Dr. A. C. Whitaker

THE PRINCIPLES AND PRACTICE OF MEDICINE

*DESIGNED FOR THE USE OF PRACTITIONERS
AND STUDENTS OF MEDICINE*

BY

WILLIAM OSLER, M. D.

Fellow of the Royal Society ; Fellow of the Royal College of Physicians,
London ; Professor of Medicine in the Johns Hopkins University and
Physician-in-chief to the Johns Hopkins Hospital, Baltimore ;
formerly Professor of the Institutes of Medicine, McGill
University, Montreal ; and Professor of Clinical Medicine
in the University of Pennsylvania, Philadelphia

THIRD EDITION

NEW YORK
D. APPLETON AND COMPANY
1900

TO THE

Memory of my Teachers:

WILLIAM ARTHUR JOHNSON,
PRIEST OF THE PARISH OF WESTON, ONTARIO.

JAMES BOVELL,
OF THE TORONTO SCHOOL OF MEDICINE, AND OF THE
UNIVERSITY OF TRINITY COLLEGE, TORONTO.

ROBERT PALMER HOWARD,
DEAN OF THE MEDICAL FACULTY AND PROFESSOR OF MEDICINE,
MCGILL UNIVERSITY, MONTREAL.

PREFACE TO THE THIRD EDITION.

At the present rate of progress in all departments, a text-book six years old needs a very thorough revision. In the second edition, issued three years ago, many corrections were made and much new matter was added. The present edition has been wholly recast. With their wonted liberality the publishers have furnished a new font of type and a somewhat enlarged page so that the additions have not materially increased the size of the volume. A paper of better quality has also been used.

The following articles have been rewritten or are new: Vaccination, Beri-Beri, The Bubonic Plague, Cerebro-spinal Fever, Pneumonia, Malta Fever, Yellow Fever, Dengue, Influenza, Leprosy, Glandular Fever, The Gonorrhoeal Infection, Cancer of the Stomach, The Gastric Neuroses, Enteroptosis, The Cirrhoses of the Liver, Jaundice, The Diseases of the Bile-passages, Diseases of the Pancreas, Diseases of the Thymus Gland, Diseases of the Spleen, Lymphatism, Addison's Disease, Encephalitis, Neurasthenia, Erythro-melalgia, and many shorter articles, as Hypertrophic Stenosis of the Pylorus, Ether Pneumonia, Anæsthesia Paralysis, Pneumaturia, Albumosuria, etc.

Into the sections on Typhoid Fever, Tuberculosis, Rheumatic Fever, Diabetes, Gout, Arthritis Deformans, Parasitic Diseases, Diseases of the Blood, Heart, Lungs, and Kidneys, much new matter has been incorporated. The section on Diseases of the Nervous System has been rearranged, and an attempt has been made to group the diseases in accordance with the modern conceptions of the anatomy and functions of the parts.

I have in all sections tried to maintain the thoroughly practical character of the work, as a guide in diagnosis, symptomatology, and treatment.

I have again to thank many friends for much valuable help, without which the revision would have been very incomplete. Dr. Flexner has not only given me great assistance in connection with the pathology and bacteriology, but has enabled me to utilize for the present edition much material from the records of the pathological department of my colleague

Dr. Welch. Dr. H. M. Thomas and Dr. L. F. Barker have given much time and invaluable help in the revision of the section on Diseases of the Nervous System. To the former I owe the excellent rearrangement of the subjects in this section.

To my associate in the chair of medicine, Dr. Thayer, and to my assistants, Drs. Futcher and McCrae, I am under many obligations. Dr. Livingood, the associate in pathology, by whose untimely death * the Johns Hopkins Medical School has suffered a grievous loss, was most kind in furnishing facts from the post-mortem records of the hospital.

Dr. Frank R. Smith has very kindly seen the edition through the press, and I have again to thank my secretary, Miss B. O. Humpton, for the preparation of the index.

And not least, since their liberal encouragement has made the revision possible, I have to thank my brethren on both sides of the Atlantic for their kind reception of the previous editions.

July 8, 1898.

---

* He was one of the victims in the Bourgogne disaster.

CONTENTS.

SECTION I.
SPECIFIC INFECTIOUS DISEASES.

SECTION II.

DISEASES DUE TO ANIMAL PARASITES.

SECTION VI.

DISEASES OF THE RESPIRATORY SYSTEM.

SECTION X.
DISEASES OF THE NERVOUS SYSTEM.

B

SECTION XI.

DISEASES OF THE MUSCLES.

CHARTS AND ILLUSTRATIONS.

---

* The red shows the two-hourly, the black the morning and evening temperature.

" Experience is fallacious and judgment difficult."

HIPPOCRATES: *Aphorisms, I.*

" And I said of medicine, that this is an art which considers the constitution of the patient, and has principles of action and reasons in each case."

PLATO: *Gorgias.*

A TEXT-BOOK ON
THE PRACTICE OF MEDICINE.

SECTION I.

SPECIFIC INFECTIOUS DISEASES.

I. TYPHOID FEVER.

Definition.—A general infection caused by the bacillus typhosus, characterized anatomically by hyperplasia and ulceration of the lymph-follicles of the intestines, swelling of the mesenteric glands and spleen, and parenchymatous changes in the other organs. While these lesions are almost constant, there are cases in which the local changes are slight or absent, and there are others with intense localization of the poison in the lungs, spleen, kidneys, or cerebro-spinal system. Clinically the disease is marked by fever, a rose-colored eruption, diarrhœa, abdominal tenderness, tympanites, and enlargement of the spleen; but these symptoms are extremely inconstant, and even the fever varies in its character.

Historical Note.—The dates 1813 and 1850 include the modern discussion of the subject. Prior to the former year many observers had noted clinical differences in the continued fevers. Huxham in particular, in his remarkable Essay on Fevers, had "taken notice of the very great difference there is between the *putrid malignant* and the *slow nervous fever.*" In 1813 Pierre Bretonneau, of Tours, distinguished "dothiénentérite" as a separate disease; and Petit and Serres described entero-mesenteric fever. Trousseau and Velpeau, students of Bretonneau, were, in 1820, instrumental in making his views known to Andral and others in Paris. In 1829 Louis' great work appeared, in which the name "typhoid" was given to the fever. At this period typhoid fever alone prevailed in Paris, and it was universally believed to be identical with the continued fever of Great Britain, where in reality typhoid and typhus coexisted; and the intestinal lesion was regarded as an accidental occurrence in the course of ordinary typhus. Louis' students returning to their homes in different countries had opportunities for studying the prevalent fevers in the thorough and systematic manner of their master. Among these were certain young American physicians, to one of whom, Gerhard, of Philadelphia, is due the great honor of having first clearly laid down the differences between the two diseases. His papers in the American Journal of the Medical Sciences, 1837, are undoubtedly the first in any language which give a full and satisfactory account of the clinical and anatomical distinctions we now recognize. No student should fail to read these articles, among the most classical in American medical literature.

Louis' influence was early felt in Boston, whither, in 1833, James Jackson, Jr., had returned from Paris. In this year he demonstrated, in his father's wards at the Massachusetts General Hospital, the identity of the typhus of this country with the typhoid of Louis. He had already, in 1830, noticed the intestinal lesions in the common fever of New England. Though cut off at the very outset of his career, we may reasonably attribute to his inspiration the two elaborate memoirs on typhoid fever which, in 1838 and 1839, were issued from the Massachusetts General Hospital, by James Jackson, Sr., and Enoch Hale. These, with Gerhard's articles, contributed to make typhoid fever, as distinguished from typhus, widely known in the profession here long before the distinctions were recognized generally in Europe. Thus, they were described with admirable clearness under different headings in the first edition of Bartlett's work on Fevers, published in 1842.

The recognition in Paris of a fever distinct from typhoid, without intestinal lesions, was due largely to the influence of the able papers of George C. Shattuck, of Boston, and Alfred Stillé, of Philadelphia, which were read before the Société médicale d'Observation in 1838. At Louis' request, Shattuck went to the London Fever Hospital to study the disease in England, where he saw the two distinct affections, and brought back a report which was very convincing to the members of the society (Medical Examiner, Philadelphia, 1840).

Stillé had the advantage of going to Paris knowing thoroughly the clinical features of typhus fever, for he had been Gerhard's house-physician at the Philadelphia Hospital during the epidemic of 1836. At La Pitié, with Louis, he saw quite a different affection, while in London, Dublin, and Naples he recognized typhus as he had seen it in Philadelphia. The results of his observations were given in an exhaustive paper which presented in tabular form the contrasts and distinctions, clinical and anatomical, which we now recognize.

In Great Britain the non-identity of typhus and typhoid was clearly established at Glasgow, where from 1836 to 1838 A. P. Stewart studied the continued fevers, and in 1840 published the results of his observations. In the decade which followed, many important works were issued and more correct views gradually prevailed; but it was not until the publication of Jenner's observations between 1849 and 1851 that the question was finally settled in England.

Etiology.—Typhoid fever prevails especially in temperate climates, in which it constitutes the most common continued fever. Widely distributed throughout all parts of the world, it probably presents everywhere the same essential characteristics, and is everywhere an index of the sanitary intelligence of a community. Defective drainage and contaminated water supply are the two special conditions favoring the distribution and growth of the bacilli; filth, overcrowding, and bad ventilation are accessories in lowering the resistance of the individuals exposed.

While improved sanitation has done much to reduce the mortality from typhoid fever, particularly in the large cities, a reduction amounting to 45.4 per cent in 21 out of 24 English towns (Dreschfeld) (figures illustrating which will be referred to under Prophylaxis), the disease is still far too prevalent, and in suburban and rural districts in this country there is evidence to show that it is on the increase. In 1890 the death-rate from typhoid fever per 100,000 of population was, in the United States, 46.27; in England and Wales, 17.9; in Italy, 65.8; in Austria, 47.0; and in Prussia, 20.4.

Season.—It prevails most in the autumn months. Of 1,889 cases admitted to the Montreal General Hospital in twenty years, more than fifty per cent were in the months of August, September, and October. Of 1,381 cases treated during twelve years at the Toronto General Hospital, 761 occurred in these months (Graham). It has been well called the autumnal fever. It has been observed to be especially prevalent in hot and dry seasons. According to Pettenkofer, epidemics are most common when the ground-water is low, under which circumstances the springs and water-sources drain more thoroughly contaminated foci and are more likely to be highly charged with poison. It may be also, as Baumgarten suggests, that in dry seasons the poison is more disseminated in the dust.

Sex.—Males and females are about equally liable to the disease, but males with typhoid are much more frequently admitted into hospitals.

Age.—Typhoid fever is a disease of youth and early adult life. The greatest susceptibility is between the ages of fifteen and twenty-five. Of 685 cases treated to January 1, 1898, in my wards at the Johns Hopkins Hospital there were under fifteen years of age, 75; between fifteen and twenty, 138; between twenty and thirty, 317; between thirty and forty, 98; between forty and fifty, 32; between fifty and sixty, 6; above sixty, 6; age doubtful in 13*. Cases are rare over sixty, although Manges believes that they are more common than the records show. As the course is often atypical the diagnosis may be uncertain. In two of my cases the disease was not recognized until the autopsy. It is not very infrequent in childhood, but infants are rarely attacked. Murchison saw a case at the sixth month. The disease may be congenital in cases in which the mother has contracted it late in pregnancy.

Immunity.—As in other fevers, not all exposed to the infection take the disease, and there are grades of susceptibility. Some families seem more disposed to infection than others. One attack usually protects. "Of 2,000 cases of enteric fever at the Hamburg General Hospital, only 14 persons were affected twice and only 1 person three times" (Dreschfeld).

The Bacillus typhosus.—The researches of Eberth, Koch, Gaffky, and others have shown that there is a special micro-organism *constantly* asso-

---

* Vols. iv, v, and vii of the Johns Hopkins Hospital Reports contain the Studies on Typhoid Fever referred to in this article as Studies I, II, and III.

ciated with typhoid fever. (*a*) *General Characters.*—It is a rather short, thick, flagellated, motile bacillus, with rounded ends, in one of which, sometimes in both (particularly in cultures), there can be seen a glistening round body, at one time believed to be a spore; but these polar structures are probably only areas of degenerated protoplasm. It grows readily on various nutritive media, and can now be differentiated from the *bacterium coli commune,* with which, and with certain other bacilli, it is apt to be confounded. This organism fulfils two of the requirements of Koch's law —it is constantly present, and it grows outside the body in a specific manner. The third requirement, the production of the disease experimentally by the cultures, has not yet been met. Probably the animals used for experimentation are not susceptible to typhoid fever. The bacilli or their toxins inoculated in large quantities into the blood of rabbits are pathogenic, and in some instances ulcerative and necrotic lesions in the intestine may be produced. But similar intestinal lesions may be caused by other bacteria, including the *bacterium coli commune.*

Cultures are killed within ten minutes when exposed to a temperature of 60° C., while they resist for days temperatures as low as − 10° C., even when frozen and thawed successively. Although the typhoid bacillus does not produce spores, it resists ordinary drying for months. The direct rays of the sun quickly injure the bacilli in cultures, and completely destroy them in from four to ten hours' exposure. Bouillon cultures are destroyed by carbolic acid, 1 to 200, and by corrosive sublimate, 1 to 2,500.

(*b*) *Distribution in the Body.*—In recent typhoid infections the bacilli are found in the lymphoid tissues of the intestines, in the mesenteric glands, in the spleen, in the bone marrow, in the liver, and in the bile. They occur also in irregular clumps in the contents of the intestines and in the stools; and since the introduction of improved methods of cultivation (Elsner, Capaldi) they have been demonstrated in the latter in about 50 per cent of the cases examined. They may, however, be incapable of demonstration even in fatal cases. The bacilli have been found in the blood and in the rose-colored spots. In the urine they may be present in numbers, where they may persist for months after recovery (Mark Richardson), and they have been found in the sweat and sputa. From the endocardial vegetations, from meningeal and pleural exudates, and from foci of suppuration in various parts, the bacilli have also been isolated.

(*c*) *The Bacilli Outside the Body.*—Outside the body, in water, the bacilli retain their vitality for weeks; but whether an increase can occur is not yet finally settled. Bolton denies it, but the general opinion seems to be that it may take place to some extent at first. They disappear from ordinary water in competition with saprophytes in a few days. In milk they undergo rapid development without changing its appearance. They may increase in the soil and retain their vitality for months. They are not killed by freezing, but, as Prudden has shown, may live in ice for months. In many epidemics the bacilli have been isolated from the infected water. The detection, however, of the typhoid bacillus in drinking-water is by no means easy, and the question in individual cases must be settled by experts

who have had special experience with this germ. Both Prudden and Ernst
have found it in water-filters. Through the use of Elsner's culture-medium
Remlinger and Schneider claim to have obtained the bacillus in small
numbers from the stools of healthy persons.

The direct infection by dust of exposed food-stuffs, such as milk, is
very probable. The bacilli retain their vitality for many weeks; in garden earth twenty-one days, in filter-sand eighty-two days, in dust of the
street thirty days, on linen sixty to seventy days, on wood thirty-two days
(Uffelmann).

Modes of Conveyance.—(*a*) *Contagion.*—The possibility of the direct
transmission through the air from one person to another must be acknowledged, although, as shown by Germano, when *completely* dried in air-cur-
rents, the specific bacillus quickly dies. There are house epidemics in which
contamination of water or food could be almost positively excluded. The
nurses and attendants who have to do with the stools and body-linen of
the patients are alone liable to direct infection. During six years one
nurse, one orderly, and one patient contracted the disease in my wards.
The contagion may be spread by means of clothing and wash-linen—a
mode of infection which is especially to be feared in military garrisons,
where the same clothing is sometimes used by different persons.

(*b*) *Infection of water* is unquestionably the most common mode of
conveyance. Many epidemics have been shown to originate in the contamination of a well or a spring. A very striking one occurred at Plym-
outh, Pa., in 1885, which was investigated by Shakespeare. The town,
with a population of 8,000, was in part supplied with drinking-water from
a reservoir fed by a mountain stream. During January, February, and
March, in a cottage by the side of and at a distance of from 60 to 80
feet from this stream, a man was ill with typhoid fever. The attendants
were in the habit at night of throwing out the evacuations on the ground
toward the stream. During these months the ground was frozen and covered with snow. In the latter part of March and early in April there was
considerable rainfall and a thaw, in which a large part of the three months'
accumulation of discharges was washed into the brook, not 60 feet distant. At the very time of this thaw the patient had numerous and copious
discharges. About the 10th of April cases of typhoid fever broke out in
the town, appearing for a time at the rate of fifty a day. In all, about
1,200 people were attacked. An immense majority of all the cases were in
the part of the town which received water from the infected reservoir.

The recent experience at Maidstone illustrates the widespread and serious character of an epidemic when the water-supply becomes badly contaminated. The outbreak began about the middle of September, and
within the first two weeks 509 cases were reported. By October 27th there
were 1,748 cases, and by November 17th 1,848 cases. In all, in a population of 35,000, about 1,900 persons were attacked. No epidemic of the
same magnitude has ever occurred in England, and it shows the terrible
danger of a badly constructed water-supply easily contaminated by surface
drainage.

(*c*) *Infection of Food.*—*Milk* may be the source of infection. One of the most thoroughly studied epidemics due to this cause was that investigated by Ballard in Islington. The milk may be contaminated by infected water used in cleansing the cans. In fresh milk it has been shown that the germs grow rapidly. Pfuhl has reported an epidemic in a military garrison caused by milk. The dairyman was nursing a son sick of typhoid and afterward became himself ill. Only those who drank the milk unboiled suffered. The milk epidemics have been collected by Ernest Hart and by Kober, of Washington.

In addition, the germs may be conveyed in ice, salads of various sorts, celery, etc.; and the food may be readily contaminated by the soiled fingers of the attendants or of the patient himself. A fly which has alighted on the soiled linen of a typhoid patient in a ward may subsequently contaminate the milk or other food.

Oysters may become infected during the process of fattening or freshening. In the Middletown epidemic, reported by H. W. Conn, the chain of circumstantial evidence seems complete; Lavis reports an epidemic occurring in Naples caused by infected oysters; and most suggestive sporadic cases have been recorded by Sir William Broadbent and others.

C. J. Foote has made an interesting bacteriological study of the subject. Oysters taken from the feeding-grounds in rivers contain a very much larger number of micro-organisms of all sorts than those from the sea. He has shown, too, that Eberth's bacillus will live in the brackish water in which oysters are fattened even when frozen; and that it will also live in the oyster itself, and for a longer time than in the water in which the oyster grows. Whether multiplication takes place in the oyster is doubtful. Chantemesse also found typhoid germs in oysters which had lain in infected sea-water even after they had been transferred to and kept in fresh water for a time.

(*d*) *Contamination of the Soil.*—Pettenkofer holds that the poison is not eliminated in a condition capable of communicating the disease directly, but that it must first undergo changes in the soil, which changes are favored by the ground-water.

Filth, bad sewers, or cesspools can not in themselves cause typhoid fever, but they furnish the conditions suitable for the preservation of the bacillus, and possibly for its propagation.

The history of typhoid fever in Munich, as told anew by Childs (Lancet, 1898, ii), indicates that the soil pollution has much to do with the occurrence of sporadic cases and of recurrent outbreaks. Robertson's studies show that the typhoid bacillus is capable of growing rapidly in certain soils, and that it can under certain conditions survive from one summer to another.

Modes of Infection.—The work of the past few years has widened considerably our conception of the intimate processes of infection in typhoid fever. Sidney Phillips, J. W. Moore, and others had reported cases of typhoid fever without enteric lesions. The wide existence of the typhoid bacilli has been repeatedly shown in cases which had the clinical features of the disease, but without lesions in the small intestine. The question has been very fully considered by Chiari and Kraus,* Hodenpyl,† Nicholls and Keenan, ‡ and by Flexner (Studies III). Typhoid fever is no more primarily intestinal than is smallpox primarily a cutaneous disease. We may recognize the following groups: 1. *Ordinary typhoid fever with marked enteric lesions.* An immense majority of all the cases are of this character. The infection has taken place through the intestines, and while the spleen and mesenteric glands are involved the lymphatic apparatus of the intestinal walls bears the brunt of the attack. 2. *Typhoid septicæmia, a general infection with the bacilli without special local manifestations.* Anatomically, as Chiari points out, these cases may not be recognizable, and the diagnosis may rest upon the existence of the Widal reaction and the demonstration of the bacilli. They present the symptoms of a severe intoxication with high fever and delirium. 3. *Typhoid fever with localizations other than enteric.* In the ordinary form it is common enough to find in conjunction with the enteric lesions special localizations in different parts of the body; but we have of late learned to recognize that these particular localizations may exist either with very slight or without any intestinal lesions. The organs attacked may be the lungs, the spleen, the kidneys, or the cerebro-spinal meninges. Clinically we have long recognized this variable character of the infection, and have spoken of cases of pneumo-typhoid, nephro-typhoid, cerebro-spinal typhoid, and spleno-typhoid. The case recently reported by Flexner illustrates very well the importance of recognizing these forms. A man aged sixty was admitted to my ward, October 28, with shortness of breath and signs of pneumonia in the lower lobe of the right lung. He died twenty-four hours after admission, after an illness of about two months' duration. The case was naturally regarded as one of senile pneumonia. The autopsy showed an extensive involvement of the lower lobe in fresh pneumonia, passing on to gangrene without any lesion of the intestine. Pure cultures of the typhoid bacillus were isolated from the lungs, liver, kidneys, and spleen. No other organisms were present. 4. *Mixed infections.* It is well to distinguish, as Dreschfeld points out, between double infections, as with the bacillus tuberculosis, the diphtheria bacillus, and the plasmodia of Laveran, in which two different diseases are present and can be readily distinguished, and the true mixed or secondary infections, in which the conditions induced by one organism favor the growth of other pathogenic forms; thus in the ordinary typhoid fever cases secondary infection with the colon bacillus, the streptococcus, staphylococcus, or the pneumococcus, is quite common. The part played by the paracolon bacillus of Widal in typhoid infection is yet to be defined. Gwyn # isolated from the blood of a typical case of typhoid fever, occurring in my wards, this organism, which agglutinated with the patient's serum, while no action was exerted upon the typhoid bacillus.

---

* Zeitschrift f. Heilkunde, 1897.   ‡ Montreal Med. Jour., 1898.
† Brit. Med. Jour., 1897, ii.   # Johns Hopkins Hospital Bulletin, 1898.

Products of the Growth of the Bacilli.—Brieger and Fraenkel have separated from bouillon cultures a poison belonging to the group of tox-albumins, to which the name typhotoxin has been applied. The chief poison, according to Pfeiffer, produced by the typhoid germ, is intimately bound up with the proteid of the bacterial cell, and goes over in small quantities into the fluids in which the bacilli are cultivated. Sterilized cultures, therefore, are still toxic. Cultures sterilized by heat or by filtration give rise, when injected into susceptible animals, to an intoxication similar to that caused by the living germs. Changes in the lymphatic apparatus of the intestine are produced by this poison as well as by that yielded by the bacillus coli communis.

Morbid Anatomy.—The statistical details under this heading are based upon eighty autopsies, a majority of which were performed at the Montreal General Hospital, and upon the records of two thousand post-mortems at the Munich Pathological Institute.*

Intestines.—A catarrhal condition exists throughout the small and large bowel, and to this is due, in all probability, the diarrhœa with the thin pea-soup-like stools. Associated with this catarrh there is some epithelial desquamation.

Specific changes occur in the lymphoid elements of the bowel, chiefly at the lower end of the ileum. The alterations which occur are most conveniently described in four stages :

1. *Hyperplasia*, which involves the glands of Peyer in the jejunum and ileum, and to a variable extent those in the large intestine. The follicles are swollen, grayish-white in color, and the patches may project to a distance of from three to five mm. In exceptional cases they may be still more prominent. The solitary glands, which range in size from a pin's head to a large pea, are usually deeply imbedded in the submucosa, but project to a variable extent. Occasionally they are very prominent, and may be almost pedunculated. Microscopical examination shows at the outset a condition of hyperæmia of the follicles. Later there is a great increase and accumulation of cells of the lymph-tissue which may even infiltrate the adjacent mucosa and the muscularis ; and the blood-vessels are more or less compressed, which gives the whitish, anæmic appearance to the follicles. The cells have all the characters of ordinary lymph-corpuscles. Some of them, however, are larger, epithelioid, and contain several nuclei. Occasionally cells containing red blood-corpuscles are seen. This so-called medullary infiltration, which is always more intense toward the lower end of the ileum, reaches its height from the eighth to the tenth day and then undergoes one of two changes, *resolution* or *necrosis*. Death very rarely takes place at this stage. Resolution is accomplished by a fatty and granular change in the cells, which are destroyed and absorbed. A curious condition of the patches is produced at this stage, in which they have a reticulated appearance, the *plaques à surface réticulée*. The swollen follicles in the patch undergo resolution and shrink more rapidly than

---

* Münchener medicinische Wochenschrift, Nos. 3 and 4, 1891.

the surrounding framework, or what is more probable the follicles alone, owing to the intense hyperplasia, become necrotic and disintegrate, leaving the little pits. In this process superficial hæmorrhages may result, and small ulcers may originate by the fusion of these superficial losses of substance.

There is nothing distinctive in the hyperplasia of the lymph-follicles in typhoid fever; but apart from this disease we rarely see in adults a marked affection of these glands with fever. In children, however, it is not uncommon when death has occurred from intestinal affections, and it is also met with in measles, diphtheria, and scarlet fever.

2. *Necrosis and Sloughing.*—When the hyperplasia of the lymph-follicles reaches a certain grade, resolution is no longer possible. The blood-vessels become choked, there is a condition of anæmic necrosis, and sloughs form which must be separated and thrown off. The necrosis is probably due in great part to the direct action of the bacilli. The process may be superficial, affecting only the upper part of the mucous coat, or it may extend to and involve the submucosa. The "slough" may sometimes lie upon the Peyer's patch, scarcely involving the epithelium (Marchand). It is always more intense toward the ileo-cæcal valve, and in very severe cases the greater part of the mucosa of the last foot of the ileum may be converted into a brownish-black eschar. The necrotic area in the solitary glands forms a yellowish cap which often involves only the most prominent point of a follicle. The extent of the necrosis is very variable. It may pass deep into the muscular coat, reaching to or even perforating the peritonæum.

3. *Ulceration.*—The separation of the necrotic tissue—the sloughing—is gradually effected from the edges inward, and results in the formation of an ulcer, the size and extent of which are directly proportionate to the amount of necrosis. If this be superficial, the entire thickness of the mucosa may not be involved and the loss of substance may be small and shallow. More commonly the slough in separating exposes the submucosa and muscularis, particularly the latter, which forms the floor of a majority of all typhoid ulcers. It is not common for an entire Peyer's patch to slough away, and a perfectly ovoid ulcer opposite to the mesentery is rarely seen. Irregularly oval and rounded forms are most common. A large patch may present three or four ulcers divided by septa of mucous membrane. The terminal 6 or 8 inches of the mucous membrane of the ileum may form a large ulcer, in which are here and there islands of mucosa. The edges of the ulcer are usually swollen, soft, sometimes congested, and often undermined. At a late period the ulcers near the valve may have very irregular sinuous borders. The base of a typhoid ulcer is smooth and clean, being usually formed of the submucosa or of the muscularis.

There may be large ulcers near the valve and swollen hyperæmic patches of Peyer in the upper part of the ileum.

4. *Healing.*—This begins with the development of a thin granulation tissue which covers the base and gives to it a soft, shining appearance.

The mucosa gradually extends from the edge, and a new growth of epithelium is formed. The glandular elements are reformed; the healed ulcer is somewhat depressed and is usually pigmented. Occasionally an appearance is seen as if an ulcer had healed in one place and was extending in another. In death during relapse healing ulcers may be seen in some patches with fresh ulcers in others.

We may say, indeed, that healing begins with the separation of the sloughs, as, when resolution is impossible, the removal of the necrosed part is the first step in the process of repair. Practically, in fatal cases, we seldom meet with evidences of cicatrization, as the majority of deaths occur before this stage is reached.

Large Intestine.—The cæcum and colon are affected in about one third of the cases. Sometimes the solitary glands are greatly enlarged. The ulcers are usually larger in the cæcum than in the colon.

Perforation of the Bowel.—*Incidence at Autopsy.*—In 114 cases of the 2,000 Munich autopsies (5.7 per cent) and in 22 instances in my series, the intestine was perforated and death caused by peritonitis. According to Chomel, "the accident is sometimes the result of ulceration, sometimes of a true eschar, and sometimes it is produced by the distention of the intestine causing the rupture of tissues weakened by disease." In only a few cases is the perforation at the bottom of a clean thin-walled ulcer. In one instance it had occurred two weeks after the temperature had become normal. The sloughs are, as a rule, adherent about the site of perforation, which in a majority of the cases occur in small deep ulcers. There may be two or three perforations; in a few instances they have been very numerous. The orifice is usually within the last foot of the ileum. In only one of my cases was it distant 18 inches. In 4 cases of my series the appendix was perforated and in 2 the large bowel. Peritonitis was present in every instance. In 167 cases collected by Fitz the ileum was perforated in 136, the large intestine in 20, the appendix in 5, Meckel's diverticulum in 4, and the jejunum in 2. In the large intestine, according to Hawkins, the sigmoid flexure is the most frequent seat of perforation.

Death from hæmorrhage occurred in 99 of the Munich cases, and in 11 of 56 deaths in my 685 cases. The bleeding seems to result directly from the separation of the sloughs. I was not able in any instance to find the bleeding vessel. In one case only a single patch had sloughed, and a firm clot was adherent to it. The bleeding may also come from the soft swollen edges of the patch.

The *mesenteric glands* at first show intense hyperæmia and subsequently become greatly swollen. Spots of necrosis are common. In several of my cases suppuration had occurred, and in one a large abscess of the mesentery was present. Fatal hæmorrhage into the peritonæum may come from rupture of a swollen gland. The bunch of glands in the mesentery, at the lower end of the ileum, is especially involved. The retroperitoneal glands are also swollen.

The *spleen* is invariably enlarged in the early stages of the disease. In only one of my cases did it exceed 20 ounces (600 grammes) in weight.

The tissue is soft, even diffluent. Infarction is not infrequent. Rupture may occur spontaneously or as a result of injury. In the Munich autopsies there were 5 instances of rupture of the spleen, one of which resulted from a gangrenous abscess.

The *liver* shows signs of parenchymatous degeneration. Early in the disease it is hyperæmic, and in a majority of instances it is swollen, somewhat pale, on section turbid, and microscopically the cells are very granular and loaded with fat. Nodular areas (microscopic) occur in many cases, as described by Handford. Reed, in Welch's laboratory, could not determine any relation between the groups of bacilli and these areas (Studies II). Some of the nodules are lymphoid, others are necrotic (Amyot). In 12 of the Munich autopsies liver abscess was found, and in 3, acute yellow atrophy. Pylephlebitis may follow abscess of the mesentery or perforation of the appendix. Affections of the gall-bladder are not uncommon, and are fully described under the clinical features.

Kidneys.—Cloudy swelling, with granular degeneration of the cells of the convoluted tubules, less commonly an acute nephritis, may be present. Rayer, Wagner, and others described the occurrence of numerous small areas infiltrated with round cells, which may have the appearance of lymphomata, or may pass on to softening and suppuration, producing the so-called *miliary abscesses*. It is usually a late change. The typhoid bacilli alone have been found by some observers in these areas. They may also be found in the urine. In 10 cases of pyuria in typhoid fever in my wards, Blumer found the bacilli in 2. Diphtheritic inflammation of the pelvis of the kidney may occur. It was present in 3 of my cases, in one of which the tips of the papillæ were also affected. Catarrh of the bladder is not uncommon. Diphtheritic inflammation of this viscus may also occur. Orchitis is occasionally met with.

Respiratory Organs.—Ulceration of the larynx occurs in a certain number of cases; in the Munich series it was noted 107 times. It may come on at the same time as the ulceration in the ileum, but the bacilli have not yet, I believe, been found in the ulcers. They occur in the posterior wall, at the insertion of the cords, at the base of the epiglottis, and on the ary-epiglottidean folds. The cartilages are very apt to become involved. In the later periods catarrhal and diphtheritic ulcers may be present.

Œdema of the glottis was present in 20 of the Munich cases, in 8 of which tracheotomy was performed. Diphtheritis of the pharynx and larynx is not very uncommon. It occurred in a most extensive form in 2 of my cases. Lobar pneumonia may be found early in the disease (see Pneumo-typhus), or it may be a late event. Hypostatic congestion and the condition of the lung spoken of as splenization are very common. Gangrene of the lung occurred in 40 cases in the Munich series; abscess of the lung in 14; hæmorrhagic infarction in 129. Pleurisy is not a very common event. Fibrinous pleurisy occurred in about 6 per cent of the Munich cases, and empyema in nearly 2 per cent.

Changes in the Circulatory System.—*Heart Lesions.*—*Endocarditis* is rare. I have met with 2 cases. The typhoid bacilli have been found in the vegetations. *Pericarditis* was present in 14 cases of the Munich autopsies. *Myocarditis* is not very infrequent. Dewèvre, in a series of 48 cases, found in 16 granular or fatty degeneration, and in 3 a proliferating endarteritis in the small vessels. It is remarkable that even in cases of death from heart-failure, with intense fever, the cell-fibres may present little or no observable change.

Lesions of the Blood-vessels—Typhoid Gangrene.—Inflammation of the arteries with thrombus formation has been frequently described in typhoid fever. Bacilli have been found in the thrombi. The artery may be blocked by a thrombus of cardiac origin—an embolus—but in the great majority of instances they are autochthonous and due to arteritis, obliterating or partial. Thrombosis in the veins is very much more frequent than in the arteries, but is not such a serious event. It is most frequent in the femoral, and in the left more often than the right. The consequences are fully considered under the *symptoms*.

Nervous System.—There are very few coarse changes met with. Meningitis is extremely rare. I have never seen a case at autopsy. It occurred in only 11 of the 2,000 Munich cases. The exudation may be either serous, sero-fibrinous, or purulent, and typhoid bacilli have been frequently isolated. Two interesting cases have recently been reported by Ohlmacher from the Cleveland City Hospital. In both bacilli were found in the meninges. In some of the cases, as Kamen's, the enteric lesions have been slight. Optic neuritis, which occurs sometimes in typhoid fever, has not, so far as I know, been described in connection with the meningitis. The anatomical lesion of the aphasia—seen not infrequently in children— is not known, possibly it is an encephalitis. Parenchymatous changes have been met with in the peripheral nerves, and appear to be not very uncommon, even when there have been no symptoms of neuritis.

The *voluntary muscles* show, in certain instances, the changes described by Zenker, which occur, however, in all long-standing febrile affections, and are not peculiar to typhoid fever. The muscle substance within the sarcolemma undergoes either a granular degeneration or a hyaline transformation. The abdominal muscles, the adductors of the thighs, and the pectorals are most commonly involved. Rupture of a rectus abdominis has been found post mortem. Hæmorrhage may occur. Abscesses may develop in the muscles during convalescence.

Symptoms.—In a disease so complex as typhoid fever it will be well first to give a general description, and then to study more fully the symptoms, complications, and sequelæ according to the individual organs.

General Description.—The period of incubation lasts from " eight to fourteen days, sometimes twenty-three " (Clinical Society), during which there are feelings of lassitude and inaptitude for work. The onset is rarely abrupt. There may be prodromal symptoms, either a rigor, which is rare, or chilly feelings, headache, nausea, loss of appetite, pains in the back and legs, and nose-bleeding. These symptoms increase in severity, and the patient at last takes to his bed. From this event, in a majority of cases, the definite onset of the disease may be dated. During the *first week* there is, in some cases (but by no means in all, as has long been taught), a steady rise in the fever, the evening record rising a degree or a degree and a half higher each day, reaching 103° or 104°. The pulse is rapid, from 100 to 110, full in volume, but of low tension and often dicrotic; the tongue is coated and white; the abdomen is slightly distended and tender. Unless the fever is high there is no delirium, but the patient complains of headache, and there may be mental confusion and wandering at night. The bowels may be constipated, or there may be two or three loose movements daily. Toward the end of the week the spleen becomes enlarged and the rash appears in the form of rose-colored spots, seen first on the skin of the abdomen. Cough and bronchitic symptoms are not uncommon at the outset.

In the *second week*, in cases of moderate severity, the symptoms become aggravated; the fever remains high and the morning remission is slight. The pulse is rapid and loses its dicrotic character. There is no longer headache, but there are mental torpor and dullness. The face looks heavy; the lips are dry; the tongue, in severe cases, becomes dry also. The abdominal symptoms, if present—diarrhœa, tympanites, and tenderness—become aggravated. Death may occur during this week, with pronounced nervous symptoms, or, toward the end of it, from hæmorrhage or perforation. In mild cases the temperature declines, and by the fourteenth day may be normal.

In the *third week*, in cases of moderate severity, the pulse ranges from 110 to 130; the temperature now shows marked morning remissions, and there is a gradual decline in the fever. The loss of flesh is now more noticeable, and the weakness is pronounced. Diarrhœa and meteorism may now occur for the first time. Unfavorable symptoms at this stage are the pulmonary complications, increasing feebleness of the heart, and pronounced delirium with muscular tremor. Special dangers are perforation and hæmorrhage.

With the *fourth week*, in a majority of instances, convalescence begins. The temperature gradually reaches the normal point, the diarrhœa stops, the tongue cleans, and the desire for food returns. In severe cases the fourth and even the fifth week may present an aggravated picture of the third; the patient grows weaker, the pulse is more rapid and feeble, the tongue dry, and the abdomen distended. He lies in a condition of profound stupor, with low muttering delirium and subsultus tendinum, and passes the fæces and urine involuntarily. Heart-failure and secondary complications are the chief dangers of this period.

In the *fifth and sixth weeks* protracted cases may still show irregular fever, and convalescence may not set in until after the fortieth day. In this period we meet with relapses in the milder forms or slight recrudescence of the fever. At this time, too, occur many of the complications and sequelæ.

Special Features and Symptoms.—*Mode of Onset.*—As a rule, the symptoms develop insidiously, and the patient is unable to fix definitely the time at which he began to feel ill. The following are the most important deviations from this common course:

(*a*) *Onset with Pronounced, sometimes Sudden, Nervous Manifestations.* —Headache, of a severe and intractable nature, is by no means an infrequent initial symptom. Again, a severe facial neuralgia may for a few days put the practitioner off his guard. In cases in which the patients have kept about and, as they say, fought the disease, the very first manifestation may be pronounced delirium. Such patients may even leave home and wander about for days. In rare cases the disease sets in with the most intense cerebro-spinal symptoms, simulating meningitis—severe headache, photophobia, retraction of the head, twitching of the muscles, and even convulsions. Occasionally drowsiness, stupor, and signs of basilar meningitis may exist for ten days or more before the characteristic symptoms develop; occasionally the onset is with mania.

(*b*) *With Pronounced Pulmonary Symptoms.*—The initial bronchial catarrh may be of great severity and obscure the other features of the disease. More striking still are those cases in which the disease sets in with a single chill, with pain in the side and all the characteristic features of lobar pneumonia, or of acute pleurisy.

(*c*) *With Intense Gastro-intestinal Symptoms.*—The vomiting may be incessant and uncontrollable. Occasionally there are cases with such intense vomiting and diarrhœa that a suspicion of poisoning may be aroused.

(*d*) *With symptoms of an acute nephritis*, smoky or bloody urine, with much albumin and tube-casts.

(*e*) *Ambulatory Form.*—Deserving of especial mention are those cases of typhoid fever in which the patient keeps about and attempts to do work, or perhaps takes a long journey to his home. He may come under observation for the first time with a temperature of 104° or 105°, and with the rash well out. Many of these cases run a severe course, and in general hospitals they contribute largely to the total mortality. Finally, there are rare instances in which typhoid is unsuspected until perforation, or a profuse hæmorrhage from the bowels occurs.

Facial Aspect.—Early in the disease the cheeks are flushed and the eyes bright. Toward the end of the first week the expression becomes more listless, and when the disease is well established the patient has a dull and heavy look. There is never the rapid anæmia of malarial fever, and the color of the lips and cheeks may be retained even to the third week.

Fever.—(*a*) *Regular Course.* (Chart I.)—In the stage of invasion the fever rises steadily during the first five or six days. The evening temperature is about a degree or a degree and a half higher than the morning remission, so that a temperature of 104° or 105° is not uncommon by the end of the first week. Having reached the fastigium or height, the fever then persists with very slight daily remissions. The fever may be singularly persistent and but little influenced by bathing or other measures. At the end of the second and throughout the third week the temperature becomes more distinctly remittent. The difference between the morning and evening record may be 3° or 4°, and the morning temperature may even be normal. It falls by lysis, and the temperature is not considered normal until the evening record is at 98.2°.

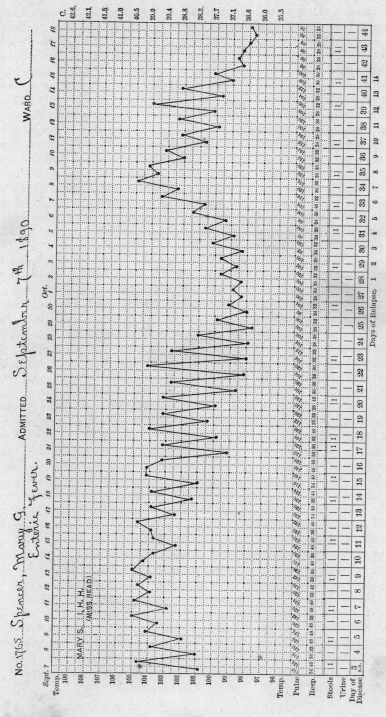

CHART 1.—Typhoid Fever with relapse.

(*b*) Variations from the typical temperature curve are common. We do not always see the gradual steplike ascent in the early stage ; the cases do not often come under observation at this time. When the disease sets in with a chill, or in children with a convulsion, the temperature may rise at once to 103° or 104°. In many cases defervescence occurs at the end of the second week and the temperature may fall rapidly, reaching the normal within twelve or twenty hours. An inverse type of temperature, high in the morning and low in the evening, is occasionally seen but has no especial significance.

Sudden falls in the temperature may occur ; thus, as shown in Chart III, a drop of 10° may follow an intestinal hæmorrhage, and the fall may be very apparent even before the blood has appeared in the stools. Sometimes during the anæmia which follows a severe hæmorrhage from the bowels there are remarkable oscillations in the temperature. Hyperpyrexia, temperature above 106°, is not very common in typhoid fever except just before death, when I have known the thermometer to register 109.5°.

(*c*) *Post-Typhoid Elevations—Fever of Convalescence.*—During convalescence, after the temperature has been normal, perhaps for five or six days, the fever may rise suddenly to 102° or 103°, and, after persisting for from one to three days or even longer, fall to normal. With this there is no constitutional disturbance, no furring of the tongue, no distention of the abdomen. These so-called recrudescences are by no means uncommon, and are of especial importance, as they cause great anxiety to the practitioner. They are attributed most frequently to errors in diet, constipation, emotions, and excitement of any sort, such as seeing friends. A long series of these cases is recorded in our reports (Studies II and III).

There are cases in which the temperature declines almost to the normal at the end of the third week, the tongue cleans, and the patient enters apparently upon a satisfactory convalescence. The evening temperature, however, does not reach 98.5°, but constantly keeps about 99.5° or 100°, and occasionally rises to 100.5°. This, in the late stages of convalescence, I have seen due to the post-typhoid anæmia. Complications should be carefully looked for, particularly insidious pleurisy or bone lesions.

In certain of these cases the persistence of the fever seems to be really a nervous phenomenon, and there is nothing in the condition of the patient to cause uneasiness except the evening elevation of temperature. If the tongue is clean, the appetite good, and there are no intestinal symptoms, it may be disregarded. I have frequently found this condition best met by allowing the patient to get up and by stopping the use of the thermometer. This prolonged slight elevation of the temperature after the disappearance of all the symptoms is most common in children and in patients of marked nervous temperament.

(*d*) *The Fever of the Relapse.*—This is a repetition in many instances of the original fever, a gradual ascent and maintenance for a few days at a certain height and then a gradual decline. It is shorter than the original pyrexia, and rarely continues more than two or three weeks. (Chart I.)

(e) *Afebrile Typhoid.*—There are cases described in which the chief features of the disease have been present without the existence of fever. They are extremely rare in this country. No instance of the kind has come under my observation. Fisk, of Denver, has met with it.

(f) *Chills* occur (a) sometimes with the fever of onset; (b) occasionally at intervals throughout the course of the disease, and followed by sweats (so-called sudoral form); (c) with the advent of complications, pleurisy, pneumonia, otitis media, periostitis, etc.; (d) with active antipyretic treatment by the coal-tar remedies; (e) occasionally during the period of defervescence without relation to any complication or sequel, probably due to a septic infection; (f) according to Herringham, chills may result from constipation. There are cases in which throughout the latter half of the disease chills recur with great severity. (See Chills in Typhoid Fever, Studies II.)

Skin.—The rash of typhoid fever is very characteristic. It consists of a variable number of rose-colored spots, which appear from the seventh to the tenth day, usually first upon the abdomen. The spots are flattened papules, slightly raised, of a rose-red color, disappearing on pressure, and ranging in diameter from 2 to 4 millimetres. They can be felt as distinct elevations on the skin. Sometimes each spot is capped by a small vesicle. The spots may be dark in color and occasionally become petechial. After persisting for two or three days they gradually disappear, leaving a brownish stain. They come out in successive crops, but rarely appear after the middle of the third week. They are present in the typical relapse. The rash is most abundant upon the abdomen and lower thoracic zone, often abounds upon the back, and may spread to the extremities or even to the face. I can not say that in my experience these cases with the more abundant eruption have been of especially severe type. The rash is not always present. Murchison states that it is frequently absent in children. In several instances within the past few years the rash has persisted after the temperature has subsided.

A branny desquamation is not rare in children; it is associated usually with abundant sudamina. Occasionally the skin may peel in large flakes.

The following accidental rashes are met with in typhoid fever:

1. *Erythema.*—It is not very uncommon in the first week of typhoid fever to find the skin of the abdomen and chest of a vivid red color; the rash may also spread to the extremities. It may possibly in some instances, but certainly not always, be due to quinine. I have seen it much more frequently in the past five years (during which time I have rarely ordered a dose of quinine in this disease) than I did in Montreal, where we used this drug largely as an antipyretic.

2. The *taches bleuâtres—Peliomata.*—These are pale-blue or steel-gray spots, subcuticular, from 4 to 10 mm. in diameter, of irregular outline and most abundant about the chest, abdomen, and thighs. They sometimes give a very striking appearance to the skin. It can be readily seen that the injection is in the deeper tissues and not superficial. This rash is quite without significance. Since my attention was called to its associa-

2

tion with body lice, I have met with no instance in which these were not present. Several French observers maintain that they are due to the irritating effects of the fluid secreted by pediculi (*vide* Hewetson, J. H. H. Bulletin, vol. v). They are not peculiar to typhoid fever (Duckworth).

3. Sudaminal and miliary eruptions are common in all cases in which there is profuse sweating.

4. Urticaria is occasionally met with ; and lastly herpes, very uncommon in typhoid fever, in comparison with its frequency in malaria and pneumonia.

The *tache cérébrale*, a red line with white borders, can be produced by drawing the nail over the skin. It is a vaso-motor phenomenon which, as in other fevers, can be readily elicited, particularly in nervous subjects. Exposure of the abdomen may be sufficient to cause a pinkish injection, which may in places change to an ivory white, giving a curious mottled appearance to the skin. A similar appearance may be seen on the arms. The general tint may be white, with irregular patches or streaks of pink or dark red. The skin of the palms of the hands may become very dry and yellow.

Sweats.—At the height of the fever the skin is usually dry. Profuse sweating is rare, but it is not very uncommon to see the abdomen or chest moist with perspiration, particularly in the reaction which follows the bath. Sweats in some instances constitute a striking feature of the disease. They may occasionally be associated with chilly sensations or actual chills. Jaccoud and others in France have especially described this *sudoral* form of typhoid fever. There may be recurring paroxysms of chill, fever, and sweats (even several in twenty-four hours), and the case may be mistaken for one of intermittent fever. The fever toward the end of the second week and during the third week may be intermittent. The characteristic rash is usually present, and, if absent, the negative condition of the blood is sufficient to exclude malaria. I have seen cases of this form in Montreal, where there could have been no suspicion of malarial infection.

Œdema of the skin occurs :

1. As the result of vascular obstruction, most commonly of a vein, as in thrombosis of the femoral vein.

2. In connection with nephritis.

3. In association with the anæmia and cachexia.

The hair is very apt to fall out after an attack of typhoid fever. Instances of permanent baldness are of extreme rarity. As in other diseases associated with fever the nutrition of the nails suffers, and during and after convalescence transverse ridges are seen.

It is stated that a peculiar odor is exhaled from the skin in typhoid fever. Whether due to a cutaneous exhalation or not, there certainly is a very distinctive smell connected with many patients. I have repeatedly had my attention directed to it by nurses. Nathan Smith describes it as of a " semi-cadaverous, musty character."

As a sequel, lines of atrophy of the skin may develop on the abdomen and lateral aspects of the thighs, similar in all respects to those seen after pregnancy. These *lineæ atrophicæ* are possibly due to neuritis, and Duckworth has reported a case in which the skin adjacent to them was hyperæsthetic.

Bed-sores are not uncommon in protracted cases, with great emaciation. As a rule, they result from pressure and are seen upon the sacrum, more rarely the ilia, the shoulders, and the heels. These are less common, I think, since the introduction of hydrotherapy. Scrupulous care and watchfulness do much for their prevention, but it is to be remembered that in cases with profound involvement of the nerve centres acute bed-sores of the back and heels may occur with very slight pressure.

Boils constitute a common and troublesome sequel of the disease. They appear to be more frequent after hydrotherapy.

Circulatory System.—The *blood* presents important changes. The following statements are based on studies which W. S. Thayer has made in my wards (Studies I and III): During the first two weeks there may be little or no change in the blood. Profuse sweats or copious diarrhœa may, as Hayem has shown, cause the corpuscles—as in the collapse stage of cholera—to rise above normal. In the third week a fall usually takes place in corpuscles and hæmoglobin, and the number may sink rapidly even to 1,300,000 per c. mm., gradually rising to normal during convalescence. When the patient first gets up, there may be a slight fall in the number of corpuscles. They diminish slightly throughout the course, and reach the lowest point toward the end of defervescence.

The amount of hæmoglobin is always reduced, and usually in a greater relative proportion than the number of red corpuscles, and during recovery the normal color standard is reached at a later period. The number of colorless corpuscles varies little from the normal standard (6,000 ± per c. mm.). They diminish slightly throughout the course and reach the lowest point when convalescence is well begun. The absence of leucocytosis may be at times of real diagnostic value in distinguishing typhoid fever from various septic fevers and acute inflammatory processes. The relative proportion of the leucocytes shows fairly constant variations, the large mononuclear and transitional forms are increased, while the polynuclear neutrophiles are diminished often below 60 or even 50 per cent. This is in marked contrast to the condition in other acute diseases in which the polynuclear neutrophiles are increased. When an acute inflammatory process occurs in typhoid fever the leucocytes show an increase in the polynuclear forms, and this may be of great diagnostic moment, as in perforation.

The accompanying blood-chart shows these changes well. (Chart II.)

The post-typhoid anæmia may reach an extreme grade. In one of my cases the blood-corpuscles sank to 1,300,000 per c. mm. and the hæmoglobin to about 20 per cent. These severe grades of anæmia are not common in my experience. In the Munich statistics there were 54 cases with general and extreme anæmia.

Of changes in the blood plasma very little is known.

The *pulse* in typhoid fever presents no special characters. It is increased in rapidity, but not always in proportion to the height of the fever. As a rule, in the first week it is above 100, full in volume and often dicrotic. There is no acute disease with which, in the early stage, a dicrotic pulse is so frequently associated. Even with high fever the pulse may not be greatly accelerated. As the disease progresses the pulse becomes more rapid, feebler, and small. In the extreme prostration of severe

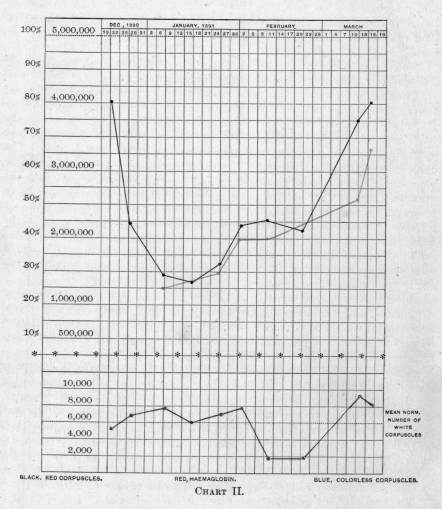

CHART II.

cases it may reach 150 or more, and is a mere undulation—the so-called running pulse. The lowered arterial pressure is manifest in the dusky lividity of the skin and coldness of the hands and feet.

During convalescence the pulse gradually returns to normal, and occasionally becomes very slow. After no other acute fever do we so frequently meet with bradycardia. I have counted the pulse as low as 30, and instances are on record of still fewer beats to the minute.

The *heart-sounds* are at first clear and loud, and free from murmur, but in severe cases, as the prostration develops, the first sound becomes feeble and there is often to be heard, at the apex and along the left sternal margin, a soft systolic murmur. The first sound may be gradually annihilated, as pointed out by Stokes. In the extreme feebleness of the graver forms, the first and second sound become very similar, and the long pause is much shortened (embryocardia). I am much impressed with the rarity of grave heart symptoms in typhoid fever.

Of cardiac complications, *pericarditis* is rare and has been met with chiefly in children and in association with pneumonia. It was not present in any of my cases and occurred in only 14 of the 2,000 Munich post-mortems. *Endocarditis* is also uncommon. I have seen only 2 cases; and there were only 11 cases noted in the Munich records. Myocarditis is more common. The following statement may be made with reference to the condition of the heart-muscle in this disease : In protracted cases the muscle-fibre is usually soft, flabby, and of a pale yellowish-brown color. The softening may be extreme, though rarely of the grade described by Stokes, in which, when held apex up by the vessels, the organ collapsed over the hand, forming a mushroom-like cap. Microscopically, the fibres may show little or no change, even when the impulse of the heart has been extremely feeble. A granular parenchymatous degeneration is common. Fatty degeneration may be present, particularly in long-standing cases with anæmia. The hyaline change is not common. The segmenting myocarditis, in which the cement substance is softened so that the muscle-cells separate, has also been found, but probably as a post-mortem change.

Complications in the Arteries.—Obliteration of large or small arterial trunks is one of the rare complications of typhoid fever. A considerable number of cases are scattered through the literature. The obliteration may be due either to embolism or to thrombosis. In a majority of cases the femoral artery is involved and gangrene of the foot and leg occurs. In several cases there has been obliteration of both femorals with extension of the clot into the aorta with gangrene of both legs. In a case which I saw with Roddick, of Montreal, the obliteration of the left femoral occurred on the sixteenth day. On the twentieth day the patient had pain in the right leg and there was no pulsation in the femoral artery. Gangrene gradually developed in both feet, and death took place in the sixth week. In these cases the condition is probably due to thrombosis, not embolism, and is associated with a blood state which favors clotting, or possibly with a local arteritis. In his recent monograph Keen refers to 46 cases of arterial gangrene, of which 8 were bilateral, 19 on the right side, and 19 on the left.

Thrombi in the Veins.—This is a much more frequent complication, and, according to Murchison, is met with in about 1 per cent of the cases. It occurs most frequently in a crural vein, and more commonly in the left than in the right; due possibly, as suggested by Liebermeister, to the fact that in the left common iliac vein, being crossed by the right iliac artery, the flow of blood is not so free as in the right vein. Thrombosis is indicated by enlargement and œdema of the limb. It is not a very unfavorable complication. In one case of my series the thrombus suppurated and there was pyæmia. Occasionally the thrombosis may extend into the pelvic veins and into the vena cava. In one instance the thrombus was in the right circumflex iliac vein alone, and the superficial veins on the right side of the abdomen were in consequence greatly enlarged. Sudden death has been caused by dislodgment of a thrombus and plugging of the pulmonary artery. Typhoid bacilli have been found in the wall of the vein and in the clot. Keen has collected 128 cases of venous coagula following typhus and typhoid. " Only 4 involved the upper extremity alone, 2 of which were followed by gangrene ; 2 involved both arm and leg, but all the other 124 cases were limited to the lower extremities." I do not think that gangrene ever results from obstruction of the vein alone.

Infarcts in the kidneys, spleen, and lungs are by no means uncommon in typhoid fever. They are associated usually with thrombosis in the arteries, rarely with embolism.

Typhoid Gangrene.—Following blocking of the femoral or popliteal arteries the leg becomes numb and cold. There may be complete anæsthesia with motor paralysis, and occasionally a good deal of pain. There is rarely much swelling ; gradually the skin becomes discolored and the process of dry gangrene begins. When both artery and vein are involved the gangrene is usually moist, and spreads more rapidly. In a number of cases the gangrene is not specially localized to vascular areas ; thus the distribution in the cases collected by Keen is as follows : Ears, 6 cases ; nose, 10 cases ; face, neck, and trunk, 47 cases ; anus, 5 cases ; genitals, 20 cases ; legs, 126 cases.

Digestive System.—Loss of appetite is early, and, as a rule, the relish for food is not regained until convalescence. Thirst is constant, and should be fully and freely gratified. Even when the mind becomes benumbed and the patient no longer asks for water, it should be freely given. The *tongue* presents the changes inevitable in a prolonged fever, but there are no distinctive characters. Early in the disease it is moist, swollen, and coated with a thin white fur, which, as the fever progresses, becomes denser. It may remain moist throughout. In severe cases, particularly those with delirium, the tongue becomes very dry, partly owing to the fact that such patients breathe with the mouth open. It may be covered with a brown or brownish-black fur, or with crusts between which are cracks and fissures. Acute glossitis occurred in one case at the onset of the relapse. In these cases the teeth and lips may be covered with a dark brownish matter called *sordes*—a mixture of food, epithelial *débris*, and micro-organisms. By keeping the mouth and tongue clean from the outset the fissures, which are extremely painful, may be prevented. During convalescence the tongue gradually becomes clean, and the fur is thrown off, almost imperceptibly or occasionally in flakes.

The secretion of saliva is often diminished ; salivation is rare.

Parotitis, not so frequent as in typhus fever, was present in 45 of the 2,000 Munich cases. It occurred in only 2 of my series of fatal cases. Of 428 instances collected by Keen occurring after typhus and typhoid, only 75 followed the latter. Usually unilateral, and in a majority of cases going on to suppuration, it is regarded as a very fatal complication, but recovery has followed in 4 or 5 of my cases. It undoubtedly may arise from extension of inflammation along Steno's duct. This is probably not so serious a form as when it arises from metastatic inflammation. The submaxillary gland may be involved alone. Parotitis may occur after the fever has subsided. A remarkable localized sweating in the parotid region is an occasional sequel of the abscess (see Studies III).

The *pharynx* may be the seat of slight catarrh. Sometimes the fauces are deeply congested. Membranous pharyngitis, a serious and fatal complication, may come on in the third week. Difficulty in swallowing may result from ulcers of the œsophagus, and in one of our cases stricture followed.* - F. A. Packard has also reported a case.

The *gastric symptoms* are extremely variable. Nausea and vomiting are not common. There are instances, however, in which vomiting, resisting all measures, is a marked feature from the outset, and may directly cause death from exhaustion. Vomiting does not often occur in the second and third week, unless associated with some serious complication. In a few of these cases ulcers have been found in the stomach.

Intestinal Symptoms.—Diarrhœa is a very variable symptom, occurring in only 25 or 30 per cent of the cases, and in only about 10 per cent of my cases have the movements been frequent. Of 99 cases under my care during 1897 diarrhœa occurred in only 12. Its absence must not be taken as an indication that the intestinal lesions are of slight extent. I have seen, on several occasions, the most extensive infiltration and ulceration of the Peyer's glands of the small intestine, with the colon filled with solid fæces. The diarrhœa is caused less by the ulcers than by the associated catarrh, and, as in tuberculosis, it is probable that when this is in the large intestine the discharges are more frequent. It is most common toward the end of the first and throughout the second week, but it may not occur until the third or even the fourth week. The number of discharges ranges from 3 to 8 or 10 in the twenty-four hours. They are usually abundant, thin, grayish-yellow, granular, of the consistency and appearance of pea-soup, and resemble very much, as Addison remarked, the normal contents of the small bowel. The reaction is alkaline and the odor offensive. On standing, the discharges separate into a thin serous layer, containing albumin and salts, and a lower stratum, consisting of epithelial *débris,* remnants of food, and numerous crystals of triple phosphates. Blood may be in small amount, and only recognized by the microscope. Sloughs of the Peyer's glands occur either as grayish-yellow fragments or occasionally as ovoid masses, an inch or more in length, in which portions of the bowel tissue

---

* Mitchell, Œsophageal Complications in Typhoid Fever (Studies III).

may be found. The bacilli are not found in the stools until the end of the first or the middle of the second week.

Hæmorrhage from the bowels is a serious complication, occurring in from 3 to 5 per cent of all cases. It had occurred in 99 of the 2,000 fatal Munich cases. In 685 cases treated in my wards, hæmorrhage occurred in 33, and proved fatal in 1.6 per cent of the total series. Of 60

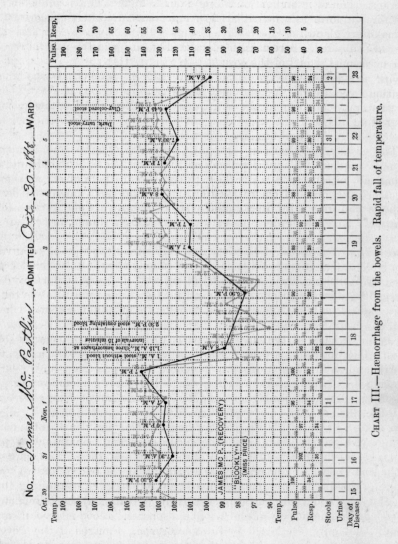

CHART III.—Hæmorrhage from the bowels. Rapid fall of temperature.

cases reported by R. G. Curtin, 28 died. It was present in 3.77 per cent of Murchison's 1,564 cases. There may be only a slight trace of blood in the stools, but too often it is a profuse, free hæmorrhage, which rapidly proves fatal. It occurs most commonly between the end of the second and the beginning of the fourth week, the time of the separation of the sloughs. Occasionally it results simply from the intense hyperæmia. It usually comes on without warning. A sensation of sinking or collapse is experienced by the patient, the temperature falls, and may, as in the annexed chart, drop 8° or 10° in a few hours. Fatal collapse may supervene before the blood appears in the stool. Hæmorrhage usually occurs in cases of considerable severity. Graves and Trousseau held that it was not a very dangerous symptom, but statistics show that death follows in from 30 to 50 per cent of the cases.

It must not be forgotten that melæna may also be part of a general hæmorrhagic tendency (to be referred to later), in which case it is associated with petechiæ and hæmaturia. There may be a special family predisposition to intestinal hæmorrhages in typhoid fever. Thus Pate * reports 34 cases in four generations in one family occurring between the years 1884 and 1891.

Meteorism, a frequent symptom, is not serious if of moderate grade, but when excessive is usually of ill omen. Owing to defective tone in the walls, in severe cases to their infiltration with serum, gas accumulates in the small and large bowels, particularly in the latter. It is rightly held to be to some extent a measure of the intensity of the local lesions. When extreme, it pushes up the diaphragm and interferes very much with the action of the heart and lungs. It undoubtedly also favors perforation.

Abdominal tenderness on pressure and *gurgling* in the right iliac fossa exist in a large proportion of all the cases. The tenderness may be more or less diffuse over the abdomen, but it is commonly limited to the right side. It is rarely excessive, and may be elicited only on deep pressure. Gurgling indicates simply the presence of gas and fluid fæces in the colon and cæcum. In a few instances the pain is very severe at the onset, localized in the right iliac fossa, and may suggest appendicitis.

Occasionally severe pain may be associated with the degeneration of the abdominal muscles, or with rupture of the recti abdominales. It is stated that the thickened ileum may be felt in typhoid fever, and also that the mesenteric glands may be palpable. This is a point of some moment. The resistance and apparent tumor have led to the diagnosis of appendicitis and operation.

Perforation.—Of my 685 cases there were 34 (4.96 per cent) with perforation. In 4,680 cases tabulated by Fitz the mortality from this accident was 6.58 per cent. It is more frequent in men than in women. It is usually indicated by the onset of sudden acute pain in the abdomen, and symptoms of collapse. It is most common at the end of the second or in the third week, but in one of my cases it occurred as early as the eighth day and in another in the sixth week, two weeks after the evening temperature had become normal. In Fitz's series 46.5 per cent occurred in the third or fourth week, 4 cases occurred in the first week, and 1 case as late as the sixteenth week. It is not infrequently associated with hæmorrhage.

---

* North Carolina Medical Journal, September, 1894.

We do not know all the circumstances which lead to perforation. There is certainly no relationship between this accident and the severity of the disease. It occurs not infrequently in very mild cases. Among causes assigned are the taking too early of indigestible food, severe vomiting, excessive meteorism, and ascarides. The tubbing has been accused of increasing the percentage, but Hare's Brisbane statistics do not show it, nor do ours. Perforation of the appendix is not very uncommon, and may cause pain in the right iliac fossa. General peritonitis or a localized abscess may result. Recovery from perforation is undoubtedly possible, though rare. Peritonitis without perforation may also occur by extension from the ulcer or occasionally by rupture of a softened mesenteric gland. It was present in 2.2 per cent of the Munich autopsies.

Symptoms of Perforation.—The cases may be grouped into (*a*) those with abrupt and well-defined onset. In about three fourths of the cases there is a sudden acute pain in the abdomen, followed by marked tenderness, rigidity of the abdominal walls, vomiting, a collapsed, pinched expression, and a small rapid pulse. In cases in which there has been marked tympanites and tenderness the symptoms may be more obscure, and I have once, at least, been deceived by the good quality of the pulse and general condition in the presence of pretty well marked local signs. (*b*) Cases in which the onset is gradual and the symptoms ill-defined. When the patient has been very ill and delirious or comatose, the increasing distention of the abdomen and signs of tenderness on deep pressure may be the only suggestive features. It is to be borne in mind that tympanitic distention is by no means a necessary accompaniment of perforation. The abdomen may be flat, with boardlike hardness. (*c*) In a small group of cases there are no symptoms whatever suggestive of perforation, and it is found accidentally post mortem. These are usually cases which have been desperately ill, and the local features are completely masked by the severity of the toxæmia. Of additional features the fall in temperature is sometimes well marked and suggestive. Obliteration of the liver dullness in front may be almost complete, and would be a very valuable sign were it not for the fact that one sometimes in extreme meteorism finds the same condition. In the absence of local abscess or otitis media the presence of a leucocytosis is a much more important symptom, the value of which in the diagnosis of perforation has been demonstrated by Thayer in several cases in my wards.

The *spleen* is invariably enlarged in typhoid fever, and in a majority of cases the edge can be felt below the costal margin. By the end of the first week the enlargement is evident, unless there is great distention of the colon, when the spleen may be pushed far back and difficult to feel. Even the normal area of dullness may not be obtainable. I have seen a very large spleen post mortem, when during life the increase in size was not observable. Toward the fourth week it diminishes in size. In four of my autopsies it weighed less than normal. Infarcts and abscesses are occasionally found. Rupture of the spleen in typhoid fever, due to a slight blow, has been seen by Bartholow. Spontaneous rupture may also occur.

Liver.—Symptoms on the part of this organ are rare.

(*a*) *Jaundice* is occasionally seen, and may be due to catarrh of the ducts, to toxæmia, to abscess, and occasionally to gall-stones.

(*b*) *Abscess.*—Solitary abscess is exceedingly rare. I have never seen an instance. It may follow the intestinal lesion or more commonly one of the complications, as parotitis or necrosis of bone. Suppurative pylephlebitis, which is more frequent than abscess, may follow perforation of the appendix. Suppurative cholangitis has been described.

(*c*) *Cholecystitis and Cholangitis.*—Recent observations have shown that the gall-bladder in fatal cases often contains typhoid bacilli : 19 of 22 cases in Chiari's series, 7 in 14 of Flexner's. They may be present without causing any mischief, or they may excite an acute inflammation with suppuration, perforation, and peritonitis. The symptoms may occur during the course of the disease or months after convalescence has been established. Three cases have been operated upon at the Johns Hopkins Hospital. Keen has collected 30 cases of perforation. Mason's paper in the Transactions of the Association of American Physicians, vol. xii, and those by Camac and myself * show how important is this complication.

(*d*) *Gall-Stones.*—Bernheim called attention to the frequency of cholelithiasis after typhoid fever. It is probably associated with the presence of typhoid bacilli in the gall-bladder (see under Gall-Stones).

Respiratory System.—*Epistaxis*, an early symptom, precedes typhoid fever more commonly than any other febrile affection. It is occasionally profuse and serious.

Laryngitis is not very common. The ulcers and the perichondritis have already been described. Œdema, apart from ulceration, is rare. In this country the laryngeal complications of typhoid fever seem much less frequent than on the Continent. I have twice only seen perichondritis; both of the cases recovered, one after the expectoration of large portions of the thyroid cartilage.

Keen and Lüning have collected 221 cases of serious surgical complications of the larynx. General emphysema may follow the perforation of an ulcer. Stenosis is a very serious sequence.

From some recent studies it would appear that paralysis of the laryngeal muscles is much more common than we have supposed. Przedborski (Volkmann's Sammlung, No 182) has systematically examined the larynx in 100 consecutive cases and found 25 with paralysis. The condition is nearly always due to neuritis, sometimes in connection with affections of other nerves.

Bronchitis is one of the most frequent initial symptoms. It is indicated by the presence of sibilant râles. The smaller tubes may be involved, producing urgent cough and even slight cyanosis. Collapse and lobular pneumonia may also occur.

Lobar pneumonia is met with under two conditions :

1. It may be the initial symptom of the disease. After an indisposition

---

* Studies in Typhoid Fever, Series III, Johns Hopkins Hospital Reports, vol. vii.

of a day or so, the patient is seized with a chill, has high fever, pain in the side, and within forty-eight hours there are signs of consolidation and the evidences of an ordinary lobar pneumonia. The intestinal symptoms may not develop until toward the end of the first week or later ; the pulmonary symptoms persist, crisis does not occur ; the aspect of the patient changes, and by the end of the second week the clinical picture is that of typhoid fever. Spots may then be present and doubts as to the nature of the case are solved. In other instances, in the absence of a characteristic eruption, the case remains doubtful, and it is impossible to say whether the disease has been pneumonia, in which the so-called typhoid symptoms have developed, or whether it was typhoid fever with early implication of the lungs. This condition may depend upon an early localization of the typhoid bacillus in the lung. I have twice performed autopsies in cases of this *pneumo-typhus*, as it is called by the French and Germans, and can speak positively of its onset with all the symptoms of a frank pneumonia.

2. Lobar pneumonia forms a serious and by no means infrequent complication of the second or third week. It was present in over 8 per cent of the Munich cases. The symptoms are usually not marked. There may be no rusty sputa, and, unless sought for, the condition is frequently overlooked. Infarction, abscess, and gangrene are occasional pulmonary complications.

Hypostatic congestion of the lungs and œdema, due to enfeebled circulation in the later periods of the disease, are very common. The physical signs are defective resonance at the bases, feeble breath-sounds, and, on deep inspiration, moist râles. Pleurisy is by no means an uncommon complication. It was present in about 8 per cent of the Munich autopsies. It may develop at the outset—pleuro-typhoid—or slowly during convalescence, in which case it is almost always purulent. Pneumothorax occasionally develops. Hale White has reported two cases, in both of which pleurisy existed. The condition may be due to straining, or to the rupture of a small pyæmic abscess. Another occasional pulmonary complication is *hæmoptysis*, which I once saw at the height of the disease. It may occur also during convalescence. After death, no lesions of the lungs or bronchi were discovered. Creagh reports a case in which the hæmoptysis caused death.

Nervous System.—*Cerebro-spinal Form.*—As already noted, the disease may set in with intense and persisting headache, or an aggravated form of neuralgia. There are cases in which the effect of the poison is manifested on the nervous system early and with the greatest intensity. There are headache, photophobia, retraction of the neck, marked twitchings of the muscles, rigidity, and even convulsions. In such cases the diagnosis of meningitis is invariably made. I have examined post mortem three such cases, in two of which the diagnosis of cerebro-spinal fever had been made. In not one of them was there any trace of meningeal inflammation, only the most intense congestion of the cerebral and spinal pia. Meningitis, however, may occur, but is extremely rare, as shown by the Munich record, in which there were only 11 among the 2,000 cases. Convulsions, marked opisthotonos, strabismus, and signs of involvement of the cranial nerves are necessary in typhoid fever, as in pneumonia, for the positive diagnosis of meningitis. A number of genuine cases have been reported of late years, and the literature is quite fully given by Ohlmacher * to May, 1897. Wolff has collected 174 cases in which a bacteriological examination was made; in only 2.87 per cent were the typhoid bacilli found. Marked convulsive movements, local or general, with coma and delirium, are seen also in thrombosis of the cerebral veins and sinuses.

Delirium, usually present in very severe cases, is certainly less frequent under a rigid plan of hydrotherapy. It may exist from the outset, but usually does not develop until the second and sometimes not until the third week. It may be slight and only nocturnal. It is, as a rule, a quiet delirium, though there are cases in which the patient is very noisy and constantly tries to get out of bed, and, unless carefully watched, may escape. The patient does not often become maniacal. In heavy drinkers the delirium may have the character of delirium tremens. Even in cases which have no positive delirium, the mental processes are usually dulled and the aspect is listless and apathetic. In severe cases the patient passes into a condition of unconsciousness. The eyes may be open, but he is oblivious to all surrounding circumstances and neither knows nor can indicate his wants. The urine and fæces are passed involuntarily. In this pseudo-wakeful state, or coma vigil, as it is called, the eyes are open and the patient is constantly muttering. The lips and tongue are tremulous; there are twitchings of the fingers and wrists—subsultus tendinum and carphologia. He picks at the bedclothes or grasps at invisible objects. These are among the most serious symptoms of the disease and always indicate danger.

Convulsions in typhoid fever are rare. In children they may occur at the onset. In September, 1896, a child of ten years was admitted in coma following a sudden convulsion after a full meal. This was the starting-point of a severe attack of typhoid. Their rarity may be gathered from the fact that in 2,960 cases Murchison only met with convulsions in 6. They may be associated with an acute encephalitis or with thrombi in the arteries or in the veins. In the case of my late assistant, Dr. Oppenheimer, the convulsions developed on the eighth day of the fever, and proved fatal in twelve hours. Thrombosis of the branches of the left middle cerebral artery was found. In other instances, as in one reported by J. W. Moore, no brain lesions are found. In very nervous women I have seen hysterical convulsions.

Neuritis, which is not uncommon, may be local, or a widespread affection of the nerves of the legs or of both arms and legs.

Local Neuritis.—This may occur during the height of the fever or after convalescence is established. It may set in with agonizing pain, and with sensitiveness of the affected nerve trunks. In two instances I have seen great tenderness of the muscles, and some of these may be cases of myo-

---

* Journal of American Medical Association, 1897, ii.

sitis. There may be extreme sensitiveness of the muscles without any signs of neuritis. The condition may subside without leaving any atrophy. The local neuritis following typhoid fever may affect the nerves of an arm or of a leg, and involve chiefly the extensors, so that there is wrist-drop or foot-drop of the affected limb. Some of the cases are very difficult to separate from those with poliomyelitis.

A curious condition, probably a local neuritis, is that which was first described by Handford as *tender toes*, and which appears to be much more common after the cold-bath treatment. The tips and pads of the toes, rarely the pads at their bases, become exquisitely sensitive, so that the patient can not bear the weight of the bedclothes. There is no discoloration and no swelling, and it disappears usually within a week or ten days.

Multiple neuritis in typhoid fever develops usually during convalescence. The legs may be affected, or the four extremities. The cases are often difficult to differentiate from those with subacute poliomyelitis. Recovery is the rule. Of 4 cases with involvement of arms and legs, 3 recovered completely and 1 improved (Studies II).

Poliomyelitis may develop with the symptoms of acute ascending paralysis and prove fatal in a few days. More frequently it is less acute, and causes either a paraplegia or a limited atrophic paralysis of one arm or leg.

Hemiplegia is a rare complication. Francis Hawkins has collected 17 cases from the literature ; aphasia was present in 12. The lesion is usually thrombosis of the arteries, less often a meningo-encephalitis. The aphasia in children often disappears (Studies III).

True *tetany* occurs sometimes, and a number of cases have developed in certain epidemics. It may set in during the full height of the disease. This complication is extremely rare in this country, and Janeway, so far as I know, has alone reported instances.

Post-febrile *insanity* is perhaps more frequent after typhoid than after any other disease. Wood regards it as confusional insanity, the result of impaired nutrition and exhaustion of the nervous centres. Five cases have come under my observation, in four of which recovery took place (Studies I).

Special Senses.—*Eye.*—Conjunctivitis, simple or phlyctenular, sometimes with keratitis and iritis, may develop. Panophthalmitis has been reported in one case in association with hæmorrhage (Finlay). Loss of accommodation may occur, usually in the asthenia of convalescence. Oculo-motor paralysis has been seen, due probably to neuritis. Retinal hæmorrhages may occur alone or in association with other hæmorrhagic features. Double optic neuritis has been described in the course of the fever. It may be independent of meningitis. Atrophy may follow, but these complications are excessively rare. Cataract may follow inflammation of the uveal tract. Other rare complications are thrombosis of the orbital veins and orbital hæmorrhage. (See De Schweinitz in Keen's monograph for full consideration of the subject.)

Ear.—Otitis media is not infrequent, 2.5 per cent in Hengst's collected cases. We have never found the typhoid bacillus in the discharge. Serious results are rare; only one case of mastoid disease occurred. The otitis may set in with a chill and an aggravation of the fever.

Renal System.—Retention of urine is an early symptom in many cases, and is more frequent in some epidemics than in others. The condition may recur for several weeks. The urine is usually diminished at first, has the ordinary febrile characters, and the pigments are increased. Later in the disease it is more abundant and lighter in color.

Ehrlich has described a reaction, which he believes is rarely met with except in typhoid fever. This so-called *diazo-reaction* is produced as follows: Two solutions are employed, kept in separate bottles: one containing a saturated solution of sulphanilic acid in a solution of hydrochloric acid (50 cc. to 1,000 cc.); the other a half per cent solution of sodium nitrite. To make the test, a few cubic centimetres of urine are placed in a small test-tube with an equal quantity of a mixture of the solution of the sulphanilic acid (40 cc.) and the sodium nitrite (1 cc.), the whole being thoroughly shaken. One cubic centimetre of ammonia is then allowed to flow carefully down the side of the tube, forming a colorless zone above the yellow urine, and at the junction of the two a deep brownish-red ring will be seen if the reaction is present. With normal urine a lighter brownish ring is produced, without a shade of red. The color of the foam of the mixed urine and reagent, and the tint they produce when largely diluted with water, are characteristic, being in both cases of a delicate rose-red if the diazo-reaction be present; but if not, brownish-yellow.

It was present in 136 of 196 cases examined at my clinic (Hewetson, Studies I). It may be present previous to the occurrence of the rash, and as late as the twenty-second day. The value of the test is lessened by its occurrence in cases of miliary tuberculosis, and occasionally in the acute diseases associated with high fever. The toxicity of the urine is much increased in typhoid fever, and the toxic products are eliminated in greater quantities in cases treated with the cold bath.

The renal complications in typhoid fever may be thus grouped:

(*a*) Febrile albuminuria, which is very common and of no special significance; thus, in the first 229 cases admitted to the Johns Hopkins Hospital albuminuria was noted in 164, with tube-casts in 103.

(*b*) Acute nephritis occurring at the onset or during the height of the disease—the *nephro-typhus* of the Germans, the *fièvre typhoïde à forme rénale* of the French—may set in, with all the symptoms of the most intense Bright's disease, masking in many instances the true nature of the malady. After an indisposition of a few days there may be fever, pain in the back, and the passage of a small amount of bloody urine. In 21 of the 229 cases evidence was present of a definite nephritis—much albumin and many tube-casts. In 10 there were also red blood-corpuscles. In 2 there was a genuine hæmorrhagic nephritis. Seven of these 21 cases died—5 from perforation, not one from the renal complication.

(*c*) The nephritis of convalescence. This is more common but less serious. It develops after the fall of the fever, and is usually associated with œdema. It does not present characters different from the ordinary post-febrile nephritis.

(*d*) The remarkable lymphomatous nephritis, described by E. Wagner and others, and already referred to in the section on morbid anatomy, produces, as a rule, no symptoms.

(*e*) *Pyuria* is a not uncommon complication. Blumer (Studies II) has reported 10 cases in my wards. In 7 the colon bacillus was present, in 2 the typhoid bacillus, and in 1 the staphylococcus albus.

(*f*) *Post-typhoid Pyelitis.*—In this the pelves of the kidney and the calices are at first covered with a membranous exudation, but erosion and ulceration may subsequently occur. There may be blood and pus in the urine. This condition occurred in 3 of my cases, in one of which it was associated with extensive membranous inflammation of the bladder.

Simple catarrh of the bladder is rare.

Orchitis is occasionally met with during convalescence. Sadrain collected 16 cases in the literature. It is usually associated with a catarrhal urethritis. Induration or atrophy may occur, and more rarely suppuration. In one case double hydrocele developed suddenly on the nineteenth day (Dunlap).

Osseous System.—Among the most common and troublesome of the sequelæ of the disease are the *bone lesions*. Of 237 cases collected by Keen there were periostitis in 110, necrosis in 85, and caries in 13. They are, I am sure, much more frequent than the figures indicate. Six cases came under my notice in the course of a year, and formed the basis of Parsons' paper (Studies II). The legs are chiefly involved. In Keen's series the tibia was affected in 91 cases, the ribs in 40. A majority of the cases occur after convalescence is established. Of 51 cases in which bacteriological examinations were made, in 13 pyogenic bacteria were found; in 38 there were typhoid bacilli (Keen). The typhoid bone lesion is apt to form what the old writers called a cold abscess. Only a few of the cases are acute. Chronicity, indolence, and a remarkable tendency to recurrence are perhaps the three most striking features of the typhoid bone lesions. If not thoroughly treated sinuses may remain, and typhoid bacilli have been found in these old lesions for as long as seven or more years.

Arthritis is fully considered in Keen's monograph. Rheumatic and septic forms are described, as well as a typhoid arthritis proper. The complication is exceedingly rare, and yet Keen has collected from the literature 84 cases. One of the most important points relating to it is the frequency with which spontaneous dislocations occur, particularly of the hip.

Typhoid Spine.—There is a remarkable disorder of convalescence to which Gibney has given this name. The patient has usually been up and about, and may have had a slight jar or shock, after which he complains of great pain in the back, and of pain on moving the legs. The condition may persist for weeks without fever or any signs of Pott's disease, spondylitis, or neuritis; but there are usually marked nervous or hysterical symptoms. The outlook is good. It is not known upon what this condition depends. It seems to be a neurosis rather than a perispondylitis (Studies I).

The *muscles* may be the seat of the degeneration already referred to, but it rarely causes any symptoms. Hæmorrhage occasionally occurs into the muscles, and late in protracted cases abscesses may develop, sometimes in or between the abdominal muscles.

Post-typhoid Septicæmia and Pyæmia.—Following severe and protracted cases there may be signs of septic infection. After the defervescence the patient may in a week or so present a slight fever, rising to 100° or 101°, with sweats and weakness, but with no signs other than fever to indicate a relapse. There may be with this recurring chills, often of great severity.*

Typhoid pyæmia has its chief manifestation in multiple abscesses, which are by no means uncommon in protracted cases. In a majority of instances these are subcutaneous, or they may take the form of boils, situated about the buttocks, the calves, the thighs, the axillæ, or shoulders. Internal abscesses are less common. We have had in the hospital several instances of extensive perirectal abscess, and I saw with Dr. Salzer an extensive perinephric abscess. In no case from the boils or from the subcutaneous abscesses has the typhoid bacillus been isolated in my wards.

Association of other Diseases.—Erysipelas is a rare complication, most commonly met with during convalescence. In 1,420 cases at Basel it occurred 10 times. Griesinger states that it is met with in 2 per cent.

Measles may develop during the fever or in convalescence. Chickenpox and noma have been reported in children. Pseudo-membranous inflammations may occur in the pharynx, larynx, or genitals. Malarial and typhoid fevers may be associated, but a majority of the cases of so-called typho-malarial fever are either remittent malarial fever or true typhoid. It is interesting to note that among the 685 cases of typhoid fever in not a single instance were the plasmodia found in the blood during the course of the disease. Many of our typhoid fever cases came from malarious regions.

Typhoid fever may attack an individual the subject of tuberculosis. In 4 of my 80 autopsies tuberculous lesions coexisted with those of typhoid fever. Miliary tuberculosis occasionally developed after it, but my personal experience does not warrant the belief held by some writers, that there is a greater susceptibility to tuberculosis after typhoid than after other fevers. Acute miliary tuberculosis and typhoid fever have been met with in the same subject.

In epilepsy and in chronic chorea the fits and movements usually cease during an attack, and in typhoid fever in a diabetic subject the sugar may be absent during the height of the disease.

Varieties of Typhoid.—Typhoid fever presents an extremely com-

---

* See paper on Chills in Typhoid Fever (Studies II).

plex symptomatology. Many forms have been described, some of which present exaggeration of common symptoms, others modification in the course, others again greater intensity of action of the poison on certain organs. As we have seen, when the nervous system is specially involved, it has been called the cerebro-spinal form; when the kidneys are early and severely affected, nephro-typhoid; when the disease begins with pulmonary symptoms, pneumo-typhoid; with pleurisy, pleuro-typhoid; when the disease is characterized throughout by profuse sweats, the sudoral form of the disease. It is a mistake, I think, to recognize or speak of these as varieties. It is enough to remember that typhoid has no fixed and constant course, that it may set in occasionally with symptoms localized in certain organs, and that many of its symptoms are extremely variable—in one epidemic uniform and text-book-like, in another slight or not met with. This diversified symptomatology has led to many clinical errors, and in the absence of the salutary lessons of morbid anatomy it is not surprising that practitioners have so often been led astray. We may recognize with Murchison the following varieties:

1. The *mild* and *abortive* forms. It is very important for the practitioner to recognize the mild type of typhoid fever, often spoken of as gastric fever or even regarded as simple febricula. In this form, the typhus *levissimus* of Griesinger, the symptoms are similar in kind but altogether less intense than in the graver attacks, although the onset may be sudden and severe. The temperature rarely reaches 103°, and the fever of onset may not show the gradual ascending evening record. The spleen is enlarged, the rose-spots may be marked; often they are very few in number. The diarrhœa is variable, often it is not present. In such cases the symptoms may persist for from ten to fourteen days.

In the abortive form the symptoms of onset may be marked with shivering and fever of 103° or even higher. The date of onset is often definite, a point upon which Jürgensen lays great stress. Rose-spots may occur from the second to the fifth day. Early in the second week or at the end of the first week the fever falls, often with profuse sweating, and convalescence is established. In this abortive form relapse may occur and may occasionally prove severe. When typhoid fever prevails extensively these cases are not uncommon. I agree with J. C. Wilson, who states that they are not nearly so common in this country as in Europe.

2. The *grave* form is usually characterized by high fever and pronounced nervous symptoms. In this category, too, come the very severe cases, setting in with pneumonia and Bright's disease, and with the very intense gastro-intestinal or cerebro-spinal symptoms.

3. The *latent* or *ambulatory* form of typhoid fever, which is particularly common in hospital practice. The symptoms are often very slight, and the patient scarcely feels ill enough to go to bed. He has languor, perhaps slight diarrhœa, but keeps about and may even attend to his work throughout the entire attack. In other instances delirium sets in. The worst cases of this form are seen in sailors, who keep up and about, though feeling ill and feverish. When brought to the hospital they often develop

symptoms of a most severe type of the disease. Hæmorrhage or perforation may be the first marked symptom of this ambulatory type. Sir W. Jenner has called attention to the dangers of this form, and particularly to the grave prognosis in the case of persons who have traveled far with the disease in progress.

Hæmorrhagic Typhoid Fever.—This is excessively rare. Among Ouskow's 6,513 cases there were only 4 deaths with general hæmorrhagic diathesis. Only one instance was present in our 685 cases.* Hæmorrhages may be marked from the outset, but more commonly they develop during the course of the disease. The condition is not necessarily fatal. Our case recovered, as did several of those reported by Nicholls from the Royal Victoria Hospital, Montreal.

An *afebrile* typhoid fever is recognized by authors. Liebermeister says that the cases were not uncommon at Basel. The patients presented lassitude, depression, headache, furred tongue, loss of appetite, slow pulse, and even the spots and enlarged spleen. I have no personal knowledge of such cases.

Typhoid Fever in Children.—Cases are not uncommon under the age of ten, but the disease is rare in infants under two years of age. Cases have been reported, however, in sucklings (nine months, Fuller; four and a half months, Ogle), and perforation has been met with in an infant five days old. Epistaxis rarely occurs; the rise in temperature is less gradual; the initial bronchial catarrh is often observed. The nervous symptoms are often prominent; there are wakefulness and delirium; diarrhœa is often absent. The rash may be very slight, but the most copious eruption I have ever seen was in a child of eight. The abdominal symptoms are often mild. Fatal hæmorrhage and perforation are rare. Among the sequelæ, aphasia, noma, and bone lesions may be mentioned as more common in children than in adults. The mortality of typhoid fever in children is low. In cases fatal early in the disease only a careful bacteriological examination can decide whether the swollen Peyer's patches and mesenteric glands—not uncommon in children with fever—depend upon infection with typhoid bacilli.

Typhoid Fever in the Aged.—After the fortieth year the disease runs a less favorable course, and the mortality is very high. Of 64 fatal cases, 7 were over forty years of age; 1 was aged sixty-three, another seventy. The fever is not so high, but complications are more common, particularly pneumonia and heart-failure.

Typhoid Fever in Pregnancy.—The disease is rare in pregnant women. Only 1 case occurred in our 685 cases. The majority of the patients are affected during the first half of pregnancy. Abortion or premature delivery follows, usually in the second week of the disease—in 199 of 310 cases collected by Sacquin. The mortality in pregnant women with typhoid fever is high—19 in 91 cases (Brieger), 17 per cent in 183 cases collected by Vinay. The experience of Brand and of the physicians of the Lyons

* Hamburger, Hæmorrhagic Form of Typhoid (Studies III).

school would show that the cold-bath treatment is not only not contra-indicated, but most efficacious.

Typhoid Fever in the Fœtus.—W. Fordyce, who has recently studied the question most thoroughly, concludes as follows: (1) That typhoid fever could be communicated to the fœtus *in utero*; (2) that as a result of this infection the fœtus might die, and be expelled prematurely; (3) that the fœtus might be born alive but weakly, and evidently suffering from the infection; (4) that the fœtus might be born alive and healthy, having passed through the infection *in utero*. Finally, the infection of the child did not necessarily follow. This last was the case in a fœtus aged five months, whose mother died of typhoid fever in my wards. Flexner found the blood and tissues sterile. J. P. C. Griffith found the Widal reaction in a child seven weeks old, born when the mother had typhoid fever.

Relapse.—Relapses vary in frequency in different epidemics, and, it would appear, in different places. The percentages of different authors range from 3 per cent (Murchison), 11 per cent (Bäumler), to 15 or 18 per cent (Immermann). In Wagner's clinic, from 1882 to 1886, there were 49 relapses in 561 cases. In 685 cases there were 54 relapses.

We may recognize the genuine, the intercurrent, and the spurious relapse.

The *true relapse* sets in after complete defervescence. Irving noted the average duration of the interval in his cases as a little over five days.

In one case there was complete apyrexia for twenty-three days, followed by a relapse of forty-one days' duration; then apyrexia for forty-two days, followed by a second relapse of two weeks' duration. As a rule, two of the three important symptoms—steplike temperature at onset, roseola, and enlarged spleen—should be present to justify the diagnosis of a relapse. The intestinal symptoms are variable. The onset may be abrupt with a chill, or the temperature may have a typical steplike ascent, as shown in Chart I. The number of relapses range from 3 to 5. Da Costa has twice seen 5 relapses. The attack is usually less severe and of shorter duration. Of Murchison's 53 cases, the mean duration of the first attack was about twenty-six days; of the relapse, fifteen days. The mortality of the relapse is not high.

The *intercurrent relapse* is quite common. A series of cases will be found in our Studies in Typhoid Fever. Many protracted cases are of this nature. The temperature drops and the patient improves; but after remaining between 100° and 102° for a few days, the fever again rises and the patient enters upon another attack, which may be even more severe than the original one.

Spurious relapses are very common. They have already been referred to on page 16, under post-typhoid elevations of temperature. They are recrudescences of the fever due to a number of causes. It is not always easy to determine whether a relapse is present, particularly in cases in which the fever persists for only five or seven days without rose-spots and without enlargement of the spleen.

The relapse shows a reinfection from within, but of the conditions favoring its occurrence we as yet know little. Errors in diet are sometimes held responsible and occasionally the rise in temperature follows abruptly upon some indiscretion. Immunity in typhoid is acquired slowly, and we know that even for a long period after the fever has disappeared the typhoid bacilli may be found in the stools, in the spleen, and in the mesenteric glands. Chiari suggests that the reinfection may be associated with the persistence of bacilli in the bile-passages; an indiscretion in diet may cause their discharge into the intestine.

Diagnosis.—There are several points which the physician should remember. In the first place, typhoid fever is the most common of all continued fevers. Secondly, it is extraordinarily variable in its manifestations. Thirdly, there is no such hybrid malady as typho-malarial fever. And lastly, errors in diagnosis are inevitable, even under the most favorable conditions. In at least 4 or 5 cases in our series the diagnosis of typhoid fever was not made until autopsy.

Data for Diagnosis.—(*a*) *General.*—No single symptom or feature is characteristic. The onset is often suggestive, particularly the occurrence of epistaxis, and (if seen from the start) the ascending fever. The steadiness of the fever for a week or longer after reaching the fastigium is an important point. The irregular remittent character in the third week and the intermittent features with chills are common sources of error. While there is nothing characteristic in the pulse, dicrotism is so much more common early in typhoid fever that its presence is always suggestive. The rash is the most valuable single sign, and with the fever usually clinches the diagnosis. The enlarged spleen is of less importance, since it occurs in all febrile conditions, but with the fever and the rash it constitutes the diagnostic triad of the disease. The absence of leucocytosis and the presence of Ehrlich's reaction are valuable accessory signs.

(*b*) *Specific.*—*The Serum Diagnosis.*—The diagnosis of typhoid fever by the isolation of the bacilli during life is difficult. Tapping of the spleen for the purpose is not a justifiable procedure. Cultures from the blood give positive results in only a small number of instances, though during the past year they have been obtained in 6 cases in my wards (N. B. Gwyn). Cultures from the typhoid stools made by the methods of Elsner, Hiss, and others are really not suitable for general clinical purposes. It was accordingly with great satisfaction that the announcement of a comparatively simple method of serum diagnosis was received. In 1894 Pfeiffer showed that cholera spirilla when introduced into the peritonæum of an immunized animal, or when mixed with the serum of immunized animals, lose their motion and break up. This "Pfeiffer's phenomenon" of agglutination and immobilization was thoroughly and systematically studied by Durham, in Gruber's laboratory. It is well, as Welch has pointed out, to bear in mind the importance of this work, since by it was determined the value of the test for the differentiation of bacterial species and for the determination of a previous attack of cholera or of typhoid fever; and also that the immobilization and agglutination was a specific effect of in-

3

fection or intoxication. Widal took the method and made it available in clinical work.

Method of Application.—The tests, as given by Widal, are as follows : (*a*) *Macroscopical.*—The blood or serum to be tested is added either " to a young bouillon culture of the typhoid bacillus or to sterile bouillon, which is then at once inoculated with the bacillus. In the former case the reaction with typhoid serum appears usually within two or three hours, and consists in clarification of the previously turbid fluid and the formation of a clumpy sediment composed of accumulated bacilli. In the latter case the tube is placed in the incubator, and within fifteen hours the reaction is manifested by growth of the bacilli in the form of a sediment at the bottom of the tube, the fluid remaining nearly or quite clear." (*b*) *Microscopic Test.*—The blood or serum is mixed with " a young bouillon culture or with a suspension in bouillon or salt solution of a fresh growth of the typhoid bacillus, and a drop or two of the mixture is examined at once under the microscope. With a dilution of 1 to 10 this microscopic typhoid reaction appears, as a rule, immediately or within a few minutes, and is evidenced by loss of motility and by clumping of the bacilli into masses of various sizes and shapes." Since then various modifications have been introduced and the dilution has been increased, as a rule to 1 to 50 or even higher. Wyatt Johnston introduced the use of the dried blood, which is of great convenience, and has developed the method of work in municipal laboratories. For fuller details the student is referred to the text-books of bacteriology.

Results.—The largest collection of cases has been given by Kneass and Stengel (Gould's Yearbook, 1898). Of 2,283 typhoid cases the reaction was present in 95.5 per cent. In 1,365 non-typhoid cases there was no reaction in 98.4 per cent. The experience in my wards of Block and Gwyn up to March, 1898, shows that in 151 cases the reaction was present in 144. In 4 of the negative cases the clinical course was not certain. A very important point is the time of appearance of the reaction. In only 46 of the last 108 cases was the reaction obtained on the day of admission. In only 26 cases of the series was the reaction present before the seventh day of the disease. It may be long delayed. In 4 cases it developed on the twenty-second, twenth-sixth, thirty-fifth, and forty-second days respectively.

While on the whole the serum reaction is of very great value, there are certain difficulties and objections which must be considered. A perfectly characteristic case with hæmorrhages, rose-spots, etc., may give no reaction throughout. A case of this sort has been reported from my wards by Gwyn, in which a so-called paracolon bacillus was repeatedly isolated from the blood. The Widal reaction was not present at any time during the course of the disease or after convalescence. Brill has reported a series of 17 cases with the clinical features of typhoid fever, but without the Widal reaction.

Common Sources of Error in Diagnosis.—An early and intense localization of the infection in certain organs may give rise to doubt at first.

Cases coming on with severe headache, photophobia, delirium, twitching of the muscles and retraction of the head are almost invariably regarded as *cerebro-spinal meningitis*. Under such circumstances it may for a few days be impossible to make a satisfactory diagnosis. I have thrice performed autopsies on cases of this kind in which no suspicion of typhoid fever had been present, the intense cerebro-spinal manifestations having dominated the scene. Until the appearance of abdominal symptoms, or the rash, it may be quite impossible to determine the nature of the case. Cerebro-spinal meningitis is, however, a rare disease; typhoid fever a very common one, and the onset with severe nervous symptoms is by no means infrequent. Fully one half of the cases of so-called brain-fever belong to this category.

I have already spoken of the misleading pulmonary symptoms, which occasionally develop at the very outset of the disease. The bronchitis rarely causes error, though it may be intense and attract the chief attention. More difficult are the cases setting in with chill and followed rapidly by *pneumonia*. I have brought such a case before the class one week as typical pneumonia, and a fortnight later shown the same case as undoubtedly one of typhoid fever. In another case, in which the onset was with definite pneumonia, no spots developed, and, though there were diarrhœa, meteorism, and the most pronounced nervous symptoms, the doubt still remains whether it was a case of typhoid fever or one of pneumonia in which severe secondary symptoms developed. There is less danger of mistaking the pneumonia which develops at the height of the disease, and yet this is possible, as in a case admitted a few years ago to my wards—a man aged seventy, insensible, with a dry tongue, tremor, ecchymoses upon the wrists and ankles, no rose-spots, enlargement of the spleen, and consolidation of his right lower lobe. It was very natural, particularly since there was no history, to regard such a case as senile pneumonia with profound constitutional disturbance, but the autopsy showed the characteristic lesions of typhoid fever. Early involvement of the pleura or the kidneys may for a time obscure the diagnosis.

Of diseases with which typhoid fever may be confounded, malaria, certain forms of pyæmia, acute tuberculosis, and tuberculous peritonitis are the most important.

From *malarial fever*, typhoid is, as a rule, readily recognized. There is no such disease as typho-malarial fever—that is, a separate and distinct malady. Typhoid fever and malarial fever in rare instances may coexist in the same patient. Of 685 cases of typhoid fever, almost all with blood examinations, and a majority of them coming from malarial regions, in not a single instance were the malarial parasites found in the blood during the fever. There is now no excuse whatever for the continued use by practitioners of the term typho-malarial fever, and still less for the falsification of vital statistics by death certificates signed with this diagnosis. The principle is bad and the practice is worse, since it gives a false sense of security, and may prevent proper measures of prophylaxis. The autumnal type of malarial fever may present a striking similarity in its early days to typhoid fever. Differentiation may be made only by the blood examination. There may be no chills, the remissions may be extremely slight, there is a history perhaps of *malaise*, weakness, diarrhœa, and sometimes vomiting. The tongue is furred and white, the cheeks flushed, the spleen slightly enlarged, and the temperature continuous, or with very slight remissions. The æstivo-autumnal variety of the malarial parasite may not be present in the circulating blood for several days. Every year we have one or two cases in which the diagnosis is in doubt for a few days.

Pyæmia.—The long-continued fever of obscure, deep-seated suppuration, without chills or sweats, may simulate typhoid. The more chronic cases of ulcerative endocarditis are usually diagnosed enteric fever. The presence or absence of leucocytosis is an important aid. The Widal reaction now offers additional and valuable help.

Acute miliary tuberculosis is not infrequently mistaken for typhoid fever. The points in differential diagnosis will be discussed under that disease. *Tuberculous peritonitis* in certain of its forms may closely simulate typhoid fever, and will be referred to in another section.

Puncture of the spleen for the purpose of obtaining cultures is justifiable only in exceptional circumstances.

Prognosis.—(*a*) *Death-rate.*—The mortality is very variable, ranging in private practice from 5 to 12 and in hospital practice from 7 to 20 per cent. In some large epidemics the death-rate has been very low. In the recent outbreak at Maidstone, England, it was between 7 and 8 per cent. In recent years the deaths from typhoid fever have certainly diminished, and, under the influence of Brand, the reintroduction of hydrotherapy has reduced the mortality in institutions in a remarkable manner, even as low as 5 or 6 per cent. Of the 685 cases treated to January 1, 1898, in my wards, 8 per cent died. The death-rate since the introduction of hydrotherapy has been 7.1 per cent. The Metropolitan Fever Hospitals still show a high rate of mortality—about 17 per cent—and Dreschfeld gives 17.18 per cent as the death-rate in the Monsall Fever Hospital for the ten years ending 1894. The last Report of the British Army Medical Department (1896) shows an increase in both incidence and mortality. In the United States army for ten years, to 1896, there was an average annual prevalence of 138.5 cases, with mortality of 19.2 per cent.

(*b*) *Special Features in Prognosis.*—Unfavorable symptoms are high fever, toxic symptoms with delirium, meteorism, and hæmorrhage. Fat subjects stand typhoid fever badly. The mortality in women is greater than in men. The complications and dangers are more serious in the ambulatory form in which the patient has kept about for a week or ten days. Early involvement of the nervous system is a bad indication; and the low, muttering delirium with tremor means a close fight for life. Prognostic signs from the fever alone are deceptive. A temperature above 104° may be well borne for many days if the nervous system is not involved.

(*c*) *Sudden Death.*—It is difficult in many cases to explain this most lamentable of accidents in the disease. There are cases in which neither cerebral, renal, nor cardiac changes have been found; there are instances too in which it does not seem likely that there could have been a special localization of the toxins in the pneumogastric centres. McPhedran, in reporting a case of the kind, in which the post mortem showed no adequate cause of death, suggests that the experiments of McWilliam on sudden cardiac failure probably explain the occurrence of death in certain of the cases in which neither embolism nor uræmia is present. Under conditions of abnormal nutrition there is sometimes induced a state of *delirium cordis*, which may develop spontaneously, or, in the case of animals, on slight irritation of the heart, with the result of extreme irregularity and finally failure of action. Sudden death occurs more frequently in men than in women, according to Dewèvre's statistics, in a proportion of 114 to 26. It may occur at the height of the fever, and, as pointed out by Graves, may also happen during convalescence.

Prophylaxis.—In cities the prevalence of typhoid fever is directly proportionate to the inefficiency of the drainage and the water-supply. There is no truer indication of the sanitary condition of a town than the returns of the number of cases of this disease. With the improvement in drainage the mortality in many cities has been reduced one half or even more. One of the most striking instances is afforded by the city of Munich. Childs has recently reviewed the sanitary history of this town as far as typhoid fever is concerned, and the figures are truly astonishing. The annual mean death-rate per 100,000 inhabitants was from 1851 to 1860, 202.4; from 1861 to 1870, 147.8; from 1871 to 1880, 116.7; from 1881 to 1890, 16; from 1891 to 1896, 5.6.

By most rigid methods of disinfection much may be done to prevent the spread of the infection.

The following procedures, suggested by Gilman Thompson, should be carried out in hospital practice, and, with modifications, in private houses:

1. The best disinfectants of typhoid urine and stools for practical use are (i) a 1 in 500 acidulated solution of corrosive sublimate; (ii) a 1 in 10 crude carbolic-acid solution; (iii) chlorinated lime.

2. Owing to the possibility of injury to plumbing, the carbolic-acid solution is preferable wherever plumbing is concerned. The lime is best for country use in privies and trenches.

3. The disinfectant should be thoroughly mixed with the stool and left in contact with it for fully two hours. Enough of the disinfectant must be added to completely cover the stool with the solution.

4. The bed-pan should be kept ready filled at all times with at least a pint of the disinfectant, into which the stool is at once discharged, and should be cleaned with scalding water and one of the disinfecting solutions.

5. Rectal thermometers, syringes, tubes, and all utensils coming in contact with any of the fecal matter must be disinfected with the corrosive sublimate or carbolic-acid solution.

6. After each stool the patient's perinæum and adjacent parts should be washed and sponged with a 1 in 2,000 corrosive sublimate solution.

7. Nurses and attendants should be cautioned to wash their own hands

thoroughly and immerse them in a 1 in 1,000 corrosive sublimate solution after handling the bed-pan, thermometer, syringe, or patient, or giving sponge- or tub-baths.

8. All linen and bed-clothing used by the patient should be soaked in a 1 in 20 carbolic-acid solution, and subsequently boiled for fully two hours.

9. Disinfection of the stools should be begun as soon as the diagnosis of enteric fever is established, and should be continued for ten days after the temperature has remained at the normal.

10. In localities where a proper drainage system is lacking, the stools should either be mixed with sawdust and cremated or buried in a trench 4 feet deep after being covered with chloride of lime.

When epidemics are prevalent the drinking-water and the milk used in families should be boiled. These precautions should be taken also by recent residents in any locality, and it is much safer for travellers to drink light wines or mineral water rather than ordinary water or milk. Care should be taken to thoroughly cook oysters which have been fattened or freshened in streams contaminated with sewage.

The physician should ever keep in mind the fact that *each individual case of typhoid fever is a focus for the spread of the disease. To carry out effective measures of prophylaxis is quite as much a part of his duty as the care of the patient.*

Antityphoid Vaccine.—A. E. Wright has prepared a vaccine, and at the Army Medical School, Netley, and at Maidstone, he has, in conjunction with D. Semple, inoculated a number of persons. The patients' blood subsequently gave the Widal reaction, and they believe them to have been rendered immune against typhoid fever.

Treatment.—(*a*) **General Management.**—The profession was long in learning that typhoid fever is not a disease to be treated mainly with drugs. Careful nursing and a regulated diet are the essentials in a majority of the cases. The patient should be in a well-ventilated room (or in summer out of doors during the day), strictly confined to bed from the outset, and there remain until convalescence is well established. The bed should be single, not too high, and the mattress should not be too hard. The woven wire bed, with soft hair mattress, upon which are two folds of blanket, combines the two great qualities of a sick-bed, smoothness and elasticity. A rubber cloth should be placed under the sheet. An intelligent nurse should be in charge. When this is impossible, the attending physician should write out specific instructions regarding diet, treatment of the discharges, and the bed-linen.

(*b*) **Diet.**—Those forms of food should be given which are digested with the greatest ease, and which leave behind the smallest amount of residue to form fæces. Some regard should be paid to the fancies of the patient. Milk is the most suitable food. If used alone, three pints at least may be given to an adult in twenty-four hours, always diluted with water, lime-water, or aërated waters. Partially peptonized milk, when not distasteful to the patient, is occasionally serviceable. The stools of a patient on a strict milk diet should be examined with great care, to see if the milk is entirely digested. Fever patients often receive more than they can utilize, in which case masses of curds are seen in the stools, or microscopically fat-corpuscles in extraordinary abundance. Under these circumstances it is best to substitute, for part of the milk, mutton or chicken broths, or beef-juice, or a clear *consommé*, all of which may be made very palatable by the addition of fresh vegetable juices. If, however, diarrhœa exists, animal broths are apt to aggravate it. Some patients will take whey, butter-milk, kumyss, or matzoon when the ordinary milk is distasteful. Thin barley-gruel, well strained, is an excellent food for typhoid-fever patients. Eggs may be given, either beaten up in milk or, better still, in the form of albumen-water. This is prepared by straining the whites of eggs through a cloth and mixing them with an equal quantity of water. It may be flav-ored with lemon, and, if the patient is taking spirits, whisky or brandy is very conveniently given with it. Patients who are unable to take milk can subsist for a time on this alone. The whole egg beaten up in milk or water may be used.

The patient should be given water freely, which may be pleasantly cold. Iced tea, barley-water, or lemonade may also be used, and there is no objec-tion to coffee or cocoa in moderate quantities. Fruits are not, as a rule, allowable, though the juice of lemon or orange may be given. Typhoid patients should be fed at stated intervals through the day. At night it depends upon the general condition of the patient whether he should be aroused from sleep or not. In mild cases it is not well to disturb the patient. When there is stupor, however, the patient should be roused for food at the regular intervals night and day.

Alcohol is not necessary in all cases, but may be given when the weak-ness is marked, the fever high, and the pulse failing. In young healthy adults, without nervous symptoms and without very high fever, it is not required; but when the heart-beat is feeble and the first sound becomes obscure, if there are a muttering delirium, subsultus tendinum, and a dry tongue, brandy or whisky should be freely given. In such a case from eight to twelve ounces of good whisky in the twenty-four hours is a moder-ate amount.

It would be too much like hoisting the teetotaler with his own petard to attribute the high rate of mortality from typhoid fever at the London Temperance Hospital—15 to 16 per cent during the past twenty years—to failure to employ alcohol.

(*c*) **Hydrotherapy.**—The use of water, inside and outside, was no new treatment in fevers at the end of the last century, when James Currie (a friend of Burns and the editor of his poems), wrote his Medical Reports on the Effects of Water, Cold and Warm, as a Remedy in Fevers and other Dis-eases. In this country it was used with great effect and recommended strongly by Nathan Smith, of Yale. Since 1861 the value of bathing in fevers has been specially emphasized by the late Dr. Brand, of Stettin.

Hydrotherapy may be carried out in several different ways, of which, in typhoid fever, the most satisfactory are by sponging, the wet pack, and the full bath.

(*a*) *Cold Sponging.*—The water may be tepid, cold, or ice-cold, according to the height of the fever. A thorough sponge-bath should take from fifteen to twenty minutes. The ice-cold sponging is quite as formidable as the full cold bath, for which, when there is an insuperable objection in private practice, it is an excellent alternative. But frequently it is difficult to get the friends to appreciate the advantages of the sponging. When such is the case, and in children and delicate persons, it can be made a little less formidable by sponging limb by limb and then the back and abdomen.

(*b*) The *cold pack* is not so generally useful in typhoid fever, but in cases with very pronounced nervous symptoms, if the tub is not available, the patient may be wrapped in a sheet wrung out of water at 60° or 65°, and then cold water sprinkled over him with an ordinary watering-pot.

(*c*) *The Bath.*—The tub should be long enough so that the patient can be completely covered except his head. In institutions a rigid system of hydrotherapy should be practiced, following Brand's instructions, with modifications to suit the individual cases. In my clinic, since the practice was introduced by Dr. Lafleur the following plan has been carried out: Every third hour, if the temperature is above 102.5°, the patient is placed in a bath (at 70° Fahr.), which is wheeled to the bedside. In this he remains from fifteen to twenty minutes, and is then taken out, wrapped in a dry sheet, and covered with a light blanket. Enough water is used to cover the patient's body to the neck. The head is sponged during the bath, and, if there is much torpor, cold water is poured over it from a height of a foot or two. The limbs and trunk are rubbed thoroughly, either with the hand or with a suitable "rubber." The rectal temperature is taken immediately after the bath, and again three quarters of an hour later. The patient often complains bitterly when in the bath, and shivering and blueness are almost a constant sequence. Food is usually given with a stimulant after the bath. The only contra-indications are peritonitis and hæmorrhage. Neither bronchitis nor pneumonia is so regarded. The accompanying chart (Chart IV) shows the number of baths and the influence on the fever during two days of treatment. The good effects of the baths are: (1) The reduction of the fever; (2) the intellect becomes clearer, the stupor lessens, and the muscular twitchings disappear; (3) a general tonic action on the nervous system and particularly on the heart; (4) insomnia is lessened, the patient usually falling asleep for two or three hours after each bath; and (5), most important of all, the mortality is, under this plan of treatment, reduced to a minimum. This *Brand method*, as it is called, has steadily advanced in favor both in hospital and private practice, in spite of the difficulties and the unpleasant features necessarily connected with it.

The spongings frequently have to be substituted for the tubs in cases of extreme weakness, or when there is much meteorism, or when there is marked collapse after the baths. While a temperature at 70° is usually well borne, in the case of children and delicate persons the luke-warm bath gradually cooled may be employed.

The results of hydrotherapy are very gratifying. By it in general hospitals from 6 to 8 patients in every hundred cases are saved. In institutions in which the expectant or other plans of treatment are employed, there is a mortality of from 12 to 15 per cent. In many it is as high as 17 per cent. There is a remarkable uniformity in the death-rate in hospitals which carry out hydrotherapy. Since July, 1890, when we introduced

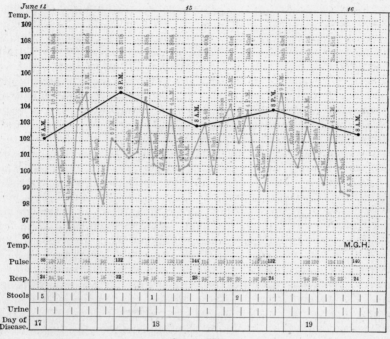

CHART IV.

hydrotherapy, there have been treated in my wards, to January 1, 1898, 652 cases. The total mortality has been 7.1 per cent. This includes all cases, those admitted and dying within twenty-four or forty-eight hours, and those in which the diagnosis was only made at autopsy.* Still more striking by contrast are the figures published by F. E. Hare from the Brisbane Hospital (Practitioner, September, 1897). Of 1,828 cases treated on the general or expectant plan, the mortality was 14.8 per cent. Of 1,902 cases treated since the introduction of hydrotherapy, the mortality was only 7.5 per cent. Equally good results have been obtained by J. C. Wilson and Tyson in Philadelphia, by Gilman Thompson in New York, and at numerous hospitals in Germany and France. The important question comes up whether the serious complications of the disease are increased by hydrotherapy. My own statistics bear out Hare's that the remarkable life-

---

* From May, 1889, when the hospital was opened, to July, 1890, the ordinary expectant plan was followed. The mortality, inclusive of this period, is 8 per cent.

saving in hydrotherapy does not depend upon a diminution in the number of fatal cases from perforation or from hæmorrhage. The percentage of perforation cases in my series was 4.96, which is a little under the average. At Brisbane it was 2.9 per cent, both before and after the introduction of bathing. Hæmorrhage occurs in from 3 to 5 per cent of the cases. In my series it occurred in 4.9 per cent of all cases since the introduction of hydrotherapy. The Brisbane statistics give before the introduction of hydrotherapy 1.8 per cent of fatal cases, and after the introduction 1.2 per cent. A careful study of the recent statistics shows that neither perforation nor hæmorrhage is more frequent with hydrotherapy. As to relapse, it is more difficult to speak, the percentage varies so widely—from 3 to 16. It must be remembered that more cases are saved to have relapse. My percentage of 7.88 is somewhat above the average, but the increase in the relapses is not so great as to seriously impugn the treatment. Hydrotherapy does not probably shorten the duration of the stay in hospital, which was forty-two days in my series. We do not, however, send out our typhoid cases until they are quite strong and well.

(*d*) **Medicinal Treatment.**—In hospital practice medicines are not often needed. A great majority of my cases do not receive a dose. In private practice it may be safer, for the young practitioner especially, to order a mild fever mixture. The question of medicinal antipyretics is important: they are used far too often and too rashly in typhoid fever. An occasional dose of antifebrin or antipyrin may do no harm, but the daily use of these drugs is most injurious. Quinine in moderate doses is still much employed. The local use of guiacol on the skin, $\mathrecorded{3}$ ss painted on the flank, causes a prompt fall in the temperature.

Antiseptic Medication.—Very laudable endeavors have been made in many quarters to introduce methods of treatment directed toward the destruction of the typhoid bacilli, or the toxic agent which they produce, but so far without success. Good results have been claimed from the carbolic acid and iodine treatment. Others advocate corrosive sublimate or calomel, β-naphthol, the salicin preparations and guiacol. I can testify to the inefficiency of the carbolic acid and iodine and of the β-naphthol. With the mercurial preparations I have no experience. Fortunately for the patients, a majority of these medicines meet one of the two objects which Hippocrates says the physician should always have in view—they do no harm. Irrigation of the colon has been recommended, with a view to washing out the toxic matters (Mosler, Seibert).

(*e*) **Eliminative and Antiseptic Treatment.**—Based on the erroneous view that the bacterial growth is chiefly in the intestine itself, Thistle and others have advocated what is known as the eliminative and antiseptic treatment. The elimination is attempted by thorough evacuation of the bowels daily, and the other factor in the treatment is the use of intestinal antiseptics, of which salol is recommended. If, as in cholera, the bacilli developed and produced the poison in the intestinal contents, there might be some reasonableness in this method, but the bacilli multiply in the intestinal walls, in the mesenteric glands, and in the spleen. They are sometimes not found in the stools until the end of the second week. An important objection to the use of purgatives is the fact that in any large series of cases those with diarrhœa do badly. Graves remarked that "the patients who have escaped active purgation before admission will get through the disease with little or no tympanites." The preliminary calomel purge, so much used, is unnecessary.

(*f*) **Antitoxine Treatment.**—In spite of many experiments and clinical trials the results are still unsatisfactory. An antityphoid serum has been placed on the market, and a few cases have been reported with rapid improvement.

(*g*) **Treatment of the Special Symptoms.**—The abdominal pain and tympanites are best treated with fomentations or turpentine stupes. The latter, if well applied, give great relief. Sir William Jenner used to lay great stress on the advantages of a well-applied turpentine stupe. He directed it to be applied as follows : A flannel roller was placed beneath the patient, and then a double layer of thin flannel, wrung out of very hot water, with a drachm of turpentine mixed with the water, was applied to the abdomen and covered with the ends of the roller.

The *meteorism* is a difficult and distressing symptom to treat. When the gas is in the large bowel, a tube may be passed or a turpentine enema given. For tympanites, with a dry tongue, turpentine was extensively used by the older Dublin physicians, and it was introduced into this country by the late George B. Wood. Unfortunately, it is of very little service in the severer cases, which too often resist all treatment. Sometimes, if beef-juice and albumen-water are substituted for milk, the distention lessens. Charcoal, bismuth, and β-naphthol may be tried.

For the *diarrhœa*, if severe—that is, if there are more than three or four stools daily—a starch and opium enema may be given ; or, by the mouth, a combination of bismuth, in large doses, with Dover's powder ; or the acid diarrhœa mixture, acetate of lead (grs. 2), dilute acetic acid (♏ 15–20), and acetate of morphia (gr. $\frac{1}{6}$–$\frac{1}{8}$). The stools should be examined to see that the diarrhœa is not aggravated by the presence of curds.

Constipation is present in many cases, and though I have never seen it do harm, yet it is well every third or fourth day to give an ordinary enema. If a laxative is needed during the course of the disease, the Hunyadijanos or Friedrichshall water may be given.

Hæmorrhage from the bowels is best treated with full doses of acetate of lead and opium. As absolute rest is essential, the greatest care should be taken in the use of the bed-pan. It is perhaps better to allow the patient to pass the motions into the draw-sheet. Ice may be freely given, and the amount of food should be restricted for eight or ten hours. If there is a tendency to collapse, stimulants should be given, and, if necessary, hypodermic injections of ether. The patient may be spared the usual styptic mixtures with which he is so often drenched. Turpentine is warmly recommended by certain authors.

Peritonitis.—In a majority of the cases this is an inevitably fatal complication, though recovery is possible. If the peritonitis be due to perforation, the question of laparotomy should be immediately discussed. Orders should be issued to the nurse, and in hospitals to the house physicians, to watch carefully for the first symptoms of peritonitis. The recent results are most gratifying. Finney (Studies III) and Keen have recently reviewed the whole question. The latter has collected 83 cases with 16 recoveries. The danger of delay is illustrated by the following figures: Of 15 cases operated on within twelve hours, 4 recovered; of 20 cases operated on between the twelfth and twenty-fourth hour, 6 recovered; of 13 cases operated on in the second twenty-four hours only 1 recovered. No case is so desperate, unless actually moribund, as to be without some hope in the hands of a good surgeon.

Bone Lesions.—The typhoid periostitis in the ribs or in the tibia does not always go on to suppuration, though, as a rule, it requires operation. Unless the practitioner is accustomed to do very thorough surgical work, he should hand over the patient to a competent surgeon, who will clear out the diseased parts with the greatest thoroughness. Recurrence is inevitable unless the operation is complete.

For the progressive *heart-weakness* alcohol, strychnine hypodermically in full doses, digitalis, and hypodermic injections of ether may be tried.

The *nervous symptoms* of typhoid fever are best treated by hydrotherapy. One special advantage of this plan is that the restlessness is allayed, the delirium quieted, and sedatives are rarely needed. In the cases which set in early with severe headache, meningeal symptoms, and high fever, the cold bath, or in private practice the cold pack, should be employed. An ice-cap may be placed on the head, and if necessary morphia administered hypodermically. The practice, in such cases, of applying blisters to the nape of the neck and to the extremities is, to paraphrase Huxham's words, an *unwholesome severity*, which should long ago have been discarded by the profession. For the nocturnal restlessness, so distressing in some cases, Dover's powder should be given. As a rule, if a hypnotic is indicated, it is best to give opium in some form. Pulmonary complications should, if severe, receive appropriate treatment.

In protracted cases very special care should be taken to guard against *bed-sores*. Absolute cleanliness and careful drying of the parts after an evacuation should be enjoined. The patient should be turned from side to side and propped with pillows, and the back can then be sponged with spirits. On the first appearance of a sore, the water- or air-bed should be used.

(*h*) **The Management of Convalescence.**—Convalescents from typhoid fever frequently cause greater anxiety than patients in the attack. The question of food has to be met at once, as the patient develops a ravenous appetite and clamors for a fuller diet. My custom has been not to allow solid food until the temperature has been normal for ten days. This is, I think, a safe rule, leaning perhaps to the side of extreme caution; but, after all, with eggs, milk toast, milk puddings, and jellies, the patient can take a fairly varied diet. Many leading practitioners allow solid food to a patient so soon as he desires it. Peabody gives it on the disappearance of the fever; the late Austin Flint was also in favor of giving solid food early. I had an early lesson in this matter which I have never forgotten. A young lad in the Montreal General Hospital, in whose case I was much interested, passed through a tolerably sharp attack of typhoid fever. Two weeks after the evening temperature had been normal, and only a day or two before his intended discharge, he ate several mutton chops, and within twenty-four hours was in a state of collapse from perforation. A small transverse rent was found at the bottom of an ulcer which was in process of healing. It is not easy to say why solid food, particularly meats, should disagree, but in so many instances an indiscretion in diet is followed by slight fever, the so-called *febris carnis*, that it is in the best interests of the patient to restrict the diet for some time after the fever has fallen. An indiscretion in diet may indeed precipitate a relapse. The patient may be allowed to sit up for a short time about the end of the first week of convalescence, and the period may be prolonged with a gradual return of strength. He should move about slowly, and when the weather is favorable should be in the open air as much as possible. He should be guarded at this period against all unnecessary excitement. Emotional disturbance not infrequently is the cause of recrudescence of the fever. Constipation is not uncommon in convalescence and is best treated by enemata. A protracted diarrhœa, which is usually due to ulceration in the colon, may retard recovery. In such cases the diet should be restricted to milk, and the patient should be confined to bed; large doses of bismuth and astringent injections will prove useful.

The recrudescence of the fever does not require special measures. The treatment of the relapse is essentially that of the original attack.

Among the dangers of convalescence may be mentioned tuberculosis, which is said by Murchison to be more common after this than after any other fever. There are facts in the literature favoring this view, but it is a rare sequel in this country.

II. TYPHUS FEVER.

Definition.—An acute infectious disease characterized by sudden onset, a maculated rash, marked nervous symptoms, and a termination, usually by crisis, about the end of the second week.

Etiology.—The disease is known by the names of hospital fever, spotted fever, jail fever, camp fever, and ship fever, and in Germany is called *exanthematic* typhus, in contradistinction to *abdominal* typhus.

Typhus is now a rare disease. Sporadic cases occur from time to time in the large centers of population, but epidemics are infrequent. In this country during the past ten years there have been very few outbreaks. In New York in 1881–'82 735 cases were admitted into the Riverside Hospital; in Philadelphia a small epidemic occurred in 1883 at the Philadelphia Hospital.

The special elements in the etiology of typhus are overcrowding and poverty. As Hirsch tersely puts it, " Die Geschichte des Typhus ist die des menschlichen Elends." Overcrowding, lack of cleanliness, intemperance, and bad food are predisposing causes. The disease still lurks in the worst quarters of London and Glasgow, and is seen occasionally in New York and Philadelphia. It is more common in Great Britain and Ireland than in other parts of Europe. During 1897 there were only 3 cases of typhus in London fever hospitals. Murchison held that typhus might originate spontaneously under favorable conditions. This opinion is suggested by the occurrence of local outbreaks under circumstances which render it difficult to explain its importation, but the analogy of other infectious diseases is directly against it. In 1877 there occurred a local outbreak of typhus at the House of Refuge, in Montreal, in which city the disease had not existed for many years. The overcrowding was so great in the basement rooms of the refuge that at night there were not more than 88 cubic feet of space to each person. Eleven individuals were affected. It was not possible to trace the source of infection.

Typhus is one of the most highly contagious of febrile affections. In epidemics nurses and doctors in attendance upon the sick are almost invariably attacked. There is no disease which has so many victims in the profession. In the extensive epidemic in the early and middle part of this century many hundred physicians died in the discharge of their duty. Casual attendance upon cases in limited epidemics does not appear to be very risky, but when the sick are aggregated in wards the poison appears concentrated and the danger of infection is much enhanced. Bedding and clothes retain the poison for a long time.

The microbe of typhus fever has not yet been determined. Streptobacilli, diplococci, and an ascomycete have been described in the blood and tissues, but the question still remains open for investigation.

Morbid Anatomy.—The anatomical changes are those which result from intense fever. The blood is dark and fluid; the muscles are of a deep red color, and often show a granular degeneration, particularly in the heart; the liver is enlarged and soft and may have a dull clay-like lustre; the kidneys are swollen; there is moderate enlargement of the spleen, and a general hyperplasia of the lymph-follicles. Peyer's glands are not ulcerated. Bronchial catarrh is usually, and hypostatic congestion of the lungs often, present. The skin shows the petechial rash.

Symptoms.—**Incubation.**—This is placed at about twelve days, but it may be less. There may be ill-defined feelings of discomfort. As a rule, however, the *invasion* is abrupt and marked by chills or a single rigor, followed by fever. The chills may recur during the first few days, and there is headache with pains in the back and legs. There is early prostration, and the patient is glad to take to his bed at once. The temperature is high at first, and may attain its maximum on the second or third day. The pulse is full, rapid, and not so frequently dicrotic as in typhoid. The tongue is furred and white, and there is an early tendency to dryness. The face is flushed, the eyes are congested, the expression is dull and stupid. Vomiting may be a distressing symptom. In severe cases mental symptoms are present from the outset, either a mild febrile delirium or an excited, active, almost maniacal condition. Bronchial catarrh is common.

Stage of Eruption.—From the third to the fifth day the eruption appears—first upon the abdomen and upper part of the chest, and then upon the extremities and face; developing so rapidly that in two or three days it is all out. There are two elements in the eruption: a subcuticular mottling, "a fine, irregular, dusky red mottling, as if below the surface of the skin some little distance, and seen through a semi-opaque medium" (Buchanan); and distinct papular rose-spots which change to petechiæ. In some instances the petechial rash comes out with the rose-spots. Collie describes the rash as consisting of three parts—rose-colored spots which disappear on pressure, dark-red spots which are modified by pressure, and petechiæ upon which pressure produces no effect. In children the rash at first may present a striking resemblance to that of measles, and give as a whole a curiously mottled appearance to the skin. The term mulberry rash is sometimes applied to it. In mild cases the eruption is slight, but even then is largely petechial in character. As the rash is largely hæmorrhagic, it is permanent and does not disappear after death. Usually the skin is dry, so that sudaminal vesicles are not common. It is stated by some authors that a distinctive odor is present. During the second week the general symptoms are much aggravated. The prostration becomes more marked, the delirium more intense, and the fever rises. The patient lies on his back with a dull expressionless face, flushed cheeks, injected conjunctivæ, and contracted pupils. The pulse increases in frequency and is feebler; the face is dusky, and the condition becomes more serious. Retention of urine is common. Coma-vigil is frequent, a condition in which the patient lies with open eyes, but quite unconscious; with it there may be subsultus tendinum and picking at the bedclothes. The tongue is dry, brown, and cracked, and there are sordes on the teeth. Respiration is accelerated, the heart's action becomes more and more enfeebled, and death takes place from exhaustion. In favorable cases, about the end of the second week occurs the crisis, in which, often after a deep sleep, the patient awakes feeling much better and with a clear mind. The temperature falls, and although the prostration may be extreme, convalescence is rapid and relapse very rare. This abrupt termination by crisis is in striking contrast to the mode of termination in typhoid fever.

Fever.—The temperature rises steadily during the first four or five days, and the morning remissions are not marked. The maximum is usually attained by the fifth day, when the temperature may be 105°, 106°, or 107°. In mild cases it seldom rises above 103°. After reaching its maximum the fever generally continues with slight morning remissions until the twelfth or fourteenth day, when the crisis occurs, during which the temperature may fall below normal within twelve or twenty-four hours. Preceding a fatal termination, there is usually a rapid rise in the fever to 108° or even 109°.

The heart may early show signs of weakness. The first sound becomes feeble and almost inaudible, and a systolic murmur at the apex is not infrequent. Hypostatic congestion of the lungs occurs in all severe cases.

The brain symptoms are usually more pronounced than in typhoid, and the delirium is more constant.

The urine in typhus shows the usual febrile increase of urea and uric acid. The chlorides diminish or disappear. Albumin is present in a large proportion of the cases, but nephritis seldom occurs.

Variations in the course of the disease are naturally common. There are malignant cases which rapidly prove fatal within two or three days; the so-called *typhus siderans*. On the other hand, during epidemics there are extremely mild cases in which the fever is slight, the delirium absent, and convalescence is established by the tenth day.

Complications and Sequelæ.—Broncho-pneumonia is perhaps the most common complication. It may pass on to gangrene. In certain epidemics gangrene of the toes, the hands, or the nose, and in children noma or cancrum oris, have occurred. Meningitis is rare. Paralyses, which are probably due to a post-febrile neuritis, are not very uncommon. Septic processes, such as parotitis and abscesses in the subcutaneous tissues and in the joints, are occasionally met with. Nephritis is rare. Hæmatemesis may occur.

Prognosis.—The mortality ranges in different epidemics from 12 to 20 per cent. It is very slight in the young. Children, who are quite as frequently attacked as adults, rarely die. After middle age the mortality is high, in some epidemics 50 per cent. Death usually occurs toward the close of the second week and is due to the toxæmia. In the third week it more commonly results from pneumonia.

Diagnosis.—During an epidemic there is rarely any doubt, for the disease presents distinctive general characters. Isolated cases may be very difficult to distinguish from typhoid fever. While in typical instances the eruption in the two affections is very different, yet taken alone it may be deceptive, since in typhoid fever a roseolous rash may be abundant and there may be occasionally a subcuticular mottling and even petechiæ. The difference in the onset, particularly in the temperature, is marked; but cases in which it is important to make an accurate diagnosis are not usually seen until the fourth or fifth day. The suddenness of the onset, the greater frequency of the chill, and the early prostration are the distinctive features in typhus. The brain symptoms too are earlier. It is easy to put down on paper elaborate differential distinctions, which are practically useless at the bedside, particularly when the disease is not prevailing as an epidemic. In sporadic cases the diagnosis is sometimes extremely difficult. I have seen Murchison himself in doubt, and more than once I have known a diagnosis to be deferred until the *sectio cadaveris*. Severe cerebro-spinal fever may closely simulate typhus at the outset, but the diagnosis is usually clear within a few days. Malignant variola also has certain features in common with severe typhus, but the greater extent of the hæmorrhages and the bleeding from the mucous membranes make the diagnosis clear within a short time. The rash at first resembles that of measles, but in the latter the eruption is brighter red in color, often crescentic or irregular in arrangement, and appears first on the face.

The frequency with which other diseases are mistaken for typhus is shown by the fact that during and following the epidemic of 1881 in New York 108 cases were wrongly diagnosed—one eighth of the entire number —and sent to the Riverside Hospital (F. W. Chapin).

Treatment.—The general management of the disease is like that of typhoid fever. Hydrotherapy should be thoroughly and systematically employed. Judging from the good results which we have obtained by this method in typhoid cases with nervous symptoms much may be expected from it. Certain authorities have spoken against it, but it should be given a more extended trial. Medicinal antipyretics are even less suitable than in typhoid, as the tendency to heart-weakness is often more pronounced. As a rule, the patients require from the outset a supporting treatment; water should be freely given, and alcohol in suitable doses, according to the condition of the pulse.

The bowels may be kept open by mild aperients. The so-called specific medication, by sulphocarbolates, the sulphides, carbolic acid, etc., is not commended by those who have had the largest experience. The special nervous symptoms and the pulmonary symptoms should be dealt with as in typhoid fever. In epidemics, when the conditions of the climate are suitable, the cases are best treated in tents in the open air.

III. RELAPSING FEVER (*Febris recurrens*).

Definition.—A specific infectious disease caused by the spirochæte (spirillum) of Obermeier, characterized by a definite febrile paroxysm which usually lasts six days and is followed by a remission of about the same length of time, then by a second paroxysm, which may be repeated three or even four times, whence the name relapsing fever.

Etiology.—This disease, which has also the names "famine fever" and "seven-day fever," has been known since the early part of the eighteenth century, and has from time to time extensively prevailed in Europe especially in Ireland. It is common in India, where the conditions for its development seem always to be present, and where it has been specially studied by Vandyke Carter, of Bombay. It was first seen in this country in 1844, when cases were admitted to the Philadelphia Hospital, which are described by Meredith Clymer in his work on fevers. Flint saw cases in 1850–'51. In 1869 it prevailed extensively in epidemic form in New York and Philadelphia; since then it has not appeared.

The special conditions under which it develops are similar to those of typhus fever. Overcrowding and deficient food are the conditions which seem to promote the rapid spread of the virus. Neither age, sex, nor season seems to have any special influence. It is a contagious disease and may be communicated from person to person, but is not so contagious as typhus. Murchison thinks it may be transported by fomites. One attack does not confer immunity from subsequent attacks. In 1873 Obermeier described an organism in the blood which is now recognized as the specific agent. This spirillum, or more correctly spirochæte, is from 3 to 6 times the length of the diameter of a red blood-corpuscle, and forms a narrow spiral filament which is readily seen moving among the red corpuscles during a paroxysm. They are present in the blood only during the fever. Shortly before the crisis and in the intervals they are not found, though small glistening bodies, which are stated to be their spores, appear in the blood. The disease has been produced in human beings by inoculation with blood taken during the paroxysm. It has also been produced in monkeys. Bed-bugs may suck out the spirilla, and Tictin reproduced the disease by injecting into a healthy monkey blood sucked by a bug from an infected monkey. Nothing is yet known with reference to the life history of the spirochæte. It has not been found in the secretions or excretions.

Morbid Anatomy.—There are no characteristic anatomical appearances in relapsing fever. If death takes place during the paroxysm the spleen is large and soft, and the liver, kidneys, and heart show cloudy swelling. There may be infarcts in the kidneys and spleen. The bone marrow has been found in a condition of hyperplasia. Ecchymoses are not uncommon.

Symptoms.—The *incubation* appears to be short, and in some instances the attack develops promptly after exposure; more frequently, however, from five to seven days elapse.

The *invasion* is abrupt, with chill, fever, and intense pain in the back and limbs. In young persons there may be nausea, vomiting, and convulsions. The temperature rises rapidly and may reach 104° on the evening of the first day. Sweats are common. The pulse is rapid, ranging from 110 to 130. There may be delirium if the fever is high. Swelling of the spleen can be detected early. Jaundice is common in some epidemics. The gastric symptoms may be severe. There are seldom intestinal symptoms. Cough may be present. Occasionally herpes is noted, and there may be miliary vesicles and petechiæ. During the paroxysm the blood invariably shows the spirochæte, and there is usually a leucocytosis (Ouskow). After the fever has persisted with severity or even with an increasing intensity for five or six days the crisis occurs. In the course of a few hours, accompanied by profuse sweating, sometimes by diarrhœa, the temperature falls to normal or even subnormal, and the period of apyrexia begins.

The crisis may occur as early as the third day, or it may be delayed to the tenth; it usually comes, however, about the end of the first week. In delicate and elderly persons there may be collapse. The convalescence is rapid, and in a few days the patient is up and about. Then in a week, usually on the fourteenth day, he again has a rigor, or a series of chills; the fever returns and the attack is repeated. A second crisis occurs from the twentieth to the twenty-third day, and again the patient recovers rapidly. As a rule, the relapse is shorter than the original attack. A second and a third may occur, and there are instances on record of even a fourth and a fifth. In epidemics there are cases which terminate by crisis on the seventh or eighth day without the occurrence of relapse. In protracted cases the convalescence is very tedious, as the patient is much exhausted.

Relapsing fever is not a very fatal disease. Murchison states that the mortality is about 4 per cent. In the enfeebled and old, death may occur at the height of the first paroxysm.

Complications are not frequent. In some epidemics nephritis and hæmaturia have occurred. Pneumonia appears to be frequent and may interrupt the typical course of the disease. The acute enlargement of the

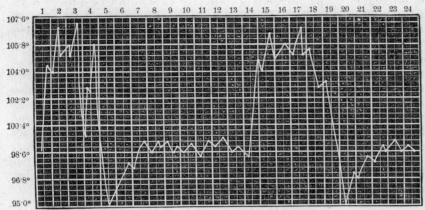

CHART V.—Relapsing Fever (Murchison).

spleen may end in rupture, and the hæmorrhage from the stomach, which has been met with occasionally, is probably associated with this enlargement. Post-febrile paralyses may occur. Ophthalmia has followed certain epidemics, and may prove a very tedious and serious complication. Jaundice has already been mentioned. In pregnant women abortion usually takes place.

Diagnosis.—The onset and general symptoms may not at first be distinctive. At the beginning of an epidemic the cases are usually regarded as anomalous typhoid; but once the typical course is followed in a case the diagnosis is clear. The blood examination is distinctive.

Treatment.—The paroxysm can neither be cut short nor can its recurrence be prevented. It might be thought that quinine, with its powerful action, would certainly meet the indications, but it does not seem to have the slightest influence. The disease must be treated like any other continued fever by careful nursing, a regular diet, and ordinary hygienic measures. Of special symptoms, pains in the back and in the limbs and joints demand opium. In enfeebled persons the collapse at the crisis may be serious, and stimulants with ammonia and digitalis should be given freely.

4

IV. SMALL-POX (*Variola*).

Definition.—An acute infectious disease characterised by an eruption which passes through the stages of papule, vesicle, pustule, and crust. The mucous membranes in contact with the air may also be affected. Severe cases may be complicated with cutaneous and visceral hæmorrhages.

Etiology.—It has not yet been determined in what country small-pox originated. The disease is said to have existed in China many centuries before Christ. The *pesta magna* described by Galen (and of which Marcus Aurelius died) is believed to be small-pox. In the sixth century it prevailed, and subsequently, at the time of the Crusades, became widespread. It was brought to America by the Spaniards early in the sixteenth century. The first accurate account was given by Rhazes, an Arabian physician who lived in the ninth century, and whose admirable description is available in Greenhill's translation for the Sydenham Society. In the seventeenth century a thorough study of the disease was made by the illustrious Sydenham, who still remains one of the most trustworthy authorities on the subject.

Special events in the history of the disease are the introduction of inoculation into Europe, by Lady Mary Wortley Montagu, in 1718, and the discovery of vaccination by Jenner, in 1796.

Small-pox is one of the most virulent of contagious diseases, and persons exposed, if unprotected by vaccination, are almost invariably attacked. There are instances on record of persons insusceptible to the disease. It is said that Diemerbroeck, a celebrated Utrecht professor in the seventeenth century, was not only himself exempt, but likewise many members of his family. One of the nurses in the small-pox department of the Montreal General Hospital stated that she had never been successfully vaccinated, and she certainly had no mark. Such instances, however, of natural immunity are very rare. An attack may not protect for life. There are undoubted cases of a second, reputed instances, indeed, of a third attack.

Age.—Small-pox is common at all ages, but is particularly fatal to young children. The *fœtus in utero* may be attacked, but only if the mother herself is the subject of the disease. The child may be born with the rash out or with the scars. More commonly the fœtus is not affected, and children born in a small-pox hospital, if vaccinated immediately, may escape the disease; usually, however, they die early.

Sex.—Males and females are equally affected.

Race.—Among aboriginal races small-pox is terribly fatal. When the disease was first introduced into America the Mexicans died by thousands, and the North American Indians have also been frequently decimated by this plague. It is stated that the negro is especially susceptible, and the mortality is greater—about 42 per cent in the black, against 29 per cent in the white (W. M. Welch).

The contagium develops in the system of the small-pox patient and is reproduced in the pustules. It exists in the secretions and excretions, and in the exhalations from the lungs and the skin. The dried scales constitute by far the most important element, and as a dust-like powder are distributed everywhere in the room during convalescence, becoming attached to clothing and various articles of furniture. The disease is probably contagious from a very early stage, though I think it has not yet been determined whether the contagion is active before the eruption develops. The poison is of unusual tenacity and clings to infected localities. It is conveyed by persons who have been in contact with the sick and by fomites. During epidemics it is no doubt widely spread in street-cars and public conveyances. It must not be forgotten that an unprotected person may contract a very virulent form of the disease from the mild varioloid. The question of aërial transmission, of great importance in connection with the situation of hospitals, can not be regarded as finally settled. Certain facts are in its favor, as those reported by Young. Of 36 cases which occurred within 500 yards of the Hastings small-pox pavilion, the percentage of small-pox attacks to population ranged from 4.2 within the 100-yard circle to 0.2 in the 400- to 500-yard circle.

The disease smoulders here and there in different localities, and when conditions are favorable becomes epidemic. Perhaps the most remarkable instance in modern times of the rapid extension of the disease occurred in Montreal in 1885. Small-pox had been prevalent in that city between 1870 and 1875, when it died out, in part owing to the exhaustion of suitable material and in part owing to the introduction of animal vaccination. The health reports show that the city was free from the disease until 1885. During these years vaccination, to which many of the French Canadians are opposed, was much neglected, so that a large unprotected population grew up in the city. On February 28th a Pullman-car conductor, who had travelled from Chicago, where the disease had been slightly prevalent, was admitted into the Hôtel-Dieu, the civic small-pox hospital being at the time closed. Isolation was not carried out, and on the 1st of April a servant in the hospital died of small-pox. Following her decease, with a negligence absolutely criminal, the authorities of the hospital dismissed all patients presenting no symptoms of contagion, who could go home. The disease spread like fire in dry grass, and within nine months there died in the city, of small-pox, 3,164 persons.

The nature of the *contagium* of small-pox is still unknown. Weigert and others have described micro-organisms in the pock, but they are the ordinary pus cocci, and the part which they play in the affection is by no means certain. Still less definite are the observations on the occurrence of sporozoa in the pocks. It is not a little remarkable that in a disease which is rightly regarded as the type of all infectious maladies, the specific virus still remains unknown.

Morbid Anatomy.—A section of a papule as it is passing into the vesicular stage shows in the *rete mucosum*, close to the true skin, an area in which the cells are smooth, granular, and do not take the staining fluid. This represents a focus of coagulation-necrosis due, according to Weigert, to the presence of micrococci. Around this area there is active inflammatory reaction, and in the vesicular stage the rete mucosum presents reticuli, or spaces, which contain serum, leucocytes, and fibrin filaments. The central depression or umbilication corresponds to the area of primary necrosis. In the stage of maturation the reticular spaces become filled with leucocytes and many of the cells of the rete mucosum become vesicular. The papillæ of the true skin below the pustule are swollen and infiltrated with embryonic cells to a variable degree. If the suppuration extends into this layer, scarring inevitably results; but if it is confined to the upper layer, this does not necessarily follow. In the hæmorrhagic cases, red corpuscles pass out in large numbers from the vessels and occupy the vesicular spaces. They infiltrate also the deeper layers of the epidermis in the skin adjacent to the papules. Frequently a hair-follicle passes through the centre of a papule.

In the mouth the pustules may be seen upon the tongue and the buccal mucosa, and on the palate. The eruption may be abundant also in the pharynx and the upper part of the œsophagus. In exceptionally rare cases the eruption extends down the œsophagus and even into the stomach. Swelling of the Peyer's follicles is not uncommon; the pustules have been seen in the rectum.

In the larynx the eruption may be associated with a fibrinous exudate and sometimes with œdema. Occasionally the inflammation penetrates deeply and involves the cartilages. In the trachea and bronchi there may be ulcerative erosions, but true pocks, such as are seen on the skin, do not occur. There are no special lesions of the lungs, but congestion and broncho-pneumonia are very common. The liver is sometimes fatty. A diffuse hepatitis, associated with intense congestion of the vessels and migration of the leucocytes, has been described; Weigert has noted small areas of necrosis.

There is nothing special in the condition of the blood, and even in the most malignant cases there are no microscopic alterations. In the blood-drop, however, it will be seen that the corpuscles, instead of forming rouleaux, are aggregated into irregular clumps. An active leucocytosis is present. The heart occasionally shows myocardial changes, parenchymatous and fatty; endocarditis and pericarditis are uncommon. French writers have described an endarteritis of the coronary vessels in connection with small-pox. The spleen is markedly enlarged. Apart from the cloudy swelling and areas of coagulation-necrosis, lesions of the kidneys are not common. Nephritis may occur during convalescence. Chiari has called attention to the frequency of orchitis in this disease; there are scattered areas of necrosis with cell infiltration.

In the hæmorrhagic form extravasations are found on the serous and mucous surfaces, in the parenchyma of organs, in the connective tissues, and about the nerve-sheaths. In one instance I found the entire retro-peritoneal tissue infiltrated with a large coagulum, and there were also extensive extravasations in the course of the thoracic aorta. Hæmorrhages in the bone-marrow have also been described by Golgi. There may be hæmorrhages into the muscles. Ponfick has described the spleen as very firm and hard in hæmorrhagic small-pox, and such was the case in seven instances which I examined. The liver has been described as fatty in these rapid cases, but in 5 of my 7 cases it was of normal size, dense, and firm. In 2 it was large and fatty; but one man had necrosis of the tibia, and the other was a drunkard. The ecchymoses are scattered over the meninges of the brain and cord, and in one case there was a clot in the right ventricle. In 5 of the cases there were areas of hæmorrhagic infarction of the lung. In four instances the pelves of the kidney were blocked with dark clots, which extended into the calices and down the ureters. In one instance the coats of the bladder were uniformly hæmorrhagic and not a trace of normal tissue could be seen. The extravasations in the mucous membrane of the stomach and intestines were numerous and large. Peyer's glands were swollen and prominent in four instances.

Symptoms.—Three forms of small-pox are described:

1. *Variola vera;* (*a*) Discrete, (*b*) Confluent.

2. *Variola hæmorrhagica;* (*a*) Purpura variolosa or black small-pox; (*b*) Hæmorrhagic pustular form, variola hæmorrhagica pustulosa.

3. *Varioloid,* or small-pox modified by vaccination.

1. **Variola Vera.**—The affection may be conveniently described under various stages: (*a*) *Incubation.*—" From nine to fifteen days; oftenest twelve." I have seen it develop on the eighth day after exposure to infection, and there are well-authenticated instances in which the stage of incubation has been prolonged to twenty days. It is unusual for patients to complain of any symptoms in this stage.

(*b*) *Invasion.*—In adults a chill and in children a convulsion are common initial symptoms. There may be repeated chills within the first twenty-four hours. Intense frontal headache, severe lumbar pains, and vomiting are very constant features. The pains in the back and in the limbs are more severe in the initial stage of this than of any other eruptive fever, and their combination with headache and vomiting is so suggestive that in epidemics precautionary measures may often be taken several days before the eruption decides positively the nature of the disease. The temperature rises quickly, and may on the first day be 103° or 104°. The pulse is rapid and full, not often dicrotic. In severe cases there may be marked delirium, particularly if the fever is high. The patient is restless and distressed, the face is flushed, and the eyes are bright and clear. The skin is usually dry, though occasionally there are profuse sweats. One can not judge from these initial symptoms whether a case is likely to be discrete or confluent, as the most intense backache and fever may precede a very mild attack.

In this stage of invasion the so-called initial rashes may occur, of which two forms can be distinguished—the diffuse, scarlatinal, and the macular or measly form; either of which may be associated with petechiæ and occupy a variable extent of surface. In some instances they are general, but as a rule they are limited, as pointed out by Simon, either to the lower abdominal areas, to the inner surfaces of the thighs, and to the lateral thoracic region, or to the axillæ. Occasionally they are found over the extensor surfaces, particularly in the neighborhood of the knees and elbows. These rashes, usually purpuric, are often associated with an erythematous or erysipelatous blush. The scarlatinal rash may come out as early as the second day and be as diffuse and vivid as in a true scarlatina. The measly rash may also be diffuse and identical in character with that of measles. Urticaria is only occasionally seen. It was present once in my Montreal cases. Apparently these initial rashes are more abundant in some epidemics

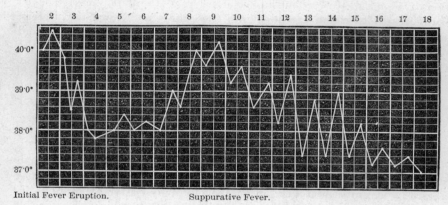

Initial Fever Eruption.   Suppurative Fever.

CHART VI.—True small-pox.

than in others; thus they were certainly more numerous in the Montreal epidemics between 1870 and 1875 than they were in the more extensive epidemic in 1885. They occur in from 10 to 16 per cent of cases. In the cases under my care in the small-pox department at the Montreal General Hospital the percentage was 13.* As will be subsequently mentioned these initial rashes have considerable diagnostic value.

(c) *Eruption.*—(1) In the *discrete form*, usually on the fourth day, small red spots appear on the forehead, particularly at the junction with the hair, and on the wrists. Within the first twenty-four hours from their appearance they occur on other parts of the face and on the extremities, and a few are seen on the trunk. As the rash comes out the temperature falls, the general symptoms subside, and the patient feels comfortable. On the fifth or sixth day the papules change into vesicles with clear summits. Each one is elevated, circular, and presents a little depression in the centre, the so-called umbilication. About the eighth day the vesicles change into pustules, the umbilication disappears, the flat top assumes a globular form and becomes grayish yellow in color, owing to the contained pus. There is an areola of injection about the pustules and the skin between them is swollen. This maturation first takes place on the face, and follows the order of the appearance of the eruption. The temperature now rises— secondary fever—and the general symptoms return. The swelling about the pustules is attended with a good deal of tension and pain in the face;

---

* The Initial Rashes of Small-pox. Canada Medical and Surgical Journal, 1875.

the eyelids become swollen and closed. There is a well-marked leucocytosis in the stage of suppuration. In the discrete form the temperature of maturation does not usually remain high for more than twenty-four or twenty-six hours, so that on the tenth or eleventh day the fever disappears and the stage of convalescence begins. The pustules rapidly dry, first on the face and then on the other parts, and by the fourteenth or fifteenth day desquamation may be far advanced on the face. There may be in addition vesicles in the mouth, pharynx, and larynx, causing soreness and swelling in these parts, with loss of voice. Whether pitting takes place depends a good deal upon the severity of the disease. In a majority of cases Sydenham's statement holds good, that " it is very rarely the case that the distinct small-pox leaves its mark."

(2) *The Confluent Form.*—With the same initial symptoms, though usually of greater severity, the rash appears on the fourth, or, according to Sydenham, on the third day. The more the eruption shows itself before the fourth day, the more sure it is to become confluent (Sydenham). The papules at first may be isolated and it is only later in the stage of maturation that the eruption is confluent. But in severer cases the skin is swollen and hyperæmic and the papules are very close together. On the feet and hands, too, the papules are thickly set; more scattered on the limbs; and quite discrete on the trunk. With the appearance of the eruption the symptoms subside and the fever remits, but not to the same extent as in the discrete form. Occasionally the temperature falls to normal and the patient may be very comfortable. Then, usually on the eighth day, the fever again rises, the vesicles begin to change to pustules, the hyperæmia about them becomes intense, the swelling of the face and hands increases, and by the tenth day the pustules have fully maturated, many of them have coalesced, and the entire skin of the head and extremities is a superficial abscess. The fever rises to 103° or 104°, the pulse is from 110 to 120, and there is often delirium. As pointed out by Sydenham, salivation in adults and diarrhœa in children are common symptoms of this stage. There is usually much thirst. The eruption may also be present in the mouth, and usually the pharynx and larynx are involved and the voice is husky. Great swelling of the cervical lymphatic glands occurs. At this stage the patient presents a terrible picture, unequalled in any other disease; one which fully justifies the horror and fright with which small-pox is associated in the public mind. Even when the rash is confluent on the face, hands, and feet, the pustules remain discrete on the trunk. The danger, as pointed out by Sydenham, is in proportion to the number upon the face. " If upon the face they are as thick as sand it is no advantage to have them few and far between on the rest of the body." In fatal cases, by the tenth or eleventh day the pulse gets feebler and more rapid, the delirium is marked, there is subsultus, sometimes diarrhœa, and with these symptoms the patient dies. In other instances between the eighth and eleventh day hæmorrhagic symptoms develop. When recovery takes place, the patient enters on the eleventh or twelfth day the period of—

(d) *Desiccation.*—The pustules break and the pus exudes and forms crusts. Throughout the third week the desiccation proceeds and in cases of moderate severity the secondary fever subsides; but in others it may persist until the fourth week. The crusts in confluent small-pox adhere for a long time and the process of scarring may take three or four weeks. The crusts on the face fall off, but the tough epidermis of the hands and feet may be shed entire. We had in the small-pox department of the Montreal General Hospital several moulds in epithelium of the hands and feet.

2. **Hæmorrhagic small-pox** occurs in two forms. In one the special symptoms appear early and death follows in from two to six days. This is the so-called petechial or black small-pox—*purpura variolosa*. In the other form the case progresses as one of ordinary variola, and it is not until the vesicular or pustular stage that hæmorrhage takes place into the pocks or from the mucous membranes. This is sometimes called *variola hæmorrhagica pustulosa.*

Hæmorrhagic small-pox is more common in some epidemics than in others. It is less frequent in children than in adults. Of 27 cases admitted to the small-pox department of the Montreal General Hospital there were 3 under ten years, 4 between fifteen and twenty, 9 between twenty and twenty-five, 7 between twenty-five and thirty-five, 3 between thirty-five and forty-five, and 1 above fifty. Young and vigorous persons seem more liable to this form. Several of my cases were above the average in muscular development. Men are more frequently affected than women; thus in my list there were 21 males and only 6 females. The influence of vaccination is shown in the fact that of the cases 14 were unvaccinated, while not one of the 13 who had scars had been revaccinated.

The clinical features of the forms of hæmorrhagic small-pox are somewhat different.

In *purpura variolosa* the illness starts with the usual symptoms, but with more intense constitutional disturbance. On the evening of the second or on the third day there is a diffuse hyperæmic rash, particularly in the groins, with small punctiform hæmorrhages. The rash extends, becomes more distinctly hæmorrhagic, and the spots increase in size. Ecchymoses appear on the conjunctivæ, and as early as the third day there may be hæmorrhages from the mucous membranes. Death may take place before the rash appears. This is truly a terrible affection and well developed cases present a frightful appearance. The skin may have a uniformly purplish hue and the unfortunate victim may even look plum-colored. The face is swollen and large conjunctival hæmorrhages with the deeply sunken corneæ give a ghastly appearance to the features. The mind may remain clear to the end. Death occurs from the third to the sixth day; thus in thirteen of my cases it took place on or before this date. The earliest death was on the third day and there were no traces of papules. There may be no mucous hæmorrhages; thus in one case of a most virulent character death occurred without bleeding early on the fourth day. Hæmaturia is perhaps most common, next hæmatemesis, and melæna was noticed in a third of the cases. Metrorrhagia was present in one only of the six females on my list. Hæmoptysis occurred in five cases. The pulse in this form of small-pox is rapid and often hard and small. The respirations are greatly increased in frequency and out of all proportion to the intensity of the fever. In the case of a negro, whose respirations the morning after admission were 32 and temperature 101°, after examining the lungs and finding nothing to account for the relatively rapid breathing, my suspicions were aroused, and even on the dark skin I was able on careful inspection to detect hæmorrhages in and about the papules.

In *variola pustulosa hæmorrhagica* the disease progresses as an ordinary case of severe variola, and the hæmorrhages do not develop until the vesicular or pustular stage. The earlier the hæmorrhage the greater is the danger. There are undoubtedly instances of recovery when the bleeding has taken place at the stage of maturation. Bleeding from the mucous membranes is also common in this form, and the great majority of the cases prove fatal, usually on the seventh, eighth, or ninth day.

There is a form of hæmorrhagic small-pox in which bleeding takes place into the pocks in the vesicular stage and is followed by a rapid abortion of the rash and a speedy recovery. Six instances of this kind came under my observation.* In 4 the hæmorrhage took place on the fourth day; in 2 on the fifth day, just at the time of transition of the papule into the vesicle. Extravasation took place chiefly into the pocks on the lower extremities and trunk, in only two instances occurring in those on the arms. The eruption in all proved abortive, and no patients under my care with an equal extent of eruption made such rapid recoveries. With these cases are to be grouped those in which the hæmorrhages occur in the pustules of the legs in patients who have in their delirium got out of bed and wandered about. This modified form of hæmorrhagic small-pox is also described by Scheby-Buch.

3. **Varioloid.**—This term is applied to the modified form of small-pox which affects persons who have been vaccinated. It may set in with abruptness and severity, the temperature reaching 103°. More commonly it is in every respect milder in its initial symptoms, though the headache and backache may be very distressing. The papules appear on the evening of the third or on the fourth day. They are few in number and may be confined to the face and hands. The fever drops at once and the patient feels perfectly comfortable. The vesiculation and maturation of the pocks take place rapidly and there is no secondary fever. There is rarely any scarring. As a rule, when small-pox attacks a person who has been vaccinated within five or six years the disease is mild, but there are instances in which it is very severe, and it may even prove fatal.

There are several forms of rash; thus in what has been known as horn-pox, crystalline pox, and wart-pox the papules come out in numbers on the third or fourth day, and by the fifth or sixth day have dried to a hard, horny consistence.

---

* Clinical Notes on Small-pox. Montreal, 1876.

Writers describe a *variola sine eruptione*, which is met with during epidemics in young persons who have been well vaccinated, and who present simply the initial symptoms of fever, headache, and backache. In a somewhat extensive experience in Montreal I do not remember to have met with an instance of this kind, or indeed to have heard of one.

We do not now see the modified form of small-pox, resulting from inoculation, in which by the seventh or eighth day a pustule forms at the seat of inoculation; after this general fever sets in, and with it, about the eleventh day, appears a general eruption, usually limited in degree.

Complications.—Considering the severity of many of the cases and the general character of the disease, associated with multiple foci of suppuration, the complications in small-pox are remarkably few.

Laryngitis is serious in three ways: it may produce a fatal œdema of the glottis; it is liable to extend and involve the cartilages, producing necrosis; and by diminishing the sensibility of the larynx, it may allow irritating particles to reach the lower air-passages, where they excite bronchitis or broncho-pneumonia.

Broncho-pneumonia is indeed one of the most common complications, and is almost invariably present in fatal cases. Lobar pneumonia is rare. Pleurisy is common in some epidemics.

The cardiac complications are also rare. In the height of the fever a systolic murmur at the apex is not uncommon; but endocarditis, either simple or malignant, is rarely met with. Pericarditis too is very uncommon. Myocarditis seems to be more frequent, and may be associated with endarteritis of the coronary vessels.

Of complications in the digestive system, parotitis is rare. In severe cases there is extensive pseudo-diphtheritic angina. Vomiting, which is so marked a symptom in the early stage, is rarely persistent. Diarrhœa is not uncommon, as noted by Sydenham, and is very constantly present in children.

Albuminuria is frequent, but true nephritis is rare. Inflammation of the testes and of the ovaries may occur.

Among the most interesting and serious complications are those pertaining to the nervous system. In children convulsions are common. In adults the delirium of the early stage may persist and become violent, and finally subside into a fatal coma. Post-febrile insanity is occasionally met with during convalescence, and very rarely epilepsy. Many of the old writers spoke of paraplegia in connection with the intense backache of the early stage, but it is probably associated with the severe agonising lumbar and crural pains and is not a true paraplegia. It must be distinguished from the form occurring in convalescence, which may be due to peripheral neuritis or to a diffuse myelitis (Westphal). The neuritis may, as in diphtheria, involve the pharynx alone, or it may be multiple. Of this nature, in all probability, is the so-called pseudo-tabes, or *ataxie variolique*. Hemiplegia and aphasia have been met with in a few instances, the result of encephalitis.

Among the most constant and troublesome complications of small-pox are those involving the skin. During convalescence boils are very frequent and may be severe. Acne and ecthyma are also met with. Local gangrene in various parts may occur.

Arthritis may develop, usually in the period of desquamation, and may pass on to suppuration. Acute necrosis of the bone is sometimes met with.

A remarkable secondary eruption (recurrent small-pox) occasionally occurs after desquamation.

Special Senses.—The eye affections which were formerly so common and serious are not now so frequent, owing to the care which is given to keeping the conjunctivæ clean. A catarrhal and purulént conjunctivitis is common in severe cases. The secretions cause adhesions of the eyelids, and unless great care is taken a diffuse keratitis is excited, which may go on to ulceration and perforation. Iritis is not very uncommon. Otitis media is an occasional complication, and usually results from an extension of the disease through the Eustachian tubes.

Prognosis.—In unprotected persons small-pox is a very fatal disease. In different epidemics the death-rate is from 25 to 35 per cent. In William M. Welch's report from the Municipal Hospital, Philadelphia, of 2,831 cases of variola, 1,534—i. e., 54.18 per cent—died, while of 2,169 cases of varioloid only 28—i. e., 1.29 per cent—died. The hæmorrhagic form is invariably fatal, and a majority of those attacked with the severer confluent forms die. In young children it is particularly fatal. In the Montreal epidemic of 1885 and 1886, of 3,164 deaths there were 2,717 under ten years. The intemperate and debilitated succumb more readily to the disease. As Sydenham observed, the danger is directly proportionate to the intensity of the disease on the face and hands. " When the fever increases after the appearance of the pustules, it is a bad sign; but, if it is lessened on their appearance, that is a good sign " (Rhazes). Very high fever, with delirium and subsultus, are symptoms of ill omen. The disease is particularly fatal in pregnant women and abortion usually takes place. It is not, however, uniformly so, and I have twice known severe cases to recover after miscarriage. Moreover, abortion is not inevitable. Very severe pharyngitis and laryngitis are fatal complications.

Death results in the early stage from the action of the poison upon the nervous system. In the later stages it usually occurs about the eleventh or twelfth day, at the height of the eruption. In children, and occasionally in adults, the laryngeal and pulmonary complications prove fatal.

Diagnosis.—During an epidemic, the initial chill, followed by fever, headache, vomiting, and the severe pain in the back, are symptoms which should put the attending physician on his guard. Mistakes arise in the initial stage owing to the presence of the scarlatinal or measly rashes which may be extremely deceptive. The scarlatinal rash has not always the intensity of the true rash of this disease. In my Montreal experience I did not meet with an instance in which this rash led to an error, though I heard of several cases in which the mistake was made. These are doubtless the instances to which the older writers refer of scarlet fever and small-pox occurring together. The measly rash can not always be distinguished from true measles, instances of which may be mistaken for the initial rash. I found in the ward one morning a young man who had been sent in on the previous evening with a diagnosis of small-pox. He had a fading macular rash with distinct small papules, which had not, however, the shotty hardness of variola. In the evening this rash was less marked, and as I felt sure that a mistake had been made, he was disinfected and sent home. In another instance a child believed to have small-pox was admitted, but it proved to have simply measles. Neither of these cases took small-pox. In a third case, which I saw at the City Hospital, the mottled papular rash was mistaken for small-pox and the young man sent to the hospital. I saw him the day after admission, when there was no question that the disease was measles and not variola. Less fortunate than the other cases, he took small-pox in a very severe form. The general condition of the patient and the nature of the prodromal symptoms are often better guides than the character of the rash. In any case it is not well, as a rule, to send a patient to a small-pox hospital until the characteristic papules appear about the forehead and on the wrists.

In the most malignant type of hæmorrhagic small-pox the patient may die before the characteristic rash develops, though as a rule small, shotty papules may be felt about the wrists or at the roots of the hairs. In only one of twenty-seven cases of hæmorrhagic small-pox, in which death occurred on the third day, did inspection fail to reveal the papules. In three cases in which death took place on the fourth day the characteristic rash was beginning to appear.

The disease may be mistaken for cerebro-spinal fever, in which purpuric symptoms are not uncommon. A four-year-old child was taken suddenly ill with fever, pains in the back and head, and on the second or third day petechiæ appeared on the skin. There were retraction of the head, and marked rigidity of the limbs. The hæmorrhages became more abundant; and finally hæmatemesis occurred and the child died on the sixth day. At the post mortem there were no lesions of cerebro-spinal fever, and in the deeply hæmorrhagic skin the papules could be readily seen. The postmortem diagnosis of small-pox was unhappily confirmed by the mother taking the disease and dying of it.

It might be thought scarcely possible to mistake any other disease for small-pox in the pustular stage. Yet I had an instance of a young man sent to me with a copious pustular eruption, chiefly on the trunk and covered portions of the body, which, so far as the pustules themselves were concerned, was almost identical with that of variola; but the history and the distribution left no question that it was a pustular syphilide. It is not to be forgotten, however, that fever, which was absent in this case, may be present in certain instances of diffuse pustular syphilis. Lastly, chicken-pox and small-pox may be confounded. Indeed, sometimes it is not easy to distinguish between them, though in well-defined cases of varicella the more vesicular character of the pustules, their irregularity, the short stage of invasion, the slight constitutional disturbance, and the greater intensity of the rash on the trunk, should make the diagnosis clear. It is stated that the Chicago case, which was the starting-point in Montreal of the epidemic of 1885, was regarded as varicella and not isolated. If so, the mistake was one which led to one of the most fatal of modern outbreaks of the disease.

Glanders in the pustular form has been mistaken for small-pox, and I know of an instance (during an epidemic) which was isolated on the supposition that it was variola.

Treatment.—In the interests of public health cases of small-pox should invariably be removed to special hospitals, since it is impossible to take the proper precautions in private houses. The general hygienic arrangements of the room should be suitable for an infectious disease. All unnecessary furniture and the curtains and carpets should be removed. The greatest care should be taken to keep the patient thoroughly clean, and the linen should be frequently changed. The bedclothing should be light. It is curious that the old-fashioned notion, which Sydenham tried so hard to combat, that small-pox patients should be kept hot and warm, still prevails; and I have frequently had to protest against the patient being, as Sydenham expresses it, stifled in his bed. Special care should be taken to sterilize thoroughly everything that has been in contact with the patient.

In the early stage the pain in the back and limbs requires opium, which, as advised by Sydenham, may be freely given. The diet should consist of milk and broths, and of " all articles which give no trouble to digestion." Cold drinks may be freely given. Barley-water and the Scotch borse (oatmeal and water) are both nutritious and palatable. After the preliminary vomiting, which is often very hard to check by ordinary measures, the appetite is usually good, and, if the throat is not very sore, patients with the confluent form take nourishment well. In the hæmorrhagic cases the vomiting is usually aggravated and persistent.

The fever when high must be kept within limits, and it is best to use either cold sponging or the cold bath. When the pyrexia is combined with delirium and subsultus, the patient should be placed in a bath at 70°, and this repeated as often as every three hours if the temperature rises above 103°. When it is not practicable to give the cold bath, the cold pack can be employed. These measures are much preferable in small-pox to the administration of medicinal antipyretics.

The treatment of the eruption has naturally engaged the special attention of the profession. The question of the preventing of pitting, so much discussed, is really not in the hands of the physician. It depends entirely upon the depth to which the individual pustules reach. After trying all sorts of remedies, such as puncturing the pustules with nitrate of silver, or treating them with iodine and various ointments, I came to Sydenham's conclusion that in guarding the face against being disfigured by the scars " the only effect of oils, liniments, and the like, was to make the white scurfs slower in coming off." There is, I believe, something in protecting the ripening papules from the light, and the constant application on the face and hands of lint soaked in cold water, to which antiseptics such as carbolic acid or bichloride may be added, is perhaps the most suitable local treatment. It is very pleasant to the patient, and for the face it is well to make a mask of lint, which can then be covered with oiled silk. When the crusts begin to form, the chief point is to keep them thoroughly moist, which may be done with oil or glycerin. This prevents the desiccation and diffusion of the flakes of epidermis. Vaseline is particularly useful, and at this stage may be freely used upon the face. It frequently relieves the itching also. For the odor, which is sometimes so characteristic and disagreeable, the dilute carbolic solutions are probably best. If the eruption is abundant on the scalp, the hair should be cut short to prevent matting and decomposition of the crusts. During convalescence frequent bathing is advisable, because it helps to soften the crusts. The care of the eyes is particularly important. The lids should be thoroughly cleansed three or four times a day, and the conjunctivæ washed with some antiseptic solution. In the confluent cases, when the eyelids are much swollen and the lids glued together, it is only by watchfulness that keratitis can be prevented. The mouth and throat should be kept clean, and if crusts form in the nose they should be softened by frequent injections. Ice can be given, and is very grateful when there is much angina. In moderate cases, so soon as the fever subsides the patient should be allowed to get up, a practice which Sydenham warmly urged. The diarrhœa, when severe, should be checked with paregoric. When the pulse becomes feeble and rapid, stimulants may be freely given. The delirium is occasionally maniacal and may require chloroform, but for the nervous symptoms the bath or cold pack is the best. For the severe hæmorrhages of the malignant cases nothing can be done, and it is only cruel to drench the unfortunate patient with iron, ergot, and other drugs. Symptoms of obstruction in the larynx, usually from œdema, may call for tracheotomy. In the late stages of the disease, should the patient be extremely debilitated and the subject of abscesses and bed-sores, he may be placed on a water-bed or treated by the continuous warm bath. During convalescence the patient should bathe daily and use carbolic soap freely in order to get rid of the crusts and scabs. He should not be considered without danger to others until the skin is perfectly smooth and clean, and free from any trace of scabs. I have not mentioned any of the so-called specifics or the internal antiseptics, which have been advised in such numbers; so far as I know, those who have had the widest experience with the disease do not favor their use.

V. VACCINIA *(Cow-pox)*—VACCINATION.

Definition.—An eruptive disease of the cow, the virus of which, inoculated into man (vaccination), produces a local pock with constitutional disturbance, which affords protection, more or less permanent, against small-pox.

The vaccine is got either directly from the calf—animal lymph—in which the disease is propagated at regular stations, or is obtained from persons vaccinated (humanized lymph).

History.—For centuries it had been a popular belief among farmer folk that cow-pox protected against small-pox. It is said that the notorious Duchess of Cleveland, replying to some joker who suggested that she would lose her occupation if she was disfigured with small-pox, said that she was not afraid of the disease, as she had had cow-pox. Jesty, a Dorsetshire farmer, had had cow-pox, and in 1774 vaccinated successfully his wife and two sons. Plett, in Holstein, in 1791, also successfully vaccinated three children. When Jenner was a student at Sodbury, a young girl, who came for advice, when small-pox was mentioned, exclaimed, " I can not take that disease, for I have had cow-pox." Jenner subsequently mentioned the subject to Hunter, who in reply gave the famous piece of advice: " Do not think, but try; be patient, be accurate." As early as 1780 the idea of the protective power of vaccination was firmly impressed on Jenner's mind. The problem which occupied his attention for many years was brought to a practical issue when, on May 14, 1796, he took matter from the hand of a dairy-maid, Sarah Nelmes, who had cow-pox, and inoculated a boy named James Phipps, aged eight years. On July 1st matter was taken from a small-pox pustule, and inserted into the boy, but no disease followed. In 1798 appeared An Inquiry into the Causes and Effects of the Variola Vaccinæ, a Disease discovered in some of the Western Counties of England, particularly Gloucestershire, and known by the Name of Cow-pox (pp. iv, 75, four plates, 4to. London, 1798). From this time on vaccination spread rapidly throughout the civilized world.

In the United States vaccination was introduced by Benjamin Waterhouse, Professor of Physic at Harvard, who on July 8, 1800, vaccinated seven of his children. President Jefferson was mainly instrumental in spreading the practice in the Southern States, and John Redman Coxe introduced it into Philadelphia.

The literature of vaccination has been greatly enriched by the publications in connection with the Jenner centenary. The centenary number of the British Medical Journal is particularly valuable. The report of the Royal Commission on vaccination, the exhaustive article in Allbutt's System by T. D. Ackland and Copeman, and Cory's recent monograph on the subject afford a large body of material. To the public health officials, who wish for distribution in handy shape Facts about Small-pox and Vaccination, the leaflets issued by the British Medical Association (British Medical Journal, 1898, vol. i, p. 632) will be of the greatest value.

Nature of Vaccinia.—Is cow-pox a separate independent disease, or is it only small-pox modified by passing through the cow? In spite of a host of observations, this question is not yet settled, as may be seen in the diametrically opposed views expressed by Copeman in Allbutt's System and by Brouardel in the Twentieth Century Practice. The experiments may be divided into two groups. First, those in which the inoculation of the small-pox matter in the heifer produced pocks corresponding in all respects to the vaccine vesicles. Lymph from the first calf inoculated into a second or third produced the characteristic lesions of cow-pox, and from the first, second, or third animal lymph used to vaccinate a child produced a typical localized vaccine vesicle without any of the generalized features of small-pox. The experiments of Ceely, of Babcock, and many other more recent workers seem to leave no question whatever that typical vaccinia may be produced in the calf by the inoculation of variolous matter. A great deal of the vaccine material at one time in use in England was obtained in this way. Secondly, against this is urged Chauveau's Lyons experiments. Seventeen young animals were inoculated with the virus of small-pox. Small reddish papules occurred which disappeared rapidly, but the animals did not acquire cow-pox. Fifteen of the seventeen animals were also vaccinated. Of these only one showed a typical cow-pox eruption. To determine the nature of the original papules one was excised and inoculated into a non-vaccinated child, which developed as a result generalized confluent small-pox. A second child inoculated from the primary pustule of the first child developed discrete small-pox. The French still hold to the Lyons experiments as demonstrating the duality of the diseases.

The weight of evidence favors the view that cow-pox and horse-pox are variola modified by transmission; or, as has been suggested, "small-pox and vaccinia are both of them descended from a common stock—from an ancestor, for instance—which resembled vaccinia far more than it resembled small-pox" (Copeman).

Bacteriology of Vaccinia.—This, too, is still unsettled. Quist, Martin, and Ernst have described various micrococci. Klein and Copeman have independently found a bacillus, while Pfeiffer and Ruffer have met with bodies believed to be of the nature of psorosperms. Walter Reed has also met with peculiar amœboid bodies in the blood.

Normal Vaccination.—*Period of Incubation.*—At first there may be a little irritation at the site of inoculation, which subsides. *Period of Eruption.*—On the third day, as a rule, a papule is seen surrounded by a reddish zone. This gradually increases, and on the fifth or sixth day shows a definite vesicle, the margins of which are raised while the centre is depressed. By the eighth day the vesicle has attained its maximum size. It is round and distended with a limpid fluid, the margin hard and prominent, and the umbilication is more distinct. By the tenth day the vesicle is still large and is surrounded by an extensive areola. The contents have now become purulent. The skin is also swollen, indurated, and often painful. On the eleventh or twelfth day the hyperæmia diminishes, the lymph becomes more opaque and begins to dry. By the end of the second week the vesicle is converted into a brownish scab, which gradually becomes dry and hard, and in about a week (that is, about the twenty-first or twenty-fifth day from the vaccination) separates and leaves a circular pitted scar. If the points of inoculation have been close together, the vesicles fuse and may form a large combined vesicle. Constitutional symptoms of a more or less marked degree follow the vaccination. Usually on the third or fourth day the temperature rises, and may persist, increasing until the eighth or ninth day. There is a marked leucocytosis. In children it is common to have with the fever restlessness, particularly at night, and irritability; but as a rule these symptoms are trivial. If the inoculation is made on the arm, the axillary glands become large and sore; if on the leg, the inguinal glands. The duration of the immunity is extremely variable, differing in different individuals. In some instances it is permanent, but a majority of persons within ten or twelve years again become susceptible.

Revaccination should be performed between the tenth and fifteenth year, and whenever small-pox is epidemic. The susceptibility to revaccination is curiously variable, and when small-pox is prevalent it is not well, if unsuccessful, to be content with a single attempt. The vesicle in revaccination is usually smaller, has less induration and hyperæmia, and the resulting scar is less perfect. Particular care should be taken to watch the vesicle of revaccination, as it not infrequently happens that a spurious pock is formed, which reaches its height early and dries to a scab by the eighth or ninth day. The constitutional symptoms in revaccination are sometimes quite severe.

Irregular Vaccination.—(*a*) *Local Variations.*—We occasionally meet with instances in which the vesicle develops rapidly with much itching, has not the characteristic flattened appearance, the lymph early becomes opaque, and the crust forms by the seventh or eighth day. The evolution of the pocks may be abnormally slow. In such cases the operation should again be performed with fresh lymph. The contents of the vesicles may be watery and bloody. In the involution the bruising or irritation of the pocks may lead to ulceration and inflammation. A very rare event is the recurrence of the pock in the same place. Sutton reports four such recurrences within six months.

(*b*) *Generalized Vaccinia.*—It is not uncommon to see vesicles in the vicinity of the primary sore. Less common is a true generalized pustular rash, developing in different parts of the body, often beginning about the wrists and on the back. The secondary pocks may continue to make their appearance for five or six weeks after vaccination. In children the disease may prove fatal. They may be most abundant on the vaccinated limb, and develop usually about the eighth to the tenth day.

(*c*) *Complications.*—In unhealthy subjects, or as a result of uncleanliness, or sometimes injury, the vesicles inflame and deep excavated ulcers result. Sloughing and deep cellulitis may follow. In debilitated children there may be with this a purpuric rash. Acland thus arranges the dates at which the possible eruptions and complications may be looked for:

1. During the first three days: Erythema; urticaria; vesicular and bullous eruptions; invaccinated erysipelas.

2. After the third day and until the pock reaches maturity: Urticaria; lichen urticatus, erythema multiforme; accidental erysipelas.

3. About the end of the first week: Generalized vaccinia; impetigo; vaccinal ulceration; glandular abscess; septic infections; gangrene.

4. After the involution of the pocks: Invaccinated diseases—for example, syphilis.

(*d*) *Transmission of Disease by Vaccination.*—Syphilis has undoubtedly been transmitted by vaccination, but such instances are very rare. A large number of the cases of alleged vaccino-syphilis must be thrown out. The

5

question has now become really of minor importance since the widespread use of animal lymph. Dr. Cory's sad experiment may here be referred to. He vaccinated himself four times from syphilitic children. The first vaccination followed, but no syphilis. Two other attempts (negative) were made. The fourth time he was vaccinated from a child the subject of congenital syphilis. The lymph was taken from the child's arm with care, avoiding any contamination with blood. At two of the points of insertion red papules appeared on the twenty-first day. On the thirty-eighth day a little ulcer was found, which Mr. Hutchinson decided was syphilitic. The diseased parts were then removed. By the fiftieth day the constitutional symptoms were well marked. Among the differences between vaccino-syphilis and vaccination ulcers the most important is perhaps that the chancre never develops before the fifteenth day, usually not until from three to five weeks, whereas the ulceration of ordinary vaccination is present by the twelfth or fifteenth day. The loss of substance in the chancre is usually quite superficial and the induration very parchment-like and specific, with but a slight inflammatory areola. The glandular swelling, too, is constant and indolent, while in the vaccination ulcer it is often absent, or, when present, chiefly inflammatory.

Tuberculosis.—" No undoubted case of invaccinated tubercle was brought before the Royal Commission on Vaccination" (Acland). The risk of transmitting tuberculosis from the calf is so slight that it need not be considered. Tuberculosis in the calf is excessively rare, and "this almost inappreciable source of danger can be avoided by the simple precaution of not using the lymph from any calf until the animal has been killed and proved to be entirely free from disease" (Acland).

The transmission of leprosy by vaccination is also open to serious doubt. In a few instances tetanus has developed during vaccination and proved fatal.

(*e*) *Influence of Vaccination upon other Diseases.*—A quiescent malady may be lighted into activity by vaccination. This has happened with congenital syphilis, occasionally with tuberculosis. An old idea was prevalent that vaccination had a beneficial influence upon existing diseases. Dr. Archer, the first medical graduate in the United States, recommended it in whooping-cough, and said that it had cured in his hands six or eight cases.

Choice of Lymph.—Calf lymph should invariably be used, and it can now be obtained from perfectly reliable sources. The practice of arm-to-arm vaccination with humanized lymph should be abandoned. If bovine lymph is not available, then the humanized lymph should be taken on the eighth day, and only from perfectly formed, unbroken vesicles, which have had a typical course. Pricking or scratching the surface, the greatest care being taken not to draw blood, allows the lymph to exude, and it may be collected on ivory points or in capillary tubes. The child from which the lymph is taken should be healthy, strong, and known to be of good stock, free from tuberculous or syphilitic taint. All possible sources of contamination with pyogenic organisms are now obviated by the use of the glycerinated calf lymph which should come into general use. The Local Government Board has recently issued a valuable report on the subject by Thorne and Copeman, giving full details as to the method of preparation. In it the statement is made that, whereas it was usual to make the lymph from one calf serve for from 200 to 300 vaccinations, the glycerinated lymph will serve for from 4,000 to 5,000 vaccinations.

Technique.—In the performance of the operation that part of the arm about the insertion of the deltoid is usually selected. Mothers " in society " prefer to have girl babies vaccinated on the leg. The skin should be cleansed and put upon the stretch. Then, with a lancet or the ivory point, cross-scratches should be made in one or more places. When the lymph has dried on the points it is best to moisten it in warm water. The clothing of the child should not be adjusted until the spot has dried, and it should be protected for a day or two with lint or a soft handkerchief. If erysipelas is prevalent, or if there are cases of suppuration in the same house, it is well to apply a pad of antiseptic cotton. Vaccination is usually performed at the second or third month. If unsuccessful, it should be repeated from time to time. A person exposed to the contagion of small-pox should always be revaccinated. This, if successful, will usually protect; but not always, as there are many instances in which, though the vaccination takes, variola also appears.

The Value of Vaccination.—Sanitation cannot account for the diminution in small-pox and for the low rate of mortality. Isolation, of course, is a useful auxiliary, but it is no substitute. Vaccination is not claimed to be an invariable and permanent preventive of small-pox, but in an immense majority of cases successful inoculation renders the person for many years insusceptible. Communities in which vaccination and revaccination are thoroughly and systematically carried out are those in which small-pox has the fewest victims. On the other hand, communities in which vaccination and revaccination are persistently neglected are those in which epidemics are most prevalent. In the German army the practice of revaccination has stamped out the disease. Nothing in recent times has been more instructive in this connection than the fatal statistics of Montreal. The epidemic which started in 1870–'71 was severe in Lower Canada, and persisted in Montreal until 1875. A great deal of feeling had been aroused among the French Canadians by the occurrence of several serious cases of ulceration, possibly of syphilitic disease, following vaccination; and several agitators, among them a French physician of some standing, aroused a popular and widespread prejudice against the practice. There were indeed vaccination riots. The introduction of animal lymph was distinctly beneficial in extending the practice among the lower classes, but compulsory vaccination could not be carried out. Between the years 1876 and 1884 a considerable unprotected population grew up and the materials were ripe for an extensive epidemic. The soil had been prepared with the greatest care, and it only needed the introduction of the seed, which in due time came, as already stated, with the Pullman-car conductor from Chicago, on the 28th of February, 1885. Within the next ten months thousands of persons were stricken with the disease, and 3,164 died.

Although the effects of a single vaccination may wear out, as we say, and the individual again become susceptible to small-pox, yet the mortality in such cases is very much lower than in persons who have never been vaccinated. The mortality in persons who have been vaccinated is from 6 to 8 per cent, whereas in the unvaccinated it is at least 35 per cent. Marson pointed out some years ago that there is a definite ratio between the number of deaths and the number of good vaccination marks in post-vaccinal small-pox. With good marks the mortality is between 3 and 4 per cent, and with indifferent marks at least 10 or 11 per cent. W. M. Welch's statistics of 5,000 cases on this point give with good cicatrices 8 per cent; with fair cicatrices, 14 per cent; with poor cicatrices, 27 per cent; post-vaccinal cases, 16 per cent; unvaccinated cases, 58 per cent.

VI. VARICELLA (*Chicken-pox*).

Definition.—An acute contagious disease of children, characterized by an eruption of vesicles on the skin.

Etiology.—The disease occurs in epidemics, but sporadic cases are also met with. It may prevail at the same time as small-pox or may follow or precede epidemics of this disease. An attack of chicken-pox is no protection against small-pox. It is a disease of childhood; a majority of the cases occur between the second and sixth years. It is rarely seen in adults. The specific germ has not yet been discovered.

There can be no question that varicella is an affection quite distinct from variola and without at present any relation whatever to it. An attack of the one does not confer immunity from an attack of the other. The case which Sharkey reported is of special importance in this connection. A boy, aged five, was admitted to St. Thomas' Hospital with a vesicular eruption, and was isolated in a ward on the same floor as the small-pox ward. The disease was pronounced chicken-pox, however, by Sir Risdon Bennett and Dr. Bristowe. The patient was then removed and vaccinated, with a result of four vesicles which ran a pretty normal course. On the eighth day from the vaccination the child became feverish. On the following day the papules appeared and the child had a well-developed attack of small-pox with secondary fever.

Symptoms.—After a period of incubation of ten or fifteen days the child becomes feverish and in some instances has a slight chill. There may be vomiting and pains in the back and legs. Convulsions are rare. The eruption usually develops within twenty-four hours. It is first seen upon the trunk, either on the back or on the chest. It may begin on the forehead and face. At first in the form of raised red papules, these are in a few hours transformed into hemispherical vesicles containing a clear or turbid fluid. As a rule there is no umbilication, but in rare instances the pocks are flattened, and a few may even be umbilicated. They are often ovoid in shape and look more superficial than the variolous vesicles. The skin in the neighborhood is neither infiltrated nor hyperæmic. At the end of thirty-six or forty-eight hours the contents of the vesicles are purulent. They begin to shrivel, and during the third and fourth days are converted into dark brownish crusts, which fall off and as a rule leave no scar. Fresh crops appear during the first two or three days of the illness, so that on the fourth day one can usually see pocks in all stages of development and decay. They are always discrete and the number may vary from eight or ten to several hundreds. As in variola, a scarlatinal rash occasionally precedes the development of the eruption. The eruption may occur on the mucous membrane of the mouth, and occasionally in the larynx (D. H. Hall).

There are one or two modifications of the rash which are interesting. The vesicles may become very large and develop into regular bullæ, looking not unlike ecthyma or pemphigus (varicella bullosa). The irritation of the rash may be excessive, and if the child scratches the pocks ulcerating sores may form, which on healing leave ugly scars. Indeed, cicatrices after chicken-pox are more common than after varioloid. The fever in varicella is slight, but it does not as a rule disappear with the appearance of the rash. The course of the disease is in a large majority of the cases favorable and no ill effects follow. The disease may recur in the same individual. There are instances in which a person has had three attacks.

In delicate children, particularly the tuberculous, gangrene (varicella escharotica) may occur about the vesicles (Hutchinson); or in other parts, as the scrotum.

Cases have been described (Andrew) of hæmorrhagic varicella with cutaneous ecchymoses and bleeding from the mucous membranes.

Nephritis may occur. Infantile hemiplegia has developed during an attack of the disease. Death has followed in an uncomplicated case from extensive involvement of the skin (Nisbet).

The *diagnosis* is as a rule easy, particularly if the patient has been seen from the outset. When a case comes under observation for the first time with the rash well out, there may be considerable difficulty. The abundance of the rash on the trunk in varicella is most important. The pocks in varicella are more superficial, more bleb-like, have not so deeply an infiltrated areola about them, and may usually be seen in all stages of development. They rarely at the outset have the hard, shotty feeling of those of small-pox. The general symptoms, the greater intensity of the onset, the prolonged period of invasion, and the more frequent occurrence of prodromal rashes in small-pox are important points in the diagnosis.

No special *treatment* is required. If the rash is abundant on the face great care should be taken to prevent the child from scratching the pustules. A soothing lotion should be applied on lint.

VII. SCARLET FEVER.

Definition.—An infectious disease characterized by a diffuse exanthem and an angina of variable intensity.

Etiology.—We owe the recognition of scarlet fever as a distinct disease to Sydenham, before whose time it was confounded with measles. It is a widespread affection, occurring in nearly all parts of the globe and attacking all races.

The disease occurs sporadically from time to time, and then under unknown conditions becomes widespread. Epidemics vary in severity.

Among predisposing factors age is most important. A large proportion of the cases occur before the tenth year. Of an enormous number of fatal cases tabulated by Murchison over 90 per cent occurred in children under this age. Adults, however, are by no means exempt. Very young infants are rarely attacked. A certain number of those coming in contact with the disease escape. In a family of children all more or less exposed one or two may not contract scarlet fever, whereas, as a rule, in the case of measles all take it. The susceptibility seems to vary in families, and we meet occasionally with sad instances in which three or more members of a family succumb in rapid succession.

Males and females are equally affected.

Epidemics prevail at all seasons, but perhaps with greater intensity in autumn and winter.

The contagion of scarlet fever is probably not developed until the eruption appears, and is particularly to be dreaded during desquamation. No doubt the poison is spread largely by the fine scaly particles which are diffused with the dust throughout the room. Even late in the disease, after desquamation has been apparently completed, a patient has conveyed the contagion. The poison clings with great persistence to clothing of all kinds and to articles of furniture in the room. In no disease is a greater tenacity displayed. Bedding and clothes which have been put away for months or even for years may, unless thoroughly disinfected, convey contagion. Physicians, nurses, and others in contact with the sick may carry the poison to persons at a distance. It is remarkable that in the case of physicians this does not more frequently occur. I know of but one instance in which I carried the contagion of this disease. The poison probably is not widely spread in the atmosphere. Observations have been recently made which indicate that it may be conveyed in milk. The epidemic investigated by Power and Klein in London in 1885 was traced by them to milk obtained from a dairy at Hendon, in which the cows were found to be suffering from a vesicular affection of the udder. The nature of this disease of the cow is doubtful, however. Crookshank holds that it was cow-pox, and had nothing to do with scarlet fever.

Some writers maintain that scarlet fever may be associated with defective house-drainage. Possibly the virus may occasionally gain entrance in this way.

One attack does not necessarily protect permanently. There are instances of one or even two recurrences.

Surgical and puerperal scarlatinas, so called, demand a word under this section. While scarlet fever may attack a person after operation, or a woman in childbed, the majority of the cases described as such belong, I believe, to those of septicæmia. In the cases which I have seen the red rash was rarely so widespread as in scarlet fever; the tongue had not the special features, nor was the throat affected. Desquamation is no criterion, as it occurs whenever hyperæmia of the skin has persisted for any length of time. It is interesting to note that these cases have become rare with the gradual disappearance of septicæmia. I. E. Atkinson suggests that in many cases these rashes are due to quinine.

The specific germ is still unknown. Streptococci are found in the skin, in the blood sometimes, and in the organs of fatal cases. It has even been urged that the disease is only a form of streptococcus infection. Throat lesions of the most malignant type may occur without the presence of the bacillus diphtheriæ, but in the infectious pavilions of hospitals the scarlet fever cases are very apt to be complicated with true diphtheria; much more so than in private practice. The streptococcus pyogenes is the common organism of the otitis media.

Morbid Anatomy.—Except in the hæmorrhagic form, the skin after death shows no traces of the rash. There are no specific lesions. Those which occur in the internal organs are due partly to the fever and partly to infection with pus-organisms.

The anatomical changes in the throat are those of simple inflammation, follicular tonsillitis, and, in extreme grades, of pseudo-membranous angina. In severe cases there is intense lymphadenitis and much inflammatory œdema of the tissues of the neck, which may go on to suppuration, or even to gangrene. Streptococci are found abundantly in the glands and in the areas of suppuration. Of changes in the digestive organs, a catarrhal state of the gastro-intestinal mucosa is not uncommon. The liver may show interstitial changes (Klein). The spleen is often enlarged.

Endocarditis and pericarditis are not infrequent. Myocardial changes are less common. The renal changes are the most important, and have been thoroughly studied by Coats, Klebs, Wagner, and others. The special nephritis of scarlet fever will be considered with the diseases of the kidney.

Affections of the respiratory organs are not frequent. When death results from the pseudo-membranous angina, broncho-pneumonia is not uncommon. Cerebro-spinal changes are rare.

Symptoms.—Incubation.—" From one to seven days, oftenest two to four."

Invasion.—The onset is as a rule sudden. It may be preceded by a slight, scarcely noticeable, indisposition. An actual chill is rare. Vomiting and, in young children, convulsions are common. The fever is intense; rising rapidly, it may on the first day reach 104° or even 105°. The skin is unusually dry and to the touch gives a sensation of very pungent heat. The tongue is furred, and as early as the first day there may be complaint of dryness of the throat. Cough and catarrhal symptoms are uncommon. The face is often flushed and the patient has all the objective features of an acute fever.

Eruption.—Usually on the second day, in some instances within twenty-four hours, the rash develops in the form of scattered red points on a deep subcuticular flush. It appears first on the neck and chest, and spreads so rapidly that by the evening of the second day it may have invaded the entire skin. After persisting for two or three days it gradually fades. In pronounced cases the rash at its height has a vivid scarlet hue, quite distinctive and unlike that seen in any other eruptive disease. It is entirely hyperæmic, and the anæmia produced by pressure instantly disappears. In a very intense rash there may be fine punctiform hæmorrhages, which do not disappear on pressure. In some cases the rash does not become uniform but remains patchy, and intervals of normal skin separate large hyperæmic areas. Tiny papular elevations may sometimes be seen, but they are not so common as in measles. At the height of the eruption sudaminal vesicles may develop, the fluid of which may become turbid. The entire skin may at the same time be covered with small yellow vesicles on a deep red background. Pronounced cases of this type were called by the older writers *scarlatina miliaris.* The blood shows an early leucocytosis, which is often extreme in fatal cases.

Occasionally there are petechiæ, which in the malignant type of the disease become widespread and large. The eruption does not always appear upon the face. There may be a good deal of swelling of the skin which feels uncomfortable and tense. The itching is variable; not as a rule intense at the height of the eruption. The rash can often be seen on the mucous membranes of the palate, the cheeks, and the tonsils, giving to these parts a vivid red, punctiform appearance. The tongue at first is red at the tip and edges, furred in the centre; and through the white fur are often seen the swollen red papillæ, which give the so-called "strawberry" appearance to the tongue. In a

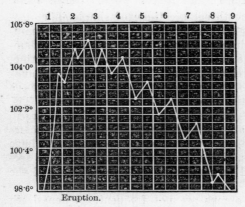

CHART VII.—Scarlet fever (Strümpell).

few days the "fur" desquamates and leaves the surface red and rough, and it is this condition which some writers call the "strawberry," or, better, the "raspberry" tongue. The breath often has a very heavy, sweet odor.

The pharyngeal symptoms vary extremely. There may be—

1. Slight redness, with swelling of the pillars of the fauces and of the tonsils.

2. A more intense grade of swelling and infiltration of these parts with a follicular tonsillitis.

3. Membranous angina with intense inflammation of all the pharyngeal structures and swelling of the glands below the jaw, and in very severe cases a thick brawny induration of all the tissues of the neck.

The fever, which sets in with such suddenness and intensity, may reach 105° or even 106°. It persists with slight morning remissions, gradually declining with the disappearance of the rash. In mild cases the temperature may not reach 103°; on the other hand, in very severe cases there may be hyperpyrexia, the thermometer registering 108° or before death even 109°.

The pulse presents the ordinary febrile characters, ranging in children from 120 to 150, or even higher. The respirations show an increase proportionate to the intensity of the fever. The gastro-intestinal symptoms are not marked after the initial vomiting, and food is usually well taken. In some instances there are abdominal pains. The edge of the spleen may be palpable. The liver is not often enlarged. With the initial fever nervous symptoms are present in a majority of the cases; but as the rash comes out the headache and the slight nocturnal wandering disappear. The urine has the ordinary febrile characters, being scanty and high colored. Slight albuminuria is by no means infrequent during the stage of eruption. Careful examination of the urine should be made every day. There is no cause for alarm in the trace of albumin which is so often present, not even if it is associated with a few tube-casts.

Desquamation.—With the disappearance of the rash and the fever the skin looks somewhat stained, is dry, a little rough, and gradually the upper layer of the cuticle begins to separate. The process usually begins about the neck and chest, and flakes are gradually detached. The degree and character of the desquamation bear some relation to the intensity of the eruption. When the latter has been very vivid and of long standing, large flakes may be thrown off. In rare instances the hair and even the nails have been shed. It must not be forgotten that there are cases in which the desquamation has been prolonged, according to Trousseau, even to the seventh or eighth week. The entire process lasts from ten to fifteen or even twenty days.

There are cases of exceptional mildness in which the rash may be scarcely perceptible. During epidemics, when several children of a household are affected, it sometimes happens that a child sickens as if of scarlet fever, and has a sore throat and the " strawberry tongue " without the development of any rash. This is the so-called *scarlatina sine eruptione*.

These mild cases of scarlet fever may be followed by the severest attacks of nephritis.

MALIGNANT SCARLET FEVER.

Atactic Form.—This presents all the characteristics of an acute intoxication. The patient, overwhelmed by the intensity of the poison, may die within twenty-four or thirty-six hours. The disease sets in with great severity—high fever, extreme restlessness, headache, and delirium. The temperature may rise to 107° or even 108°, and rare cases have been observed in which the thermometer has registered even higher. Convulsions may occur in children. The initial delirium rapidly gives place to coma. The dyspnœa may be urgent; the pulse is very rapid and feeble.

Hæmorrhagic Form.—In some instances hæmorrhages occur into the skin. There are hæmaturia and epistaxis. In the erythematous rash there are at first scattered petechiæ, which gradually become more extensive, and ultimately the skin may be universally involved. Death may take place on the second or on the third day. While this form is perhaps more common in enfeebled children, I have twice known it to attack persons apparently in full health.

Anginose Form.—The throat symptoms may appear early and progress rapidly. The fauces and tonsils are swollen. Membranous exudation occurs. It may extend to the posterior wall of the pharynx, forward into the mouth, and upward into the nostrils. The glands of the neck rapidly enlarge. Necrosis occurs in the tissues of the throat, the fœtor is extreme, the constitutional disturbance profound, and the child dies with the clinical picture of a malignant diphtheria. Occasionally the membrane extends into the trachea and the bronchi. The Eustachian tubes and the middle ear are usually involved. When death does not take place rapidly from toxæmia there may be extensive abscess formation in the tissues of the neck and sloughing. In the separation of deep sloughs about the tonsils the carotid artery may be opened, causing fatal hæmorrhage.

Complications and Sequelæ.—(a) *Nephritis.*—At the height of the fever there is often a slight trace of albumin in the urine, which is not of special significance. In a majority of cases the kidneys escape without greater damage than occurs in other acute febrile affections.

Nephritis is most common in the second or third week and may develop after a very mild attack. It may be delayed until the third or fourth week. As a rule, the earlier it develops the more severe it is. It varies greatly in intensity, and three grades of cases may be recognized:

1. Very severe cases with suppression of urine or the passage of a small quantity of dark bloody urine laden with albumin and tube-casts. Vomiting is constant, there are convulsions, and the child dies with the symptoms of acute uræmia.

2. Less severe cases without any serious acute symptoms. There is a puffy appearance of the eyelids, with slight œdema of the feet; the urine is diminished in quantity, smoky in appearance, and contains albumin and tube-casts. The kidney symptoms then dominate the entire case, the dropsy persists, and there may be effusion into the serous sacs. The condition may drag on and become chronic, or the patient may succumb to uræmic accidents. Fortunately, in a majority of the cases the disease yields to judicious treatment and recovery takes place.

3. Cases so mild that they can scarcely be termed nephritis. The urine contains albumin and a few tube-casts, but rarely blood. The œdema is extremely slight or transient, and the convalescence is scarcely interrupted. Occasionally, however, in these mild attacks serious symptoms may supervene. Œdema of the glottis may prove rapidly fatal, and in one case of the kind a child under my care died of acute effusion into the pleural sacs.

Occasionally œdema occurs without albuminuria or signs of nephritis. Possibly in some of these case the œdema may be hæmic and due to the anæmia; but there are instances in which marked changes have been found in the kidney after death, even when the urine did not show the features characteristic of nephritis.

(b) *Arthritis.*—During the subsidence of the fever, rarely at its height, pains and swellings in the joints may develop and present all the characteristics of acute rheumatism. In all probability it is not, however, true rheumatism, but is analogous to gonorrhœal arthritis. The effusion may pass on to suppuration, in which case it most commonly involves only a single joint.

(*c*) *Cardiac Complications.*—Simple endocarditis is not uncommon, and many cases of chronic valvular disease originate probably in a latent endocarditis during this disease. Malignant endocarditis is rare. Pericarditis is probably not more frequent, but is less likely to be overlooked than endocarditis. It usually develops during convalescence; the effusion may be sero-fibrinous or purulent. The cardiac complications are sometimes found in association with arthritis. Myocarditis is not uncommon.

(*d*) *Pleurisy* may follow *pneumonia*, though this is rare. More often it occurs during convalescence, is insidious in its course, and as a rule purulent. This serious complication of scarlet fever is not sufficiently recognized. It was one upon which my teacher, R. P. Howard,* in Montreal, specially insisted in his lectures. Sheriff, in a number of the same journal, reports two cases, occurring at the same time in brothers, one of whom died suddenly after a slight exertion.

(*e*) *Ear Complications.*—These are common and serious. They are due to extension of the inflammation from the throat through the Eustachian tubes, and rank among the most frequent causes of deafness. The severe forms of membranous angina are almost always associated with inflammation of the middle ear, which goes on to suppuration and to perforation of the drum. The suppuration may extend to the labyrinth and rapidly produce deafness. In other instances there is suppuration in the mastoid cells. In the necrosis which follows the middle-ear disease, the facial nerve may be involved and paralysis follow. Later, still more serious complications may follow the otitis, such as thrombosis of the lateral sinus, meningitis, or abscess of the brain.

(*f*) *Adenitis.*—In comparatively mild cases of scarlet fever the submaxillary lymph-glands may be swollen. In severer cases the swelling of the neck becomes extreme and extends beyond the limits of the glands. Acute phlegmonous inflammations may occur, leading to widespread destruction of tissue, in which vessels may be eroded and fatal hæmorrhage ensue. The suppurative processes may also involve the retro-pharyngeal tissues.

The swelling of the lymph-glands usually subsides, and within a few weeks even the most extensive enlargement gradually disappears. There are rare instances, however, in which the lymphadenitis becomes chronic, and the neck remains with a glandular collar which almost obliterates its outline. This may prove intractable to all ordinary measures of treatment. A case came under my observation in which, two years after scarlet fever, the neck was enormously enlarged and surrounded by a mass of firm brawny glands.

(*g*) *Nervous Complications.*—Chorea occasionally develops in connection with the arthritis and endocarditis. Sudden convulsions followed by hemiplegia may occur. Progressive paralysis of the limbs with wasting may develop with the features of a subacute, ascending spinal paralysis.

---

* Canada Medical and Surgical Journal, December, 1872.

Thrombosis of the cerebral veins may occur.   Mental symptoms, mania and melancholia, have been described.

(h) Other rare complications and sequelæ are œdema of the eyelids, without nephritis (S. Philips), symmetrical gangrene, enteritis, noma, and perforation of the soft palate (Goodall). Pearson and Littlewood have reported a case of dry gangrene after scarlet fever in a boy of four, which developed on the ninth day of the disease, and involved both legs, necessitating amputation at the upper third of the thighs. The child recovered.

Diagnosis.—The diagnosis of scarlet fever is not difficult, but there are cases in which the true nature of the disease is for a time doubtful. The following are the most common conditions with which it may be confounded:

1. *Acute Exfoliating Dermatitis.*—This pseudo-exanthem simulates scarlet fever very closely. It has a sudden onset, with fever. The eruption spreads rapidly, is uniform, and after persisting for five or six days begins to fade. Even before it has entirely gone, desquamation usually begins. Some of these cases can not be distinguished from scarlet fever in the stage of eruption. The throat symptoms, however, are usually absent, and the tongue rarely shows the changes which are so marked in scarlet fever. In the desquamation of this affection the hair and nails are commonly affected. It is, too, a disease liable to recur. Some of the instances of second and third attacks of scarlet fever have been cases of this form of dermatitis.

2. *Measles,* which is distinguished by the longer period of invasion, the characteristic nature of the prodromes, and the later appearance of the rash. The greater intensity of the measly rash upon the face, the more papular character and the irregular crescentic distribution are distinguishing features in a majority of the cases. Other points are the absence in measles of the sore throat, the peculiar character of the desquamation, and the absence of leucocytosis.

3. *Rötheln.*—The rash of rubella is sometimes strikingly like that of scarlet fever, but in the great majority of cases the mistake could not arise. In cases of doubt the general symptoms are our best guide.

4. *Septicæmia.*—As already mentioned, the so-called puerperal or surgical scarlatina shows an eruption which may be identical in appearance with that of true scarlet fever.

5. *Diphtheria.*—The practitioner may be in doubt whether he is dealing with a case of scarlet fever with intense membranous angina, a true diphtheria with an erythematous rash, or coexisting scarlet fever and diphtheria. In the angina occurring early in, and during the course of scarlet fever, though the clinical features may be those of true diphtheria, Loeffler's bacilli are rarely found. On the other hand, in the membranous angina occurring during convalescence, the bacilli are usually present. The rash in diphtheria is, after all, not so common, is limited usually to the trunk, is not so persistent, and is generally darker than the scarlatinal rash.

Scarlatina and diphtheria may coexist, but in a case presenting widespread erythema and extensive membranous angina with Loeffler's bacilli, it would puzzle Hippocrates to say whether the two diseases coexisted, or whether it was only an intense scarlatinal rash in diphtheria. Desquamation occurs in either case. The streptococcus angina is not so apt to extend to the larynx, nor are recurrences so common; but it is well to bear in mind that general infection may occur, that the membrane may spread downward with great rapidity, and, lastly, that all the nervous sequelæ of the Klebs-Loeffler diphtheria may follow the streptococcus form.

6. *Drug Rashes.*—These are partial, and seldom more than a transient hyperæmia of the skin. Occasionally they are diffuse and intense, and in such cases very deceptive. They are not associated, however, with the characteristic symptoms of invasion. There is no fever, and with care the distinction can usually be made. They are most apt to follow the use of belladonna, quinine, and iodide of potassium.

Coexistence of other Diseases.—Of 48,366 cases of scarlet fever in the Metropolitan Asylum Board Hospitals which were complicated by some other disease, in 1,094 cases the secondary infection was diphtheria, in 899 cases chicken-pox, in 703 measles, in 404 whooping-cough, in 55 erysipelas, in 11 enteric fever, and in 1 typhus fever (F. F. Caiger).

How long is a Child Infective?—Usually after desquamation is complete, in four or five weeks the danger is over, but the occurrence of so-called " return cases " show that patients remain infective even when free from desquamation. In 1894, with 2,593 patients from the Glasgow fever hospitals sent to their homes convalescent, fresh cases appeared in 70 of the houses (Chalmers). With 15,000 cases submitted to an average period of isolation of forty-nine days or under, the percentage of return cases was 1.86; with an average period of fifty to fifty-six days, the percentage was 1.12; where the isolation extended to between fifty-seven and sixty-five days, the percentage of return cases was 1 (Neech). This author suggests eight weeks as a minimum and thirteen weeks as a maximum.

Prognosis.—Epidemics differ in severity and the mortality is extremely variable. Among the better classes the death-rate is much lower than in hospital practice. There are physicians who have treated consecutively a hundred or more cases without a death. On the other hand, in hospitals and among the poorer classes the death-rate is considerable, ranging from 5 to 10 per cent in mild epidemics to 20 or 30 per cent in the very severe.

The younger the child the greater the danger. In infants under one year the death-rate is very high. The great proportion of fatal cases occurs in children under six years of age.

The unfavorable symptoms are very high fever, early mental disturbance with great jactitation, the occurrence of hæmorrhages (cutaneous or visceral), intense membranous angina with cervical bubo, and signs of laryngeal obstruction.

Nephritis is always a serious complication and when setting in with suppression of the urine may quickly prove fatal. It is noteworthy, however, that a large majority of the cases of scarlatinal nephritis recover.

Treatment.—The disease can not be cut short. In the presence of the severer forms we are still too often helpless. There is no disease, however, in which the successful issue and the avoidance of complications depends more upon the skilled judgment of the physician and the care with which his instructions are carried out.

The child should be isolated and placed in charge of a competent nurse. The temperature of the room should be constant and the ventilation thorough. The child should wear a light flannel night-gown, and the bedclothing should not be too heavy. The diet should consist of milk, broths, and fresh fruits; water should be freely given. With the fall of the temperature, the diet may be increased and the child may gradually return to ordinary fare. When desquamation begins the child should be thoroughly rubbed every day, or every second day, with sweet oil, or carbolated vaseline, or a 5-per-cent hydro-naphthol soap, which prevents the drying and the diffusion of the scales. An occasional warm bath may then be given. At any time during the attack the skin may be sponged with warm water. The patient may be allowed to get up after the temperature has been normal for ten days, but for at least three weeks from this time great care should be exercised to prevent exposure to cold. It must not be forgotten, also, that the renal complications are very apt to develop during the convalescence, and after all danger is apparently past. Ordinary cases do not require any medicine, or at the most a simple fever mixture, and during convalescence a bitter tonic. The bowels should be carefully regulated.

Special symptoms in the severe cases call for treatment.

When the fever is above 103° the extremities may be sponged with tepid water. In severe cases, with the temperature rapidly rising, this will not suffice, and more thorough measures of hydrotherapy should be practised. With pronounced delirium and nervous symptoms the cold pack should be used. When the fever is rising rapidly but the child is not delirious, he should be placed in a warm bath, the temperature of which can be gradually lowered. The bath with the water at 80° is beneficial. In giving the cold pack a rubber sheet and a thick layer of blankets should be spread upon a sofa or a bed, and over them a sheet, wrung out of cold water. The naked child is then laid upon it and wrapped in the blankets. An intense glow of heat quickly follows the preliminary chilling, and from time to time the blankets may be unfolded and the child sprinkled with cold water. The good effects which follow this plan of treatment are often striking, particularly in allaying the delirium and jactitation, and procuring quiet and refreshing sleep. Parents will object less, as a rule, to the warm bath gradually cooled than to any other form of hydrotherapy. The child may be removed from the warm bath, placed upon a sheet wrung out of tolerably cold water, and then folded in blankets. The ice-cap is very useful and may be kept constantly applied in cases in which there is high fever. Medicinal antipyretics are not of much service in comparison with cold water.

The throat symptoms, if mild, do not require much treatment. If severe, the local measures mentioned under diphtheria should be used. Cold applications to the neck are to be preferred to hot, though it is sometimes difficult to get a child to submit to them. In connection with the throat, the ears should be specially looked after, and a careful disinfection of the mouth and fauces by suitable antiseptic solutions should be practised. When the inflammation extends through the tubes to the middle ear, the practitioner should either himself examine daily the condition of the drum, or, when available, a specialist should be called in to assist him in the case. The careful watching of this membrane day by day and the puncturing of it if the tension becomes too great may save the hearing of the child. With the aid of cocaine the drum is readily punctured. The operation may be repeated at intervals if the pain and distention return. No complication of the disease is more serious than this extension of the inflammatory process to the ear.

The nephritis should be dealt with as in ordinary cases; indications for treatment will be found under the appropriate section. It is worth mentioning, however, that Jaccoud insists upon the great value of milk diet in scarlet fever as a preventive of nephritis.

Among other indications for treatment in the disease is cardiac weakness, which is usually the result of the direct action of the poison, and is best met by stimulants.

Many specifics have been vaunted in scarlet fever, but they are all useless.

VIII. MEASLES.

Definition.—An acute, highly infectious disorder, characterized by an initial coryza and a rapidly spreading eruption.

Etiology.—The infection of measles is very intense and immunity against attack not nearly so common as in scarlet fever. It is a disease of childhood, but unprotected adults are liable to the infection. Indeed, measles is more frequent in adults than is scarlet fever. Within the first six months of life the liability is not so marked, though infants of a month or three weeks may be attacked. The sexes are equally affected. The contagion is communicated by the breath and by the secretions, particularly those of the nose. It may be conveyed by a third person and by fomites.

The disease is practically endemic in large centres of population, and from time to time spreads and prevails epidemically. It occurs at all seasons, but prevails more extensively during the colder months. There is no infectious disease in which recurrence is more frequent. There may be a second, third, or even a fourth attack.

The *contagium* of the disease is unknown. No one of the various organisms which have been described meets the requirements of Koch's law.

Morbid Anatomy.—Measles itself rarely kills, but the complications and sequelæ combine to make it a very fatal affection in children. There are no characteristic post-mortem appearances. The skin changes are those associated with an intense hyperæmia.

There is a catarrhal condition of the mucous membranes, particularly of the bronchi. The fatal cases show almost invariably either bronchopneumonia, capillary bronchitis with patches of collapse, or less frequently lobar pneumonia. The bronchial glands are invariably swollen. Pleurisy

is less common. During convalescence from measles there is a special liability to tuberculous invasion, and tuberculous broncho-pneumonia claims
a large number of victims. The bronchial glands may also be affected.

The gastro-intestinal mucosa may be hyperæmic. Swelling of Peyer's
glands is not at all uncommon and may reach a very intense grade in the
patches.

Symptoms.—Incubation.—"From seven to eighteen days; oftenest
fourteen." The disease has been frequently inoculated. In such cases
the incubation period is less than ten days.

Invasion.—The disease usually begins with symptoms of a feverish
cold. There are shiverings (not often a definite chill), marked coryza,
sneezing, running at the nose, redness of the eyes and lids, with photophobia, and within twenty-four hours cough. These early catarrhal symptoms are more marked in measles than in any other infectious disease of
children. There may be the symptoms so commonly associated with an
on-coming fever—nausea, vomiting, and headache. The tongue is furred.
Examination of the throat may show a reddish hyperæmia or in some instances a distinct punctiform rash.
Occasionally this spreads over the
whole mucous membrane of the
mouth with the exception of the
tongue. The temperature at this
stage is usually high, reaching from
103° to 104°, ascending gradually
through the second and third days.

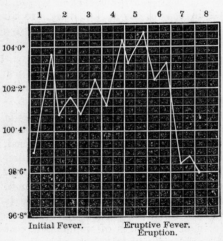

CHART VIII.—Measles (Strümpell).

Eruption. — Usually on the
fourth day, when the fever and
general symptoms have reached
their height, the rash appears
upon the cheeks or forehead in
the form of small red papules,
which increase in size and spread
over the neck and thorax. When
the eruption becomes well developed the face is swollen and covered with reddish blotches, which
often have rounded or crescentic outlines. Here and there is an intervening
portion of unaffected skin. At this stage the cervical lymph-glands may
be slightly swollen and sore; sometimes also the glands in the groins,
axillæ, and at the elbows. The papules can now be felt with the finger.
Sometimes they are quite shotty, but do not extend deep into the skin. On
the trunk and extremities the swelling of the skin is not so noticeable,
the color of the rash not so intense and often less uniform. The mottled,
blotchy character of the rash appears most clearly on the chest or the abdomen. The rash is hyperæmic and disappears on pressure, but in the more
malignant cases it may become hæmorrhagic. The general symptoms do
not abate with the occurrence of the eruption. They persist until the end
of the fifth or the sixth day, when in the majority of the cases all the symp-

toms become mitigated. Among the peculiarities of the rash may be mentioned the development of numerous miliary vesicles and the occurrence of petechiæ, which are seen occasionally even in cases of moderate severity.

Desquamation.—After persisting for two or three days the rash gradually fades and desquamation occurs in the form of very fine branny scales, which may be difficult to see and are wholly unlike the coarse exfoliation in scarlet fever.

The catarrhal symptoms gradually disappear and convalescence is rapidly established.

In epidemics of measles atypical cases are common. The rash may appear early, within thirty-six hours of the onset of the symptoms; or, on the other hand, it may be delayed until the sixth day. As in other exanthems, when many cases occur in a household, one of the children may have all the initial symptoms and "sicken for the disease," as it is said, but no eruption appears.

The most serious variety of measles is that in which hæmorrhages occur—the *morbilli hæmorrhagici.* In general practice these cases are very uncommon. Occasionally in institutions, particularly when the hygienic surroundings are bad, one or two cases develop during an epidemic. It has been frequently seen in camps and when the disease is freshly imported into a native population, as in the Fiji Islands. During the civil war, as shown by Smart's statistics, some cases occurred.

In this form the disease sets in with much greater intensity, the rash becomes petechial, hæmorrhages occur from the mucous membranes, the constitutional depression is very great, and death occurs early from toxæmia.

Complications and Sequelæ.—The existing bronchitis is apt to extend into the smaller tubes and lead to collapse and broncho-pneumonia. When limited in extent, this causes only aggravation of the cough and persistence of the fever (symptoms which gradually abate), and convalescence is rapid; but in debilitated children, more particularly in institutions and among the lower classes, this complication is extremely grave and is responsible for the high death-rate from measles in the community. In some instances the clinical picture is that of a suffocative catarrh, the result of a widespread involvement of the smaller tubes. The description of the condition will be found under Broncho-pneumonia. Lobar pneumonia is less common and perhaps less dangerous.

Laryngitis is not uncommon: the voice becomes husky and the cough croupy in character. Œdema of the glottis is very rare. Pseudo-membranous inflammation of the pharynx and larynx may occur and prove fatal. In debilitated infants severe stomatitis, *cancrum oris,* or ulcerative vulvitis may develop.

Catarrhal inflammation of the middle ear is not very uncommon, and may proceed to suppuration and to perforation of the drum. The conjunctival catarrh rarely leads to further trouble, though occasionally the inflammation becomes purulent.

Intestinal catarrh is common in some epidemics, and there may be the symptoms of acute colitis.

6

Nephritis is an exceedingly rare complication.

Of the sequelæ of measles, tuberculosis is the most important—either an involvement of the bronchial glands, a miliary tuberculosis, or a tuberculous broncho-pneumonia. Arthritis is rare. I have known anchylosis of the jaw to follow measles in a child of four years.

Among the rarer sequelæ are paralyses. Hemiplegia is very rare, but cases of paraplegia have been described. Thomas Barlow reports a fatal case in which the symptoms occurred early, the paralysis extended rapidly and involved the upper limbs, and death took place on the eleventh day. Marked vascular changes were found in the gray matter of the spinal cord, and were believed to depend on an early disseminated myelitis. Examination of the peripheral nerves was not made. While some of these cases are due to an ascending myelitis, others are probably the result of a post-febrile polyneuritis.

Diagnosis.—From scarlet fever, with which it is most likely to be confounded, measles is distinguished by the longer initial stage with characteristic symptoms, and the blotchy irregular character of the rash, which is so unlike the diffuse uniform erythema of scarlet fever. Occasionally in measles, when the throat is very sore and the eruption pretty diffuse, there may at first be difficulty in determining which disease is present, but a few days should suffice to make the diagnosis clear. As a rule there is no leucocytosis. It may be extremely difficult to distinguish from rötheln. I have more than once known practitioners of large experience unable to agree upon a diagnosis. The shorter prodromal stage, the slighter fever in many cases, are perhaps the most important features. It is difficult to speak definitely about the distinctions in the rash, though perhaps the more uniform distribution and the absence of the crescentic arrangement are more constant in rötheln. In Africans the disease is easily recognized, even in the black; the papules stand out with great plainness, often in groups; the hyperæmia is to be seen on all but the very black skins. The distribution of the rash, the coryza, and the rash in the mouth are important points.

The conditions under which measles may be mistaken for small-pox have already been described. Of drug eruptions, that induced by copaiba is very like measles, but is readily distinguished by the absence of fever and catarrh.

Prognosis.—The mortality bills of large cities show what a serious disease measles is in a community. Among the eruptive fevers it ranks third in the death-rate. The mortality from the disease itself is not high, but the pulmonary complications render it one of the most serious of the diseases of children.

In some epidemics the disease is of great severity. In institutions and in armies the death-rate is often high. The fever itself is rarely a source of danger. The extension of the catarrhal symptoms to the finer bronchial tubes is the most serious indication.

Treatment.—Confinement to bed in a well-ventilated room and a light diet are the only measures necessary in cases of uncomplicated measles. The fever rarely reaches a dangerous height. If it does it may be lowered by sponging or by the tepid bath gradually reduced. If the rash does not come out well, warm drinks and a hot bath will hasten its maturation. The bowels should be freely opened. If the cough is distressing, paregoric and a mixture of ipecacuanha wine and squills should be given. The patient should be kept in bed for a few days after the fever subsides. During desquamation the skin should be oiled daily, and warm baths given to facilitate the process. The convalescence from measles is the most important stage of the disease. Watchfulness and care may prevent serious pulmonary complications. The frequency with which the mothers of children with simple or tuberculous broncho-pneumonia tell us that " the child caught cold after measles," and the contemplation of the mortality bills should make us extremely careful in our management of this affection.

IX. RUBELLA (*Rötheln, German Measles*).

This exanthem has also the names of *rubeola notha*, or epidemic roseola, and, as it is supposed to present features common to both, has been also known as hybrid measles or hybrid scarlet fever. It is now generally regarded, however, as a separate and distinct affection.

Etiology.—It is propagated by contagion and spreads with great rapidity. It frequently attacks adults, and the occurrence of either measles or scarlet fever in childhood is no protection against it. The epidemics of it are often very extensive.

Symptoms.—These are usually mild, and it is altogether a less serious affection than measles. Very exceptionally, as in the epidemics studied by Cheadle, the symptoms are severe.

The stage of incubation ranges from ten to twelve days.

In the stage of invasion there are chilliness, headache, pains in the back and legs, and coryza. D. H. Hall insists that slight sore throat is a constant symptom, on which account, indeed, it was that it was originally regarded as a hybrid, having the sore throat of scarlet fever and the rash of measles. There may be very slight fever. In 30 per cent of Edwards's cases the temperature did not rise above 100°. The duration of this stage is somewhat variable. The rash usually appears on the first day, some writers say on the second, and others again give the duration of the stage of invasion as three days. Griffith places it at two days. The eruption comes out first on the face, then on the chest, and gradually extends so that within twenty-four hours it is scattered over the whole body. It may be the first symptom noted by the mother. The eruption consists of a number of round or oval, slightly raised spots, pinkish-red in color, usually discrete, but sometimes confluent.

The color of the rash is somewhat brighter than in measles. The patches are less distinctly crescentic. After persisting for two or three days (sometimes longer), it gradually fades and there is a slight furfuraceous desquamation. The rash persists as a rule longer than in scarlet fever or measles, and the skin is slightly stained after it. The lymphatic glands of the neck are frequently swollen, and, when the eruption is very intense and diffuse, the lymph-glands in the other parts of the body.

There are no special complications. The disease usually progresses favorably; but in rare instances, as in those reported by Cheadle, the symptoms are of greater severity. Albuminuria may occur and even nephritis. Pneumonia and colitis have been present in some epidemics. Icterus has been seen.

Diagnosis.—The mildness of the case, the slightness of the prodromal symptoms, the mildness or the absence of the fever, the more diffuse character of the rash, its rose-red color, and the early enlargement of the cervical glands, are the chief points of distinction between rötheln and measles.

The treatment is that of a simple febrile affection. It is well to keep the child in bed, though this may be difficult, as the patient rarely feels ill.

X. EPIDEMIC PAROTITIS (*Mumps*).

Definition.—An infectious disease, characterized by inflammation of the parotid gland. The testes in males and the ovaries and breasts in females are sometimes involved.

Etiology.—The nature of the virus is unknown.

The affection has all the characters of an epidemic disease. It is said to be endemic in certain localities, and probably is so in large centres of population. At certain seasons, particularly in the spring and autumn months, the number of cases increases rapidly. It is met most frequently in childhood and adolescence. Very young infants and adults are seldom attacked. Males are somewhat more frequently affected than females. In institutions and schools the disease has been known to attack over 90 per cent of all the children. It may be curiously localized in a city or district. The disease is contagious and spreads from patient to patient.

A remarkable idiopathic, non-specific parotitis may follow injury or disease of the abdominal or pelvic organs (see Diseases of the Salivary Glands).

Symptoms.—The period of incubation is from two to three weeks, and there are rarely any symptoms during this stage. The invasion is marked by fever, which is usually slight, rarely rising above 101°, but in exceptionally severe cases going up to 103° or 104°. The child complains of pain just below the ear on one side. Here a slight swelling is noticed, which increases gradually, until, within forty-eight hours, there is great enlargement of the neck and side of the cheek. The swelling passes forward in front of the ear, and back beneath the sterno-cleido muscle. The other side usually becomes affected within a day or two. The other salivary glands are rarely involved. The greatest inconvenience is experienced in taking food, for the patient is unable to open the mouth, and even speech and deglutition become difficult. There may be an increase in the secretion of the saliva, but the reverse is sometimes the case. There is seldom great pain, but, instead, an unpleasant feeling of tension and tightness. There may be earache, even otitis media, and slight impairment of hearing.

After persisting for from seven to ten days, the swelling gradually subsides and the child rapidly regains his strength and health. Relapse rarely if ever occurs.

Occasionally the disease is very severe and characterized by high fever, delirium, and great prostration. The patient may even lapse into a typhoid condition.

Orchitis.—Excessively rare before puberty, it develops usually as the parotitis subsides, or indeed a week or ten days later. One or both testicles may be involved. The swelling may be great, and occasionally effusion takes place into the tunica vaginalis. The orchitis may develop before the parotitis, or in rare instances may be the only manifestation of the infection (*orchitis parotidea*). The inflammation increases for three or four days, and resolution takes place gradually. There may be a muco-purulent discharge from the urethra. In severe cases atrophy may follow, fortunately as a rule only in one organ; occurring in both before puberty the natural development is usually checked. Even when both testicles are atrophied and small, sexual vigor may be retained. The proportion of cases of orchitis varies in different epidemics; 211 cases occurred in 699 cases, and 103 cases of atrophy followed 163 instances of orchitis (Comby).

A vulvo-vaginitis sometimes occurs in girls, and the breasts may become enlarged and tender. Mastitis has been seen in boys. Involvement of the ovaries is rare.

Complications and Sequelæ.—Of these the cerebral affections are perhaps the most serious. As already mentioned, there may be delirium and high fever. In rare instances meningitis has been found. Hemiplegia and coma may also occur. A majority of the fatal cases are associated with meningeal symptoms. These, of course, are very rare in comparison with the frequency of the disease; yet, in the Index Catalogue, under this caption, there are six fatal cases mentioned. In some epidemics the cerebral complications are much more marked than in others. Acute mania has occurred, and there are instances on record of insanity following the disease.

Arthritis, albuminuria, even acute uræmia with convulsions, endocarditis, facial paralysis, hemiplegia, and peripheral neuritis are occasional complications.

Suppuration of the gland is an extremely rare complication in genuine idiopathic mumps. Gangrene has occasionally occurred. The special senses may be seriously involved. Many cases of deafness have been described in connection with or following mumps. It, unfortunately, may be permanent. Affections of the eye are rare, but atrophy of the optic nerve has been described. The lachrymal glands may be involved.

Relapse may occur, even two or three, and chronic hypertrophy of the gland may follow.

The diagnosis of the disease is usually easy. The position of the swelling in front of and below the ear and the elevation of the lobe on the affected side definitely fix the locality of the swelling. In children inflammation of the parotid, apart from ordinary mumps, is excessively rare.

Treatment.—It is well to keep the patient in bed during the height of the disease. The bowels should be freely opened, and the patient given a light liquid diet. No medicine is required unless the fever is high, in which case aconite may be given. Cold compresses may be placed on the gland, but children, as a rule, prefer hot applications. A pad of cotton wadding covered with oiled silk is the best application. Suppuration is hardly ever to be dreaded, even though the gland become very tense. Should redness and tenderness develop, leeches may be used. With delirium and head symptoms the ice-cap may be applied. In a robust subject, unless the signs of constitutional depression are extreme, a free venesection may do good. For the orchitis, rest, with support and protection of the swollen gland with cotton-wool, is usually sufficient.

XI. WHOOPING-COUGH.

Definition.—A specific affection characterized by convulsive cough and a long-drawn inspiration, during which the "whoop" is produced.

Etiology.—The disease occurs in epidemic form, but sporadic cases appear in a community from time to time. It is directly contagious from person to person; but dwelling-rooms, houses, school-rooms, and other localities may be infected by a sick child. It is, however, in this way less infectious than other diseases, and is probably most often taken by direct contact. Koplik, Czaplewski, and Hensel have described a bacillus in the sputum, which may probably be the specific organism. The bacilli are present in the mucous clumps, with other forms as a rule, but they can be separated by proper means. Koplik found them in 13 of 16 cases of whooping-cough. It is a small bacillus with rounded ends, a little larger than the influenza bacillus. It is a facultative anærobe, and is pathogenic for mice. There are still doubtful points regarding the organism. Epidemics prevail for two or three months, usually during the winter and spring, and have a curious relation to other diseases, often preceding or following epidemics of measles, less frequently of scarlet fever.

Children between the first and second dentitions are commonly affected. Sucklings are, however, not exempt, and I have seen very severe attacks in infants under six weeks. It is stated that girls are more subject to the disease than boys. Adults and old people are sometimes attacked, and in the aged it may be a very serious affection. Many persons possess immunity against the disease, and, though frequently exposed, escape. As a rule, one attack protects. Delicate anæmic children with nasal or bronchial catarrh are more subject to the disease than others. According to the United States Census Reports, the disease is more than twice as fatal in the negro race than in others.

Morbid Anatomy.—Whooping-cough itself has no special pathological changes. In fatal cases pulmonary complications, particularly broncho-pneumonia, are usually present. Collapse and compensatory emphysema, vesicular and interstitial, are found, and the tracheal and bronchial glands are enlarged.

Symptoms.—Catarrhal and paroxysmal stages can be recognized. There is a variable period of incubation of from seven to ten days. In the *catarrhal stage* the child has the symptoms of an ordinary cold, which may begin with slight fever, running at the nose, injection of the eyes, and a bronchial cough, usually dry, and sometimes giving indications of a spasmodic character. The fever is usually not high, and slight attention is paid to the symptoms, which are thought to be those of a simple catarrh. After lasting for a week or ten days, instead of subsiding, the cough becomes worse and more convulsive in character.

The *paroxysmal stage,* marked by the characteristic cough, dates from the first appearance of the " whoop." The fit begins with a series of from fifteen to twenty short coughs of increasing intensity, and then with a deep inspiration the air is drawn into the lungs, making the " whoop," which may be heard at a distance and from which the disease takes its name. This loud inspiratory sound may sometimes precede the series of spasmodic expiratory efforts. Several coughing-fits may succeed each other until a tenacious mucus is ejected. This may be small in amount, but after a series of coughing-fits a considerable quantity may be expectorated. Not infrequently it is brought up by vomiting or by a combination of cough and regurgitation. There may be only four or five of these attacks in the day, or in severe cases they may recur every half-hour. During the paroxysm the thorax is very strongly compressed by the powerful expiratory efforts, and, as very little air passes in through the glottis, there are signs of defective aëration of the blood; the face becomes swollen and congested, the veins are prominent, the eyeballs protrude, and the conjunctivæ become deeply engorged. Suffocation indeed seems imminent, when with a deep, crowing inspiration air enters the lungs and the color is quickly restored. Children are usually terrified at the onset, and run at once to the mother or nurse to be supported during the attack. Few diseases are more painful to witness. In severe paroxysms vomiting is frequent and the sphincters may be opened. The urine is said to be of high specific gravity (1022–1032), pale yellow, and to contain much uric acid.

An ulcer under the tongue is a very common event, and was thought at one time to be the cause of the disease.

During the attack, if the chest be examined, the resonance is defective in the expiratory stage, full and clear during the deep, crowing inspiration; but on auscultation during the latter there may be no vesicular murmur heard, owing to the slowness with which the air passes the narrowed glottis. Bronchial râles are occasionally heard.

Among circumstances which precipitate a paroxysm are emotion, such as crying, and any irritation about the throat. Even the act of swallowing sometimes seems sufficient. In a close dusty atmosphere the coughing-fits are more frequent. After lasting for three or four weeks the attacks become lighter and finally cease. In cases of ordinary severity the course of the disease is rarely under six weeks.

The complications and sequelæ of whooping-cough are important. During the extensive venous congestion hæmorrhages are very apt to occur in the form of petechiæ, particularly about the forehead, ecchymosis of the conjunctivæ, epistaxis, and occasionally hæmoptysis. Hæmorrhage from the bowels is rare. Convulsions are not very uncommon, due perhaps to the extreme engorgement of the cerebral cortex. Very rarely hemiplegia or monoplegia follows. Sudden death has been caused by extensive subdural hæmorrhage. Whooping-cough must be regarded as a very unusual cause of cerebral palsy in children. It was associated with 3 of my series of 120 cases, but in none of them did the hemiplegia come on during the paroxysm, as in a case reported by S. West. Bernhardt has described an acutely developing spastic paraplegia.

The persistent vomiting may induce marked anæmia and wasting. The pulmonary complications which follow whooping-cough are extremely serious. During the severe coughing-spells interstitial emphysema may be induced, more rarely pneumothorax. I saw one instance in which rupture occurred, evidently near the root of the lung, and the air passed along the trachea and reached the subcutaneous tissues of the neck, a condition which has been known to become general. Broncho-pneumonia, with its accompanying collapse, is the most frequent pulmonary complication and carries off a large number of children. It may be simple, but in a considerable proportion of the cases the process is tuberculous. Pleurisy is sometimes met with and occasionally lobar pneumonia. Enlargement of the bronchial glands is very common in whooping-cough and has been thought to cause the disease. It may sometimes be sufficient to produce dulness over the manubrium. During the spasm the radial pulse is small, the right heart engorged, and during and after the attack the cardiac action is very much disturbed. Serious damage may result, and possibly some of the cases of severe valvular disease in children who have had neither rheumatism nor scarlet fever may be attributed to the terrible heart strain during a prolonged attack of whooping-cough. Koplik regards the swelling about the face and eyes as an important sign of the heart strain. Serious renal complications are very uncommon, but albumin not infrequently and sugar occasionally is found in the urine. An unusually marked leucocytosis appears early, chiefly of the lymphocytes (Meunier).

Diagnosis.—So distinctive is the "whoop" of the disease that the diagnosis is very easy; but occasionally there are doubtful cases, particularly during epidemics, in which a series of expiratory coughs occurs without any inspiratory crow.

Prognosis.—Taken with its complications, whooping-cough must be regarded as a very fatal affection. According to Dolan, it ranks third among the fatal diseases of children in England, where the death-rate per 1,000,000 from this disease is 5,000 annually. The younger the infant the greater is the probability of serious complications. The deaths are chiefly among children of the poor and among delicate infants.

Treatment.—Parents should be warned of the serious nature of whooping-cough, the gravity of which is scarcely appreciated by the public. Particular care should be taken that children suspected of the disease are not sent to the public schools or exposed in any way so that other children can become contaminated. There is more reprehensible neglect in connection with this than with any other disease. The patient should be isolated, and if the paroxysms are at all severe, at rest in bed. Fresh air, night and day, is a most essential element in the treatment of the disease. The medicinal treatment of whooping-cough is most unsatisfactory. In the catarrhal stage when there is fever the child should be in bed and a saline fever mixture administered. If the cough is distressing, ipecacuanha wine and paregoric may be given. For the paroxysmal stage a suspiciously long list of remedies has been recommended, twenty-two in one popular text-book on therapeutics. If the disease is due, as seems probable, to a germ growing upon and irritating the bronchial mucosa, a germicidal plan of treatment seems highly rational, and persistent attempts should be made to discover a suitable remedy. Quinine is one of the best drugs. One sixth of a grain may be given three times a day for each month of age, and 1½ grain for each year in children under five years. Resorcin in a 1-per-cent solution, swabbed frequently on the throat; 2 or 3 grains of iodoform to an ounce of starch powder; a spray of carbolic acid —have all been warmly recommended. J. Lewis Smith advises the use of the steam atomizer with a solution of carbolic acid, chlorate of potassium, and bromide of potassium in glycerin. Bromoform, in doses of 1 to 5 minims suspended in syrup, has been warmly recommended of late. Jacobi regards belladonna as the most satisfactory remedy. He gives it in full doses, as much as one sixth of a grain of the extract to a child of six or eight months three times a day. It should be given in sufficient doses to produce the cutaneous flush. For the nervous element in the disease anti-pyrin has been used with apparent success.

After the severity of the attack has passed and convalescence has begun, the child should be watched with the greatest care. It is just at this period that the fatal broncho-pneumonias are apt to develop. The cough sometimes persists for months and the child remains weak and delicate. Change of air should be tried. Such a patient should be fed with care, and given tonics and cod-liver oil.

XII. INFLUENZA (La Grippe).

Definition.—A pandemic disease, appearing at irregular intervals, characterized by extraordinary rapidity of extension and the large number of people attacked. Following the pandemic there are, as a rule, for several years endemic or epidemic outbreaks in different regions. Clinically, the disease has protean aspects, but with a special tendency to attack the respiratory mucous membranes.

History.—Great pandemics have been recognized since the sixteenth century. There have been four with their succeeding epidemics during the present century—1830-'33, 1836-'37, 1847-'48, and 1889-'90. The last pandemic began, as others had done before, in some of the distant provinces of Russia (hence the name Russian fever) in October, and by the beginning of November it had reached Moscow. By the middle of November Berlin was attacked. By the middle of December it was in London, and by the end of the month it had invaded New York, and was widely distributed over the entire continent. Within a year it had visited nearly all parts of the earth.

The duration of an epidemic in any one locality is from six to eight weeks. With the exception, perhaps, of dengue, there is no disease which attacks indiscriminately so large a proportion of the inhabitants. Fortunately, as in dengue, the rate of mortality is very low, but the last epidemic taught us to recognize in influenza, particularly its sequels and complications, one of the most serious of all specific diseases. The opportunity for studying the disease in the last epidemic has thrown much light upon many problems. Among the most notable productions were the work of Pfeiffer in discovering the specific germ, the elaborate Berlin report by von Leyden and Senator, and the Local Government Board's report by Parsons. Leichtenstern's article in Nothnagel's Handbuch is the most masterly and systematic consideration of the disease in the literature.

Etiology.—What relation has the epidemic influenza to the ordinary influenza cold or catarrhal fever (commonly also called the *grippe*), which is constantly present in the community? Leichtenstern answers this question by making the following divisions: (1) Epidemic *influenza vera*, caused by Pfeiffer's bacillus; (2) endemic-epidemic *influenza vera*, which often develops for several years in succession after a pandemic, also caused by the same bacillus; (3) endemic *influenza nostras*, pseudo-influenza or catarrhal fever, commonly called the *grippe*, which is a special disease, still of unknown etiology, and which bears the same relation to the true influenza as cholera nostras does to Asiatic cholera.

The epidemics which followed the great pandemic of 1889–'90 during the years 1891 to 1895 varied in intensity and extent in different localities.

The disease is highly contagious; it spreads with remarkable rapidity, which, however, is not greater than modern methods of conveyance. In the great pandemic of 1889–'90 some of the large prisons escaped entirely. The outbreak of epidemics is independent of all seasonal and meteorological conditions, though the worst have been in the colder seasons of the year. One attack does not necessarily protect from a subsequent one. A few persons appear not to be liable to the disease.

Bacteriology.—In 1892 Pfeiffer isolated a bacillus from the nasal and bronchial secretions, which is recognized as the cause of the disease. It is a small, non-motile organism, which stains well in Loeffler's methylene blue, or in a dilute, pale-red solution of carbol-fuchsin in water. On culture media it grows only in the presence of hæmoglobin. The bacilli are present in enormous numbers in the nasal and bronchial secretions of patients, in the latter almost in pure cultures. They persist often after the severe symptoms have subsided.

The much-discussed question whether during the presence of an epidemic human influenza attacks animals must be answered in the negative. In great pandemics of influenza the general rule holds good that other diseases do not prevail to the same extent. Anders has brought forward statistics to indicate that the outbreaks of malaria are very much diminished during the prevalence of influenza.

Symptoms.—The incubation period is "from one to four days; oftenest three to four days." The onset is usually abrupt, with fever and its associated phenomena.

Types of the Disease.—The manifestations are so extraordinarily complex that it is best to describe them under types of the disease.

1. *Respiratory.*—The mucous membrane of the respiratory tract from the nose to the air-cells of the lungs may be regarded as the seat of election of the influenza bacilli. In the simple forms the disease sets in with coryza, and presents the features of an acute catarrhal fever, with perhaps rather more prostration and debility than is usual. In other cases the catarrhal symptoms persist, bronchitis develops, the fever continues, there is delirium and much prostration, and the picture may even be that of severe typhoid. The graver respiratory conditions are bronchitis, pleurisy, and pneumonia. The bronchitis has really no special peculiarities. The sputum is supposed by many to be distinctive. Sometimes it is in extraordinary amounts, very thin, and containing purulent masses. Pfeiffer regards sputum of a greenish-yellow color and in coin-like lumps as almost characteristic of influenza. In other cases there may be a dark red, bloody sputum. One of the most distressing sequels of the influenza bronchitis is diffuse bronchiectasis, of which I have seen at least one instance. It occasionally happens that the bronchitis is of great intensity and reaches the finer tubes, so that the patient becomes cyanosed or even asphyxiated.

Influenza pneumonia is one of the most serious manifestations, and may depend upon Pfeiffer's bacillus itself, or is the result of a mixed infection. The true influenza pneumonia is most commonly lobular or catarrhal, less often croupous. Much of the mortality of the disease depends upon the fatal character of this complication. The clinical course of the cases is often irregular and the symptoms are obscure or masked.

Influenza pleurisy is more rare, but cases of primary involvement of the pleura are reported. It is very apt to lead to empyema. Pulmonary tuberculosis is usually much aggravated by an attack of influenza.

2. *Nervous Form.*—Without any catarrhal symptoms there may be severe headache, pain in the back and joints, with profound prostration. Many remarkable nervous manifestations were noted during the last epidemic. Among the more serious may be mentioned meningitis and encephalitis, the latter leading to hemiplegia or monoplegia. Abscess of the brain has followed in acute cases. All forms of neuritis are not uncommon, and in some cases are characterized by marked disturbance of motion and sensation. Judging from the accounts in the literature, almost every form of disease of the nervous system may follow influenza.

To involvement of the nerves may be ascribed some of the common cardiac symptoms, such as persistent irregularity, tachycardia or bradycardia, and attacks of angina pectoris. Among the most important of the nervous sequelæ are depression of spirits, melancholia, and in some cases dementia.

3. *Gastro-intestinal Form.*—With the onset of the fever there may be nausea and vomiting, or the attack may set in with abdominal pain, profuse diarrhœa, and collapse. In some epidemics jaundice has been a common symptom. In a considerable number of the cases there is enlargement of the spleen, depending chiefly upon the intensity of the fever.

4. *Febrile Form.*—The fever in influenza is very variable, but it is

important to recognize that it may be the only manifestation of the disease. It is sometimes markedly remittent, with chills; or in rare cases there is a protracted, continued fever of several weeks duration, which simulates typhoid closely.

While these are perhaps the most common forms with their complications, there are many others, among which may be mentioned the following: Various renal affections have been noted. G. Baumgarten has called attention to the frequency of nephritis in the recent epidemic. Orchitis has been also seen. Endocarditis and pericarditis, phlebitis and thrombosis of the various vessels are reported. Herpes is common. A diffuse erythema sometimes occurs, occasionally purpura. Catarrhal conjunctivitis is a frequent event. Iritis, and in rare instances optic neuritis, have been met with. Acute otitis media was a common complication. I have seen severe and persistent vertigo follow influenza, probably from involvement of the labyrinth.

Since the late severe epidemics it has been the fashion to date various ailments or chronic ill-health from influenza. In many cases this is correct. It is astonishing the number of people who have been crippled in health for years after an attack.

Diagnosis.—During a pandemic the cases offer but slight difficulty. The profoundness of the prostration, out of all proportion to the intensity of the disease, is one of the most characteristic features. In the respiratory form the diagnosis may be made by the bacteriological examination of the sputum, a procedure which should be resorted to early in a suspected epidemic. The differentiation of the various forms has been already sufficiently considered.

Treatment.—Isolation should be practised when possible, and old people should be guarded against all possible sources of infection. The secretions, nasal and bronchial, should be thoroughly disinfected. In every case the disease should be regarded as serious, and the patient should be confined to bed until the fever has completely disappeared. In this way alone can serious complications be avoided. From the outset the treatment should be supporting, and the patient should be carefully fed and well nursed. The bowels should be opened by a dose of calomel or a saline draught. At night 10 grains of Dover's powder may be given. At the onset a warm bath is sometimes grateful in relieving the pain in the back and limbs, but great care should be taken to have the bed well warmed, and the patient should be given after it a drink of hot lemonade. If the fever is high and there is delirium, small doses of antipyrin may be given and an ice-cap applied to the head. The medicinal antipyretics should be used with caution, as profound prostration sometimes develops in these cases. Too much stress should not be laid upon the mental features. Delirium may be marked even with slight fever. In the cases with great cardiac weakness stimulants should be given freely, and during convalescence strychnia in full doses.

The intense bronchitis, pneumonia, and other complications should receive their appropriate treatment. The convalescence requires careful management, and it may be weeks or months before the patient is restored to full health. A good nutritious diet, change of air, and pleasant surroundings are essential. The depression of spirits following this disease is one of its most unpleasant and obstinate features.

XIII. DENGUE.

Definition.—An acute infectious disease of tropical and subtropical regions, characterized by febrile paroxysms, pains in the joints and muscles, an initial erythematous, and a terminal polymorphous eruption.

It is known as *break-bone* fever from the atrocious character of the pain, and *dandy fever* from the stiff, dandified gait. The word dengue is supposed to be derived from a Spanish, or possibly Hindoostanee, equivalent of the word dandy.

History and Geographical Distribution.—The disease was first recognized in 1779 in Cairo and in Java, where Brylon described the outbreak in Batavia. The description by Benjamin Rush of the epidemic in Philadelphia in 1780 is one of the first, and one of the very best accounts of the disease. Between 1824 and 1828 it was prevalent at intervals in India and in the Southern States. S. H. Dickson gives a graphic description of the disease as it appeared in Charleston in 1828. Since that date there have been four or five widespread epidemics in tropical countries and on this continent along the Gulf States, the last in the summer of 1897. None of the recent epidemics have extended into the Northern States, but in 1888 it prevailed as far north as Virginia.

Etiology.—The rapidity of diffusion and the pandemic character are the two most important features of dengue. There is no disease, not even influenza, which attacks so large a proportion of the population. In Galveston, in 1897, 20,000 people were attacked within two months. It appears to belong to the group of exanthematic fevers, and has their highly infectious characters. A micrococcus has been found in the blood of patients by McLaughlin, of Texas.

As the disease is rarely fatal, no observations have been made upon its pathological anatomy.

Symptoms.—The period of incubation is from three to five days, during which the patient feels well. The attack sets in suddenly with headache, chilly feelings, and intense aching pains in the joints and muscles. The temperature rises gradually, and may reach 106° or 107°. The pulse is rapid, and there are the other phenomena associated with acute fever—loss of appetite, coated tongue, slight nocturnal delirium, and concentrated urine. The face has a suffused, bloated appearance, the eyes are injected, and the visible mucous membranes are flushed. There is a congested, erythematous state of the skin. Rush's description of the pains is worth quoting, as in it the epithet break-bone occurs in the literature for the first time. "The pains which accompanied this fever were exquisitely severe in the head, back, and limbs. The pains in the head were sometimes in the back parts of it, and at other times they occupied only the eyeballs. In some people the pains were so acute in their backs and hips that they could not lie in bed. In others, the pains affected the neck and arms, so as to produce in one instance a difficulty of moving the fingers of the right hand. They all complained more or less of a soreness in the seats of these pains, particularly when they occupied the head and eyeballs. A few complained of their flesh being sore to the touch in every part of the body. From these circumstances the disease was sometimes believed to be a rheumatism, but its more general name among all classes of people was the break-bone fever." The large and small joints are affected, sometimes in succession, and become swollen, red, and painful. In some cases cutaneous hyperæsthesia has been noted. Hæmorrhage from the mucous membranes was noted by Rush. Black vomit has also been described by several observers.

The fever gradually reaches its maximum by the third or fourth day; the patient then enters upon the apyretic period, which may last from two to four days, and in which he feels prostrated and stiff. A second paroxysm of fever then occurs, and the pains return. In a large number of cases an eruption is common, which, judging from the description, has nothing distinctive, being sometimes macular, like that of measles, sometimes diffuse and scarlatiniform, or papular, or lichen-like. In other instances the rash has been described as urticarial, or even vesicular. Certain writers describe inflammation and hyperæmia of the mucous membrane of the nose, mouth, and pharynx. Enlargement of the lymph-glands is not uncommon, and may persist for weeks after the disappearance of the fever. Convalescence is often protracted, and there is a degree of mental and physical prostration out of all proportion to the severity of the primary attack. The pains in the joints or muscles, sometimes very local, may persist for weeks. Rush refers to the former, stating that a young lady after recovery said it should be called break-heart, not break-bone, fever. The average duration of a moderate attack is from seven to eight days. Dengue is very seldom fatal. Dickson saw three deaths in the Charleston epidemic.

Complications are rare. Insomnia and occasionally delirium, resembling somewhat the alcoholic form, have been observed, and convulsions in children. A relapse may occur even as late as two weeks.

The *diagnosis* of the disease, prevailing as it does in epidemic form and attacking all classes indiscriminately, rarely offers any special difficulty. Isolated cases might be mistaken at first for acute rheumatism. The important question of the differentiation between yellow fever and dengue will be considered later.

Treatment.—This is entirely symptomatic. Quinine is stated to be a prophylactic, but on insufficient grounds. Hydrotherapy may be employed to reduce the fever. The salicylates or antipyrin may be tried for the pains, which usually, however, require opium. During convalescence iodide of potassium is recommended for the arthritic pains, and tonics are indicated.

XIV. CEREBRO-SPINAL MENINGITIS.

Definition.—A specific infectious disease, occurring sporadically and in epidemics, caused by the diplococcus intracellularis, characterized by inflammation of the cerebro-spinal meninges and a clinical course of great irregularity.

The affection is also known by the names of malignant purpuric fever, petechial fever, and spotted fever.

History.—Vieusseux first described a small outbreak in Geneva in 1805. In 1806 L. Danielson and E. Mann (Medical and Agricultural Register, Boston) gave an account of "a singular and very mortal disease which lately made its appearance in Medford, Mass."

The disease attracted much attention and was the subject of several very careful studies. The Massachusetts Medical Society, in 1809, appointed James Jackson, Thomas Welch, and J. C. Warren to investigate it. Elisha North's little book (1811) gives a full account of the early epidemics. Stillé's monograph (1867) and the elaborate section in vol. i of Joseph Jones' works contain details of the later American outbreaks. The history of the disease in Europe and elsewhere is to be found in Hirsch's Geographical Pathology, and a detailed statement of the epidemics in the United Kingdom is given as an appendix by Ormerod in his article in Allbutt's System. Hirsch divides the outbreaks into four periods: From 1805 to 1830, in which the disease was most prevalent throughout the United States; a second period, from 1837 to 1850, when the disease prevailed extensively in France, and there were a few outbreaks in the United States; a third period, from 1854 to 1874, when there were outbreaks in Europe and several extensive epidemics in this country. During the civil war there were comparatively few cases of the disease. It prevailed extensively in the Ottawa Valley early in the seventies. In the fourth period, from 1875 to the present time, the disease has broken out in a great many regions. There was a serious epidemic in western Maryland in 1892 and in New York in 1893. From the spring of 1896 to the date of writing, April, 1898, the disease has prevailed in Boston and the neighboring towns, and has been made the subject of careful study by Councilman, Mallory, and Wright, whose monograph, issued by the Massachusetts State Board of Health, is the most important contribution made in this country to the pathology of epidemic meningitis.

Etiology.—Cerebro-spinal meningitis presents several remarkable peculiarities. The outbreaks are localized, occurring in certain regions, and are rarely very widespread. As a rule, country districts have been more afflicted than cities. The epidemics have occurred most frequently in the winter and spring. The concentration of individuals, as of troops in large barracks, seems to be a special factor, and epidemics on the Continent show how liable recruits and young soldiers are to the disease. In civil life children and young adults are most susceptible. Over-exertion, long marches in the heat, depressing mental and bodily surroundings, and the misery and squalor of the large tenement houses in cities are predisposing causes. The disease seems not to be directly contagious, and is probably not transmitted by clothing or the excretions. It is very rare to have more than one or two cases in a house, and in a city epidemic the distribution of the cases is very irregular. Councilman has found five instances in which the same individual is reported to have had the disease twice.

Sporadic cases occur from time to time in the larger cities and country districts on this continent. After the first epidemic in Montreal in 1873 occasional instances occurred. In Philadelphia, since its appearance in 1863, there have been cases reported every year in the mortality bills. Without autopsy the diagnosis of many of these is extremely doubtful; but there can be no question that the disease, though rare, still lingers. Judging from my own experience in three of the hospitals of that city, in which in five years I saw only three instances, I would regard it as very much less frequent than the reports of the Health Office would seem to indicate.

It is greatly to be desired that observers hereafter pay very special attention to these cases, particularly to the bacteriological study, in order to determine the character of the exciting organism.

Bacteriology.—In 1887 Weichselbaum described an organism, the *Diplococcus intracellularis meningitidis,* which was probably the same as one previously found by Leichtenstern. In the tissues the organism is almost constantly within the polynuclear leucocytes. In cultures it has well-characterized features, and is distinguishable from the pneumococcus. Since Weichselbaum's observations this is the organism which has usually been met with in the carefully studied epidemics of the disease, particularly by Jäger. In the recent Boston outbreak, in 35 of the cases on which post-mortem examinations were made, the diplococci were demonstrated in all but 4, in one of which they had previously been found in fluid withdrawn by spinal puncture. The other 3 cases were chronic. Cultures may fail to give the organism even when abundantly present, as shown on cover-slips. In 7 cases the pneumococcus was found in connection with the diplococcus intracellularis, and once Friedländer's bacillus. Lumbar puncture was performed in 55 cases, in 38 of which diplococci were found.

Morbid Anatomy.—In malignant cases there may be no characteristic changes, the brain and spinal cord showing only extreme congestion, which was the lesion described by Vieusseux. In a majority of the acutely fatal cases death occurs within the first week. There is intense injection of the pia-arachnoid. The exudate is usually fibrino-purulent, most marked at the base of the brain, where the meninges may be greatly thickened and plastered over with it. On the cortex there may be much lymph along the larger fissures and in the sulci; sometimes the entire cortex is covered with a thick, purulent exudate. It deserves to be recorded that Danielson and Mann made five autopsies and were the first to describe " a fluid resembling pus between the dura and pia mater." The cord is always involved with the brain. The exudate is more abundant on the posterior surface, and involves, as a rule, the dorsal and lumbar regions more than the cervical portion.

In the more chronic cases there is general thickening of the meninges and scattered yellow patches mark where the exudate has been. The ventricles in the acute cases are dilated and contain a turbid fluid, or in the posterior cornua pure pus. In the chronic cases the dilatation may be very great. The brain substance is usually a little softer than normal and has a pinkish tinge; foci of hæmorrhage and of encephalitis may be found. The cranial nerves are usually involved, particularly the second, fifth, seventh, and eighth. The spinal nerve roots are also found imbedded in the exudate.

Microscopically, the exudate consists largely of polynuclear leucocytes closely packed in a fibrinous material. Flexner and Barker describe larger cells, from two to eight times the diameter of a leucocyte. The lesions in the tissue of the brain and cord, according to Councilman, are more marked in this than in other forms. They consist chiefly in infiltration of the tissue with pus cells, which extend downward in the perivascular spaces. In some instances there are foci of purulent infiltration and hæmorrhage. The neuroglia cells are swollen, with large, clear, and vesicular nuclei. The ganglion cells show less marked changes. Diplococci are found in variable numbers in the exudate, being more numerous in the brain than in the cord.

Lesions in Other Parts.—In one of the Boston cases, examination of the nasal secretion during life showed diplococci, and in this instance there was found post mortem a purulent infiltration of the mucous membrane. In two other cases this membrane was normal.

Lungs.—Pneumonia and pleurisy have been described in the disease. Councilman reports that in the recent epidemic in 13 cases there was congestion with œdema, in 7 broncho-pneumonia, in 2 characteristic croupous pneumonia with pneumococci; in 8 pneumonia due to the diplococcus intracellularis was present.

Spleen.—The organ varies a good deal in size. In only three of the Boston fatal cases was it found much enlarged. The *liver* is rarely abnormal. Acute *nephritis* is sometimes present. The intestines show sometimes swelling of the follicles, but this was not present in any of the Boston cases.

Symptoms.—Cases differ remarkably in their characters. Many different forms have been described. These are perhaps best grouped into three classes:

1. **Malignant Form.**—This fulminant or apoplectic type is found with variable frequency in epidemics. It may occur sporadically. The onset is sudden, usually with violent chills, headache, somnolence, spasms in the muscles, great depression, moderate elevation of temperature, and feeble pulse, which may fall to fifty or sixty in the minute. Usually a purpuric rash develops. In a Philadelphia case, in 1888, a young girl, apparently quite well, died within twenty hours of this form. There are cases on record in which death has occurred within a shorter time. Stillé tells of a child of five years, in whom death occurred after an illness of ten hours; and refers to a case reported by Gordon, in which the entire duration of the illness was only five hours. Two of Vieusseux's cases died within twenty-four hours.

2. **Ordinary Form.**—The stage of incubation is not known. The disease usually sets in suddenly. There may be premonitory symptoms: headache, pains in the back, and loss of appetite. More commonly, the onset is with headache, severe chill, and vomiting. The temperature rises to 101° or 102°. The pulse is full and strong. An early and important symptom is a painful stiffness of the muscles of the neck. The headache increases, and there are photophobia and great sensitiveness to noises.

7

Children become very irritable and restless. In severe cases the contraction of the muscles of the neck sets in early, the head is drawn back, and, when the muscles of the back are also involved, there is orthotonos, which is more common than opisthotonos. The pains in the back and in the limbs may be very severe. The motor symptoms are most characteristic. Tremor of the muscles may be present, with tonic or clonic spasms in the arms or legs. Rigidity of the muscles of the back or neck is very common, and the patient lies with the body stiff and the head drawn so far back that the occiput may be between the shoulder-blades. Except in early childhood convulsions are not common. Strabismus is a frequent and important symptom. Spasm of the muscles of the face may also occur. Cases have been described in which the general rigidity and stiffness was such that the body could be moved like a statue. Paralysis of the trunk muscles is rare, but paralysis of the muscles of the eye and the face is not uncommon.

Of sensory symptoms, headache is the most dominant and persists from the outset. It is chiefly in the back of the head, and the pain extends into the neck and back. There may be great sensitiveness along the spine, and in many cases there is marked hyperæsthesia.

The psychical symptoms are pronounced. Delirium occurs at the onset, occasionally of a furious and maniacal kind. The patient may display at the start marked erotic symptoms. The delirium gives place in a few days to stupor, which, as the effusion increases, deepens to coma.

The temperature is irregular and variable. Remissions occur frequently, and there is no uniform or typical curve during the disease. In some instances there has been little or no fever. In others the temperature may reach 105° or 106°, or, before death, 108°. The pulse may be very rapid in children; in adults it is at first usually full and strong. In some cases it is remarkably slow, and may not be more than fifty or sixty in the minute. Sighing respirations and Cheyne-Stokes breathing are met with in some instances. Unless there is pneumonia the respirations are not often increased in frequency.

The cutaneous symptoms of the disease are important. Herpes occurs with even greater frequency than in pneumonia or in intermittent fever. The petechial rash, which has given the name spotted fever to the disease, is very variable. Stillé states that of 98 cases in the Philadelphia Hospital, no eruption was observed in 37. In the Montreal cases petechiæ and purple spots were common. They appear to have been more frequent in the epidemics on this continent than in Europe. The petechiæ may be numerous and cover the entire skin. An erythema or dusky mottling may be present. In some instances there have been rose-colored hyperæmic spots like the typhoid rash. Urticaria or erythema nodosum, ecthyma, pemphigus, and in rare instances gangrene of the skin have been noted.

There is a leucocytosis, a point which may help in the diagnosis from typhoid fever. In the recent Boston epidemic blood counts were made in 33 cases. The highest number of leucocytes in any one was 31,000. The increase is chiefly in the polynuclear variety.

As already stated, vomiting may be a special feature at the onset; but, as a rule, it gradually subsides. In some instances, however, it persists and becomes the most serious and distressing of the symptoms. Diarrhœa is not common. The bowels are usually confined. The abdomen is not tender. In the acute form the spleen is usually enlarged.

The urine is sometimes albuminous and the quantity may be increased. Glycosuria has been noted in some instances, and in the malignant types hæmaturia.

The course of the disease is extremely variable. Hirsch rightly states that it may range between a few hours and several months. More than half of the deaths occur within the first five days. In favorable cases, after the symptoms have persisted for five or six days, improvement is indicated by a lessening of the spasm, reduction of the fever, and a return of the intelligence. A sudden fall in the temperature is of bad omen. Convalescence is extremely tedious, and may be interrupted by complications and sequelæ to be noted.

3. Anomalous Forms.

(a) *Abortive Type.*—The attack sets in with great severity, but in a day or two the symptoms subside and convalescence is rapid. Strümpell would distinguish between this abortive variety, which begins with such intensity, and the mild ambulant cases described by certain writers. He reports a case in which the meningeal symptoms set in with the greatest intensity and persisted for four days, the temperature rising to 40.9° C. On the fifth day the patient entered upon a rapid and satisfactory convalescence. In the mild cases, as distinguished from the abortive, the patients complain of headache, nausea, sensations of discomfort in the back and limbs, and stiffness in the neck. There is little or no fever, and only moderate vomiting. These cases could be recognized only during the prevalence of an epidemic.

(b) *An Intermittent Type* has been observed in many epidemics, and is recognized by von Ziemssen and Stillé. It is characterized by exacerbations of fever, which may recur daily or every second day, or follow a curve of an intermittent or remittent character. The pyrexia resembles that of pyæmia rather than malaria.

(c) *Chronic Form.*—Heubner states that this is a relatively frequent form, though it does not seem to be recognized by many writers on the subject. An attack may be protracted for from two to five or even six months, and may cause the most intense marasmus. It is characterized by a series of recurrences of the fever, and may present the most complex symptomatology. It is not improbable that these protracted cases depend upon chronic hydrocephalus or abscesses of the brain. This form differs distinctly from the intermittent type. A very remarkable instance of it is described by Worthington, in which the disease lasted for fourteen weeks.

Complications.—Pleurisy, pericarditis, and parotitis are not uncommon.

Pneumonia is described as frequent in certain outbreaks. Immermann found, during the Erlangen epidemic, many instances of the combination of pneumonia with meningitis, but it does not seem possible to determine whether, in such cases, pneumonia is the primary disease and the meningitis secondary, or *vice versa*. The frequency with which inflammation of the meninges of the brain complicates pneumonia is well known. Councilman suggests that the pneumonia of the disease is not the true croupous form, but due to the diplococcus meningitidis. This was found in eight of the Boston cases, and in one it was so extensive that it could have been mistaken for the ordinary croupous pneumonia. Arthritis has been the most frequent complication in certain epidemics. Many joints are affected simultaneously, and there are swelling, pain, and exudation, sometimes serous, sometimes purulent. This was first observed by James Jackson, Sr., in the epidemic which he described. Enteritis is rare.

Headache may persist for months or years after an attack. Chronic hydrocephalus develops in certain instances in children. The symptoms of this are " paroxysms of severe headache, pains in the neck and extremities, vomiting, loss of consciousness, convulsions, and involuntary discharges of fæces and urine " (von Ziemssen). Von Ziemssen regards chronic hydrocephalus as by no means a rare sequela. Mental feebleness and aphasia have occasionally been noted.

Paralysis of individual cranial nerves or of the lower extremities may persist for some time. In some of these cases there may be peripheral neuritis, as Mills suggested.

Special Senses.—*Eye.*—These are due to three causes: First, neuritis following involvement of the nerve in the exudation at the base. This may affect the third nerve or the optic nerves, leading to acute papillitis, which was found in 6 out of 40 cases examined by Randolph. Secondly, the inflammation may extend directly into the eye along the pia-arachnoid of the optic nerve, causing purulent choroido-iritis or even keratitis. Thirdly, a neuritis of the fifth nerve may be followed by keratitis and purulent conjunctivitis.

Ear.—Deafness very often follows inflammation of the labyrinth. Otitis media, with mastoiditis, may develop from direct extension. In 64 cases of meningitis which recovered, Moos found that 55 per cent were deaf. He suggests that the abortive form of the disease may be responsible for many cases of early acquired deafness. In children this not infrequently leads to deaf-mutism. Von Ziemssen states that in the deaf and dumb institutions of Bamberg and Nuremberg, in 1874, a majority of the pupils had become deaf from epidemic cerebro-spinal meningitis.

Nose.—Coryza is not infrequent early in the disease, and Strümpell says that in many of his cases nasal catarrh preceded the meningitis. He suggests that the latter may be caused by infection from the nose. Certainly the nasal secretion appears frequently to contain the diplococci—in 18 cases examined by Scherrer, and in 10 out of 15 of the Boston cases.

Diagnosis.—Is cerebro-spinal meningitis present? This is not always easy to answer. In certain manifestations typhoid fever, typhus fever, and pneumonia closely simulate cerebro-spinal meningitis. I am quite certain that many cases reported to the health boards as the last-named disease belong to the cerebral form of typhoid fever or pneumonia. Such cases present high fever, delirium, retraction of the neck, tremor, and rigidity of the muscles, and a certain diagnosis may only be made at autopsy. Stokes' statement, that "there is no single nervous symptom which may not and does not occur independently of any appreciable lesion of the brain, nerves or spinal cord," can not be too often repeated. I have already referred to the fact that the malignant form of small-pox may be mistaken for cerebro-spinal meningitis.

The second question, Is the disease cerebro-spinal fever? is usually easy to answer when an epidemic is prevailing, as the practitioner then soon learns to recognize the different types of which I have spoken. The chief difficulty is in differentiating sporadic cases of cerebro-spinal fever from other forms of meningitis. The matter is of importance chiefly with reference to the prognosis, which is so much more favorable in cerebro-spinal fever. Neither the tuberculous nor the streptococcus forms offer, as a rule, special difficulties. The pneumococcus meningitis may occur alone or as a complication of a pneumonia, latent or manifest. Leichtenstern states that "in meningitis following pneumonia contraction of the muscles of the neck is often absent, while in epidemic meningitis it is almost invariably present. Pneumonia-meningitis soon leads to delirium and coma, while in the epidemic form the sensorium may be normal throughout the entire course. Pneumonia-meningitis, moreover, is rapidly fatal, while the epidemic form is frequently recovered from." Councilman concludes that the difference between the clinical history of pneumococcus meningitis as compared with the epidemic form is the absence or slight development in the former of symptoms, pointing to extensive infection of the meninges of the cord and of the roots of the spinal and cranial nerves. Probably the most reliable method in diagnosis is Quincke's lumbar puncture, which is easily performed and free from danger. In the recent Boston epidemic it was carried out in 55 cases, and diplococci were found in 38. The negative cases were chiefly early in the outbreak. Toward the end of the epidemic there were no negative results when the spinal puncture was made early, and the tubes were inoculated with a large amount of material. The puncture should be made between the second and third or the third and fourth lumbar vertebræ with an ordinary exploratory or "antitoxine" needle. At a depth of about 4 cm. in children and 7 or 8 cm. in adults the needle passes through the membranes, and the fluid comes out drop by drop. It is not, as a rule, necessary to use aspiration. For bacteriological study from 5 to 10 cc. should pass into a perfectly sterilized test-tube, which should then be stoppered with cotton. The experience of F. H. Williams and of Wentworth in Boston shows that puncture is not only harmless, but the results are sometimes positively beneficial. Hereafter this procedure should be used early in all sporadic cases, and careful studies made of the organisms.

Prognosis.—Hirsch states that the mortality has ranged in various epidemics from 20 to 75 per cent. In children the death-rate is much higher than in adults. Cases with deep coma, repeated convulsions, and high fever rarely recover. The outlook in the protracted cases is not good, though Heubner gives an instance of a lad of seven, who was ill from the end of February until the end of June, with repeated recurrences, was worn to a skeleton, and yet completely recovered.

Treatment.—The high rate of mortality which has existed in most epidemics indicates the futility of the various therapeutical agents which have been recommended. When we consider the nature of the local disease and the fact that, so far as we know, simple or tuberculous cerebrospinal meningitis is invariably fatal, we may wonder rather that recovery follows in any well-developed case.

In strong robust patients the local abstraction of blood by wet cups on the nape of the neck relieves the pain. General bloodletting is rarely indicated. Cold to the head and spine, which was used in the first epidemics by New England physicians, is of great service. A bladder of ice to the head, or an ice-cap, and the spinal ice-bag may be continuously employed. The latter is very beneficial. Judging from the remarkable effects of the general bath in typhoid with pronounced cerebro-spinal symptoms, hydrotherapy should be systematically employed if the temperature is above 102.5°. In private practice the cold pack or sponging may be substituted. If any counter-irritation is thought necessary, the skin of the back of the neck may be lightly touched with the Paquelin thermocautery. Blisters, which have been used so much, are of doubtful benefit. Of internal remedies opium may be given freely, best as morphia hypodermically. Stillé recommends giving a grain of opium every hour in severe cases or every two hours in cases of moderate severity; von Ziemssen advises the hypodermic injection of morphia, from one third to one half grain in adults. Mercury has no special influence on meningeal inflammation. Iodide of potassium is warmly recommended by some writers. Quinine in large doses, ergot, belladonna and Calabar bean have had advocates. Bromide of potassium may be employed in the milder cases, but it is not so useful as morphia to control the spasms.

The diet should be nutritious, consisting of milk and strong broths while the fever persists. Many cases are very difficult to feed, and Heubner recommends forced alimentation with the stomach-tube. The cases seem to bear stimulants well, and whisky or brandy may be given freely when there are signs of a failing heart.

XV. LOBAR PNEUMONIA.

(Croupous or Fibrinous Pneumonia; Pneumonitis; Lung Fever.)

Definition.—An infectious disease characterized by inflammation of the lungs, toxæmia of varying intensity, and a fever that terminates abruptly by crisis. Secondary infective processes are common. The micrococcus lanceolatus of Fraenkel is present in a large proportion of the cases.

Incidence.—Pneumonia is the most widespread and the most fatal of all acute diseases. In the United States during the census year 1890 there died of it 76,496, a death-rate per 100,000 of population of 186.94. "More deaths are attributed to it than to any single form of disease except consumption" (Census Report). During the year 1897 there died of pneumonia in Baltimore 644 persons. It came next on the list to pulmonary tuberculosis. The Census Reports of 1870, 1880, and 1890 show that pneumonia as a cause of death has increased but slightly. C. F. Folsom has brought forward evidence to show that in the State of Massachusetts there has been between 1852 and 1894 a progressive increase in the death-rate from pneumonia. The same is true for the city of Glasgow. On the other hand, in England there is a slight diminution. Hospital statistics show that the ratio of pneumonia to other admissions is in the proportion of 20 to 30 per 1,000.

Etiology.—*Age.*—To the sixth year the predisposition to pneumonia is marked; it diminishes to the fifteenth year, but then for each subsequent decade it increases. For children Holt's statistics of 500 cases give: First year, 15 per cent; from the second to the sixth year, 62 per cent; from the seventh to the eleventh year, 21 per cent; from the twelfth to the fourteenth year, 2 per cent. Lobar pneumonia has been met with in the newborn. The relation to age is well shown in the last Census Report. The death-rate in persons from fifteen to forty-five years was 100.05 per 100,000 of population; from forty-five to sixty-five years it was 263.12; and in persons sixty-five years of age and over it was 733.77. Pneumonia may well be called the friend of the aged. Taken off by it in an acute, short, not often painful illness, the old man escapes those " cold gradations of decay " so distressing to himself and to his friends.

Sex.—Males are more frequently affected than females. The Census Report for 1890 gives 42,739 males against 33,757 females.

Race.—In this country pneumonia is more fatal in the colored race than among the whites, the death-rate being 278.97 against 182.24.

Social Condition.—The disease is more common in the cities. The census figures give 234.07 deaths per 100,000 of population for the cities against 141.09 for rural districts. Individuals who are much exposed to hardship and cold are particularly liable to the disease. New-comers and immigrants are stated to be less susceptible than native inhabitants.

Personal Condition.—Debilitating causes of all sorts render individuals more susceptible. Alcoholism is perhaps the most potent predisposing factor. Robust, healthy men are, however, often attacked.

Previous Attack.—No acute disease recurs in the same individual with such frequency. Instances are on record of individuals who have had ten or more attacks. The percentage of recurrences has been placed as high as 50. Netter gives it as 31, and he has collected the statistics of eleven observers who place the percentage at 26.8. Among the highest figures for recurrences are those of Benjamin Rush, 28, and Andral, 16.

Trauma.—Occasionally the disease directly follows an injury, particularly of the chest. Litten, who has described these *contusion-pneumoniæ*, saw 14 cases in the course of six years. Jürgensen, however, met with only one case among 768 pneumonia patients. There can be no question that an acute inflammation of the lungs may follow immediately upon injury to the chest without fracture of the ribs. Harris has reported a remarkable case in which a pneumonia of this kind appears to have been infected from obsolescent tuberculous foci in the same lung. Workers in certain phosphate factories, where they breathe a very dusty atmosphere, according to Ballard, are particularly prone to pneumonia.

Cold has been for years regarded as an important etiological factor. The frequent occurrence of an initial chill has been one reason for this widespread belief. As to the close association of pneumonia with exposure there can be no question. We see the disease occur either promptly after a wetting or a chilling due to some unusual exposure, or come on after an ordinary catarrh of one or two days' duration. Cold is now regarded simply as a factor in lowering the resistance of the bronchial and pulmonary tissues.

Climate and Season.—Climate does not appear to have very much influence, as pneumonia prevails equally in hot and cold countries. It is stated to be more prevalent in the Southern than in the Northern States, but an examination of the last Census Report shows that there is very little difference in the various State groups.

Much more important is the influence of *season*. Statistics are unanimous in placing the highest incidence of the disease in the winter and spring months. In Montreal January, the coldest month of the year, but with steady temperature, has usually a comparatively low death-rate from pneumonia. The large statistics of Seitz from Munich and of Seibert of New York give the highest percentage in February and March.

Bacteriology of Acute Lobar Pneumonia.—(*a*) *The Micrococcus lanceolatus, Pneumococcus or Diplococcus Pneumoniæ, of Fraenkel.*— In September, 1880, Sternberg inoculated rabbits with his own saliva and isolated a micrococcus. The publication was not made until April 30, 1881. Pasteur discovered the same organism in the saliva of a child dead of hydrophobia in December, 1880, and the priority of the discovery belongs to him, as his publication is dated January 18, 1881. There was, however, no suspicion that this organism was concerned in the etiology of lobar pneumonia, and it was not really until April, 1884, that A. Fraenkel determined that the organism found by Sternberg and Pasteur in the saliva, and known as the coccus of sputum septicæmia, was the most frequent organism in acute pneumonia. At first there was a good deal of confusion between this and the organism described by Friedländer, November, 1883, and which is now known as the pneumo-bacillus. The subsequent investigations of Fraenkel and those of Weichselbaum have demonstrated that in a very large proportion of all cases of croupous pneumonia the diplococcus is present.

The organism is a somewhat elliptical, lance-shaped coccus, usually occurring in pairs; hence the term diplococcus. It is readily demonstrated in cover-glass preparations with the usual solutions and by the Gram method. About the organism in the sputum a capsule can always be demonstrated. Its cultural and biological properties present many variations, for a consideration of which the student is referred to the textbooks on bacteriology. Scarcely any peculiarity is constant. A large number of varieties have been cultivated. Its kinship to the streptococcus pyogenes is regarded by many as very close.

Distribution in the Body.—In the bronchial secretions and in the affected lung it is readily demonstrated in cover-slips, and in the latter in sections. During life in cases of pneumonia the organism has been isolated from the blood in a number of cases, in 4 out of 32 by Kohn.

Micrococcus lanceolatus under other Conditions.—In this connection a very important point is the presence of the organism in the mouth and bronchial secretions of healthy individuals—20 per cent, according to Netter's observations. It persists for months or even for years in the saliva of persons who have had pneumonia.

In other Diseases.—The organism is very widely distributed, and is found in many other conditions besides croupous pneumonia. It has been met with in pure cultures in the inflammations of the serous membranes— pleurisy, pericarditis, meningitis, peritonitis, acute synovitis, and in endocarditis, etc.

An acute general infection with the micrococcus lanceolatus without localized foci may prove rapidly fatal, constituting a *Pneumococcus septicæmia* comparable to the typhoid septicæmia already described. Townsend has reported a remarkable case of a girl aged six, who had pain in the abdomen, vomiting, and a temperature of 104.2°. There was no exudate in the throat. Twenty-four hours from the beginning of the symptoms she had a convulsion and died six hours later. There was found a general infection with the pneumococcus, which occurred in the blood, lungs, spleen, and kidneys. In Flexner's study of terminal infections the micrococcus lanceolatus was found four times in acute peritonitis, eleven times in acute pericarditis, five times in acute endocarditis, three times in acute pleurisy, and three times in acute meningitis.

Outside the body the organism has been found in the dust and sweepings of rooms.

(*b*) *The Bacillus pneumoniæ of Friedländer.*—This is a larger organism than the pneumococcus, and appears in the form of small, short rods. It also shows a capsule, but presents marked biological and cultural differences from Fraenkel's pneumococcus. It is not found nearly so often in the lung as the pneumococcus. It occurred in 9 of Weichselbaum's 129 cases. Its etiological relation to the disease is still in question.

(*c*) *Other Organisms.*—In a variable number of cases of pneumonia the staphylococcus and the streptococcus pyogenes occur, rarely alone, usually in association with the pneumococcus. The streptococcus pyogenes may be the only organism present, particularly in children, but this type of pneumonia probably differs from the true fibrinous form. Other organisms have been met with in pneumonia—the bacillus typhosus, the bacillus diphtheriæ, and the influenza bacillus.

Clinically, the *infectious nature* of pneumonia was recognized long before we knew anything of the pneumococcus. Among the features which favored this view were the following: First, the disease is similar to other infections in its mode of outbreak. It may occur in endemic form, localized in certain houses, in barracks, jails, and schools. As many as ten occupants of one house have been attacked, and in hospital practice it is not infrequent to have 2 or 3 cases admitted from the same house. I have seen three members of a family consecutively attacked with a most malignant type of pneumonia. Among the more remarkable endemic outbreaks is that reported by W. B. Rodman, of Frankfort, Ky. In a prison with a population of 735 there occurred in one year 118 cases of pneumonia with 25 deaths. At the penitentiary at Amberg during a period of five months there were 161 cases, with a mortality above 28 per cent. The disease may assume epidemic proportions. In the Middlesborough epidemic, so carefully studied by Ballard, there were 682 persons attacked with a mortality of 21 per cent. During some years pneumonia is so prevalent that it is practically pandemic. Direct contagion is suggested by the fact that a patient in the next bed to a pneumonia case may take the disease, or 2 or 3 cases may follow in rapid succession in a ward. It is very exceptional, however, for nurses or doctors to be attacked.

Secondly, the clinical course of the disease is that of an acute infection. It is the very type of a self-limited disease, running a definite cycle in a way seen only in infectious disorders.

Thirdly, as in other acute infections, the constitutional symptoms may bear no proportion whatever to the severity of the local lesion. As is well known, a patient may have a very small apex pneumonia which does not seriously impair the breathing capacity, but which may be accompanied with the most intense toxic features.

Immunity and Serum Therapy.—The observations of the Klemperers, Foa, Washbourn, and others on the production of immunity and on the cure of the disease are of great importance. The Klemperers found that immunity was readily obtained in animals either by subcutaneous or intravenous injections of large quantities of the filtered bouillon cultures, or by the injection of the glycerine extract. The immunity, though rarely lasting more than six months, was transmitted to the offspring born within this period. Still more interesting are their observations upon the cure of the experimentally produced disease. They found that the serum and fluids of the body of an animal which had been rendered immune had the property not only of producing immunity when introduced into the circulation of another susceptible animal, but actually of curing the disease after infection had been in progress for some time. In infected animals with a body temperature of from 40° to 41° C., the fever fell to normal in twenty-four hours after the injection of serum from another animal which possessed immunity. They believe that the pneumococcus produces a poisonous albumin (pneumotoxin) which when introduced into the circulation of an animal causes elevation of temperature and the subsequent production in the body of a substance (antipneumotoxin) which possesses the power of neutralizing the poisonous albumin which is formed by the bacteria. In man they hold that during the pneumonic process there is a constant absorption into the circulation of this poisonous albumin produced by the bacteria in the lungs. This continues until eventually the same antidotal substance is produced in the circulation that has been seen to occur experimentally. It is then that the crisis occurs. The bacteria are neither destroyed nor is their power to produce the poisonous albumin lessened; but the third factor, the antitoxic element, now exists and neutralizes the toxic substances as they are produced. They demonstrated that the serum of the blood of patients after the crisis of pneumonia contained the antitoxic substance and was capable, in a fair number of cases, of curing the disease when injected into infected animals.

Not much progress has as yet been made in establishing a satisfactory serum therapy for the disease in men. Washbourn has obtained large quantities of the serum by immunizing ponies, but, so far as I can ascertain, a trustworthy antipneumococcic serum is at present not in the market.

Morbid Anatomy.—Since the time of Laennec, pathologists have recognized three stages in the inflamed lung—engorgement, red hepatization, and gray hepatization.

In the stage of *engorgement* the lung tissue is deep red in color, firmer to the touch, and more solid, and on section the surface is bathed with blood and serum. It still crepitates, though not so distinctly as healthy lung, and excised portions float. The air-cells can be dilated by insufflation from the bronchus. Microscopical examination shows the capillary vessels to be greatly distended, the alveolar epithelium swollen, and the air-cells occupied by a variable number of blood-corpuscles and detached alveolar cells. In the stage of *red hepatization* the lung tissue is solid, firm, and airless. If the entire lobe is involved it looks voluminous, and shows indentations of the ribs. On section the surface is dry, reddish brown in color, and has lost the deeply congested appearance of the first stage. One of the most remarkable features is the friability; in striking contrast to the healthy lung, which is torn with difficulty, a hepatized organ can be readily broken by the finger. Careful inspection shows that the surface is distinctly granular, the granulations representing fibrinous plugs filling the air-cells. The distinctness of this appearance varies greatly with the size of the alveoli, which are about 0.10 mm. in diameter in the infant, 0.15 or 0.16 in the adult, and from 0.20 to 0.25 in old age. On scraping the surface with a knife a reddish viscid serum is removed, containing small granular masses. The smaller bronchi often contain fibrinous plugs. If the lung has been removed before the heart, it is not uncommon to find solid moulds of clot filling the blood-vessels. Microscopically, the air-cells are seen to be occupied by coagulated fibrin in the meshes of which are red blood-corpuscles, polynuclear leucocytes, and alveolar epithelium. The alveolar walls are infiltrated and leucocytes are seen in the interlobular tissues. Cover-glass preparations from the exudate, and thin sections show, as a rule, the diplococci already referred to, many of which are contained within cells. Staphylococci and streptococci may also be seen in some cases. In the stage of *gray hepatization* the tissue has changed from a reddish-brown to a grayish-white color. The surface is moister, the exudate obtained on scraping is more turbid, the granules in the acini are less distinct, and the lung tissue is still more friable. Histologically, in gray hepatization, it is seen that the air-cells are densely filled with leucocytes, the fibrin network and the red blood-corpuscles have disappeared. A more advanced condition of gray hepatization is that known as *purulent infiltration*, in which the lung tissue is softer and bathed with a purulent fluid.

The stage of gray hepatization appears to be the first step in the process of *resolution*. The exudate is softened, the cell elements are disintegrated and rendered capable of absorption. When the purulent infiltration of the lung tissue reaches the grade sometimes seen post mortem, it is probable that resolution could not take place. Small abscess cavities may arise, and by their fusion larger ones. Often in one lung, or even in one lobe, the various stages of the process may be seen, and the passage of the engorgement into red hepatization and of the latter into the gray stage can be readily traced.

The general details of the morbid anatomy of pneumonia may be gathered from the following facts, based on 100 autopsies, made by me at the General Hospital, Montreal: In 51 cases the right lung was affected; in 32, the left; in 17, both organs. In 27 cases the entire lung, with the exception, perhaps, of a narrow margin at the apex and anterior border, was consolidated. In 34 cases, the lower lobe alone was involved; in 13 cases, the upper lobe alone. When double, the lower lobes were usually affected together, but in three instances the lower lobe of one and the upper lobe of the other were attacked. In three cases also, both upper lobes were affected. Occasionally the disease involves the greater part of both lungs; thus, in one instance the left organ with the exception of the anterior border was uniformly hepatized, while the right was in the stage of gray hepatization, except a still smaller portion in the corresponding region. In a third of the cases, red and gray hepatization existed together. In 22 instances there was gray hepatization. As a rule the unaffected portion of the lung is congested or œdematous. When the greater portion of a lobe is attacked, the uninvolved part may be in a state of almost gelatinous œdema. The unaffected lung is usually congested, particularly at the posterior part. This, it must be remembered, may be largely due to post-mortem subsidence. The uninflamed portions are not always congested and œdematous. The upper lobe may be dry and bloodless when the lower lobe is uniformly consolidated. The average weight of a normal lung is about 600 grammes, while that of an inflamed organ may be 1,500, 2,000, or even 2,500 grammes.

The bronchi contain, as a rule, at the time of death a frothy serous fluid, rarely the tenacious mucus so characteristic of pneumonic sputum. The mucous membrane is usually reddened, rarely swollen. In the affected areas the smaller bronchi often contain fibrinous plugs, which may extend into the larger tubes, forming perfect casts. The bronchial glands are swollen and may even be soft and pulpy. The pleural surface of the inflamed lung is invariably involved when the process becomes superficial. Commonly, there is only a thin sheeting of exudate, producing slight turbidity of the membrane. In only two of the hundred instances the pleura was not involved. In some cases the fibrinous exudate may form a creamy layer an inch in thickness. A serous exudation of variable amount is not uncommon.

Lesions in other Organs.—The heart is distended with firm, tenacious coagula, which can be withdrawn from the vessels as dendritic moulds. In no other acute disease do we meet with coagula of such solidity and firmness. The distention of the right chambers of the heart is particularly marked. The left chambers are rarely distended to the same degree. The spleen is often enlarged, though in only 35 of the 100 cases was the weight above 200 grammes. The kidneys show parenchymatous swelling,

turbidity of the cortex, and, in a very considerable proportion of the cases
—25 per cent—chronic interstitial changes.

Pericarditis is not infrequent, and occurs more particularly with pneumonia of the left side and with double pneumonia. In 5 of the 100 autopsies it was present, and in 4 of them the lappet of lung overlying the pericardium with its pleura was involved. Endocarditis is more frequent and
occurred in 16 of the 100 cases. In 5 of these the endocarditis was of the
simple character; in 11 the lesions were ulcerative. Fatty degeneration
of the heart is not common except in protracted cases.

Meningitis is not infrequently found, and in many cases is associated
with malignant endocarditis. It was present in 8 of the 100 autopsies.
Of 20 cases of meningitis in ulcerative endocarditis 15 occurred in pneumonia. The meningeal inflammation in these cases is usually cortical.

Croupous or diphtheritic inflammation may occur in other parts. A
croupous colitis, as pointed out by Bristowe, is not very uncommon. It
occurred in 5 of my 100 post-mortems. It is usually a thin, flaky exudation, most marked on the tops of the folds of the mucous membrane. In
1 case there was a patch of croupous gastritis, covering an area of 12 by
8 cm., situated to the left of the cardiac orifice.

The liver shows parenchymatous changes and often extreme engorgement of the hepatic veins.

Symptoms.—*Course of the Disease in Typical Cases.*—We know but
little of the incubation period in lobar pneumonia. It is probably very
short. There are sometimes slight catarrhal symptoms for a day or two.
As a rule, the disease sets in abruptly with a severe chill, which lasts from
fifteen to thirty minutes or longer. In no acute disease is an initial chill
so constant or so severe. The patient may be taken abruptly in the midst
of his work, or may awaken out of a sound sleep in a rigor. The temperature taken during the chill shows that the fever has already begun. If
seen shortly after the onset, the patient has usually features of an acute
fever, and complains of headache and general pains. Within a few hours
pain in the side develops, often of an agonizing character; a short, dry,
painful cough begins, and the respirations are increased in frequency.
When seen on the second or third day, the picture in typical pneumonia
is quite pathognomonic; more so, perhaps, than that presented by any
other acute disease. The patient lies flat in bed, often on the affected
side; the face is flushed, particularly one or both cheeks; the breathing is
hurried, accompanied often with a short expiratory grunt; the alæ nasi
dilate with each inspiration; herpes is usually present on the lips or nose;
the eyes are bright, the expression is anxious, and there is a frequent short
cough which makes the patient wince and hold his side. The expectoration is blood-tinged and extremely tenacious. The temperature may be
104° or 105°. The pulse is full and bounding and the pulse-respiration
ratio much disturbed. Examination of the lung shows the physical signs
of consolidation—blowing breathing and fine râles. After persisting for
from seven to ten days the crisis occurs, and with a fall in the temperature
the patient passes from a condition of extreme distress and anxiety to one
of comparative comfort.

Special Features.—*The fever* rises rapidly, and the height may be 104° or 105° within twelve hours. Having reached the fastigium, it is

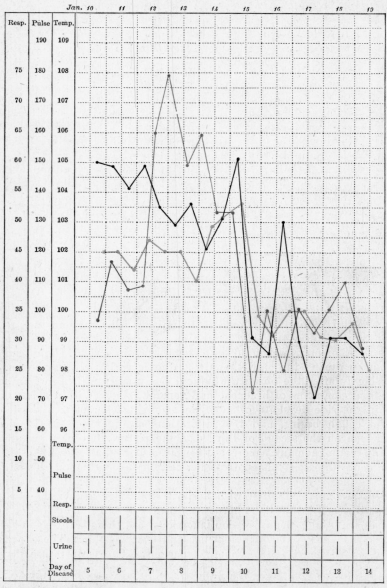

BLACK, TEMPERATURE ;   RED, PULSE ;   BLUE, RESPIRATION.

CHART IX.—Fever, pulse, and respirations in lobar pneumonia.

remarkably constant. Often the two-hour temperature chart will not show for two days more than a degree of variation. In children and in cases without chill the rise is more gradual. In old persons and in drunkards the temperature range is lower than in children and in healthy individuals; indeed, one occasionally meets with an afebrile pneumonia.

The Crisis.—After the fever has persisted for from five to nine or ten days there is an abrupt drop, known as the crisis, which is perhaps the most characteristic feature of lobar pneumonia. The day of the crisis is variable. It is very uncommon before the third day, and rare after the twelfth. I have twice seen it as early as the third day. From the time of Hippocrates it has been thought to be more frequent on the uneven days, particularly the fifth and seventh. A precritical rise of a degree or two may occur. In one case the temperature rose from 105° to nearly 107°, and then in a few hours fell to normal. Not even after the chill in malarial fever do we see such a prompt and rapid drop in the temperature. The usual time is from five to twelve hours, but often in an hour there may occur a fall of six or eight degrees (S. West). The temperature may be subnormal after the crisis, as low as 96° or 97°. Usually with the crisis there is an abundant sweat, and the patient sinks into a comfortable sleep. The day after the crisis there may be a slight post-critical rise. A pseudocrisis is not very uncommon, in which on the fifth or sixth day the temperature drops from 104° or 105° to 102°, and then rises again. When the fall takes place gradually within twenty-four hours it is called a protracted crisis. If the fever persists beyond the twelfth day, the fall is likely to be by lysis. In children this mode of termination is common, and occurred in one third of a series of 183 cases reported by Morrill. Occasionally in debilitated individuals the temperature drops rapidly just before death; more frequently there is an ante-mortem elevation. In cases of delayed resolution the fever may persist for weeks. The crisis is the most remarkable single phenomenon of pneumonia. With the fall in the fever the respirations become reduced almost to normal, the pulse slows, and the patient passes from perhaps a state of extreme hazard and distress to one of safety and comfort, and yet, so far as the physical examination indicates, there is with the crisis no special change in the local condition in the lung.

Pain.—On the affected side there is early a sharp, agonizing pain, generally referred to the region of the nipple or lower axilla. It is much aggravated on deep inspiration and on coughing. It is associated with the accompanying dry pleurisy of the disease. It is absent in central pneumonia, and much less frequent in apex pneumonia. In exceptional cases the pain is in the abdomen, and I have twice known the suspicion of appendicitis raised by the sudden acute onset of the pain, once in the region of the navel and once low on the right side. The pain may be severe enough to require a hypodermic injection of morphia.

Dyspnœa is an almost constant feature. Even early in the disease the respirations may be 30 in the minute, and on the second or third day between 40 and 50. The movements are shallow, evidently restrained, and if the patient is asked to draw a deep breath he cries out with the pain. Expiration is frequently interrupted by an audible grunt. At first with the increased respiration there may be no sensation of distress. Later this may be present in a marked degree. In children the respirations may be

80 or even 100. Many factors combine to produce the shortness of breath—the pain in the side, the toxæmia, the fever, and the loss of function in a considerable area of the lung tissue. Sometimes there appear to be nervous factors at work. That it does not depend upon the consolidation is shown by the fact that after the crisis, without any change in the local condition of the lung, the number of respirations may drop to normal. The ratio between the respirations and the pulse may be 1 to 2 or even 1 to 1.5, a disturbance rarely so marked in any other disease.

Cough.—This usually comes on with the pain in the side, and at first is dry, hard, and without any expectoration. Later it becomes very characteristic—frequent, short, restrained, and associated with great pain in the side. In old persons, in drunkards, in the terminal pneumonias, and sometimes in young children there may be no cough. After the crisis the cough usually becomes much easier and the expectoration more easily expelled. The cough is sometimes persistent, continuous, and by far the most aggravated and distressing symptom of the disease. Paroxysms of coughing of great intensity after the crisis suggest a pleural exudate.

Sputum.—A brisk hæmoptysis may be the initial symptom. At first the sputum may be mucoid, but usually after twenty-four hours it becomes blood-tinged, viscid, and very tenacious. At first quite red from the unchanged blood, it gradually becomes rusty or of an orange yellow. The tenacious viscidity of the sputum is remarkable; it often has to be wiped from the lips of the patient, and a spit-cup half full may be inverted without spilling. In low types of the disease the sputum may be fluid and of a dark brown color, resembling prune juice. The amount is very variable. In children and in old people there may be none, and even in adults cases are not very uncommon in which from beginning to close there is no expectoration. A common amount is from 150 to 300 cc. daily. After the crisis the quantity is variable, abundant in some cases, absent in others.

Microscopically, the sputum consists of leucocytes, mucus corpuscles, red blood-corpuscles in all stages of degeneration, and bronchial and alveolar epithelium. Hæmatoidin crystals are occasionally met with. Of micro-organisms the pneumococcus is usually present, and sometimes Friedländer's bacillus. Very interesting constituents are small cell moulds of the alveoli and the fibrinous casts of the bronchioles; the latter may be very plainly visible to the naked eye, and sometimes may form good-sized dendritic casts. Chemically, the expectoration is particularly rich in calcium chloride.

Physical Signs.—*Inspection.*—The position of the patient is not constant. He usually rests more comfortably on the affected side, or he is propped up with the spine curved toward it. Orthopnœa is not nearly so frequent as in heart-disease.

Inspection of the thorax may show at first no differences between the two sides; usually if the lower lobe of a lung is involved the movement is less on the affected side. Later this deficient expansion is marked, and may be both seen and felt. The compensatory increased movement on the sound side is sometimes very noticeable even before the patient's chest is bared. The intercostal spaces are not usually obliterated. When the cardiac lappet of the left upper lobe is involved there may be a marked increase in the area of visible cardiac pulsation. Pulsation of the affected lung may cause a marked movement of the chest wall (Graves). Other points to be noticed in the inspection are the frequency of the respiration, the action of the accessory muscles, such as the sterno-cleido-mastoids and scaleni, and the dilatation of the nostrils with each inspiration.

Mensuration may show a definite increase in the volume of the side affected, rarely more, however, than 1 or 1½ cm.

Palpation.—The lack of expansion on the affected side is sometimes more readily perceived by touch than by sight. The pleural friction may be felt. On asking the patient to count, the voice fremitus is greatly increased in comparison with the corresponding point on the healthy side. It is to be remembered that if the bronchi are filled with thick secretion, or if, in what is known as massive pneumonia, they are filled with fibrinous exudate, the tactile fremitus may be diminished. It is always well to ask the patient to cough before testing the fremitus.

Percussion.—In the stage of engorgement the note is higher pitched and may have a somewhat tympanitic quality, the so-called Skoda's resonance. This can often be obtained over the lung tissue just above a consolidated area. When the lung is hepatized, the percussion note is dull, the quality varying a good deal from a note which has in it a certain tympanitic quality to one of absolute flatness. There is not the wooden flatness of effusion and the sense of resistance is not so great. During resolution the tympanitic quality of the percussion note usually returns. For weeks or months after convalescence there may be a higher-pitched note on the affected side. Among variations to be noticed are that Wintrich's change in the percussion note when the mouth is open may be very well marked in pneumonia of the upper lobe. Occasionally there is an almost metallic quality over the consolidated area, and when this exists with a very pronounced amphoric quality in the breathing the presence of a cavity may be suggested. In deep-seated pneumonias there may be for several days no change in the percussion note, and in a few rare cases percussion shows no change throughout the disease.

Auscultation.—Quiet, suppressed breathing in the affected part is often a marked feature in the early stage, and is always suggestive. Very early there is heard at the end of inspiration the fine crepitant râle, a series of minute cracklings heard close to the ear, and perhaps not audible until a full breath is drawn. This is probably a fine pleural crepitus, as J. R. Learning maintained; it is usually believed to be produced in the air-cells and finer bronchi by the separation of the sticky exudate. At this stage, before consolidation has occurred, the breath-sounds may be, as before mentioned, much feebler than in health, but on drawing a long breath they may have a harsh quality, to which the term broncho-vesicular has been applied. In the stage of red hepatization and when dulness is well defined, the respiration is tubular, similar to that heard in health over the larger bronchi. With this blowing breathing there may be no râles, and it may present an intensity unknown in any other pulmonary affection. It is simply the propagation of the laryngeal and tracheal sounds through the bronchi and the consolidated lung tissue. The permeability of the bronchi is essential to its production. Tubular breathing is absent in certain cases of massive pneumonia in which the larger bronchi are completely filled with exudation. When resolution begins mucous râles of all sizes can be heard. At first they are small and have been called the *redux-crepitus*. The voice-sounds are transmitted through the consolidated lung with great intensity. This bronchophony may have a curious nasal quality to which the term ægophony has been given. There are cases in which the consolidation is deeply seated—so-called central pneumonia, in which the physical signs are slight or even absent, yet the cough, the rusty expectoration, and general features make the diagnosis certain.

Circulatory Symptoms.—During the chill the *pulse* is small, but in the succeeding fever it becomes full and bounding. In cases of moderate severity it ranges from 100 to 116. It is not often dicrotic. In strong, healthy individuals and in children there may be no sign of failing pulse throughout the attack. With extensive consolidation the left ventricle may receive a very much diminished amount of blood and the pulse in consequence may be small. In the old and feeble it may be small and rapid from the outset. The pulse may be full, soft, very deceptive, and of no value whatever in prognosis. The *heart-sounds* are usually loud and clear. During the intensity of the fever, particularly in children, *bruits* are not uncommon both in the mitral and in the pulmonic areas. The second sound over the pulmonary artery is accentuated. Attention to this sign gives a valuable indication as to the condition of the lesser circulation. With distention of the right chambers and failure of the right ventricle to empty itself completely the pulmonary second sound becomes much less distinct. When the right heart is engorged there may be an increase in the dulness to the right of the sternum. With gradual heart weakness and signs of dilatation the long pause is greatly shortened, the sounds approach each other in tone and have a fœtal character (embryocardia).

There may be a sudden early collapse of the heart with very feeble, rapid pulse and increasing cyanosis. I have known this to occur on the third day. Even when these symptoms are very serious recovery may take place. I saw with Dr. Hollyday a robust man of thirty-six who at the end of the second week of a severe pneumonia had two serious attacks of heart weakness, in which the pulse became exceedingly feeble, scarcely perceptible; there was marked pallor, an ashy appearance of the face, and profuse sweating. Both attacks appeared to be most critical, but he recovered perfectly. In other instances without any special warning death may occur even in robust, previously healthy men.[*] Endocarditis and pericarditis will be considered under complications.

Blood.—Anæmia is rarely seen. Bollinger has called attention to an oligæmia due to the large amount of exudate, and thinks that the collapse features are in part due to it. There is in most cases a leucocytosis, which appears early, persists, and disappears with the crisis. The leucocytes may number from 12,000 to 40,000 or 50,000, or even more, per cubic millimetre. The fall in the leucocytes is often slower than the drop in the fever, par-

---

[*] For illustrative cases see Prognosis in Pneumonia, Am. Jr. Med. Sci., Jan., 1897.

ticularly when resolution is delayed. The annexed chart from J. S. Billings'
paper (J. H. H. Bulletin, No. 43) shows well the coincident drop in the
fever and in the number of the leucocytes. A point of considerable prognostic importance is that in malignant pneumonia the leucocytosis may
be absent, and in any case the continuous absence may be regarded as an
unfavorable sign. Of 50 cases shown in my clinic during the sessions of

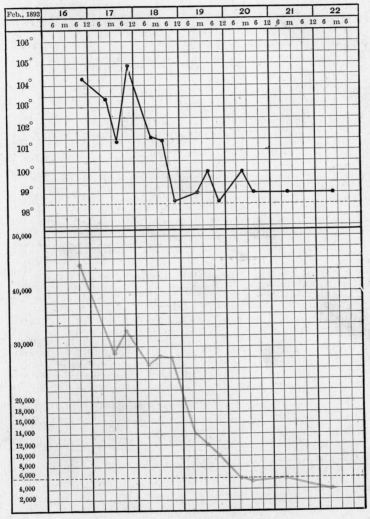

CHART X.

1896–'97 and 1897–'98, the highest leucocytosis was 63,000, the lowest
10,200. A striking feature in the blood-slide is the richness and density of
the fibrin network. This corresponds to the great increase in the fibrin

elements, which has long been known to occur in pneumonia, the proportion rising from 4 to 10 parts per thousand. Hayem describes the blood-plates as greatly increased. The micrococci can very rarely be demonstrated in the blood.

Digestive Organs.—The tongue is white and furred, and in severe toxic cases rapidly becomes dry. Vomiting is not uncommon at the onset in children. The appetite is lost. Constipation is more common than diarrhœa. A distressing and sometimes dangerous symptom is meteorism. On several occasions I have seen great distress from the enlarged, tympanitic abdomen pushing up the diaphragm. The spleen is usually enlarged, and the edge can be felt during a deep inspiration. With extreme engorgement of the right heart there may be perceptible increase in the volume of the liver.

Skin.—Among *cutaneous* symptoms one of the most interesting is the association of herpes with pneumonia. Not excepting malaria, we see labial herpes more frequently in this than in any other disease, occurring, as it does, in from 12 to 40 per cent of the cases. It is supposed to be of favorable prognosis, and figures have been quoted in proof of this assertion. It may also occur on the nose, genitals, and anus. Its significance and relation to the disease are unknown. It is scarcely necessary to mention the theory which has been advanced, that it is an external expression of a neuritis which involves the pneumogastric and induces the pneumonia. At the height of the disease sweats are not common, but at the crisis they may be profuse. Redness of one cheek is a phenomenon long recognized in connection with pneumonia, and is usually on the same side as the disease.

Urine.—Early in the disease it presents the usual febrile characters of high color, high specific gravity, and increased acidity. A trace of albumin is very common. There may be tube-casts and in a few instances the existence of albumin, tube-casts, and blood indicate the presence of an acute nephritis. In a large proportion of all cases the albumin is a febrile or toxic feature. The urea and uric acid are usually increased at first, but may be much diminished before the crisis, to increase greatly with its onset. The chlorides are absent or greatly reduced during the height of the fever, owing to the amount exuded in the hepatized lung. At the crisis there may be a marked increase in the amount of urine, which is heavily laden with urates and extractives. When jaundice occurs there is bile pigment. I saw profuse hæmaturia on the seventeenth day of a severe pneumonia. The boy had recently had gonorrhœa.

Cerebral Symptoms.—Headache is common. Convulsions occur frequently at the outset in children. Apart from meningitis, which will be considered separately, one may group the cases with marked cerebral features into—

First, the so-called cerebral pneumonias of children, in which the disease sets in with a convulsion and there are high fever, headache, delirium, great irritability, muscular tremor, and perhaps retraction of the head and neck. The diagnosis of meningitis is usually made, and the local affection may be overlooked.

Secondly, the cases with maniacal symptoms. These may occur at the very outset, and I once performed an autopsy on a case in which there was no suspicion whatever that the disease was other than acute mania. The house physician should give instructions to the nurses to watch such cases very carefully. On March 22, 1894, a patient who had been doing very well, with the exception of slight delirium, while the orderly was out of the room for a few moments, got up, raised the window, and jumped out, sustaining a fracture of the leg and of the upper lumbar vertebræ, of which he died.

Thirdly, alcoholic cases with the features of delirium tremens. It should be an invariable rule, even if fever be not present, to examine the lungs in a case of *mania a potu*.

Fourthly, cases with toxic features, resembling rather those of uræmia. Without a chill and without cough or pain in the side, a patient may develop fever, a little shortness of breath, and then gradually grow dull mentally, and within three days be in a condition of profound toxæmia with low, muttering delirium.

It is stated that apex pneumonia is more often accompanied with severe delirium. Occasionally the cerebral symptoms develop immediately after the crisis. Mental disturbance may persist during and after convalescence, and in a few instances delusional insanity follows, the outlook in which is favorable.

Complications.—Compared with typhoid fever, pneumonia has but few complications and still fewer sequelæ. The most important are the following:

Pleurisy is an inevitable event when the inflammation reaches the surface of the lung, and thus can scarcely be termed a complication. But there are cases in which the pleuritic features take the first place—cases to which the term pleuro-pneumonia is applicable. The exudation may be sero-fibrinous with copious effusion, differing from that of an ordinary acute pleurisy in the greater richness of the fibrin, which may form thick, tenacious, curdy layers. Pneumonia on one side with extensive pleurisy on the other is sometimes a puzzling complication to diagnose and an aspirator needle may be required to settle the question. The bacteriological examination of the fluid has demonstrated, in a large number of cases, the presence of the pneumococcus. Empyema frequently follows pneumonia. The pleurisy caused by the streptococcus is much more dangerous and is a not infrequent fatal complication. Effusion may not have been suspected during the height of the disease, but after the temperature has been normal for some days a slight rise occurs and an irregular fever persists. Dulness continues at the base, or may have extended. The breathing is feeble and there are no râles. Such a condition may be closely simulated, of course, by the thickened pleural layers which are so commonly found after the pneumonia. The question should be settled at once by the introduction of the needle. It is by no means an uncommon complication, and many cases of empyema supposed to be primary are in reality secondary to a slight pneumonia. The persistence of the leucocytosis is an important point.

8

Pericarditis is more common in the pneumonia of children, particularly when double, and it is said with the pneumonia of the left side. It is particularly apt to follow or to be associated with acute rheumatism. It was present, as I stated, in 5 of my 100 autopsies. Though usually plastic, there may be much serous effusion. There is rarely any difficulty in the diagnosis, but when the pneumonia involves the portion of lung covering the pericardium, there may be difficulty in determining, by physical signs, the existence of fluid. The increase in the dyspnœa, the greater feebleness of the pulse, and the gradual suppression of the heart-sounds will give the most valuable indications. In some instances the fluid is purulent. Though a very serious event, it is surprising how often recovery takes place even in the most desperate cases of pneumonia complicated with pericarditis, a point to which I have heard Murchison refer.

Endocarditis is still more frequent, and in my 100 autopsies was present in 16. I called attention in the Gulstonian lectures for 1885 to the great frequency of this complication. Of 209 cases of malignant endocarditis collected from the literature, 54 occurred in this disease. Subsequent observations have fully confirmed this statement. Kanthack found an antecedent pneumonia in 14.2 per cent of all instances of infective endocarditis. It is much more common in the left heart than in the right. It is particularly liable to attack persons with old valvular disease. The pneumococcus has been found in the vegetations. There may be no symptoms indicative of this complication even in very severe cases. It may, however, be suspected in cases (1) in which the fever is protracted and irregular; (2) when signs of septic mischief arise, such as chills and sweats; (3) when embolic phenomena appear. The frequent complication of meningitis with the endocarditis of pneumonia, which has already been mentioned, gives prominence to the cerebral symptoms in these cases. The physical signs may be very deceptive. There are instances in which no cardiac murmurs have been heard. In others the development under observation of a loud, rough murmur, particularly if diastolic, is extremely suggestive.

Myocarditis is rare.

Heart-clots.—Ante-mortem coagula are uncommon in pneumonia, even in extreme grades of dilatation of the right chamber. In not a single instance of my autopsies were there globular thrombi in the auricles or in the apices of the ventricles. In protracted cases thrombi occasionally form in the veins. A rare complication is *embolism* of one of the larger arteries. I saw in Montreal an instance of embolism of the femoral artery at the height of pneumonia, which necessitated amputation at the thigh. The patient recovered. *Aphasia* has been met with in a few instances, setting in abruptly with or without hemiplegia.

Meningitis is perhaps the most serious complication of pneumonia. It varies very much at different times and in different regions. My Montreal experience is rather exceptional, as 8 per cent of the fatal cases had this complication. It usually comes on at the height of the fever, and in the majority of the cases is not recognized unless, as before mentioned, the base is involved, which is not common. Meningitis may develop later in the disease, and is then more easily diagnosed. In some cases it is associated with infective endocarditis. The pneumococcus has been found in the exudate.

Peripheral neuritis is a rare complication, of which several cases have been described. I saw one well-marked instance following pneumonia and influenza in the spring of 1890. There was neuritis of the left arm with considerable wasting.

Gastric complications are rare. A croupous gastritis has already been mentioned. The *croupous colitis* may induce severe diarrhœa. *Jaundice* is one of the most interesting complications of pneumonia and occurs with curious irregularity in different outbreaks of the disease. It sets in early, is rarely very intense, and has not the characters of obstructive jaundice. There are cases in which it assumes a very serious form. The mode of production is not well ascertained. It does not appear to bear any definite relation to the degree of hepatic engorgement and it is certainly not due to catarrh of the ducts. Possibly it may be, in great part, hæmatogenous.

Parotitis occasionally occurs, commonly in association with endocarditis. In children middle-ear disease is not an infrequent complication.

Bright's disease does not often follow pneumonia. *Peritonitis* is exceedingly rare.

The relations of *rheumatism* and pneumonia are very interesting. The arthritis may precede the onset, and the pneumonia, possibly with endocarditis and pleurisy, may occur as a complication of the rheumatism. In other instances at the height of an ordinary pneumonia one or two joints may become red and sore. On the other hand, after the crisis has occurred pains and swelling may come on in the joints.

Relapse.—There are cases in which from the ninth to the eleventh day the fever subsides, and after the temperature has been normal for a day or two a rise occurs and fever may persist for another ten days or even two weeks. Though this might be termed a relapse, it is more correct to regard it as an instance of an anomalous course of delayed resolution. Wagner, who has studied the subject carefully, says that in his large experience of 1,100 cases he met with only 3 doubtful cases. When it does occur, the attack is usually abortive and mild. In the case of Z. R. (Medical No. 4223), with pneumonia of the right lower lobe, crisis occurred on the seventh day, and after a normal temperature for thirteen days he was discharged. That night he had a shaking chill, followed by fever, and he had recurring chills with reappearance of the pneumonia. In a second case (Medical No. 4538) crisis occurred on the third day, and there was recurrence of pneumonia on the thirteenth day.

Recurrence is more common in pneumonia than in any other acute disease. Rush gives an instance in which there were 28 attacks. Other authorities narrate cases of 8, 10, and even more attacks.

Convalescence in pneumonia is usually prompt and rapid, and sequelæ are rare. Some authors speak of a sudden fatal collapse when the patients are allowed to get up and go about too soon. With the onset of fever and persistence of the leucocytes the affected side should be very carefully examined for pleurisy. With a persistence of the dulness the physical signs may be obscure, but the use of a small exploratory needle will be found very satisfactory.

Clinical Varieties.—1. Local variation are responsible for some of the most marked deviations from the usual type.

Apex pneumonia is said to be more often associated with adynamic features and with marked cerebral symptoms. The expectoration and cough may be slight. I can not say that in my experience the cerebral symptoms in adults have been more marked in this form, nor do I think it necessarily graver than if situated at the base.

Migratory or *creeping pneumonia,* a form which successively involves one lobe after the other.

Double pneumonia has no peculiarities other than the greater danger connected with it.

Massive pneumonia is a rare form, in which not alone the air-cells but the bronchi of an entire lobe or even of a lung are filled with the fibrinous exudate. The auscultatory signs are absent; there is neither fremitus nor tubular breathing, and on percussion the lung is absolutely flat. It closely resembles pleurisy with effusion. The moulds of the bronchi may be expectorated in violent fits of coughing.

Central Pneumonia.—The inflammation may be deep-seated at the root of the lung or centrally placed in a lobe, and for several days the diagnosis may be in doubt. It may not be until the third or fourth day that a pleural friction is detected, or that dulness or blowing breathing and râles are recognized. I saw recently with Dr. Henry Adler and Dr. Chew an instance in which at the end of the fourth day in a young, thin-chested girl all the usual symptoms of pneumonia were present without any physical signs other than a few clicking râles at the left apex behind. The thinness of the patient greatly facilitated the examination. The general features of pneumonia continued, and the crisis occurred on the seventh day.

2. *Pneumonia in Infants.*—It is sometimes seen in the newborn. In infants it very often sets in with a convulsion. The summit of the lung seems more frequently involved than in adults, and the cerebral symptoms are more marked. The torpor and coma, particularly if they follow convulsions, and the preliminary stage of excitement, may lead to the diagnosis of meningitis. Pneumonic sputum is rarely seen in children.

3. *Pneumonia in the Aged.*—The disease may be latent and set in without a chill; the cough and expectoration are slight, the physical signs ill-defined and changeable, and the constitutional symptoms out of all proportion to the extent of the local lesion.

4. *Pneumonia in Alcoholic Subjects.*—The onset is insidious, the symptoms masked, the fever slight, and the clinical picture usually that of delirium tremens. The thermometer alone may indicate the presence of an acute disease. Often the local condition is overlooked, as the patient makes no complaint of pain, and there may be very little shortness of breath, no cough, and no sputum.

5. *Terminal Pneumonia.*—The wards and the post-mortem room show a very striking contrast in their pneumonia statistics, owing to the occurrence of what may be called terminal pneumonia. During the winter

months patients with chronic pulmonary tuberculosis, arterio-sclerosis, heart disease, Bright's disease, and diabetes are not infrequently carried off by a pneumonia which may give few or no signs of its presence. There may be a slight elevation of temperature, with increase in the respirations, but the patient is near the end and perhaps not in a condition in which a thorough physical examination can be made. The autopsy may show pneumonia of the greater part of one lower lobe or of the apex, which had entirely escaped notice. In diabetic patients the disease often runs a rapid and severe course, and may end in abscess or gangrene.

Some of the most remarkable variations in the clinical course of pneumonia depend probably upon the severity, possibly upon the nature of the infective agent. Further investigation may enable us to say how far the associated organisms, so often present, may be responsible for the differences in the clinical course.

6. *Secondary Pneumonias.*—These are met with chiefly in the specific fevers, particularly diphtheria, typhoid fever, typhus, influenza, and the plague. Anatomically, they rarely present the typical form of red or gray hepatization. The surface is smoother, not so dry, and it is often a pseudolobar condition, a consolidation caused by closely set areas of lobular involvement. Histologically, they are characterized in many instances by a more cellular, less fibrinous exudate, which may also infiltrate the alveolar walls. Bacteriologically, a large number of different organisms have been found, the specific microbe of the primary disease, usually in association with the streptococcus pyogenes or the staphylococcus; in some instances the colon bacillus has been present. Finkler has attempted to separate a special form, which he calls the *acute cellular pneumonia,* to which most of these secondary types conform and which have the histological characters already referred to (Die Acuten Lungenentzundungen, 1891).

The symptoms of the secondary pneumonias often lack the striking definiteness of the primary croupous pneumonia. The pulmonary features may be latent or masked altogether. There may be no cough and only a slight increase in the number of respirations. The lower lobe of one lung is most commonly involved, and the physical signs are obscure and rarely amount to more than impaired resonance, feeble breathing, and a few crackling râles. In some instances when the consolidation is extensive the breathing is distinctly tubular.

7. *Epidemic pneumonia* has already been referred to. It is, as a rule, more fatal, and often displays minor complications which differ in different outbreaks. In some the cerebral manifestations are very marked; in others, the cardiac; in others, again, the gastro-intestinal.

8. *Larval Pneumonia.*—Mild, abortive types are seen, particularly in institutions when pneumonia is prevailing extensively. A patient may have the initial symptoms of the disease, a slight chill, moderate fever, a few indefinite local signs, and herpes. The whole process may only last for two or three days; some authors recognize even a one-day pneumonia.

9. *Asthenic, Toxic, or Typhoid Pneumonia.*—The toxæmic features dominate the scene throughout. The local lesions may be slight in extent and the subjective phenomena of the disease absent. The nervous symp-

toms usually predominate. There are delirium, prostration, and early weakness. Very frequently there is jaundice. Gastro-intestinal symptoms may be present, particularly diarrhœa and meteorism. In such a case, seen about the end of the first week, it may be difficult to say whether the condition is one of asthenic pneumonia or one of typhoid fever which has set in with early localization in the lung. Here the Widal reaction would be an important aid. In these cases there is really a pneumococcus septicæmia, and the organisms may sometimes be isolated from the blood. Possibly, too, there is a mixed infection, and the streptococcus pyogenes may be in large part responsible for the toxic features of the disease.

10. *Association of Pneumonia with other Diseases.*—(*a*) *With Malaria.* —A malarial pneumonia is described by many observers and thought to be particularly prevalent in some parts of this country. One hears of it, indeed, even where true malaria is rarely seen. With our large experience in malaria, amounting now to nearly 2,000 cases, and a considerable number of pneumonia patients every year, we have only had a few cases in which the latter disease has developed during malarial fever, or *vice versa*. In either case the malaria yields promptly to the action of quinine. So far as the Southern States are concerned, the question of a special form was thrashed out years ago in a discussion between Manson and W. T. Howard, and was decided in the negative. A form of pneumonia directly dependent upon the malarial parasite is unknown. We have not been able to recognize here a pneumonia which is influenced in any way by the malarial poison. Such a case as the following we see occasionally: A patient was admitted, March 16, 1894, with tertian malarial fever. The lungs were clear. A pneumonia began thirty-six hours after admission. Quinine was given that evening, and the malarial organisms rapidly disappeared from the blood. There was successive involvement of the right lower, the middle, and the left lower lobe. The temperature fell by crisis on the 24th, and there were no features in the disease whatever suggestive of malaria. In other instances we have found a chill in the course of an ordinary pneumonia to be associated with a malarial infection, and quinine has rapidly and promptly caused the disappearance of the parasites from the blood.

(*b*) *Pneumonia and Acute Rheumatism.*—We have already spoken under complications of this association, which is more frequently seen in children.

(*c*) *Pneumonia and Tuberculosis.*—Many subjects of chronic pulmonary tuberculosis die of an acute croupous pneumonia. A point to be specially borne in mind is the fact that acute tuberculous pneumonia may set in with all the features and physical signs of fibrinous pneumonia (see page 290).

For the consideration of the association of pneumonia with typhoid fever and influenza, the reader is referred to the sections on those diseases.

11. *Post-operation Pneumonia.*—Before the days of anæsthesia, lobar pneumonia was a well-recognized cause of death after surgical injuries and operations. Norman Cheevers, in an early number of the Guy's Hospital Reports, calls attention to it as one of the most frequent causes of death after surgical procedures, and Erichsen states that of 41 deaths after surgical injuries 23 cases exhibited signs of pneumonia. The lobular form

is the most frequent. I have already referred to the contusion-pneumonia described by Litten.

12. *Ether Pneumonia.*—The question of a direct relation between ether narcosis and pneumonia has been much discussed within the past year, having been raised by Mr. Lucas, of Guy's Hospital. The statistics are by no means unanimous. Prescott, of Boston, in 40,000 cases found only 3 of acute lobar pneumonia. The London anæsthetists, particularly Hewitt and Silk, seem also to have had a fortunate experience, Silk having found among 5,000 cases 13 of pneumonia; 8 of these were tongue or jaw cases. The German experience is very different. Von Beck states that, owing to the injurious after-effects upon the respiratory tract, the use of ether has been largely restricted in Czerny's clinic. Gurlt reports 52,177 cases, with 30 cases of pneumonia and 15 deaths. On the surgical side of the Johns Hopkins Hospital, Dr. Bloodgood tells me there have been 15 cases of pneumonia following anæsthesia; 12 of these have been broncho-pneumonias; 7 deaths and 8 recoveries; 79 per cent of the cases followed abdominal section or hernia operations. Czerny suggests that the relation of these ether pneumonias to abdominal operations is associated with the pain on coughing, which leads to an accumulation of secretion, and through this to retention or aspiration pneumonia. Among the various views brought forward to account for it are the rapid evaporation of the ether, causing chilling of the pulmonary tissues, chilling of the patient at the time of operation, infection from the inhaler, and direct action of the ether.

The probability is that the prolonged etherization lowers the vitality of the tissues of the finer bronchi and permits the pathogenic organisms (which are almost always present) to do their work. The pneumonia is more frequently lobular than lobar. Neuwerck, and subsequently Whitney, have suggested thorough disinfection of the mouth and throat before operation.

13. *Delayed Resolution in Pneumonia.*—The lung is restored to its normal state partly by the expectoration of the exudate, partly by its liquefaction and absorption. There are cases in which resolution takes place rapidly without any increase in or, indeed, without any expectoration; on the other hand, during resolution it is not uncommon to find in the sputa the little plugs of fibrin and leucocytes which have been loosened from the air-cells and expelled by coughing. In a majority of cases both processes are probably at work. A variable time is taken in the restoration of the lung. Sometimes within a week or ten days the dulness is greatly diminished, the breath-sounds become clear, and, so far as physical signs are any guide, the lung seems perfectly restored. It is to be remembered that in any case of pneumonia with extensive pleurisy a certain amount of dulness will persist for months, owing to thickening of the pleura.

Delayed resolution is a condition which causes much anxiety to the physician. While it is perhaps more frequent in debilitated persons, yet it is met with in robust, previously healthy individuals, and in cases which have had a very typical onset and course. The condition is stated to be most frequent in apex pneumonia. Venesection has been assigned as a cause. There is no question that the solid exudate can persist for weeks and yet the integrity of the lung may ultimately be restored. Grissole describes the lung from a patient who died on the sixtieth day, in which the affected part showed a condition not unlike that of the acute stage.

Clinically, there are several groups of cases: First, those in which the crisis occurs naturally, the temperature falls and remains normal, but the local features persist—well-marked flatness with tubular breathing and râles. Resolution may occur very slowly and gradually, taking from two to three weeks. In a second group of cases the temperature falls by lysis, and with the persistence of the local signs there is slight fever, sometimes sweats and rapid pulse. The condition may persist for three or four weeks, or, as in one of my cases, for eleven weeks, and ultimately perfect resolution occur. During all this time there may be little or no sputum. The practitioner is naturally much exercised, and he dreads lest tuberculosis should supervene. In a third group the crisis occurs or the fever falls by lysis, but the consolidation persists and there may be intense bronchial breathing, with few or no râles, or the fever may recur and the patient may die exhausted. In 1 of my 100 autopsies a patient, aged fifty-eight, had died on the thirty-second day from the initial chill. The right lung was solid, grayish in color, firm, and presented in places a translucent, semi-homogeneous aspect. In these areas the alveolar walls were thickened, and the plugs filling the air-cells were undergoing transformation into new connective tissue. This fibroid induration may proceed gradually and be associated with shrinkage of the affected side, and the gradual production of a cirrhosis or chronic interstitial pneumonia.

Ordinary fibrinous pneumonia never terminates in tuberculosis. The instances of caseous pneumonia and softening which have followed an acute pneumonic process, have been from the outset tuberculous (see page 290).

14. *Termination in Abscess.*—This occurred in 4 of my 100 autopsies. Usually the lung breaks down in limited areas and the abscesses are not large, but they may fuse and involve a considerable proportion of a lobe. The condition is recognized by the sputa, which is usually abundant and contains pus and elastic tissue, sometimes cholesterin crystals and hæmatoidin crystals. The cough is often paroxysmal and of great severity; usually the fever is remittent, or in protracted cases intermittent in character, and there may be pronounced hectic symptoms. When a case is seen for the first time it may be difficult to determine whether it is one of abscess of the lung or a local empyæma which has perforated the lung.

15. *Gangrene.*—This is most commonly seen in old debilitated persons. It was present in 3 of my 100 autopsies. It very often occurs with abscess. The gangrene is associated with the growth of the saprophytic bacteria on a soil made favorable by the presence of the pneumococcus or the streptococcus. Clinically, the gangrene is rendered very evident by the horribly fetid odor of the expectoration and its characteristic features. In some instances the gangrene may be found post-mortem when clinically there has not been any evidence of its existence.

Prognosis.—Pneumonia is the most fatal of all acute diseases, killing more than diphtheria, and ranking next to consumption as a cause of death.

Hospital statistics show that the mortality ranges from 20 to 40 per cent. Of 1,012 cases at the Montreal General Hospital, the mortality was 20.4 per cent. It appears to be somewhat more fatal in southern climates. Of 3,969 cases treated at the Charity Hospital, New Orleans, the death-rate was 38.01 per cent. Of the first 124 cases admitted to or developing in the Johns Hopkins Hospital, 37 died, a mortality of 29.8 per cent. In 704 cases at the Pennsylvania Hospital the mortality was 29 per cent. At the Boston City Hospital in 1,443 cases the mortality was 29.1 per cent. It has been urged that the mortality in this disease has been steadily increasing, and attempts have been made to connect this increase with the expectant plan of treatment at present in vogue. But the careful and thorough analysis by C. N. Townsend and A. Coolidge, Jr., of 1,000 cases at the Massachusetts General Hospital indicates clearly that, when all circumstances are taken into consideration, this conclusion is not justified. They found that when all fatal cases over fifty years of age were omitted, and those patients who were delicate, intemperate, or the subject of some complication, there was very little variation from decade to decade, and that, excluding these cases, the rate was but little over 10 per cent. In answer to the assertion that the modified treatment is in part responsible for the increased mortality, these authors show clearly that the rise in death-rate took place in the period prior to 1860, when the treatment was entirely or in great part heroic.

According to the analysis of 708 cases at St. Thomas's Hospital by Hadden, H. W. G. McKenzie, and W. W. Ord, the mortality progressively increases from the twentieth year, rising from 3.7 per cent under that age to 22 per cent in the third decade, 30.8 per cent in the fourth, 47 per cent in the fifth, 51 per cent in the sixth, 65 per cent in the seventh decade. Of 223,730 cases collected by Wells from various sources, 40,276 died, a mortality of 18.1 per cent.

The mortality in private practice varies greatly. R. P. Howard treated 170 cases with only 6 per cent of deaths. Fussell has recently reported 134 cases with a mortality of 17.9 per cent. The mortality in children is sometimes very low. Morrill has recently reported 6 deaths in 123 cases of frank pneumonia. On the other hand, Goodhart had 25 deaths in 120 cases.

The following are among the circumstances which influence the prognosis:

Age.—As Sturges remarks, the old are likely to die, the young to recover. Under one year it is more fatal than between two and five. Fussell lost 5 out of 8 cases in yearlings. At about sixty the death-rate is very high, amounting to 60 or 80 per cent. So fatal is it in this country, at least, that one may say that to die of pneumonia is the natural end of old people.

As already stated, the disease is more fatal in the negro than in the white race.

Previous habits of life and the condition of bodily health at the time of the attack form the most important factors in the prognosis of pneumonia. In analyzing a series of fatal cases one is very much impressed with the number of cases in which the organs show signs of degeneration. In 25 of my 100 autopsies at the Montreal General Hospital the kidneys showed extensive interstitial changes. Individuals debilitated from sickness or poor food, hard drinkers, and that large class of hospital patients, composed of robust-looking laborers between the ages of forty-five and sixty, whose organs show signs of wear and tear, and who have by excesses in alcohol weakened the reserve power, fall an easy prey to the disease. Very few fatal cases occur in robust, healthy adults. Some of the statistics given by army surgeons show better than any others the low mortality from pneumonia in healthy picked men. The death-rate in the German army in over 40,000 cases was only 3.6 per cent.

Certain *complications* and terminations are particularly serious. The meningitis of pneumonia is probably always fatal. Endocarditis is extremely grave, much more so than pericarditis. Apart from these serious complications, the fatal event in pneumonia is due either to a gradual toxæmia or to mechanical interference with the respiration and circulation.

Toxæmia is the important prognostic feature in the disease, to which in a majority of the cases the degree of pyrexia and the extent of consolidation are entirely subsidiary. It is not at all proportionate to the degree of lung involved. A severe and fatal toxæmia may develop with the consolidation of only a small part of one lobe. On the other hand, a patient with complete solidification of one lung may have no signs of a general infection. The question of individual resistance seems to be the most important one, and one sees even most robust-looking individuals fatally stricken within a few days.

Much stress has been laid of late upon the factor of *leucocytosis* as an element in the prognosis. A very slight or complete absence of a leucocytosis is regarded as very unfavorable. Of the 22 cases from my wards reported by Billings, only 1 showed a complete absence during the entire course of the disease. In 6 fatal cases there was an absence of leucocytosis at some period of the disease. As a rule, it may be said that the continuous absence of leucocytosis is unfavorable.

Death from direct interference with the function of respiration is rare. It may happen in extensive double pneumonia, but even with involvement of a very large section of both lungs recovery may take place. A very important element in the prognosis is the condition of the heart, from failure of which quite as many die as from the intoxication. The heart weakness may be due either to the specific action of the poison, to the prolonged fever, or to over-distention of the right chambers. All three factors may be at work together. I have already referred to the sudden onset of serious cardiac weakness; more commonly there is a gradually increased rapidity with increasing weakness of the heart muscle. The pulse is not always a safe guide; since, as I mentioned before, it may be full and soft and not very rapid within a few hours of a fatal termination, even in cases without pronounced toxæmia.

Diagnosis.—No disease is more readily recognized in a large majority of the cases. The external characters, the sputa, and the physical signs combine to make one of the clearest of clinical pictures. After a study in the post-mortem room of my own and others' mistakes, I think that the ordinary lobar pneumonia of adults is rarely overlooked. Errors are particularly liable to occur in the intercurrent pneumonias, in those complicating chronic affections, and in the disease as met with in children, the aged, and drunkards. Tuberculo-pneumonic phthisis is frequently confounded with pneumonia. Pleurisy with effusion is, I believe, not often mistaken except in children. The diagnostic points will be referred to under pleurisy.

In diabetes, Bright's disease, chronic heart-disease, pulmonary phthisis, and cancer, an acute pneumonia often ends the scene, and is frequently overlooked. In these cases the temperature is perhaps the best index, and should, more particularly if cough develops, lead to a careful examination of the lungs. The absence of expectoration and of pulmonary symptoms may make the diagnosis very difficult.

In children there are two special sources of error; the disease may be entirely masked by the cerebral symptoms and the case mistaken for one of meningitis. It is remarkable in these cases how few indications there are of pulmonary trouble. The other condition is pleurisy with effusion, which in children often has deceptive physical signs. The breathing may be intensely tubular and tactile fremitus may be present. The exploratory needle is sometimes required to decide the question. In the old and debilitated a knowledge that the onset of pneumonia is insidious, and that the symptoms are ill-defined and latent, should put the practitioner on his guard and make him very careful in the examination of the lungs in doubtful cases. In chronic alcoholism the cerebral symptoms may predominate and completely mask the local process. As mentioned, the disease may assume the form of violent mania, but more commonly the symptoms are those of delirium tremens. In any case rapid pulse, rapid respiration, and fever are symptoms which should invariably excite suspicion of inflammation of the lungs. Under cerebro-spinal meningitis will be found the points of differential diagnosis between pneumonia and that disease.

Pneumonia is rarely confounded with ordinary consumption, but to differentiate acute tuberculo-pneumonic phthisis is often difficult. The case may set in with a chill. It may be impossible to determine which condition is present until softening occurs and elastic tissue and tubercle bacilli appear in the sputum. A similar mistake is sometimes made in children. With typhoid fever, pneumonia is not infrequently confounded. There are instances of pneumonia with the local signs well marked in which the patient rapidly sinks into what is known as the typhoid state, with dry tongue, rapid pulse, and diarrhœa. Unless the case is seen from the outset it may be very difficult to determine the true nature of the malady. On the other hand, there are cases of typhoid fever which set in with symptoms of lobar pneumonia—the so-called pneumo-typhus. It may be impossible to make a differential diagnosis in such a case unless the characteristic eruption develops or the Widal reaction be found.

Prophylaxis.—The question of the prevention of pneumonia is a difficult one, which has hardly yet come within the sphere of practical knowledge. More care should be taken with pneumonic sputum than has been done heretofore, and it should be carefully disinfected. Individuals who have had pneumonia should be specially careful to keep the mouth and throat thoroughly cleansed, and any house in which several cases of pneumonia have occurred in rapid succession should be thoroughly disinfected.

Treatment.—Pneumonia is a self-limited disease, which can neither be aborted nor cut short by any known means at our command. Even under the most unfavorable circumstances it may terminate abruptly and naturally, without a dose of medicine having been administered. A patient was admitted into the Philadelphia Hospital on the evening of the seventh day after the chill, in which he had been seen by one of my assistants, who had ordered him to go to a hospital. He remained, however, in his house alone, without assistance, taking nothing but a little milk and bread and whisky, and was brought into the hospital by the police in a condition of active delirium. That night his temperature was 105° and his pulse above 120. In his delirium he came near escaping through the window of the ward. The following morning—the eighth day—the crisis occurred, and at ward class his temperature was below 98°. The entire lower lobe of the right side was found involved, and he entered upon a rapid convalescence. So also, under the favoring circumstances of good nursing and careful diet, the experience of many physicians in different lands has shown that pneumonia runs its course in a definite time, terminating sometimes spontaneously on the third or the fifth day, or continuing until the tenth or twelfth.

There is no specific treatment for pneumonia. The young practitioner may bear in mind that patients are more often damaged than helped by the promiscuous drugging, which is still only too prevalent.

1. *General Management of a Case.*—The same careful hygiene of the bed and of the sick-room should be carried out as in typhoid fever. The patient should not be too much bundled up with clothing. For the heavy flannel undershirts should be substituted a thin, light flannel jacket, open in front, which enables the physician to make his examinations without unnecessarily disturbing the patient. The room should be bright and light, letting in the sunshine if possible, and thoroughly well ventilated. Only one or two persons should be allowed in the room at a time. Even when not called for on account of the high fever, the patient should be carefully sponged each day with tepid water. This should be done with as little disturbance as possible. Special care should be taken to keep the mouth and gums cleansed.

2. *Diet.*—Plain water, a pleasant table water, or lemonade should be given freely. When the patient is delirious the water should be given at fixed intervals. The food should be liquid, consisting chiefly of milk, either alone or, better, mixed with food prepared from some one of the cereals, and eggs, either soft boiled or raw.

3. *Special Treatment.*—Certain measures are believed to have an influence in arresting, controlling, or cutting short the disease. It is very difficult for the practitioner to arrive at satisfactory conclusions on this question in a disease so singularly variable in its course. How natural, when

on the third or fourth day the crisis occurs and convalescence set in, to attribute the happy result to the effect of some special medication! How easy to forget that the same unexpected early recoveries occur under other conditions! The following are among the measures which are believed by many to be of benefit:

(a) *Bleeding.*—The reproach of Van Helmont, that "a bloody Moloch presides in the chairs of medicine," can not be brought against this generation of physicians. Before Louis' iconoclastic paper on bleeding in pneumonia it would have been regarded as almost criminal to treat a case without venesection. We employ it nowadays much more than we did a few years ago, but more often late in the disease than early. To bleed at the very onset in robust, healthy individuals in whom the disease sets in with great intensity and high fever is, I believe, a good practice. I have seen instances in which it was very beneficial in relieving the pain and the dyspnœa, reducing the temperature, and allaying the cerebral symptoms.

(b) *Drugs.*—Certain drugs are credited with the power of reducing the intensity and shortening the duration of the attack. Among them veratrum viride still holds a place, doses of ℳ ii–v of the tincture given every two hours. Tartar emetic—a remedy which had great vogue some years ago—is now very rarely employed. To a third drug, digitalis, has been attributed of late great power in controlling the course of the disease. Petresco gives at one time as much as from 4 to 12 grammes of the powdered leaves, and claims that these colossal doses are specially efficacious in shortening the course of the disease and diminishing the mortality.

(c) *Antipneumonic Serum.*—This is still in the trial stage. The Klemperer brothers, Auld, Washbourn, and others have reported favorable results. The serum is injected into the subcutaneous tissues. Washbourn recommends as a dose 20 cc., and thinks it is well to make an injection twice a day until the patient is convalescent. Fortunately, the serum appears to be harmless. I have no personal experience with it.

4. *Symptomatic Treatment.*—(a) *To relieve the Pain.*—The stitch in the side at onset, which is sometimes so agonizing, is best relieved by a hypodermic injection of a quarter of a grain of morphia. When the pain is less intense and diffuse over one side, the Paquelin cautery applied lightly is very efficacious, or hot or cold applications may be tried. When the disease is fairly established the pain is not, as a rule, distressing, except when the patient coughs, and for this the Dover's powder may be used in 5-grain doses, according to the patient's needs. Hot poultices, formerly so much in use, relieve the pain, though not more than the cold applications. For children they are often preferable.

(b) *To combat the Toxæmia.*—Herein lies our chief weakness in dealing with pneumonia. We have as yet no specific, either drug or the product of the bacteriological laboratory, which safely and surely neutralizes the poison of the disease. We may reasonably hope that such a remedy ere long will be forthcoming, but meantime we must be content with measures which aim at keeping up the strength of the patient in his fight against the progressive toxæmia.

(c) The third and all-important indication in the treatment of pneumonia is *to support the heart*. The practitioner must ever be on the alert to prevent the onset of cardiac weakness, and to treat it should that condition arise.

To prevent the Onset of Cardiac Weakness.—We can not at present separate the effects of the fever from those of the poisons circulating in the blood. It is possible, indeed, as some suppose, that the fever itself may be beneficial. Undoubtedly, however, high and prolonged pyrexia is dangerous to the heart, and should be combated. For this our most trusty weapon is *hydrotherapy*, which in pneumonia is used in several different ways. The ice-bag to the affected side is one of the most convenient and serviceable. Its good effects have been strongly insisted upon by Mays. I have used ice systematically in my wards for the past six or seven years. It allays the pain, reduces the fever slightly, and, as a rule, the patient says he feels very much more comfortable. Broad, flat ice-bags are now easily obtained for the purpose, and if these are not available an ice poultice can be readily made, and by the use of oil-silk the clothing and bedding of the patient can be protected from the water. Cold sponging should, I think, be employed as a routine measure in cases of pneumonia. When done limb by limb the patient is but little disturbed, and it is refreshing and beneficial. With very pronounced nervous symptoms and persistent high temperature, or with hyperpyrexia, a cold bath of ten minutes' duration may be given. Von Jürgensen, one of the best of living students of the disease, strongly advises it under these conditions. Personally, my experience with the full cold bath is not large enough to enable me to express a positive opinion. In this country we have not, I think, used it sufficiently in the toxic cases, in which in typhoid fever we see such good results.

Of medicinal antipyretics, *quinine* has been much vaunted in doses of from 30 to 60 grains daily. Unfortunately, it is apt to disturb the stomach and cause unpleasant ringing in the ears; according to some, also, it is very depressing, but I must say I have never seen any injurious effects from it, though I have not used it for some years. *Antipyrin, antifebrin*, and *phenacetin* have been thoroughly tried in pneumonia, and the general opinion at present is decidedly against their systematic employment.

Alcohol may be used with benefit in a majority of cases of pneumonia. In moderate doses it diminishes slightly the temperature, increases the appetite, obviates the tendency to heart weakness, and is a conservator of energy, being itself consumed in supplying heat in place of the body tissues. Two or three ounces of good whisky in the twenty-four hours may be used in ordinary cases.

To treat Heart Weakness when Present.—Now the resources and judgment of the physician are taxed to the utmost. Is the heart weakness due to progressive distention and overfilling of the right heart? This is usually indicated by increasing cyanosis, increasing shortness of breath, signs of œdematous infiltration in the uninvolved parts of the lung, and a small and feeble radial pulse. Under these circumstances a free *venesection* is sometimes helpful, though I must say that my personal experience has not been very satisfactory. I have, however, within the past three years seen 2 cases in which it seemed to be timely, even life-saving. Too often the progressive cardiac asthenia is due to the action of the fever and of the poisons, partly upon the heart muscle itself, partly upon the nerve centres, cardiac and respiratory. An increase in the amount of *alcohol* is advisable when the pulse becomes small, frequent, and feeble or very compressible, and when the heart-sounds, particularly the second pulmonic, begin to lose their force. The amount will vary with the age of the patient and with his habits. It may be increased, if necessary, to 12 or 16 ounces in the twenty-four hours. *Strychnia* is a most valuable cardiac tonic in pneumonia. It may be given in doses of from one sixtieth to one thirtieth of a grain hypodermically, or, if the heart's action becomes more feeble, in still larger doses, up to one twentieth or even one twelfth of a grain every three or four hours. The precise indications for the use of *digitalis* in pneumonia are not easy to estimate. I rarely use it unless the heart's action becomes very rapid, or if, as above stated, there is a sudden onset of cardiac weakness, indicated by a very quick and irregular pulse. Then it may be given freely, either in the form of the tincture, 15 or 20 minims every two hours until 2 drachms are given, or a good digitalin hypodermically in doses of from a thirtieth to a twentieth of a grain. Other remedies still much in use are the aromatic spirits of ammonia, camphor, musk, and the hypodermic injections of ether. Two other measures may be referred to under this section.

Oxygen Gas.—It is doubtful whether the inhalation of oxygen in pneumonia is really beneficial. Personally, when called in consultation to a case, if I see the oxygen cylinder at the bedside I feel the prognosis to be extremely grave. It does sometimes seem to give transitory relief and to diminish the cyanosis. It is harmless, its exhibition is very simple, and the process need not be at all disturbing to the patient. The gas may be allowed to flow gently from the nozzle directly under the nostrils of the patient, or it may be administered every alternate fifteen minutes through a mask. As already stated, Bollinger regards the heart weakness as in part due to an oligæmia from the loss of a large amount of solid exudate in the lung. The use of *saline injections* hypodermically has been advocated. I have seen it do good in helping to tide over a critical period of cardiac depression. As much as a couple of pints may be allowed to run beneath the skin by gravity, a rubber bag and either a large hypodermic or a middle-sized aspirator needle being used. The injection may be made in the flanks or in the thighs.

Treatment of Complications.—If the fever persists it is important to look out for pleurisy, particularly for the meta-pneumonic empyema. The exploratory needle should be used if necessary. A sero-fibrinous effusion should be aspirated, a purulent opened and drained. In a complicating pericarditis with a large effusion aspiration may be necessary. Delayed resolution is a difficult condition to treat. Riess has recommended pilocarpine, which I have tried in one or two cases without much benefit.

XVI. DIPHTHERIA.

Definition.—A specific infectious disease, characterized by a local fibrinous exudate, usually upon a mucous membrane, and by constitutional symptoms due to toxins produced at the site of the lesion. The presence of the Klebs-Loeffler bacillus is the etiological criterion by which true diphtheria is distinguished from other forms of membranous inflammation.

The clinical and bacteriological conceptions of diphtheria are at present not in full accord. On the one hand, there are cases of simple sore throat which the bacteriologists, finding the Klebs-Loeffler bacillus, call true diphtheria. On the other hand, cases of membranous, sloughing angina, diagnosed by the physician as diphtheria, are called by the bacteriologists, in the absence of the Klebs-Loeffler bacillus, pseudo-diphtheria or diphtheroid angina.

The term *diphtheroid* may be used for the present to designate those forms in which the Klebs-Loeffler bacillus is not present. Though usually milder, severe constitutional disturbance, and even paralysis, may follow these so-called pseudo-diphtheritic processes.

Historical Note.—The disease was known to Aretæus and to Galen. Epidemics occurred throughout the middle ages. It appeared early among the settlers of New England, and accounts are extant of epidemics in this country in the seventeenth and eighteenth centuries. Huxham and Fothergill gave excellent descriptions of the disease. An admirable account was given by Samuel Bard,* of New York, whose essay is one of the most solid contributions made to medicine in America. It was reserved for Pierre Bretonneau, of Tours, to grasp the fact that *angina suffocativa*, "*cynanche maligna*," the "putrid," and other forms of malignant sore throat, were one and the same disease, to which he gave the name "*diphthérite.*"

Etiology.—The disease is endemic in the larger centres of population, and becomes epidemic at certain seasons of the year. While other contagious diseases have diminished within the past decade, diphtheria has increased, particularly in cities. It has prevailed also with great severity in country districts, in which indeed the affection seems to be specially virulent. A close relation between imperfect drainage or a polluted water-supply and diphtheria has not been determined.

Diphtheria is a highly contagious disease, readily communicated from person to person. The bacilli may be received, " (1) from the membranous exudate or discharges from diphtheria patients; (2) from the secretions of the nose and throat of convalescent cases of diphtheria in which the virulent bacilli persist; (3) from the throats of healthy individuals who have acquired the bacilli from being in contact with others having virulent germs on their person or clothing: in such cases the bacilli may sometimes live and develop for days or weeks in the throat without causing any lesion " (Park and Beebe). In the tenement districts of New York these authors recognized two varieties of local epidemics. In one, the cases were evi-

---

* Transactions of the American Philosophical Society, vol. i, Philadelphia, 1770.

dently from neighborhood infection; while in the other, the infection was derived from schools, since a whole district would suddenly become the seat of scattered cases. "At times in a certain area of the city, from which several schools drew their scholars, all the cases of diphtheria would occur (as investigation showed) in families whose children attended one school, the children of the other schools being for the time exempt."

No disease of temperate regions proves more fatal to physicians and nurses. There seems to be particular danger in the examination and swabbing of the throat, for in the gagging, coughing, and spluttering efforts the patient may cough mucus and flakes of membrane into the physician's face. The virus attaches itself to the clothing, the bedding, and the room in which the patient has lived, and has in many instances displayed great tenacity. It has been found to live on blood serum for one hundred and fifty-five days, in gelatin for eighteen months, dried on silk threads for one hundred and seventy-two days, on a child's plaything which had been kept in a dark place for five months, and in bits of dried membrane for from fourteen to twenty weeks. An instance has been reported (Golay) in which the bacilli were present in the throat for three hundred and sixty-two days. During this period there were three acute relapses. They have been found, too, in the dust of a diphtheria pavilion, and in the hair and clothing of the nurses in attendance upon diphtheria babies (Wright and Emerson). Forbes isolated diphtheria bacilli from a vessel which was regarded as the cause of the disease in twenty-four families. The bacilli grow readily in milk without changing its appearance. From cheese which was made on a farm on which diphtheria prevailed, pure cultures of diphtheria bacilli were obtained (New York Board of Health Report, 1894).

The disease may be transmitted by inoculation.

Calves, cats, and fowls are subject to contagious membranous diseases, which are, however, not identical with diphtheria in man and are not communicable to him.

As in other infectious disorders, individual susceptibility plays an important *rôle*. Not only do very many of those exposed escape, but even of those in whose throats the bacilli lodge and grow.

Of predisposing causes age is one of the most important. Very young children are rarely attacked, but Jacobi states that he has seen three instances of the disease in the newly born. Between the second and the fifteenth year a large majority of the cases occur. In this period the greatest number of deaths is between the second and the fifth years. Girls are attacked in larger numbers than boys, probably because they are brought into closer contact with the sick. Adults are frequently affected. The disease is most prevalent in the cold autumn weather. The secondary pseudo-membranous inflammations, caused usually by the streptococcus, attack debilitated persons, the subjects of fevers, particularly of scarlet fever, typhoid, and measles.

Caillé regards as special predisposing elements in children enlarged tonsils, chronic naso-pharyngeal catarrh, carious teeth, and an unhealthy condition of the mucous membrane of the mouth and throat.

Epidemics vary in intensity. While in some the affection is mild and

9

rarely fatal, in others it is characterized by wide extension of the membrane, and shows a special tendency to attack the larynx.

The Klebs-Loeffler bacillus occurs in a large percentage of all suspected cases. It is found chiefly in the false membrane, and does not extend into the subjacent mucosa. In the majority of instances the organisms are localized, and only a few penetrate into the interior. In exceptional instances the bacilli are found in the blood and in the internal organs. It may be the predominating or sole organism in the bronchopneumonia so common in the disease. Outside the throat, the common site of its morbid action, the Klebs-Loeffler bacillus has been found in diphtheritic conjunctivitis, in otitis media, sometimes in wound diphtheria, in fibrinous rhinitis, and in an attenuated condition by Howard in a case of ulcerative endocarditis.

Morphological Characters.—The bacillus is non-motile, varies from 2.5 to 3 μ in length, and from 0.5 to 0.8 μ in thickness. It appears as a straight or slightly bent rod with rounded ends; irregular, bizarre forms, such as rods with one or both ends swollen and simple branching forms, are more or less common. The bacillus stains in sections or on the cover-glass by the Gram method.

It grows best upon a mixture of glucose bouillon and blood serum (Loeffler), forming large, elevated, grayish-white colonies with opaque centres. It grows also upon all the ordinary culture media. The growth usually ceases at temperatures below 20° C.

The bacillus is very resistant, and cultures have been made from a bit of membrane preserved for five months in a dry cloth. Incorporated with dust and kept moist, the bacilli were still cultivatable at the end of eight weeks; kept in a dried state they no longer grew at the end of this period (Ritter).

Variation in Virulence.—For testing the virulence the guinea-pig is used, being most susceptible to the poison. An amount of a forty-eight hour bouillon culture equalling one half per cent of the weight of the animal is injected subcutaneously. "A fully virulent culture is one which causes the death of a guinea-pig within three days or less; a culture of medium virulence one which causes the death of the animal in from three to five days. Cultures which only produce local necrosis and ulceration or death after a greater number of days may be considered as of slight virulence" (J. H. Wright). At the seat of the inoculation there is local necrosis with fibrinous exudate which contains the bacilli, and there is also a more or less extensive œdema of the subcutaneous tissue. The Klebs-Loeffler bacillus evidently has very varying grades of virulence down even to complete absence of pathogenic effects. The name pseudo-bacillus of diphtheria should not be given to this avirulent organism.

The Presence of the Klebs-Loeffler Bacillus in Non-membranous Angina and in Healthy Throats.—The bacillus has been isolated from cases which show nothing more than a simple catarrhal angina, of a mild type without any membrane, with diffuse redness, and perhaps huskiness and signs of catarrhal laryngitis. In other cases the anatomical picture may be that of a lacunar tonsillitis.

During the prevalence of an epidemic the organisms may be met with in perfectly healthy throats, particularly in persons in the same house, or the ward attendants and nurses in fever hospitals.

Following an attack of diphtheria the bacilli may persist in the throat after all the membrane has disappeared for weeks or months. Schäfer notes a case in which they were present six months after the attack, and in a nurse in my ward the bacilli persisted for eighty-four days.

Toxine of the Klebs-Loeffler Bacillus.—Roux and Yersin showed that a fatal result following the inoculation with the bacillus was not caused by any extension of the micro-organisms within the body; and they were enabled in bouillon cultures to separate the bacilli from the poison. The toxine so separated killed with very much the same effects as those caused by the inoculation of the bacilli; the pseudo-membrane, however, is not formed. These results were confirmed by many observers, particularly by Sidney Martin, who separated a toxic albumose. The precise composition of the body and whether it is a proteid at all is still doubtful.

Production of Immunity.—Susceptible animals may be rendered immune from diphtheritic infection by injecting weakened cultures of the bacillus or, what is better, suitable doses of the diphtheria toxine. The result of the injections is a febrile reaction which soon passes away and leaves the animal less susceptible to the poison or the living bacilli. By repeating and gradually increasing the quantity of poison injected a high degree of immunity can be produced in large animals (goat, horse). During the reaction following the injections the immunity temporarily falls only to exceed the previous degree at its end. This form of immunity, denominated antitoxic, is associated with the development of a curative substance, which is contained within the humors and cells of the body, and in the form of the preserved serum of the blood (horse) is known commercially as diphtheria antitoxine. It has the power to neutralize the effects of the toxine.

The Bacteria associated with the Diphtheria Bacillus.—The most common is the streptococcus pyogenes. Others, in addition to the organisms constantly found in the mouth, are the micrococcus lanceolatus, the bacillus coli communis, and the staphylococcus aureus and albus. Of these, probably the streptococcus pyogenes is the most important, as cases of general infection with this organism have been found in diphtheria. The suppuration in the lymph-glands and the broncho-pneumonia are usually (though not always) caused by this organism.

Pseudo-Diphtheria Bacillus.—As mentioned above, the Klebs-Loeffler bacillus varies very much in its virulence, and it exists in a form entirely devoid of pathogenic properties. This organism should not be designated the pseudo-diphtheria bacillus. The name " should be confined to bacilli which, though resembling the diphtheria bacillus, differ from it not only by absence of virulence, but also by cultural peculiarities, the most important of the latter being greater luxuriance of growth on agar, and the preservation of the alkaline reaction of the bouillon cultures " (Welch). Neisser has just proposed a differential method of staining to discriminate between these organisms that gives useful results.

Diphtheroid Inflammations.—Under the term *diphtheroid* may be grouped those membranous inflammations which are not associated with the Klebs-Loeffler bacillus. It is perhaps a more suitable designation than pseudo-diphtheria or secondary diphtheria. As in a great majority of cases the streptococcus pyogenes is the active organism, the term " streptococcus diphtheritis " is often employed. The name " diphtheritis " is best used in an anatomical sense to designate an inflammation of a mucous membrane or integumentary surface characterized by necrosis and a fibrinous exudate, whereas the term " diphtheria " should be limited to the disease caused by the Klebs-Loeffler bacillus. The proportion of cases of diphtheroid inflammation varies greatly in the different statistics. Of the large number of observations made by Park and Beebe (5,611) in New York, 40 per cent were diphtheroid. Figures from other sources do not show so high a percentage.

It is not to be inferred from these statistics that any considerable number of the cases which present the appearances of typical and characteristic primary diphtheria are due to other micro-organisms than the Klebs-Loeffler bacillus. Nearly all such cases, when carefully examined by a competent bacteriologist, are found to be due to the diphtheria bacillus. It is the less characteristic cases, with more or less suspicion of diphtheria, which are most likely to be caused by other bacteria than the Klebs-Loeffler bacillus. It is also to be remembered that in the routine examination of a large number of cases for boards of health and diphtheria wards of hospitals, some cases of genuine diphtheria may escape recognition from lack of such repeated and thorough bacteriological tests as are sometimes required for the detection of cases presenting unusual difficulties.

Conditions under which the Diphtheroid Affection occurs.—Of 450 cases (Park and Beebe), 300 occurred in the autumn months and 150 in the spring; 198 occurred in children from the first to the seventh year. In a large proportion of all the cases the disease develops in children, and can only be differentiated from diphtheria proper by the bacteriological examination. In many of the cases it is simply an acute catarrhal angina with lacunar tonsillitis.

The diphtheroid inflammations are particularly prone to develop in connection with the acute fevers.

(*a*) *Scarlet Fever.*—In a large proportion of the cases of angina in scarlet fever the Klebs-Loeffler bacillus is not present. Booker has reported 11 cases complicating scarlet fever, in all of which the streptococci were the predominant organisms. Of the 450 cases of Park and Beebe, 42 complicated scarlet fever. The angina of this disease is not always, however, due to the streptococcus. Where diphtheria is prevalent and opportunities are favorable for exposure, a large proportion of the cases of membranous throats in scarlet fever may be genuine diphtheria, as is shown by the statistics of Williams and Morse in the Boston City Hospital. Here, of 97 cases of scarlet fever, membranous angina was present in 35; in 12 with the Klebs-Loeffler bacillus, and in 23 with other organisms. Morse reports 99 cases of angina in scarlet fever in which 76 were diphtheritic. This large proportion of cases in which scarlet fever was associated with true diphtheria is attributed to local conditions in the hospital.

(*b*) *Measles.*—Membranous angina is much less common in this disease. It occurred in 6 of the 450 diphtheroid cases in New York. Of 4 cases with severe membranous angina at the Boston City Hospital, 1 only presented the Klebs-Loeffler bacillus.

(*c*) *Whooping-cough* may also be complicated with membranous angina. The bacteriological examinations have not been very numerous. Escherich gives 4 cases, in all of which the Klebs-Loeffler bacillus was found.

(*d*) *Typhoid Fever.*—Membranous inflammations in this disease are not very infrequent; they may occur in the throat, the pelvis of the kidney, the bladder, or the intestines. The complication may be caused by the Klebs-Loeffler bacillus, which was present in 4 cases described by Morse. It is frequently, however, a streptococcus infection.

Ernst Wagner has remarked upon the greater frequency of these membranous inflammations in typhoid fever when diphtheria is prevailing.

Clinical Features of the Diphtheroid Affection.—The cases, as a rule, are milder, and the mortality is low, only 2.5 per cent in the 450 cases of Park and Beebe. The diphtheroid inflammations complicating the specific fevers are, however, often very fatal, and a general streptococcus infection is by no means infrequent. As in the Klebs-Loeffler angina, there may be only a simple catarrhal process. In other instances the tonsils are covered with a creamy, pultaceous exudate, without any actual membrane. An important group may begin as a simple lacunar tonsillitis, while in others the entire fauces and tonsils are covered by a continuous membrane, and there is a foul sloughing angina with intense constitutional disturbance.

Are the diphtheroid cases infectious? General clinical experience warrants the statement that the membranous angina associated with the fevers is rarely communicated to other patients. The health department of New York does not keep the diphtheroid cases under supervision. Their investigation of the 450 diphtheroid cases seems to justify this conclusion. Park and Beebe say that "it did not seem that the secondary cases were any less liable to occur where the primary case was isolated than when it was not."

Sequelæ of the Diphtheroid Angina.—The usual mildness of the disease is in part, no doubt, due to the less frequent systemic invasion. Some of the worst forms of general streptococcus infection are, however, seen in this disease. There are no peculiarities, local or general, which can be in any way regarded as distinctive; and if the observation of Bourges should be corroborated, even the most extensive paralysis may follow an angina caused by it.

Morbid Anatomy.—A majority of the cases die of the faucial or of the laryngeal disease. The exudation may occur in the mouth and cover the inner surfaces of the cheeks; it may even extend beyond the lips on to the skin. This was met once in 30 autopsies at the Montreal General Hospital. The amount of exudation varies in different cases. Usually the tonsils and the pillars of the fauces are swollen and covered with the false membrane. More commonly, in the fatal cases, the exudation is very extensive, involving the uvula, the soft palate, the posterior nares, and the lateral and posterior walls of the pharynx. These parts are covered with a dense pseudo-membrane, in places firmly adherent, in others beginning to separate. In extreme cases the necrosis is advanced and there is a gangrenous condition of the parts. The membrane is of a dirty greenish or gray color, and the tonsils and palate may be in a state of necrotic sloughing. The erosion may be deep enough in the tonsils to open the carotid artery, or a false aneurism may be produced in the deep tissues of the neck. The nose may be completely blocked by the false membrane, which may also extend into the conjunctivæ and through the Eustachian tubes into the middle ear. In cases of laryngeal diphtheria the exudate in the pharynx may be extensive. In many cases, however, it is slight upon the tonsils and fauces and abundant upon the epiglottis and the larynx, which may be completely occluded by false membrane. In severe cases the exudate extends into the trachea and to the bronchi of the third or fourth dimension. This occurred in nearly half of my 30 Montreal autopsies.

In all these situations the membrane varies very much in consistence, depending greatly upon the stage at which death has taken place. If death has occurred early, it is firm and closely adherent; if late, it is soft, shreddy, and readily detached. When firmly adherent it is torn off with difficulty and leaves an abraded mucosa. In the most extreme cases, in which there is extensive necrosis, the parts look gangrenous. In fatal cases the lymphatic glands of the neck are enlarged, and there is a general infiltration of the tissues with serum; the salivary glands, too, may be swollen. In rare instances the membrane extends to the gullet and stomach.

On inspection of the larynx of a child dead of membranous croup, the *rima* is seen filled with mucus or with a shreddy material which, when washed off carefully, leaves the mucosa covered by a thin grayish-yellow membrane, which may be uniform or in patches. It covers the ary-epiglottic folds and the true cords, and may be continued into the ventricles or even into the trachea. Above, it may involve the epiglottis. It varies much in consistency. I have seen fatal cases in which the exudation was not actually membranous, but rather friable and granular. It may form a thick, even stratified membrane, which fills the entire glottis. The exudation may extend down the trachea and into the bronchi, and may pass beyond the epiglottis to the fauces. Usually it is readily stripped off from the mucous membrane of the larynx and leaves exposed the swollen and injected mucosa. On examination it is seen that the fibrinous material has involved chiefly the epithelial lining and has not greatly infiltrated the subjacent tissues.

Histological Changes.—We owe largely to the labors of Wagner, Weigert, and more particularly to the splendid work of Oertel, our knowledge of the minute changes which take place in diphtheria. The following is a brief abstract of the views of the last-named author:

The diphtheritic poison induces first a necrosis or death of cells with which it comes in contact, particularly the superficial epithelium and the leucocytes. The deeper cells of the mucosa and of the other parts reached by the poison may also be affected. The second change is hyaline transformation of the dead cells, or, as Weigert terms it, the production of coagulation-necrosis. The bacilli excite inflammation with the migration of leucocytes, which are destroyed by the poison and undergo the hyaline change. The superficial epithelial layers undergo a similar alteration, and what we know as the false membrane represents in large part an aggregation of dead cells, most of which have undergone the transformation into hyaline material, and have become much distorted in shape. Genuine fibrinous exudate is, however, associated with this coagulation-necrosis of cells. This is in all probability a conservative process by which, in a measure, the poison is localized and prevented from reaching the deeper structures. The laminated condition of the exudate is probably produced by the inflammation of different layers. The formation of these foci of necrobiosis, starting from the epithelium and proceeding inward, is, according to Oertel, the distinguishing characteristic of diphtheria. The action of the poison is by no means confined to the superficial mucosa on which the bacilli grow. Although they do not themselves penetrate deeply, the contiguous bronchial glands show extensive foci of necrosis. In severe cases these necrotic areas are found in the internal organs, in the solitary glands of the intestines, and in the mesenteric glands.

The blood-vessels may themselves be much altered and the capillaries may show extensive hyaline degeneration. Every one of the histological changes described by Oertel in human diphtheria may be paralleled in the experimental disease induced by the Klebs-Loeffler bacillus. Welch and Flexner have shown that similar foci of necrosis with nuclear fragmentation in lymphatic glands, the liver, spleen, intestinal mucosa, and other parts, occur in the experimental diphtheria of guinea-pigs, and they have demonstrated that these necroses are due to the so-called tox-albumin of the diphtheria bacillus. The local exudate is caused by the bacilli themselves and cannot be produced by the tox-albumin alone.

The changes in the *other organs* are variable. When death has occurred from asphyxia there is general congestion of the viscera.

Capillary bronchitis, areas of collapse, and patches of broncho-pneumonia are almost constantly found in fatal cases. The broncho-pneumonia complicating diphtheria often contains the Klebs-Loeffler bacillus, but usually in combination with the streptococcus pyogenes or the diplococcus pneumoniæ. These latter organisms, particularly the streptococcus, are the most frequent cause of the pulmonary complications of diphtheria. In very malignant cases the blood may be fluid. Fibrinous coagula may be found in the heart, but the widespread idea that they may cause sudden death is erroneous. Myocardial changes are not infrequent, and in certain cases sudden death is due to heart-failure in consequence of degeneration of the muscle-fibres. Endocarditis is extremely rare. It was not present in one of my thirty autopsies. The serous membranes often show ecchymoses. The kidneys present parenchymatous changes, such as are associated with acute febrile affections. There may, however, be acute nephritis. The spleen and liver show the usual febrile changes. The spleen is not always enlarged. General streptococcus septicæmia or lesions of internal organs due to localizations of the streptococcus pyogenes are common and most dangerous complications of diphtheria. The Klebs-Loeffler bacillus may be found at autopsy in the blood and internal organs, but usually only in small number.

Symptoms.—The period of incubation is "from two to seven days, oftenest two."

The initial symptoms are those of an ordinary febrile attack—slight chilliness, fever, and aching pains in the back and limbs. In mild cases these symptoms are trifling, and the child may not feel ill enough to go to bed. Usually the temperature rises within the first twenty-four hours to 102.5° or 103°; in severe cases to 104°. In young children there may be convulsions at the outset.

Pharyngeal Diphtheria.—In a typical case there is at first redness of the fauces, and the child complains of slight difficulty in swallowing. The membrane first appears upon the tonsils, and it may be a little difficult to distinguish a patchy diphtheritic pellicle from the exudate of the tonsillar crypts. The pharyngeal mucous membrane is reddened, and the tonsils themselves are swollen. By the third day the membrane has covered the tonsils, the pillars of the fauces, and perhaps the uvula, which is thickened and œdematous, and may fill completely the space between the swollen tonsils. The membrane may extend to the posterior wall of the pharynx. At first grayish-white in color, it changes to a dirty gray, often to a yellow-white. It is firmly adherent, and when removed leaves a bleeding, slightly eroded surface, which is soon covered by fresh exudate. The glands in the neck are swollen, and may be tender. The general condition of a patient in a case of moderate severity is usually good; the temperature not very high, in the absence of complications ranging from 102° to 103°. The pulse range is from 100 to 120. The local condition of the throat is not of great severity, and the constitutional depression is slight. The symptoms gradually abate, the swelling of the neck diminishes, the membranes separate, and from the seventh to the tenth day the throat becomes clear and convalescence sets in.

Clinically atypical forms are extremely common, and I follow here Koplik's division:

(a) There may be no local manifestation of membrane, but a simple catarrhal angina associated sometimes with a croupy cough. The detection in these cases of the Klebs-Loeffler bacillus can alone determine the diagnosis. Such cases are of great moment, inasmuch as they may communicate the severer disease to other children.

(b) There are cases in which the tonsils are covered by a pultaceous exudate, not a consistent membrane.

(c) Cases presenting a punctate form of membrane, isolated, and usually on the surface of the tonsils.

(d) Cases which begin and often run their entire course with the local picture of a typical lacunar amygdalitis. They may be mild, and the local exudate may not extend, but in other cases there are rapid development of membrane, and extension of the disease to the pharynx and the nose, with severe septic and constitutional symptoms.

(*e*) Under the term "latent diphtheria" Heubner has described cases, usually secondary, occurring chiefly in hospital practice, in young persons the subject of wasting affections, such as rickets and tuberculosis. There are fever, naso-pharyngeal catarrh, and gastro-intestinal disturbances. Diphtheria may not be suspected until severe laryngeal complications develop, or the condition may not be determined until autopsy.

Systemic Infection.—The constitutional disturbance in mild diphtheria is very slight. There are instances, too, of extensive local disease without grave systemic symptoms. As a rule, the general features of a case bear a definite relation to the severity of the local disease. There are rare instances in which from the outset the constitutional prostration is extreme, the pulse frequent and small, the fever high, and the nervous phenomena are pronounced; the patient may sink in two or three days overwhelmed by the intensity of the toxæmia. There are cases of this sort in which the exudate in the throat may be slight, but usually the nasal symptoms are pronounced. The temperature may be very slightly raised or even subnormal. More commonly the severe systemic symptoms appear at a later date when the pharyngeal lesion is at its height. They are constantly present in extensive disease, and when there is a sloughing, fœtid condition. The lymphatic glands become greatly enlarged; the pallor is extreme; the face has an ashen-gray hue; the pulse is rapid and feeble, and the temperature sinks below normal. In the most aggravated forms there are gangrenous processes in the throat, and in rare instances, when life is prolonged, extensive sloughing of the tissues of the neck.

Escherich accounts for the discrepancy sometimes observed between the severity of the constitutional disturbance and the intensity of the local process, by assuming varying degrees of susceptibility to the diphtheria bacillus on the one hand, and to its poison on the other hand. With high local susceptibility of a part to the action of the bacillus, with little general susceptibility to the toxine, there is extensive local exudate with mild constitutional symptoms, or *vice versa*, severe systemic disturbance with limited local inflammation.

A leucocytosis is present in diphtheria. Morse does not think it of any prognostic value, since it is present and may be pronounced in mild cases.

Nasal Diphtheria.—In cases of pharyngeal diphtheria the Klebs-Loeffler bacillus is found on the mucous membrane of the nose and in the secretions, even when no membrane is present, but it may apparently produce two affections similar enough locally but widely differing in their general features.

In membranous or fibrinous rhinitis, a very remarkable affection seen usually in children, the nares are occupied by thick membranes, but there is an entire absence of any constitutional disturbance. The condition has been studied very carefully by Park, Abbott, Gerber and Podack, and others. Ravenel has collected 77 cases (Medical News, 1895, I), in 41 of which a bacteriological examination was made, in 33 the Klebs-Loeffler bacillus being present. All the cases ran a benign course, and in all but a few the membrane was limited to the nose, and the constitutional symptoms were either absent or very slight. Remarkable and puzzling features are that the disease runs a benign course, and that infection of other children in the family is extremely rare.

On the other hand, nasal diphtheria is apt to present a most malignant type of the disease. The infection may be primary in the nose, and in a case recently in my wards there was otitis media, and the Klebs-Loeffler bacillus was separated from the discharge before the condition of nasal diphtheria was suspected. While some cases are of mild character, others are very intense, and the constitutional symptoms most profound. The glandular inflammation is usually very intense, owing, as Jacobi points out, to the great richness of the nasal mucosa in lymphatics. From the nose the inflammation may extend through the tear-ducts to the conjuctivæ and into the antra.

Laryngeal Diphtheria.—*Membranous Croup.*—With a very large proportion of all the cases of membranous laryngitis the Klebs-Loeffler bacillus is associated; in a much smaller number other organisms, particularly the streptococcus, are found. Membranous croup, then, may be said to be either genuine diphtheria or diphtheroid in character. Of 286 cases in which the disease was confined to the larynx or bronchi, in 229 the Klebs-Loeffler bacilli were found. In 57 they were not present, but 17 of these cultures were unsatisfactory (Park and Beebe). The streptococcus cases are more likely to be secondary to other acute diseases.

Symptoms.—Naturally, the clinical symptoms are almost identical in the non-specific and specific forms of membranous laryngitis.

The affection begins like an acute laryngitis with slight hoarseness and rough cough, to which the term croupy has been applied. After these symptoms have lasted for a day or two with varying intensity, the child suddenly becomes worse, usually at night, and there are signs of impeded respiration. At first the difficulty in breathing is paroxysmal, due probably to more or less spasm of the muscles of the glottis. Soon the dyspnœa becomes continuous, inspiration and expiration become difficult, particularly the latter, and with the inspiratory movements the epigastrium and lower intercostal spaces are retracted. The voice is husky and may be reduced to a whisper. The color gradually changes and the imperfect aëration of the blood is shown in the lividity of the lips and finger-tips. Restlessness comes on and the child tosses from side to side, vainly trying to get breath. Occasionally, in a severer paroxysm, portions of membrane are coughed out. The fever in membranous laryngitis is rarely very high and the condition of the child is usually very good at the time of the onset. The pulse is always increased in frequency and if cyanosis be present is small. In favorable cases the dyspnœa is not very urgent, the color of the face remains good, and after one or two paroxysms the child goes to sleep and wakes in the morning, perhaps without fever and feeling comfortable. The attack may recur the following night with greater severity. In unfavorable cases the dyspnœa becomes more and more urgent, the cyanosis deepens, the child, after a period of intense restlessness, sinks into a semi-comatose state, and death finally occurs from poisoning of the nerve centres by carbon dioxide. In other cases the onset is less sudden and is preceded by a longer period of indisposition. As a rule, there are pharyngeal symptoms. The constitutional disturbance may be more severe, the fever higher, and there may be swelling of the glands of the neck. Inspection of the fauces may show the presence of false membranes on the pillars or on the tonsils. Bacteriological examination can alone determine whether these are due to the Klebs-Loeffler bacillus or to the streptococcus. Fagge held that non-contagious membranous croup may spread upward from the larynx just as diphtheritic inflammation is in the habit of spreading downward from the fauces. Ware, of Boston, whose essay on croup is perhaps the most solid contribution to the subject made in this country, reported the presence of exudate in the fauces in 74 out of 75 cases of croup. These observations were made prior to 1840, during periods in which diphtheria was not epidemic to any extent in Boston. In protracted cases pulmonary symptoms may develop, which are sometimes due to the difficulty in expelling the muco-pus from the tubes; in others, the false membrane extends into the trachea and even into the bronchial tubes. During the paroxysm the vesicular murmur is scarcely audible, but the laryngeal stridor may be loudly communicated along the bronchial tubes.

Diphtheria of Other Parts.—Primary diphtheria occurs occasionally in the *conjunctiva*. It follows in some instances the affection of the nasal mucous membrane. Some of the cases are severe and serious, but it has been shown by C. Fränkel and others that the diphtheria bacilli may be present in a conjunctivitis catarrhal in character, or associated with only slight croupous deposits.

Diphtheria of the *external auditory meatus* is seen in rare instances in which there are diphtheritic otitis media and extension through the tympanic membrane.

Diphtheria of the *skin* is most frequently seen in the severer forms of pharyngeal diphtheria, in which the membrane extends to the mouth and lips, and invades the adjacent portions of the skin of the face. The skin about the anus and genitals may also be attacked. Pseudo-membranous inflammation is not uncommon on ulcerated surfaces and wounds. In very many of these cases it is a streptococcus infection, but in a majority, perhaps, in which the patient is suffering with diphtheria, the Klebs-Loeffler bacillus will be found in the fibrinous exudate. As proposed by Welch, the term " wound diphtheria " should be limited to infection of a wound by the Klebs-Loeffler bacillus. This " may manifest itself as a simple inflammation, or inflammation with superficial necrosis, or inflammation with more or less adherent pseudo-membrane. The conditions as regards varying intensity and character of the infection, association with other bacteria, particularly streptococci, and the necessity of a bacteriological examination to establish the diagnosis, are in no way different in the diphtheria of wounds from those in diphtheria of mucous membranes. Wound diphtheria may occur without demonstrable connection with cases of diphtheria and without affection of the throat in the individual attacked, but such occurrences are rare " (Welch). Paralysis may follow wound diphtheria. Pseudo-membranous inflammations of wounds are caused more frequently by other micro-organisms, particularly the streptococcus pyogenes, than by the Klebs-Loeffler bacillus. The fibrinous membrane so common in the neighborhood of the tracheotomy wound in diphtheria is rarely associated with the Klebs-Loeffler bacillus. Diphtheria of the genitals is occasionally seen.

Complications and Sequelæ.—Of local complications, hæmorrhage from the nose or throat may occur in the severe ulcerative cases. Skin rashes are not infrequent, particularly the diffuse erythema. Occasionally there is urticaria and in the severe cases purpura. The pulmonary complications are extremely important. Fatal cases almost invariably show capillary bronchitis with broncho-pneumonia and large patches of collapse. In very bad cases, with extensive sloughing, the septic particles may reach the bronchi and excite gangrenous processes which may lead to severe and fatal hæmorrhage.

Renal complications are common. *Albuminuria* is present in all severe cases. It may cause with the usual tests only a slight turbidity of the urine, the ordinary febrile albuminuria. In others there is a large amount of albumin, curdy in character. It is only when the albumin is in considerable quantity and associated with epithelial or blood casts that the condition indicates parenchymatous nephritis and is alarming. The nephritis may appear quite early in the disease. It sets in occasionally with complete suppression of the urine. In comparison with scarlet fever the renal changes lead less frequently to general dropsy. Mention has already been made of the frequency and gravity of septicæmia and local infection of internal parts due to invasion of the streptococcus pyogenes, which is nearly a constant attendant of the Klebs-Loeffler bacillus in the human body.

Of the sequelæ of diphtheria, *paralysis* is by far the most important. This can be experimentally produced in animals, as already noted, by the inoculation of the toxic material produced by the bacilli. The paralysis occurs in a variable proportion of the cases, ranging from 10 to 15 and even to 20 per cent. It is strictly a sequel of the disease, coming on usually in the second or third week of convalescence. Occasionally it occurs as early as the seventh or eighth day of the disease. It may follow very mild cases; indeed, the local lesion may be so trifling that the onset of the paralysis alone calls attention to the true nature of the trouble. It is proportionately less frequent in children than in adults.

The disease is a toxic neuritis, due to the absorption of the poison, and, like other forms of multiple neuritis, has an extremely complex symptomatology, according to the nerves which are affected. The paralysis may be local or general.

Of the local paralyses the most common is that which affects the palate. This gives a nasal character to the voice, and, owing to a return of liquids through the nose, causes a difficulty in swallowing. These may be the only symptoms. The palate is seen to be relaxed and motionless, and the sensation in it is also much impaired. The affection may extend to the constrictors of the pharynx, and deglutition become embarrassed. Within two or three weeks or even a shorter time the paralysis disappears. In many cases the affection of the palate is only part of a general neuritis. Of other local forms perhaps the most common are paralysis of the eye-muscles, intrinsic and extrinsic. There may be strabismus, ptosis, and loss of power of accommodation. Facial paralysis may develop, and in one case, two and a half years later, it still persisted with contractures. The neuritis may be confined to the nerves of one limb, though more commonly the legs or the arms are affected together. Very often with the palatal paralysis is associated a weakness of the legs without definite palsy but with loss of the knee-jerk.

Heart symptoms are not uncommon. There may be great retardation, even to thirty beats in the minute. Bradycardia and tachycardia may alternate in the same patient. Heart-failure and fatal syncope may occur at the height of the disease or during convalescence. If they occur during the fever, the child, perhaps after an exaggeration of symptoms, presents an unusual pallor. The pulse becomes weak and rapid, but may fall to fifty, forty, or even lower. The extremities are cold, the temperature sinks, and death takes place, with all the features of collapse, within a few hours. More frequently the fatal collapse comes during convalescence, even as late as the sixth or seventh week after apparent recovery. The attack may set in abruptly, perhaps following a sudden exertion. More commonly there have been symptoms pointing to disturbed cardiac rhythm, or even fainting-spells. In some instances vomiting has preceded the serious cardiac attack. There may be no physical signs other than slight increase in the cardiac dulness and a gallop-rhythm indicating dilatation. These symptoms were formerly ascribed to cardiac thrombosis or to endocarditis. Possibly in some of the cases the result is due, as pointed out by Mosler and Leyden, to an infectious myocarditis, but in a majority of the cases the symptoms are probably due to a neuritis of the cardiac nerves.

The multiple form of diphtheritic neuritis is not uncommon. It may begin with the palatal affection, or with loss of power of accommodation and loss of the tendon reflexes. This last is an important sign, which, as Bernhardt, Buzzard, and R. L. MacDonnell have shown, may occur early, but is not necessarily followed by other symptoms of neuritis. There is paraplegia, which may be complete or involve only the extensors of the feet. The paralysis may extend and involve the arms and face and render the patient entirely helpless. The muscles of respiration may be spared. The chief danger in these severer forms comes from the involvement of the heart and of the muscles of respiration; but the outlook is in many cases not so bad as the patient's condition would indicate. Of 13 cases collected by Cadet de Gassicourt 6 died. The sphincters may be involved, though they are often spared.

Diagnosis.—The presence of the Klebs-Loeffler bacillus is regarded by bacteriologists as the sole criterion of true diphtheria, and as this organism may be associated with all grades of throat affections, from a simple catarrh to a sloughing, gangrenous process, it is evident that in many instances there will be a striking discrepancy between the clinical and the bacteriological diagnosis. One inestimable value of the recent studies has been the determination of the diphtheritic character of many of the milder forms of tonsillitis and pharyngitis.

The bacteriological diagnosis is simple. The plan adopted by the New York Health Department is a model which may be followed with advantage in other cities. Outfits for making cultures, consisting of a box containing a tube of blood-serum and a sterilized swab in a test-tube, are distributed to about forty stations at convenient points in the city. A list of these places is published, and a physician can obtain the outfit free of cost. The directions are as follows: " The patient should be placed in a good light, and, if a child, properly held. In cases where it is possible to get a good view of the throat, depress the tongue and rub the cotton swab gently but freely against any visible exudate. In other cases, including those in which the exudate is confined to the larynx, avoiding the tongue, pass the swab far back and rub it freely against the mucous membrane of the pharynx and tonsils. Without laying the swab down, withdraw the cotton plug from the culture-tube, insert the swab, and rub that portion of it which has touched the exudate gently but thoroughly all over the surface of the blood-serum. Do not push the swab into the bloodserum, nor break the surface in any way. Then replace the swab in its own tube, plug both tubes, put them in the box, and return the culture outfit at once to the station from which it was obtained." The culture-tubes which have been inoculated are kept in an incubator at 37° C. for twelve hours and are then ready for examination. Some prefer a method by which the material from the throat collected on a sterile swab, or, as recommended by von Esmarch, on small pieces of sterilized sponge, is sent to the laboratory where the cultures and microscopical examination are made by a bacteriologist.

An immediate diagnosis without the use of cultures is often possible by making a smear preparation of the exudate from the throat. The Klebs-Loeffler bacilli may be present in sufficient numbers, and may be quite characteristic to an expert. In this connection may be given the following statement by Park, who has had such an exceptional experience: " The examination by a competent bacteriologist of the bacterial growth in a blood-serum tube which has been properly inoculated and kept for fourteen hours at the body temperature can be thoroughly relied upon in cases where there is visible membrane in the throat, if the culture is made during the period in which the membrane is forming, and no antiseptic, especially no mercurial solution, has lately been applied. In cases in which the disease is confined to the larynx or bronchi, surprisingly accurate results can be obtained from cultures, but in a certain proportion of cases no diphtheria bacilli will be found in the first culture, and yet will be abundantly present in later cultures. We believe, therefore, that absolute reliance for a diagnosis cannot be placed upon a single culture from the pharynx in purely laryngeal cases."

Where a bacteriological examination cannot be made, the practitioner must regard as suspicious all forms of throat affections in children, and carry out measures of isolation and disinfection. In this way alone can serious errors be avoided. It is not, of course, in the severer forms of membranous angina that mistake is likely to occur, but in the various lighter forms, many of which are in reality due to the Klebs-Loeffler bacillus.

A large proportion of the cases of diphtheroid inflammation of the throat are due to the streptococcus pyogenes. They are usually milder, and the liability to general infection is less intense; still, in scarlet fever and other specific fevers some of the most virulent cases of throat disease which we see, with intense systemic infection, are caused by this micro-organism. These streptococcus cases are probably much less numerous than the figures which I have given would indicate. The more careful examinations in the diphtheria pavilions of hospitals, particularly in Europe, have shown that in the large majority of cases admitted the Klebs-Loeffler bacillus is present. I have already referred, under the section on scarlet fever, to the question of the diagnosis between scarlet fever with severe angina and diphtheria.

Prognosis.—In hospital practice the disease is very fatal, the percentage of deaths ranging from thirty to fifty. This is due in great part to the admission only of the severer forms. In country places the disease may display an appalling virulence. In cases of ordinary severity the outlook is usually good. Death results from involvement of the larynx, septic infection, sudden heart-failure, diphtheritic paralysis, occasionally from uræmia, and sometimes from broncho-pneumonia developing during convalescence.

Prophylaxis.—Isolation of the sick, disinfection of the clothing and of everything that has come in contact with the patient, careful scrutiny of the milder cases of throat disorder, and more stringent surveillance in the period of convalescence are the essential measures to prevent the spread of the disease. Suspected cases in families or schools should be at once isolated or removed to a hospital for infectious disorders. When a death has occurred from diphtheria, the body should be wrapped in a sheet which has been soaked in a corrosive-sublimate solution (1 to 3,000), and placed in a closely sealed coffin. The funeral should always be private.

In cases of well-marked diphtheria these precautions are usually carried out, but the chief danger is from the milder cases, particularly the ambulatory form, in which the disease has perhaps not been suspected. But from such patients mingling with susceptible children the disease is often conveyed. The healthy children in a family in which diphtheria exists may carry the disease to their school-fellows. A striking illustration of the way in which diphtheria is spread is given by Park and Beebe: " The child of a man who kept a candy store developed diphtheria; there were four other children in the family, and these were in no way isolated from the patient, yet none of them developed diphtheria; but children who bought candy at the store, and other children coming in contact with these in school, developed diphtheria. The secondary cases ceased to develop so soon as the candy store had been closed."

A very important matter in the prophylaxis relates to the period of convalescence. It has been shown by numerous observations that, after all the membrane has cleared away, virulent bacilli may persist in the throat from periods ranging from six weeks to six months, or even longer. There is evidence to show that the disease may be communicated by such patients, so that isolation should be continued in any given case until the bacteriological examination shows that the throat is free.

It cannot be too strongly emphasized that the important elements in the prophylaxis of diphtheria are the rigid scrutiny of the milder types of throat affection, and the thorough isolation and disinfection of the individual patients.

Careful attention should be given to the throats and mouths of children, particularly to the teeth and tonsils, as Caillé has urged. Swollen and enlarged tonsils should be removed. In persons exposed, the antiseptic mouth washes, such as corrosive sublimate (1 to 10,000), chlorine water (1 to 1,100), or swabbing the throat with a diluted Loeffler's solution, should be employed.

Treatment.—The important points are hygienic measures to prevent the spread of the malady, local treatment of the throat to destroy the bacilli, medication, general or specific, to counteract the effects of the toxines, and, lastly, to meet the complications and sequelæ.

(*a*) **Hygienic Measures.**—The patient should be in a room from which the carpets, curtains, and superfluous furniture have been removed. The temperature should be about 68°, and thorough ventilation should be secured. The air may be kept moist by a kettle or a steam-atomizer. If possible, only the nurse, the child's mother, and the doctor should come in contact with the patient. During the visit the physician should wear a linen overall, and on leaving the room he should thoroughly wash his hands and face in a corrosive-sublimate solution. The strictest quarantine should be employed against other members in the house.

(*b*) **Local Treatment.**—In mild cases the throat symptoms are alone prominent. Vigorous local treatment from the outset should be carried out, taking especial care in all instances to avoid mechanical injury to the tissues. A very large number of solutions have been recommended. They are best employed with a swab of cotton-wool or a soft sponge, or irrigation with hot antiseptic solutions may be used. The direct application with a swab of cotton-wool or sponge is, as a rule, effective. In many young children it is really a most trying procedure to carry out the treatment, and sometimes one is compelled to desist. The nurse should hold the child on her knees, well wrapped in a shawl, with its head resting on her shoulder. The nose is then held, and so soon as the child opens its mouth a cork should be placed between the molar teeth. The local application can then be made, or thorough irrigation carried out. In infants the disinfecting fluids are sometimes better applied through the nostrils. The following solutions may be employed:

Loeffler's solution: Menthol, 10 grammes dissolved in toluol to 36 cc. Liq. Ferri sesquichlorati, 4 cc.; alcohol absol., 60 cc.

Corrosive sublimate, 1 to 1,000, either alone or with tartaric acid, 5 grammes to the litre.

Carbolic acid, 3 per cent in 30 per cent alcohol solution, is much employed; some prefer to touch the small spots of exudate with pure carbolic acid.

Another solution is: The tincture of the perchloride of iron, a drachm and a half, in glycerine, one ounce, water, one ounce, with from 15 to 20 minims of carbolic acid. Chlorine water, boric acid, peroxide of hydrogen, iodoform, lactic acid, trypsin, and papain are also recommended.

Loeffler's solution, which has been given a very thorough trial, is perhaps the most satisfactory.

Nasal diphtheria requires prompt and thorough disinfection of the passages. Jacobi recommends chloride of sodium, saturated boric acid, or 1 part of bichloride of mercury, 35 of chloride of sodium, and 1,000 of water, or the 1-per-cent solution of carbolic acid. Loeffler's solution may be diluted and applied with a syringe or a spray. To be effectual the injection must be properly given. The nurse should be instructed to pass the nozzle of the syringe horizontally, not vertically; otherwise the fluid will return through the same nostril.

When the larynx becomes involved, a steam tent may be arranged upon the bed, so that the child may breathe an atmosphere saturated with moisture. If the dyspnœa becomes urgent, an emetic of sulphate of zinc or ipecacuanha may be given. When the signs of obstruction are marked there should be no delay in the performance of intubation or tracheotomy.

Hot applications to the neck are usually very grateful, particularly to young children, though in the case of older children and adults the ice poultices are to be preferred.

(c) **General Measures.**—The food should be liquid—milk, beef juices, barley water, albumen water, and soups. The child should be encouraged to drink water freely. When the pharyngeal involvement is very great and swallowing painful, nutritive enemata should be used. In cases with severe constitutional symptoms stimulants should be given early.

Medicines given internally are of very little avail in the disease. There is still a widespread belief in the profession that forms of mercury are beneficial. The tincture of the perchloride of iron is also very warmly recommended. We are still, however, without drugs which can directly counteract the tox-albumins of this disease, and we must rely on general measures of feeding and stimulants to support the strength.

The convalescence of the disease is not without its dangers, and patients should be very carefully watched, particularly if there are signs of heart weakness.

The diphtheritic paralysis requires rest in bed, and in those cases in which the heart rhythm is disturbed the avoidance of sudden exertion. In the chronic forms with wasting, massage, electricity, and strychnine are invaluable aids. If swallowing becomes very difficult, the patient must be fed with the stomach-tube, which is very much preferable to feeding *per rectum.*

(d) **Antitoxine Treatment.**—As above mentioned, animals may be rendered immune against diphtheria, and the blood of an animal so treated when introduced into another animal protects it from infection with the bacilli of the disease. The observations of Behring, Roux, and others have shown that the use of the blood-serum of animals rendered artificially immune against diphtheria has an important healing influence upon diphtheria spontaneously acquired in man. In preparing the blood-serum it is very desirable, of course, to have a uniform standard of strength. One tenth of one cubic centimetre of what Behring calls his normal serum

10

will counteract ten times the minimum of diphtheria poison fatal for a guinea-pig weighing 300 grammes. One cubic centimetre of this normal serum he calls an antitoxine unit. Holt gives the following directions for the use of the antitoxine: "The general experience of the profession thus far is, that for children over two years old the initial dose should be from 1,500 to 2,000 units in all severe cases, including those of laryngeal stenosis; this dose to be repeated in from eighteen to twenty-four hours if no improvement is seen, and again in twenty-four hours if the course of the disease is unfavorable. The third dose is rarely necessary. Exceptional cases of great severity, especially when seen late, should receive somewhat larger doses than those mentioned—i. e., 3,000 units. Mild cases should receive 1,000 units for the first injection, a second being rarely required. For children under two years old, the initial dose in a severe case or one of laryngeal stenosis should be 1,000 units, to be repeated as above indicated; in a mild case, 600 units. The most concentrated serum is to be preferred, and only that obtained from a reliable source should be used."

A large number of preparations are now on the market, and some caution has to be exercised by the practitioner as to the serum which he employs.

In favorable cases the effects of the serum are seen in a marked amelioration of both the local and general symptoms. Within twenty-four hours the swelling of the fauces subsides and the membrane begins to disappear. At the same time the temperature falls, the pulse becomes slower, and the general condition of the patient improves in every way. In cases of moderate severity, when the injections are employed early, the improvement in both the throat and constitutional symptoms is certainly very striking. The earlier the cases come under treatment the better are the results. There are cases, however, of great severity in which the antitoxine has been employed early and yet has not saved life.

Among the untoward effects of the treatment may be the development of a local abscess, which, however, is rare, diffuse erythema and urticaria, joint pains, and albuminuria. None of these are serious, and the evidence is not conclusive that the incidence of albuminuria is greater in the cases treated with antitoxine.

During the past three years evidence has been accumulating from all parts of the world as to the beneficial effects of the antitoxine treatment in diphtheria, but figures need no longer be quoted in illustration. The following statement from Holt's work expresses the opinion of those best able to judge of the matter: "The serum is much less efficacious in the cases of so-called mixed infection or septic diphtheria, and is valueless in the membranous inflammations which are due to streptococci. In a child the serum should be injected upon a clinical diagnosis of diphtheria without waiting for the bacterial examination. In a mild case in an older child this perhaps may be waited for, but not in a severe one, and particularly not in a laryngeal case. The most concentrated preparation of antitoxine which can be obtained should be employed. In cases injected during the first two days the mortality is less than 5 per cent. The evidence is conclusive that in laryngeal diphtheria the serum in sufficient doses largely prevents the extension of membrane into the trachea and bronchi, and thus prevents broncho-pneumonia. While much still remains to be learned regarding immunization, present knowledge justifies the statement that for a period—approximately a month—the protection conferred is practically complete. Immunizing doses should therefore be given to every child in an infected household or institution."

The question of immunizing those exposed to the disease is a very practical one. It has been carried out on a large scale in some institutions with satisfactory results. An injection of the No. 1 Behring is given, and if thought proper repeated in a few days. The immunity appears to be transient, only persisting for a few weeks.

XVII. ERYSIPELAS.

Definition.—An acute, contagious disease, characterized by a special inflammation of the skin caused by the streptococcus erysipelatos (streptococcus pathogenes longus).

Etiology.—Erysipelas is a widespread affection, endemic in most communities, and at certain seasons epidemic. We are as yet ignorant of the atmospheric or telluric influences which favor the diffusion of the poison.

It is particularly prevalent in the spring of the year. Of 2,012 cases collected by Anders, 1,214 occurred during the first five months of the year. April had the largest number of cases. The affection prevails extensively in old, ill-ventilated hospitals and institutions in which the sanitary conditions are defective. With the improved sanitation of late years the number of cases has materially diminished. It has been observed, however, to break out in new institutions under the most favorable hygienic circumstances. Erysipelas is both contagious and inoculable; but, except under special conditions, the poison is not very virulent and does not seem to act at any great distance. It can be conveyed by a third person. The poison certainly attaches itself to the furniture, bedding, and walls of rooms in which patients have been confined.

The disposition to the disease is widespread, but the susceptibility is specially marked in the case of individuals with wounds or abrasions of any sort. Recently delivered women and persons who have been the subjects of surgical operations are particularly prone to it. A wound, however, is not necessary, and in the so-called idiopathic form, although it may be difficult to say that there was not a slight abrasion about the nose or lips, in very many cases there certainly is no observable external lesion.

Chronic alcoholism, debility, and Bright's disease are predisposing agents. Certain persons show a special susceptibility to erysipelas, and it may recur in them repeatedly. There are instances, too, of a family predisposition.

The specific agent of the disease is a streptococcus growing in long chains, which is included under the group name *Streptococcus pyogenes*, with which the *Streptococcus erysipelatos* appears to be identical. The fever and constitutional symptoms are due in great part to the toxins; the more serious visceral complications are the result of secondary metastatic infection.

Immunity.—Susceptible animals can be rendered immune to virulent streptococci by repeated non-lethal injections of cultures. Marmorek has attempted to prepare a curative serum by injecting animals (donkey, horse, sheep) with cultures intensified by being grown on human serum-bouillon. Such a serum is said to have both immunizing and curative properties. The tests thus far made are not particularly promising.

Morbid Anatomy.—Erysipelas is a simple inflammation. In its uncomplicated forms there is seen, post mortem, little else than inflammatory œdema. Investigations have shown that the cocci are found chiefly in the lymph-spaces and most abundantly in the zone of spreading inflammation. In the uninvolved tissue beyond the inflamed margin they are to be found in the lymph-vessels, and it is here, according to Metschnikoff and others, that an active warfare goes on between the leucocytes and the cocci (phagocytosis). In more extensive and virulent forms of the disease there is usually suppuration. It is stated that the inflammation may pass inward from the scalp through the skull to the meninges. This I have never seen, but in one case I traced the extension from the face along the fifth nerve to the meninges, where an acute meningitis and thrombosis of the lateral sinus were excited.

The visceral complications of erysipelas are numerous and important. The majority of them are of a septic nature. Infarcts occur in the lungs, spleen, and kidneys, and there may be the general evidences of pyæmic infection.

Some of the worst cases of malignant endocarditis are secondary to erysipelas; thus, of 23 cases, 3 occurred in connection with this disease. Septic pericarditis and pleuritis also occur.

As just mentioned, the disease may in rare cases extend and involve the meninges. Pneumonia is not a very common complication.

Acute nephritis is also met with; it is often ingrafted upon an old chronic trouble.

Symptoms.—The following description applies specially to erysipelas of the face and head, the form of the disease which the physician is most commonly called upon to treat.

The *incubation* is variable, probably from three to seven days.

The stage of *invasion* is often marked by a rigor, and followed by a rapid rise in the temperature and other characteristics of an acute fever. When there is a local abrasion, the spot is slightly reddened; but if the disease is idiopathic, there is seen within a few hours slight redness over the bridge of the nose and on the cheeks. The swelling and tension of the skin increase and within twenty-four hours the external symptoms are well marked. The skin is smooth, tense, and œdematous. It looks red, feels hot, and the superficial layers of the epidermis may be lifted as small blebs. The patient complains of an unpleasant feeling of tension in the skin; the swelling rapidly increases; and during the second day the eyes are usually closed. The first-affected parts gradually become pale and less swollen as the disease extends at the periphery. When it reaches the forehead it progresses as an advancing ridge, perfectly well defined and raised; and often, on palpation, hardened extensions can be felt beneath the skin which is not yet reddened. Even in a case of moderate severity, the face is enormously swollen, the eyes are closed, the lips greatly œdematous, the ears thickened, the scalp is swollen, and the patient's features are quite unrecognizable. The formation of blebs is common on the eyelids, ears, and forehead. The cervical lymph-glands are swollen, but are usually masked in the œdema of the neck. The temperature keeps high without marked remissions for four or five days and then defervescence takes place by crisis. Leucocytosis is present. Kirkbride has noted the presence in one case of leucin and tyrosin in the urine. The general condition of the patient varies much with his previous state of health. In old and debilitated persons, particularly in those addicted to alcohol, the constitutional depression from the outset may be very great. Delirium is present, the tongue becomes dry, the pulse feeble, and there is marked tendency to death from toxæmia. In the majority of cases, however, even with extensive lesions, the constitutional disturbance, considering the height of the fever range, is slight. The mucous membrane of the mouth and throat may be swollen and reddened. The erysipelatous inflammation may extend to the larynx, but the severe œdema of this part occasionally met with is commonly due to the extension of the inflammation from without inward.

There are cases in which the inflammation extends from the face to the neck, and over the chest, and may gradually migrate or wander over the greater part of the body (*E. migrans*).

The close relation between the erysipelas coccus and the pus organisms is shown by the frequency with which suppuration occurs in facial erysipelas. Small cutaneous abscesses are common about the cheeks and forehead and neck, and beneath the scalp large collections of pus may accumulate. Suppuration seems to occur more frequently in some epidemics than in others, and at the Philadelphia Hospital one year nearly all the cases in the erysipelas wards presented local abscesses.

Complications.—Meningitis is rare. The cases in which death occurs with marked brain symptoms do not usually show, post mortem, meningeal affection. The delirium and coma are due to the fever, or to toxæmia.

Pneumonia is an occasional complication. Ulcerative endocarditis and septicæmia are more common. Albuminuria is almost constant, particularly in persons over fifty. True nephritis is occasionally seen. Da Costa has called attention to curious irregular returns of the fever which occur during convalescence without any aggravation of the local condition. Malaria may coexist with erysipelas. L. F. Barker has reported such a case occurring in my wards.

The diagnosis rarely presents any difficulty. The mode of onset, the rapid rise in fever, and the characters of the local disease are quite distinctive. Acute necrosis of bone may sometimes be regarded as erysipelas, a mistake which I once saw made in connection with the lower end of the femur.

Prognosis.—Healthy adults rarely die. The general mortality in hospitals is about 7 per cent, in private practice about 4 per cent (Anders). In the new-born, when the disease attacks the navel, it is almost always fatal. In drunkards and in the aged erysipelas is a serious affection, and death may result either from the intensity of the fever or, more commonly, from toxæmia. The wandering or ambulatory erysipelas, which has a more protracted course, may cause death from exhaustion.

Treatment.—Isolation should be strictly carried out, particularly in hospitals. A practitioner in attendance upon a case of erysipelas should not attend cases of confinement.

The disease is self-limited and a large majority of the cases get well without any internal medication. I can speak definitely on this point, having, at the Philadelphia Hospital, treated many cases in this way. The diet should be nutritious and light. Stimulants are not required except in the old and feeble. For the restlessness, delirium, and insomnia, chloral or the bromides may be given; or, if these fail, opium. When the fever is high the patient may be bathed or sponged, or, in private practice, if there is an objection to this, antipyrin or antifebrin may be given.

Of internal remedies believed to influence the disease, the tincture of the perchloride of iron has been highly recommended. At the Montreal General Hospital this was the routine treatment, and doses of half a drachm to a drachm were given every three or four hours. I am by no means convinced that it has any special action; nor, so far as I know, has any medicine, given internally, a definite control over the course of the disease.

Of local treatment, the injection of antiseptic solutions at the margin of the spreading areas has been much practised. Two-per-cent solutions of carbolic acid, the corrosive sublimate and the biniodide of mercury have been much used. The injection should be made not into but just a little beyond the border of the inflamed patch. F. P. Henry has treated a large number of cases at the Philadelphia Hospital with the last-mentioned drug, and this mode of practice is certainly most rational.

Of local applications, ichthyol is at present much used. The inflamed region may be covered with salicylate of starch. Perhaps as good an application as any is cold water, which was highly recommended by Hippocrates.

XVIII. SEPTICÆMIA AND PYÆMIA.

In these days of asepsis physicians see many more cases of septicæmia and pyæmia than do the surgeons. For one case in the post-mortem room with the anatomical diagnosis of *septicæmia* which comes from the surgical or gynæcological departments of the Johns Hopkins Hospital, at least fifteen or twenty come from my medical wards. Certain terms must first be defined.

An *infection* is the morbid process induced by the invasion and growth in the body of pathogenic micro-organisms. An infection may be local, as in a boil, or general, as in some cases of anthrax.

An *intoxication* is the morbid condition caused by the absorption of toxines, in large part derived from pathogenic organisms. The term *sapræmia* is the equivalent of septic intoxication.

A hard-and-fast line cannot be drawn between an infection and an intoxication, but agents of infection alone are capable of reproduction, whereas those of intoxication are chemical poisons, some of which are produced by the agency of bacteria, or by vegetable and animal cells. Infectious diseases which are communicated directly from one person to another are termed contagious, and the infecting agent is sometimes spoken of as a contagium. " Whether or not an infectious disease is contagious in the ordinary sense depends upon the nature of the infectious agent, and especially upon the manner of its elimination from and reception by the body. Most but not all contagious diseases are infectious. Scabies is a contagious disease, but it is not infectious " (Welch).

There are three chief clinical types of infection.

1. LOCAL INFECTIONS WITH THE DEVELOPMENT OF TOXINES.

This is the common mode of invasion of many of the diseases which we have already considered. Tetanus, diphtheria, erysipelas, and pneumonia are diseases which have sites of local infection in which the pathogenic organisms develop; but the constitutional effects are caused by the absorption of the poisonous products. The diphtheria toxine produces all the general symptoms, the tetanus toxine every feature, of the disease without the presence of their respective bacilli. Certain of the symptoms following the absorption of the toxines are general to all; others are special and peculiar, according to the organism which produces them. A chill, fever, general malaise, prostration, rapid pulse, restlessness, and headache are the most frequent. With but few exceptions the febrile disturbance is the most common feature. The most serious effects are seen upon the nervous system and upon the heart, and the gravity of the symptoms on the part of these organs is to some extent a measure of the intensity of the intoxication. The organisms of certain local infections produce poisons which have special actions; thus the diphtheria toxine, besides having the effects already referred to, is especially prone to attack the nervous system and to cause peripheral neuritis. The tetanus toxine has a specific action on the motor neurones.

2. SEPTICÆMIA.

Formerly, and in a surgical sense, the term " septicæmia " was used to designate the invasion of the blood and tissues of the body by the organisms of suppuration, but in the medical sense the term may be applied to any condition in which, with or without a local site of infection, there is microbic invasion of the blood and tissues, but in which there are no foci of suppuration. Owing to the great development of bacteria in the blood, and in order to separate it sharply from local infectious processes with toxic invasion of the body, it is proposed to call this condition bacteræmia; toxæmia denotes the latter state.

(*a*) **Progressive Septicæmia from Local Infection.**—The common streptococcus and staphylococcus infection is as a rule first local, and the toxines alone pass into the blood. In other instances the cocci appear in the
blood and throughout the tissues, causing a septicæmia which intensifies
greatly the severity of the case. Other infections in which the bacterial
invasion, local at first, may become general are pneumonia, typhoid fever,
anthrax, gonorrhœa, and puerperal fever.

The clinical features of this form are well seen in the cases of puerperal septicæmia or in dissection wounds, in which the course of the infection may be traced along the lymphatics. The symptoms usually set in
within twenty-four hours, and rarely later than the third or fourth day.
There is a chill or chilliness, with moderate fever at first, which gradually
rises and is marked by daily remissions and even intermissions. The pulse
is small and compressible, and may reach 120 or higher. Gastro-intestinal
disturbances are common, the tongue is red at the margin, and the dorsum
is dry and dark. There may be early delirium or marked mental prostration and apathy. As the disease progresses there may be pallor of the face
or a yellowish tint. Capillary hæmorrhages are not uncommon.

The outlook is serious in streptococcus cases. Death may occur within
twenty-four hours, and in fatal cases life is rarely prolonged for more than
seven or eight days. On post-mortem examination there may be no gross
focal lesions in the viscera, and the seat of infection may present only slight
changes. The spleen is enlarged and soft, the blood may be extremely
dark in color, and hæmorrhages are common, particularly on the serous
surfaces. Neither thrombi nor emboli are found.

Many instances of septicæmia are combined infections; thus in diphtheria streptococcus septicæmia is a common, and the most serious, event.
The local disease and the symptoms produced by absorption of the toxines dominate the clinical picture; but the features are usually much
aggravated by the systemic invasion. A similar infection may develop in
typhoid fever and in tuberculosis, and may obscure the typical picture,
leading to serious errors in diagnosis. The septicæmia is not always due
to the streptococcus.

(*b*) **General Septicæmia without Recognizable Local Infection.**—*Cryptogenetic Septicæmias.*—This is a group of very great interest to the physician, the full importance of which we are only now beginning to recognize.

The subjects when attacked may be in perfect health; more commonly
they are already weakened by acute or chronic illness. The pathogenic
organisms are varied. The streptococcus pyogenes is the most common;
the forms of staphylococcus more rare. Other occasional causal agents are
the micrococcus lanceolatus (pneumococcus), the bacillus proteus, and the
bacillus pyocyaneus. Between May 1, 1892, and June 1, 1895, there were
sent to the post-mortem room from my wards 21 cases of general infection,
of which 13 were due to the streptococcus pyogenes, 2 to the staphylococcus
pyogenes, and 6 to the pneumococcus. In 19 of these cases the patients
were already the subjects of some other malady, which was aggravated, or
in most instances terminated, by the general septicæmia. The symptoms
vary somewhat with the character of the micro-organisms. In the strep-

tococcus cases there may be chills with high, irregular fever, and a more characteristic *septic* state than in the pneumococcus infection.

Most of these cases come correctly under the term "cryptogenetic septicæmia" as employed by Leube, inasmuch as the local focus of infection is not evident during life, and may not be found after death. Although most of these cases are terminal infections, yet it is well to bear in mind that there are instances of this type of affection coming on in apparently healthy persons. The fever may be extremely irregular, characteristically septic, and persist for many weeks. Foci of suppuration may not develop, and may not be found even at autopsy. I have on several occasions met with cases of an intermittent pyrexia persisting for weeks, in which it seemed impossible to give any explanation of the phenomena, and some which ultimately recovered, and in which tuberculosis and malaria could be almost positively excluded. These cases require to be carefully studied bacteriologically. Dreschfeld has described them as idiopathic intermittent fever of pyæmic character. Local symptoms may be absent, though in three of his cases there was enlargement of the liver, and in two the condition was a diffuse suppurative hepatitis. The pyocyanic disease, or cyano-pyæmia, is an extremely interesting form of infection with the bacillus pyocyaneus, of which a large number of cases have been reported of late years. (See Wollstein's paper, Archives of Pediatrics, October, 1897, and Barker, Jour. Am. Med. Assoc., 1897.)

3. SEPTICO-PYÆMIA.

The pathogenic micro-organisms which invade the blood and tissues may settle in certain foci and there cause suppuration. When multiple abscesses are thus produced in connection with a general infection, the condition is known as pyæmia or, perhaps better, septico-pyæmia. There are no specific organisms of suppuration, and the condition of pyæmia may be produced by organisms other than the streptococci and staphylococci, though these are the most common. Other forms which may invade the system and cause foci of suppuration are the micrococcus lanceolatus, the gonococcus, the bacillus coli communis, the bacillus typhi abdominalis, the bacillus proteus, the bacillus pyocyaneus, the bacillus influenzæ, and very probably the bacillus aerogenes capsulatus. In a large proportion of all cases of pyæmia there is a focus of infection, either a suppurating external wound, an osteo-myelitis, a gonorrhœa, an otitis media, an empyæma, or an area of suppuration in a lymph-gland or about the appendix. In a large majority of all these cases the common pus cocci are present.

In a suppurating wound, for example, the pus organisms induce hyaline necrosis in the smaller vessels with the production of thrombi and purulent phlebitis. The entrance of pus organisms in small numbers into the blood does not necessarily produce pyæmia. Commonly the transmission to various parts from the local focus takes place by the fragments of thrombi which pass as emboli to different parts, where, if the conditions are favorable, the pus organisms excite suppuration. A thrombus which is not septic or contaminated, when dislodged and impacted in a distant vessel, produces at most only a simple infarction; but, coming from an infected source and containing pus microbes, an independent centre of infection is established wherever the embolus may lodge. These independent suppurative centres in pyæmia, known as *embolic* or *metastatic abscesses*, have the following distribution:

(*a*) In external wounds, in osteo-myelitis, and in acute phlegmon of the skin, the embolic particles very frequently excite suppuration in the lungs, producing the well-known wedge-shaped pyæmic infarcts; but in some cases the infected particles pass through the lungs, and there are foci of inflammation in the heart and kidneys.

(*b*) Suppurative foci in the territory of the portal system, particularly in the intestines, produce metastatic abscesses in the liver with or without suppurative pylephlebitis.

Endocarditis is an event which is very liable to occur in all forms of septicæmia, and modifies materially the character of the clinical features. Streptococci and staphylococci are the most common organisms present in the vegetations, but the pneumococci, gonococci, tubercle bacilli, typhoid bacilli, anthrax bacilli, and other forms have been isolated. The vegetations which develop at the site of the valve lesion become covered with thrombi, particles of which may be dislodged and carried as emboli to different parts of the body, causing multiple abscesses or infarcts.

Symptoms of Septico-pyæmia.—In a case of wound infection, prior to the onset of the characteristic symptoms, there may be signs of local trouble, and in the case of a discharging wound the pus may change in character. The onset of the disease is marked by a severe rigor, during which the temperature rises to 103° or 104° and is followed by a profuse sweat. These chills are repeated at intervals, either daily or every other day. In the intervals there may be slight pyrexia. The constitutional disturbance is marked and there are loss of appetite, nausea, and vomiting, and, as the disease progresses, rapid emaciation. Transient erythema is not uncommon. Local symptoms usually develop. If the lungs become involved there are dyspnœa and cough. The physical signs may be slight. Involvement of the pleura and pericardium is common. The tint of the skin is changed; at first pale and white, it subsequently becomes bile-tinged. The spleen is enlarged, and there may be intense pain in the side, pointing to perisplenitis from embolism. Usually in the rapid cases a typhoid state develops, and the patient dies comatose.

In the chronic cases the disease may be prolonged for months; the chills recur at long intervals, the temperature is irregular, and the condition of the patient varies from month to month. The course is usually slow and progressively downward.

Diagnosis.—Pyæmia is a disease frequently overlooked and often mistaken for other affections.

Cases following a wound, an operation, or parturition are readily recognized. On the other hand, the following conditions may be overlooked:

Osteo-myelitis.—Here the lesion may be limited, the constitutional symptoms severe, and the course of the disease very rapid. The cause of the trouble may be discovered only post mortem.

So, too, acute septico-pyæmia may follow *gonorrhœa* or a *prostatic abscess*.

Cases are sometimes confounded with *typhoid fever*, particularly the more chronic instances, in which there are diarrhœa, great prostration, delirium, and irregular fever. The spleen, too, may be enlarged. The marked leucocytosis is an important differential point.

In some of the instances of *ulcerative endocarditis* the diagnosis is very difficult, particularly in what is known as the typhoid, in contradistinction to the septic, type of this disease. In *acute miliary tuberculosis* the symptoms occasionally resemble those of septicæmia, more commonly those of typhoid fever.

The *post-febrile arthritides*, such as occur after scarlet fever and gonorrhœa, are really instances of mild septic infection. The joints may sometimes suppurate and pyæmia develop. So, also, in *tuberculosis of the kidneys* and *calculous pyelitis* recurring rigors and sweats due to septic infection are common. In this latitude septic and pyæmic processes are too often confounded with *malaria*. In early tuberculosis, or even when signs of excavation are present in the lungs, and in cases of suppuration in various parts, particularly empyema and abscess of the liver, the diagnosis of malaria is made. The practitioner may take it as a safe rule, to which he will find very few exceptions, *that an intermittent fever which resists quinine is not malaria*.

Other conditions associated with chills which may be mistaken for pyæmia are profound anæmia, certain cases of Hodgkin's disease, the hepatic intermittent fever associated with the lodgment of gall-stones at the orifice of the common duct, rare cases of essential fever in nervous women, and the intermittent fever sometimes seen in rapidly developing cancer.

Treatment.—The treatment of septicæmia and pyæmia is largely a surgical problem. The cases which come under the notice of the physician usually have visceral abscesses or ulcerative endocarditis, conditions which are irremediable. We have no remedy which controls the fever. Quinine and the new antipyretics may be tried, but they are of little service. Quinine is probably better than antipyrin and antifebrin, which lower the temperature for a time, but when a careful two-hourly twenty-four-hour chart is taken, it is often found that the depression under the influence of the drug is made up at some other period of the day; a morning may be substituted for an afternoon fever.

The brilliant and remarkable results which follow complete evacuation of the pus with thorough drainage give the indication for the only successful treatment of this condition.

Unfortunately, in too many cases which the physician is called upon to treat, the region of suppuration is not accessible, and we have to be content with the employment of general measures for the support of the patient's strength.

TERMINAL INFECTIONS.

It may seem paradoxical, but there is truth in the statement that persons rarely die of the disease with which they suffer. Secondary infections, or, as we are apt to call them in hospital work, terminal infections, carry off many of the incurable cases in the wards. Flexner * has analyzed 255 cases of chronic renal and cardiac disease in which complete bacteriological examinations were made at autopsy. Excluding tuberculous infection, 213 gave positive and 42 negative results.

The infections may be local or general. The former are extremely common, and are found in a large proportion of all cases of Bright's disease, arterio-sclerosis, heart-disease, cirrhosis of the liver, and other chronic disorders. Affections of the serous membranes (acute pleurisy, acute pericarditis, or peritonitis), meningitis, and endocarditis are the most frequent lesions. It is perhaps safe to say that the majority of cases of advanced arterio-sclerosis and of Bright's disease succumb to these intercurrent infections. The infective agents are very varied. The streptococcus pyogenes is perhaps the most common, but the pneumococcus, staphylococcus aureus, the bacillus proteus, the gonococcus, the gas bacillus, and the bacillus pyocyaneus are also met with.

Particular mention may be here made of the terminal form of acute miliary tuberculosis. It is surprising in how many instances of arterio-sclerosis, of chronic heart-disease, of Bright's disease, and more particularly of cirrhosis of the liver, the fatal event is determined by an acute tuberculosis of the peritonæum or pleura.

The general terminal infections are somewhat less common. Of 85 cases of chronic renal disease in which Flexner found micro-organisms at autopsy, 38 exhibited general infections; of 48 cases of chronic cardiac disease, in 14 the distribution of bacteria was general. The blood-serum of persons suffering from advanced chronic disease was found by him to be less destructive to the staphylococcus aureus than normal human serum. Other diseases in which general terminal infection may occur are Hodgkin's disease, leukæmia, and chronic tuberculosis.

And, lastly, probably of the same nature is the terminal entero-colitis so frequently met with in chronic disorders.

XIX. RHEUMATIC FEVER.

Definition.—An acute, non-contagious fever, dependent upon an unknown infective agent, and characterized by multiple arthritis and a marked tendency to inflammation of the fibrous tissues.

Etiology.—*Distribution and Prevalence.*—It prevails in temperate and humid climates. Church has collected interesting statistics on this point. Oddly enough, the two countries with the highest admission in the army per thousand of strength—Egypt, 7.02, and Canada, 6.26—have climates the most diverse. The returns, however, from Canada for the six years from 1886 to 1892 are perhaps more correct, 2.83 per thousand of strength. The death-rate for the five years 1881–'85 in Great Britain was 97 per million. In the United States there are no satisfactory statistics; the disease is not

---

* Jour. Exp. Med., i, 1896.

dealt with in the last Census Report as a cause of death. So far as my personal observation goes, it certainly seemed to be more prevalent in Montreal than in Philadelphia or Baltimore. The general impression is that the disease prevails more in the British Isles than elsewhere; but, as Church remarks, the returns are very imperfect (this holds good everywhere), and probably the death-rate from rheumatic fever itself is very much lower than the figures would indicate, as very many different diseases are grouped under this heading. In Norway, where cases of rheumatic fever are notified, there were for the four years 1888–'92 13,654 cases, with 250 deaths.

Season.—In London the cases reach the maximum in the months of September and October. In the Montreal General Hospital Bell's statistics of 456 cases show that the largest number was admitted in February, March, and April. Newsholme has brought forward statistics to show that the disease prevails most in the dry years or a succession of such, and is specially prevalent when the subsoil water is abnormally low and the temperature of the earth high.

Age.—Young adults are most frequently affected, but the disease is by no means uncommon in children between the ages of ten and fifteen years. Sucklings are rarely attacked, and probably many of the cases which have been described belong to a totally different affection, the arthritis of infants. In exceptional cases, however, true rheumatism does occur. The following age table is based upon 456 cases admitted to the Montreal General Hospital: Under fifteen years, 4.38 per cent; from fifteen to twenty-five years, 48.68 per cent; from twenty-five to thirty-five years, 25.87 per cent; from thirty-five to forty-five years, 13.6 per cent; above forty-five years, 7.4 per cent. Of the 655 cases analyzed by Whipham for the Collective Investigation Committee of the British Medical Association, only 32 cases occurred under the tenth year and 80 per cent between the twentieth and fortieth year. These figures scarcely give the ratio of cases in children.

Sex.—If all ages are taken, males are affected oftener than females. In the Collective Investigation Report there were 375 males and 279 females. Up to the age of twenty, however, females predominate. Between the ages of ten and fifteen girls are more prone to the disease.

Heredity.—It is a deeply grounded belief with the public and the profession that rheumatism is a family disease, but Church thinks the evidence is still imperfect. Its not rare occurrence in several members of the same family is used by those who believe in the infectious origin as an argument in favor of its being a house disease.

The *occupations* which necessitate exposure to cold and great changes of temperature predispose strongly to rheumatic fever. The disease is met with oftenest in drivers, servants, bakers, sailors, and laborers.

Chill.—Exposure to cold, a wetting, or a sudden change of temperature are among the most important factors in determining the onset of an attack.

Immunity is not afforded by an attack; on the contrary, as in pneumonia, one attack predisposes the subject to the disease.

Rheumatic Fever as an Acute Infectious Disease.—(*a*) *General Evidence.* —Rheumatic fever, as Newsholme has shown, occurs in epidemics without regular periodicity, recurring at intervals of three, four, or six years, and varying much in intensity. A severe epidemic is apt to be followed by two or three mild outbreaks. " The curves of the mortality statistics . . . approximate very closely to those of pyæmia, puerperal fever, and erysipelas, diseases which are certainly associated with specific micro-organisms " (Church). The constancy also of the seasonal variations is an additional support to this view.

(*b*) *Clinical Features.*—Physicians have long been impressed with the striking similarity of the symptoms of rheumatic fever to those of septic infection. In the character of the fever, the mode of involvement of the joints, the tendency to relapse, the sweats, the anæmia, the leucocytosis, and, above all, the great liability to endocarditis and involvement of the serous membranes, acute rheumatic fever resembles pyæmia very closely, and may, indeed, be taken as the very type of an acute infection. But, as Stephen Mackenzie remarks, acute rheumatism should be considered not simply from the point of view of the rheumatic polyarthritis of the adult, but as a whole in its manifestations at different periods of life; yet even from this standpoint the multiform manifestations of the rheumatic poison in childhood and young adults may very reasonably be referred to the effect of the toxines of micro-organisms.

(*c*) *Special Evidence.*—The bacteriology of acute rheumatism has lately attracted a great deal of attention. Mantle, Sahli, Leyden, Chvostek, Singer, Achalme, and others have contributed important studies. A review of their work, however, justifies the conclusion that no positive proof has as yet been offered of the constant association of any special micro-organism with the disease. Singer in an extensive monograph attempts to show that in rheumatic fever the organisms, consisting chiefly of staphylococci and streptococci, are discharged in numbers in the urine. Special stress has been laid upon the tonsils as the point of entrance of the infection. It has long been known that tonsillitis is a very frequent initial symptom in the disease—28 out of 66 cases in Singer's series. Indeed, some have gone so far as to say that there is always a primary infective trouble in the lacunæ of the tonsils, to which the rheumatic fever is secondary, arising from the absorption of microbes or their products.

Other views as to the nature of rheumatism are the *metabolic or chemical:* that it depends upon a morbid material produced within the system in defective processes of assimilation. It has been suggested that this material is lactic acid (Prout) or certain combinations with lactic acid (Latham). Our knowledge of the chemical relations of the various products produced in the regressive nutritive changes is too limited to warrant much reliance upon these views. Richardson claims to have produced rheumatism by injecting lactic acid and by its internal administration.

Nervous Theory of Acute Rheumatism.—This was specially advocated by the late Dr. J. K. Mitchell, of Philadelphia. According to this view, either the nerve centres are primarily affected by cold and the local lesions are really trophic in character, or the primary nervous disturbance leads to errors in metabolism and the accumulation of lactic acid in the system. The advocates of this view regard as analogous the arthropathies of myelitis, locomotor ataxia, and chorea.

Morbid Anatomy.—There are no changes characteristic of the disease. The affected joints show hyperæmia and swelling of the synovial membranes and of the ligamentous tissues. There may be slight erosion of the cartilage. The fluid in the joint is turbid, albuminous in character, and contains leucocytes and a few fibrin flakes. Pus is very rare in uncomplicated cases. Rheumatism rarely proves fatal, except when there are serious complications, such as pericarditis, endocarditis, myocarditis, pleurisy, or pneumonia. The conditions found show nothing peculiar, nothing to distinguish them from other forms of inflammation. In death from hyperpyrexia no special changes occur. The blood usually contains an excessive amount of fibrin. In the secondary rheumatic inflammations, as pleurisy and pericarditis, various pus organisms have been found, possibly the result of a mixed infection.

Symptoms.—As a rule, the disease sets in abruptly, but it may be preceded by irregular pains in the joints, slight *malaise,* sore throat, and particularly by tonsillitis. A definite rigor is uncommon; more often there is slight chilliness. The fever rises quickly, and with it one or more of the joints become painful. Within twenty-four hours from the onset, the disease is fully developed. The temperature range is from 102° to 104°. The pulse is frequent, soft, and usually above 100. The tongue is moist, and rapidly becomes covered with a white fur. There are the ordinary symptoms associated with an acute fever, such as loss of appetite, thirst, constipation, and a scanty, highly acid, highly colored urine. In a majority of the cases there are profuse, very acid sweats, of a peculiar sour odor. Sudaminal and miliary vesicles are abundant, the latter usually surrounded by a minute ring of hyperæmia. The mind is clear, except in the cases with hyperpyrexia. The affected joints are painful to move, soon become swollen and hot, and present a reddish flush. The knees, ankles, elbows, and wrists are the joints usually attacked, not together, but successively. For example, if the knee is first affected, the redness may disappear from it as the wrists become painful and hot. The disease is seldom limited to a single articulation. The amount of swelling is variable. Extensive effusion into a joint is rare, and much of the enlargement is due to the infiltration of the periarticular tissues with serum. The swelling may be limited to the joint proper, but in the wrists and ankles it sometimes involves the sheaths of the tendons and produces great enlargement of the hands and feet. Corresponding joints are often affected. In attacks of great severity every one of the larger joints may be involved. The vertebral, sterno-clavicular, and phalangeal articulations are less often inflamed in acute than in gonorrhœal rheumatism. Perhaps no disease is more painful than acute polyarthritis. The inability to change the posture without agonizing pain, the drenching sweats, the prostration and utter helplessness, combine to make it one of the most distressing of febrile affections. A special feature of the disease is the tendency of the inflammation to subside in one joint while developing with great intensity in another.

The temperature range in an ordinary attack is between 102° and 104°. It is peculiarly irregular, with marked remissions and exacerbations, depending very much upon the intensity and extent of the articular inflammation. Defervescence is usually gradual. The profuse sweats materially influence the temperature curve. If a two-hourly chart is made and observations upon the sweats are noted, the remissions will usually be found coincident with the sweats. The perspiration is sour-smelling and acid at first; but, when persistent, becomes neutral or even alkaline.

The blood is profoundly and rapidly altered in acute rheumatism. There is, indeed, no acute febrile disease in which the anæmia develops with greater rapidity. There is a well-marked leucocytosis.

With the high fever a murmur may often be heard at the apex region. Endocarditis is also a common cause of an apex *bruit*. The heart should be carefully examined at the first visit and subsequently each day.

The urine is, as a rule, reduced in amount, of high density and high color. It is very acid, and, on cooling, deposits urates. The chlorides may be greatly diminished or even absent. Febrile albuminuria is not uncommon.

The saliva may become acid in reaction and is said to contain an excess of sulphocyanides.

Subacute Rheumatism.—This represents a milder form of the disease, in which all the symptoms are less pronounced. The fever rarely rises above 101°; fewer joints are involved; and the arthritis is less intense. The cases may drag on for weeks or months, and the disease may finally become chronic. It should not be forgotten that in children this mild or subacute form may be associated with endocarditis or pericarditis.

Complications.—These are important and serious.

(1) **Hyperpyrexia.**—The temperature may rise rapidly a few days after the onset, and be associated with delirium; but not necessarily, for the temperature may rise to 108° or, as in one of Da Costa's cases, 110°, without cerebral symptoms. Hyperpyrexia is most common in first attacks, 57 of 107 cases (Church). It is most apt to occur during the second week. The delirium may precede or follow the onset of the hyperpyrexia. As a rule, with the high fever, the pulse is feeble and frequent, the prostration is extreme, and finally stupor supervenes.

(2) **Cardiac Affections.**—(a) *Endocarditis,* the most frequent and serious complication, occurs in a considerable percentage of all cases. Of 889 cases, 494 had signs of old or recent endocarditis (Church). The liability to endocarditis diminishes as age advances. It increases directly with the number of attacks. Of 116 cases in the first attack, 58.1 per cent had endocarditis, 63 per cent in the second attack, and 71 per cent in the third attack (Stephen Mackenzie). The mitral segments are most frequently involved and the affection is usually of the simple, verrucose variety. Ulcerative endocarditis in the course of acute rheumatism is very rare. Of 209 cases of this disease which I analyzed, in only 24 did the symptoms of a severe endocarditis arise during the progress of acute or subacute rheumatism. This complication, in itself, is rarely dangerous. It produces few symptoms and is usually overlooked. Unhappily, though the valve at the

time may not be seriously damaged, the inflammation starts changes which lead to sclerosis and retraction of the segments, and so to chronic valvular disease.

(b) *Pericarditis* may occur independently of or together with endo-carditis. It may be simple fibrinous, sero-fibrinous, or in children puru-lent. Clinically we meet it more frequently in connection with rheuma-tism than all other affections combined. The physical signs are very char-acteristic. The condition will be fully described under its appropriate sec-tion. A peculiar form of delirium may develop during the progress of rheumatic pericarditis.

(c) *Myocarditis* is most frequent in connection with endo-pericardial changes. As Sturges insisted, the term *carditis* is applicable to many cases. The anatomical condition is a granular or fatty degeneration of the heart-muscle, which leads to weakening of the walls and to dilatation. It is not, I think, nearly so common as the other cardiac affections. S. West has re-ported instances of acute dilatation of the heart in rheumatic fever, in one of which marked fatty changes were found in the heart-fibres.

(3) **Pulmonary Affections.**—Pneumonia and pleurisy occurred in 9.94 per cent of 3,433 cases (Stephen Mackenzie). They frequently accompany the cases of endo-pericarditis. According to Howard's analysis of a large number of cases, there were pulmonary complications in only 10.5 per cent of cases of rheumatic endocarditis; in 58 per cent of cases of peri-carditis; and in 71 per cent of cases of endo-pericarditis. Congestion of the lung is occasionally found, and in several cases has proved rapidly fatal.

(4) **Cerebral Complications.**—These are due, in part, to the hyper-pyrexia and in part to the special action upon the brain of the toxic agent of the disease. They may be grouped as follows: (a) *Delirium.* This is usually associated with the hyperpyrexia, but may be independent of it. It may be active and noisy in character; more rarely a low muttering delirium, passing into stupor and coma. Special mention must be made of the delirium which occurs in connection with rheumatic pericarditis. Delirium, too, may be excited by the salicylate of soda, either shortly after its administration, or more commonly a week or ten days later. (b) *Coma,* which is more serious, may develop without preliminary delirium or con-vulsions, and may prove rapidly fatal. Certain of these cases are associ-ated with hyperpyrexia; but Southey has reported the case of a girl who, without previous delirium or high fever, became comatose, and died in less than an hour. A certain number of such cases, as those reported by Da Costa, have been associated with marked renal changes and were evidently uræmic. The coma may develop during the attack, or after convalescence has set in. (c) *Convulsions* are less common, though they may precede the coma. Of 127 observations cited by Besnier, there were 37 of delirium, only 7 of convulsions, 17 of coma and convulsions, 54 of delirium, coma, and convulsions, and 3 of other varieties (Howard). (d) *Chorea.* The relations of this disease and rheumatism will be subsequently discussed. It is sufficient here to say that in only 88 out of 554 cases which I have analyzed from the Infirmary for Diseases of the Nervous System, Phila-

11

delphia, were chorea and rheumatism associated. It is most apt to develop in the slighter attacks in childhood. (*e*) *Meningitis* is extremely rare, though undoubtedly it does occur. It must not be forgotten that in ulcerative endocarditis, which is occasionally associated with acute rheumatism, meningitis is frequent.

(5) **Cutaneous Affections.**—Sweat-vesicles have already been mentioned as extremely common. A red miliary rash may also develop. Scarlatiniform eruptions are occasionally seen. Purpura, with or without urticaria, may occur, and various forms of erythema. It is doubtful whether the cases of extensive purpura with urticaria and arthritis—peliosis rheumatica—belong truly to acute rheumatism.

(6) **Rheumatic Nodules.**—These curious structures, in the form of small subcutaneous nodules attached to the tendons and fasciæ, have been known for some years; but special attention has been paid to them of late, since their careful study by Barlow and Warner. While not so common in this country as in England, the cases are by no means infrequent (Futcher. J. H. H. Bulletin, 1895). They vary in size from a small shot to a large pea, and are most numerous on the fingers, hands, and wrists. They also occur about the elbows, knees, the spines of the vertebræ, and the scapulæ. They are not often tender. They do not necessarily come on during the fever, but may be found on its decline, or even independently altogether of an acute attack. The nodules may develop with great rapidity and usually last for weeks or months. They are more common in children than in adults, and in the former their presence may be regarded as a positive indication of rheumatism. They have been noted particularly in association with severe and chronic rheumatic endocarditis. Subcutaneous nodules occur also in migraine, gout, and arthritis deformans. Histologically they are made up of round and spindle-shaped cells. In addition to these firm, hard nodules, there occur in rheumatism and in chronic vegetative endocarditis remarkable small bodies, which have been called by Féréol " nodosités cutanées éphémères." In a case of chronic vegetative endocarditis (without arthritis), which I saw with Dr. J. K. Mitchell, there were, in addition to occasional elevated spots resembling urticaria, infiltrated areas of soreness in the skin, from two to three lines in diameter, not elevated, but pale pink, and exquisitely tender and painful even without being touched.

The *course* of acute rheumatism is extremely variable. It is, as Austin Flint first showed, a self-limited disease, and it is not probable that medicines have any special influence upon its *duration* or *course*. Gull and Sutton, who likewise studied a series of 62 cases without special treatment, arrived at the same conclusion.

Sudden death in rheumatic fever is due most frequently to myocarditis. Herringham has reported a case in which on the fourteenth day there was fatty degeneration and acute inflammation of the myocardium. In a few rare cases it results from embolism. I saw one case at the Montreal General Hospital in which we thought possibly the sudden death was due to Fuller's alkaline treatment, which had been kept up by mistake. There was slight endocarditis but no myocardial changes. Alarming symptoms of depression sometimes follow excessive doses of the salicylate of soda.

Diagnosis.—Practically, the recognition of acute rheumatism is very easy; but there are several affections which, in some particulars, closely resemble it.

(1) **Multiple Secondary Arthritis.**—Under this term may be embraced the various forms of arthritis which come on or follow in the course of the infective diseases, such as gonorrhœa, scarlet fever, dysentery, and cerebro-spinal meningitis. Of these the gonorrhœal form will receive special consideration and is the type of the entire group.

(2) **Septic Arthritis,** which develops in the course of pyæmia from any cause, and particularly in puerperal fever. No hard and fast line can be drawn between these and the cases in the first group; but the inflammation rapidly passes on to suppuration and there is more or less destruction of the joints. The conditions under which the arthritis develops give a clew at once to the nature of the case. Under this section may also be mentioned:

(a) *Acute necrosis* or *acute osteo-myelitis,* occurring in the lower end of the femur, or in the tibia, and which may be mistaken for acute rheumatism. Sometimes, too, it is multiple. The greater intensity of the local symptoms, the involvement of the epiphyses rather than the joints, and the more serious constitutional disturbances are points to be considered. The condition is unfortunately often mistaken for acute arthritis, and, as the treatment is essentially surgical, the error is one which may cost the life of the patient.

(b) *The acute arthritis of infants* must be distinguished from rheumatism. It is a disease which is usually confined to one joint (the hip or knee), the effusion in which rapidly becomes purulent. The affection is most common in sucklings and is undoubtedly pyæmic in character. It may also develop in the gonorrhœal ophthalmia or vaginitis of the newborn, as pointed out by Clement Lucas.

(3) **Gout.**—While the localization in a single, usually a small, joint, the age, the history, and the mode of onset are features which enable us to recognize acute gout, there are in this country many cases of acute arthritis, called rheumatic fever, which are in reality gout. The involvement of several of the larger joints is not so infrequent in gout, and unless tophi are present, or unless a very accurate analysis of the urine is made, the diagnosis may be difficult.

Treatment.—The bed should have a smooth, soft, yet elastic mattress. The patient should wear a flannel night-gown, which may be opened all the way down the front and slit along the outer margin of the sleeves. Three or four of these should be made, so as to facilitate the frequent changes required after the sweats. He may wear also a light flannel cape about the shoulders. He should sleep in blankets, not in sheets, so as to reduce the liability to catch cold and obviate the unpleasant clamminess consequent upon heavy sweating. Chambers insisted that the liability to endocarditis and pericarditis was much reduced when the patients were in blankets.

Milk is the most suitable diet. It may be diluted with alkaline mineral waters. Lemonade and oatmeal or barley water should be freely given. The thirst is usually great and may be fully satisfied. There is no objection to broths and soups if the milk is not well borne. The food should be given at short and stated intervals. As convalescence is established a fuller diet may be allowed, but meat should be used sparingly.

The local treatment is of the greatest importance. It often suffices to wrap the affected joints in cotton. If the pain is severe, hot cloths may be applied, saturated with Fuller's lotion (carbonate of soda, 6 drachms; laudanum, 1 oz.; glycerine, 2 oz.; and water, 9 oz.). Tincture of aconite or chloral may be employed in an alkaline solution. Chloroform liniment is also a good application. Fixation of the joints is of great service in allaying the pain. I have seen, in a German hospital, the joints enclosed in plaster of Paris, apparently with great relief. Splints, padded and bandaged with moderate firmness, will often be found to relieve pain. Friction is rarely well borne in an acutely inflamed joint. Cold compresses are much used in Germany. The application of blisters above and below the joint often relieves the pain. This method, which was used so much a few years ago, is not to be compared with the light application of the Paquelin thermo-cautery.

Medicines have little or no control over the duration or course of the disease, which, like other self-limited affections, practically takes its own time to disappear. Salicyl compounds, which were regarded so long as specific, are now known to act chiefly by relieving pain. R. P. Howard's elaborate analysis shows that they do not influence the duration of the disease. Nor do they prevent the occurrence of cardiac complications, while under their use relapses are considerably more frequent than in any other method of treatment. In acute cases with severe pain the salicyl compounds give prompt relief and rarely disappoint us in their action. Sodium salicylate, in fifteen-grain doses for eight or ten doses, may be given. The bicarbonate of potassium in twenty-grain doses may be used with it. Many prefer salicin (gr. 20) in wafers; others the salicylic acid (gr. 20) or salol. I have for the past five or six years used the oil of wintergreen, recommended by Kinnicutt, and have found it quite as efficacious. Twenty minims may be given every two hours in milk. The salicyl compounds are best given in full doses at the outset of the disease, to relieve the pain. Then the dose should be reduced in frequency, or, if the symptoms have abated, stopped altogether, as relapses are certainly more frequent under their use.

Alkalies may be combined with the salicylates, or may be used alone. The potassium bicarbonate in half-drachm doses may be given every three or four hours until the urine is rendered alkaline. Fuller, who so warmly supported this method of treatment, was in the habit of ordering a drachm and a half of the sodium bicarbonate with half a drachm of potassium acetate in three ounces of water, rendered effervescent at the time of administration by half a drachm of citric acid or an ounce of lemon-juice. This is given every three or four hours, and usually by the end of twenty-four hours the urine is alkaline in reaction. The alkali is then reduced, and the amount subsequently regulated by the degree of acidity of the urine, only enough being given to keep the secretion alkaline. Opinion is almost unanimous that, under the alkaline treatment, cardiac complications are less common. The combination of the salicylates with the alkali is probably the most satisfactory. Care must be taken to watch the heart during the administration of these remedies, since, if given freely, they are very depressing.

To allay the pain opium may be given in the form of Dover's powder, or morphia hypodermically. Antipyrin, antifebrin, and phenacetin are useful sometimes for the purpose. During convalescence iron is indicated in full doses, and quinine is a useful tonic. Of the complications, hyperpyrexia should be treated by the cold bath or the cold pack. The treatment of endocarditis and pericarditis and the pulmonary complications will be considered under their respective sections.

To prevent and arrest endocarditis Caton urges the use of a series of small blisters along the course of the third, fourth, fifth, and sixth intercostal nerves of the left side, applied one at a time and repeated at different points. Potassium or sodium iodide is given in addition to the salicylates. The patients are kept in bed for about six weeks.

XX. CHOLERA ASIATICA.

Definition.—A specific, infectious disease, caused by the comma bacillus of Koch, and characterized clinically by violent purging and rapid collapse.

Historical Summary.—Cholera has been endemic in India from a remote period, but only within the present century has it made inroads into Europe and America. An extensive epidemic occurred in 1832, in which year it was brought in immigrant ships from Great Britain to Quebec. It travelled along the lines of traffic up the Great Lakes, and finally reached as far west as the military posts of the upper Mississippi. In the same year it entered the United States by way of New York. There were recurrences of the disease in 1835–'36. In 1848 it entered the country through New Orleans, and spread widely up the Mississippi Valley and across the continent to California. In 1849 it again appeared. In 1854 it was introduced by immigrant ships into New York and prevailed widely throughout the country. In 1866 and in 1867 there were less serious epidemics. In 1873 it again appeared in the United States, but did not prevail widely. In 1884 there was an outbreak in Europe, and again in 1892 and 1893. Although occasional cases have been brought by ship to the quarantine stations in this country, the disease has not gained a foothold here since 1873.

Etiology.—In 1884 Koch announced the discovery of the specific organism of this disease. Subsequent observations have confirmed his statement that the comma bacillus, as it is termed, occurs constantly in the true cholera, and in no other disease. It has the form of a slightly bent rod, which is thicker, but not more than about half the length of the tubercle bacillus, and sometimes occurs in corkscrew-like or S forms. It is not a true bacillus, but really a spirochæte. The organisms grow upon a great variety of media and display distinctive and characteristic appearances. Koch found them in the water-tanks in India, and they were isolated from the Elbe water during the Hamburg epidemic of 1892. During epidemics virulent bacilli may be found in the fæces of healthy persons. The bacilli are found in the intestine, in the stools from the earliest period of the disease, and very abundantly in the characteristic rice-water evacuations, in which they may be seen as an almost pure culture. They very rarely occur in the vomit. Post mortem, they are found in enormous numbers in the intestine. In acutely fatal cases they do not seem to invade the intestinal wall, but in those with a more protracted course they are found in the depths of the glands and in the still deeper tissues. Experimental animals are not susceptible to cholera germs administered per os. But if introduced after neutralization of the gastric contents, and if kept in contact with the intestinal mucosa by controlling peristalsis with opium, guinea-pigs succumb after showing cholera-like symptoms. The intestines are filled with thin, watery contents, containing comma bacilli in almost pure culture.

Cholera Toxine.—Koch in his studies of cholera failed to find the spirilla in the internal organs. He concluded that the constitutional symptoms of the disease resulted from the absorption of toxic bodies from the intestine. In old cholera cultures ptomaines are contained; these probably have nothing to do with the intoxication of human cholera. R. Pfeiffer has shown that the cholera toxine is intimately associated with the proteid of the bacterial cells, and, being of a very labile nature, cannot be separated. Dead cultures are toxic; and the symptoms produced by the introduction of even minimal amounts are often comparable with those of the algid stage of cholera asiatica. The symptoms develop very rapidly, and death often results in eight to twelve hours; in non-fatal cases recovery is often equally as rapid. The intracellular cholera toxine is poisonous to animals if introduced into the blood, peritoneal cavity, or subcutaneous tissues. No absorption takes place from the intestine unless the epithelial layer has been injured.

Immunity.—Lazarus found that the blood-serum of human beings who had recovered from cholera contained an antidotal substance which would prevent the fatal result of intraperitoneal injections of cholera vibrios in guinea-pigs. R. Pfeiffer showed, contrary to Lazarus, that this substance was not of the nature of an antitoxine, but was actively bactericidal, and caused rapid disintegration of the introduced bacilli. The blood-serum of animals rendered immune to the bacillus contains this body. Upon its presence depends the success of the "Pfeiffer serum reaction" for the identification of the true cholera vibrio and its differentiation from all other forms which resemble it. Haffkine has carried out immunizing injections of cholera cultures in India on a large scale with very promising results.

Modes of Infection.—As in other diseases, individual peculiarities count for much, and during epidemics virulent cholera bacilli have been isolated from the normal stools of healthy men. Cholera cultures have also been swallowed with impunity.

The disease is not highly contagious; physicians, nurses, and others in close contact with patients are not often affected. On the other hand, washerwomen and those who are brought into very close contact with the linen of the cholera patients, or with their stools, are particularly prone to catch the disease. There have been several instances of so-called "laboratory cholera," in which students, having been accidentally infected while working with the cultures, have developed the disease, and at least one death has resulted from this cause.*

Vegetables which have been washed in the infected water, particularly lettuces and cresses, may convey the disease. Milk may also be contaminated. The bacilli live on fresh bread, butter, and meat, for from six to eight days. In regions in which the disease prevails the possibility of the infection of food by flies should be borne in mind, since it has been shown that the bacilli may live for at least three days in their intestines.

Infection through the air is not to be much dreaded, since the germs when dried die rapidly.

The disease is propagated chiefly by contaminated water used for drinking, cooking, and washing. The virulence of an epidemic in any region is in direct proportion to the imperfection of its water-supply. In India the demonstration of the connection between drinking-water and cholera infection is complete. The Hamburg epidemic is a most remarkable illustration. The unfiltered water of the Elbe was the chief supply, although taken from the river in such a situation that it was of necessity directly contaminated by sewage. It is not known accurately from what source the contagion came, whether from Russia or from France, but in August, 1892, there was a sudden explosive epidemic, and within three months nearly 18,000 persons were attacked, with a mortality of 42.3 per cent. The neighboring city of Altona, which also took its water from the Elbe, but which had a thoroughly well-equipped modern filtration system, had in the same period only 516 cases.

Two main types of epidemics of cholera are recognized: the first, in which many individuals are attacked simultaneously, as in the Hamburg outbreak, and in which no direct connection can be traced between the individual cases. In this type there is widespread contamination of the drinking-water. In the other the cases occur in groups, so-called cholera nests; individuals are not attacked simultaneously but successively. A direct connection between the cases may be very difficult to trace. Again, both these types may be combined, and in an epidemic which has started in a widespread infection through water, there may be other outbreaks, which are examples of the second or chain-like type.

Pettenkofer, on the other hand, denies the truth of this drinking-water theory, and maintains that the conditions of the soil are of the greatest importance; particularly a certain porosity, combined with moisture and contamination with organic matter, such as sewage. He holds that germs develop in the subsoil moisture during the warm months, and that they rise into the atmosphere as a miasm.

The disease always follows the lines of human travel. In India it has,

---

* Reincke, Deut. med. Wochenschr., 1894.

in many notable cases, been widely spread by pilgrims. It is carried also by caravans and in ships. It is not conveyed through the atmosphere.

Places situated at the sea-level are more prone to the disease than inland towns. In high altitudes the disease does not prevail so extensively. A high temperature favors the development of cholera, but in Europe and America the epidemics have been chiefly in the late summer and in the autumn.

The disease affects persons of all ages. It is particularly prone to attack the intemperate and those debilitated by want of food and by bad surroundings. Depressing emotions, such as fear, undoubtedly have a marked influence. It is doubtful whether an attack furnishes immunity against a second one.

Morbid Anatomy.—There are no characteristic anatomical changes in cholera; but a post-mortem diagnosis of the nature of the disease could be made by any competent bacteriologist, as the micro-organisms are specific and distinctive. The body has the appearances associated with profound collapse. There is often marked post-mortem elevation of temperature. The *rigor mortis* sets in early and may produce displacement of the limbs. The lower jaw has been seen to move and the eyes to rotate. Various movements of the arms and legs have also been noted. The blood is thick and dark, and there is a remarkable diminution in the amount of its water and salts. The peritonæum is sticky, and the coils of intestines are congested and look thin and shrunken. There is nothing special in the appearance of the stomach. The small intestine usually contains a turbid serum, similar in appearance to that which was passed in the stools. The mucosa is, as a rule, swollen, and in very acute cases slightly hyperæmic; later the congestion, which is not uniform, is more marked, especially about the Peyer's patches. Post mortem the epithelial lining is sometimes denuded, but this is probably not a change which takes place freely during life. In the stools, however, large numbers of columnar epithelial cells have been described by many observers. The bacilli are found in the contents of the intestine and in the mucous membrane. The spleen is usually small. The liver and kidneys show cloudy swelling, and the latter extensive coagulation-necrosis and destruction of the epithelial cells. The heart is flabby; the right chambers are distended with blood and the left chambers are usually empty. The lungs are collapsed, and congested at the bases.

The above appearances are those met with in cases which prove rapidly fatal. When the patient survives and death occurs during reaction, there may be more definite inflammatory appearances in the intestines leading to extensive necrosis and fibrinous exudation, and more pronounced changes in the kidneys and liver.

In the acute cases the rice-water discharges contain the vibrios in practically pure cultures; at a somewhat later stage other bacteria make their appearance, while in the stage of cholera-typhoid the comma bacilli are demonstrated with difficulty.

Symptoms.—A period of incubation of uncertain length, probably not more than from two to five days, precedes the development of the symptoms.

Three stages may be recognized in the attack: the preliminary diarrhœa, the collapse stage, and the period of reaction.

(*a*) *The preliminary diarrhœa* may set in abruptly without any previous indications. More commonly there are, for one or two days, colicky pains in the abdomen, with looseness of the bowels, perhaps vomiting, with headache and depression of spirits. There may be no fever.

(*b*) *Collapse Stage.*—The diarrhœa increases, or, without any of the preliminary symptoms, sets in with the greatest intensity, and profuse liquid evacuations succeed each other rapidly. There are in some instances griping pains and tenesmus. More commonly there is a sense of exhaustion and collapse. The thirst becomes extreme, the tongue is white; cramps of great severity occur in the legs and feet. Within a few hours vomiting sets in and becomes incessant. The patient rapidly sinks into a condition of collapse, the features are shrunken, the skin has an ashy gray hue, the eyeballs sink in the sockets, the nose is pinched, the cheeks are hollow, the voice becomes husky, the extremities are cyanosed, and the skin is shrivelled, wrinkled, and covered with a clammy perspiration. The temperature sinks. In the axilla or in the mouth it may be from five to ten degrees below normal, but in the rectum and in the internal parts it may be 103° or 104°. The pulse becomes extremely feeble and flickering, and the patient gradually passes into a condition of coma, though consciousness is often retained until near the end.

The fæces are at first yellowish in color, from the bile pigment, but soon they become grayish white and look like turbid whey or rice-water; whence the term " rice-water stools." There are found in them numerous small flakes of mucus and granular matter, and at times blood. The reaction is usually alkaline. The fluid contains albumin and the chief mineral ingredient is chloride of sodium. Microscopically, mucus and epithelial cells and innumerable bacteria are seen, the majority of the latter being the comma bacilli.

The condition of the patient is largely the result of the concentration of the blood consequent upon the loss of serum in the stools. There is almost complete arrest of secretion, particularly of the saliva and the urine. On the other hand, the sweat-glands increase in activity, and in nursing women it has been stated that the lacteal flow is unaffected. This stage sometimes lasts not more than two or three hours, but more commonly from twelve to twenty-four. There are instances in which the patient dies before purging begins—the so-called *cholera sicca*.

(*c*) *Reaction Stage.*—When the patient survives the collapse, the cyanosis gradually disappears, the warmth returns to the skin, which may have for a time a mottled color or present a definite erythematous rash. The heart's action becomes stronger, the urine increases in quantity, the irritability of the stomach disappears, the stools are at longer intervals, and there is no abdominal pain. In the reaction the temperature may not rise above normal. Not infrequently this favorable condition is interrupted by a recurrence of severe diarrhœa and the patient is carried off in a relapse. Other cases pass into the condition of what has been called *cholera-typhoid*, a state in which the patient is delirious, the pulse rapid and feeble, and the tongue dry. Death finally occurs with coma. These symptoms have been attributed to uræmia.

During epidemics attacks are found of all grades of severity. There are cases of diarrhœa with griping pains, liquid, copious stools, vomiting, and cramps, with slight collapse. To these the term *cholerine* has been applied. They resemble the milder cases of *cholera nostras*. At the opposite end of the series there are the instances of *cholera sicca*, in which death may occur in a few hours after the onset, without diarrhœa. There are also cases in which the patients are overwhelmed with the poison and die comatose, without the preliminary stage of collapse.

Complications and Sequelæ. —The typhoid condition has already been referred to. The consecutive nephritis rarely induces dropsy. Diphtheritic colitis has been described. There is a special tendency to diphtheritic inflammation of the mucous membranes, particularly of the throat and genitals. Pneumonia and pleurisy may develop, and destructive abscesses may occur in different parts. Suppurative parotitis is not very uncommon. In rare instances local gangrene may develop. A troublesome symptom of convalescence is cramps in the muscles of the arms and legs.

Diagnosis.—The only affection with which Asiatic cholera could be confounded is the *cholera nostras*, the severe choleraic diarrhœa which occurs during the summer months in temperate climates. The clinical picture of the two affections is identical. The extreme collapse, vomiting, and rice-water stools, the cramps, the cyanosed appearance, are all seen in the worst forms of cholera nostras. In enfeebled persons death may occur within twelve hours. It is of course extremely important to be able to diagnose between the two affections. This can only be done by one thoroughly versed in bacteriological methods, and conversant with the diversified flora of the intestines. The comma bacillus is present in the dejections of a great majority of the cases and can be seen on cover-glass preparations. Though the eye of the expert may be able to differentiate between the bacillus of true cholera and that which occurs in cholera nostras, cultures should be made, from which alone positive results can be obtained.

Attacks very similar to Asiatic cholera are produced in poisoning by arsenic, corrosive sublimate, and certain fungi; but a difficulty in diagnosis could scarcely arise.

The *prognosis* is always uncertain, as the mortality ranges in different epidemics from 30 to 80 per cent. Intemperance, debility, and old age are unfavorable conditions. The more rapidly the collapse sets in, the greater is the danger, and as Andral truly says of the malignant form, " It begins where other diseases end—in death." Cases with marked cyanosis and very low temperature rarely recover.

Prophylaxis.—Preventive measures are all-important, and isolation of the sick and thorough disinfection have effectually prevented the disease entering England or the United States since 1873. On several occasions since that date cholera has been brought to various ports in America, but has been checked at quarantine. During epidemics the greatest care should be exercised in the disinfection of the stools and linen of the patients. When an epidemic prevails, persons should be warned not to drink water unless previously boiled. Errors in diet should be avoided. As the disease is not more contagious than typhoid fever, the chance of a person passing safely through an epidemic depends very much upon how far he is able to carry out thoroughly prophylactic measures. Digestive disturbances are to be treated promptly, and particularly the diarrhœa, which so often is a preliminary symptom. For this, opium and acetate of lead and large doses of bismuth should be given.

Medicinal Treatment. —During the initial stage, when the diarrhœa is not excessive but the abdominal pain is marked, opium is the most efficient remedy, and it should be given hypodermically as morphia. It is advisable to give at once a full dose, which may be repeated on the return of the pain. It is best not to attempt to give remedies by the mouth, as they disturb the stomach. Ice should be given, and brandy or hot coffee. In the collapse stage, writers speak strongly against the use of opium. Undoubtedly it must be given with caution, but, judging from its effects in cholera nostras, I should say that collapse *per se* was not a contra-indication. The patient may be allowed to drink freely. For the vomiting, which is very difficult to check, cocaine may be tried, and lavage with hot water. Creasote, hydrocyanic acid, and creolin have been found useless. Rumpf advises calomel (gr. $\frac{1}{8}$) every two hours.

External applications of heat should be made and a hot bath may be tried. Warm applications to the abdomen are very grateful. Hypodermic injections of ether will be found serviceable.

Irrigation of the bowel—enteroclysis—with warm water and soap, or tannic acid (2 per cent), should be used. With a long, soft-rubber tube, as much as 3 or 4 litres may be slowly injected. Not only is the colon cleansed, but the small bowel may also be reached, as shown by the fact that the tannic-acid solutions have been vomited.

Owing to the profuse serous discharges the blood becomes concentrated, and absorption takes place rapidly from the lymph-spaces. To meet this, intravenous injections were introduced by Latta, of Leith, in the epidemic of 1832. My preceptor, Bovell, first practised the intravenous injections of milk in Toronto, in the epidemic of 1854. A litre of salt solution at 107° may be injected, and repeated in a few hours if no reaction follows. Less risky and equally efficacious is the subcutaneous injection of a saline solution. For this, common salt should be used in the proportion of about four grammes to the liter. With rubber tubing, a cannula from an aspirator, or even with a hypodermic needle, the warm solution may be allowed to run by pressure beneath the skin. It is rapidly absorbed, and the process may be continued until the pulse shows some sign of improvement. This is really a valuable method, thoroughly physiological, and should be tried in all severe cases.

In the stage of reaction special pains should be taken to regulate the diet and to guard against recurrences of the severe diarrhœa.

XXI. YELLOW FEVER.

Definition.—A fever of tropical and subtropical countries, character-ized by a toxæmia of varying intensity, with jaundice, albuminuria, and a marked tendency to hæmorrhage, especially from the stomach, causing the " black vomit." A specific bacillus has been described by Sanarelli, but its causal relationship with the disease cannot be said to have been definitely established.

Etiology.—The disease prevails endemically in the West Indies and in certain sections of the Spanish Main. From these regions it occasionally extends and, under suitable conditions, prevails epidemically in the South-ern States. Now and then it is brought to the large seaports of the Atlantic coast. Formerly it occurred extensively in the United States. In the latter part of the last century and the beginning of this, frightful epi-demics prevailed in Philadelphia and other Northern cities. The epidemic of 1793, in Philadelphia, so graphically described by Matthew Carey, was the most serious that has ever visited any city of the Middle States. The mortality, as given by Carey, during the months of August, September, October, and November, was 4,041, of whom 3,435 died in the months of September and October. The population of the city at the time was only 40,000. Epidemics occurred in the United States in 1797, 1798, 1799, and in 1802, when the disease prevailed slightly in Boston and extensively in Baltimore. In 1803 and 1805 it again appeared; then for many years the outbreaks were slight and localized. In 1853 the disease raged throughout the Southern States. In New Orleans alone there was a mortality of nearly 8,000. In 1867 and 1873 there were moderately severe epidemics. In 1878 the last extensive epidemic occurred, chiefly in Louisiana, Alabama, and Mississippi. The total mortality was nearly 16,000. There have since been local outbreaks, the last in 1897, in which in New Orleans from Sep-tember 8th to December 11th there were, according to the Marine Hospital Reports, 1,902 cases, with 288 deaths. In Europe it has occasionally gained a foothold, but there have been no widespread epidemics except in the Spanish ports. The disease exists on the west coast of Africa. It is some-times carried to ports in Great Britain and France, but it has never ex-tended into those countries. The history of the disease and its general symptomatology are exhaustively treated of in the classical works of Réné La Roche and Bérenger-Féraud.

Guitéras recognizes three areas of infection: (1) The focal zone in which the disease is never absent, including Havana, Vera Cruz, Rio, and other Spanish-American ports. (2) The perifocal zone or regions of periodic epi-demics, including the ports of the tropical Atlantic in America and Africa. (3) The zone of accidental epidemics, between the parallels of 45° north and 35° south latitude.

The epidemics are invariably due to the introduction of the poison either by patients affected with the disease or through infected articles. Unquestionably the poison may be conveyed by fomites. The channels of infection are believed to be the digestive canal and the lungs. Individuals of all ages and races are attacked. The negro is much less susceptible than the white, but he does not enjoy an immunity. Residents in southern countries, in which the disease is prevalent, are not so susceptible as strangers and temporary residents. Males are more frequently affected and the mortality is greater among them, owing probably to greater exposure.

Very young children usually escape; but in the epidemics of large cities the number under five attacked is large, since they constitute a considerable proportion of the population unprotected by previous attack. Guitéras states that the " foci of endemicity of yellow fever are essentially maintained by the creole infant population, which is subject to the disease in a very mild form." Immunity is acquired by passing through an attack or by prolonged residence in a locality in which the disease is endemic. The statement so often made that the creoles are exempt from yellow fever has been abundantly disproved. They certainly are not so susceptible, but in severe epidemics they die in numbers. The evidence in favor of inherited immunity is not conclusive.

Conditions favoring the Development of Epidemics.—Yellow fever is a disease of the sea-coast, and rarely prevails in regions with an elevation above 1,000 feet. Its ravages are most serious in cities, particularly when the sanitary conditions are unfavorable. It is always most severe in the badly drained, unhealthy portions of a city, where the population is crowded together in ill-ventilated, badly drained houses. The disease prevails during the hot season. Humidity, heat, darkness, and want of air seem to be the proper coefficients for the preservation of the poison (Sanarelli). In Havana the death-rate is greatest during the months of June, July, and August. The epidemics in the United States have always been in the summer and autumn months, disappearing rapidly with the onset of cold weather.

Bacteriology of Yellow Fever.—Sanarelli,[*] the director of the Institute of Experimental Medicine at Montevideo, has described an organism, which he calls the *bacillus icteroides*, with the following characters: It is a slender rod from 2 to 4 mikrons in length, a facultative anærobe, ciliated and motile. It decolorizes by Gram's method, grows well on ordinary media, does not coagulate milk, ferments saccharine fluids, and is pathogenic to lower animals. In man, dogs, and monkeys it is stated to produce a clinical picture similar to that of the natural disease. The bacillus is found only in the blood and tissues, never in the stomach or bowels. It occurs in very small numbers, but produces a toxine of extraordinary intensity. It has only been found in rather more than half of the

---

[*] The work of Sanarelli has been marred by a series of unjustifiable experiments upon men, which should receive the unqualified condemnation of the profession. In one sense every dose of medicine given is an experiment, since who can tell the nature of the reaction? But the limitation of deliberate experimentation on human beings should be clearly defined. Voluntarily, if with full knowledge, a fellow-creature may submit to certain tests and trials, just as a physician may experiment on himself. Drugs, the value of which has been carefully tested on animals (if found harmless), may be tried on patients, since in this way alone can progress be made. But deliberate experiments such as Sanarelli carried out with cultures of known and tested virulence, and which were followed by serious, nearly fatal illness, are simply criminal.

cases. This, Sanarelli claims, is owing to the almost constant intervention of secondary infections, in which streptococci, staphylococci, or the colon bacilli overspread the body, before the death of the patient, with such a quantity of toxic products that they kill or attenuate the bacillus icteroides. This is a very weak point in his statement. The bacillus possesses a remarkable resistance to drying and to the action of sea-water. The presence of moulds favors its vitality and growth. The amaril poison, as Sanarelli calls the product of the bacillus icteroides, is said to possess three special properties—emetic, hæmorrhagic, and steatogenic. The injection of the filtered cultures into man produced " the fever, congestions, hæmorrhages, vomiting, steatosis of the liver, cephalalgia, nephritis, anuria, uræmia, icterus, delirium, and collapse "! The results of inoculation into dogs are equally remarkable. Both the bacilli by themselves and the toxines produce fever, diarrhœa, vomiting, and an early hæmatemesis. The most characteristic changes are in the liver, which presents large patches of yellow color, made up of hepatic cells, which have undergone complete fatty degeneration. The kidneys show an acute parenchymatous nephritis.

An interesting point, one which favors the specificity of the bacillus icteroides, and supplements in an important way Sanarelli's work, is the existence of an agglutinative reaction in the blood of yellow fever patients. The Archinards of New Orleans and Woodson of the United States army state that in 50 cases of yellow fever studied during the recent epidemic the agglutination with cessation of motion was obtained in over 70 per cent. The work was done with cultures of the bacillus icteroides of Sanarelli obtained from the Pasteur Institute, and with cultures made from the local cases. Should this fact be confirmed in subsequent epidemics, it will solve the all-important question of the early diagnosis of the disease. Blood taken as early as the second day gave a prompt and characteristic reaction. Surgeon-General Sternberg, whose researches on yellow fever have been so important, described an organism which he called the bacillus X, and which he claims to be the same as Sanarelli's bacillus. It has much the same characters, but presents minor peculiarities. The question of the identity of the two has not yet been settled.

Morbid Anatomy.—The skin is more or less jaundiced. Cutaneous hæmorrhages may be present. No specific or distinctive internal lesions have been found. The blood-serum contains hæmoglobin, owing to destruction of the red cells, just as in pernicious malaria. The heart sometimes, not invariably, shows fatty change; the stomach presents more or less hyperæmia of the mucosa with catarrhal swelling. It contains the material which, ejected during life, is known as the *black vomit*. The essential ingredient in this is transformed blood-pigment. In the two specimens which I have had an opportunity of examining it differed in no respect from the material found in other affections associated with hæmatemesis. There is no proof that this black material depends upon the growth of a micro-organism. The liver is usually of a pale yellow or brownish-yellow color, and the cells are in various stages of fatty degeneration. From the date of Louis' observations at Gibraltar in 1828, the appearances of this organ have been very carefully studied, and some have thought the changes in it to be characteristic. Councilman has described remarkable appearances in the liver-cells which he believes are distinctive and peculiar. Fatty degeneration and regions of necrosis are present in all cases. The kidneys often show traces of diffuse nephritis. The epithelium of the convoluted tubules is swollen and very granular; there may also be necrotic changes. In both liver and kidneys bacteria of various sorts have been described.

Symptoms.—The incubation is usually three or four days, but it may be less than twenty-four hours or prolonged to seven days. The onset is sudden, as a rule, without premonitory symptoms, and in the early hours of the morning. Chilly feelings are common, and are usually associated with headache and very severe pains in the back and limbs. The fever rises rapidly and the skin feels very hot and dry. The tongue is furred, but moist; the throat sore. Nausea and vomiting are present, and become more intense on the second or third day. The bowels are usually constipated. The following, in detail, are the more important characteristics:

Facies.—Even as early as the first morning the patient may present a very characteristic facies, according to Guitéras, one of the three distinguishing features of the disease. The following description is taken from him: The face is decidedly flushed, more so than in any other acute infectious disease at such an early period. The eyes are injected, the color is a bright red, and there may be a slight tumefaction of the eyelids and of the lips. Even at this early date there is to be noticed in connection with the injection of the superficial capillaries of the face and conjunctivæ an element of icterus, and " the early manifestation of jaundice is undoubtedly the most characteristic feature of the facies of yellow fever." It has to be looked for very carefully.

The Fever.—On the morning of the first day the temperature may vary between 100° and 106°, usually between 102° and 103°. During the evening of the first day and the morning of the second day the temperature keeps about the same. There is a slight diurnal variation on the second and third day. In very mild cases the fever may fall on the evening of the second or on the morning of the third day, or in abortive cases or in undeveloped cases in children even at the end of twenty-four hours. In cases that are to terminate favorably the defervescence takes place by lysis during a period of two or three days. The remission or stage of *calm,* as it has been called, is succeeded by a febrile reaction or secondary fever, which lasts one, two, or three days, and in favorable cases falls by a short lysis. On the other hand, in fatal cases the temperature rises rapidly, becomes higher than in the initial fever, and death follows shortly.

The Pulse.—On the first day the pulse is rarely more than 100 or 110. On the second or third day, while the fever still keeps up, the pulse begins to fall, and may have become slower by as much as 20 beats while the temperature has risen 1.5° or 2°. On the evening of the third day there may be a temperature range of 103° and a pulse of only 75, or "a temperature between 103° and 104° with a pulse running from 70 to 80." This important diagnostic feature was first described by Faget, of New Orleans. During the defervescence the pulse may become still slower, down to 50, 48, or 45, or even as low as 30. A slow pulse with the defervescence is not the special circulatory feature of the disease, but *the slowing of the pulse with a steady or even rising temperature.*

Albuminuria.—This, regarded by Guitéras as the third characteristic symptom of the disease, occurs as early as the evening of the third day. He says very truly that it is very rare so early in other fevers except those of an unusually severe type. " Even in the mild cases that do not go to bed— cases of ' walking yellow fever '—on the second, third, or fourth day of the disease albuminuria will show itself." It may be quite transient. In the severer cases the amount of albumin is large, and there may be numerous tube-casts and all the signs of an intense acute nephritis; or complete suppression of the urine may supervene, and death may occur in uræmic convulsions or coma within twenty-four or thirty-six hours. Guitéras insists that the evening urine should be specially examined. He states that the presence of albumin on the first day and its persistence on the second indicate a severe case. With the secondary rise in temperature the jaundice becomes more intense.

Gastric Features.—" *Black Vomit.*"—Irritability of the stomach is present from the very outset, and the vomited matter consists of the contents of the stomach, and subsequently of mucus and a grayish fluid. In the second stage of the disease the vomiting becomes more pronounced and in the severe cases is characterized by the presence of blood. It may be copious and forcible, producing much pain in the abdomen and along the gullet. There is nothing specific in the " black vomit " of yellow fever. It consists of altered blood. " Black vomit " is not necessarily a fatal symptom, though it occurs only in the severer forms of the disease. Other hæmorrhagic features may be present—petechiæ on the skin and bleeding from the gums or from other mucous membranes. The bowels are usually constipated, the stools not clay-colored, as in jaundice from obstruction. They are sometimes tarry from the presence of altered blood.

Mental Features.—In very severe cases the onset may be with active delirium. " As a rule, in a majority of cases, even when there is black vomit, there is a peculiar alertness; the patient watches everything going on about him with a peculiar intensity and liveliness. This may be due in part to the terror the disease inspires " (Guitéras). The first signs of mental cloudiness may be due to the uræmic coma.

Relapses occasionally occur. Among the varieties of the disease it is important to recognize the mild cases. These are characterized by slight fever, continuing for one or two days, and succeeded by a rapid convalescence. Such cases would not be recognized as yellow fever in the absence of a prevailing epidemic. Cases of greater severity have high fever and the features of the disease are well marked—vomiting, prostration, and hæmorrhages. And lastly, there are malignant cases in which the patient is overwhelmed by the intensity of the fever, and death takes place in two or three days.*

---

* For a full discussion of the morbid anatomy and symptomatology of the disease the student is referred to the works of Joseph Jones, of New Orleans, and to his papers in the Journal of the American Medical Association, 1895, I.

In severe cases convalescence may be complicated by the occurrence of parotitis, abscesses in various parts of the body, and diarrhœa. An attack confers an immunity which persists, as a rule, through life.

Diagnosis.—(*a*) *From Dengue.*—The difficulty in the differential diagnosis of these two diseases lies in their frequent coexistence, as during the epidemic of 1897 in parts of the Southern States. For example, whether yellow fever existed last year in Galveston is still unsettled, some observers claiming that dengue alone prevailed, others, including Guitéras and West, affirming that there were a certain number of cases of true yellow fever. On the one hand, if the suspicious cases were dengue, we must acknowledge that break-bone fever may be a much more serious disease than writers state, and that certain of the symptoms, particularly the hæmorrhages, occur in a larger proportion of cases than has been heretofore acknowledged. Of the other symptoms, too, one writer states that jaundice of mild grade was the rule from first to last. Albumin was not infrequently present in the urine, and the lack of correlation between the pulse and the temperature was so frequent as to be almost the rule. There was no case of black vomit. Dengue, as I have stated in the article on that disease, prevailed to a remarkable extent in the city of Galveston. On the other hand, if the cases examined by Guitéras and declared by him to be yellow fever were truly examples of that disease, there is the anomalous—indeed, unique—fact of an outbreak of yellow fever in a city which had not had the disease in epidemic form since 1867, and in which it did not assume epidemic proportions and did not increase the death-rate, which for the months of August, September, and October of 1897 was lower than for the corresponding three months in 1896 and 1895. After a review of the local literature on the question, I confess myself to be quite unable to decide upon the points at issue. I have dwelt upon this matter in order that practitioners may realize how difficult the diagnosis may be under certain circumstances. It is quite useless to emphasize in parallel columns the differential points between the two diseases. Doubtless in a majority of all the cases the three diagnostic points upon which Guitéras lays stress—the facies, the albuminuria, and the slowing of the pulse with maintenance or elevation of the fever—are sufficient for the diagnosis. He states, too, that jaundice, which does sometimes occur in dengue, rarely appears as early as the second or third day of the disease, and on this much stress should be laid. Hæmorrhages are much less common in dengue, but that they do occur has been recognized by authorities ever since the time of Rush. It is most sincerely to be hoped that the work of the Archinards and Woodson on the serum diagnosis may prove final, in which case we shall have a positive diagnostic criterion, such as we now have for malarial fever.

(*b*) *From Malarial Fever.*—In the early stages of an epidemic cases are very apt to be mistaken for forms of malarial fever. In the Southern States the outbreaks have usually been in the late summer months, the very season in which the æstivo-autumnal irregular malarial fever prevails. Among the points to be specially noted are the absence of early jaundice in malarial fever. Even in the most intense types of infection the color of the skin is rarely changed within four or five days. To the experienced eye

12

the facies would be of considerable help. Albumin is rarely present in the urine so early as the second day in a malarial infection. Other important points are the marked swelling of the spleen in malaria, while in yellow fever it is not often enlarged. Hæmorrhages, and particularly the black vomit, are very rare in the acute forms of æstivo-autumnal malarial infection. In the so-called hæmorrhagic malarial fever the patient has usually had previous attacks of malaria. Hæmaturia is a prominent feature, while in yellow fever it is by no means frequent. Two special points of more importance, perhaps, than any of these general symptomatic features are (1) the examination of the blood for malarial parasites. The forms to be looked for are the small, ring-shaped organisms of the æstivo-autumnal infections. As a rule, their presence is readily determined by any one familiar with their general characters. They are, however, of all forms the most difficult to recognize, and, while they may be very abundant, there are cases in which the organisms are extremely scanty in the peripheral circulation. Under such circumstances in a case of doubt it might be justifiable to tap the spleen. (2) If Sanarelli's researches are confirmed, the agglutination test will be a very important aid in the diagnosis of doubtful cases.

Prognosis.—In its graver forms, yellow fever is one of the most fatal of epidemic diseases. The mortality has ranged, in various epidemics, from 15 to 85 per cent. In heavy drinkers and those who have been exposed to hardships the death-rate is much higher than among the better classes. In the epidemic of 1878, in New Orleans, while the mortality in hospitals was over 50 per cent of the white and 21 per cent of the colored patients, in private practice it was not more than 10 per cent among the white patients. The death-rate was very low in the epidemic of 1897. Favorable symptoms are a low grade of fever, slight jaundice, absence of hæmorrhages, and a free secretion of urine. If the temperature rise above 103° or 104° during the first two days, the outlook is serious. Black vomit is not an invariably fatal symptom. Cases with suppression of urine, delirium, coma, and convulsions rarely recover.

Prophylaxis.—The measures to be taken are—

(a) " Exclusion of the exotic germ of the disease by the sanitary supervision, at the port of departure, of ships sailing from infected ports, and thorough disinfection at the port of arrival, when there is evidence or reasonable suspicion that they are infected; (b) isolation of the sick on shipboard, at quarantine stations, and, so far as practicable, in recently infected places; (c) disinfection of excreta, and of the clothing and bedding used by the sick, and of localities into which cases have been introduced, or which have become infected in any way; (d) depopulation of infected places —i. e., the removal of all susceptible persons whose presence is not necessary for the care of the sick " (Sternberg). During an epidemic, individuals who must remain in the locality should avoid the regions in which the disease prevails most; they should live temperately, avoiding all excesses, and should be careful not to get overheated, either in the sun or by exercise.

Treatment.—Careful nursing and a symptomatic plan of treatment probably give the best results. Bleeding has long since been abandoned.

How much patients will stand in this disease is illustrated by Rush's practice, which was of the most heroic character. He says: "From a newly arrived Englishman I took 144 ounces, at twelve bleedings, in six days; four were in twenty-four hours. I gave within the course of the same six days nearly 150 grains of calomel, with the usual proportions of jalap and gamboge." * With the courage of his convictions this modern Sangrado himself submitted to two bleedings in one day, and had his infant of six weeks old bled twice! Neither emetics nor purgatives are now employed. Of special remedies quinine is warmly recommended, and, when hæmorrhage sets in, the perchloride of iron. Digitalis, aconite, and jaborandi have been employed. Sternberg advises the following mixture: Bicarbonate of soda, 150 grains; bichloride of mercury, $\frac{1}{3}$ grain; pure water, 1 quart. Three tablespoonfuls every hour. This is given on the view that the specific agent is in the intestine, and that its growth may possibly be restrained by this antacid and antiseptic mixture. The fever is best treated by hydrotherapy. There are several reports of the good effects of cold baths, sponging, and the application of ice-cold water to the head and the extremities in this disease. Vomiting is a very difficult symptom to control. Morphia hypodermically and ice in small quantities are probably the best remedies. Medicines given by the mouth for this purpose are said to be rarely efficacious.

We have no drug which can be depended upon to check the hæmorrhages. Ergot and acetate of lead and opium are recommended. The uræmic symptoms are best treated by the hot bath. Stimulants should be given freely during the second stage, when the heart's action becomes feeble and there is a tendency to collapse. The patient should be carefully fed; but when the vomiting is incessant it is best not to irritate the stomach, but to give nutritive enemata until the gastric irritation is allayed.

Serum Treatment in Yellow Fever.—Sanarelli's most recent communication, March 8, 1898, gives an account of the use of the blood-serum from two horses, one of which had been under treatment for eighteen months, the other for twelve. Altogether of the 22 cases treated with the serum 5 died, a mortality of 22.7 per cent. He has been testing the prophylactic power of this *antiamarilic* serum, but so far on too small a scale to judge of its efficacy.

XXII. BUBONIC PLAGUE.

Definition.—A specific, infectious disease of extraordinary virulence and very rapid course, characterized by inflammation of the lymphatic glands (buboes), carbuncles, and often hæmorrhages.

History and Geographical Distribution.—The disease was probably not known to the classical Greek writers. The earliest positive account dates from the second century of our era. The plague of Athens and the pestilence of the reign of Marcus Aurelius were apparently not this disease (Payne). From the great plague in the days of Justinian (sixth

---

* Manuscript letter to Redman Coxe.

century) to the middle of the seventeenth century epidemics of varying severity occurred in Europe. Among the most disastrous was the famous " black death " of the fourteenth century, which overran Europe and destroyed a fourth of the population. In the seventeenth century it raged virulently, and during the great plague of London, in 1665, about 70,000 people died. During the present century the plague in Europe has been confined almost exclusively to Turkey and southern Russia. The last outbreak was a small epidemic in 1878–'79. There are now five independent endemic centres of the disease—(1) the province of Tripoli, (2) southwestern Arabia, (3) a large section of Asia, comprising Mesopotamia, Persia, and Kurdestan, (4) the districts of Kumaon and Gurwhal in northwestern India, and (5) southwestern China (Payne).

Renewed interest has recently been aroused in the disease by the epidemic at Hong-kong in 1894, from which in the space of three months 2,500 people died. Far more serious has been the outbreak in India in the presidency of Bombay. It began in the city of Bombay in September, 1896, during three months developed gradually, maintained a great intensity for three months, and then slowly declined. In the nine months at least 20,000 people died. After a period of quiescence in the city of Bombay it again broke out with great virulence during the early part of the present year (1898). At the time of writing it has spread widely throughout the presidency, and is in many respects the most ominous of recent epidemics.

Etiology.—The specific organism of the disease is a bacillus discovered by Kitasato and carefully studied by Yersin and others. It resembles somewhat the bacillus of chicken cholera, and grows in a perfectly characteristic manner. The bacillus pestis occurs in the blood and in the organs of the body, and has also been found in the dust and in the soil of houses in which the patients have lived. Flies and fleas die from the disease, and may convey the infection. Rats, mice, and dogs are readily infected, and diseased animals will convey the plague to healthy ones.

The disease prevails most frequently in hot seasons, though an outbreak may occur during the coldest weather of winter. Persons of all ages are attacked. It spreads chiefly among the poorer classes, in the slums of the great cities, and, in fact, wherever the hygienic conditions are most faulty. There is much in favor of the view that the plague is a soil disease, the virus of which, like that of anthrax and tetanus, resides permanently in the soil of the affected districts (see Payne in Allbutt's System). The method of spread was well recognized by De Foe: " No one in this whole nation ever received the sickness or infection but who received it in the ordinary way of infection from somebody, or the clothes, or touch, or stench of somebody that was infected before."

While the virus of the plague may be communicated from one person to another through the air, the disease has not the extreme contagiousness of small-pox or of scarlet fever. It attaches itself particularly to houses and to the clothing and bedding. In the Bombay epidemic few attendants upon the sick—nurses and physicians—have been attacked, and a writer states that among the hundreds of British troops daily employed on cordon duty and search parties and in the disinfection of houses not a single case occurred.

Clinical Forms.—Most writers recognize three varieties—*pestis siderans,* or the fulminant variety, *pestis major,* and *pestis minor.* In the *pestis siderans* death may occur within twenty-four hours. It is an intense septicæmia, with or without the development of hæmorrhages, and rarely with glandular enlargements. The *pestis major* is the common severe bubonic form—*malignant adenitis,* as Cantlie terms it. The *pestis minor* is usually met with before the outbreak of the severe epidemic, and is characterized by glandular swellings but very slight fever and constitutional disturbances, and is rarely fatal.

A very interesting form has been recognized during the Bombay epidemic; namely, the primary plague pneumonia, which begins with a chill, pain in the side, and cough, with rusty expectoration. There are rarely swellings of the lymph glands. The Bombay Plague Committee give the following interesting classification:

1. With enlarged glands (gravity according to symptoms and severity of attack).
   - Femoral.
   - Inguinal.
   - Axillary.
   - Cervical.
   - Tonsillar.

2. Without enlarged glands (almost always fatal).
   - Septicæmic.
   - Pneumonic.
   - Mesenteric, enteric, or gastro-intestinal.
   - Nephritic.
   - Cerebral.

Symptoms.—The following is a brief summary of the symptoms of the ordinary bubonic form:

The stage of incubation is rarely more than three or four days.

The stage of invasion is characterized by headache, backache, stiffness in the limbs, a feeling of anxiety and restlessness, and great depression of spirits. The breathing is hurried, and hæmorrhages, particularly from the nose or from the lungs, may occur. After these symptoms have persisted for from twelve to thirty-six hours, the temperature rises and the pulse becomes rapid. The fever may reach 104° or even 106°; the tongue becomes brown, collapse symptoms are apt to supervene, and in very severe infections the patient may die at this stage. In at least two thirds of all cases, however, a fourth period is reached, characterized by the development of glandular swellings or buboes. The inguinal glands are most often affected, then in order the axillary, the cervical, and the popliteal. The first sign of the swelling appears usually from the third to the fifth day. Resolution may occur, or suppuration, or in rare cases gangrene. Carbuncles also may develop in different parts of the skin, particularly on the legs, buttocks, or back. Suppuration is a favorable feature. De Foe recognized this in his graphic account of the London plague, stating that " if these swellings could be brought to a head or to break and run, or, as the surgeons call it, to digest, the patient generally recovered."

At this stage petechiæ very commonly show themselves, and may be very extensive. These have been called the " plague spots," or the " tokens of the disease," and gave to it in the middle ages the name of the Black Death. Hæmorrhages from the mucous membranes may also occur; in some epidemics hæmoptysis has been especially frequent.

Convalescence may proceed rapidly, or may be much prolonged by the suppurating buboes.

The mortality of the disease is the highest of any known infection, reaching from 70 to 90 per cent of all attacked. In the Hong-kong Hospital during the recent epidemic it is stated that the mortality was 95 per cent.

Prophylaxis.—The following brief extract is taken from Kitasato's report: " The disease prevails especially under faulty hygienic conditions; it is therefore urged that general hygienic measures be carried out. Proper receptacles for sewage should be provided; a pure water-supply afforded; houses and streams are to be cleansed; all persons sick of the disease isolated; the furniture of the sick-room washed with a 2-per-cent carbolic solution in milk of lime; old clothes and bedding are to be steamed at 100° C. for at least an hour, or exposed for a few hours to sunlight. If feasible, all infected articles should be burned. The evacuations of the sick are to be mixed with milk of lime, and those who die of the disease are to be buried at a depth of three metres, or preferably cremated. After recovery the patient is to be kept in isolation at least one month. All contact with the sick is to be avoided, and great care is to be exercised with reference to food and drink." For the disinfection of buildings, Haffkine suggests sulphuric acid of the strength of 1 to 200.

Treatment.—In a disease the mortality of which may reach as high as 80 or 90 per cent the question of treatment resolves itself into making the patient as comfortable as possible, and following out certain general principles such as guide us in the care of fever patients. Cantlie recommends purgation and stimulation from the outset, and the use of morphia for the pain. The local treatment of the buboes is important, and good results apparently follow the injection of the bichloride of mercury.

Preventive inoculation has been introduced by Haffkine. Sterilized bouillon cultures of the plague bacillus are used. Injections with increasing quantities of these soluble toxines are practised, which are followed by mild reactionary symptoms. Some thousands of persons have been inoculated by him in India. Haffkine claims for the method very positive success, and quotes the following in support of his contention: " First, as regards animals being rendered immune. Twenty rats from a ship newly arrived from Europe were seized; of these, 10 were inoculated. Subsequently the 20 rats were kept together in a cage, into which a rat suffering from plague was introduced. Of the uninoculated, 9 were seized with plague and died, whereas of those rendered immune only 1 contracted the disease. Secondly, at Uran, a village possessing 1,000 inhabitants, when plague broke out 429 persons were inoculated by the serum in question. Of these, only 7 were attacked by plague, and all recovered, whilst of the uninoculated 26 were seized and 24 died. Thirdly, in the town of Lower

Damaun 2,197 persons were inoculated, 6,033 remaining unprotected. Of the latter, 1,482 died, whereas only 36 of the persons inoculated succumbed to the disease. Fourthly, at Lanowli, a village with 700 inhabitants, some two hours' distance from Bombay, 323 persons were inoculated, and 377 were content to remain unprotected. Among the former there were 14 cases and 7 deaths; among the latter—that is, the uninoculated—78 persons contracted the disease, of whom 58 died. Fifthly, at Kirkee, out of a total of 1,530 inhabitants, 671 availed themselves of the treatment, while 859 remained unprotected. Of the latter, 143 had plague, with 98 deaths; whereas of the inoculated 32 cases occurred, with 17 deaths only " (British Med. Jour., 1898, I).

A serum therapy has been introduced by Yersin, the immunizing serum being obtained from the horse. In Canton good results appear to have followed the use of the serum, but the recent reports from Bombay are not so favorable.

XXIII. DYSENTERY.

Definition.—Under this clinical term are described several different forms of intestinal flux, characterized by frequent stools, and in the acute stage by tormina and tenesmus. Anatomically there is inflammation and usually ulceration of the large bowel.

Etiology.—Dysentery is one of the four great epidemic diseases of the world. In the tropics it destroys more lives than cholera, and it has been more fatal to armies than powder and shot.

While especially severe in the tropics, sporadic cases constantly occur in more temperate climates, and under favoring circumstances epidemics are found even in the more northern countries, such as Canada and Norway. It has become less frequent of late years, owing to improved sanitary conditions. The statistics of the Montreal General Hospital, for the twenty years ending May 1, 1889, show a remarkable decrease in the disease. In the decade ending May, 1879, 150 cases were admitted; whereas in the last ten years there have been only 31 admissions. There has been a similar decrease at the Pennsylvania Hospital.

In the Southern cities of this country dysentery is more prevalent; even when not epidemic, sporadic cases are common. In Baltimore it prevails every summer, and has on several occasions been epidemic.

Epidemics of dysentery have occurred in the United States for more than a century, and Woodward has collected the data which show the various outbreaks. Perhaps the most serious was that which prevailed from 1847 to 1856. During the war of secession the disease existed to an alarming extent in both armies. According to Woodward's report,[*] there were in the Federal service in all 259,071 cases of acute and 28,451 cases of chronic dysentery. Probably a considerable proportion of the 182,586 cases of chronic diarrhœa should also come in this category. The decen-

---

* Medical and Surgical History of the War of the Rebellion, Medical, vol. ii ; the most exhaustive treatise extant on intestinal fluxes—an enduring monument to the industry and ability of the author.

nial census reports since 1850 show a progressive decrease in the total number of deaths from this disease. It prevails most extensively in the summer and autumn. Sudden changes of temperature appear more harmful than variations in moisture. The effluvia from decomposing animal matter have been thought by some to predispose to or even to cause the disease. That dysenteric affections are more frequent in malarial localities has long been known, and is probably connected with external conditions favoring their development. With reference to the influence of drinking-water, Woodward is doubtless correct in stating that the effects of dissolved mineral matters have been greatly exaggerated. On the other hand, from the days of the old Greek physicians, it has been held that the impurities in the stagnant water of marshy districts and ponds may give rise to diarrhœa and dysentery. Here, however, it is not probable that the vegetable impurities are directly causative, but that the organic matter renders the water a more favorable medium for the development of the organisms which cause the disease.

Dyspeptic conditions, particularly those caused by the ingestion of bad food and unripe fruit, seem to predispose to the disease. Great stress has been laid by German authorities on the importance of constipation as a causal factor.

Dysentery occurs at all ages. There is no race immunity. The contagiousness of the disease is doubtful. The experience of the civil war is decidedly against it, but the possibility, as with typhoid fever, must be acknowledged.

Clinical Forms.—(*a*) **Acute Catarrhal Dysentery.**—This may occur sporadically or endemically, and is the variety most frequently found in temperate climates.

Morbid Anatomy.—The lesions are confined to the large bowel; sometimes the ileum also is involved. The mucous membrane is injected, swollen, and often covered with tenacious blood-stained mucus. The most striking feature is the enlargement of the solitary follicles, which stand out prominently from the mucous membrane. In very acute forms, as in children, the picture is that of an acute follicular colitis. In more protracted cases the follicles suppurate or are capped with an area of necrotic tissue. In other instances the sloughs have separated and the entire colon presents numerous ulcers, most of which have developed from the follicles, while others have resulted from necrosis and sloughing of the intervening tissue.

Symptoms.—There may be preliminary dyspepsia or slight pains in the abdomen. Chills are rare. Diarrhœa is the most constant initial symptom, and at first is not painful. Usually within thirty-six hours the characteristic features of the disease develop—abdominal pain of a colicky, griping character and frequent stools, which are passed with straining and tenesmus; the constitutional disturbance is variable, and in mild cases may be slight. The temperature is not high; at the outset the range may be 102° or 103°. The tongue is furred and moist, and as the disease progresses becomes red and glazed. Nausea and vomiting may be present, but as a rule the patient retains nourishment. The constant desire to go to stool and the straining or tenesmus are the most distressing symptoms. The abdomen may be flat and hard. The thirst is often excessive. The stools in this variety of dysentery have the following characters: During the first twenty-four or forty-eight hours they consist of more or less clear mucus and blood mixed with small fæcal scybala. After this they become purely gelatinous and bloody, and are small and frequent, from fifteen to two hundred in twenty-four hours, according to the severity of the case. About the end of the first week the mucus becomes opaque, the proportion of blood diminishes, and grayish or brownish shreddy material appears in the stools, which become gradually reduced in frequency. At this time they may be wholly composed of a greenish pultaceous material with mucus. As the disease subsides, fæcal matter again appears in the stools, increasing in amount until they become normal. Microscopical examination of the glairy bloody stools shows red blood-corpuscles, few or many leucocytes, and constantly large, swollen, round or oval epithelioid cells, containing fat-drops and vacuoles. These are not infrequently mistaken for amœbæ. Occasionally the *cercomonas intestinalis* is seen in large numbers. The bacillus pyocyaneus has been found by F. C. Curtis in a recent epidemic at Hartwick, N. Y. Not only was it present in the stools in large numbers, but it was isolated from the drinking-water in almost pure culture.

Course of the Disease.—The milder cases run a course, as Flint has shown, of about eight days; severer ones rarely terminate within four weeks. The affection occasionally becomes chronic. Peritonitis and liver abscess are extremely rare. Of abscesses of the liver among the first 1,000 autopsies at the Johns Hopkins Hospital, not more than two or three were associated with dysentery other than amœbic.

(*b*) **Tropical Dysentery—Amœbic Dysentery.**—This form of intestinal flux is characterized by irregular diarrhœa and the constant presence in the stools of the *amœba coli* (Lösch), *amœba dysenteriæ* (Councilman and Lafleur). It is this variety which prevails extensively in the tropical and subtropical regions, and which proves so fatal in epidemic form. The amœba is a unicellular, protoplasmic, motile organism, from 15 to 30 μ in diameter, consisting of a clear outer zone, ectosarc, and a granular inner zone, endosarc, containing a nucleus and one or more vacuoles. It was first described by Lambl in 1859, and subsequently by Lösch, who considered it the cause of the disease. In the endemic dysentery of Egypt, Kartulis, in 1883, found these amœbæ constantly in the stools, in the intestines, and in the liver abscesses. He was afterward enabled to cultivate them in straw infusion, and reproduced the disease experimentally in cats. In 1890 I reported a case of dysentery with abscess of the liver, originating in Panama, in which the amœbæ were found in the stools and in the pus from the abscess; and Councilman and Lafleur * have described the clinical features and anatomical lesions in a series of cases of this form of dysentery in my wards. Dock has demonstrated their presence in a number of cases in Galveston, and Musser has found them in Philadelphia. A careful study has been made recently of 35 cases by H. F. Harris. Amœbæ are

---

* Johns Hopkins Hospital Reports, vol. ii.

occasionally found in the stools of healthy men. Quincke and Roos recognize three forms of parasitic amœbæ, two of which are pathogenic. The disease is very common in tropical and subtropical countries. It is, however, found more or less widely distributed throughout Europe and North America. The sources of infection are not known, but it seems probable that one of them is drinking-water.

Morbid Anatomy.—The lesions are found in the large intestine, sometimes in the lower portion of the ileum. Abscess of the liver is a common sequence. Perforation into the right lung is not infrequent.

Intestines.—The lesions consist of ulceration, produced by preceding infiltration, general or local, of the submucosa, due to an œdematous condition and to multiplication of the fixed cells of the tissue. In the earliest stage these local infiltrations appear as hemispherical elevations above the general level of the mucosa. The mucous membrane over these soon becomes necrotic and is cast off, exposing the infiltrated submucous tissue as a grayish-yellow gelatinous mass, which at first forms the floor of the ulcer, but is subsequently cast off as a slough.

The individual ulcers are round, oval, or irregular, with infiltrated, undermined edges. The visible aperture is often small compared to the loss of tissue beneath it, the ulcers undermining the mucosa, coalescing, and forming sinuous tracts bridged over by apparently normal mucous membrane. According to the stage at which the lesions are observed, the floor of the ulcer may be formed by the submucous, the muscular, or the serous coat of the intestine. The ulceration may affect the whole or some portion only of the large intestine, particularly the cæcum, the hepatic and sigmoid flexures, and the rectum. In severe cases the whole of the intestine is much thickened and riddled with ulcers, with only here and there islands of intact mucous membrane.

The disease advances by progressive infiltration of the connective-tissue layers of the intestine, which produces necrosis of the overlying structures. Thus, in severe cases there may be in different parts of the bowel sloughing *en masse* of the mucosa or of the muscularis, and the same process is observed, but not so conspicuously, in the less severe forms.

In some cases a secondary diphtheritic inflammation complicates the original lesions.

Healing takes place by the gradual formation of fibrous tissue in the floor and at the edges of the ulcers, which may ultimately result in partial and irregular strictures of the bowel.

Microscopical examination shows a notable absence of the products of purulent inflammation. In the infiltrated tissues polynuclear leucocytes are seldom found, and never constitute purulent collections. On the other hand, there is proliferation of the fixed connective-tissue cells. Amœbæ are found more or less abundantly in the tissues at the base of and around the ulcers, in the lymphatic spaces, and occasionally in the blood-vessels.

The lesions in the *liver* are of two kinds: firstly, local necroses of the parenchyma, scattered throughout the organ and possibly due to the action of chemical products of the amœbæ; and, secondly, abscesses. These may be single or multiple. When single they are generally in the right lobe, either toward the convex surface near its diaphragmatic attachment, or on the concave surface in proximity to the bowel. Multiple abscesses are small and generally superficial. In an early stage the abscesses are grayish-yellow, with sharply defined contours, and contain a spongy necrotic material, with more or less fluid in its interstices. The larger abscesses have ragged necrotic walls, and contain a more or less viscid, greenish-yellow or reddish-yellow purulent material mixed with blood and shreds of liver-tissue. The older abscesses have fibrous walls of a dense, almost cartilaginous toughness. A section of the abscess wall shows an inner necrotic zone, a middle zone in which there is great proliferation of the connective-tissue cells and compression and atrophy of the liver-cells, and an outer zone of intense hyperæmia. There is the same absence of purulent inflammation as in the intestine, except in those cases in which a secondary infection with pyogenic organisms has taken place. The material from the abscess cavity shows chiefly fatty and granular detritus, few cellular elements, and amœbæ in variable numbers, which are also found in the abscess walls, chiefly in the inner necrotic zone. Mallory has devised a differential stain, by which they can be distinguished in tissues. Cultures are usually sterile. Lesions in the lungs are seen when an abscess of the liver—as so frequently happens—points toward the diaphragm and extends by continuity through it into the lower lobe of the right lung. An exhaustive study of the amœbic abscess of the liver has recently been made by W. T. Howard, Jr., and C. F. Hoover, of Cleveland (American Journal of the Medical Sciences, 1897, ii).

Symptoms.—The onset may be sudden, as in catarrhal dysentery, or gradual, beginning as a trifling and perhaps transient diarrhœa. In severe gangrenous cases the abrupt onset is more common. The subsequent course is a very irregular diarrhœa, marked by exacerbations and intermissions, and progressive loss of strength and flesh. There is moderate fever as a rule, but many cases are afebrile throughout the greater part of their course. Abdominal pain and tenesmus, usually present at the onset, especially in severe cases, may be entirely absent, and vomiting and nausea are only occasionally observed. The stools vary very much in number and appearance in different cases and at different periods in the same cases. They may be very frequent, bloody, and mucoid at the outset, as in catarrhal dysentery; but their main characteristic, when the disease is well established, is fluidity. From six to twelve yellowish-gray liquid stools, containing mucus and occasionally blood in varying proportions, are passed daily for weeks. Actively moving amœbæ are found in these stools, more abundantly during exacerbations of the diarrhœa, and disappear gradually as the stools become formed.

Abscess of the liver, and especially of the liver and lung, is a frequent and formidable complication. In India it occurs once in every four or five cases.

The duration of the disease in uncomplicated cases varies from six to twelve weeks. Recovery is tedious, owing to anæmia and muscular weakness, often delayed by relapses, and there is in all cases a constant tendency to chronicity. The mortality is much higher than in catarrhal dysentery. A fatal issue is due either to the initial gravity of the intestinal lesions, to exhaustion in prolonged cases, or to involvement of the liver.

(c) **Diphtheritic Dysentery.**—A form of colitis or entero-colitis in which areas of necrosis occur in the mucous membranes, which on separation leave ulcers. This occurs: (a) As a *primary* disease coming on acutely and sometimes proving fatal. In its milder grades the tops of the folds of the colon are capped with a thin, yellow exudate. In severer forms the colon is enormously enlarged, the walls are thickened, stiff, and infiltrated, and the mucosa, from the ileo-cæcal valve to the rectum, is represented by a tough, yellowish material, in which on section no trace of the glandular elements can be seen. The condition is one of extensive necrosis of the mucosa. There are cases in which this necrosis is superficial, involving only the upper layers of the mucous membrane; but in the most advanced forms it may be, as in the description by Rokitansky, " a black, rotten, friable, charred mass." The areas of necrosis may be more localized, and large sloughs are formed which may be a half to three fourths of an inch in thickness and extend to the serosa. There are instances in which this condition is confined to the lower portion of the large bowel. A sailor from the Mediterranean was admitted to the Montreal General Hospital under my care with symptoms resembling typhoid fever. The autopsy showed enormous sloughs in the rectum and in the sigmoid flexure, but scarcely any disease in the transverse or ascending colon. In cases which last for many weeks the sloughs separate and may be thrown off, sometimes in large tubular pieces.

(b) *Secondary Diphtheritic Dysentery.*—This occurs as a terminal event in many acute and chronic diseases. It is not infrequent in chronic heart affections, in Bright's disease, and in cachectic states generally. In acute diseases it is, as pointed out by Bristowe, most frequently associated with pneumonia. Anatomically there may be only a thin, superficial infiltration of the upper layer of the mucosa in localized regions, particularly along the ridges and folds of the colon, often extending into the ileum. In severer forms the entire mucosa may be involved and necrotic, sometimes having a rough, granular appearance. In the secondary colitis of pneumonia the exudation may be pseudo-membranous and form a firm, thin, white pellicle which seems to lie upon, not within, the mucous membrane.

Symptoms.—The clinical features of diphtheritic dysentery are very varied. In the acute *primary* cases the patient from the outset is often extremely ill, with high fever, great prostration, pain in the abdomen, and frequent discharges. Delirium may be early and the clinical features may closely resemble those of severe typhoid. I have, on more than one occasion, known this mistake to be made. The abdomen is distended and often tender. The discharges are frequent and diarrhœal in character, and tenesmus may not be a striking symptom. Blood and mucus may be found early, but are not such constant features as in the follicular disease. This primary form is very fatal, but the sloughs may separate and the condition become chronic. In the *secondary* form there may have been no symptoms to attract attention to the large bowel. In a majority of the cases the patient has a diarrhœa—three, four, or more movements in the day, which are often profuse and weakening. A little blood and mucus may be passed at first, but they are not specially characteristic elements in the stools.

In all forms of dysentery death usually results from asthenia. The pulse becomes weaker and more rapid, the tongue dry, the face pinched, the skin cool and covered with sweat, and the patient falls into a drowsy, torpid condition. Consciousness may be retained until the last, but in the protracted cases there is a low delirium deepening into collapse.

(d) **Chronic Dysentery.**—This usually succeeds an acute attack, though the amœbic form may be subacute from the outset and not present an acute period. Anatomical changes in the large intestine in chronic dysentery are variable. There may be no ulceration, and the entire mucosa presents a rough, irregular puckered appearance, in places slate-gray or blackish in color. The submucosa is thickened and the muscular coats are hypertrophied. There may be cystic degeneration of the glandular elements, as is beautifully figured in Woodward's volume.

Ulcers are usually present, often extensive and deeply pigmented, in places perhaps healing. The submucous and muscular coats are thickened and the calibre of the bowel may be reduced. Stricture, however, is very rare.

The *symptoms* of chronic dysentery are by no means definite, and it is not always possible to separate the cases from those of chronic diarrhœa. Many of the characteristic symptoms of the acute disease are absent. Tenesmus and severe griping pains rarely occur except in acute exacerbations. The character of the stools varies very much. Blood and necrotic shreddy tissue are not often found. Mucus is passed in variable amounts. On a mixed diet the fæces are thin, often frothy, and contain particles of food. The motions vary from four or five to twelve or more in the twenty-four hours. There are cases in which marked constipation alternates with attacks of diarrhœa, and scybala may be passed with much mucus. In many cases the fæces have a semi-fluid consistency, and a yellowish or brown color depending on the amount of bile. Fragments of undigested food may be found, and the discharges have the character of what is termed a lienteric diarrhœa. Indeed, variations in the bile and in the food give at once corresponding differences in the character of the stools. In the amœbic form recurrences are common in which blood and mucus again appear in the stools, accompanied perhaps by pus. Flatulence is in some cases distressing, and there is always more or less tenderness along the course of the colon. The appetite is capricious, the digestion disordered, and unless the patient is on a strictly regulated diet the number of stools is greatly increased. The tongue is not often furred; it is more commonly red, glazed, and beefy, and becomes dry and cracked toward the end in protracted cases. There is always anæmia and the emaciation may be extreme; with the exception of gastric cancer, we rarely see such ghastly faces as in patients with prolonged dysentery. The complications are those already referred to in the acute form. The greater debility renders the patient more liable to the intercurrent affections, such as pneumonia and tuberculosis. Ulceration of the cornea was frequently noted during the civil war.

Complications and Sequelæ.—A local peritonitis may arise by extension, or a diffuse inflammation may follow perforation, which is usually fatal. When this occurs about the cæcal region, perityphlitis results; when low down in the rectum, periproctitis. In 108 autopsies collected by Woodward perforation occurred in 11. By far the most serious complication is abscess of the liver, which occurs frequently in the tropics and is not very uncommon in this country. It was not, however, a frequent complication in dysentery during the civil war. In this latitude it is certainly not uncommon. It usually comes on insidiously. The symptoms will be discussed in connection with hepatic abscess.

In extensive epidemics, however, Woodward states that cases of ordinary dysentery occur associated with all the phenomena of malaria. We have had a number of instances of the coexistence of the two diseases. With reference to typhoid fever, as a complication, this author mentions that the combination was exceedingly frequent during the civil war, and characteristic lesions of both diseases coexisted. In civil practice it is extremely rare.

Sydenham noted that dysentery was sometimes associated with rheumatic pains, and in certain epidemics joint swellings have been especially prevalent. They are probably not of the nature of true rheumatism, but rather analogous to those of gonorrhœal arthritis. In severe, protracted cases there may be pleurisy, pericarditis, endocarditis, and occasionally pyæmic manifestations, among which may be mentioned pylephlebitis. Chronic Bright's disease is also an occasional sequel. In protracted cases there may be an anæmic œdema. An interesting sequel of dysentery is paralysis. Woodward reports 8 cases. Weir Mitchell mentions it as not uncommon, occurring chiefly in the form of paraplegia. As in other acute fevers, this is due probably to a neuritis. Intestinal stricture is a rare sequence—so rare that no case was reported at the Surgeon-General's office during the war. Among the sequelæ of chronic dysentery, in persons who have recovered a certain measure of health, may be mentioned persistent dyspepsia and irritability of the bowels.

Diagnosis.—The recognition of the acute follicular form is easy; the frequency of the passages, the presence of blood and mucus, and the tenesmus forming a very characteristic picture. Local affections of the rectum, particularly syphilis and epithelioma, may produce tenesmus with the passage of mucoid and bloody stools. The acute diphtheritic form, coming on with great intensity and with severe constitutional disturbances, is not infrequently mistaken for typhoid fever, to which indeed in many cases the resemblance is extremely close. The higher grade of fever, the more pronounced intestinal symptoms, the presence, particularly in the early stage, of a small amount of blood in the stools, the absence of enlargement of the spleen, the rose rash, and the Widal reaction should lead to a correct diagnosis. In the amœbic form the diagnosis can readily be made by examination of the stools. A characteristic feature of these cases is their irregular, chronic course. A patient may be about and in fairly good condition, with well-formed stools and very slight intestinal disturbance, in whose fæces the amœbæ may still be discovered, and in whom the disease is at any time likely to recur with intensity. In some cases, complicated by abscess of the liver and lung discharging through a bronchus, the diagnosis may rest on the detection of amœbæ in the sputa, when they cannot be found in the stools owing to the latency of the intestinal disturbance. Leucocytosis is rare except when complications arise. Instances have occurred in my wards.

Treatment.—Flint has shown that sporadic dysentery is, in its slighter grades at least, a self-limited disease, which runs its course in eight or nine days. Reading a report of his cases, one is struck, however, with their comparative mildness.

The enormous surface involved, amounting to many square feet, the constant presence of irritating particles of food, and the impossibility of getting absolute rest, are conditions which render the treatment of dysentery peculiarly difficult. Moreover, in the severer cases, when necrosis of the mucosa has occurred, ulceration necessarily follows, and cannot in any way be obviated. When a case is seen early, particularly if there has been constipation, a saline purge should be given. The free watery evacuations produced by a dose of salts cleanse the large bowel with the least possible irritation, and if necessary, in the course of the disease, particularly if scybala are present, the dose may be repeated. Purgatives are, as a rule, objectionable, and the profession has largely given up their use. Of medicines given by the mouth which are supposed to have a direct effect upon the disease, ipecacuanha still maintains its reputation in the tropics. It did not, however, prove satisfactory during the civil war; nor can I say that in cases of sporadic dysentery I have ever seen the marked effect described by the Anglo-Indian surgeons. The usual method of administration is to give a preliminary dose of opium, in the form of laudanum or morphia, and half an hour after from 20 to 60 grains of ipecacuanha. If rejected by vomiting, the dose is repeated in a few hours.

Minute doses of corrosive sublimate, one hundredth of a grain every two hours, are warmly recommended by Ringer. Large doses of bismuth, half a drachm to a drachm every two hours, so that the patient may take from 12 to 15 drachms in a day, have in many cases had a beneficial effect. To do good it must be given in large doses, as recommended by Monneret, who gave as high as 70 grammes a day. It certainly is more useful in the chronic than the acute cases. It is best given alone. Opium is an invaluable remedy for the relief of the pain and to quiet the peristalsis. It should be given as morphia, hypodermically, according to the needs of the patient.

The treatment of dysentery by topical applications is by far the most rational plan. A serious obstacle, however, in the acute cases, is the extreme irritability of the rectum and the tenesmus which follows any attempt to irrigate the colon. A preliminary cocaine suppository or the injection of a small quantity of the 4-per-cent solution will sometimes relieve this, and then with a long tube the solution can be allowed to flow in slowly. The patient should be in the dorsal position with a pillow under the hips, so as to get the effect of gravitation. Water at the temperature of 100° is very soothing, but the irritability of the bowel is such that large quantities can rarely be retained for any time. When the acute symptoms' subside, the injections are better borne. Various astringents may be used—alum, acetate of lead, sulphate of zinc and copper, and nitrate of silver. Of these remedies the nitrate of silver is the best, though, I think, not in very acute cases. In the chronic form it is perhaps the most satisfactory method of treatment which we have. It is useless to give it in the small injections of two or three ounces with 1 to 2 grains of the salt to the ounce. It must be a large irrigating injection, which will reach all parts of the colon. This plan was introduced by Hare, of Edinburgh, and is highly recommended by Stephen MacKenzie and H. C. Wood. The solution must be fairly strong, 20 to 30 grains to the pint, and if possible from 3 to 6 pints of fluid must be injected. To begin with it is well to use not more than a drachm to the 2 pints or $2\frac{1}{2}$ pints, and to let the warm fluid run in slowly through a tube passed far into the bowel. It is at times intensely painful and is rejected at once. Argyria, so far as I know, has never followed the prolonged use of nitrate of silver injections in chronic dysentery. In the cases of amœbic dysentery we have been using at the Johns Hopkins Hospital with great benefit warm injections of quinine in strength of 1 to 5,000, 1 to 2,500, and 1 to 1,000. The amœbæ are rapidly destroyed by the drug. These large injections are said not to be without a certain degree of danger. I have never seen any ill effects, even with the very large amounts. When there is not much tenesmus, a small injection of thin starch with half a drachm to a drachm of laudanum gives great relief, but for the tormina and tenesmus, the two most distressing symptoms, a hypodermic of morphia is the only satisfactory remedy. Local applications to the abdomen, in the form of light poultices or turpentine stupes, are very grateful.

The diet in acute cases must be restricted to milk, whey, and broths, and during convalescence the greatest care must be taken to provide only the most digestible articles of food. In chronic dysentery, diet is perhaps the most important element in the treatment. The number of stools can frequently be reduced from ten or twelve in the day to two or three, by placing the patient in bed and restricting the diet. Many cases do well on milk alone, but the stools should be carefully watched and the amount limited to that which can be digested. If curds appear, or if much oily matter is seen on microscopical examination, it is best to reduce the amount of milk and to supplement it with beef-juice or, better still, egg-albumen. The large doses of bismuth seem specially suitable in the chronic cases, and the injections of nitrate of silver, in the way already mentioned, should always be given a trial.

XXIV. MALARIAL FEVER.

Definition.—An infectious disease characterized by: (*a*) paroxysms of intermittent fever of quotidian, tertian, or quartan type; (*b*) a continued fever with marked remissions; (*c*) certain pernicious, rapidly fatal forms; and (*d*) a chronic cachexia, with anæmia and an enlarged spleen.

With the disease are invariably associated the hæmatozoa describéd by Laveran.*

Etiology.—(1) **Geographical Distribution.**—In Europe, southern Russia and certain parts of Italy are now the chief seats of the disease. It is not widely prevalent in Germany, France, or England, and the foci of epidemics are becoming yearly more restricted.

In the United States malaria has progressively diminished in extent and severity during the past fifty years. The records of the health boards of the larger cities on the Atlantic coast which give a high mortality from the disease are quite untrustworthy. From New England, where it once prevailed extensively, it has gradually disappeared, but there has of late years been a slight return in some places. In the city of New York the milder forms of the disease are not uncommon. In Philadelphia and along the valleys of the Delaware and Schuylkill Rivers, formerly hot-beds of malaria, the disease has become much restricted. In Baltimore a few cases develop in the autumn, but a majority of the patients seeking relief are from the outlying districts and one or two of the inlets of Chesapeake Bay. Throughout the Southern States there are many regions in which malaria prevails; but here, too, the disease has diminished in prevalence and intensity. In the Northwestern States malaria is almost unknown. It is rare on the Pacific coast. In the region of the Great Lakes malaria prevails only in the Lake Erie and Lake St. Clair regions. The St. Lawrence districts remain free from the disease.

In India malaria is very prevalent, particularly in the great river basins. In Burma and Assam severe types are met with, and recently the anomalous form of fever known as the *Kála-ázar* of Assam has been shown to be malarial (Rogers).

In Africa the malarial fevers form the great obstacle to European settlements on the coast and along the river basins. The *black-water* or West African fever of the Gold Coast is a very fatal type of malarial hæmoglobinuria.

(2) **Telluric Conditions.**—The importance of the state of the soil in the etiology of malaria is universally recognized. It is seen particularly in low, marshy regions which have an abundant vegetable growth. Estuaries, badly drained, low-lying districts, the course of old river-beds, tracts of land which are rich in vegetable matter, and particularly districts such as the Roman Campagna, which have been allowed to fall out of cultivation, are favorite localities for the development of the malarial poison. These conditions are most frequently found, of course, in tropical and subtropical regions, but nothing can be truer than the fact that reeking marshes of the most pestilent appearance may be entirely devoid of the poison, and the disappearance of the disease from a locality is not neces-

---

* For a full consideration of the malaria problem as it has presented itself to us in Baltimore during the past nine years, the reader is referred to the monograph of Thayer and Hewetson, and the article of Barker in vol. v of the Johns Hopkins Hospital Reports, to the exhaustive article by Welch and Thayer in Loomis and Thompson's System of Medicine, and to Thayer's Lectures on the Malarial Fevers, New York, 1897.

sarily associated with any material improvement in the condition of the marshes or of the soil. Thus, in New England and in parts of western Canada, in which malaria formerly was very prevalent, the increased salubrity is usually attributed to the clearing of the forests and the better drainage of the ground; but these improvements alone can scarcely explain the disappearance, since in many districts there are marshy tracts and low-lying lands in every respect like those in which, even in the same latitude, the disease still prevails. In short, it is impossible to ascertain from the nature of the soil and climate in any given place whether it is malarial or not. In the absence of accurate knowledge as to the habitat of the hæmatozoa, the only means of deciding this point is by noticing the effect of residence in such a place on the human subject, preferably one of the Caucasian race.

(3) **Season.**—In the tropics there are minimal and maximal periods, the former corresponding to the summer and winter, the latter to the spring and autumn months. In temperate regions, like the central Atlantic States, there are only a few cases in the spring, usually in the month of May, and a large number of cases in September and October, and sometimes in November.

(4) **Meteorological Conditions.**—(*a*) *Heat.*—A tolerably high temperature is one of the essential conditions for the development of the virus. It is more prevalent after prolonged hot summers.

(*b*) *Moisture.*—In the tropics the malarial fevers are most prevalent in the rainy seasons. In the temperate climates the relation between the rainfall and malaria is not so clear, and cases are more numerous after a dry summer; but if either heat or moisture is excessive, the development of the virus is checked for a time.

(*c*) *Winds.*—Many facts are on record which seem to indicate that the poison may be carried to some distance by winds. The planting of trees has been held to interfere with the transmission by prevailing winds. Possibly, however, the quickly growing trees, such as the *Eucalyptus globulus,* have acted more beneficially by drying the soil.

(5) **Specific Gravity.**—That the distribution of the poison of malaria is influenced by gravity has long been conceded. Persons dwelling in the upper stories, or in buildings elevated some distance above the ground, are exempt in a marked degree.

The Specific Germ.—As Hirsch correctly remarks, the late J. K. Mitchell "was the first to approach in a scientific spirit the nature of infective disease and particularly in malarial fever." Many attempts were made to discover a constant and characteristic organism. In 1880 Laveran, a French army surgeon, announced the discovery of a parasite in the blood of patients attacked by malarial fever. During the next three years he published nine additional communications, but for a time these observations attracted little attention. The Italian observers Marchiafava, Celli, and Golgi corroborated Laveran's statements. In this country Laveran's work was confirmed by Councilman, by myself, Walter James, Dock, and many others. In India, Vandyke Carter's good work on the subject has been followed up by a number of observers. So far as I know, not a single observer, who has had the necessary training and the material at his command, has failed to demonstrate the existence of these parasites.

The bodies which have been found invariably associated with all forms of malarial fevers belong to the protozoa and to a group of organisms known as the *hæmocytozoa*, usually placed among the sporozoa. Parasites of the red blood-corpuscles have been met with abundantly in the blood of fish, turtles, and many species of birds (see papers by W. G. Macallum and Opie in Journal of Experimental Medicine, vol. ii).

The parasites are true hæmocytozoa, existing and pursuing their cycle of existence within the red blood-corpuscles of the infected individual. The youngest forms, small, hyaline, amœboid bodies, enter the red blood-corpuscles and develop, accumulating, as they increase in size, fine granules of dark pigment, which is formed at the expense of the hæmoglobin of the including corpuscle. When the organisms have reached their full development and destroyed their hosts, the pigment granules gather into a central clump or block, and the parasites break up into a number of small round or ovoid hyaline bodies, each one of which represents a fresh young organism ready to attack a new corpuscle and begin again a cycle of existence.

Several varieties of the parasite have been separated, each of which is associated with a characteristic type of fever. These varieties are: (1) The parasite of tertian fever; (2) the parasite of quartan fever; (3) the parasite associated with the more irregular fevers occurring in temperate climates, in the later summer and autumn—the "æstivo-autumnal fever" of the Italians. Golgi first pointed out the remarkable fact that the parasites of the regularly intermittent fevers—the tertian and quartan parasites —exist in the blood in great groups, all the members of which are approximately at the same stage of development. Thus an entire group of myriads of parasites undergoes sporulation within a period of several hours. *The sporulation of such a group of parasites is always followed by the malarial paroxysm*, which very possibly depends upon some toxic substance which is developed at the time of sporulation. The tertian parasite requires about forty-eight hours to accomplish its cycle of development and undergo sporulation. Thus with infections with a single group of tertian parasites, sporulation occurs every other day, resulting, as might be expected, in tertian paroxysms. More often, however, infections with two groups of tertian parasites are seen—groups reaching maturity on alternate days, and causing quotidian paroxysms. Very rarely infections with multiple groups of the parasite are met with.

The cycle of existence of the quartan parasite lasts about seventy-two hours, and if but one group of organisms be present, typical quartan fever results. The presence of two groups—double quartan infection—is associated with paroxysms on two successive days, followed by a day of intermission; the presence of three groups gives rise to quotidian paroxysms. Very rarely more than three groups may be present.

The parasite of the autumnal type possesses a cycle of development the exact duration of which is still a subject of dispute; it is probably variable, lasting from twenty-four hours or less to forty-eight hours or even more, the variations depending upon conditions not wholly known. While at the beginning of the infection the arrangement of the parasites in groups may be made out, this regular arrangement often disappears, and organisms at different stages of development may be found at the same time.

Segmentation may thus occur at irregular intervals, sometimes almost continuously. The resulting fever may be regularly intermittent, but is often irregular and sometimes continuous.

The parasite of tertian fever begins its cycle of development as a small, hyaline, amœboid body. This rapidly accumulates fine brown pigment granules which are thrown into active motion; the including corpuscle becomes expanded and decolorized as the parasite grows. The full-grown tertian organism is about the size of a normal red corpuscle. In sporulation the segments number from fifteen to twenty, or even more.

The parasite of quartan fever is very similar in its appearance to the tertian organism. The amœboid movements are, however, slower, and the pigment granules are coarser, darker, and in less active motion. The fully developed parasite is smaller, while the corpuscle in which the organism develops, instead of becoming expanded and decolorized, as in the tertian infections, rather shrinks about the parasite and assumes a deeper, greenish, somewhat brassy color. In sporulation the segments are fewer, from five to ten in number. They are arranged with great regularity about the central pigment clump or block, forming beautiful "rosettes."

The parasite of the æstivo-autumnal fever is considerably smaller than the other varieties; at full development it is often less than one half the size of a red blood-corpuscle. The pigment is much scantier, often consisting of a few minute granules. At first only the earlier stages of development, small, hyaline bodies, sometimes with one or two pigment granules, are to be found in the peripheral circulation; the later stages are ordinarily only to be seen in the blood of certain internal organs, the spleen and bone marrow particularly. The corpuscles containing the parasites become not infrequently shrunken, crenated, and brassy-colored. After the process has existed for about a week, larger, refractive, crescentic, ovoid, and round bodies, with central clumps of coarse pigment granules, begin to appear. These bodies are characteristic of æstivo-autumnal fever. Their significance is a matter of dispute.

From the full-grown tertian and quartan parasites, and from the round bodies with central pigment clumps in æstivo-autumnal infections, long, actively moving flagella may develop; these may at times break loose and move about free among the corpuscles. The observations of W. G. MacAllum suggest that flagellation is a sexual process, the flagella representing the male elements. Manson thinks that the flagella represent the forms in which the parasites exist outside the body. Ross, in India, observed the flagellation in blood taken from the stomach of mosquitoes which had been allowed to feed upon malarial subjects. Manson suggests that the mosquito is the intermediate host in the life history of the parasite.

The general symptoms and morbid anatomy of malaria are in harmony with the changes which these parasites induce. The remarkable periodicity of the manifestations of paludism are well explained when we consider the relations which these manifestations bear to the life history of the parasite. The destruction of the red blood-corpuscles by the organism can be traced in all stages. The *presence of pigment* in the blood and viscera so characteristic of malaria results from the transformation of the hæmoglobin by the parasites. The anæmia is a direct consequence of the widespread destruction of the corpuscles themselves. The severe cerebral symptoms in pernicious cases, as well as the occasional cases of choleriform malaria, have been shown to be associated with the special localization of the parasites in capillaries of the brain, or in the mucous membrane of the gastro-intestinal tract.

The Mosquito and Malaria.—Since the first printing of this edition the observations of Ross, of the Indian Medical Service, have shown that the malarial organism undergoes development in the body of the mosquito. In birds he has proved that the mosquito is the intermediate host of the proteosoma, a parasite very similar to the malarial organism in man. Grassi believes that there are three varieties of the mosquito associated with the malarial fevers—the *Anopheles claviger*, the *Culex penicillaris*, and the *Culex malariæ*. Bignami has produced malaria experimentally by obtaining adult mosquitoes from a malarious district and allowing them to bite an individual who had lived for six years in a hospital in which no case of malaria had ever been known to develop.

Meantime, awaiting further knowledge, advantage may be taken of the constant presence of the parasite in malaria. This alone, without reference to the true nature of the organism, is a fact of the highest importance. To be able, everywhere and under all circumstances, to differentiate between malaria and other forms of fever is one of the most important advances which has been made of late years in practical medicine.

Morbid Anatomy.—The changes result from the disintegration of the red blood-corpuscles, accumulation of the pigment thereby formed, and possibly the influence of toxic materials produced by the parasite. Cases of simple malarial infection, the ague, are rarely fatal, and our knowledge of the morbid anatomy of the disease is drawn from the pernicious malaria or the chronic cachexia. Rupture of the enlarged spleen may occur spontaneously, but more commonly from trauma. A case of the kind was admitted under my colleague, Halsted, in June, 1889, and Dock has recently reported two cases.

(1) **Pernicious Malaria.**—The blood is hydræmic and the serum may even be tinged with hæmoglobin. The red blood-corpuscles present the endoglobular forms of the parasite and are in all stages of destruction. The *spleen* is enlarged, often only moderately; thus, of two fatal cases in my wards the spleens measured 13×8 cm. and 14×8 cm. respectively. In a fresh infection, the spleen is usually very soft, and the pulp lake-colored and turbid. In cases of intense reinfection the spleen may be enlarged and firm. The amount of pigment in the spleen elements is greatly increased. The pulp contains large numbers of red corpuscles enclosing parasites. Enormous numbers of phagocytes, large and small, are to be seen, some of the larger being necrotic. The *liver* is swollen and turbid. In very acute cases there is not necessarily any macroscopic pig-

mentation, though microscopically the capillaries may be packed with phagocytes, which may almost occlude the vessels. Parasites may be present in considerable numbers, usually within the red corpuscles. Areas of disseminated necrosis closely similar to those observed in typhoid fever, diphtheria, and other acute infectious diseases, have been described by Guarnieri, Bignami, and Barker. In association with these areas, Barker describes capillary thrombosis. Perivascular (portal) infiltration has been found in a very acute case in a young man (Dock). The *kidneys* show only moderate pigmentation, with more or less parenchymatous degeneration. In severe cases with hæmoglobinuria there may be extensive necrosis of the epithelium of the convoluted tubes with hæmorrhages into the glomeruli and interstitial tissue. The *brain* usually shows interesting changes. In severe cases of some duration the tissue is stained, sometimes chocolate-colored. In mild cases the discoloration is present, but less marked. The blood-vessels, especially the arterioles and capillaries, contain large numbers of parasites, with partial or total destruction of red blood-corpuscles, and phagocytes. Occlusions of arterioles by parasites are often seen, together with perivascular infection and punctate hæmorrhages. In some instances changes of this sort occurring in special areas have given rise to focal symptoms.

In some acute pernicious cases with choleraic symptoms, the capillaries of the gastro-intestinal mucosa may be packed with parasites.

(2) **Malarial Cachexia.**—In fatal cases of chronic paludism death occurs usually from anæmia or the hæmorrhage associated with it.

The anæmia is profound, particularly if the patient has died of fever. The spleen is greatly enlarged, and may weigh from seven to ten pounds. If the disease has persisted for any length of time, it is firm and resists cutting. The capsule is thickened, the parenchyma brownish or yellowish-brown, with areas of pigmentation, or in very protracted cases it is extremely melanosed, particularly in the trabeculæ and about the vessels.

The liver may be greatly enlarged; but, as a rule, the increase in size is moderate in proportion to that of the spleen. It may present to the naked eye a grayish-brown or slate color, due to the large amount of pigment. In the portal canals and beneath the capsule the connective tissue is impregnated with melanin. Varying with the duration of the disease, the shade of color of the liver ranges from a light gray to a deep slate-gray tint. The texture is firm, but there is not necessarily any great increase in the connective tissue. Histologically, the pigment is seen in the Kupffer's cells and the perivascular tissue.

The kidneys may be enlarged and present a grayish-red color, or areas of pigmentation may be seen. The pigment may be diffusely scattered and particularly marked about the blood-vessels and the Malpighian bodies. The peritonæum is usually of a deep slate-color. The mucous membrane of the stomach and intestines may have the same hue, due to the pigment in and about the blood-vessels. In some cases this is confined to the lymph nodules of Peyer's patches, causing the shaven-beard appearance.

(3) **The Accidental and Late Lesions of Malarial Fever.**

(a) *The Liver.*—Paludal hepatitis plays a very important *rôle* in the history of malaria, as described by French writers. Kelsch and Kiêner devote over sixty pages to a description of the various forms, parenchymatous and interstitial, describing under the latter three different varieties. The existence of a cirrhosis dependent upon the irritation of large quantities of pigment in the liver is unquestioned, but only those cases in which the history of chronic malaria is definite, and in which the melanosis of both liver and spleen coexist, should be regarded as of paludal origin.

(*b*) *Pneumonia* is believed by many authors to be common in malaria, and even to depend directly upon the malarial poison, occurring either in the acute or in the chronic forms of the disease. I have no personal knowledge of such a special pneumonia. It certainly does not occur in the intermittent or remittent fevers which prevail in Philadelphia and Baltimore. The two diseases may be concurrent. Inflammation of the lungs may develop during a simple intermittent, and the quinine may check the chills without influencing in any way the pneumonia.

(*c*) *Nephritis.*—Moderate albuminuria is a frequent occurrence, having occurred in 46.4 per cent of the cases in my wards. It is much more frequent in the æstivo-autumnal infections.

Acute nephritis is a not unusual complication of the disease. Rare in the milder forms, it is relatively frequent in æstivo-autumnal infections, having occurred in over 4.5 per cent of my cases. Chronic nephritis occasionally follows long-continued or frequently repeated infections.

Clinical Forms of Malarial Fever.—(1) **The Regularly Intermittent Fevers.**—(*a*) Tertian fever; (*b*) quartan fever. These forms are characterized by recurring paroxysms of what are known as ague, in which, as a rule, chill, fever, and sweat follow each other in orderly sequence. The stage of *incubation* is not definitely known; it probably varies much according to the amount of the infectious material absorbed. Experimentally the period of incubation varies from thirty-six hours to fifteen days, being a trifle longer in quartan than in tertian infections. Attacks have been reported within a very short time after the apparent exposure. On the other hand, the ague may be, as is said, "in the system," and the patient may have a paroxysm months after he has removed from a malarial region, though I doubt if this can be the case unless he has had the disease when living there.

Description of the Paroxysm.—The patient generally knows he is going to have a chill a few hours before its advent by unpleasant feelings and uneasy sensations, sometimes by headache. The paroxysm is divided into three stages—cold, hot, and sweating.

Cold Stage.—The onset is indicated by a feeling of lassitude and a desire to yawn and stretch, by headache, uneasy sensations in the epigastrium, sometimes by nausea and vomiting. Even before the chill begins the thermometer indicates some rise in temperature. Gradually the patient begins to shiver, the face looks cold, and in the fully developed rigor the whole body shakes, the teeth chatter, and the movements may often be violent enough to shake the bed. Not only does the patient look cold and blue, but a surface thermometer will indicate a reduction of the skin temperature. On the other hand, the axillary or rectal temperature may,

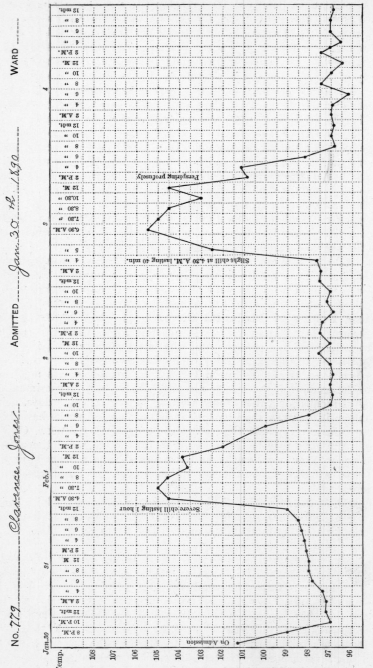

CHART XI.

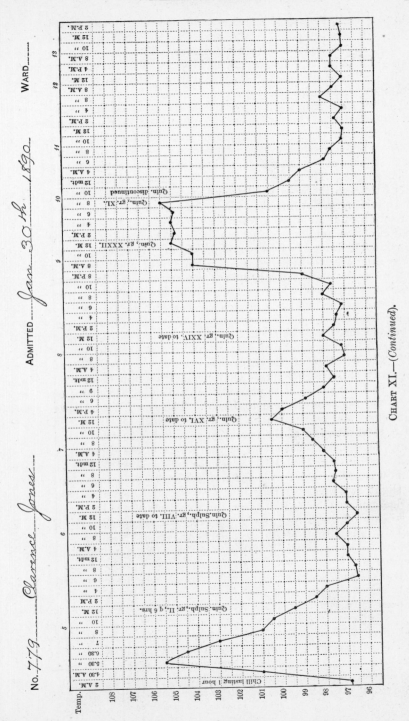

CHART XI.—(Continued).

during the chill, be greatly increased, and, as shown in the chart, the fever may rise during the chill to 105° or 106°. Of symptoms associated with the chill, nausea and vomiting are common. There may be intense headache. The pulse is quick, small, and hard. The urine is increased in quantity. The chill lasts for a variable time, from ten or twelve minutes to an hour, or even longer.

The *hot stage* is ushered in by transient flushes of heat; gradually the coldness of the surface disappears and the skin becomes intensely hot. The contrast in the patient's appearance is striking: the face is flushed, the hands are congested, the skin is reddened, the pulse is full and bounding, the heart's action is forcible, and the patient may complain of a throbbing headache. There may be active delirium. A patient in this stage jumped through the ward window and sustained fatal injuries. The rectal temperature may not increase much during this stage; in fact, by the termination of the chill the fever may have reached its maximum. The duration of the hot stage varies from half an hour to three or four hours. The patient is intensely thirsty and drinks eagerly of cold water.

Sweating Stage.—Beads of perspiration appear upon the face and gradually the entire body is bathed in a copious sweat. The uncomfortable feeling associated with the fever disappears, the headache is relieved, and within an hour or two the paroxysm is over and the patient usually sinks into a refreshing sleep. The sweating varies much. It may be drenching in character or it may be slight.

Chart XI is a fac-simile of a ward temperature chart in a case of tertian ague. The duration of the paroxysms on February 1st, 3d, and 5th was from twelve to sixteen hours. Quinine in two-grain doses was given on the 5th and was sufficient to prevent the on-coming paroxysms on the 7th, though the temperature rose to 100.5°. The small doses, however, were not effective, and on the 9th he had a severe chill.

The total duration of the paroxysm averages from ten to twelve hours, but may be shorter. Variations in the paroxysm are common. Thus the patient may, instead of a chill, experience only a slight feeling of coldness. The most common variation is the occurrence of a hot stage alone, or with very slight sweating. During the paroxysm the spleen is enlarged and the edge can usually be felt below the costal margin. In the interval or intermission of the paroxysm the patient feels very well, and, unless the disease is unusually severe, he is able to be up. Bronchitis is a common symptom. Herpes, usually labial, is perhaps as frequently seen in ague as in pneumonia.

Types of the Regularly Intermittent Fevers.—As has been stated in the description of the parasites, two distinct types of the regularly intermittent fevers have been separated. These are (*a*) tertian fever and (*b*) quartan fever.

(*a*) *Tertian Fever.*—This type of fever depends upon the presence in the blood of the tertian parasite, an organism which, as stated above, is usually present in sharply defined groups, whose cycle of development lasts approximately forty-eight hours, sporulation occurring every third day. In infections with one group of the tertian parasite the paroxysms occur synchronously with sporulation at remarkably regular intervals of about forty-eight hours, every third day—hence the name *tertian*. Very commonly, however, there may be two groups of parasites which reach maturity on alternate days, resulting thus in daily (*quotidian*) paroxysms—*double tertian infection*. Quotidian fever, depending upon double tertian infection, is the most frequent type in the acute intermittent fevers in this latitude.

(*b*) *Quartan Fever.*—This type of fever depends upon infection with the quartan parasite, an organism which occurs in well-defined groups, whose cycle of existence lasts about seventy-two hours. In infection with one group of parasites the paroxysm occurs every fourth day; hence the term *quartan*. At times, however, two groups of the parasites may be present; under these circumstances paroxysms occur on two successive days, with a day of intermission following. In infection with three groups of parasites there are daily paroxysms.

Thus a quotidian intermittent fever may be due to infection with either the tertian or quartan parasites.

Course of the Disease.—After a few paroxysms, or after the disease has persisted for ten days or two weeks, the patient may get well without any special medication. I have repeatedly known the chills to stop spontaneously. Such cases, however, are very liable to recurrence. Persistence of the fever leads to anæmia and hæmatogenous jaundice, owing to the destruction of the red blood-disks by the parasites. Ultimately the condition may become chronic, and will be described under malarial cachexia. The regularly intermittent fevers yield promptly and immediately to treatment with quinine.

(2) **The more Irregular, Remittent, or Continued Fevers. — Æstivo autumnal Fever.**—This type of fever occurs in temperate climates, chiefly in the later summer and fall; hence the term given to it by Marchiafava and Celli, *æstivo-autumnal fever*. The severer forms of it prevail in the Southern States and in tropical countries, where it is known chiefly as *bilious remittent fever*. The entire group of cases included under the terms *remittent fever*, *bilious remittent*, and *typho-malarial fevers* requires to be studied anew.

This type of fever is associated with the presence in the blood of the æstivo-autumnal parasite, an organism the length of whose cycle of development is probably subject to variations, while the existence of multiple groups of the parasite, or the absence of arrangement into definite groups, is not infrequent.

The *symptoms* are therefore, as might be expected, often irregular. In some instances there may be regular intermittent fever occurring at uncertain intervals of from twenty-four to forty-eight hours, or even more. In the cases with longer remissions the paroxysms are longer. Some of the quotidian intermittent cases may closely resemble the quotidian fever depending upon double tertian or triple quartan infection. Commonly, however, the paroxysms show material differences; their length averages over twenty hours, instead of from ten or twelve; the onset occurs often without chills and even without chilly sensations. The rise in temperature is frequently gradual and slow, instead of sudden, while the fall may occur by lysis instead of by crisis. There is a marked tendency toward anticipation in the paroxysms, while frequently, from the anticipation of one paroxysm or the retardation of another, more or less continuous fever may result. Sometimes there is continuous fever without sharp paroxysms. In these cases of continuous and remittent fever the patient, seen fairly early in the disease, has a flushed face and looks ill. The tongue is furred, the pulse is full and bounding, but rarely dicrotic. The temperature may range from 102° to 103°, or is in some instances higher. The general appearance of the patient is strongly suggestive of typhoid fever—a suggestion still further borne out by the existence of acute splenic enlargement of moderate grade. As in intermittent fever, an initial bronchitis may be present. The course of these cases is variable. The fever may be continuous, with remissions more or less marked; definite paroxysms with or without chills may occur, in which the temperature rises to 105° or 106°. Intestinal symptoms are usually absent. A slight hæmatogenous jaundice may develop early. Delirium of a mild type may occur. The cases vary very greatly in severity. In some the fever subsides at the end of the week, and the practitioner is in doubt whether he has had to do with a mild typhoid or a simple febricula. In other instances the fever persists for from ten days to two weeks; there are marked remissions, perhaps chills, with a furred tongue and low delirium. Jaundice is not infrequent. These are the cases to which the term *bilious remittent* and *typho-malarial* fevers are applied. In other instances the symptoms become grave and assume the character of the pernicious type. It is in this form of malarial fever that so much confusion still exists. The similarity of the cases to typhoid fever is most striking, more particularly the appearance of the facies, and the patient *looks* very ill. The cases develop, too, in the autumn, at the very time when typhoid fever occurs. The fever yields, as a rule, promptly to quinine, though here and there cases are met with—rarely indeed in my experience—which are refractory. It is just in this group that the observations of Laveran will be found of the greatest value. Several of the charts in Thayer and Hewetson's report show how closely, in some instances, the disease may simulate typhoid fever.

The *diagnosis* of malarial remittent fever may be definitely made by the examination of the blood. The small, actively motile, hyaline forms of the æstivo-autumnal parasite are to be found, while, if the case has lasted over a week, the larger crescentic and ovoid bodies are usually seen. In many cases here we are at first unable to distinguish between typhoid and continued malarial fever without a blood examination. A more widespread use of this means of diagnosis will enable us to bring some order out of the confusion which exists in the classification of the fevers of the South. At present the following febrile affections are recognized by various physicians as occurring in the subtropical regions of this continent: (*a*) Typhoid fever; (*b*) typho-malarial fever—a typhoid modified by malarial infection, or the result of a combined infection; (*c*) the malarial remittent fever; and (*d*) continued thermic fever (Guitéras). In these various forms, all of which may be characterized by a continued pyrexia with remissions or with chills and sweats (for we must remember that chills and sweats in typhoid fever are by no means rare), the blood examination will enable us to discover those which depend upon the malarial poison. In many of these cases of continued or remittent fever careful inquiry will show that at the beginning the patient had several intermittent paroxysms. In this latitude we have not the opportunity of seeing many of the protracted and severe cases, but I am inclined to think that future observations will show that, apart from the thermic fever, there are only two forms of these continued fevers in the South—the one due to the *typhoid* and the other to the *malarial* infection. The typhoid fever of Philadelphia and Baltimore presents no essential difference from the disease as it occurs in Montreal, a city practically free from malaria. Dock has shown conclusively that cases diagnosed in Texas as continued malarial fever were really true typhoid. The Widal reaction is now an important aid in diagnosis.

Pernicious Malarial Fever.—This is fortunately rare in temperate climates, and the number of cases which now occur, for example, in Philadelphia and Baltimore, is very much less than it was thirty or forty years ago. Among the cases of malaria which have been under observation during the past eight years there were only seven of the pernicious form. Pernicious fever is always associated with the æstivo-autumnal parasite. The following are the most important types:

(*a*) The *comatose form*, in which a patient is struck down with symptoms of the most intense cerebral disturbance, either acute delirium or, more frequently, a rapidly developing coma. A chill may or may not precede the attack. The fever is usually high, and the skin hot and dry. The unconsciousness may persist for from twelve to twenty-four hours, or the patient may sink and die. After regaining consciousness a second attack may come on and prove fatal. In these instances, as has been stated, the special localization of the infection is in the brain, where actual thrombi of parasites with marked secondary changes in the surrounding tissues have been found.

(*b*) *Algid Form.*—In this, the attack sets in usually with gastric symptoms; there are vomiting, intense prostration, and feebleness out of all proportion to the local disturbance. The patient complains of feeling cold, although there may be no actual chill. The temperature may be normal, or even subnormal; consciousness may be retained. The pulse is feeble and small, and the respirations are increased. There may be most severe diarrhœa, the attack assuming a choleriform nature. The urine is often diminished, or even suppressed. This condition may persist with slight exacerbations of fever for several days and the patient may die in a condition of profound asthenia. This is essentially the same as described as the *asthenic* or *adynamic* form of the disease. In the cases with vomiting and diarrhœa, Marchiafava has shown that the gastro-intestinal mucosa is often the seat of a special invasion by the parasites, actual thrombosis of the small vessels with superficial ulceration and necrosis occurring. Similar lesions were found by Barker in the gastro-intestinal tract of a case from my wards.

(*c*) *Hæmorrhagic Forms.*—In all the severe types of malarial infection, especially if persistent, hæmorrhage may occur from the mucous membranes. An important form is the malarial *hæmaturia*, which in some instances assumes a very malignant type. Paroxysms of ague may precede the attack, but in many cases called malarial hæmaturia there is no febrile paroxysm. The condition is usually an hæmoglobinuria, though blood-corpuscles are present also. In severe cases there is bleeding from the mucous membranes. Jaundice is present, but to a variable extent, and is hæmatogenous, due to the destruction of the red blood-corpuscles. Malarial hæmaturia occurs in epidemic form in many regions of the Southern States, and in some seasons proves very fatal.

Many different forms of pernicious malarial fever—diaphoretic, syncopal, pneumonic, pleuritic, choleraic, cardiac, gastric, and gangrenous—all of which depend upon some special symptom, have been described.

Malarial Cachexia.—The symptoms of chronic malarial poisoning are very varied. It may follow the frequent recurrence of ordinary intermittent fever, a common sequence in this country. A patient has chills for several weeks, is improperly or imperfectly treated, and on exposure the chills recur. This may be repeated for several months until the patient presents the two striking features of malarial cachexia—namely, *anæmia* and an *enlarged spleen*. Cases developing without chills or without febrile paroxysms are almost unknown in this region. They may occur, however, in intensely malarial districts, but in such cases the patients have fever, though chills may not supervene. The most pronounced types of malarial cachexia which we meet with here are in sailors from the West Indies and Central America. There is profound anæmia; the blood count may be as low as one million per cubic millimetre; the skin has a saffron-yellow or lemon tint, not often the light yellow tint of pernicious anæmia, but a darker, dirtier yellow. The spleen is greatly enlarged, firm, and hard. It rarely reaches the dimensions of the large leukæmic organ, but comes next to it in size.

The general symptoms are those of ordinary anæmia—breathlessness on exertion, œdema of the ankles, hæmorrhages, particularly into the retina, as noted by Stephen Mackenzie. Occasionally the bleeding is severe, and I have twice known fatal hæmatemesis to occur in association with the enlarged spleen. The fever is variable. The temperature may be low for days, not going above 99.5°. In other instances there may be irregular fever, and the temperature rises gradually to 102.5° or 103°. The cases in fact present a picture of splenic anæmia.

With careful treatment the outlook is good, and a majority of cases recover. The spleen is gradually reduced in size, but it may take several months or, indeed, in some instances, several years before the ague-cake entirely disappears.

Among the rarer symptoms which may develop as a result of malarial intoxication may be mentioned *paraplegia*, cases of which have been described by Gibney, Suckling, and others. Some of the cases are doubtful, and have been attributed to malaria simply because the paralysis was intermittent. It is a condition of extreme rarity. No case is mentioned by

Kelsch and Kiêner. Suckling's case had had several attacks of malaria, the last of which preceded by about two weeks the onset of the nervous symptoms, which were headache, giddiness, loss of speech, and paraplegia. The attack was transient, but he had a subsequent attack which also followed an ague-fit. The patient was an old soldier who had had syphilis, a point which somewhat complicated the case. *Orchitis* has been described as developing in malaria by Charvot in Algiers and Fedeli in Rome.

Diagnosis.—The blood, as one might expect, shows marked changes in malarial fever. In the regularly intermittent fevers there is a loss in red corpuscles after each paroxysm, which may be considerable, but which is rapidly compensated during the intermissions. In æstivo-autumnal fever the losses are oftener greater and more permanent. In any case of malaria which has existed for any length of time there is always considerable anæmia. The hæmoglobin, as in all secondary anæmias, is diminished, usually in greater proportion than the corpuscles. The leucocytes are almost invariably diminished in number in malarial fever. The reduction is greatest just after the paroxysms, the number increasing slightly at the beginning of the febrile paroxysm. The differential count shows a relative diminution in polynuclear leucocytes, with a relative increase in the large mononuclear forms, exactly the same condition that is seen in typhoid fever. Sometimes in fatal post-malarial anæmia the blood shows all the characteristics of true pernicious anæmia; in other instances of fatal anæmia, where the blood during life has shown an absence of leucocytosis, or of nucleated red corpuscles, the marrow of the long bones has been found to be perfectly yellow, showing no evidence of regenerative activity.

The diagnosis of the various forms of malaria is usually easy. The continued remittent and certain of the pernicious cases offer difficulties, which, however, are now greatly lessened or entirely overcome since Laveran's researches have given us a positive diagnostic indication. Many forms of intermittent pyrexia are mistaken for malarial fever, particularly the initial chills of tuberculosis and of septic infection. In these instances the blood shows leucocytosis, which is rare in malaria. If the practitioner will take to heart the lesson that an intermittent fever which resists quinine is not malarial, he will avoid many errors in diagnosis. In the so-called masked intermittent or dumb ague, the febrile manifestations are more irregular and the symptoms less pronounced; but occasionally chills occur, and the therapeutical test usually removes every doubt in the diagnosis.

The malarial poison is supposed to influence many affections in a remarkable way, giving to them a paroxysmal character. A whole series of minor ailments and some more severe ones, such as neuralgia, are attributed to certain occult effects of paludism. The more closely such cases are investigated the less definite appears the connection with malaria. Practitioners in districts entirely exempt from the disease have to deal with ailments which present the same odd periodicity, and which the physicians of the Atlantic coast attribute to a " touch of malaria."

Treatment.—We do not know as yet how the poison reaches the system. Infection seems most liable to occur at night. In regions in which the disease prevails extensively mosquito netting should be used, as the researches of Ross render it highly probable that the disease is transmitted in this way. Persons going to a malarial region should take about 10 grains of quinine daily, though Sézary found that 2 grains three times a day was a sufficient protection against the disease. During the paroxysm the patient should, in the cold stage, be wrapped in blankets and given hot drinks. The reactionary fever is rarely dangerous even if it reaches a high grade. The body may, however, be sponged. In quinine we possess a specific remedy against malarial infection. Experiment has shown that the parasites are most easily destroyed by quinine at the stage when they are free in the circulation—that is, during and just after sporulation. While in most instances the parasites of the regularly intermittent fevers may be destroyed, even in the intra-corpuscular stage, in æstivo-autumnal fever this is much more difficult. It should, then, be our object, if we wish to most effectually eradicate the infection, to have as much quinine in circulation at the time of the paroxysm and shortly before as is possible, for this is the period at which sporulation occurs. In the regularly intermittent fevers from 10 to 30 grains in divided doses throughout the day will in many instances prevent any fresh paroxysms. If the patient comes under observation shortly before an expected paroxysm, the administration of a good dose of quinine just before its onset may be advisable to obtain a maximum effect upon that group of parasites. The quinine will not prevent the paroxysm, but will destroy the greater part of the group of organisms and prevent its further recurrence. It is safer to give at least 20 to 30 grains daily for the first three days, and then to continue the remedy in smaller doses for the next two or three weeks. In æstivo-autumnal fever larger doses may be necessary, though in relatively few instances is it necessary to give more than 30 to 40 grains in the twenty-four hours.

The quinine should be ordered in solution or in capsules. The pills and compressed tablets are more uncertain, as they may not be dissolved.

A question of interest is the efficient dose of quinine necessary to cure the disease. I have a number of charts showing that grain doses three times a day will in many cases prevent the paroxysm, but not always with the certainty of the larger doses. In cases of æstivo-autumnal fever with pernicious symptoms it is necessary to get the system under the influence of quinine as rapidly as possible. In these instances the drug should be administered hypodermically as the bisulphate in 30-grain doses, with 5 grains of tartaric acid, every two or three hours. The muriate of quinine and urea is also a good form in which to administer the drug hypodermically; 10, 15, or 20 grain doses may be necessary. In the most severe instances some observers advise the intravenous administration of quinine, for which the very soluble bimuriate is well adapted. Fifteen grains with a grain of sodium chloride may be injected in about 2 drachms of distilled water. For extreme restlessness in these cases opium is indicated, and cardiac stimulants, such as alcohol and strychnine, are necessary. If in the comatose form the internal temperature is raised, the patient should be put in a bath and doused with cold water. For malarial anæmia, iron and arsenic are indicated.

An interesting question is much discussed, whether quinine does not cause or at any rate aggravate the hæmoglobinuria. We have not yet seen a case in which this condition has occurred as a result of the use of the drug. It seems localized in certain sections; and Bastianelli states that it is not seen in the Roman malarial fevers. He recommends that in any case of hæmoglobinuria if the blood shows parasites quinine should be administered freely. In the post-malarial forms quinine aggravates the attack. In an active malarial infection the patient runs less risk with the quinine.

XXV. MALTA FEVER.

(*Undulant Fever.*)

Definition.—An endemic fever, characterized by an irregular course, undulatory pyrexial relapses, profuse sweats, rheumatic pains, arthritis, and an enlarged spleen. An organism, the micrococcus Melitensis, is present in all cases.

The greater part of our knowledge of this remarkable disease we owe to the work of the army surgeons stationed at Gibraltar and Malta, particularly to Marston, to Bruce, and recently to Hughes, whose important work on the subject I have used freely for this article.

Distribution.—The disease prevails extensively at Malta, and is also met with in the countries bordering on the Mediterranean; hence the name Mediterranean fever. It is known in Gibraltar as Rock fever, and in Sicily and Italy it is known as Neapolitan fever. It probably is also met with in India and China. Hughes suggests that some of the indefinite forms of fever in America conform to this type, but the evidence before us at present is certainly against this view.

Etiology.—The disease is not contagious. It prevails in summer, and in infected regions is endemic, occasionally assuming epidemic characters. Insanitary conditions favor its spread, but we cannot as yet say whether the poison is air-borne or water-borne. Hughes thinks that the former is the more probable view, Bruce the latter. Young, healthy adults are chiefly attacked.

The micrococcus Melitensis, discovered by Bruce, has not yet been isolated from the blood, but occurs in large numbers in the spleen. It is constantly present in fatal cases. The morphological and cultural characters have been accurately studied by H. E. Durham. Inoculations into monkeys produce a disease somewhat similar to that in man, and the micrococcus can be isolated from the infected animal.

Symptoms.—There is no specific fever which presents the same remarkable group of phenomena. The period of incubation is from six to ten days. " Clinically the fever has a peculiarly irregular temperature curve, consisting of intermittent waves or undulations of pyrexia, of a distinctly remittent character. These pyrexial waves or undulations last, as a rule,

14

from one to three weeks, with an apyrexial interval, or period of temporary abatement of pyrexial intensity between, lasting for two or more days. In rare cases the remissions may become so marked as to give an almost intermittent character to the febrile curve, clearly distinguishable, however, from the paroxysms of paludic infection. This pyrexial condition is usually much prolonged, having an uncertain duration, lasting for even six months or more. Unlike paludism, its course is not markedly affected by the administration of quinine or arsenic. Its course is often irregular and even erratic in nature. This pyrexia is usually accompanied by obstinate constipation, progressive anæmia, and debility. It is often complicated with and followed by neuralgic symptoms referred to the peripheral or central nervous system, arthritic effusions, painful inflammatory conditions of certain fibrous structures, of a localized nature, or swelling of the testicles " (Hughes). This author recognizes a malignant type, in which the disease may prove fatal within a week or ten days; an undulatory type —the common variety—in which the fever is marked by intermittent waves or undulations of variable length, separated by periods of apyrexia and freedom from symptoms. In this really lie the peculiar features of the disease, and the unfortunate victim may suffer a series of relapses which may extend from three months, the average time, to two years. Lastly, there is an intermittent type, in which the patient may simply have daily pyrexia toward evening, without any special complications, and may do well and be able to go about his work, and yet at any time the other serious features of the disease may develop.

The mortality is slight, only about 2 per cent. There are no characteristic morbid lesions. The seriousness of the disease is in its protracted course, so that in the army the loss of time is a very grave item. Malta fever has to be distinguished carefully from typhoid fever and from malaria. From the latter it can be now readily differentiated by the examination of the blood. A characteristic serum reaction is present. From Durham's observations on animals it is probable that the organism may be isolated from the urine even after apparent recovery.

Treatment.—General measures suitable to typhoid fever are indicated. Fluid food should be given during the febrile period. Hydrotherapy, either the bath or the cold pack, should be used every third hour when the temperature is above 103° F. Otherwise the treatment is symptomatic. No drugs appear to have any special influence on the fever. A change of climate seems to promote convalescence.

XXVI. BERI-BERI.

Definition.—An endemic and epidemic multiple neuritis of unknown etiology, occurring in tropical and subtropical countries, characterized by motor and sensory paralysis and anasarca.

History.—The disease is believed to be of great antiquity in China, and is possibly mentioned in the oldest known medical treatise. In the early years of this century it attracted much attention among the Anglo-

Indian surgeons, and we may date the modern scientific study of the disease from Malcolmson's monograph, published in Madras in 1835. The opening of Japan gave an opportunity to the German physicians holding university positions, particularly Baelz, Scheube, and more recently Grimm, to investigate the disease. The studies of the native Japanese physicians, particularly Miura and Takagi, and of the Dutch physicians in the East, have contributed much to our knowledge. An added interest has been given to the subject by the discovery of the disease among the Cape Cod fishermen, and by the recurring outbreaks of endemic neuritis at the Richmond Asylum in Dublin and at the State Insane Hospital at Tuscaloosa, Ala.

Distribution.—Beri-beri, Kakke, or endemic neuritis prevails most extensively in the Malay Archipelago; in certain of the Dutch colonies the mortality among the coolies is simply frightful. It is widely distributed through parts of China and Japan. In India it has become less common, but is still prevalent in parts of Burma. Localized outbreaks have occurred in Australia. It prevails extensively in parts of South America and in the West Indies, and from the ports of these countries cases occasionally reach the United States. Birge, of Provincetown, and J. J. Putnam encountered beri-beri among the fishermen on the Newfoundland Banks. Birge writes (March 10, 1898) that he has seen 47 cases of both the wet and the dry form. The disease is not entirely confined to the fishermen on the Grand Banks, but develops occasionally among those living on shore or making "shore trips." In 1895–'96 a remarkable outbreak of endemic neuritis occurred at the State Insane Hospital at Tuscaloosa, Ala., which has been described fully by E. D. Bondurant.* Between February, 1895, and October, 1896, in a population of 1,200 there were 71 cases with 21 deaths. None occurred among the 200 employees of the hospital. The negroes were relatively less affected than the whites. The chief symptoms were "muscular weakness, tenderness, pain, paræsthesiæ, loss of deep reflexes, followed by atrophy of muscles and the electrical reaction of degeneration, accompanied by rise of temperature, gastro-intestinal disturbance, general anasarca, and tachycardia." At the Arkansas State Insane Asylum at Little Rock, in 1895, there was an outbreak of between 20 and 30 cases possibly of beri-beri.

In Great Britain the disease is not infrequent at the seaports.

At the Richmond Asylum, Dublin, there have been extensive outbreaks in the years 1894, 1896, 1897, under conditions of shameful overcrowding.

Etiology.—Two main views prevail as to the nature of the disease—that it is an infection, and that it is a toxæmia caused by food.

1. *Beri-beri as an Acute Infection.*—Baelz and Scheube, with many of the Dutch physicians, hold that the disease is due to a living germ. In favor of this view, Scheube refers to the fact that strong, well-nourished young people are attacked, that the disease has definite foci in which it prevails, definite seasonal relations, and has of late years spread in some countries as an epidemic without any special change in the diet of the

---

* New York Medical Journal, 1897, ii.

inhabitants. So far as seasonal and telluric influences are concerned, it is a disease which resembles malaria, with which, in fact, some authors have confounded it. It is probably not directly contagious. On the other hand, Scheube, Manson and others bring forward evidence to show that beri-beri may probably be conveyed from one district to another. Many bacteriological studies have been made in the disease, particularly by Dutch physicians, but there is no unanimity as to the results, and we may say that no specific organism has as yet been determined upon.

2. The food theory of beri-beri is widely held in Japan, some believing that it is due to the eating of bad rice, and others that it is associated with the use of certain fish. In favor of the dietetic view of its origin is adduced the extraordinary change which has taken place in the Japanese navy since the introduction by Takagi of an improved diet, allowing a larger portion of nitrogenous food, and forbidding the use of fresh fish altogether. Subsequent to this there has certainly been the most remarkable diminution in the number of cases—a reduction from about a fourth of the entire strength attacked annually to a practical abolition of the disease.

A recent number of Janus gives the experience of the Dutch physicians in Java, many of whom regard rice as the important cause of the disease. It is stated that in the prisons of Java the proportion of cases is 1 to 39 when the rice is eaten completely shelled, 1 to 10,000 when the grain is eaten with its pericarp; in some places the disease has disappeared when the unshelled rice has been substituted for the shelled. Miura, with whose studies of the disease all readers of Virchow's Archiv are familiar, regards beri-beri as a form of chronic poisoning due to the use of the flesh of certain fish eaten raw or improperly prepared. Grimm, in his recent monograph, regards the immunity of Europeans as in great part owing to the fact that they do not follow the Japanese custom of eating various kinds of raw fish.

Among the most important factors are the following: Overcrowding, as in ships, jails, and asylums, hot and moist seasons, and exposure to wet. Europeans under good hygienic conditions rarely contract the disease in beri-beri regions. The natives and the imported coolies are the most often attacked. Males are more subject to the disease than females. Young men from sixteen to twenty-five are most often affected.

Symptoms.—The incubation period is unknown, but it probably extends over several months. The following forms of the disease are recognized by Scheube:

1. **The incomplete or rudimentary form** which often sets in with catarrhal symptoms, followed by pains and weakness in the limbs and a lowering of the sensibility in the legs, with the development of paræsthesiæ. Slight œdema sometimes appears. After a time paræsthesiæ may develop in other parts of the body, and the patient may complain of palpitation of the heart, uneasy sensations in the abdomen, and sometimes shortness of breath. There may be weakness and tenderness of the muscles. After lasting from a few days to many months, these symptoms all disappear, but

with the return of the warm weather there may be a recurrence. One of Scheube's patients suffered in this way for twenty years.

2. **The atrophic form** sets in with much the same symptoms, but the loss of power in the limbs progresses more rapidly, and very soon the patient is no longer able to walk or to move the arms. The atrophy, which is associated with a good deal of pain, may extend to the muscles of the face. The œdematous symptoms and heart troubles play a minor *rôle* in this form, which is known as the dry or paralytic variety.

3. **The Wet or Dropsical Form.**—Setting in as in the rudimentary variety, the œdema soon becomes the most marked feature, extending over the whole subcutaneous tissue, and associated with effusions into the serous sacs. The atrophy of the muscles and disturbance of sensation are not such prominent symptoms. On the other hand, palpitation and rapid action of the heart and dyspnœa are common. The wasting may not be apparent until the dropsy disappears.

4. **The acute, pernicious, or cardiac form** is characterized by threatenings of an acute cardiac failure, developing rapidly after the existence of slight symptoms, such as occur in the rudimentary form. In the most acute type death may follow within twenty-four hours; more commonly the symptoms extend over several weeks.

The mortality of the disease varies greatly, from 2 or 3 per cent to 40 or 50 per cent among the coolies in certain of the settlements of the Malay Archipelago.

Morbid Anatomy.—The most constant and striking features are changes in the peripheral nerves and degenerative inflammation involving the axis cylinder and medullary sheaths. In the acute cases this is found not only in the peripheral nerves, but also in the pneumogastric and in the phrenic. The fibres of the voluntary muscles, as well as of the myocardium, are also much degenerated.

Diagnosis.—In tropical countries there is rarely any difficulty in the diagnosis. In cases of peripheral neuritis, associated with œdema, coming from tropical ports, the possibility of this disease should be remembered. Scheube states that rarely any difficulty offers in the diagnosis of the different forms. An interesting question arises as to the true nature of the endemic neuritis in the Richmond Asylum and at Tuscaloosa. Bondurant's report certainly shows a disease conforming with beri-beri in a majority of its features. The statement is made that the Dutch committee which studied the epidemic at the Richmond Asylum did not regard the disease as quite identical with the tropical beri-beri.

Treatment.—Much has been done to prevent the disease, particularly in Japan. There is no more remarkable triumph of modern hygiene than that which followed Takagi's dietetic reforms in the Japanese navy. In beri-beri districts Europeans should use a diet rich in nitrogenous ingredients. In the dietary of prisons and asylums the experience of the Javanese physicians with reference to the remarkable diminution of the disease with the use of unshelled rice should be borne in mind. In ships, prisons, and asylums the disease has rarely occurred except in connection with overcrowding, an element which prevailed both at the Richmond Asylum and at the State Hospital for the Insane at Tuscaloosa.

Baelz recommends in early cases a free use of the salicylates, 15 or 20 grains four or five times a day. Others advise early free purgation. In very severe acute cases, both Anderson and Baelz advise blood-letting. The more chronic cases demand, in addition to dietetic measures, drugs to support the heart and treatment of the atrophied muscles with electricity and massage.

XXVII. ANTHRAX.

(Splenic Fever; Charbon; Wool-sorter's Disease.)

Definition.—An acute infectious disease caused by the *bacillus anthracis*. It is a widespread affection in animals, particularly in sheep and cattle. In man it occurs sporadically or as a result of accidental inoculations with the virus.

Etiology.—The infectious agent is a non-motile, rod-shaped organism, the *bacillus anthracis*, which has, by the researches of Pollender, Davaine, Koch, and Pasteur, become the best known perhaps of all pathogenic microbes. The bacillus has a length of from two to ten times the diameter of a red blood-corpuscle; the rods are often united. They multiply by fission with great rapidity and grow with facility on various culture media, extending into long filaments which interlace and produce a dense network. The spore formation is seen with great readiness in these filaments; but an asporogenous variety is known, and can be produced artificially in cultures. The bacilli themselves are readily destroyed, but the spores are very resistant, and survive after prolonged immersion in a 5-percent solution of carbolic acid, and resist for some minutes a temperature of 212° Fahr. They are capable also of resisting gastric digestion. Outside the body the spores are in all probability very durable.

Geographically and zoölogically the disease is the most widespread of all infectious disorders. It is much more prevalent in Europe and in Asia than in America. Its ravages among the herds of cattle in Russia and Siberia, and among sheep in certain parts of Europe, are not equalled by any other animal plague. In this country the disease is rare. So far as I know, it has never prevailed on the ranches in the Northwest, but cases were not infrequent about Montreal.

A protective inoculation with a mitigated virus has been introduced by Pasteur, and has been adopted in certain anthrax regions. Hankin has isolated from the cultures an albumose which renders animals immune against the most intense virus.

In animals the disease is conveyed sometimes by direct inoculation, as by the bites and stings of insects, by feeding on carcasses of animals which have died of the disease, but more commonly by feeding in pastures in which the germs have been preserved. Pasteur believes that the earth-worm plays an important part in bringing to the surface and distributing the bacilli which have been propagated in the buried carcass of an infected animal. Certain fields, or even farms, may thus be infected for an indefinite period of time. It seems probable, however, that if the carcass is not opened or the blood spilt, spores are not formed in the buried animal and the bacilli quickly die.

Animals vary in susceptibility: the herbivora come first, then the omnivora, and lastly the carnivora. The disease does not occur spontaneously in man, but always results from infection, either through the skin, the intestines, or in rare instances through the lungs. It is found in persons whose occupations bring them into contact with animals or animal products, as stablemen, shepherds, tanners, butchers, and those who work in wool and hair.

Various forms of the disease have been described, and two chief groups may be recognized: the external anthrax and the internal anthrax, of which there are pulmonary and intestinal forms.

Symptoms.—(1) External Anthrax.

(a) *Malignant Pustule.*—The inoculation is usually on an exposed surface—the hands, arms, or face. At the site of inoculation there are, within a few hours, itching and uneasiness. Gradually a small papule develops, which becomes vesicular. Inflammatory induration extends around this, and within thirty-six hours, at the site of inoculation there is a dark brownish eschar, at a little distance from which there may be a series of small vesicles. The brawny induration may be extreme. The œdema produces very great swelling of the parts. The inflammation extends along the lymphatics, and the neighboring lymph-glands are swollen and sore. The fever at first rises rapidly, and the concomitant phenomena are marked. Subsequently the temperature falls, and in many cases becomes subnormal. Death may take place in from three to five days. In cases which recover the constitutional symptoms are slighter, the eschar gradually sloughs out, and the wound heals. The cases vary much in severity. In the mildest form there may be only slight swelling. At the site of inoculation a papule is formed, which rapidly becomes vesicular and dries into a scab, which separates in the course of a few days.

(b) *Malignant Anthrax Œdema.*—This form occurs in the eyelid, and also in the head, hand, and arm, and is characterized by the absence of the papule and vesicle forms, and by the most extensive œdema, which may follow rather than precede the constitutional symptoms. The œdema reaches such a grade of intensity that gangrene results, and may involve a considerable surface. The constitutional symptoms then become extremely grave, and the cases invariably prove fatal.

The greatest fatality is seen in cases of inoculation about the head and face, where the mortality, according to Nasarow, is 26 per cent; the least in infection of the lower extremities, where it is 5 per cent.

In a recent case, in a hair-picker, there was most extensive enteritis, peritonitis, and endocarditis, which last lesion has been described by Eppinger.

A feature in both these forms of malignant pustule, to which many writers refer, is the absence of feeling of distress or anxiety on the part of the patient, whose mental condition may be perfectly clear. He may be without any apprehension, even though his condition is very critical.

The *diagnosis* in most instances is readily made from the character of the lesion and the occupation of the patient. When in doubt, the examination of the fluid from the pustule may show the presence of the anthrax bacilli. Cultures should be made, or a mouse or guinea-pig inoculated from the local lesion. It is to be remembered that the blood may not show the bacilli in numbers until shortly before death.

(2) Internal Anthrax.

(*a*) *Intestinal Form, Mycosis intestinalis.*—In these cases the infection usually is through the stomach and intestines, and results from eating the flesh or drinking the milk of diseased animals; it may, however, follow an external infection if the germs are carried to the mouth. The symptoms are those of intense poisoning. The disease may set in with a chill, followed by vomiting, diarrhœa, moderate fever, and pains in the legs and back. In acute cases there are dyspnœa, cyanosis, great anxiety and restlessness, and toward the end convulsions or spasms of the muscles. Hæmorrhage may occur from the mucous membranes. Occasionally there are small phlegmonous areas on the skin, or petechiæ develop. The spleen is enlarged. The blood is dark and remains fluid for a long time after death. Late in the disease the bacilli may be found in the blood.

This is one of the forms of acute poisoning which may affect many individuals together. Thus Butler and Karl Huber describe an epidemic in which twenty-five persons were attacked after eating the flesh of an animal which had had anthrax. Six died in from forty-eight hours to seven days.

(*b*) *Wool-sorter's Disease.*—This important form of anthrax is found in the large establishments in which wool or hair is sorted and cleansed. The hair and wool imported into Europe from Russia and South America appear to have induced the largest number of cases. Many of these show no external lesion. The infective material has been swallowed or inhaled with the dust. There are rarely premonitory symptoms. The patient is seized with a chill, becomes faint and prostrated, has pains in the back and legs, and the temperature rises to 102° or 103°. The breathing is rapid, and he complains of much pain in the chest. There may be a cough and signs of bronchitis. So prominent in some instances are these bronchial symptoms that a pulmonary form of the disease has been described. The pulse is feeble and very rapid. There may be vomiting, and death may occur within twenty-four hours with symptoms of profound collapse and prostration. Other cases are more protracted, and there may be diarrhœa, delirium, and unconsciousness. The cerebral symptoms may be most intense; in at least four cases the brain seems to have been chiefly affected, and its capillaries stuffed with bacilli (Merkel). The recognition of wool-sorter's disease as a form of anthrax is due to J. H. Bell, of Bradford, England.

In certain instances these profound constitutional symptoms of internal anthrax are associated with the external lesions of malignant pustule.

The *rag-picker's disease* has been made the subject of an exhaustive study by Eppinger (Die Hadernkrankheit, Jena, 1894), who has shown that it is a local anthrax of the lungs and pleura, with general infection.

The diagnosis of internal anthrax is by no means easy, unless the history points definitely to infection in the occupation of the individual.

Treatment.—In malignant pustule the site of inoculation should be destroyed by the caustic or hot iron, and powdered bichloride of mercury may be sprinkled over the exposed surface. The local development of the bacilli about the site of inoculation may be prevented by the subcutaneous injections of solutions of carbolic acid or bichloride of mercury. The injections should be made at various points around the pustule, and may be repeated two or three times a day. The internal treatment should be confined to the administration of stimulants and plenty of nutritious food. Davies-Colley advises ipecacuanha powder in doses of from 5 to 10 grains every three or four hours.

In malignant forms, particularly the intestinal cases, little can be done. Active purgatives may be given at the outset, so as to remove the infecting material. Quinine in large doses has been recommended.

XXVIII. HYDROPHOBIA.

(*Lyssa; Rabies.*)

Definition.—An acute disease of warm-blooded animals, dependent upon a specific virus, and communicated by inoculation to man.

Etiology.—In man the disease is very variously distributed. In Russia it is common. In North Germany it is extremely rare, owing to the wise provision that all dogs shall be muzzled; in England and France it is much more common. In this country the disease is very rare. Dulles could collect only 78 cases in the five and a half years ending December 31, 1893.

Canines are specially liable to the disease. It is found most frequently in the dog, the wolf, and the cat. All animals are, however, susceptible; and it is communicable by inoculation to the ox, horse, or pig. The disease is propagated chiefly by the dog, which seems specially susceptible. In the Western States the skunk is said to be very liable to the disease. The nature of the poison is as yet unknown. It is contained chiefly in the nervous system and is met with in some of the secretions, particularly in the saliva.

A variable time elapses between the introduction of the virus and the appearance of the symptoms. Horsley states that this depends upon the following factors: " (*a*) Age. The incubation is shorter in children than in adults. For obvious reasons the former are more frequently attacked. (*b*) Part infected. The rapidity of onset of the symptoms is greatly determined by the part of the body which may happen to have been bitten. Wounds about the face and head are especially dangerous; next in order in degrees of mortality come bites on the hands, then injuries on the other parts of the body. This relative order is, no doubt, greatly dependent upon the fact that the face, head, and hands are usually naked, while the other parts are clothed; it would also appear to depend somewhat upon the richness in nerves of the part. (*c*) The extent and severity of the wound. Puncture wounds are the most dangerous; the lacerations are fatal in proportion to the extent of the surface afforded for absorption of the virus. (*d*) The animal conveying the infection. In order of decreasing severity come: first, the wolf; second, the cat; third, the dog; and fourth, other animals." Only a limited number of those bitten by rabid dogs become affected by the disease; according to Horsley, not more than 15 per cent. On the other hand, the death-rate of those persons bitten by wolves is higher, not less than 40 per cent. Babes gives the mortality as from 60 to 80 per cent.

The incubation period in man is extremely variable. The average is from six weeks to two months. In a few cases it has been under two weeks. It may be prolonged to three months. It is stated that the incubation may be prolonged for a year or even two years, but this has not been definitely settled.

Symptoms.—Three stages of the disease are recognized:

(1) *Premonitory stage*, in which there may be irritation about the bite, pain, or numbness. The patient is depressed and melancholy; and complains of headache and loss of appetite. He is very irritable and sleepless, and has a constant sense of impending danger. There is often greatly increased sensibility. A bright light or a loud voice is distressing. The larynx may be injected and the first symptoms of difficulty in swallowing are experienced. The voice also becomes husky. There is a slight rise in the temperature and the pulse.

(2) *Stage of Excitement.*—This is characterized by great excitability and restlessness, and an extreme degree of hyperæsthesia. "Any afferent stimulant—i. e., a sound or a draught of air, or the mere association of a verbal suggestion—will cause a violent reflex spasm. In man this symptom constitutes the most distressing feature of the malady. The spasms, which affect particularly the muscles of the larynx and mouth, are exceedingly painful and are accompanied by an intense sense of dyspnœa, even when the glottis is widely opened or tracheotomy has been performed" (Horsley). Any attempt to take water is followed by an intensely painful spasm of the muscles of the larynx and of the elevators of the hyoid bone. It is this which makes the patient dread the very sight of water and gives the name *hydrophobia* to the disease. These spasmodic attacks may be associated with maniacal symptoms. In the intervals between them the patient is quiet and the mind unclouded. The temperature in this stage is usually elevated and may reach from 100° to 103°. In some instances the disease is afebrile. The patient rarely attempts to injure his attendants, and in the intense spasms may be particularly anxious to avoid hurting any one. There are, however, occasional fits of furious mania, and the patient may, in the contractions of the muscles of the larynx and pharynx, give utterance to odd sounds. This stage lasts from a day and a half to three days and gradually passes into the—

(3) *Paralytic Stage.*—In rodents the preliminary and furious stages are absent, as a rule, and the paralytic stage may be marked from the outset—the so-called dumb rabies. This stage rarely lasts longer than from six to eighteen hours. The patient then becomes quiet; the spasms no

longer occur; unconsciousness gradually supervenes; the heart's action becomes more and more enfeebled, and death occurs by syncope.

Morbid Anatomy.—The lesions are in the cerebro-spinal system. The blood-vessels are congested; there is perivascular exudation of leucocytes; and there are minute hæmorrhages. According to Gowers, these are particularly intense in the medulla. The pharynx is congested, the mucous membrane of the stomach is hyperæmic, and not infrequently covered with a blood-stained mucus. The larynx, trachea, and bronchi show acute congestion. There are no special changes in the abdominal or thoracic viscera. The inoculation experiments show that the virus is not present in the liver, spleen, or kidneys, but is abundant in the spinal cord, brain, and peripheral nerves.

Treatment.—Prophylaxis is of the greatest importance, and by a systematic muzzling of dogs the disease can be, as in Germany, practically eradicated.

The bites should be carefully washed and thoroughly cauterized with caustic potash or concentrated carbolic acid. It is best to keep the wound constantly open for at least five or six weeks. When once established the disease is hopelessly incurable. No measures have been found of the slightest avail, consequently the treatment must be palliative. The patient should be kept in a darkened room, in charge of not more than two careful attendants. To allay the spasm, chloroform may be administered and morphia given hypodermically. It is best to use these powerful remedies from the outset, and not to temporize with chloral, bromide of potassium, and other less potent drugs. By the local application of cocaine, the sensitiveness of the throat may be diminished sufficiently to enable the patient to take liquid nourishment. Sometimes he can swallow readily. Nutrient enemata should be administered.

Preventive Inoculation.—Pasteur has found that the virus, when propagated through a series of rabbits, increases rapidly in its virulence; so that whereas subdural inoculation from the brain of a mad dog takes from fifteen to twenty days to produce the disease, in successive inoculations in a series of rabbits the incubation period is gradually reduced to seven days (*virus fixe*). The spinal cords of these rabbits contain the virus in great intensity, but when they are preserved in dry air this gradually diminishes. If now dogs are inoculated from cords preserved for from twelve to fifteen days, and then from cords preserved for a shorter period, i. e., with a progressively stronger virus, they gradually acquire immunity against the disease. A dog treated in this way will resist inoculation with the *virus fixe*, which otherwise would inevitably have proved fatal. Relying upon these experiments, Pasteur began inoculations in the human subject, using, on successive days, material from cords in which the virus was of varying degrees of intensity.

There is still some discussion as to the full value of this method, but the statistics published annually from the Pasteur Institute seem to prove conclusively its importance as a protective measure in man. The figures given by Pottevin, being the cases treated in Paris from 1886 to 1894 inclusive, show that of 13,817 persons bitten the mortality was 0.5 per cent.

Of these, 1,347 were bitten on the head, the mortality being 1.26 per cent; 8,722 on the hands, with 0.76 per cent of deaths; and 5,746 on other parts of the body, with a mortality of 0.28 per cent.

Diagnosis.—After the symptoms of the disease have developed in man the diagnosis should offer no especial difficulties. It is advisable, in cases attended with any doubts, as soon as possible after the injury has been inflicted, to secure the medulla oblongata of the supposed rabid animal for the purpose of inoculating rabbits. The subdural inoculation of rabbits with a small quantity of the central nervous system of a rabid animal will be followed by the development of the paralytic form of the disease in from fifteen to twenty days.

Pseudo-hydrophobia (Lyssophobia).—This is a very interesting affection, which may closely resemble hydrophobia, but is really nothing more than a neurotic or hysterical manifestation. A nervous person bitten by a dog, either rabid or supposed to be rabid, develops within a few months, or even later, symptoms somewhat resembling the true disease. He is irritable and depressed. He constantly declares his condition to be serious and that he will inevitably become mad. He may have paroxysms in which he says he is unable to drink, grasps at his throat, and becomes emotional. The temperature is not elevated and the disease does not progress. It lasts much longer than the true rabies, and is amenable to treatment. It is not improbable that a majority of the cases of alleged recovery in this disease have been of this hysterical form. In a case which Burr reported from my clinic a few years ago the patient had paroxysmal attacks in which he could not swallow. He was greatly excited and alarmed at the sight of water and was extremely emotional. The symptoms lasted for a couple of weeks and yielded to treatment with powerful electrical currents.

XXIX. TETANUS.
(*Lockjaw.*)

Definition.—An infectious malady characterized by tonic spasms of the muscles with marked exacerbations. The virus is produced by a bacillus which occurs in earth and sometimes in putrefying fluids and manure.

Etiology.—It occurs as an idiopathic affection or follows trauma. It is frequent in some localities and has prevailed extensively in epidemic form among new-born children, when it is known as tetanus or trismus neonatorum. It is more common in hot than in temperate climates, and in the colored than in the Caucasian race. This is particularly the case with tetanus following confinement and in tetanus neonatorum. In certain of the West Indian Islands more than one half of the mortality among the negro children has been due to this cause. St. Hilda, one of the western Hebrides, had been scourged for years by the " eight days' sickness " among the new-born. Of 125 children, 84 died within fourteen days of birth. Since the discovery of the tetanus bacillus, some philanthropic people in Glasgow sent a nurse to the island, who taught the midwives to use iodoform on the navel. The disease has now practically disappeared (Turner). In a majority of the cases there is an injury which may be of the most trifling character. It is more common after punctured and contused than after incised wounds, and frequently follows those of the hands and feet. The symptoms usually appear within two weeks of the injury. In some military campaigns tetanus has prevailed extensively, but in others, as in the late civil war, the cases have been comparatively few. Idiopathic tetanus is rare in man, but it has sometimes followed exposure to cold or sleeping on the damp ground. The disease has occurred after prolonged use of the hypodermic needle for morphia and quinine injections.

The infectious nature of tetanus was suggested by its endemic occurrence and from the manner of its behavior in certain institutions. Veterinarians have long been of this belief, as cases are apt to occur together in horses in one stable. On the eastern end of Long Island, where formerly the disease was very prevalent, it is now rarely seen.

The Tetanus Bacillus.—The observations of Rosenbach, Nicolaïer, and Kitasato have demonstrated that there is in connection with the disease a specific organism which can be isolated and cultivated. The bacillus forms a slender rod, which may grow into long threads. One end is often swollen and occupied by a spore. It is motile, grows at ordinary temperatures, and is anaërobic. The bacilli develop at the site of the wound (and do not invade the blood and organs), where alone the toxine is manufactured. With small quantities of the culture the disease may be transmitted to animals, which die with symptoms of tetanus. The poison is a tox-albumin of extraordinary potency, which has been separated by Brieger and Cohn in a state of tolerable purity. It is perhaps the most virulent poison known. Whereas the fatal dose of strychnine for a man weighing 70 kilos is from 30 to 100 milligrammes, that of the tetanus toxine is estimated at 0.23 milligrammes. Every feature of the disease can be produced by it experimentally without the presence of the bacilli. The symptoms do not develop immediately, as in the case of ordinary poisons, but slowly, and it has been suggested that it acts only after undergoing some further changes in the body. Another point of interest is the fact that immunity can be procured by inoculating an animal with the blood of another which has had the disease. The organism has been found in the earth and in putrefying fluids, and Nicolaïer has caused the disease by inoculating with different sorts of surface soil. Animals have been rendered immune to the tetanus poison and a curative serum has been prepared. This serum has been used successfully in preventing and even curing the experimental form of the disease. The results in man are as yet doubtful.

Morbid Anatomy.—No characteristic lesions have been found in the cord or in the brain. Congestions occur in different parts, and perivascular exudations and granular changes in the nerve-cells have been found. The condition of the wound is variable. The nerves are often found injured, reddened, and swollen. In the tetanus neonatorum the umbilicus may be inflamed.

Symptoms.—After an injury the disease sets in usually within ten days. In Yandell's statistics in at least two fifths, and in Joseph Jones's in four fifths, the symptoms occurred before the fifteenth day. The patient complains at first of slight stiffness in the neck, or a feeling of tightness in the jaws, or difficulty in mastication. Occasionally chilly feelings or actual rigors may precede these symptoms. Gradually a tonic spasm of the muscles of these parts develops, producing the condition of trismus or lockjaw. The eyebrows may be raised and the angles of the mouth drawn out, causing the so-called sardonic grin—*risus sardonicus*. In children the spasm may be confined to these parts. Sometimes the attack is associated with paralysis of the facial muscles and difficulty in swallowing—the head-tetanus of Rose, which has most commonly followed injuries in the neighborhood of the fifth nerve. Gradually the process extends and involves the muscles of the body. Those of the back are most affected, so that during the spasm the unfortunate victim may rest upon the head and heels—a position known as *opisthotonos*. The rectus abdominalis muscle has been torn across in the spasm. The entire trunk and limbs may be perfectly rigid—*orthotonos*. Flexion to one side is less common—*pleurothotonos;* while spasm of the muscles of the abdomen may cause the body to be bent forward—*emprosthotonos*. In very violent attacks the thorax is compressed, the respirations are rapid, and spasm of the glottis may occur, causing asphyxia. The paroxysms last for a variable period, but even in the intervals the relaxation is not complete. The slightest irritation is sufficient to cause a spasm. The paroxysms are associated with agonizing pain, and the patient may be held as in a vice, unable to utter a word. Usually he is bathed in a profuse sweat. The temperature may remain normal throughout, or show only a slight elevation toward the close. In other cases the pyrexia is marked from the outset; the temperature reaches 105° or 106°, and before death 109° or 110°. In rare instances it may go still higher. Death either occurs during the paroxysm from heart-failure or asphyxia, or is due to exhaustion.

The cephalic tetanus (*Kopftetanus* of Rose) originates usually from a wound on one side of the head, and is characterized by stiffness of the muscles of the jaw and paralysis of the facial muscles on the same side as the wound, with difficulty in swallowing.

The prognosis is good in the chronic cases; of these, in Willard's table only 8 of 32 died; but in the acute form, of 45 cases, only 4 recovered.

Diagnosis.—Well-developed cases following a trauma could not be mistaken for any other disease. The spasms are not unlike those of strychnia-poisoning, and in the celebrated Palmer murder trial this was the plea for the defence. The jaw-muscles, however, are never involved early, if at all, and between the paroxysms in strychnia-poisoning there is no rigidity. In tetany the distribution of the spasm at the extremities, the peculiar position, the greater involvement of the hands, and the condition under which it occurs, are sufficient to make the diagnosis clear. In doubtful cases cultures should be made from the pus of the wound.

Prognosis.—Two of the Hippocratic aphorisms express tersely the general prognosis even at the present day: " The spasm supervening on a wound is fatal," and " such persons as are seized with tetanus die within four days, or if they pass these they recover."

The mortality in the traumatic cases is not less than 80 per cent (Conner); in the idiopathic cases it is under 50 per cent. According to Yandell, the mortality is greatest in children. Favorable indications are: late onset of the attack, localization of the spasms to the muscles of the neck and jaw, and an absence of fever.

Treatment.—Local treatment of the wound is essential, as the poison is manufactured here. Tizzoni advises nitrate of silver as the best germicide for the tetanus bacillus. Thorough excision and antiseptic treatment should be carried out. The patient should be kept in a darkened room, absolutely quiet, and attended by only one person. All possible sources of irritation should be avoided. Veterinarians appreciate the importance of this complete seclusion, and in well-equipped infirmaries there may be seen a brick padded chamber in which the horses are treated.

When the lockjaw is extreme the patient may not be able to take food by the mouth, under which circumstances it is best to use rectal injections, or to feed by a catheter passed through the nose. The spasm should be controlled by chloroform, which may be repeatedly exhibited at intervals. It is more satisfactory to keep the patient thoroughly under the influence of morphia given hypodermically. Chloral hydrate, bromide of potassium, Calabar bean, curara, Indian hemp, belladonna, and other drugs have been recommended, and recovery occasionally follows their use. It is very difficult to estimate the value of the blood-serum therapy in this disease. Tizzoni and Cantani have used an antitoxine prepared from the blood-serum of immunized animals. The material, which is now to be obtained from Merck, is in the dried state, and comes in tubes containing 4 to 5 grammes. It can be bought in this country from his agents. An antitoxine serum is also prepared by Behring and by Roux. Of the fluid serum 20 to 30 cc. may be used for the first dose and 15 to 20 cc. every five or ten hours after. Tizzoni advises 2.25 grammes of his antitoxine for the first dose and 0.6 grammes for subsequent doses. Gooderich has collected 113 cases treated with the antitoxine, with 63 per cent of recoveries. The Tizzoni product has been the most successful.

XXX. GLANDERS (*Farcy*).

Definition.—An infectious disease of the horse, communicated occasionally to man. In the horse it is characterized by the formation of nodules, chiefly in the nares (glanders) and beneath the skin (farcy).

Etiology.—The disease belongs to the infective granulomata. The local manifestations in the nostrils and the skin of the horse are due to one and the same cause. The specific germ, *bacillus mallei*, was discovered by Loeffler and Schütz. It is a short, non-motile bacillus, not unlike that of tubercle, but exhibits different staining reactions. It grows readily on the ordinary culture media. For the full recognition of glanders in man we are indebted to the labors of Rayer, whose monograph remains one of the best descriptions ever given of the disease. Man becomes infected by contact with diseased animals, and usually by inoculation on an abraded surface of the skin. The contagion may also be received on the mucous membrane. In one of the Montreal cases a gentleman was probably infected by the material expelled from the nostril of his horse, which was not suspected of having the disease.

Morbid Anatomy.—As in the horse, the disease may be localized in the nose (glanders) or beneath the skin (farcy). The essential lesion is the granulomatous tumor, characterized by the presence of numerous lymphoid and epithelioid cells, among and in which are seen the glanders bacilli. These nodular masses tend to break down rapidly, and on the mucous membrane result in ulcers, while beneath the skin they form abscesses. The glanders nodules may also occur in the internal organs.

Symptoms.—An acute and a chronic form of glanders may be recognized in man, and an acute and a chronic form of farcy.

Acute Glanders.—The period of incubation is rarely more than three or four days. There are signs of general febrile disturbance. At the site of infection there are swelling, redness, and lymphangitis. Within two or three days there is involvement of the mucous membrane of the nose, the nodules break down rapidly to ulcers, and there is a muco-purulent discharge. An eruption of papules, which rapidly become pustules, breaks out over the face and about the joints. It has been mistaken for variola. This was carefully studied by Rayer and is figured in his monograph. In a Montreal case this copious eruption led the attending physician to suspect small-pox, and the patient was isolated. There is great swelling of the nose. The ulceration may go on to necrosis, in which case the discharge is very offensive. The lymph-glands of the neck are usually much enlarged. Subacute pneumonia is very apt to develop. This form runs its course in about eight or ten days, and is invariably fatal.

Chronic glanders is rare and difficult to diagnose, as it is usually mistaken for a chronic coryza. There are ulcers in the nose, and often laryngeal symptoms. It may last for months, or even longer, and recovery sometimes takes place. Tedeschi has described a case of chronic osteomyelitis, due to the bacillus mallei, which was followed by a fatal glanders meningitis. The diagnosis may be extremely difficult. In such cases a suspension of the secretion, or of cultures upon agar-agar made from the secretion, should be injected into the peritoneal cavity of a male guinea-pig. At the end of two days, in positive cases, the testicles are found to be swollen and the skin of the scrotum reddened. The testicles continue to increase in size, and finally suppurate. Death takes place after the lapse of two or three weeks, and generalized glanders nodules are found in the viscera. The use of mallein for diagnostic purposes is highly recommended. The principles and methods of application are the same as for tuberculin.

Acute farcy in man results usually from the inoculation of the virus into the skin. There is an intense local reaction with a phlegmonous inflammation. The lymphatics are early affected, and along their course there are nodular subcutaneous enlargements, the so-called farcy buds, which may rapidly go on to suppuration. There are pains and swelling in the joints and abscesses may form in the muscles. The symptoms are those of an acute infection, almost like an acute septicæmia. The nose is not involved and the superficial skin eruption is not common. The bacilli have been found in the urine in acute cases in man and animals.

The disease is fatal in a large proportion of the cases, usually in from twelve to fifteen days.

Chronic farcy is characterized by the presence of localized tumors, usually in the extremities. These tumors break down into abscesses, and sometimes form deep ulcers, without much inflammatory reaction and without special involvement of the lymphatics. The disease may last for months or even years. Death may result from pyæmia, or occasionally acute glanders develops. The celebrated French veterinarian Bouley had it and recovered.

The disease is transmissible also from man to man. Washerwomen have been infected from the clothes of a patient. In the diagnosis of this affection the occupation is very important. Nowadays, in cases of doubt, the inoculation should be made in animals, as in this way the disease can be readily determined. Mallein, a product of the growth of the bacilli, is now used for the purpose of diagnosing glanders in animals. Several instances of cured glanders have been reported in animals treated with small and repeated doses of mallein (Pilavios, Babes).

Treatment.—If seen early, the wound should be either cut out or thoroughly destroyed by caustics and an antiseptic dressing applied. The farcy buds should be early opened. In the acute cases there is very little hope. In the chronic cases recovery is possible, though often tedious.

XXXI. ACTINOMYCOSIS.

Definition.—A chronic infective disorder produced by the actinomyces or ray-fungus, the *Streptothrix actinomyces*.

Etiology.—The disease is widespread among cattle, and occurs also in the pig. It was first described by Bollinger in the ox, in which it forms the affection known in this country as "big-jaw." Examples of the disease were common in the cattle killed at the abattoir in Montreal. In man it was mentioned by von Langenbeck, who observed the "sulphur grains" in the characteristic purulent material. The first accurate description of the disease was given by James Israel, and subsequently Ponfick insisted upon the identity of the disease in man and cattle.

In this country to May 1, 1898, about 41 cases have been recognized (Ruhräh); in England the disease is rare. It is not uncommon in Germany and Russia. To the end of 1892 about 450 cases had been described (Leith, Edinburgh Hospital Reports, vol. ii). It is nearly three times as common in men as in women.

The *parasite* belongs probably to the *Streptothrix* group of bacteria. In both man and cattle it can be seen in the pus from the affected region as yellowish or opaque granules from one half to two millimetres in diameter, which are made up of cocci and radiating threads, which present bulbous, club-like terminations. The youngest granules are gray in color and semi-translucent; in these the bulbous extremities are wanting. It

15

was shown by Boström that the clubbed ends are the result of a hyaline, degenerative change taking place in the filaments. The organism is strikingly pleomorphic.

The parasite has been successfully cultivated, and the disease has been inoculated both with the natural and artificially grown organism.

The Mode of Infection.—There is no evidence of direct infection with the flesh or milk of diseased animals. The streptothrix has not been detected outside the body. It seems highly probable that it is taken in with the food. The site of infection in a majority of cases in man and animals is in the mouth or neighboring passages. In the cow, possibly also in man, barley and rye have been carriers of the germ.

Morbid Anatomy.—In the earliest stages of its growth the parasite gives rise to a small granulation tumor not unlike that produced by the *bacillus tuberculosis*, which contains, in addition to small round cells, epithelioid elements and giant cells. After it reaches a certain size there is great proliferation of the surrounding connective tissue, and the growth may, particularly in the jaw, look like, and was long mistaken for, osteosarcoma. Finally suppuration occurs, which in man, according to Israel, may be produced directly by the streptothrix itself.

Clinical Forms.—(*a*) **Alimentary Canal.**—Israel is said to have found the fungus in the cavities of carious teeth. The jaw has been involved in a number of cases in man. The patient comes under observation with swelling of one side of the face, or with a chronic enlargement of the jaw which may simulate sarcoma.

The tongue has been involved in several cases, showing small growths, either primary or following disease of the jaw. In the intestines the disease may occur either as a primary or secondary affection. Cases have been reported of pericæcal abscess due to the germ. An actinomycotic appendicitis has been described; primary actinomycosis of the large intestine with metastases has also been described. Ransom has found the actinomyces in the stools. The liver may be affected primarily, as in the case reported by Sharkey and Acland. The actinomycotic abscesses present a reticular or honeycomb-like arrangement (Leith).

(*b*) **Pulmonary Actinomycosis.**—In September, 1878, James Israel described a remarkable mycotic disease of the lungs, which subsequent observation showed to be the affection described the year before by Bollinger in cattle. Since that date many instances have been reported in which the lungs were affected. It is a chronic infectious pulmonary disorder, characterized by cough, fever, wasting, and a muco-purulent, sometimes foetid, expectoration. The lesions are unilateral in a majority of the cases. Hodenpyl classifies them in three groups: (1) Lesions of chronic bronchitis; the diagnosis has been made by the presence of the actinomyces in the sputum. (2) Miliary actinomycosis, closely resembling miliary tubercle, but the nodules are seen to be made up of groups of fungi, surrounded by granulation tissue. This form of pulmonary actinomycosis is not infrequent in oxen with advanced disease of the jaw or adjacent structures. (3) The cases in which there is more extensive destructive disease of the lungs, broncho-pneumonia, interstitial changes, and abscesses, the latter forming cavities large enough to be diagnosed during life. Actinomycotic lesions of other organs are often present in connection with the pulmonary disease; erosion of the vertebræ, necrosis of the ribs and sternum, with node-like formations, subcutaneous abscesses, and occasionally metastases in all parts of the body.

Symptoms.—The fever is of an irregular type and depends largely on the existence of suppuration. The cough is an important symptom, and the diagnosis in 18 of the cases was made during life by the discovery of the actinomyces. Death results usually with septic symptoms. Occasionally there is a condition simulating typhoid fever. The average duration of the disease was ten months. Recovery is very rare. Clinically the disease closely resembles certain forms of pulmonary tuberculosis and of fœtid bronchitis. It is not to be forgotten in the examination of the sputum that, as Bizzozero mentions, certain degenerated epithelial cells may be mistaken for the organism. The radiating leptothrix threads about the epithelium of the mouth sometimes present a striking resemblance.

(*c*) **Cutaneous Actinomycosis.**—In several instances in connection with chronic ulcerative diseases of the skin the ray-fungus has been found. It is a very chronic affection resembling tuberculosis of the skin, associated with the development of tumors which suppurate and leave open sores, which may remain for years.

(*d*) **Cerebral Actinomycosis.**—Bollinger has reported an instance of primary disease of the brain. The symptoms were those of tumor. A second remarkable case has been reported by Gamgee and Delepine. The patient was admitted to St. George's Hospital with left-sided pleural effusion. At the post mortem three pints of purulent fluid were found in the left pleura; there was an actinomycotic abscess of the liver, and in the brain there were abscesses in the frontal, parietal, and temporo-sphenoidal lobes which contained the mycelium, but no clubs. A third case, reported by O. B. Keller, had *empyema necessitatis*, which was opened and actinomycétes were found in the pus. Subsequently she had Jacksonian epilepsy, for which she was trephined twice and abscesses opened, which contained actinomyces grains. Death occurred after the second operation.

Diagnosis.—The disease is in reality a chronic pyæmia. The only test is the presence of the actinomyces in the pus. Metastases may occur as in pyæmia and in tumors. The tendency, however, is rather to the production of a local purulent affection which erodes the bones and is very destructive. In cattle the disease may cause metastases without any suppuration; thus in a Montreal case the jaw and tongue were the seat of the most extensive disease with very slight suppuration, while the lungs presented numbers of secondary growths containing the organisms.

Treatment.—This is largely surgical and is practically that of pyæmia. Incision of the abscess, removal of the dead bone, and thorough irrigation are appropriate measures. Thomassen has recommended iodide of potassium, which, in doses of from 40 to 60 grains daily, has proved curative in a number of recent cases.

XXXII. SYPHILIS.

Definition.—A specific disease of slow evolution, propagated by inoculation (acquired syphilis), or by hereditary transmission (congenital syphilis). In the acquired form the site of inoculation becomes the seat of a special tissue change—*primary lesion*. Within two or three months constitutional symptoms develop, with affections of the skin and mucous membranes—*secondary lesions*. After a period of months or years granulomatous growths develop in the viscera, muscles, bones, or skin—*tertiary lesions*. And, finally, there are certain diseases, as tabes and general paresis, which are peculiarly prone to develop on the syphilitic soil—*para-* or *meta-syphilitic affections*.

I. GENERAL ETIOLOGY AND MORBID ANATOMY.

The nature of the virus is still doubtful. Lustgarten found in the hard chancre and in gummata a rod-shaped bacillus of 3 or 4 μ in length, which he claims is specific and peculiar to the disease. This organism closely resembles the smegma bacillus, which is found beneath the prepuce, but from its occurrence in gummatous growths it is hardly possible that they can be identical. Further observations are required before the question can be considered settled.

Syphilis is peculiar to man, and cannot be transmitted to the lower animals. All are susceptible to the contagion, and it occurs at all ages.

Modes of Infection.—(1) In a large majority of all cases the disease is transmitted by *sexual congress*, but the designation *venereal* disease (*lues venerea*) is not always correct, as there are many other modes of inoculation.

(2) *Accidental Infection.*—In surgical and in midwifery practice physicians are not infrequently inoculated. It is surprising that infection from these sources is not more common. I have known personally of 10 cases. Midwifery chancres are usually on the fingers, but I have met with one instance on the back of the hand. The lip chancre is the most common of these erratic or extra-genital forms, and may be acquired in many ways apart from direct infection. Mouth and tonsillar sores result as a rule from improper practices. Wet-nurses are sometimes infected on the nipple, and it occasionally happens that relatives of the child are accidentally contaminated. One of the most lamentable forms of accidental infection is the transmission of the disease in humanized vaccine lymph. This, however, is extremely rare. The conditions under which it occurs have been already referred to (see Vaccination).

(3) *Hereditary Transmission.*—This may be, and is, most common from (*a*) the father, the mother being healthy (sperm inheritance). It is, unfortunately, an every-day experience to see cases of congenital syphilis in which the infection is clearly paternal. A syphilitic father may, however, beget a healthy child, even when the disease is fresh and full-blown. On the other hand, in very rare instances, a man may have had syphilis when young, undergo treatment, and for years present no signs of disease, and yet his first-born may show very characteristic lesions. Happily, in a

large majority of instances, when the treatment has been thorough, the offspring escape. The closer the begetting to the primary sore, the greater the chance of infection. A man with tertiary lesions may beget healthy children. As a general rule it may be said that with judicious treatment the transmissive power rarely exceeds three or four years.

(*b*) Maternal transmission (germ inheritance). It is a remarkable and interesting fact that a woman who has borne a syphilitic child is herself immune, and cannot be infected, though she may present no signs of the disease. This is known as Colles' law, and was thus stated by the distinguished Dublin surgeon: "That a child born of a mother who is without obvious venereal symptoms, and which, without being exposed to any infection subsequent to its birth, shows this disease when a few weeks old, this child will infect the most healthy nurse, whether she suckle it, or merely handle and dress it; and yet this child is never known to infect its own mother, even though she suckle it while it has venereal ulcers of the lips and tongue." In a majority of these cases the mother has received a sort of protective inoculation, without having had actual manifestations of the disease.

A woman with acquired syphilis is liable to bear infected children. The father may not be affected. In a large number of instances both parents are diseased, the one having infected the other, in which case the chances of fœtal infection are greatly increased.

(*c*) Placental transmission. The mother may be infected after conception, in which case the child may be, but is not necessarily, born syphilitic.

Morbid Anatomy.—The *primary lesion,* or chancre, shows: (*a*) A diffuse infiltration of the connective tissue with small, round cells. (*b*) Larger epithelioid cells. (*c*) Giant cells. (*d*) The Lustgarten bacilli, in small numbers. (*e*) Changes in the small arteries, chiefly thickening of the intima, and alterations in the nerve-fibres going to the part (Berkley). The sclerosis is due in part to this acute obliterative endarteritis. Associated with the initial lesions are changes in the adjacent lymph-glands, which undergo hyperplasia, and finally become indurated.

The *secondary lesions* of syphilis are too varied for description here. They consist of condylomata, skin eruptions, affections of the eye, etc.

The *tertiary lesions* consist of circumscribed tumors known as gummata, and of an arteritis, which, however, is not peculiar to the disease.

Gummata.—Syphilomata develop in the bones or periosteum—here they are called nodes—in the muscles, skin, brain, lung, liver, kidneys, heart, testes, and adrenals. They vary in size from small, almost microscopic, bodies to large, solid tumors from 3 to 5 cm. in diameter. They are usually firm and hard, but in the skin and on the mucous membranes they tend to break down rapidly and ulcerate. On cross-section a medium-sized gumma has a grayish-white, homogeneous appearance, presenting in the centre a firm, caseous substance, and at the periphery a translucent, fibrous tissue. Often there are groups of three or more surrounded by dense sclerotic tissue.

The arteritis will be considered in a separate section.

II. Acquired Syphilis.

Primary Stage.—This extends from the appearance of the initial sore until the onset of the constitutional symptoms, and has a variable duration of from six to twelve weeks. The initial sore appears within a month after inoculation, and it first shows itself as a small red papule, which gradually enlarges and breaks in the centre, leaving a small ulcer. The tissue about this becomes indurated so that it ultimately has a gristly, cartilaginous consistence—hence the name, hard or indurated chancre. The size attained is variable, and when small the sore may be overlooked, particularly if it is just within the urethra. The glands in the lymph-district of the chancre enlarge and become hard. Suppuration both in the initial lesion and in the glands may occur as a secondary change. The general condition of the patient in this stage is good. There may be no fever and no impairment of health.

Secondary Stage.—The first constitutional symptoms are usually manifested within three months of the appearance of the primary sore. They rarely develop earlier than the sixth or later than the twelfth week. The symptoms are: (a) *Fever*, slight or intense, and very variable in character. A mild continuous pyrexia is not uncommon, the temperature not rising above 101°. The fever may have a distinctly remittent character; but the most remarkable and puzzling type, which is very apt to lead to error in diagnosis, is the intermittent syphilitic fever. It may come on within a month after exposure and rise to 104° or 105°, with oscillations of 5° or 6° (Yeo). A remarkable case is reported by Sidney Phillips, in which pyrexia persisted for months, with paroxysms resembling in all respects tertian ague, and which resisted quinine and yielded promptly to mercury and potassium iodide. Although usually a secondary manifestation, the fever of syphilis may occur late in the disease. Practitioners are scarcely alive to the frequency and importance of syphilitic fever. Janeway has recently called attention to cases in which the diagnosis of pulmonary tuberculosis had been made.

(b) *Anæmia.*—In many cases the syphilitic poison causes a pronounced anæmia which gives to the face a muddy pallor, and there may even be a light-yellow tingeing of the conjunctivæ or of the skin, a hæmatogenous icterus. This syphilitic cachexia may in some instances be extreme. The red blood-corpuscles do not show any special alterations. The blood-count may fall to three millions per cubic millimetre, or even lower. The anæmia may develop suddenly. In a case of syphilitic arthritis in a young girl following three or four inunctions of mercury the blood-count fell below two millions per cubic millimetre in a few days.

(c) *Cutaneous Lesions.*—Skin eruptions of all forms may develop. The earliest and most common is a rash—*macular syphilide* or *syphilitic roseola* —which occurs on the abdomen, the chest, and on the front of the arms. The face is often exempt. The spots, which are reddish-brown and symmetrically arranged, persist for a week or two. Next in frequency is a *papular syphilide*, which may form acne-like indurations about the face and trunk, often arranged in groups. Other forms are the *pustular rash*, which may so closely simulate variola that the patient may be sent to a small-pox hospital. A *squamous syphilide* occurs, not unlike ordinary psoriasis, except that the scales are less abundant. The rash is more copper-colored and not specially confined to the extensor surfaces.

In the moist regions of the skin, such as the perinæum and groins, the axillæ, between the toes, and at the angles of the mouth, the so-called *mucous patches* develop, which are flat, warty outgrowths, with well-defined margins and surfaces covered with a grayish secretion. They are among the most distinctive lesions of syphilis.

Frequently the hair falls out (alopecia), either in patches or by a general thinning. Occasionally the nails become affected (syphilitic onychia).

(*d*) *Mucous Lesions.*—With the fever and the roseolous rash the throat and mouth become sore. The pharyngeal mucosa is hyperæmic, the tonsils are swollen and often present small, kidney-shaped ulcers with grayish-white borders. Mucous patches are seen on the inner surfaces of the cheeks and on the tongue and lips. Sometimes on the tongue there are whitish spots (leucomata), which are seen most frequently in smokers, and which Hutchinson regards as the joint result of syphilitic glossitis and the irritation of hot tobacco-smoke. Hypertrophy of the papillæ in various portions of the mucous membrane produces the syphilitic warts or condylomata which are most frequent about the vulva and anus.

(*e*) *Other Lesions.*—*Iritis* is common, and usually affects one eye before the other. It develops in from three to six months after the chancre. There may be only slight ciliary congestion in mild cases, but in severer forms there is great pain, and the condition is serious and demands careful management. *Choroiditis* and *retinitis* are rare secondary symptoms. Ear affections are not common in the secondary stage, but instances are found in which sudden deafness develops, which may be due to labyrinthine disease; more commonly the impaired hearing is due to the extension of inflammation from the throat to the middle ear. Epididymitis and parotitis are occasional secondary lesions.

Tertiary Stage.—No hard and fast line can be drawn between the lesions of the secondary and those of the tertiary period; and, indeed, in exceptional cases, manifestations which usually appear late may set in even before the primary sore has properly healed. The special affections of this stage are certain skin eruptions, gummatous growths in the viscera, and amyloid degenerations.

(*a*) The late *syphilides* show a greater tendency to ulceration and destruction of the deeper layers of the skin, so that in healing scars are left. They are also more scattered and seldom symmetrical. One of the most characteristic of the tertiary syphilides is rupia, the dry stratified crusts of which cover an ulcer which involves the deeper layers of the skin and in healing leaves a scar.

(*b*) *Gummata.*—These may develop in the skin, subcutaneous tissue, muscles, or internal organs. The general character has been already described. When they develop in the skin they tend to break down and ulcerate, leaving ugly sores which heal with difficulty. In the solid organs they undergo fibroid transformation and produce puckering and deformity.

On the mucous membranes these tertiary lesions lead to ulceration, in the healing of which cicatrices are formed; thus, in the larynx great narrowing may result, and in the rectum ulceration with fibroid thickening and retraction may lead to stricture.

(c) *Amyloid Degeneration.*—Syphilis plays a most important *rôle* in the production of this affection. Of 244 instances analyzed by Fagge, 76 had syphilis, and of these 42 had no bone lesions. It follows the acquired form and is very common in association with rectal syphilis in women. In congenital lues amyloid degeneration is rare.

(d) *Para- or Metasyphilitic Affections.*—Certain disorders not actually syphilitic, yet so closely connected that a large proportion of the cases have had the disease, are termed by Fournier parasyphilitic (Les Affections Parasyphilitiques, 1894). These affections are not exclusively and necessarily caused by syphilis, and they are not influenced by specific treatment. The chief of them are locomotor ataxia, dementia paralytica, certain types of epilepsy, and, we may add, arterio-sclerosis.

III. Congenital Syphilis.

With the exception of the primary sore, every feature of the acquired disease may be seen in the congenital form.

The intra-uterine conditions leading to the death of the fœtus do not here concern us. The child may be born healthy-looking, or with well-marked evidences of the disease. In the majority of instances the former is the case, and within the first month or two the signs of the disease appear.

Symptoms.—(a) *At Birth.*—When the disease exists at birth the child is feebly developed and wasted, and a skin eruption is usually present, commonly in the form of bullæ about the wrists and ankles, and on the hands and feet (pemphigus neonatorum). The child snuffles, the lips are ulcerated, the angles of the mouth fissured, and there is enlargement of the liver and spleen. The bone symptoms may be marked, and the epiphyses may even be separated. In such cases the children rarely survive long.

(b) *Early Manifestations.*—When born healthy the child thrives, is fat and plump, and shows no abnormity whatever; then from the fourth to the eighth week, rarely later, a nasal catarrh develops, *syphilitic rhinitis*, which impedes respiration, and produces the characteristic symptom which has given the name *snuffles* to the disease. The discharge may be sero-purulent or bloody. The child nurses with great difficulty. In severe cases ulceration takes place with necrosis of the bone, leading to a depression at the root of the nose and a deformity characteristic of congenital syphilis. This coryza may be mistaken at first for an ordinary catarrh, but the co-existence of other manifestations usually makes the diagnosis clear. The disease may extend into the Eustachian tubes and middle ears and lead to deafness.

The *cutaneous lesions* develop with or shortly after the onset of the snuffles. The skin often has a sallow, earthy hue. The eruptions are first noticed about the nates. There may be an erythema or an eczematous condition, but more commonly there are irregular reddish-brown patches with well-defined edges. A papular syphilide in this region is by no means uncommon. Fissures develop about the lips, either at the angles of the mouth or in the median line. These *rhagades*, as they are called, are very characteristic. There may be marked ulceration of the muco-cutaneous surfaces. The secretions from these mouth lesions are very virulent, and it is from this source that the wet-nurse is usually infected. Not only the nurse, but members of the family, may be contaminated. There are instances in which other children have been accidentally inoculated from a syphilitic infant. The hair of the head or of the eyebrows may fall out. The syphilitic *onychia* is not uncommon. Enlargement of the glands is not so frequent in the congenital as in the acquired disease. When the cutaneous lesions are marked, the contiguous glands can usually be felt. As pointed out by Gee, the spleen is enlarged in many cases. The condition may persist for a long time. Enlargement of the liver, though often present, is less significant, since in infants it may be due to various causes. These are among the most constant symptoms of congenital syphilis, and usually develop between the third and twelfth weeks. Frequently they are preceded by a period of restlessness and wakefulness, particularly at night. Some authors have described a peculiar syphilitic cry, high-pitched and harsh. Among rarer manifestations are hæmorrhages—the *syphilis hæmorrhagica neonatorum*. The bleeding may be subcutaneous, from the mucous surfaces, or, when early, from the umbilicus. All of such cases, however, are not syphilitic, and the disease must not be confounded with the acute hæmoglobinuria of new-born infants, which Winckel describes as occurring in epidemic form, and which is probably an acute infectious disorder.

(*c*) *Late Manifestations.*—Children with congenital syphilis rarely thrive. Usually they present a wizened, wasted appearance, and a prematurely aged face. In the cases which recover, the general nutrition may remain good and the child may show no further manifestations of the disease; commonly, however, at the period of second dentition or at puberty the disease reappears. Although the child may have recovered from the early lesions, it does not develop like other children. Growth is slow, development tardy, and there are facial and cranial characteristics which often render the disease recognizable at a glance. A young man of nineteen or twenty may neither look older nor be more developed than a boy of ten or twelve. Fournier describes this condition as *infantilism*. The forehead is prominent, the frontal eminences are marked, and the skull may be very asymmetrical. The bridge of the nose is depressed, the tip *retroussé*. The lips are often prominent, and there are striated lines running from the corners of the mouth. The *teeth* are deformed and may present appearances which Jonathan Hutchinson claims are specific and peculiar. The upper central incisors of the permanent set are the teeth which give information. The specific alterations are—the teeth are peg-shaped, stunted in length and breadth, and narrower at the cutting edge than at the root. On the anterior surface the enamel is well formed, and not eroded or honeycombed. At the cutting edge there is a single notch, usually shallow, sometimes deep, in which the dentine is exposed.

Among late manifestations, particularly apt to appear about puberty, is the interstitial *keratitis*, which usually begins as a slight steaminess of the corneæ, which present a ground-glass appearance. It affects both eyes, though one is attacked before the other. It may persist for months, and usually clears completely, though it may leave opacities, which prevent clear vision. *Iritis* may also occur. Of *ear affections*, apart from those which develop as a sequence of the pharyngeal disease, a form occurs about the time of puberty or earlier, in which deafness comes on rapidly and persists in spite of all treatment. It is unassociated with obvious lesions, and is probably labyrinthine in character. *Bone lesions*, occurring oftenest after the sixth year, are not rare among the late manifestations of hereditary syphilis. The tibiæ are most frequently attacked. It is really a chronic gummatous periostitis, which gradually leads to great thickening of the bone. The nodes of congenital syphilis, which are often mistaken for rickets, are more commonly diffuse and affect the bones of the upper and lower extremities. They are generally symmetrical and rarely painful. They may develop late, even after the twenty-first year.

Joint lesions are rare. Clutton has described a symmetrical synovitis of the knee in hereditary syphilis. Enlargement of the spleen, sometimes with the lymph-glands, may be one of the late manifestations, and may occur either alone or in connection with disease of the liver.

Gummata of the liver, brain, and kidneys have been found in late hereditary syphilis.

Is syphilis transmitted to the third generation? The general opinion is that the recorded cases scarcely stand criticism. Occasionally, however, cases of pronounced congenital syphilis are met with in the children of parents who are perfectly healthy, and who have not, so far as is known, had syphilis, and yet, as remarked by Coutts, who reported such a group of cases, they do not bear careful scrutiny. This is the opinion of the leading syphilographers. Personally, I have never met with even a suspicious instance. On the other hand, I know now a number of perfectly healthy children, one of whose grandfathers was syphilitic.

IV. Visceral Syphilis.

A. **Syphilis of the Brain and Cord.**—The following lesions occur:

(1) *Gummata*, forming definite tumors, ranging in size from a pea to a walnut. They are usually multiple and attached to the pia mater, sometimes to the dura. Very rarely they are found unassociated with the meninges. When small they present a uniform, translucent appearance, but when large the centre undergoes a fibro-caseous change, while at the periphery there is a firm, translucent, grayish tissue. They may closely resemble large tuberculous tumors. The growths are most common in the cerebrum. They may be multiple and may even attain a considerable size without becoming caseous. Occasionally gummata undergo cystic degeneration. In the cord large gummatous growths are not so common. In

an instance recently reported by me a tumor, from three eighths to one fourth of an inch in diameter, was completely within the cord opposite the fourth cervical nerve, and there were numerous gummata in the cauda equina.

(2) *Gummatous Meningitis.*—This constantly occurs in the neighborhood of the larger growths, and there may be local meningeal thickening several centimetres in extent, in which the pia is infiltrated and the arteries greatly thickened. This by no means uncommon form may run a subacute or a chronic course.

(3) *Gummatous Arteritis.*—The lesions may be confined to the arteries which present the nodular tumors to be described hereafter.

(4) Foci of *sclerosis,* which Lancereaux holds may be distinguished from non-specific forms by a much greater tendency of the neuroglia elements to undergo fatty transformation, and by the secondary alterations, as areas of softening, which occur in the neighborhood. Neither the diffuse nor the nodular cerebral sclerosis, met with particularly in children, appears to have any special relation to inherited syphilis.

(5) Whether a localized encephalitis or myelitis can result from the action of the syphilitic poison without involvement of the blood-vessels is doubtful. In a case of multiple arterial gummata recently in my ward, Thomas found in the lumbar region of the cord foci of inflammatory softening.

Secondary Changes.—In the brain gummatous arteritis is one of the common causes of softening, which may be extensive, as when the middle cerebral artery is involved, or when there is a large patch of syphilitic meningitis. In such instances the process is really a meningo-encephalitis, and the symptoms are due to the secondary changes in the brain-substance, not directly to the gumma. In the neighborhood of a gummatous growth intense encephalitis or myelitis may develop, and within a few days change the clinical picture. Gummatous arteritis may lead to weakening of the wall of the vessel and rupture with meningeal hæmorrhage.

Syphilitic disease of the nerve-centres may occur in the inherited or acquired form, more commonly in the latter. In the congenital cases the tumors usually develop early, but may be as late as the twenty-first year (H. C. Wood). In the acquired form the nerve lesions belong, as a rule, to the late manifestations, and patients may have quite forgotten the existence of a primary infection, and in very many instances the secondary manifestations have been slight. Heubner, to whom we owe so much in connection with this subject, has seen them as late as the thirtieth year. On the other hand, in exceptional instances, they may occur very early, and severe convulsions with hemiplegia have been reported within three months of the primary sore. The discussion at the Royal Medical and Chirurgical Society (B. M. J., 1895, vol. i), and Lydston's paper (Jour. Am. Med. Assoc., 1895, vol. i), show that various affections of the nervous system are by no means uncommon during the secondary stage of the disease.

Symptoms.—The chief features of cerebral syphilis are those of tumor, which will be considered subsequently under that section. They may be classified here as follows:

(1) Psychical features. A sudden and violent onset of delirium may be the first symptom. In other instances prior to the occurrence of delirium there have been headache, alteration of character, and loss of memory. The condition may be accompanied by convulsions. There may be no neuritis, no palsy, and no localizing symptoms.

(2) More commonly following headache, giddiness, or an excited state which may amount to delirium, the patient has an epileptic seizure or develops hemiplegia, or there is involvement of the nerves of the base. Some of these cases display a prolonged torpor, a special feature of brain syphilis to which both Buzzard and Heubner have referred, which may persist for as long as a month. H. C. Wood describes with this a state of automatism occurring particularly at night, in which the patient behaves like a "restless nocturnal automaton rather than a man."

(3) A clinical picture of general paralysis—dementia paralytica. The question is still in dispute whether this syphilitic encephalopathy, which so closely resembles general paralysis, is a distinct and independent affection. Mickle, who has carefully reviewed the subject, concludes that syphilis may directly produce the inflammatory changes in the brain, while in other instances it directly predisposes to this affection. It is a somewhat remarkable feature that the cases which present the clinical picture of general paresis are most frequently those which have not had any localizing symptoms, and they may not have convulsions until the disease is well advanced.

(4) Many cases of cerebral syphilis display the symptoms of brain tumor—headache, optic neuritis, vomiting, and convulsions. Of these symptoms convulsions are the most important, and both Fournier and Wood have laid great stress on the value of this symptom in persons over thirty. The first symptoms may, however, rather resemble those of embolism or thrombosis; thus there may be sudden hemiplegia, with or without loss of consciousness.

The symptoms of *spinal syphilis* are extremely varied and may be caused by large gummatous growths attached to the meninges, in which case the features are those of tumor; by gummatous arteritis with secondary softening; by meningitis with secondary cord changes; or by scleroses developing late in the disease, the relation of which to syphilis is still obscure. Erb's syphilitic myelitis will be considered under the spastic paraplegias.

Diagnosis.—The history is of the first importance, but it may be extremely difficult to get a reliable account. Careful examination should be made for traces of the primary sore, for the cicatrices of bubo, for scars of the skin eruption or throat ulcers, and for bone lesions. The character of the symptoms is often of great assistance. They are multiform, variable, and often such as could not be explained by a single lesion; thus there may be anomalous spinal symptoms or involvement of the nerves of the brain on both sides. And lastly the result of treatment has a definite bearing on the diagnosis, as the symptoms may clear up and disappear with the use of antisyphilitic remedies.

B. **Syphilis of the Lung.**

This is a very rare disease. During twenty-five years I have not seen more than half a dozen specimens in which there was no question as to the nature of the trouble. Fowler states that he has recently visited the museums of the London hospitals and at the Royal College of Surgeons, and can find only twelve specimens illustrating syphilitic lesions of the lungs, two of which are doubtful. For the most full and satisfactory consideration of pulmonary syphilis, the reader is referred to chapter xxxvii of Fowler and Godlee's work on Diseases of the Lungs.

Etiology and Morbid Anatomy.—Syphilis of the lung occurs under the following forms:

(1) The *white pneumonia of the foetus*. This may affect large areas or an entire lung, which then is firm, heavy, and airless, even though the child may have been born alive. On section it has a grayish-white appearance—the so-called white hepatization of Virchow. The chief change is in the alveolar walls, which are greatly thickened and infiltrated, so that, as Wagner expressed it, the condition resembles a diffuse syphiloma. In the early stages, for example, in a seven or eight months' foetus, there may be scattered miliary foci of this induration chiefly about the arteries. The air-cells are filled with desquamated and swollen epithelium.

(2) In the form of definite *gummata*, which vary in size from a pea to a goose-egg. They occur irregularly scattered through the lung, but, as a rule, are more numerous toward the root. They present a grayish-yellow caseous appearance, are dry and usually imbedded in a translucent, more or less firm, connective tissue. In a case from my wards described by Councilman, there was extensive involvement of the root of the lungs. Bands of connective tissue passed inward from the thickened pleura and between these strands and surrounding the gummata there was in places a mottled red pneumonic consolidation. In the caseous nodules there is typical hyaline degeneration. Councilman describes as the primary lesion, atrophy of the alveolar walls with hyaline degeneration of the capillaries; not the syphilitic endarteritis, which is well marked, and to which the lesions are attributed. The bronchi are usually involved, and surrounding the gummata there may be a diffuse broncho-pneumonia, which does not appear to have any peculiar characters.

(3) A majority of authors follow Virchow in recognizing the fibrous interstitial pneumonia at the root of the lung and passing along the bronchi and vessels as probably syphilitic. This much may be said, that in certain cases gummata are associated with these fibroid changes. Again, this condition alone is found in persons with well-marked syphilitic history or with other visceral lesions. It seems in many instances to be a purely sclerotic process, advancing sometimes from the pleura, more commonly from the root of the lung, and invading the interlobular tissue, gradually producing a more or less extensive fibroid change. It rarely involves more than a portion of a lobe or portions of the lobes at the root of the lung. The bronchi are often dilated.

Symptoms.—Is there a syphilitic phthisis, an ulcerative and destructive disease, due to lues? Personally I have no knowledge of such an affection, either clinically or anatomically, and the cases which I have seen demonstrated do not seem to me to have characters distinctive enough to separate them from ordinary tuberculous phthisis. Certain French writers recognize not only a chronic syphilitic phthisis but an acute syphilitic pneumonia in adults, simulating acute pneumonic phthisis. Clinically, pulmonary syphilis is not of much importance, as the cases can rarely be diagnosed, and the symptoms which arise are usually those of bronchiectasis or of chronic interstitial pneumonia. The white pneumonia is usually found in the still-born.

Diagnosis.—It is to be borne in mind, in the first place, that hospital physicians and pathologists the world over bear witness to the extreme rarity of lung syphilis. In the second place, the therapeutic test upon which so much reliance is placed is by no means conclusive. With pulmonary tuberculosis there should now be no confusion, owing to the readiness with which the presence of bacilli is determined. Bronchiectasy in the lower lobe of a lung, dependent upon an interstitial pneumonia of syphilitic origin, could not be distinguished from any other form of the disease. In persons with well-marked syphilitic lesions elsewhere, when obscure pulmonary symptoms occur, or if there are signs of chronic interstitial pneumonia with dilated bronchi, and no tubercle bacilli are present, the condition may possibly be due to syphilis. So far as my experience goes, tuberculous phthisis occurring in a syphilitic subject has no special peculiarities. The lesions of syphilis and tuberculosis could of course co-exist in a lung.

c. Syphilis of the Liver.

This occurs in three forms: (a) *Diffuse Syphilitic Hepatitis.*—This is most common in cases of congenital syphilis. The liver preserves its form, is large, hard, and resistant. Sometimes it has a yellow look, compared by Trousseau to sole-leather, or an appearance not unlike the amyloid liver. Careful inspection shows grayish or whitish points and lines corresponding to the interlobular new growth. Microscopically, great increase in the connective tissue is seen, and in many places foci of small-celled infiltration. Sometimes these nodules are visible, forming firm miliary gummata which in cicatrizing produce more or less deformity. Larger gummata may also be present.

(b) *Gummata.*—As a result of congenital syphilis these may occur in childhood or in adult life. In acquired syphilis they rarely come on before the second year after infection. In the early stage there are pale grayish nodules, varying in size from a pea to a marble. The larger present yellowish centres at first; but later there is a " pale yellowish, cheese-like nodule of irregular outline, surrounded by a fibrous zone, the outer edge of which loses itself in the lobular tissue, the lobules dwindling gradually in its grasp. This fibrous zone is never very broad; the cheesy centre varies in consistence from a gristle-like toughness to a pulpy softness; it is sometimes mortar-like, from cretaceous change " (Wilks). When numerous, the most extensive deformity of the liver is produced in the gradual healing of these gummata. On the surface there are deep, scar-like depressions, and the entire organ may be divided into a cluster of irregular masses, held together by fibrous tissue. To this condition the term *botyroid* has been given, from its resemblance to a bunch of grapes. As a rule, the gummata gradually undergo fibroid transformation. They may, however, soften and liquefy, and, according to Wilks, may form a fluctuating tumor.

(*c*) Occasionally the syphilitic changes are chiefly manifested in *Glisson's sheath*, in a thickening of the capsule, producing perihepatitis, and increase in the connective tissue in the *portal canals*, so that on section the organ presents a number of branching fibrous scars which may cause considerable deformity.

Symptoms.—The symptoms of syphilitic hepatitis are very variable. In the new-born icterus is not uncommon, but the condition of the liver can scarcely be recognized. In the adult there are three groups of cases:

The patient presents a picture of cirrhosis of the liver; there are digestive disturbances, slight icterus, loss of weight, and ascites. If signs of syphilis are present in other organs, the condition may be suspected, or if after removal of the fluid the liver is felt to be extremely irregular, the diagnosis may be made almost with certainty. These cases are common, and with proper treatment get well; they form an important contingent of the reputed recoveries in ordinary cirrhosis of the liver.

In a second group of cases the patient is anæmic, passes large quantities of pale urine containing albumin and tube-casts; the liver is enlarged, perhaps irregular, and the spleen also is enlarged. Dropsical symptoms may supervene, or the patient may be carried off by some intercurrent disease. Extensive amyloid degeneration of the spleen, the intestinal mucosa, and of the liver, with gummata, are found.

Thirdly, the gummata may form an irregular tumor on the right or left lobe, perhaps with very few or very obscure symptoms. The diagnosis may be doubtful until some other evidence of syphilis develops. I have recorded several illustrative cases in my Lectures on Abdominal Tumors.

The *diagnosis* of syphilis of the liver is very important, since upon it the proper treatment depends. If with a history of infection the liver is enlarged and irregular, and the general health fairly good, the condition is probably syphiloma.

D. Syphilis of the Digestive Tract.

The *œsophagus* is very rarely affected. Stenosis is the usual result. Syphilis of the *stomach* is excessively rare. Flexner has reported a remarkable case in association with gummata of the liver. He has collected 14 cases in the literature. Syphilitic ulceration has been found in the small intestine and in the cæcum.

The most common seat of syphilitic disease in this tract is the *rectum*. The affection is found most commonly in women, and results from the development of gummata in the submucosa above the internal sphincter. The process is slow and tedious, and may last for years before it finally induces stricture. The symptoms are usually those of narrowing of the lower bowel. The condition is readily recognized by rectal examination. The history of gradual on-coming stricture, the state of the patient, and the fact that there is a hard, fibrous narrowing, not an elevated crater-like ulcer, usually render easy the diagnosis from malignant disease. In medical practice these cases come under observation for other symptoms, particularly amyloid degeneration; and the rectal disease may be entirely overlooked, and only discovered post mortem.

E. Circulatory System.

Syphilis of the Heart.—A fresh, warty endocarditis due to syphilis is not recognized, though occasionally in persons dead of the disease this form is present, as is not uncommon in conditions of debility. Outgrowths on the valves in connection with gummata have been reported by Janeway and others. In a recent study of the subject Loomis groups the lesions into: (1) Gummata, recent or old; (2) fibroid induration, localized or diffuse; (3) amyloid degeneration; and (4) endarteritis obliterans. I. Adler claims that changes in the blood-vessels of the walls of the heart are common both in congenital and acquired syphilis, even in cases without clinical symptoms or gross lesions.

Rupture may take place, as in the cases reported by Dandridge and Nalty, or sudden death, as in the cases of Cayley and Pearce Gould; indeed, sudden death is frequent, occurring in 21 of 63 cases (Mracek).

Syphilis of the Arteries.—Syphilis is believed to play an important *rôle* in arterio-sclerosis and aneurism. Its connection with these processes will be considered later; here we shall refer only to the syphilitic arteritis, which occurs in two forms:

(*a*) An *obliterating endarteritis*, characterized by a proliferation of the subendothelial tissue. The new growth lies within the elastic lamina, and may gradually fill the entire lumen; hence the term obliterating. The media and adventitia are also infiltrated with small cells. This form of endarteritis described by Heubner is not, however, characteristic of syphilis, and its presence alone in an artery could not be considered pathognomonic. If, however, there are gummata in other parts, or if the condition about to be described exists in adjacent arteries, the process may be regarded as syphilitic.

(*b*) *Gummatous Periarteritis.*—With or without involvement of the intima, nodular gummata may develop in the adventitia of the artery, producing globular or ovoid swellings, which may attain considerable size. They are not infrequently seen in the cerebral arteries, which seem to be specially prone to this affection. This form is specific and distinctive of syphilis. The disease usually affects the smaller vessels and may be found in the coronary arteries, and particularly in those of the brain.

F. Renal Syphilis.

(*a*) Gummata occasionally develop in the kidneys, particularly in cases in which there is extensive gummatous hepatitis. They are rarely numerous, and occasionally lead to scattered cicatrices. Clinically the affection is not recognizable.

(*b*) *Acute Syphilitic Nephritis.*—This condition has been carefully studied by the French writers and by Lafleur, of Montreal. It is estimated to occur in the secondary stage in about 3.8 per cent, and may develop in from three to six months, sometimes later, from the initial lesion. The outlook is good, though often the albuminuria may persist for months; more rarely chronic Bright's disease develops. In a few instances syphilitic nephritis has proved rapidly fatal in a fortnight or three weeks. The lesions are not specific, but are similar to those in other acute infections.

G. **Syphilitic Orchitis.**—This affection is of special significance to the physician, as its detection frequently clinches the diagnosis in obscure internal disorders. Syphilis occurs in the testes in two forms:

(a) The *gummatous growth*, forming an indurated mass or group of masses in the substance of the organ, and sometimes difficult to distinguish from tuberculous disease. The area of induration is harder and it affects the body of the testes, while tubercle more commonly involves the epididymis. It rarely tends to invade the skin, or to break down, soften, and suppurate, and is usually painless.

(b) There is an *interstitial orchitis* regarded as syphilitic, which leads to fibroid induration of the gland and gradually to atrophy. It is a slow, progressive change, coming on without pain, usually involving one organ more than another.

General Diagnosis of Syphilis.—There is seldom any doubt concerning the existence of syphilitic lesions. The negative statements of the patient must be taken with extreme caution, as persons will lie deliberately with reference to primary infection, when it is in their best interest to make a straightforward truthful statement. It is to be remembered that syphilis is common in the community, and there are probably more families with a luetic than with a tuberculous taint. It is possible that the primary sore may have been of trifling extent, or urethral and masked by a gonorrhœa, and the patient may not have had severe secondary symptoms, but such instances are extremely rare. Inquiries should be made into the history to ascertain if the patient has had skin rashes, sore throat, or if the hair has fallen out. Careful inspection should be made of the throat and skin for signs of old lesions. Scars in the groins, the result of buboes, may be taken as positive evidence of infection (Hutchinson). The cicatrices on the legs are often copper-colored, though this cannot be regarded as peculiar to syphilis. The bones should be examined for nodes. In doubtful cases the scar of the primary sore may be found, or there may be signs of atrophy or of hardening of the testes. In women, special stress has been laid upon the occurrence of frequent miscarriages, which, in connection with other circumstances, are always suggestive.

In the congenital disease, the occurrence within the first three months of snuffles and skin rash is conclusive. Later, the characters of the syphilitic facies, already referred to, often give a clew to the nature of some obscure visceral lesion. Other distinctive features are the symmetrical development of nodes on the bones, and the interstitial keratitis.

In doubtful cases much stress is laid by some writers upon the therapeutic test, by placing the patient upon antisyphilitic treatment. In the case of an obstinate skin rash of doubtful character, which has resisted all other forms of medication, this has much greater weight than in obscure visceral lesions. I have on several occasions known such marked improvement to follow large doses of iodide of potassium that the diagnosis of syphilitic lesion was greatly strengthened, but the subsequent course and the post mortem have shown that the disease was not syphilis.

16

Prophylaxis.—Irregular intercourse has existed from the beginning of recorded history, and unless man's nature wholly changes—and of this we can have no hope—will continue. Resisting all attempts at solution, the social evil remains the great blot upon our civilization, and inextricably blended with it is the question of the prevention of syphilis. Two measures are available—the one personal, the other administrative.

Personal purity is the prophylaxis which we, as physicians, are especially bound to advocate. Continence may be a hard condition (to some harder than to others), but it can be borne, and it is our duty to urge this lesson upon young and old who seek our advice in matters sexual. Certainly it is better, as St. Paul says, to marry than to burn, but if the former is not feasible there are other altars than those of Venus upon which a young man may light fires. He may practise at least two of the five means by which, as the physician Rondibilis counselled Panurge, carnal concupiscence may be cooled and quelled—hard work of body and hard work of mind. Idleness is the mother of lechery; and a young man will find that absorption in any pursuit will do much to cool passions which, though natural and proper, cannot in the exigencies of our civilization always obtain natural and proper gratification.

The second measure is a rigid and systematic regulation of prostitution. The state accepts the responsibility of guarding citizens against small-pox or cholera, but in dealing with syphilis the problem has been too complex and has hitherto baffled solution. On the one hand, inspection, segregation, and regulation are difficult, if not impossible, to carry out; on the other hand, public sentiment, in Anglo-Saxon communities at least, is as yet bitterly opposed to this plan. While this feeling, though unreasonable, as I think, is entitled to consideration, the choice lies between two evils—licensing, even imperfectly carried out, or widespread disease and misery. If the offender bore the cross alone, I would say, forbear; but the physician behind the scenes knows that in countless instances syphilis has wrought havoc among innocent mothers and helpless infants, often entailing life-long suffering. It is for them he advocates protective measures.

Treatment.—We must admit that various constitutions react very differently to the poison of syphilis. There are individuals who, although receiving brief and unsatisfactory treatment, display for years no traces of the disease. On the other hand, there are persons thoroughly and systematically treated from the outset who from time to time show well-marked indications of syphilis. Certainly there are grounds for the opinion that persons who have suffered very slightly from secondary symptoms are more prone to have the severer visceral lesions of the later stage.

When we consider that syphilis is one of the most amenable of all diseases to treatment, it is lamentable that the later stages which come under the charge of the physician are so common. This results, in great part, from carelessness of the patient, who, wearied with treatment, cannot understand why he should continue to take medicine after all the symptoms have disappeared; but, in part, the profession also is to blame for not insisting more urgently in every instance that acquired syphilis is not cured in a few months, but takes at least two years, during which time the patient should be under careful supervision. The treatment of the disease is now practically narrowed to the use of two remedies, justly termed specifics—namely, mercury and iodide of potassium. The former is of special service in the secondary, the latter in the tertiary manifestations of the disease; but they are often combined with advantage.

Mercury may be given by the mouth in the form of gray powder, the hydrargyrum cum cretâ, which Hutchinson recommends to be given in pills, one-grain doses with a grain of Dover's powder. One pill from four to six times a day will usually suffice. I warmly endorse the excellent results which are obtained by this method, under which the patient often gains rapidly in weight, and the general health improves remarkably. It may be continued for months without any ill effects. Other forms given by the mouth are the pilules of the biniodide (gr. $\frac{1}{16}$), or of the protiodide (gr. $\frac{1}{4}$), three times a day. "If mercury be begun as soon as the state of the sore permits of diagnosis, and continued in small but adequate doses, the patient will usually escape both sore throat and eruption" (Jonathan Hutchinson).

Inunction is a still more effective means. A drachm of the ordinary mercurial ointment is thoroughly rubbed into the skin every evening for six days; on the seventh a warm bath is taken, and on the eighth the mercurial course is resumed. At least half an hour should be given to each inunction. It is well to apply it at different places on successive days. The sides of the chest and abdomen and the inner surfaces of the arms and thighs are the best positions.

The mercury may be given by direct injection into the muscles. If proper precautions are taken in sterilizing the syringe, and if the injections are made into the muscles, not into the subcutaneous tissue, abscesses rarely result. One third of a grain of the bichloride in twenty drops of water may be injected once a week, or from one to two grains of calomel in glycerin (20 minims).

Still another method, greatly in vogue in certain parts of the Continent and in institutions, is fumigation. It may be carried out effectively by means of Lee's lamp. The patient sits on a chair wrapped in blankets, with the head exposed. The calomel is volatilized and deposited with the vapor on the patient's skin. The process lasts about twenty minutes, and the patient goes to bed wrapped in blankets without washing or drying the skin. A patient under mercurial treatment should avoid stimulants and live a regular life, not necessarily abstaining from business. Green vegetables and fruit should not be taken. Salivation is to be avoided. The teeth should be cleansed twice a day, and if the gums become tender, the breath fetid, or the tongue swollen and indented, the drug should be suspended for a week or ten days.

In congenital syphilis the treatment of cases born with bullæ and other signs of the disease is not satisfactory, and the infants usually die within a few days or weeks. The child should be nursed by the mother alone, or, if this is not feasible, should be hand-fed, but under no circumstances should a wet-nurse be employed. The child is most rapidly and thoroughly brought under the influence of the drug by inunction. The mercurial ointment may be smeared on the flannel roller. This is not a very cleanly method, and sometimes rouses the suspicion of the mother. It is preferable to give the drug by the mouth, in the form of gray powder, half a grain three times a day. In the late manifestations associated with bone lesions, the combination of mercury and iodide of potassium is most suitable and is well given in the form of Gilbert's syrup, which consists of the biniodide of mercury (gr. j), of potassium iodide (℥ ss.), and water (℥ ij). Of this a dose for a child under three is from five to ten drops three times a day, gradually increased. Under these measures, the cases of congenital syphilis usually improve with great rapidity. The medication should be continued at intervals for many months, and it is well to watch these patients carefully during the period of second dentition and at puberty, and if necessary to place them on specific treatment.

In the treatment of the visceral lesions of syphilis, which come more distinctly within the province of the physician, iodide of potassium is of equal or even greater value than mercury. Under its use ulcers rapidly heal, gummatous tumors melt away, and we have an illustration of a specific action only equalled by that of mercury in the secondary stages, by iron in certain forms of anæmia, and by quinine in malaria. It is as a rule well borne in an initial dose of 10 grains, or 10 minims of the saturated solution; given in milk the patient does not notice the taste. It should be gradually increased to 30 or more grains three times a day. In syphilis of the nervous system it may be used in still larger doses. Seguin, who specially insisted upon the advantage of this plan, urged that the drug should be pushed, as good effects were not obtained with the moderate doses.

When syphilitic hepatitis is suspected the combination of mercury and iodide of potassium is most satisfactory. If there is ascites, Addison's or Niemeyer's pill (as it is often called) of calomel, digitalis, and squills will be found very useful. A patient of mine with recurring ascites, on whom paracentesis was repeatedly performed and who had an enlarged and irregular liver, took this pill for more than a year with occasionally intermissions, and ultimately there was a complete disappearance of the dropsy and an extraordinary reduction in the volume of the liver. Occasionally the iodide of sodium is more satisfactory than the iodide of potassium. It is less depressing and agrees better with the stomach. Many patients possess a remarkable idiosyncrasy to the iodide, but as a rule it is well borne. Severe coryza with salivation, and œdema about the eyelids, are its most common disagreeable effects. Skin eruptions also are frequent. I have known patients unable to take more than from 20 to 30 grains without suffering from an erythematous rash; much more common is the acne eruption. Occasionally an urticarial rash may develop with spots of purpura. Some of these iodide eruptions may closely resemble syphilis. Hutchinson has reported instances in which they have proved fatal.

Upon the question of syphilis and marriage the family physician is often called to decide. He should insist upon the necessity of two full years elapsing between the date of infection and the contracting of marriage. This, it should be borne in mind, is the earliest possible limit, and there should be at least a year of complete immunity from all manifestations of the disease.

In relation to life insurance, an individual with syphilis cannot be regarded as a first-class risk unless he can furnish evidence of prolonged and thorough treatment and of immunity for two or three years from all manifestations. Even then, when we consider the extraordinary frequency of the cerebral and other complications in persons who have had this disease and who may even have undergone thorough treatment, the risk to the company is certainly increased.

XXXIII. GONORRHŒAL INFECTION.

Gonorrhœa, one of the most widespread and serious of infectious diseases, presents many features for consideration. As a cause of ill-health and disability the gonococcus occupies a position of the very first rank among its fellows. While the local lesion is too often thought to be trifling, in its singular obstinacy, in the possibilities of permanent sexual damage to the individual himself and still more in the " grisly troop " which may follow in its train, gonorrhœal infection does not fall very far short of syphilis in importance.

The immediate and remote effects of the gonococcus may be considered under—

I. The primary infection.

II. The spread in the genito-urinary organs by direct continuity of surface.

III. Systemic gonorrhœal infection.

I. The primary lesion we need not here consider, but we may call attention to the frequency of the complications, such as periurethral abscess, gonorrhœal prostatitis in the male, and vaginitis, endocervicitis, and inflammation of the glands of Bartholini in the female.

II. Perhaps the most serious of all the sequels of gonorrhœa are those which result from the spread by direct continuity of tissues, particularly in women, in whom gonorrhœal salpingitis has been shown to be a not infrequent event. Metritis and ovaritis are also occasionally met with, and peritonitis, due to the escape of pus from the Fallopian tubes, has been described. Equally important is the development of cystitis, which is probably much more frequently the result of a mixed infection than due to the gonococcus itself. A great risk is the extension upward through the ureters to the kidneys. The pyelitis, like the cystitis, is usually a mixed infection.

III. Systemic Gonorrhœal Infection.

1. *Gonorrhœal Septicæmia and Pyæmia.*—The fever associated with the primary disease is not an indication of a general infection, but probably follows the absorption of toxines. The presence of the gonococcus has been demonstrated in the blood in a few cases, usually in connection with some local lesion, as in Thayer's and Blumer's case from my wards, in

which the patient succumbed to an acute endocarditis. Instances of severe, rapidly fatal general infection in gonorrhœa are probably always associated with foci of suppuration in the urinary tract. I held an autopsy in Montreal on a remarkable case of rapid gonorrhœal sepsis in a young man, who within ten days of the primary lesion was seized with severe chills and high fever. He rapidly became unconscious, the fever persisted, and he fell into a condition of profound toxæmia and died early on the morning of the fourth day from the chill. At the autopsy, which was made about twelve hours after death, there was an acute urethritis and a small prostatic abscess not more than 2 or 3 cm. in diameter. The blood was fluid, tarry black, and unlike anything I have ever seen before or since.

Gonorrhœal Endocarditis.—R. L. MacDonnell found 4 cases of endocarditis in 27 instances of gonorrhœal arthritis. Two remarkable cases have been reported from my wards lately by Thayer and Blumer and Thayer and Lazear. They are of special interest, as in both the gonococci were isolated from the blood during life and after death from the affected valves. Thayer and Lazear have analyzed 30 instances of fatal ulcerative endocarditis in gonorrhœa. Of these, 22 were in men, 8 in women. As a rule, the arthritis preceded the cardiac affection, but in a number of instances the cardiac complication occurred without or before the development of joint symptoms.

Of other cardiac lesions, pericarditis occurred in 7 of the fatal cases. Acute myocarditis was present in Councilman's case.

2. *Gonorrhœal Arthritis.*—In many respects this is the most damaging, disabling, and serious of all the complications of gonorrhœa. It not only occurs in the adult, but in children after the gonorrhœal conjunctivitis. It occurs more frequently in males than in females. In a series of 252 cases collected by Northrup, 230 were in males; 130 cases were between twenty and thirty years of age. It occurs, as a rule, during an acute attack of gonorrhœa. In 208 of Northrup's series there was a urethral discharge while in hospital. It may occur as the attack subsides, or even when it has become chronic. A gonorrhœal arthritis of great intensity may develop in a newly married woman infected by an old gleet in her husband. As a rule, many joints are affected. In Northrup's series three or more joints were affected in 175 cases, one joint in 56 cases. It is peculiar in attacking certain joints which are rarely involved in acute rheumatism, as the sterno-clavicular, the intra-vertebral, the temporo-maxillary and sacroiliac.

The *anatomical changes* are variable. The inflammation is often periarticular, and extends along the sheaths of the tendons. When effusion occurs in the joints it rarely becomes purulent. It has more commonly the characters of a synovitis. About the wrist and hand suppuration sometimes occurs in the sheaths. It has been suggested that the simple arthritis or synovitis follows absorption of ptomaines from the urethral discharge, while the more severe suppurating forms are due to infection with pus organisms. It has now been definitely shown that the gonococcus itself may be present in the inflamed joint or in the peri-arthritic exudate. Within the past eighteen months Young has obtained the gonococcus in pure culture in 7 cases of gonorrhœal arthritis in the Johns Hopkins Hospital. Sometimes the cultures are negative; in other instances there is a mixed infection with staphylococci or streptococci.

Clinical Course.—Variability and obstinacy are the two most distinguishing features. The following are the most important clinical forms:

(*a*) *Arthralgic*, in which there are wandering pains about the joints, without redness or swelling. These persist for a long time.

(*b*) *Polyarthritic*, in which several joints become affected, just as in subacute articular rheumatism. The fever is slight; the local inflammation may fix itself in one joint, but more commonly several become swollen and tender. In this form cerebral and cardiac complications may occur.

(*c*) *Acute gonorrhœal arthritis*, in which a single articulation becomes suddenly involved. The pain is severe, the swelling extensive, and due chiefly to peri-articular œdema. The general fever is not at all proportionate to the intensity of the local signs. The exudate usually resolves, though suppuration occasionally supervenes.

(*d*) *Chronic Hydrarthrosis.*—This is usually mono-articular, and is particularly apt to involve the knee. It comes on often without pain, redness, or swelling. Formation of pus is rare. It occurred only twice in 96 cases tabulated by Nolen.

(*e*) *Bursal and Synovial Form.*—This attacks chiefly the tendons and their sheaths and the bursæ and the periosteum. The articulations may not be affected. The bursæ of the patella, the olecranon, and the tendo Achillis are most apt to be involved.

(*f*) *Septicæmic.*—In which with an acute arthritis the gonococci invade the blood, and the picture is that of an intense septico-pyæmia, usually with endocarditis.

The disease is much more intractable than ordinary rheumatism, and relapses are extremely common. It may become chronic and last for years.

Complications.—Iritis is not infrequent and may recur with successive attacks. The visceral complications are rare. Endocarditis, pericarditis, and pleurisy may occur.

Treatment.—The salicylates are of very little service, nor do they often relieve the pains in this affection. Iodide of potassium has also proved useless in my hands, even in large doses. A general tonic treatment seems much more suitable—quinine, iron, and, in the chronic cases, arsenic.

The local treatment of the joints is very important. The thermocautery may be used to allay the pain and reduce the swelling. In acute cases, fixation of the joints is very beneficial, and in the chronic forms, massage and passive motion. I have seen very good results follow in a few cases the use of the dry hot air. The surgical treatment of this affection, as carried out nowadays, is more satisfactory, and I have seen strikingly good effects from incision and irrigation.

XXXIV. TUBERCULOSIS.

I. General Etiology and Morbid Anatomy.

Definition.—An infective disease, caused by the *bacillus tuberculosis*, the lesions of which are characterized by nodular bodies called tubercles or diffuse infiltrations of tuberculous tissue which undergo caseation or sclerosis and may finally ulcerate, or in some situations calcify.

Etiology.—1. **Zoological Distribution.**—Tuberculosis is one of the most widespread of maladies.

In cold-blooded animals it is rare, owing doubtless to temperature conditions unfavorable to the development of the bacillus. Among reptiles in confinement it is, however, occasionally seen (Sibley). In fowls it is an extremely common disease, but there are differences in avian tuberculosis sufficient to warrant its separation from the ordinary form.

Among domestic animals tuberculosis is widely but unevenly distributed. Among ruminants, bovines are chiefly affected. The percentage for oxen and cows at the Berlin abattoir in the year 1892–'93 was 15.1. In this country much has been done, particularly in Massachusetts and Pennsylvania, to determine the presence of the disease in the dairy herds, for which purpose the tuberculin test has been extensively employed. The results show a widespread prevalence of the disease.

Of 5,297 cattle slaughtered in Maryland only 159 were tuberculous (A. W. Clement). Of 15,506 slaughtered at the Brighton abattoir, Boston, only 29 were tuberculous (A. Burr). The tuberculin test has shown in some places a percentage of from 15 to 30.

In sheep the disease is very rare. In pigs it is common, but not so common in this country as in Europe. In the inspection of 1,000 hogs, which was made by A. W. Clement and myself in Montreal in 1880, tuberculosis was seen only once or twice. At the Berlin abattoir in 1887–'88 there were 6,393 pigs affected with the disease.

Horses are rarely attacked. Dogs and cats are not prone to the disease, but cases are described in which infection of pet animals has taken place from phthisical masters. Among the semi-domestic animals, such as the rabbit and guinea-pig, the disease under natural conditions is rare, although these animals, particularly the latter, are extremely susceptible to the disease when inoculated. Among apes and monkeys in the wild state, tuberculosis is unknown, but in confinement it is the most formidable disease with which they have to contend.

The important etiological fact in connection with tuberculosis in animals is the widespread occurrence of the disease in bovines, from which class we derive nearly all the milk and a very large proportion of the meat used for food.

2. **General Statistics of the Disease in Man.**—Tuberculosis is the most universal scourge of the human race. It prevails more particularly in the large cities and wherever the population is massed together. One seventh of all deaths are due to it. In the United States Census Report for 1890, 102,188 deaths were reported to be due to consumption. At a low esti-

mate one can say that at least 150,000 persons die annually in the United States of some form of tuberculosis. An estimation based on the Census Report gives the total number of persons in this country infected with tuberculosis as 1,050,000, or 1 in every 60 of the population (Vaughan).

Geographical position has very little influence. The disease is perhaps more prevalent in the temperate regions than in the tropics, but altitude is a more potent factor than latitude; in the high regions of the Alps and Andes and in the central plateau of Mexico the death-rate from tuberculosis is very low.

The influence of race, which has been much studied, is probably less owing to any inherent differences than to the conditions under which the individuals live. The Indians of this continent are very prone to the disease. Matthews states that the death-rate in the older reservations in the East was three times as great as that of the Indians still living in the Northwest. In this country the Irish and the negroes appear specially prone to the disease; on the other hand, the Hebrews possess a relative immunity. For the six years ending May 31, 1890, the average annual death-rate from consumption in New York city per 100,000 of population was: For the Irish, 645.73; for the colored, 531.35; for the Germans, 328.80; for the American whites, 205.14; and for the Russian-Polish Jews, 76.72 (J. S. Billings).

The Decrease of Tuberculosis.—E. F. Wells, who has tabulated an immense body of statistics on this subject, states that the evidence is in favor of a very positive decline in the prevalence of the disease. While the last decennial census of the United States does not show any decrease, yet in many of the larger cities there has been a striking diminution. The question has been considered very carefully by James B. Russell, of Glasgow, in his Sanitary History of that city. One or two of the sentences from his report may be quoted with advantage: " Between the five years 1870–'74 and the five years 1890–'94 there was a decrease of 41 per cent in the death-rate. If we start from the maximum period of fatality (1860–'64), the decrease amounts to 44 per cent. The acceptance of the doctrine that every case of phthisis is the result of a specific infection—that, consequently, no one is foredoomed to have phthisis or any other form of tuberculous disease—gives great precision to our ideas of prevention." He attributes a good deal to the diffusion of the knowledge that the existence and distribution of the tubercle bacillus is the first condition of infection, and also to the successful administrative efforts in securing " ventilation, especially of houses and byres; the removal of dampness by subsoil drainage and precautions adapted to the foundations and walls of houses; the abolition of dark spaces and inclosures; the dissemination of direct sunlight."

The diminution of pulmonary tuberculosis in Massachusetts is remarkable, the death-rate having fallen from 42 per 10,000 inhabitants in 1853 to 21.8 per 10,000 in 1895. A remarkable reduction has also taken place in New York.

3. **The Bacillus Tuberculosis.**—The history of the discovery of the bacillus presents many points of interest. Confidently expected by such observers as Villemin, Chauveau, Cohnheim, and others, and claimed to

have been demonstrated by many, notably by Klebs and Aufrecht, it remained for Koch to demonstrate its existence and its invariable association with the disease. The investigations which he had previously made upon anthrax and experimental traumatic infections, by perfecting the methods of research, paved the way for this brilliant discovery. His preliminary article * and his more elaborate later work † should be carefully studied by any one who wishes to appreciate the value of scientific methods. It forms one of the most masterly demonstrations of modern medicine. Its thoroughness appears in the fact that in the years which have elapsed since its appearance the innumerable workers on the subject have not, so far as I know, added a solitary essential fact to those presented by Koch.

Morphological Characters.—The tubercle bacillus occurs usually as a short, fine rod, often slightly bent or curved, and has an average length of nearly half the diameter of a red blood-corpuscle (3 to 4 μ); more rarely it shows lateral outgrowths or simple branches. When stained it often presents a beaded appearance, which some have attributed to the presence of spores.

With the basic aniline dyes it stains slowly, except at the body temperature, but retains the dye after treatment with acids—a characteristic which separates it from all other known forms of bacteria, with the exception of the bacillus of leprosy.

Modes of Growth.—It grows on blood-serum, glycerin-agar, bouillon, or on potato—most readily on the first. The cultures must be kept at blood-heat. They grow slowly, and do not appear until about the end of the second week. The colonies form thin, grayish-white, dry, scale-like masses on the surface of the culture medium. Successive inoculations may be made from the cultures, and at the end of an indefinite series material from one of them inoculated into a guinea-pig will produce tuberculosis.

Variations.—(*a*) *In Form.*—The small branching forms are found not infrequently in tuberculous lesions. Some investigators claim to have produced more complex structures, resembling the " drüsen " of the actinomyces.

(*b*) *In Virulence.*—Koch was of the opinion that tubercle bacilli from various sources possess the same degree of virulence. Theobald Smith has found cultures of bovine tuberculosis more highly virulent for rabbits than cultures of sputum bacilli. The morphology of the organisms from the two sources was also different. Arloing and his students have long claimed that material from scrofula and bone tuberculosis is less virulent than from other varieties of human tuberculosis.

The bacillus tuberculosis avium tends to appear in more irregular forms, grows more readily and more rapidly in artificial cultures, and is more resistant to age and high temperature, and, while highly pathogenic for the hen, produces only local inflammatory processes in mammals. It is probable that infection with avian tuberculosis sometimes occurs in man (Pausini).

Products of the Growth.—Little is yet known of the chemical charac-

---

* Berliner klinische Wochenschrift, 1882.
† Mittheilungen a. d. k. Gesundheitsamte, Bd. 2.

ters of the materials which result from the growth of the tubercle bacilli. Koch's tuberculin is stated to be a glycerin extract of the cultures. Crookshank and Herroun have separated an albumose and a ptomaine.

Distribution of the Bacilli.—The bacilli are found in all tuberculous lesions; in some in great abundance, in others sparsely. They are particularly numerous in actively developing tubercles, but in the chronic tuberculous processes of lymph-glands and of the joints they are scanty. When a tuberculous focus communicates with a vein or with lymph-vessels, the bacilli may be spread widely throughout the body. In old lesions they may not be found in the sections, and the demonstration of the true nature may be possible only by culture or inoculation.

The Bacilli outside the Body.—Patients with advanced pulmonary tuberculosis throw off in the expectoration countless millions of the bacilli daily. Some idea of the extraordinary numbers may be gained from the studies of Nuttall. From a patient with moderately advanced disease, the amount of whose expectoration was from 70 to 130 cc. daily, he estimated by his method that there were in sixteen counts, between January 10th and March 1st, from one and a half to four and a third billions of bacilli thrown off in the twenty-four hours. These figures emphasize the danger associated with phthisical sputa unless most carefully dealt with. When expectorated and allowed to dry, the sputum rapidly becomes dust, and is distributed far and wide. The observations made by Cornet under Koch's supervision are in this connection most instructive. He collected the dust from the walls and bedsteads of various localities, and determined its virulence or innocuousness by inoculation into susceptible animals. Material was gathered from 21 wards of 7 hospitals, 3 asylums, 2 prisons, from the surroundings of 62 phthisical patients in private practice, and from 29 other localities in which tuberculous patients were only transient frequenters (out-patient departments, streets, etc.). Of 118 dust samples from hospital wards or the rooms of phthisical patients, 40 were infective and produced tuberculosis. Negative results were obtained with the 29 dust samples from the localities occasionally occupied by consumptives. Virulent bacilli were obtained from the dust of the walls of 15 out of 21 medical wards. It is interesting to note that in 2 wards with many phthisical patients the results were negative, indicating that the dust in such regions is not necessarily infective. The infectiousness of the dust of the medical and surgical divisions of a hospital is in the proportion of 76.6 to 12.5. In a room in which a tuberculous woman had lived the dust from the wall in the neighborhood of the bed was infective six weeks after her death. No bacilli were found in the dust of an inhalation-chamber for consumptives. The experiments of Strauss at the Charité Hospital, Paris, are important. In the nostrils of 29 assistants, nurses, and ward-tenders he placed plugs of cotton-wool to collect the dust of the wards. In 9 of the 29 cases these contained tubercle bacilli and proved infective to animals. The question of the increase of tuberculosis among the permanent residents of health resorts frequented by consumptives is one of great interest. Gardiner has studied the problem at Colorado Springs, in which for twenty years tuberculous patients have been living, and he finds the number of cases of tuberculosis originating in the city to be very small.

Pseudo-tuberculosis.—While lesions resembling the nodules of tuberculosis, but due to a variety of bacteria, protozoa, and nematodes, are not uncommon in animals, pseudo-tuberculous processes are very rare in human beings. Flexner * has described, under the name *pseudo-tuberculosis hominis streptothrica*, a condition in human beings in which the lungs presented the appearance of a caseous pneumonia and numerous tubercle-like nodules existed in the peritonæum. The micro-organism found in the lesions was a streptothrix, which differed greatly from the known forms of the bacillus tuberculosis and streptothrix actinomyces.

4. Modes of Infection.—(*a*) *Hereditary Transmission.*—The possible methods of transmission of the germ in direct inheritance are three—transmission by the sperm, transmission by the ovum, and transmission through the blood by means of the placenta.

There is no clinical evidence to support the view that direct transmission can occur through the sperm. In order that the disease could be transmitted by the sperm it would be necessary that the tubercle bacilli should lodge in the individual spermatozoön which fecundates the ovum. The chances that such a thing could occur are extremely small, looking at the subject from a numerical point of view, although we know that tubercle bacilli do occasionally exist in the semen; they become still smaller when we consider that the spermatozoön is made up of nuclear material, which the tubercle bacillus is never known to attack. Experimentation is all opposed to sperm transmission, the work of Gärtner and others showing that the young of healthy female rabbits impregnated by tuberculous males are never tuberculous, even though the females themselves often contract the disease.

The possibility of transmission by the ovum must be accepted. Baumgarten has in one instance been able to detect the tubercle bacillus in the ovum of a female rabbit which he had artificially fecundated with tuberculous semen. The work of Pasteur on *pébrine* has shown the possibility of this form of transmission in the lower forms, though the question as to what effect such inoculation would have upon the human ovum cannot of course be answered.

Probably the almost constant method of transmission in congenital tuberculosis is through the blood current, the tubercle bacilli penetrating by way of the placenta. Certain authors hold that in these cases the placenta itself is invariably the seat of tuberculosis, and tubercles, indeed, have been demonstrated in several cases; but there are undoubted instances in which, with an apparently sound placenta, both the placental blood and the fœtal organs contained tubercle bacilli, notwithstanding the fact that the organs also appeared normal.

Possible Latency of the Tubercle Germs.—Baumgarten and his followers assume that the tubercle bacilli can lie latent in the tissues and subsequently develop when, for some reason or other, the individual resistance

---

* Journal of Experimental Medicine, 1898.

is lowered. He likens such cases of latent tuberculosis to the late hereditary forms of syphilis, and explains the lack of development of the germs by the greater resisting power of the tissues of children. In the discussion on *latency* before the Royal Medical and Chirurgical Society of London, Kingston Fowler expressed the sensible opinion that it was not necessary seriously to consider the question of latency in tuberculosis until direct transmission from mother to child was proved to be of frequent occurrence. Baumgarten bases his belief in germ transmission upon two main factors—the great frequency of the disease in early life and the localization of tuberculous lesions in children.

The mortality from tuberculosis in the first years of life is relatively high. Of 2,576 autopsies made on children, 27.8 per cent who died in the first year were tuberculous (Botz). Of 182 autopsies on children one year or under, 17 were tuberculous (Comby). The localization of tuberculous lesions in children in the bones or joints is very common, Cnopp's statistics showing that out of 298 tuberculous children of from a few days to twelve years of age, 147 had bone or joint tuberculosis, and only 8 of these showed evidence of visceral disease. Baumgarten is of the opinion that the accidental conveyance of tubercle bacilli to these points would not account for such a large proportion of cases, and expresses the view that the bacilli have been present since birth and have developed when favorable conditions offered. The evidence in favor of Baumgarten's view is both clinical and experimental.

The clinical evidence exists in the form of undoubted cases of congenital tuberculosis, of which there are now, in man alone, about 20 examples in the literature; besides these, a number of spontaneous cases of congenital tuberculosis in the lower animals have been reported.

A number of laboratory workers have been able to show that congenital tuberculosis can be produced experimentally, the most prominent of these being Gärtner, who was able to cause tuberculosis in young mice by inoculating the mother with tuberculosis, either into the peritoneal cavity or into the blood stream. Mafucci has shown that after injecting eggs with avian tuberculosis the disease may remain latent in the chick for weeks or even months.

Against Baumgarten's theory are the facts that the percentage of cases of congenital tuberculosis is extremely small, and that in the great majority of instances the organs of fœtuses born of tuberculous mothers give negative results when inoculated into guinea-pigs.

No circumstance, perhaps, has contributed more to the belief in the hereditary transmission of the disease than the frequency with which tuberculosis is met with in the ascendants of those affected. The estimates range from 10 per cent to 25 per cent, or even in some instances to 50 per cent. Some of the statistics on this point are worth quoting: In 1,000 cases Williams found 48.4 per cent with family predisposition, 12 per cent with parental, 1 per cent with grandparental, and 34.4 per cent with collateral heredity. Of 250 cases in which Solly made very careful inquiries on this point, there were 28.8 per cent with parental, 7.6 per cent with grandparental, and 19.2 per cent with a history of collateral heredity. Of 427 cases at the Johns Hopkins Hospital, there were 53 in which the mother had had tuberculosis, 52 in which the father had been affected, and 105 in which a brother or sister had had the disease. The question of family infection is the all-important one, and Hilton Fagge very wisely remarks that it is impossible to draw a line between hereditary and accidental tuberculosis, as naturally the children of an affected parent are more liable to accidental contamination. In a recent careful study of heredity in phthisis, Squire concludes that there is but a small difference between the incidence of the disease in the offspring of phthisical and non-phthisical parents.

While the demonstration of the contagiousness of tuberculosis has in some quarters intensified the dread with which the disease is regarded, the terrible *Ate* of hereditary transmission has been in great part abolished, to the great gain of suffering humanity.

(*b*) *Inoculation.*—The infective nature of tuberculosis was first demonstrated by Villemin, who showed conclusively in 1865 that it could be transmitted to animals by inoculation. The beautiful experiments of Cohnheim and Salamonson, who produced tuberculosis in the eyes of guinea-pigs and rabbits by inoculating fresh tubercle into the anterior chamber, confirmed and extended Villemin's original observations and paved the way for the reception of Koch's announcement. It is now universally conceded that *only* tuberculous matter can produce, when inoculated, tuberculosis. In man tuberculosis is not often transmitted by inoculation, and when it does occur the disease usually remains local. This mode of infection is seen in persons whose occupation brings them in contact with dead bodies or animal products. Demonstrators of morbid anatomy, butchers, and handlers of hides are subject to a local tubercle of the skin, which forms a reddened mass of granulation tissue, usually capping the dorsal surfaces of the hands or fingers. This is the so-called post-mortem wart, the *verruca necrogenica* of Wilks. The demonstration of its nature is shown by the presence of tubercle bacilli, and by inoculation experiments in animals.

The statement that Laennec contracted phthisis from this source is probably false, since he did not die until twenty years after the inoculation and in the interval presented no manifestations. The possibility, however, of general infection must be borne in mind. Gerber reports that after accidental inoculation in the hand from a case of phthisis he had for months a "Leichen-tubercle," which was excised. Shortly afterward the lymph-glands of the axilla became enlarged and painful, and when removed showed characteristic tuberculous changes, with bacilli.

In the performance of the rite of circumcision children have been accidentally inoculated. Infection in these cases is probably always associated with disease in the operator, and occurs in connection with the habit of cleansing the wound by suction.

Other means of inoculation have been described: as the wearing of ear-rings, washing the clothes of phthisical patients, the bite of a tuberculous subject, or inoculation from a cut by a broken spit-glass of a consumptive; and Czerny has reported two cases of infection by transplantation of skin.

It has been urged by the opponents of vaccination that tuberculosis, as well as syphilis, may be thus conveyed, but of this there is no evidence, and the lymph from the vesicles of revaccinated consumptives has been shown by many observers to be non-infective. It may be said, on the whole, that inoculation in man plays a trifling *rôle* in the transmission of tuberculosis.

(c) *Infection by Inhalation.*—A belief in the contagiousness of pulmonary tuberculosis has existed from the days òf the early Greek physicians, and has persisted among the Latin races. The investigations of Cornet afford conclusive proof that the dust of a room or other locality frequented by patients with pulmonary tuberculosis is infective. The bacilli are attached to fine particles of dust and in this way gain entrance to the system through the lungs.

Flügge denies that the bacillus-containing dust is the dangerous element in infection. Experimentally he has only succeeded in producing the disease when there is some lesion in the respiratory tract. He thinks that the danger of infection by the dry sputum is very improbable. On the other hand, he thinks that the infection is chiefly conveyed by the free, finely divided particles of sputum produced in the act of coughing, and that these tiny fragments are suspended in the atmosphere. Those who cough very much and with the mouth open are most liable to infect the surrounding air.

It is well remarked by Cornet, " The consumptive in himself is almost harmless, and only becomes harmful through bad habits." It has been fully shown that the expired air of consumptives is not infective. The virus is only contained in the sputum, which when dry is widely disseminated in the form of dust, and constitutes the great medium for the transmission of the disease. " In order to be air-borne the sputum must be dried and broken up into dust. If discharged into a handkerchief, it speedily dries, especially if it is put into the pocket or beneath the pillow. In the last stages of consumption the patient becomes weak, the sputum is expelled imperfectly, pillows, sheets, and handkerchiefs are soiled. If a male, the beard or moustache is smeared. Even in the hands of the cleanly, without special precautions, such circumstances all tend to the production around the patient of a halo of infected dust maintained by every process of bedmaking or of cleaning which includes the pernicious process happily described as ' dusting.' In the hands of the careless and the dirty the infectivity is, of course, greatly aggravated. It attains its maximum òf intensity where the filthy habit of spitting on the floor prevails, especially if it is carpeted " (James B. Russell).

The following are some of the facts in favor of infection by inhalation:

(1) Primary tuberculous lesions are in a majority of all cases connected with the respiratory system. The frequency with which foci are met with in the lungs and in the bronchial glands is extraordinary, and the statistics of the Paris morgue show that a considerable proportion of all persons dying of accident or by suicide present evidences of the disease in these parts. The post-mortem statistics of hospitals show the same widespread prevalence of infection through the air-passages. Biggs reports that more

than 60 per cent of his post mortems showed lesions of pulmonary tuberculosis. In 125 autopsies at the Foundling Hospital, New York, the bronchial glands were tuberculous in every case. In adults the bronchial glands may be infected and the individual remain in good health. H. P. Loomis found in 8 of 30 cases in which there were no signs of old or recent tuberculous lesions that the bronchial glands were infective to rabbits.

(2) The greater prevalence of tuberculosis in institutions in which the residents are confined and restricted in the matter of fresh air and a free open life—conditions which would favor, on the one hand, the presence of the bacilli in the atmosphere, and, on the other, lower the vital resistance of the individual. The investigations of Cornet upon the death-rate from consumption among certain religious orders devoted to nursing give some striking facts in illustration of this. In a review of 38 cloisters, embracing the average number of 4,028 residents, among 2,099 deaths in the course of twenty-five years, 1,320 (62.88 per cent) were from tuberculosis. In some cloisters more than three fourths of the deaths are from this disease, and the mortality in all the residents, up to the fortieth year, is greatly above the average, the increase being due entirely to the prevalence of tuberculosis. It has been stated that nurses are not more prone to the disease than other individuals, but Cornet says that of 100 nurses deceased, 63 died of tuberculosis. The more perfect the prophylaxis and hygienic arrangements of an asylum or institution, the lower the death-rate from tuberculosis. The mortality in prisons has been shown by Baer to be four times as great as outside. The death-rate from phthisis is estimated at 15 per cent of the total mortality, while in prisons it constitutes from 40 to 50 per cent, and in some countries, as Austria, over 60 per cent. Flick has studied the distribution of the deaths from tuberculosis in a single city ward in Philadelphia for twenty-five years. His researches go far to show that it is a house disease. About 33 per cent of infected houses have had more than one case. Less than one third of the houses of the ward became infected with tuberculosis during the twenty-five years prior to 1888. Yet more than one half of the deaths from this disease during the year 1888 occurred in those infected houses. There are, however, opposing facts. The statistics of the Brompton Consumption Hospital show that doctors, nurses, and attendants are rarely attacked. Dettweiler claims that no case of tuberculosis has been contracted among his nurses or attendants at Falkenstein. On the other hand, in the Paris hospitals tuberculosis decimates the attendants.

(3) Special danger exists when the contact is very intimate, such, for instance, as between man and wife. On this point much difference of opinion exists, but the figures seem to indicate that under these circumstances the husband or wife is much more liable subsequently to die of consumption. Of 427 cases of pulmonary tuberculosis at the Johns Hopkins Hospital, in 25 either husband or wife had been affected with it or had died of tuberculosis. In response to a question as to contagion, asked by the Collective Investigation Committee of the British Medical Association, there were 261 replies in the affirmative, among which were 158 cases of supposed contagion through marriage. Weber's cases are of special in-

terest. One of his patients lost four wives in succession, one lost three, and four lost two each.

(d) *Infection by Milk.*—The milk of an animal suffering from tuberculosis may contain the virus, and is capable of communicating the disease, as shown by Gerlach, Bang, Bollinger, and others. Striking illustrations of this are sometimes afforded in the lower animals. The pigs, for instance, of a tuberculous sow have been shown to present intestinal tuberculosis of the most exquisite form. Of late years the experimental proof has been entirely conclusive. It was formerly thought that the cow must present tuberculous disease of the udder, but Ernst has shown that the bacilli may be present and the milk be infective in a large proportion of cases in which there is no tuberculous mammitis; an observation made also by Hirschberger and others. This author states the interesting fact that an owner of a herd known to be tuberculous withdrew the milk from market and used it without boiling to fatten his pigs, which, almost without exception, became tuberculous, so that the whole stock had to be slaughtered. Sidney Martin could not induce the disease artificially in animals inoculated or fed with milk of tuberculous cows with healthy udders. Butter made from the milk of tuberculous cows has proved infective (Bang). There is no reason to believe that young children, or even adults, are less susceptible to the virus than calves or pigs, so that the danger of the disease from this source is real and serious. The great frequency of intestinal and mesenteric tuberculosis in children no doubt finds here its explanation. As noted in Woodhead's analysis of 127 cases of fatal tuberculosis in children, the mesenteric glands were involved in 100.

(e) *Infection by Meat.*—The meat of tuberculous animals is not necessarily infective. The results of experiments with the flesh of cows are not in accord. This mode of infection probably plays a minor *rôle* in the etiology of human tuberculosis, as usually the flesh is thoroughly cooked before eating. The possibility, however, must be borne in mind, and it would certainly be safer in the interests of a community to confiscate the carcasses of all tuberculous animals. Experiments in Bollinger's laboratory show that the flesh of tuberculous subjects is very infective to guinea-pigs. Martin suggests that when the meat is infective it commonly acquires this property by accidental contamination with tuberculous matter during its removal.

5. Conditions Influencing Infection.—(a) *General.*—Environment is an all-important predisposing factor. Dwellers in cities are much more prone to the disease than residents of the country. Not only is the liability to infection very much greater, but the conditions of life are such that the powers of resistance are apt to be weakened. As already stated, sunlight is one of the most powerful agents in destroying the tubercle bacillus, so that in imperfectly ventilated dwellings and workshops, and in residences in close, dark alleys, and in tenement houses the liability to infection is very much increased. The influence of environment was never better demonstrated than in the now well-known experiment of Trudeau, who found that rabbits inoculated with tuberculosis if confined in a dark, damp place without sunlight and fresh air rapidly succumbed, while others

17

treated in the same way, but allowed to run wild, either recovered or showed very slight lesions. The occupants of prisons, asylums, and poorhouses, too often, indeed, in barracks and large workshops, are in the position of Trudeau's rabbits in the cellar, and under conditions most favorable to foster the development of the bacilli which may have lodged in their tissues. The frequent respiration of air already breathed, upon which MacCormac of Belfast laid so much stress, appears to render the lungs less capable of resisting infection.

Soil and locality are believed by many to have a very important bearing on the development of tuberculosis. The observations of Henry I. Bowditch in this country and of Buchanan in England show that the disease prevails more widely in the wet, ill-drained districts—an increase which is associated with heightened vulnerability and greater liability to catarrhal affections of all kinds. The influence of the dwelling has been already referred to in connection with Flick's work. No single condition is of greater importance than that which relates to the proper arrangement and ventilation of the dwelling houses.

(b) *Individual Predisposition.*—The fathers of medicine, more particularly Hippocrates, Aretæus, and Galen, laid great stress upon the bodily conformation of those prone to consumption. A great deal was written on the so-called *habitus phthisicus*, which Hippocrates described in the following terms: " The form of body peculiar to subjects of phthisical complaints was the smooth, the whitish, that resembling the lentil; the reddish, the blue-eyed, the leuco-phlegmatic; and that with the scapulæ having the appearance of wings." Undoubtedly the long, narrow, flat chest with depressed sternum is commonly enough seen in tuberculous patients, but there are only too many individuals with perfectly well-shaped chests who fall victims annually to the disease. The tuberculous or scrofulous diathesis, upon which formerly so much stress was laid, is now regarded simply as an indication of a type of conformation in which the tissues are more vulnerable and less capable of resisting infection. Beneke's investigations on the viscera of phthisical patients indicate that the heart is relatively small, the arteries proportionately narrow, and the pulmonary artery relatively wider than the aorta. He suggests that this may lead to increase in the intrapulmonary blood pressure, and so favor catarrhal processes. The lung volume he found relatively greater in those affected with tuberculosis. A study of the composite portraiture of pulmonary tuberculosis has been made by Galton and Mahomed. In 442 patients they separated two types of face—one ovoid and narrow, the other broad and coarse-featured. This corresponds in an interesting way to the diathetic states formerly recognized—namely, the tuberculous, with thin skin, bright eyes, oval face, and long, thin bones; and the scrofulous, with thick lips and nose, opaque skin, large, thick bones, and heavy figure. These conditions, on which so much stress was formerly laid, indicate, as Fagge states, nothing more than delicacy of constitution, incomplete growth, and imperfect development.

(c) *Influence of Age.*—No age is exempt. The disease is met with in the suckling and in the octogenarian. Pulmonary tuberculosis occurs most frequently, as stated by Hippocrates, from the eighteenth to the thirty-fifth year. From the fifth to the tenth year individuals are less prone to the disease. At different ages different organs are more prone to be involved. During the first decade the bones, meninges, and lymph-glands are more frequently affected than at subsequent periods.

(d) *Sex.*—The influence of sex is very slight. Women are perhaps somewhat more frequently attacked than men, possibly from the fact that in a more sedentary, indoor life they are more liable to infection. Pregnancy and lactation also are two conditions which are apt to lower, perhaps, the resistance of the organism.

(e) *Race.*—The negro, who it is stated is not specially prone to the disease in Africa, is in America and in the West Indies very subject to tuberculosis. The relative immunity of the Jews has been mentioned (page 259).

(f) *Occupation* is an important predisposing factor. The inhalation of impure air in occupations associated with a very dusty atmosphere renders the lungs less capable of resisting infection. The incidence of pulmonary tuberculosis among the workers in mills and factories is very high, and certain occupations, such as those of glass-workers, stone-cutters, and coal-miners, and the whole group of trades, which lead to pneumonokoniosis, favor the development of tuberculosis.

(g) Certain *local conditions* influence infection, among which the following are the most important:

Catarrhal bronchitis. The influence of catarrh of the respiratory passages in pulmonary tuberculosis is well recognized. How often is a neglected cold blamed as the starting-point of the disease! It seems to act by lowering the resistance and favoring the conditions which enable the bacilli either to enter the system or, when once in it, to develop. The liability of lymphatic tuberculosis in children is probably associated with the common catarrhal processes in the tonsils, throat, and bronchi.

Certain of the specific fevers predispose to tuberculosis, among which measles and whooping-cough stand pre-eminent. They are often associated with a bronchial catarrh. In some of the cases it is probably not a fresh infection which follows, but the blazing of a smouldering fire. Typhoid fever is thought by some to predispose to tuberculosis, but my experience is opposed to this view. Of other affections, influenza, variola, and syphilis are all believed to favor the development of the disease. Diabetes, as is well known, very often terminates in pulmonary tuberculosis, particularly in young persons.

Chronic heart-disease, arterio-sclerosis, aneurism of the aorta, forms of chronic nephritis, cirrhosis of the liver, and the various forms of cerebrospinal sclerosis, all are conditions which favor infection. It is remarkable in how many of the subjects of these disorders in general hospital practice the fatal event is a terminal acute tuberculosis, most frequently of the serous membranes. Subjects of congenital or acquired contraction of the orifice of the pulmonary artery usually die of tuberculosis. On the other hand, mitral valve disease, particularly stenosis, is stated to antagonize the disease (J. E. Graham). In children catarrhal entero-colitis probably favors the development of tabes mesenterica.

The influence of hæmoptysis and pleurisy will be referred to later.

Trauma. Surgeons have laid great stress upon this as an etiological factor in tuberculous processes. Experiments indicate that tissues which have been bruised, and which would in health have readily and rapidly destroyed organisms, promote their growth under the altered conditions. Probably in the case of tuberculosis following trauma the injured part is for a time a *locus minoris resistentiæ*, and if bacilli are present they may by it receive a stimulus to growth or under the altered conditions be capable of multiplying. Not only in arthritis, but in pulmonary tuberculosis, traumatism may play a part. The question has been thoroughly studied by Mendelssohn, who reports 9 cases in which, without fracture of the rib or laceration of the lung, tuberculosis developed shortly after contusion of the chest. Operation upon tuberculous lesions may be followed by a general infection. Resection of a strumous joint is occasionally followed by acute tuberculosis. Of 837 resections, 225 ended fatally, 26 with acute tuberculosis (Wartmann).

General Morbid Anatomy and Histology of Tuberculous Lesions.

(1) **Distribution of the Tubercles in the Body.**—The organs of the body are variously affected by tuberculosis. In adults, the lungs may be regarded as the seat of election; in children, the lymph-glands, bones, and joints. In 1,000 autopsies there were 275 cases with tuberculous lesions. With but two or three exceptions the lungs were affected. The distribution in the other organs was as follows: Pericardium, 7; peritonæum, 36; brain, 31; spleen, 23; liver, 12; kidneys, 32; intestines, 65; heart, 4; and generative organs, 8.

The tuberculosis which comes under the care of the surgeon has a different distribution, as shown by the following figures from the Würzburg clinic. Among 8,873 patients, 1,287 were tuberculous, with the following distribution of lesions: Bones and joints, 1,037; lymph-glands, 196; skin and connective tissues, 77; mucous membranes, 10; genito-urinary organs, 20.

(2) **The Changes produced by the Tubercle Bacilli.**

(*a*) *The Nodular Tubercle.*—The body which we term a "tubercle" *presents in its early formation nothing distinctive or peculiar, either in its components or in their arrangement.* Identical structures are produced by other parasites, such as the actinomyces, and by the strongylus in the lungs of sheep.

The researches of Baumgarten have enabled us to follow in detail the evolution of a tubercle.

(*a*) The multiplication of the tubercle bacilli, which is rapid and is accompanied by their dissemination in the surrounding tissues partly by growth, partly in the lymph currents.

(*β*) The multiplication of the fixed cells, especially those of connective tissue and the endothelium of the capillaries, and the gradual production from them of rounded, cuboidal, or polygonal bodies with vesicular nuclei —the *epithelioid cells*—inside some of which the bacilli are soon seen.

(*γ*) From the vessels of the infected focus, leucocytes, chiefly polynuclear, migrate in numbers and accumulate about the focus of infection. They do not subdivide. Many undergo rapid destruction. Later, as the little tubercle grows, the leucocytes are chiefly of the mononuclear variety (lymphocytes), which do not undergo the rapid degeneration of the polynuclear forms.

(δ) A reticulum of fibres is formed by the fibrillation and rarefaction of the connective-tissue matrix. This is most apparent, as a rule, at the margin of the growth.

(ε) In some, but not all, tubercles *giant cells* are formed by an increase in the protoplasm and in the nuclei of an individual cell, or possibly by the fusion of several cells. The giant cells seem to be in inverse ratio to the number and virulence of the bacilli. In lupus, joint tuberculosis, and scrofulous glands, in which the bacilli are scanty, the giant cells are numerous; while in miliary tubercles and all lesions in which the bacilli are abundant the giant cells are few in number.

The bacilli then cause, in the first place, a proliferation of the fixed elements, with the production of epithelioid and giant cells; and, secondly, an inflammatory reaction, associated with exudation of leucocytes. How far the leucocytes attack and destroy the bacilli has not been definitely settled—Metschnikoff claiming, Baumgarten denying, an active phagocytosis.

(3) **The Degeneration of Tubercle.**—There are two chief forms of degeneration:

(a) *Caseation.*—At the central part of the growth, owing to the direct action of the bacilli or their products, a process of coagulation necrosis goes on in the cells, which lose their outline, become irregular, no longer take stains, and are finally converted into a homogeneous, structureless substance. Proceeding from the centre outward, the tubercle may be gradually converted into a yellowish-gray body, in which, however, the bacilli are still abundant. No blood-vessels are found in them. Aggregated together these form the cheesy masses so common in tuberculosis, which may undergo softening, fibroid limitation (encapsulation), or calcification.

(b) *Sclerosis.*—With the necrosis of the cell elements at the centre of the tubercle, hyaline transformation proceeds, together with great increase in the fibroid elements; so that the tubercle is converted into a firm, hard structure. Often the change is rather of a fibro-caseous nature; but the sclerosis predominates. In some situations, as in the peritonæum, this seems to be the natural transformation of tubercle, and it is by no means rare in the lungs.

In all tubercles two processes go on: the one—caseation—destructive and dangerous; and the other—sclerosis—conservative and healing. The ultimate result in a given case depends upon the capabilities of the body to restrict and limit the growth of the bacilli. There are tissue-soils in which the bacilli are, in all probability, killed at once—*the seed has fallen by the wayside.* There are others in which a lodgment is gained and more or less damage done, but finally the day is with the conservative, protecting forces—*the seed has fallen upon stony ground.* Thirdly, there are tissue-soils in which the bacilli grow luxuriantly, caseation and softening, not limitation and sclerosis, prevail, and the day is with the invaders—*the seed has fallen upon good ground.*

The action of the bacilli injected directly into the blood-vessels illustrates many points in the histology and pathology of tuberculosis. If into the vein of a rabbit a pure culture of the bacilli is injected, the microbes accumulate chiefly in the liver and spleen. The animal dies usually within two weeks, and the organs apparently show no trace of tubercles. Microscopically, in both spleen and liver the young tubercles in process of formation are very numerous, and karyokinesis is going on in the liver-cells. After an injection of a more dilute culture, or one whose virulence has been mitigated by age, instead of dying within a fortnight the animal survives for five or six weeks, by which time the tubercles are apparent in the spleen and liver, and often in the other organs.

(4) **The diffused Inflammatory Tubercle.**—This is most frequently seen in the lungs. Only a great master like Virchow could have won the profession from a belief in the *unity of phthisis*, which the genius of Laennec had, on anatomical ground, announced. Here and there a teacher, as Wilson Fox, protested, but the heresy prevailed, and we repeated the striking aphorism of Niemeyer, " The greatest evil which can happen to a consumptive is that he should become tuberculous." It was thought that the products of any simple inflammation might become caseous, and that ordinary catarrhal pneumonia terminated in phthisis. It was peculiarly fitting that from Germany, in which the dualistic heresy arose, the truth of Laennec's views should receive incontestable proof, in the demonstration by Koch of the etiological unity of all the various processes known as tuberculous and scrofulous.

Infiltrated tubercle results from the fusion of many small foci of infection—so small indeed that they may not be visible to the naked eye, but which histologically are seen to be composed of scattered centres, surrounded by areas in which the air-cells are filled with the products of exudation and of the proliferation of the alveolar epithelium. Under the influence of the bacilli, caseation takes place, usually in small groups of lobules, occasionally in an entire lobe, or even the greater part of a lung. In the early stage of the process, the tissue has a gray gelatinous appearance, the *gray infiltration* of Laennec. The alveoli contain a sero-fibrinous fluid with cells, and the septa are also infiltrated. These cells accumulate and undergo coagulation necrosis, forming areas of caseation, the *infiltration tuberculeuse jaune* of Laennec, the scrofulous or cheesy pneumonia of later writers. There may also be a diffuse infiltration and caseation without any special foci, a widespread tuberculous pneumonia induced by the bacilli.

After all, the two processes are identical. As Baumgarten states: " There is no well-marked difference between miliary tubercle and chronic caseous pneumonia. Speaking histologically, miliary tuberculosis is nothing else than a chronic caseous miliary pneumonia, and chronic caseous pneumonia is nothing but a tuberculosis of the lungs."

(5) **Secondary Inflammatory Processes.**—(*a*) The irritation caused by the bacilli invariably produces an inflammation which may, as has been described, be limited to exudation of leucocytes and serum, but may also be

much more extensive, and which varies with varying conditions. We find, for example, about the smaller tubercles in the lungs, pneumonia—either catarrhal or fibrinous, proliferation of the connective-tissue elements in the septa (which also become infiltrated with round cells), and changes in the blood and lymph-vessels.

(b) In processes of minor intensity the inflammation is of the slow reactive nature, which results in the production of a cicatricial connective tissue which limits and restricts the development of the tubercles and is the essential conservative element in the disease. It is to be remembered that in chronic pulmonary tuberculosis much of the fibroid tissue which is present is not in any way associated with the action of the bacilli.

(c) Suppuration. Do the bacilli themselves induce suppuration? In so-called cold tuberculous abscess the material is not histologically pus, but a débris consisting of broken-down cells and cheesy material. It is moreover sterile—that is, does not contain the usual pus organisms. The products of the tubercle bacilli are probably able to induce suppuration, as in joint and bone tuberculosis pus is frequently produced, although this may be due to a mixed infection. Koch, it will be remembered, states that the " tuberculin " is one of the best agents for the production of experimental suppuration. In tuberculosis of the lungs the suppuration is largely the result of an infection with pus organisms.

II. Acute Tuberculosis.

The truly infective nature of tubercle is best shown in this affection, which is characterized by an eruption of miliary tubercles in various parts of the body. The clinical picture varies with the general or localized distribution of the growths. The tubercles are found upon the pleura and peritonæum; in the lungs, liver, kidneys, lymph-glands, and spleen; upon the membranes of the brain, occasionally in the choroid coat of the eye, and in the bone-marrow. They may be abundant in some organs and scanty in others. Thus, in the meninges of the brain they may be thickly set, while there are few or none in the abdominal viscera or in the lungs. On the other hand, the lungs may be studded with granulations while the meninges of the brain are free. In other cases, again, the distribution is uniform in all the viscera.

The etiology has been in part considered, and the only additional statement necessary is that in a great majority of all cases it is an auto-infection, arising from a pre-existing tuberculous focus, which may be latent and unsuspected. The following are the most common sources of general infection: Local disease of the lungs, which may be quite limited and unproductive of symptoms; tuberculous affection of the lymph-glands, particularly in children; and tuberculosis of the bones and of the kidneys. Of these sources perhaps the most common are the tracheal and bronchial lymph-glands, which are so often the seat of local tuberculosis. Weigert has shown that in many cases the infection results from the rupture of a caseous pulmonary nodule into a vein, or of a caseous bronchial gland into one of the pulmonary veins. A general infection may, as shown by Ponfick, result from invasion of the thoracic duct by tubercles. With special care the source of infection can usually be discovered at post-mortem examination. The connection between tuberculous lymph-glands and veins has often been demonstrated. In many instances it is impossible to say what determines the sudden and violent onset of the disease. It would seem sometimes as if general rather than local conditions influenced the outbreak. After certain fevers, particularly measles and whooping-cough in children—affections, it is true, which are associated with long-continued bronchitis—miliary tuberculosis is not uncommon. The prostration and constitutional weakness which follow protracted fevers frequently seem in the adult to be a predisposing cause.

Clinical Forms.—For practical purposes the cases may be divided into those with the symptoms of *acute general infection* without special localization; cases with marked *pulmonary* symptoms; and cases with *cerebral* or *cerebro-spinal* symptoms.

Other forms have been recognized, but this division covers a large majority of the cases.

Taking any series of cases it will be found that the meningeal form of acute tuberculosis exceeds in numbers the cases with general or marked pulmonary symptoms.

1. General or Typhoid Form.—*Symptoms.*—The patient here presents the symptoms of an infectious disease with few if any local signs. The cases simulate and are frequently mistaken for typhoid fever. After a period of failing health, with loss of appetite, the patient becomes feverish and weak. Occasionally the disease sets in more abruptly, but in many instances the anamnesis closely resembles that of typhoid fever. Nose-bleeding, however, is rare. The temperature increases, the pulse becomes rapid and feeble, the tongue dry; delirium becomes marked and the cheeks are flushed. The pulmonary symptoms may be very slight; usually bronchitis exists, but not more severe than is common with typhoid fever. The pulse is seldom dicrotic, but is rapid in proportion to the pyrexia. Perhaps the most striking feature of the temperature is the irregularity; and if seen from the outset there is not the steady ascent noted in typhoid fever. There is usually an evening rise to 103°, sometimes 104°, and a morning remission of from two to three degrees. Sometimes the pyrexia is intermittent, and the thermometer may register below normal during the early morning hours. The inverse type of temperature, in which the rise takes place in the morning, is held by some writers to be more frequent in general tuberculosis than in other diseases. In rare instances there may be little or no fever. On two occasions I have had a patient admitted to my wards in a condition of profound debility, with a history of illness of from three to four weeks' duration, with rapid pulse, flushed cheeks, dry tongue, and very slight elevation in temperature, in whom (post mortem) the condition proved to be general tuberculosis. In one instance there was tolerably extensive disease at the right apex. Reinhold, from Bäumler's clinic, has recently called attention to these afebrile forms of acute tuberculosis. In 9 of 52 cases there was no fever, or only a transient rise.

In a considerable number of these cases the respirations are increased in frequency, particularly in the early stage, and there may be signs of diffuse bronchitis and slight cyanosis. Cheyne-Stokes breathing develops toward the close.

Active delirium is rare. More commonly there are torpor and dulness, gradually deepening into coma, in which the patient dies. In some cases the pulmonary symptoms become more marked; in others, meningeal or cerebral features develop.

Diagnosis.—The differential diagnosis between general miliary tuberculosis without local manifestations and typhoid fever is extremely difficult. A point of importance, to which reference has already been made, is the irregularity of the temperature curve. The greater frequency of the respirations and the tendency to slight cyanosis is much more common in tuberculosis. There are cases, however, of typhoid fever in which the initial bronchitis is severe and may lead to dyspnœa and disturbed oxygenation. The cough may be slight or absent. Diarrhœa is rare in tuberculosis; the bowels are usually constipated; but diarrhœa may occur and persist for days. In certain cases the diagnosis has been complicated still further by the occurrence of blood in the stools. Enlargement of the spleen occurs in general tuberculosis, but is neither so early nor so marked as in typhoid fever. In children, however, the enlargement may be considerable. The urine may show traces of albumin, and unfortunately Ehrlich's diazo-reaction, which is so constant in typhoid fever, is also met with in general tuberculosis. The absence of the characteristic roseola is an important feature. Occasionally in acute tuberculosis reddish spots may develop and for a time cause difficulty, but they do not come out in crops, and rarely have the characters of the true typhoid eruption. Herpes is perhaps more common in tuberculosis. Toward the close, petechiæ may appear on the skin, particularly about the wrists. A rare event is jaundice, due possibly to the eruption of tubercles in the liver. It is to be remembered that the lesions of acute tuberculosis and of typhoid fever have been demonstrated in the same body.

In a few instances the presence of tubercle bacilli has been demonstrated in the blood, which in doubtful cases should therefore be examined. The spleen has been punctured and cultivations made to determine the presence or absence of the typhoid bacilli, but in the acute splenic tumor this is a dangerous procedure. The eye-grounds should be carefully examined for choroidal tubercles. The blood may show a slight leucocytosis, but in the very acute cases where there are no suppurating foci this is absent. The Widal reaction is now a most important help in the diagnosis.

2. Pulmonary Form.—*Symptoms.*—From the outset the pulmonary symptoms are marked. The patient may have had a cough for months or for years without much impairment of health, or he may be known to be the subject of chronic pulmonary tuberculosis. In other instances, particularly in children, the affection follows measles or whooping-cough, and is of a distinctly broncho-pneumonic type. The disease begins with the symptoms of diffuse bronchitis. The cough is marked, the expectoration muco-purulent, occasionally rusty. Hæmoptysis has been noted in a few instances. From the outset dyspnœa is a striking feature and may be out of proportion to the intensity of the physical signs. There is more or less cyanosis of the lips and finger-tips, and the cheeks are suffused. Apart from emphysema and the later stages of severe pneumonia I know of no other pulmonary condition in which the cyanosis is so marked. The physical signs are those of bronchitis. In children there may be defective resonance at the bases, from scattered areas of broncho-pneumonia; or, what is equally suggestive, areas of hyper-resonance. Indeed, the percussion note, particularly in the front of the chest, in some cases of miliary tuberculosis, is full and clear, and it will be noted (post mortem) that the lungs are unusually voluminous. This is probably the result of more or less widespread acute emphysema. On auscultation, the râles are either sibilant and sonorous or small, fine, and crepitant. There may be fine crepitation from the occurrence of tubercles on the pleura (Jürgensen). In children there may be high-pitched tubular breathing at the bases or toward the root of the lung. Toward the close the râles may be larger and more mucous. The temperature rises to 102° or 103°, and may present the inverse type. The pulse is rapid and feeble. In the very acute cases the spleen is always enlarged. The disease may prove fatal in ten or twelve days, or may be protracted for weeks or even months.

Diagnosis.—The diagnosis of this form offers less difficulty and is more frequently made. There is often a history of previous cough, or the patient is known to be the subject of local disease of the lung, or of the lymph-glands, or of the bones. In children these symptoms following measles or whooping-cough indicate in the majority of cases acute miliary tuberculosis, with or without broncho-pneumonia. Occasionally the sputum contains tubercle bacilli.

The choroidal tubercle occurs in a limited number of cases and may help the diagnosis. More important in an adult is the combination of dyspnœa with cyanosis and the signs of a diffuse bronchitis. In some instances the occurrence of cerebral symptoms at once gives a clew to the nature of the trouble.

3. Meningeal Form (*Tuberculous Meningitis, Basilar Meningitis*).—This affection, which is also known as acute hydrocephalus or "water on the brain," is essentially an acute tuberculosis in which the membranes of the brain, sometimes of the cord, bear the brunt of the attack. Our first accurate knowledge of this affection dates from the publication of Robert Whytt's Observations on the Dropsy of the Brain, Edinburgh, 1768. The literature is very fully given in the last edition of Barthez and Sannée.

Though Guersant had as early as 1827 used the name *granular meningitis* for this form of inflammation of the meninges, it was not until 1830 that Papavoine demonstrated the nature of the granules and noted their occurrence with tubercles in other parts.

In 1832 and 1833, W. W. Gerhard, of Philadelphia, made a very careful study of the disease in the Children's Hospital at Paris, and his publications, more than those of any other author, served to place the disease on a firm anatomical and clinical basis.

There are several special *etiological* factors in connection with this form. It is much more common in children than in adults. It is rare during the first year of life, more frequent between the second and the fifth years. In a majority of the cases a focus of old tuberculous disease will be found, commonly in the bronchial or mesenteric glands. In a few instances the affection seems to be primary in the meninges. It is very difficult, however, in an ordinary post mortem to make an exhaustive search, and the lesion may be in the bones, sometimes in the middle ear, or in the genito-urinary organs. In those instances in which no primary focus has been discovered it has been suggested that the bacilli reach the meninges through the cribriform plate of the ethmoid from the upper part of the nostrils, but this is not probable.

Morbid Anatomy.—Tuberculous meningitis presents a very characteristic picture. The meninges at the base are most involved, hence the term basilar meningitis. The parts about the optic chiasm, the Sylvian fissures, and the interpeduncular space are affected. There may be only slight turbidity and matting of the membranes, and a certain stickiness with serous infiltration; but more commonly there is a turbid exudate, fibrino-purulent in character, which covers the structures at the base, surrounds the nerves, extends out into the Sylvian fissures, and appears on the lateral, rarely on the upper, surfaces of the hemispheres. The tubercles may be very apparent, particularly in the Sylvian fissures, appearing as small, whitish nodules on the membranes. They vary much in number and size, and may be difficult to find. The amount of exudate bears no definite relation to the abundance of tubercles. The arteries of the anterior and posterior perforated spaces should be carefully withdrawn and searched, as upon them nodular tubercles may be found when not present elsewhere. In doubtful cases the middle cerebral arteries should be very carefully removed, spread on a glass plate with a black background, and examined with a low objective. The tubercles are then seen as nodular enlargements on the smaller arteries. The lateral ventricles are dilated (acute hydrocephalus) and contain a turbid fluid; the ependyma may be softened, and the septum lucidum and fornix are usually broken down. The convolutions are often flattened and the sulci obliterated owing to the increased intra-ventricular pressure. There is a tuberculous endarteritis with the formation of intimal tubercles, due to implantation of bacilli from the blood (Hektoen). Proliferation in the adventitia, with invasion of the media and intima are common, forming nodular circumscribed tubercles. The lumen of the vessel is narrowed and thrombosis may result. The meninges are not alone involved, but the contiguous cerebral substance is more or less œdematous and infiltrated with leucocytes, so that anatomically the condition is in reality a *meningo-encephalitis*.

There are instances in which the acute process is associated with chronic meningeal tuberculosis; cases which may for months present the clinical picture of brain tumor.

Although in a majority of instances the process is cerebral, the spinal meninges may also be involved, particularly those of the cervical cord. There are cases indeed in which the symptoms are chiefly spinal. A sailor, who had fallen on the deck three weeks before his death, was admitted to the Montreal General Hospital. He presented signs of meningitis, chiefly spinal, which were naturally attributed to traumatism. The post mortem showed absence of tubercles and lymph at the base of the brain, and an extensive eruption of miliary tubercles with much turbid lymph over the entire spinal meninges. There were small cheesy masses at the apices of the lungs.

Symptoms.—Tuberculous meningitis presents an extremely complex clinical picture. It will be best to describe the form found in children.

Prodromal symptoms are common. The child may have been in failing health for some weeks, or may be convalescent from measles or whooping-cough. In many instances there is a history of a fall. The child gets thin, is restless, peevish, irritable, loses its appetite, and the disposition may completely change. Symptoms pointing to the disease may then set in, either quite suddenly with a convulsion, or more commonly with headache, vomiting, and fever, three essential symptoms of the onset which are rarely absent. The pain may be intense and agonizing. The child puts its hand to its head and occasionally, when the pain becomes worse, gives a short, sudden cry, the so-called hydrocephalic cry. Sometimes the child screams continuously until utterly exhausted. I saw in West Philadelphia a case of basilar meningitis in a girl of thirteen, who for three days, when not under the influence of a powerful sedative or of chloroform, screamed at the top of her voice so as to be heard a square or more away. The vomiting is without apparent cause, and is independent of taking of food. Constipation is usually present. The fever is slight, but gradually rises to 102° or 103°. The pulse is at first rapid, subsequently irregular and slow. The respirations are rarely altered. During sleep the child is restless and disturbed. There may be twitchings of the muscles, or sudden startings; or the child may wake up from sleep in great terror. In this early stage the pupils are usually contracted. These are the chief symptoms of the initial stage, or, as it is termed, the *stage of irritation.*

In the second period of the disease these irritative symptoms subside; vomiting is no longer marked, the abdomen becomes retracted, boat-shaped or *carinated.* The bowels are obstinately constipated, the child no longer complains of headache, but is dull and apathetic, and when roused is more or less delirious. The head is often retracted and the child utters an occasional cry. The pupils are dilated or irregular, and a squint may develop. Sighing respiration is common. Convulsions may occur, or rigidity of the muscles of one side or of one limb. The temperature is variable, ranging from 100° to 102.5°. A blotchy erythema is not uncommon on the skin. If the finger-nail is drawn across the skin of any region a red line comes out quickly, the so-called *tache cérébrale,* which, however, has no diagnostic significance.

In the final period, or stage of *paralysis,* the coma increases and the child cannot be roused. Convulsions are not infrequent, and there are spasmodic contractions of the muscles of the back and neck. Spasms may occur in the limbs of one side. Optic neuritis and paralysis of the ocular muscles may be present. The pupils become dilated, the eyelids are only partially closed, and the eyeballs are rolled up so that the corneæ are only covered in part by the upper eyelids. Diarrhœa may develop, the pulse becomes rapid, and the child may sink into a typhoid state with dry tongue, low delirium, and involuntary passages of urine and fæces. The temperature often becomes subnormal, sinking in rare instances to 93° or 94°. In some cases there is an ante-mortem elevation of temperature, the fever rising to 106°. The entire duration of the disease is from a fortnight to three or four weeks. A leucocytosis is not infrequently present throughout the disease.

There are cases of tuberculous meningitis which pursue a more rapid course. They set in with great violence, often in persons apparently in good health, and may prove fatal within a few days. In these instances, more commonly seen in adults, the convex surface of the brain is usually involved. There are again instances which are essentially chronic and display symptoms of a limited meningitis; sometimes with pronounced psychical symptoms, and sometimes with those of cerebral tumor.

There are certain features which call for special comment.

The irregularity and slowness of the pulse in the early and middle stages of the disease are points upon which all authors agree. Toward the close, as the heart's action becomes weaker, the pulsations are more frequent. The temperature is usually elevated, but there are instances in which it does not rise in the whole course of the disease much above 100°. It may be extremely irregular, and the oscillations are often as much as three or four degrees in the day. Toward the close the temperature may sink to 95°, occasionally to 94°, or there may be hyperpyrexia. In a case of Bäumler's the temperature rose before death to 43.7° C. (110.7° F.).

The ocular symptoms of the disease are of special importance. In the early stages narrowing of the pupils is the rule. Toward the close, with increase in the intra-cranial pressure, the pupils dilate and are irregular. There may be conjugate deviation of the eyes. Of ocular palsies the third nerve is most frequently involved, sometimes with paralysis of the face, limbs, and hypoglossal nerve on the opposite side (syndrome of Weber), due to a lesion limited to the inferior and internal part of the crus. The changes in the eye-grounds are very important. Neuritis is the most common. According to Gowers, the disk at first becomes full colored and has hazy outlines, and the veins are dilated. Swelling and striation become pronounced, but the neuritis is rarely intense. Of 26 cases studied by Garlick, in 6 the condition was of diagnostic value. The tubercles in the choroid are rare and much less frequently seen during life than post-mortem figures would indicate. Thus Litten found them (post mortem) in 39 out of 52 cases. They were present in only 1 of the 26 cases of tuberculous meningitis examined by Garlick. Heinzel examined with negative results 41 cases.

Among the motor symptoms convulsions are most common, but there are other changes which deserve special mention. A tetanic contraction of one limb may persist for several days, or a cataleptic condition. Tremor and athetoid movements are sometimes seen. The paralyses are either hemiplegias or monoplegias. Hemiplegia may result from disturbance in the cortical branches of the middle cerebral artery, occasionally from softening in the internal capsule, due to involvement of the central branches.

Of monoplegias, that of the face is perhaps most common, and if on the right side it may occur with aphasia. In two of my cases in adults aphasia developed. Brachial monoplegia may be associated with it. In the more chronic cases the symptoms persist for months, and there may be a characteristic Jacksonian epilepsy when the tubercles involve the meninges of the motor cortex.

The diagnosis of tuberculous meningitis is rarely difficult, and points upon which special stress is to be laid are the existence of a tuberculous focus in the body, the mode of onset and the symptoms, and the evidence obtained on lumbar puncture. The fluid withdrawn is usually turbid, and in it, on centrifugalizing, the bacilli may be discovered. A sterile fluid, which is sometimes present, also favors the diagnosis of tuberculous meningitis.

The *prognosis* in this form of meningitis is always most serious. I have neither seen a case which I regarded as tuberculous recover, nor have I seen post-mortem evidence of past disease of this nature. Cases of recovery have been reported by reliable authorities, but they are extremely rare, and there is always a reasonable doubt as to the correctness of the diagnosis. The differential features and treatment will be considered in connection with acute meningitis.

III. Tuberculosis of the Lymphatic System.

1. Tuberculosis of the Lymph-glands (*Scrofula*).

Scrofula is tubercle, as it has been shown that the bacillus of Koch is the essential element. Formerly special attention was given to different types of scrofula, of which two important forms were recognized—the sanguine, in which the child was slightly built, tall, with small limbs, a fine clear skin, soft silky hair, and was mentally very bright and intelligent; and the phlegmatic type, in which the child was short and thick-set, with coarse features, muddy complexion, and a dull, heavy aspect. It is not yet definitely settled whether the virus which produces the chronic tuberculous adenitis or scrofula differs from that which produces tuberculosis in other parts, or whether it is the local conditions in the glands which account for the slow development and milder course. The experiments of Arloing would indicate that the virus was attenuated or milder, for he has shown that the caseous material of a lymph-gland killed guinea-pigs, while rabbits escaped. The guinea-pig, as is well known, is the more susceptible animal of the two. The observations of Lingard are still more conclusive, as showing a variation in the virulence of the tubercle bacillus. Guinea-pigs inoculated with ordinary tubercle showed lymphatic infection within the first week, and the animals died within three months; infected with material from scrofulous glands, the lymphatic enlargement did not appear until the second or third week, and the animals survived for six or seven months. He showed, moreover, that the virulence of the infection obtained from the scrofulous glands increased in intensity by passing through a series of guinea-pigs. Eve's experiments show that scrofulous material invariably produces tuberculosis in guinea-pigs and very often in rabbits.

Tuberculous adenitis is met with at all ages. It is more common in children than in adults, but it is not infrequent in the middle period of life, and may occur in old age.

The tubercle bacillus is ubiquitous. All are exposed to infection, and upon the local conditions, whether favorable or unfavorable, depend the fate of those organisms which find lodgment in our bodies. It is possible, of course, that tuberculous adenitis may be congenital, but such instances must be extremely rare. A special predisposing factor in lymphatic tuberculosis is catarrhal inflammation of the mucous membranes, which in itself excites slight adenitis of the neighboring glands. In a child with constantly recurring naso-pharyngeal catarrh, the bacilli which lodge on the mucous membranes find in all probability the gateways less strictly guarded and are taken up by the lymphatics and passed to the nearest glands. The importance of the tonsils as an infection-atrium has of late been urged. In conditions of health the local resistance, or, as some would put it, the phagocytes, would be active enough to deal with the invaders, but the irritation of a chronic catarrh weakens the resistance of the lymph-tissue and the bacilli are enabled to develop and gradually to change a simple into a tuberculous adenitis. The frequent association of tuberculous adenitis of the bronchial glands with whooping-cough and with measles, and the frequent development of tubercle in the mesenteric glands in children with intestinal catarrh, find in this way a rational explanation. After all, as Virchow pointed out, an increased vulnerability of the tissue, however brought about, is the important factor in the disease.

The following are some of the features of interest in tuberculous adenitis:

(a) The local character of the disease. Thus, the glands of the neck, or at the bifurcation of the bronchi, or those of the mesentery, may be alone involved.

(b) The tendency to spontaneous healing. In a large proportion of the cases the battle which ensues between the bacilli and the tissue-cells is long; but the latter are finally successful, and we find in the calcified remnants in the bronchial and mesenteric lymph-glands evidences of victory. Too often in the bronchial glands a truce only is declared and hostilities may break out afresh in the form of an acute tuberculosis.

(c) The tendency of tuberculous adenitis to pass on to suppuration. The frequency with which, particularly in the glands of the neck, we find the tuberculous processes associated with pus is a special feature of this form of adenitis. In nearly all instances the pus is sterile. Whether the suppuration is excited by the bacilli or by their products, or whether it is the result of a mixed infection with pus organisms, which are subsequently destroyed, has not been settled.

(d) The existence of an unhealed focus of tuberculous adenitis is a constant menace to the organism. It is safe to say that in three fourths of the instances of acute tuberculosis the infection is derived from this source. On the other hand, it has been urged that scrofula in childhood gives a sort of protection against tuberculosis in adult life. We certainly do meet with many persons of exceptional bodily vigor who in childhood had enlarged glands, but the evidence which Marfan brings forward in support of this view is not conclusive.

Clinical Forms.—1. **Generalized Tuberculous Lymphadenitis.**—In exceptional instances we find diffuse tuberculosis of nearly all the lymph-glands of the body with little or no involvement of other parts. The most extreme cases of it, which I have seen, have been in negro patients. Two well-marked cases occurred at the Philadelphia Hospital. In a woman, the chart from April, 1888, until March, 1889, showed persistent fever, ranging from 101° to 103°, occasionally rising to 104°. On December 16th the glands on the right side of the neck were removed. After an attack of erysipelas, on February 17th, she gradually sank and died March 5th. The lungs presented only one or two puckered spots at the apices. The bronchial, retro-peritoneal, and mesenteric glands were greatly enlarged and caseous. There was no intestinal, uterine, or bone disease. The continuous high fever in this case depended apparently upon the tuberculous adenitis, which was much more extensive than was supposed during life. In these instances the enlargement is most marked in the retro-peritoneal, bronchial, and mesenteric glands, but may be also present in the groups of external glands. Occurring acutely, it presents a picture resembling Hodgkin's disease. In a case which died in the Montreal General Hospital this diagnosis was made. The cervical and axillary glands were enormously enlarged, and death was caused by infiltration of the larynx. In infants and children there is a form of general tuberculous adenitis in which the various groups of glands are successively, more rarely simultaneously, involved, and in which death is caused either by cachexia, or by an acute infection of the meninges.

2. **Local Tuberculous Adenitis.**—(a) *Cervical.*—This is the most common form met with in children. It is seen particularly among the poor and those who live continuously in the impure atmosphere of badly ventilated lodgings. Children in foundling hospitals and asylums are specially prone to the disease. In this country it is most common in the negro race. As already stated, it is often met with in catarrh of the nose and throat, or chronic enlargement of the tonsils; or the child may have had eczema of the scalp or a purulent otitis.

The submaxillary glands are first involved, and are popularly spoken of as enlarged *kernels*. They are usually larger on one side than on the other. As they increase in size, the individual tumors can be felt; the surface is smooth and the consistence firm. They may remain isolated, but more commonly they form large, knotted masses, over which the skin is, as a rule, freely movable. In many cases the skin ultimately becomes adherent, and inflammation and suppuration occur. An abscess points and, unless opened, bursts, leaving a sinus which heals slowly. The disease is frequently associated with coryza, with eczema of the scalp, ear, or lips, and with conjunctivitis or keratitis. When the glands are large and growing actively, there is fever. The subjects are usually anæmic, particularly if suppuration has occurred. The progress of this form of adenitis is slow and tedious. Death, however, rarely follows, and many aggravated cases in children ultimately get well. Not only the submaxillary group, but the glands above the clavicle and in the posterior cervical triangle, may be involved. In other instances the cervical and axillary glands are involved together, forming a continuous chain which extends beneath the clavicle and the pectoral muscle. With them the bronchial glands may also be enlarged and caseous. Not infrequently the enlargement of the supra-clavicular and axillary group of glands on one side precedes the development of a tuberculous pleurisy or of pulmonary tuberculosis.

(b) *Tracheo-bronchial.*—The mediastinal lymph-glands constitute filters in which lodge the various foreign particles which escape the normal phagocytes of bronchi and lungs. Among these foreign particles, and probably attached to them, tubercle bacilli are not uncommon, and we find tubercles and caseous matter with great frequency in the mediastinal glands, particularly those about the bronchi. It is stated that this process is always secondary to a focus, however small, in the lungs, but my experience does not bear out such a statement. As already mentioned, Northrup found them involved in every one of 127 cases at the New York Foundling Hospital. This tuberculous adenitis may, in the bronchial glands, attain the dimensions of a tumor of large size. But even when this occurs there may be no pressure symptoms. In children the bronchial adenitis is apt to be associated with suppuration. The effects of these enlarged glands are very varied, and for full details the reader is referred to the elaborate section in the Traité of Barthez and Sannée (tome iii). It is sufficient here to say that there are instances on record of compression of the superior cava, of the pulmonary artery, and of the azygos vein. The trachea and bronchi, though often flattened, are rarely seriously compressed. The pneumogastric nerve may be involved, particularly the recurrent laryngeal branch. More important really are the perforations of the enlarged and softened glands into the bronchi or trachea, or a sort of secondary cyst may be formed between the lung and the trachea. Asphyxia has been caused by blocking of the larynx by a caseous gland which has ulcerated through the bronchus (Voelcker), and Cyril Ogle has reported a case in which the ulcerated gland practically occluded both bronchi. Perforations of the vessels are much less common, but the pulmonary artery and the aorta have been opened. Perforation of the œsophagus has been described in several cases. One of the most serious effects is infection of the lung or pleura by the caseous glands situated deep along the bronchi. This may, as is often clearly seen, be by direct contact, and it may be difficult to determine in some sections where the caseous bronchial gland terminates and the pulmonary tissue begins. In other instances it takes place along the root of the lung and is subpleural. Among other sequences may be mentioned diverticulum of the œsophagus following adhesion of an enlarged gland and its subsequent retraction; and, in the case of the anterior mediastinal and aortic groups, the frequent production of pericarditis, either by contact or by rupture of a softened gland into the sac.

A serious danger is systemic infection, which takes place through the vessels.

(c) *Mesenteric; Tabes mesenterica.*—In this affection, the abdominal scrofula of old writers, the glands of the mesentery and retro-peritonæum

18

become enlarged and caseate; more rarely they suppurate or calcify. A slight tuberculous adenitis is extremely common in children, and is often accidentally found (post mortem) when the children have died of other diseases. It may be a primary lesion associated with intestinal catarrh, or it may be secondary to tuberculous disease of the intestines.

The primary cases are very common in children, as may be gathered from Woodhead's figures, already given. The general involvement of the glands interferes seriously with nutrition, and the patients are puny, wasted, and anæmic. The abdomen is enlarged and tympanitic; diarrhœa is a constant feature; the stools are thin and offensive. There is moderate fever, but the general wasting and debility are the most characteristic features. The enlarged glands cannot often be felt, owing to the distended condition of the bowels. These cases are often spoken of as consumption of the bowels, but in a majority of them the intestines do not present tuberculous lesions. In a considerable number of the cases of tabes mesenterica the peritonæum is also involved, and in such the abdomen is large and hard, and nodules may be felt.

In adults tuberculous disease of the mesenteric glands may occur as a primary affection, or in association with pulmonary disease. Gairdner gives a remarkable instance of the kind in a man aged twenty-one. Instances of this sort are not uncommon in the literature. Large tumors may exist without tuberculous disease in the intestines or in any other part.

The diagnosis of local and general tuberculous adenitis from lymphadenoma will be subsequently considered.

2. Tuberculosis of the Serous Membranes.

General Serous Membrane Tuberculosis.—The serous membranes may be chiefly involved, either simultaneously or consecutively, forming a distinctive and readily recognizable clinical type of tuberculosis. There are three groups of cases. First, those in which an acute tuberculosis of the peritonæum and pleuræ develops rapidly, caused by local disease of the tubes in women, or of the mediastinal or bronchial lymph-glands. Secondly, cases in which the disease is more chronic, with exudation into both peritonæum and pleuræ, the formation of cheesy masses, and the occurrence of ulcerative and suppurative processes. Thirdly, there are cases in which the pleuro-peritoneal affection is still more chronic, the tubercles hard and fibroid, the membranes much thickened, and with little or no exudate. In any one of these three forms the pericardium may be involved with the pleuræ and peritonæum. It is important to bear in mind that there may be in these cases no visceral tuberculosis.

Tuberculosis of the Pleura.—1. Acute tuberculous pleurisy. It is difficult in the present state of our knowledge to estimate the proportion of instances of acute pleurisy due to tuberculosis (see Acute Pleurisy). The cases are rarely fatal. In the study of those in the Johns Hopkins Hospital, which I made for the Shattuck Lecture (Boston Med. and Surg. Journal, 1893), there were three groups of cases: (a) Acute tuberculous pleurisy with subsequent chronic course. (b) Secondary and terminal forms of acute pleurisy (these are not uncommon in hospital practice).

And (c) a form of acute tuberculous suppurative pleurisy. A considerable number of the purulent pleurisies, designated as latent and chronic, are caused by tubercle bacilli, but the fact is not so widely recognized that there is an acute, ulcerative, and suppurative disease which may run a very rapid course. The pleurisy sets in abruptly, with pain in the side, fever, cough, and sometimes with a chill. There may be nothing to suggest a tuberculous process, and the subject may have a fine physique and come of healthy stock. 2. The subacute and chronic tuberculous pleurisies are more common. The largest group of cases comprises those with sero-fibrinous effusion. The onset is insidious, the true character of the disease is frequently overlooked, and in almost every instance there are tuberculous foci in the lungs and in the bronchial glands. These are cases in which the termination is often in pulmonary tuberculosis or general miliary tuberculosis. In not a few of them the exudate becomes purulent.

And, lastly, there is a chronic adhesive pleurisy, a primary proliferative form which is of long standing, may lead to very great thickening of the membrane, and sometimes to invasion of the lung. For a fuller consideration the reader is referred to my Shattuck Lecture or to the section on tuberculosis in Loomis and Thompson's System of Medicine.

Secondary tuberculous pleurisy is very common. The visceral layer is always involved in pulmonary tuberculosis. Adhesions usually form and a chronic pleurisy results, which may be simple, but usually tubercles are scattered through the adhesions. An acute tuberculous pleurisy may result from direct extension. The fluid may be sero-fibrinous or hæmorrhagic, or may become purulent. And, lastly, a very common event in pulmonary tuberculosis is the perforation of a superficial spot of softening, and the production of *pyo-pneumothorax*.

The general symptomatology of these forms will be considered under disease of the pleura.

Tuberculosis of the Pericardium.—Miliary tubercles may occur as a part of a general infection, but the term is properly limited to those cases in which, either as a primary or secondary process, there is extensive disease of the membrane. Tuberculosis is not so common in the pericardium as in the pleura and peritonæum, but it is certainly more common than the literature would lead us to suppose. Seventeen cases had come under my observation to January, 1893 (American Journal of the Medical Sciences).

We may recognize four groups of cases: First, those in which the condition is entirely latent, and the disease is discovered accidentally in individuals who have died of other affections or of chronic pulmonary tuberculosis.

A second group, in which the symptoms are those of cardiac insufficiency following the dilatation and hypertrophy consequent upon a chronic adhesive pericarditis. The symptoms are those of cardiac dropsy, and suggest either idiopathic hypertrophy and dilatation, or, if there is a loud blowing systolic murmur at the apex, mitral valve disease, either insufficiency or stenosis. There are cases of adherent pericardium in which a bruit is heard which resembles the rumbling presystolic murmur (Hale White). The condition of adherent pericardium is usually overlooked.

In a third group the clinical picture is that of an acute tuberculosis, either general or with cerebro-spinal manifestations, which has had its origin from the tuberculous pericardium or tuberculous mediastinal lymph-glands.

A fourth group, with symptoms of acute pericarditis, includes cases in which the affection is acute and accompanied with more or less exudation of a sero-fibrinous, hæmorrhagic, or purulent character. There may be no suspicion whatever of the tuberculous nature of the trouble.

(*d*) **Tuberculosis of the Peritonæum.**—In connection with miliary and chronic pulmonary tuberculosis it is not uncommon to find the peritonæum studded with small gray granulations. They are constantly present on the serous surface of tuberculous ulcers of the intestines. Apart from these conditions the membrane is often the seat of extensive tuberculous disease, which occurs in the following forms:

(1) *Acute miliary tuberculosis* with sero-fibrinous or bloody exudation.

(2) *Chronic tuberculosis*, characterized by larger growths, which tend to caseate and ulcerate. It may lead to perforation of the intestinal coils. The exudate is purulent or sero-purulent, and is often sacculated.

(3) *Chronic fibroid tuberculosis*, which may be subacute from the onset, or which may represent the final stage of an acute miliary eruption. The tubercles are hard and pigmented. There is little or no exudation, and the serous surfaces are matted together by adhesions.

The process may be primary and local, which was the case in 5 of my 17 post mortems. In children the infection appears to pass from the intestines, and in adults this is the source in the cases associated with chronic phthisis. In women the disease extends commonly from the Fallopian tubes. In at least 30 or 40 per cent of the instances of laparotomy in this affection reported by gynæcologists the infection was from them. The prostate or the seminal vesicles may be the starting-point. In many cases the peritonæum is involved with the pleura and pericardium, particularly with the former membrane.

It is interesting to note that certain morbid conditions of the abdominal organs predispose to the development of the disease; thus patients with cirrhosis of the liver very often die of an acute tuberculous peritonitis. The frequency with which the condition is met with in operations upon ovarian tumors has been commented upon by gynæcologists. Many cases have followed trauma of the abdomen. A very interesting feature is the development of tuberculosis in hernial sacs. The condition is not very uncommon. In a majority of the instances it has been discovered accidentally during the operation for radical cure or for strangulation. In 7 instances the sac alone was involved.

It is generally stated that males are attacked oftener than females. In my own series of 21 cases, 15 were males. The recent laparotomies, however, which have been performed in this disease have been chiefly in females; so that in the collected statistics I find the cases to be twice as numerous in females as in males; in the ratio, indeed, of 131 to 60.

Tuberculous peritonitis occurs at all ages. It is common in children associated with intestinal and mesenteric disease. The incidence is most frequent between the ages of twenty and forty. It may occur in advanced life. In one of my cases the patient was eighty-two years of age. Of 357 cases collected from the literature,* there were under ten years, 27; between ten and twenty, 75; from twenty to thirty, 87; between thirty and forty, 71; from forty to fifty, 61; from fifty to sixty, 19; from sixty to seventy, 4; above seventy, 2. In America it is more common in the negro than in the white race.

Symptoms.—In certain special features the tuberculous varies considerably from other forms of peritonitis. It presents a symptom-complex of extraordinary diversity.

In the first place, the process may be *latent* and not cause a single symptom. Such are the cases met with accidentally in the operation for hernia or for ovarian tumor. In direct contrast are the instances in which the onset is so sudden and violent that the diagnosis of *enteritis* or *hernia* is made. The operation for strangulated hernia has, indeed, been performed. Many cases set in acutely with fever, abdominal tenderness, and the symptoms of ordinary acute peritonitis. Cases with a slow onset, abdominal tenderness, tympanites, and low continuous fever resemble *typhoid fever* very closely, and may lead to error in diagnosis.

Ascites is frequent, but the effusion is rarely large. It is sometimes hæmorrhagic. In this form the diagnosis may rest between an acute miliary cancer, cirrhosis of the liver, and a chronic simple peritonitis—conditions which usually offer no special difficulties in differentiation. A most important point is the simultaneous presence of a pleurisy. The tuberculin test may be used. *Tympanites* may be present in the very acute cases, when it is due to loss of tone in the intestines, owing to inflammatory infiltration; or it may occur in the old, long-standing cases when universal adhesion has taken place between the parietal and visceral layers. *Fever* is a marked symptom in the acute cases, and the temperature may reach 103° or 104°. In many instances the fever is slight. In the more chronic cases subnormal temperatures are common, and for days the temperature may not rise above 97°, and the morning record may be as low as 95.5°. An occasional symptom is pigmentation of the skin, which in some cases has led to the diagnosis of Addison's disease. A striking peculiarity of tuberculous peritonitis is the frequency with which either the condition simulates or is associated with *tumor*. These may be:

(*a*) *Omental*, due to puckering and rolling of this membrane until it forms an elongated firm mass, attached to the transverse colon and lying athwart the upper part of the abdomen. This cord-like structure is found also with cancerous peritonitis, but is much more common in tuberculosis. Gairdner has called special attention to this form of tumor, and in children has seen it undergo gradual resolution. A resonant percussion note may sometimes be elicited above the mass. Though usually situated near the

---

* Johns Hopkins Hospital Reports, vol. ii.

umbilicus, the omental mass may form a prominent tumor in the right iliac region.

(b) *Sacculated exudation,* in which the effusion is limited and confined by adhesions between the coils, the parietal peritonæum, the mesentery, and the abdominal or pelvic organs. This encysted exudate is most common in the middle zone, and has frequently been mistaken for ovarian tumor. It may occupy the entire anterior portion of the peritonæum, or there may be a more limited saccular exudate on one side or the other. It may lie completely within the pelvis proper, associated with tuberculous disease of the Fallopian tubes.

(c) In rare cases the tumor formations may be due to great retraction or thickening of the *intestinal coils.* The small intestine is found shortened, the walls enormously thickened, and the entire coil may form a firm knot close against the spine, giving on examination the idea of a solid mass. Not the small intestine only, but the entire bowel from the duodenum to the rectum, has been found forming such a hard nodular tumor.

(d) *Mesenteric glands,* which occasionally form very large, tumor-like masses, more commonly found in children than in adults. This condition may be confined to the abdominal glands. Ascites may coexist. The condition must be distinguished from that in children, in which, with ascites or tympanites—sometimes both—there can be felt irregular nodular masses, due to large caseous formations between the intestinal coils. No doubt in a considerable number of cases of the so-called tabes mesenterica, particularly in those with enlargement and hardness of the abdomen—the condition which the French call *carreau*—there is involvement also of the peritonæum.

The *diagnosis* of these peritoneal tumors is sometimes very difficult. The omental mass is a less frequent source of error than any other; but, as already mentioned, a similar condition may occur in cancer. The most important problem is the diagnosis of the saccular exudation from ovarian tumor. In fully one third of the recorded cases of laparotomy in tuberculous peritonitis, the diagnosis of cystic ovarian disease had been made. The most suggestive points for consideration are the history of the patient and the evidence of old tuberculous lesions. The physical condition is not of much help, as in many instances the patients have been robust and well nourished. Irregular febrile attacks, gastro-intestinal disturbance, and pains are more common in tuberculous disease. Unless inflamed there is usually not much fever with ovarian cysts. The local signs are very deceptive, and in certain cases have conformed in every particular to those of cystic disease. The outlines in saccular exudation are rarely so well defined. The position and form may be variable, owing to alterations in the size of the coils of which in parts the walls are composed. Nodular cheesy masses may sometimes be felt at the periphery. Depression of the vaginal wall is mentioned as occurring in encysted peritonitis; but it is also found in ovarian tumor. Lastly, the condition of the Fallopian tubes, of the lungs and of the pleuræ, should be thoroughly examined. The association of salpingitis with an ill-defined anomalous mass in the abdomen should arouse suspicion, as should also involvement of the pleura, the apex of one lung, or a testis in the male.

IV. PULMONARY TUBERCULOSIS (*Phthisis, Consumption*).

Three clinical groups may be conveniently recognized: (1) *tuberculo-pneumonic phthisis*—acute phthisis; (2) *chronic ulcerative phthisis;* and (3) *fibroid phthisis.*

According to the mode of infection there are two distinct types of lesions:

(*a*) When the bacilli reach the lungs through the blood-vessels or lymphatics the primary lesion is usually in the tissues of the alveolar walls, in the capillary vessels, the epithelium of the air-cells, and in the connective-tissue framework of the septa. The process of cell division proceeds as already described in the general histology of tubercle. The irritation of the bacilli produces, within a few days, the small, gray miliary nodules, involving several alveoli and consisting largely of round, cuboidal, uninuclear epithelioid cells. Depending upon the number of bacilli which reach the lung in this way, either a localized or a general tuberculosis is excited. The tubercles may be uniformly scattered through both lungs and form a part of a general miliary tuberculosis, or they may be confined to the lungs, or even in great part to one lung. The changes which the tubercles undergo have already been referred to. The further stages may be: (1) Arrest of the process of cell division, gradual sclerosis of the tubercle, and ultimately complete fibroid transformation. (2) Caseation of the centre of the tubercle, extension at the periphery by proliferation of the epithelioid and lymphoid cells, so that the individual tubercles or small groups become confluent and form diffuse areas which undergo caseation and softening. (3) Occasionally as a result of intense infection of a localized region through the blood-vessels the tubercles are thickly set. The intervening tissue becomes acutely inflamed, the air-cells are filled with the products of a desquamative pneumonia, and many lobules are involved.

(*b*) When the bacilli reach the lung through the bronchi—inhalation or aspiration tuberculosis—the picture differs. The smaller bronchi and bronchioles are more extensively affected; the process is not confined to single groups of alveoli, but has a more lobular arrangement, and the tuberculous masses from the outset are larger, more diffuse, and may in some cases involve an entire lobe or the greater part of a lung. It is in this mode of infection that we see the characteristic peri-bronchial granulations and the areas of the so-called nodular broncho-pneumonia. These broncho-pneumonic areas, with on the one hand caseation, ulceration, and cavity formation, and on the other sclerosis and limitation, make up the essential elements in the anatomical picture of tuberculous phthisis.

1. Acute Pneumonic Tuberculosis of the Lungs.

This form, known also by the name of *galloping consumption*, is met with both in children and adults. In the former many of the cases are mistaken for simple broncho-pneumonia.

Two types may be recognized, the *pneumonic* and *broncho-pneumonic.*

(*a*) In the *pneumonic form* one lobe may be involved, or in some instances an entire lung. The organ is heavy, the affected portion airless; the pleura is usually covered with a thin exudate, and on section the picture resembles closely that of ordinary hepatization. The following is an extract from the post-mortem report of a case in which death occurred twenty-nine days after the onset of the illness, having all the characters of an acute pneumonia: " Left lung weighs 1,500 grammes (double the weight of the other organ) and is heavy and airless, crepitant only at the anterior margins. Section shows a small cavity the size of a walnut at the apex, about which are scattered tubercles in a consolidated tissue. The greater part of the lung presents a grayish-white appearance due to the aggregation of tubercles which in some places have a continuous, uniform appearance, in others are surrounded by an injected and consolidated lung-tissue. Toward the margins of the lower lobe strands of this firm reddish tissue separate anæmic, dry areas. There are in the right lung three or four small groups of tubercles but no caseous masses. The bronchial glands are not tuberculous." Here the intense local infection was due to the small focus at the apex of the lung, probably an aspiration process.

Only the most careful inspection may reveal the presence of miliary tubercles, or the attention may be arrested by the detection of tubercles in the other lung or in the bronchial glands. The process may involve only one lobe. There may be older areas which are of a peculiarly yellowish-white color and distinctly caseous. The most remarkable picture is presented by cases of this kind in which the disease lasts for some months. A lobe or an entire lung may be enlarged, firm, airless throughout, and converted into a dry, yellowish-white, cheesy substance. Cases are met with in which the entire lung from apex to base is in this condition, with perhaps only a small, narrow area of air-containing tissue on the margin. More commonly, if the case has lasted for two or three months, rapid softening has taken place at the apex with extensive cavity formation.

In a recent study A. Fraenkel and Troje found tubercle bacilli alone in 11 of 12 cases. They suggest that in these cases of infection by aspiration the large areas of exudative inflammation, at some distance even from the seat of growth of the bacilli, are due to the presence of some diffusible poison produced by the germs.

Symptoms.—The attack sets in abruptly with a chill, usually in an individual who has enjoyed good health, although in many cases the onset has been preceded by exposure to cold, or there have been debilitating circumstances. The temperature rises rapidly after the chill, there are pain in the side, and cough, with at first mucoid, subsequently rusty-colored expectoration which may contain tubercle bacilli. The dyspnœa may become extreme and the patient may have suffocative attacks. The physical examination shows involvement of one lobe or of one lung, with signs of consolidation, dulness, increased fremitus, at first feeble or suppressed vesicular murmur, and subsequently well-marked bronchial breathing. The upper or lower lobe may be involved, or in some cases the entire lung.

At this time, as a rule, no suspicion enters the mind of the practitioner that the case is anything but one of frank lobar pneumonia. Occasionally there may be suspicious circumstances in the history of the patient or in his family; but, as a rule, no stress is laid upon them in view of the intense and characteristic mode of onset. Between the eighth and tenth day, instead of the expected crisis, the condition becomes aggravated, the temperature is irregular, and the pulse more rapid. There may be sweating, and the expectoration becomes muco-purulent and greenish in color—a point of special importance, to which Traube called attention. Even in the second or third week, with the persistence of these symptoms, the physician tries to console himself with the idea that the case is one of unresolved pneumonia, and that all will yet be well. Gradually, however, the severity of the symptoms, the presence of physical signs indicating softening, the existence of elastic tissue and tubercle bacilli in the sputa present the mournful proofs that the case is one of acute pneumonic phthisis. Death may occur before softening takes place, even in the second or third week. In other cases there is extensive destruction at the apex, with rapid formation of cavity, and the case may drag on for two or three months or may become one of chronic phthisis.

Diagnosis.—It is by no means widely recognized in the profession that there is a form of acute phthisis which may closely simulate ordinary pneumonia. Waters, of Liverpool, gave an admirable description of these cases, and called attention to the difficulty in distinguishing them from ordinary pneumonia. Certainly the mode of onset affords no criterion whatever. A healthy, robust-looking young Irishman, a cab-driver, who had been kept waiting on a cold, blustering night until three in the morning, was seized the next afternoon with a violent chill, and the following day was admitted to my wards at the University Hospital, Philadelphia. He was made the subject of a clinical lecture on the fifth day, when there was absent no single feature in history, symptoms, or physical signs of acute lobar pneumonia of the right upper lobe. It was not until ten days later, when bacilli were found in his expectoration, that we were made aware of the true nature of the case. I know of no criterion by which cases of this kind can be distinguished in the early stage. The tubercle bacilli may not be present at first, but in one of Fraenkel and Troje's cases they existed alone in the typical pneumonic sputum. A point to which Traube called attention, and which is also referred to as important by Hérard and Cornil, is the absence of breath-sounds in the consolidated region; but this, I am sure, does not hold good in all cases. The tubular breathing may be intense and marked as early as the fourth day; and again, how common it is to have, as one of the earliest and most suggestive symptoms of lobar pneumonia, suppression or enfeeblement of the vesicular murmur! In many cases, however, there are suspicious circumstances in the onset: the patient has been in bad health, or may have had previous pulmonary trouble, or there are recurring chills. Careful examination of the sputa and a study of the physical signs from day to day can alone determine the true nature of the case. A point of some moment is the character of the fever, which in true pneumonia is more continuous, particularly in severe cases, whereas in this form of tuberculosis remissions of 1.5° or 2° are not infrequent.

(b) *Acute tuberculous broncho-pneumonia* is more common, particularly in children, and forms a majority of the cases of *phthisis florida,* or "galloping consumption." It is an acute caseous broncho-pneumonia, starting in the smaller tubes, which become blocked with a cheesy substance, while the air-cells of the lobule are filled with the products of a catarrhal pneumonia. In the early stages the areas have a grayish-red, later an opaque-white, caseous appearance. By the fusion of contiguous masses an entire lobe may be rendered nearly solid, but there can usually be seen between the groups areas of crepitant air tissue. This is not an uncommon picture in the acute phthisis of adults, but it is still more frequent in children. The following is an extract from the post-mortem report of a case on a child aged four months, which died in the sixth week of illness: " On section, the right upper lobe is occupied with caseous masses from 5 to 12 mm. in diameter, separated from each other by an intervening tissue of a deep-red color. The bronchi are filled with cheesy substance. The middle and lower lobes are studded with tubercles, many of which are becoming caseous. Toward the diaphragmatic surface of the lower lobe there is a small cavity the size of a marble. The left lung is more crepitant and uniformly studded with tubercles of all sizes, some as large as peas. The bronchial glands are very large, and one contains a tuberculous abscess."

There is a form of tuberculous aspiration pneumonia, to which Bäumler has called attention, developing as a sequence of hæmoptysis, and due to the aspiration of blood and the contents of pulmonary cavities into the finer tubes. Following the hæmoptysis, which may have occurred in an individual without suspected lesion, there are fever, dyspnœa, and signs of a diffuse broncho-pneumonia. Some of these cases run a very rapid course, and are examples of galloping consumption following hæmoptysis. This accident may occur not alone early in the disease, but may follow hæmorrhage in a well-developed case of pulmonary tuberculosis.

In children the enlarged bronchial glands usually surround the root of the lung, and even pass deeply into the substance, and the lobules are often involved by direct contact.

In other cases the caseous broncho-pneumonia involves groups of alveoli or lobules in different portions of the lungs, more commonly at both apices, forming areas from 1 to 3 cm. in diameter. The size of the mass depends largely upon that of the bronchus involved. There are cases which probably should come in this category, in which, with a history of an acute illness of from four to eight weeks, the lungs are extensively studded with large gray tubercles, ranging in size from 5 to 10 mm. In some instances there are cheesy masses the size of a cherry. All of these are grayish-white in color, distinctly cheesy, and between the adjacent ones, particularly in the lower lobe, there may be recent pneumonia, or the condition of lung which has been termed splenization. In a case of this kind at the Philadelphia Hospital death took place about the eighth week from the abrupt onset of the illness with hæmorrhage. There were no extensive areas of consolidation, but the cheesy nodules were uniformly scattered throughout both lungs. No softening had taken place.

Secondary infections are not uncommon; but Prudden was able to show that the tubercle bacillus could produce not only distinct tubercle nodules, but also the various kinds of exudative phenomena, the exudates varying in appearance in different cases, which phenomena occurred absolutely without the intervention of other organisms. The fact that these latter had not subsequently crept in was shown by cultures at the autopsy on the affected animal.

Symptoms.—The symptoms of acute broncho-pneumonic phthisis are very variable. In adults the disease may attack persons in good health, but who are overworked or "run down" from any cause. Hæmorrhage initiates the attack in a few cases. There may be repeated chills; the temperature is high, the pulse rapid, and the respirations are increased. The loss of flesh and strength is very striking.

The physical signs may at first be uncertain and indefinite, but finally there are areas of impaired resonance, usually at the apices; the breath-sounds are harsh and tubular, with numerous râles. The sputa may early show elastic tissue and tubercle bacilli. In the acute cases, within three weeks, the patient may be in a marked typhoid state, with delirium, dry tongue, and high fever. Death may occur within three weeks. In other cases the onset is severe, with high fever, rapid loss of flesh and strength, and signs of extensive unilateral or bilateral disease. Softening takes place; there are sweats, chills, and progressive emaciation, and all the features of *phthisis florida*. Six or eight weeks later the patient may begin to improve, the fever lessens, the general symptoms abate, and a case which looks as if it would certainly terminate fatally within a few weeks drags on and becomes chronic.

In *children* the disease most commonly follows the infectious diseases, particularly measles and whooping-cough.* The profession is gradually recognizing the fact that a majority of all such cases are tuberculous. At least *three groups* of these tuberculous broncho-pneumonias may be recognized. In the *first* the child is taken ill suddenly while teething or during convalescence from fever; the temperature rises rapidly, the cough is severe, and there may be signs of consolidation at one or both apices with râles. Death may occur within a few days, and the lung shows areas of broncho-pneumonia, with perhaps here and there scattered opaque grayish-yellow nodules. Macroscopically the affection does not look tuberculous, but histologically miliary granulations and bacilli may be found. Tubercles are usually present in the bronchial glands, but the appearance of the broncho-pneumonia may be exceedingly deceptive, and it may require careful microscopical examination to determine its tuberculous character. The *second group* is represented by the case of the child previously quoted, which died at the sixth week with the ordinary symptoms of severe broncho-pneumonia. And the *third group* is that in which, during the convalescence from an infectious disease, the child is taken ill with fever, cough, and shortness of breath. The severity of the symptoms abates within the first fortnight; but there is loss of flesh, the general condition is bad, and the physical examination shows the presence of scattered râles

---

* "Tussis convulsiva vestibulum tabis" (Willis).

throughout the lungs, and here and there areas of defective resonance. The child has sweats, the fever becomes hectic in character, and in many cases the clinical picture gradually develops into that of chronic phthisis.

2. Chronic Ulcerative Tuberculosis of the Lungs.

Under this heading may be grouped the great majority of cases of pulmonary tuberculosis, in which the lesions proceed to ulceration and softening, and ultimately produce the well-known picture of chronic phthisis. At first a strictly tuberculous affection, it ultimately becomes, in a majority of cases, a mixed disease, many of the most prominent symptoms of which are due to septic infection from purulent foci and cavities.

Morbid Anatomy.—Inspection of the lungs in a case of chronic phthisis shows a remarkable variety of lesions, comprising nodular tubercles, diffuse tuberculous infiltration, caseous masses, pneumonic areas, cavities of various sizes, with changes in the pleura, bronchi, and bronchial glands.

1. The Distribution of the Lesions.—For years it has been recognized that the most advanced lesions are at the apices, and that the disease progresses downward, usually more rapidly in one of the lungs. This general statement, which has passed current in the text-books ever since the masterly description of Laennec, has recently been carefully elaborated by Kingston Fowler, who finds that the disease in its onward progress through the lungs follows, in a majority of the cases, distinct routes. In the upper lobe the primary lesion is not, as a rule, at the extreme apex, but from an inch to an inch and a half below the summit of the lung, and nearer to the posterior and external borders. The lesion here tends to spread downward, probably from inhalation of the virus, and this accounts for the frequent circumstance that examination behind, in the supraspinous fossa, will give indications of disease before any evidences exist at the apex in front. Anteriorly this initial focus corresponds to a spot just below the centre of the clavicle, and the direction of extension in front is along the anterior aspect of the upper lobe, along a line running about an inch and a half from the inner ends of the first, second, and third interspaces. A second less common site of the primary lesion in the apex " corresponds on the chest wall with the first and second interspaces below the outer third of the clavicle." The extension is downward, so that the outer part of the upper lobe is chiefly involved.

In the middle lobe of the right lung the affection usually follows disease of the upper lobe on the same side. In the involvement of the lower lobe the first secondary infiltration is about an inch to an inch and a half below the posterior extremity of its apex, and corresponds on the chest wall to a spot opposite the fifth dorsal spine. This involvement is of the greatest importance clinically, as " in the great majority of cases, when the physical signs of the disease at the apex are sufficiently definite to allow of the diagnosis of phthisis being made, the lower lobe is already affected." Examination, therefore, should be made carefully of this posterior apex in all suspicious cases. In this situation the lesion spreads downward and laterally along the line of the interlobular septa, a line which is marked by the vertebral border of the scapula, when the hand is placed on the opposite scapula and the elbow raised above the level of the shoulder. Once present in an apex, the disease usually extends in time to the opposite upper lobe; but not, as a rule, until the apex of the lower lobe of the lung first affected has been attacked.

Of 427 cases above mentioned, the right apex was involved in 172, the left in 130, both in 111.

Lesions of the base may be primary, though this is rare. Percy Kidd makes the proportion of basic to apicic phthisis 1 to 500, a smaller number than existed in my series. In very chronic cases there may be arrested lesions at the apex and more recent lesions at the base.

2. **Summary of the Lesions in Chronic Ulcerative Phthisis.**—(a) *Miliary Tubercles.*—They have one of two distributions: (1) A dissemination due to aspiration of tuberculous material, the tubercles being situated in the air-cells or the walls of the smaller bronchi; (2) the distribution due to dissemination of tubercle bacilli by the lymph current, the tubercles being scattered about the old foci in a radial manner—the secondary crop of Laennec. Much more rarely there is a scattered dissemination from infection here and there of the smaller vessels, the tubercles then being situated in the vessel walls. Sometimes, in cases with cavity formation at the apex, the greater part of the lower lobes presents many groups of firm, sclerotic, miliary tubercles, which may indeed form the distinguishing anatomical feature—a chronic miliary tuberculosis.

(b) *Tuberculous Broncho-pneumonia.*—In a large proportion of the cases of chronic phthisis the terminal bronchiole is the point of origin of the process, consequently we find the smaller bronchi and their alveolar territories blocked with the accumulated products of inflammation in all stages of *caseation*. At an early period a cross-section of an area of tuberculous broncho-pneumonia gives the most characteristic appearance. The central bronchiole is seen as a small orifice, or it is plugged with cheesy contents, while surrounding it is a caseous nodule, the so-called peribronchial tubercle. The longitudinal section has a somewhat dendritic or foliaceous appearance. The condition of the picture depends much upon the slowness or rapidity with which the process has advanced. The following changes may occur:

Ulceration.—When the caseation takes place rapidly or ulceration occurs in the bronchial wall, the mass may break down and form a small cavity.

Sclerosis.—In other instances the process is more chronic. Fibroid changes gradually produce a sclerosis of the affected area, a condition which is sometimes called *cirrhosis nodosa tuberculosa*. The sclerosis may be confined to the margin of the mass, forming a limiting capsule, within which is a uniform, firm, cheesy substance, in which lime salts are often deposited. This represents the healing of one of these areas of caseous broncho-pneumonia. It is only, however, when complete fibroid transformation or calcification has occurred that we can really speak of healing. In many instances the colonies of miliary tubercles about these masses show that the virus is still active in them. Subsequently, in ulcerative processes, these calcareous bodies—lung-stones, as they are sometimes called —may be expectorated.

(c) *Pneumonia.*—An important though secondary place is occupied by inflammation of the alveoli surrounding the tubercles, which become filled with epithelioid cells. The consolidation may extend for some distance about the tuberculous foci and unite them into areas of uniform consolidation. Although in some instances this inflammatory process may be simple, in others it is undoubtedly specific. It is excited by the tubercle bacilli and is a manifestation of their action. It may present a very varied appearance; in some instances resembling closely ordinary red hepatization, in others being more homogeneous and infiltrated, the so-called *infiltration tuberculeuse* of Laennec. In other cases the contents of the alveoli undergo fatty degeneration, and appear on the cut surface as opaque white or yellowish-white bodies. In early phthisis much of the consolidation is due to this pneumonic infiltration, which may surround for some distance the smaller tuberculous foci.

(d) *Cavities.*—A vomica is a cavity in the lung tissue, produced by necrosis and ulceration. It differs materially from the bronchiectatic form. The process usually begins in the wall of the bronchus in a tuberculous area. Dilatation is produced by retained secretion, and necrosis and ulceration of the wall occur with gradual destruction of the contiguous tissues. By extension of the necrosis and ulceration the cavity increases, contiguous ones unite, and in an affected region there may be a series of small excavations communicating with a bronchus. In nearly all instances the process extends from the bronchi, though it is possible for necrosis and softening to take place in the centre of a caseous area without primary involvement of the bronchial wall. Three forms of cavities may be recognized.

The *fresh ulcerative,* seen in acute phthisis, in which there is no limiting membrane, but the walls are made up of softened, necrotic, and caseous masses. Small vomicæ of this sort, situated just beneath the pleura, may rupture and cause pneumothorax. In cases of acute tuberculo-pneumonic phthisis they may be large, occupying the greater portion of the upper lobe. In the chronic ulcerative phthisis, cavities of this sort are invariably present in those portions of the lung in which the disease is advancing. At the apex there may be a large old cavity with well-defined walls, while at the anterior margin of the upper lobes, or in the apices of the lower lobes, there are recent ulcerating cavities communicating with the bronchi.

Cavities with Well-defined Walls.—A majority of the cavities in the chronic form of phthisis have a well-defined limiting membrane, the inner surface of which constantly produces pus. The walls are crossed by trabeculæ which represent remnants of bronchi and blood-vessels. Even the vomicæ with the well-defined walls extend gradually by a slow necrosis and destruction of the contiguous lung tissue. The contents are usually purulent, similar in character to the grayish nummular sputa coughed up by phthisical patients. Not infrequently the membrane is vascular or it may be hæmorrhagic. Occasionally, when gangrene has occurred in the wall, the contents are horribly fœtid. These cavities may occupy the greater portion of the apex, forming an irregular series which communicate with each other and with the bronchi, or the entire upper lobe except the anterior margin may be excavated, forming a thin-walled cavity. In rare instances the process has proceeded to total excavation of the lung, not a remnant of which remains, except perhaps a narrow strip at the anterior margin. In a case of this kind, in a young girl, the cavity held 40 fluid ounces.

Quiescent Cavities.—When quite small and surrounded by dense cicatricial tissue communicating with the bronchi they form the *cicatrices fistuleuses* of Laennec. Occasionally one apex may be represented by a series of these small cavities, surrounded by dense fibrous tissue. The lining membrane of these old cavities may be quite smooth, almost like a mucous membrane. Cavities of any size do not heal completely.

Cases are often seen in which it has been supposed that a cavity has healed; but the signs of excavation are notoriously uncertain, and there may be pectoriloquy and cavernous sounds with gurgling, resonant râles in an area of consolidation close to a large bronchus.

In the formation of vomicæ the blood-vessels gradually become closed by an obliterating inflammation. They are the last structures to yield and may be completely exposed in a cavity, even when the circulation is still going on in them. Unfortunately, the erosion of a large vessel which has not yet been obliterated is by no means infrequent, and causes profuse and often fatal hæmorrhage. Another common event is the development of aneurisms on the arteries running in the walls of cavities. These may be small, bunch-like dilatations, or they may form sacs the size of a walnut or even larger. Rasmussen, Douglas Powell, and others have called attention to their importance in hæmoptysis, under which section they are dealt with more fully.

And finally, about cavities of all sorts, the connective tissue develops and tends to limit the extent. The thickening is particularly marked beneath the pleura, and in chronic cases an entire apex may be converted into a mass of fibrous tissue, enclosing a few small cavities.

(*e*) *Pleura.*—Practically, in all cases of chronic phthisis the pleura is involved. Adhesions take place which may be thin and readily torn, or dense and firm, uniting layers of from 2 to 5 mm. in thickness. This pleurisy may be simple, but in many cases it is tuberculous, and miliary tubercles or caseous masses are seen in the thickened membrane. Effusion is not at all infrequent, either serous, purulent, or hæmorrhagic. Pneumothorax is a common accident.

(*f*) Changes in the *smaller bronchi* control the situation in the early stages of tuberculous phthisis, and play an important *rôle* throughout the disease. The process very often begins in the walls of the smaller tubes and leads to caseation, distention with products of inflammation, and broncho-pneumonia of the lobules. In many cases the visible implication of the bronchus is an extension upward of a process which has begun in the smallest bronchiole. This involvement weakens the wall, leading to bronchiectasis, not an uncommon event in phthisis. The mucous membrane of the larger bronchi, which is usually involved in a chronic catarrh, is more or less swollen, and in some instances ulcerated. Besides these specific lesions, they may be the seat, especially in children, of inflammation due to secondary invasion, most frequently by the micrococcus lanceolatus, with the production of a broncho-pneumonia.

(g) The *bronchial glands*, in the more acute cases, are swollen and œdematous. Miliary tubercles and caseous foci are usually present. In cases of chronic phthisis the caseous areas are common, calcification may occur, and not infrequently purulent softening.

(h) *Changes in the other Organs.*—Of these, tuberculosis is the most common. In my series of autopsies the brain presented tuberculous lesions in 31, the spleen in 33, the liver in 12, the kidneys in 32, the intestines in 65, and the pericardium in 7. Other groups of lymphatic glands besides the bronchial may be affected.

Certain degenerations are common. *Amyloid change* is frequent in the liver, spleen, kidneys, and mucous membrane of the intestines. The *liver* is often the seat of extensive fatty infiltration, which may cause marked enlargement. The *intestinal tuberculosis* occurs in advanced cases and is responsible in great part for the troublesome diarrhœa.

Endocarditis is not very uncommon, and was present in 12 of my post mortems and in 27 of Percy Kidd's 500 cases. Tubercle bacilli have been found in the vegetations. The subject has been considered in an important monograph by Teissier (Paris, 1894). Tubercles may be present on the endocardium, particularly of the right ventricle. As pointed out by Norman Chevers, and confirmed by subsequent writers, the subjects of congenital stenosis of the pulmonary orifice very frequently have phthisis.

The *larynx* is frequently involved, and ulceration of the vocal cords and destruction of the epiglottis are not at all uncommon.

Modes of Onset.—We have already seen that tuberculosis of the lungs may occur as the chief part of a general infection, or may set in with symptoms which closely simulate acute pneumonia. In the ordinary type of pulmonary tuberculosis the invasion is gradual and less striking, but presents an extraordinarily diverse picture, so that the practitioner is often led into error. Among the most characteristic of these types of onset are the following:

(a) There is a small but important group of cases in which the disease makes considerable progress before there are serious symptoms to arouse the attention of the patient. This *latent form* of the disease is seen most frequently in workingmen, and the disease may even advance to excavation of an apex before they seek advice. In some of these cases it is not a little remarkable how slight the lung symptoms have been.

A different type of latent pulmonary tuberculosis is the form in which the symptoms are masked by the existence of serious disease in other organs, as in the peritonæum, intestines, or bones.

(b) *With Symptoms of Dyspepsia and Anæmia.*—The gastric mode of onset is very common, and the early manifestations may be great irritability of the stomach with vomiting or a type of acid dyspepsia with eructations. In young girls (and in children) with this dyspepsia there is very frequently a pronounced chloro-anæmia, and the patient complains of palpitation of the heart, increasing weakness, slight afternoon fever, and amenorrhœa.

(*c*) In a considerable number of cases the onset of pulmonary tuberculosis is with symptoms which suggest *malarial fever.* The patient has repeated paroxysms of chills, fevers, and sweats, which may recur with great regularity. In districts in which intermittents prevail there is no more common mistake than to confound the initial rigors of pulmonary tuberculosis with malaria.

(*d*) *Onset with Pleurisy.*—The first symptoms may be a dry pleurisy over an apex, with persistent friction murmur. In other instances the pulmonary symptoms have followed an attack of pleurisy with effusion. The exudate gradually disappears, but the cough persists and the patient becomes feverish, and gradually signs of disease at one apex become manifest. Of 90 cases of pleurisy with effusion, the history of which was followed by H. I. Bowditch, one third developed pulmonary tuberculosis.

(*e*) *With Laryngeal Symptoms.*—The primary localization may be in the larynx, though in a majority of the instances in which huskiness and laryngeal symptoms are the first noticeable features of the disease there are doubtless foci already existing in the lung. The group of cases in which for many months throat and larynx symptoms precede the graver manifestations of pulmonary phthisis is a very important one.

(*f*) *Onset with Hæmoptysis.*—Frequently the very first symptom of the disease is a brisk hæmorrhage from the lungs, following which the pulmonary symptoms may develop with great rapidity. In other cases the hæmoptysis recurs, and it may be months before the symptoms become well established. In a majority of these cases the local tuberculous lesion exists at the date of the hæmoptysis.

(*g*) *With Tuberculosis of the Cervico-axillary Glands.*—Preceding the onset of pulmonary phthisis for months, or even for years, the lymphglands of the neck or of the neck and axilla of one side may be enlarged. These cases are by no means infrequent, and they are of importance because of the latency of the pulmonary lesions. Nowadays, when operative interference is so common, it is well to bear in mind that in such patients the corresponding apex of the lung may be extensively involved.

(*h*) And, lastly, in by far the largest number of all cases the onset is with a *bronchitis*, or, as the patient expresses it, a neglected cold. There has been, perhaps, a liability to catch cold easily or the patient has been subject to naso-pharyngeal catarrh; then, following some unusual exposure, a bronchial cough develops, which may be frequent and very irritating. The examination of the lungs may reveal localized moist sounds at one apex and perhaps wheezing bronchitic râles in other parts. In a few cases the early symptoms are often suggestive of asthma with marked wheezing and diffuse piping râles.

Symptoms.—In discussing the symptoms it is usual to divide the disease into three periods: the first embracing the time of the growth and development of the tubercles; the second, in which they soften; and the third, in which there is a formation of cavities. Unfortunately, these ana-

19

tomical stages cannot be satisfactory correlated with corresponding clinical periods, and we often find that a patient in the third stage with well-marked cavity is in a far better condition and has greater prospects of recovery than a patient in the first stage with diffuse consolidation. It is therefore better perhaps to disregard them altogether.

1. **Local Symptoms.**—*Pain* in the chest may be early and troublesome or absent throughout. It is usually associated with pleurisy, and may be sharp and stabbing in character, and either constant or felt only during coughing. Perhaps the commonest situation is in the lower thoracic zone, though in some instances it is beneath the scapula or referred to the apex. The attacks may recur at long intervals. Intercostal neuralgia occasionally develops in the course of ordinary phthisis.

Cough is one of the earliest symptoms, and is present in the majority of cases from beginning to end. There is nothing peculiar or distinctive about it. At first dry and hacking, and perhaps scarcely exciting the attention of the patient, it subsequently becomes looser, more constant, and associated with a glairy, muco-purulent expectoration. In the early stages of the disease the cough is bronchial in its origin. When cavities have formed it becomes more paroxysmal, and is most marked in the morning or after a sleep. Cough is not a constant symptom, however, and a patient may present himself with well-marked excavation at one apex who will declare that he has had little or no cough. So, too, there may be well-marked physical signs, dulness and moist sounds, without either expectoration or cough. In well-established cases the nocturnal paroxysms are most distressing and prevent sleep. The cough may be of such persistence and severity as to cause vomiting, and the patient becomes rapidly emaciated from loss of food—Morton's cough (Phthisiologia, 1689, p. 101). The laryngeal complications give a peculiarly husky quality to the cough, and when erosion and ulceration have proceeded far in the vocal cords the efforts of coughing are much less effective.

Sputum.—This varies greatly in amount and character at the different stages of ordinary phthisis. There are cases with well-marked local signs at one apex, with slight cough and moderately high fever, without from day to day a trace of expectoration. So, also, there are instances with the most extensive consolidation (caseous pneumonia), and high fever, but, as in a recent instance under observation for several months, without enough expectoration to enable an examination for bacilli to be made. In the early stage of pulmonary tuberculosis the sputum is chiefly catarrhal and has a glairy, sago-like appearance, due to the presence of alveolar cells which have undergone the myelin degeneration. There is nothing distinctive or peculiar in this form of expectoration, which may persist for months without indicating serious trouble. The earliest trace of characteristic sputum may show the presence of small grayish or greenish-gray purulent masses. These, when coughed up, are always suggestive and should be the portions picked out for microscopical examination. As softening comes on, the expectoration becomes more profuse and purulent, but may still contain a considerable quantity of alveolar epithelium. Finally, when cavities exist, the sputa assume the so-called nummular form; each mass is isolated, flattened, greenish-gray in color, quite airless, and sinks to the bottom when spat into water.

By the microscopical examination of the sputum we determine whether the process is tuberculous, and whether softening has occurred. For *tubercle bacilli* the Ehrlich-Weigert method is the best. Eleven centimetres of a saturated solution of fuchsin in absolute alcohol is added to 100 cm. of the saturated solution of commercial aniline oil (made by shaking up the oil in water and then filtering). This should be made fresh every third or fourth day. A small bit of the sputum is picked out on a needle or platinum wire and spread thin on the top-cover so as to make a uniformly thin layer. The top-cover is slowly dried about a foot above a Bunsen burner. Sufficient of the staining fluid is then dropped upon the top-cover, which is held at a little distance above the flame until the fluid boils. The staining fluid is then washed off in distilled water or put under the tap, decolorized in 30 per cent nitric-acid fluid, again washed off in water, and mounted on the slide. In doubtful cases the long process is used, the cover-slips remaining twenty-four hours in the stain. The bacilli are seen as elongated, slightly curved, red rods, sometimes presenting a beaded appearance. They are frequently in groups of three or four, but the number varies considerably. Only one or two may be found in a preparation, or, in some instances, they are so abundant that the entire field is occupied.

The presence of these bacilli in the sputum is an infallible indication of the existence of tuberculosis.

Sometimes they are found only after repeated examination. They may be abundant early in the disease and are usually numerous in the nummular sputum of the later stages.

Elastic tissue may be derived from the bronchi, the alveoli, or from the arterial coats; and naturally the appearance of the tissue will vary with the locality from which it comes. In the examination for this it is not necessary to boil the sputum with caustic potash. For years I have used a simple plan which was shown to me at the London Hospital by Sir Andrew Clark. This method depends upon the fact that in almost all instances if the sputum is spread in a sufficiently thin layer the fragments of elastic tissue can be seen with the naked eye. The thick, purulent portions are placed upon a glass plate 15 × 15 cm. and flattened into a thin layer by a second glass plate 10 × 10 cm. In this compressed grayish layer between the glass slips any fragments of elastic tissue show on a black background as grayish-yellow spots and can either be examined at once under a low power or the uppermost piece of glass is slid along until the fragment is exposed, when it is picked out and placed upon the ordinary microscopic slide. Fragments of bread and collections of milk-globules may also present an opaque white appearance, but with a little practice they can readily be recognized. Fragments of epithelium from the tongue, infiltrated with micrococci, are still more deceptive, but the microscope at once shows the difference.

The bronchial elastic tissue forms an elongated network, or two or three long, narrow fibres are found close together. From the blood-vessels

a somewhat similar form may be seen and occasionally a distinct sheeting
is found as if it had come from the intima of a good-sized artery. The
elastic tissue of the alveolar wall is quite distinctive; the fibres are branched
and often show the outline of the arrangement of the air-cells. The elastic
tissue from bronchus or alveoli indicates extensive erosion of a tube and
softening of the lung-tissue.

Another occasional constituent of the sputum is blood, which may be
present as the chief characteristic of the expectoration in hæmoptysis or
may simply tinge the sputum. In chronic cases with large cavities, in
addition to bacteria, various forms of fungi may develop, of which the
aspergillus is the most important. Sarcinæ may also occur.

Calcareous Fragments.—Formerly a good deal of stress was laid upon
their presence in the sputum, and Morton described a phthisis *a calculis in
pulmonibus generatis.* Bayle also described a separate form of *phthisie cal-
culeuse.* The size of the fragments varies from a small pea to a large cherry.
As a rule, a single one is ejected; sometimes large numbers are coughed
up in the course of the disease. They are formed in the lung by the calcification of caseous masses, and it is said also occasionally in obstructed
bronchi. They may come from the bronchial glands by ulceration into
the bronchi, and there is a case on record of suffocation in a child from
this cause.

The daily amount of expectoration varies. In rapidly advancing cases,
with much cough, it may reach as high as 500 cc. in the day. In cases with
large cavities the chief amount is brought up in the morning. The expectoration of tuberculous patients usually has a heavy, sweetish odor, and
occasionally it is fetid, owing to decomposition in the cavities.

Hæmoptysis.—One of the most famous of the Hippocratic axioms
says, "From a spitting of blood there is a spitting of pus." The older
writers thought that the phthisis was directly due to the inflammatory
or putrefactive changes caused by the hæmorrhage into the lung. Morton,
however, in his interesting section, Phthisis ab Hæmoptöe, rather doubted
this sequence. Laennec and Louis, and later in the century Traube, regarded the hæmoptysis as an evidence of existing disease of the lung. From
the accurate views of Laennec and Louis the profession was led away by
Graves, and particularly by Niemeyer, who held that the blood in the air-
cells set up an inflammatory process, a common termination of which was
caseation. Since Koch's discovery we have learned that many cases in
which the physical examination is negative show, either during the period
of hæmorrhage or immediately after it, tubercle bacilli in the sputa, so that
opinion has veered to the older view, and we now regard the appearance of
hæmoptysis as an indication of existing disease. In young, apparently
healthy persons, cases of hæmoptysis may be divided into three groups. In
the first the bleeding has come on without premonition, without overexertion or injury, and there is no family history of tuberculosis. The
physical examination is negative, and the examination of the expectoration
at the time of the hæmorrhage and subsequently shows no tubercle bacilli.
Such instances are not uncommon, and, though one may suspect strongly
the presence of some focus of tuberculosis, yet the individuals may retain

good health for many years, and have no further trouble. Of the 386 cases of hæmoptysis noted by Ware in private practice, 62 recovered, and pulmonary disease did not subsequently develop.

In a second group individuals in apparently perfect health are suddenly attacked, perhaps after a slight exertion or during some athletic exercises. The physical examination is also negative, but tubercle bacilli are found sometimes in the bloody sputa, more frequently a few days later.

In a third set of cases the individuals have been in failing health for a month or two, but the symptoms have not been urgent and perhaps not noticed by the patients. The physical examination shows the presence of well-marked tuberculous disease, and there are both tubercle bacilli and elastic tissue in the sputa.

A very interesting systematic study of the subject of hæmoptysis, particularly in its relation to the question of tuberculosis, has been completed in the Prussian army by Franz Stricker. During the five years 1890–'95 there were 900 cases admitted to the hospitals, which is a percentage of 0.045 of the strength (1,728,505). Of the cases, in 480 the hæmorrhage came on without recognizable cause. Of these 417 cases, 86 per cent were certainly or probably tuberculous. In only 221, however, was the evidence conclusive.

In a second group of 213 cases the hæmorrhage came on during the military exercise, and of these 75 patients were shown to be tuberculous.

In 118 cases the hæmorrhage followed certain special exercises, as in the gymnasium or in riding or in consequence of swimming. In 24 cases it developed during the exercise of the voice in singing or in giving command or in the use of wind instruments. A very interesting group is reported of 24 cases in which the hæmorrhage followed trauma, either a fall or a blow upon the thorax. In 7 of these tuberculosis was positively present, and in 6 other cases there was a strong probability of its existence.

Among the conclusions which Stricker draws the following are the most important: namely, that soldiers attacked with hæmoptysis without special cause are in at least 86.8 per cent tuberculous. In the cases in which the hæmoptysis follows the special exercises, etc., of military service, at least 74.4 per cent are tuberculous. In the cases which come on during swimming or as a consequence of direct injury to the thorax about one half are not associated with tuberculosis.

Hæmoptysis occurs in from 60 to 80 per cent of all cases of pulmonary tuberculosis. It is more frequent in males than in females.

In a majority of all cases the bleeding recurs. Sometimes it is a special feature throughout the disease, so that a hæmorrhagic or hæmoptysical form has been recognized. The amount of blood brought up varies from a couple of drachms to a pint or more. In 69 per cent of 4,125 cases of hæmoptysis at the Brompton Hospital the amount brought up was under half an ounce.

A distinction may be drawn between the hæmoptysis early in the disease and that which occurs in the later periods. In the former the bleeding is usually slight, is apt to recur, and fatal hæmorrhage is very rare. In these instances the bleeding is usually from small areas of softening or from early erosions in the bronchial mucosa. In the later periods, after cavities have formed, the bleeding is, as a rule, more profuse and is more apt to be fatal. Single large hæmorrhages, proving quickly fatal, are very rare, except in the advanced stages of the disease. In these cases the bleeding comes either from an erosion of a good-sized vessel in the wall of a cavity or from the rupture of an aneurism of the pulmonary artery.

The bleeding, as a rule, sets in suddenly. Without any warning the patient may notice a warm salt taste and the mouth fills with blood. It may come up with a slight cough. The total amount may not be more than a few drachms, and for a day or two the patient may spit up small quantities. When a large vessel is eroded or an aneurism bursts, the amount of blood brought up is large, and in the course of a short time a pint or two may be expectorated. Fatal hæmorrhage may occur into a very large cavity without any blood being coughed up. The character of the blood is, as a rule, distinctive. It is frothy, mixed with mucus, generally bright red in color, except when large amounts are expectorated, and then it may be dark. The sputa may remain blood-tinged for some days or there are brownish-black streaks in the sputa, or " friable nodules consisting entirely of blood-corpuscles " may be coughed up. Blood moulds of the smaller bronchi are sometimes expectorated.

The microscopical examination of the sputum in tuberculous cases is most important. If carefully spread out,.there may be noted, even in an apparently pure hæmorrhagic mass, little portions of mucus from which bacilli or elastic tissue may be obtained.

Dyspnœa is not a common accompaniment of ordinary phthisis. The greater part of one lung may be diseased and local trouble exist at the other apex without any shortness of breath. Even in the paroxysms of very high fever the respirations may not be much increased. Rapid advance of a broncho-pneumonia, or the development of miliary tubercles throughout the lung, causes great increase in the number of respirations. A degree of dyspnœa leading to cyanosis is almost unknown, apart from extensive invasion of the sound portions by miliary tubercles.

In long standing cases, with contracted apices or great thickening of the pleura, the right heart is enlarged, and the dyspnœa may be cardiac.

2. General Symptoms.—*Fever.*—To get a correct idea of the temperature range in pulmonary tuberculosis it is necessary, as Ringer pointed out, to make tolerably frequent observations. The usual 8 A. M. and 8 P. M. record is, in a majority of the cases, very deceptive, giving neither the minimum nor maximum. The former usually occurs between 2 and 6 A. M. and the latter between 2 and 6 P. M.

A recognition of various forms of fever, viz., of tuberculization, of ulceration, and of absorption, emphasizes the anatomical stages of growth, softening and cavity formation; but practically such a division is of little use, as in a majority of cases these processes are going on together.

Fever is the most important initial symptom and throughout the entire course the thermometer is the most trustworthy guide as to the progress of the affection. With pyrexia a patient loses in weight and strength, and the local disease usually progresses. The periods of apyrexia are those of gain in weight and strength and of limitation of the local lesion. It by no means necessarily follows that a patient with tuberculosis has pyrexia. There may be quite extensive disease without coexisting fever. At one time, I have had 18 instances of chronic phthisis under observation, of whom 10 were practically free from fever. But in the early stage, when tubercles are developing and caseous areas are in process of formation and when softening is in progress, fever is a constant symptom. It was present in 100 consecutive cases in my dispensary service.

Two types of fever are seen—the remittent and the intermittent. These may occur indifferently in the early or in the late stages of the disease

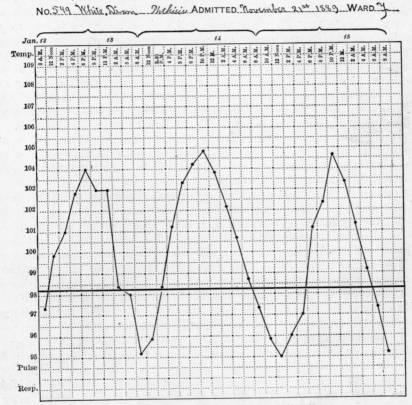

CHART XII. Three days. Chronic tuberculosis.

or may alternate with each other, a variability which depends upon the fact that phthisis is a progressive disease and that all stages of lesions may be found in a single lung. Special stress should be laid upon the fact, particularly in malarial regions, that tuberculosis may set in with a fever typically intermittent in character—a daily chill, with subsequent fever and sweat. In Montreal, where malaria is practically unknown, this was always regarded as a suggestive symptom; but in Philadelphia and Baltimore, where ague prevails, it is no exaggeration to say that yearly scores of cases of early tuberculosis are treated for ague. These are often cases that pursue a rapid course. The fever of onset—tuberculization—may be almost continuous, with slight daily exacerbations; and at any time during the course of chronic phthisis, if there is rapid extension, the remissions become less marked.

A remittent fever, in which the temperature is constantly above normal but drops two or three degrees toward morning, is not uncommon in the middle and later stages and is usually associated with softening or extension of the disease. Here, too, a simple morning and evening register may give an entirely erroneous idea as to the range of the fever. With breaking down of the lung-tissue and formation of cavities, associated as these processes always are with suppuration and with more or less systemic contamination, the fever assumes a characteristically intermittent or hectic type. For a large part of the day the patient is not only afebrile, but the temperature is subnormal. In the annexed two-hourly chart, from a case of chronic tuberculosis of the lungs, it will be seen that from 10 P. M. to 8 or 12 A. M., the temperature continuously fell and went as low as 95°. A slow rise then took place through the late morning and early afternoon hours and reached its maximum between 6 and 10 P. M. As shown in the chart, there were in the three days about forty-three hours of pyrexia and twenty-nine hours of apyrexia. The rapid fall of the temperature in the early morning hours is usually associated with sweating. This hectic, as it is called, which is a typical fever of septic infection, is met with when the process of cavity formation and softening is advanced and extending.

A continuous fever with remissions of not more than a degree, developing in the course of pulmonary tuberculosis, is suggestive of acute pneumonia. When a two-hourly chart is made, the remissions even in acute tuberculous pneumonia are usually well marked. A continued fever, such as is seen in the first week of typhoid, or in some cases of inflammation of the lung, is rare in tuberculosis.

Sweating.—Drenching perspirations are common in phthisis and constitute one of the most distressing features of the disease. They occur usually with the drop in the fever in the early morning hours, or at any time in the day when the patient sleeps. They may come on early in the disease, but are more persistent and frequent after cavities have formed. Some patients escape altogether.

The *pulse* is increased in frequency, especially when the fever is high. It is often remarkably full, though soft and compressible. Pulsation may sometimes be seen in the capillaries and in the veins on the back of the hand.

Emaciation is a pronounced feature, from which the two common names of the disease have been derived. The loss of weight is gradual but, if the disease is extending, progressive. The scales give one of the best indications of the progress of the case.

3. **Physical Signs.**—(*a*) *Inspection.*—The shape of the chest is often suggestive, though it is to be remembered that pulmonary tuberculosis may be met with in chests of any build. Practically, however, in a consider-

able proportion of cases the thorax is long and narrow, with very wide intercostal spaces, the ribs more vertical in direction and the costal angle very narrow. The scapulæ are "winged," a point noted by Hippocrates. Another type of chest which is very common is that which is flattened in the antero-posterior diameter. The costal cartilages may be prominent and the sternum depressed. Occasionally the lower sternum forms a deep concavity, the so-called funnel breast (*Trichter-Brust*). Inspection gives valuable information in all stages of the disease. Special examination should be made of the clavicular regions to see if one clavicle stands out more distinctly than the other, or if the spaces above or below it are more marked. Defective expansion at one apex is an early and important sign. The condition of expansion of the lower zone of the thorax may be well estimated by inspection. The condition of the præcordia should also be noted, as a wide area of impulse, particularly in the second, third, and fourth interspaces, often results from disease of the left apex. From a point behind the patient, looking over the shoulders, one can often better estimate the relative expansion of the apices.

(*b*) *Palpation.*—Deficiency in expansion at the apices or bases is perhaps best gauged by placing the hands in the subclavicular spaces and then in the lateral regions of the chest and asking the patient to draw slowly a full breath. Standing behind the patient and placing the thumbs in the supraclavicular and the fingers in the intraclavicular spaces one can judge accurately as to the relative mobility of the two sides. Disease at an apex, though early and before dulness is at all marked, may be indicated by deficient expansion. On asking the patient to count, the tactile fremitus is increased wherever there is local growth of tubercle or extensive caseation. In comparing the apices it is important to bear in mind that normally the fremitus is stronger over the right than the left. So too at the base, when there is consolidation of the lung, the fremitus is increased; whereas, if there is pleural effusion, it is diminished or absent. In the later stages, when cavities form, the tactile fremitus is usually much exaggerated over them. When the pleura is greatly thickened the fremitus may be somewhat diminished.

(*c*) *Percussion.*—Tubercles, inflammatory products, fibroid changes, and cavities produce important changes in the pulmonary resonance. There may be localized disease, even of some extent, without inducing much alteration; as when the tubercles are scattered and have air-containing tissue between them. One of the earliest and most valuable signs is defective resonance upon and above a clavicle. In a considerable proportion of all cases of phthisis the dulness is first noted in these regions. The comparison between the two sides should be made also when the breath is held after a full inspiration, as the defective resonance may then be more clearly marked. In the early stages the percussion note is usually higher in pitch, and may require an experienced ear to detect the difference. In recent consolidation from caseous pneumonia the percussion note often has a tubular or tympanitic quality. A wooden dulness is rarely heard except in old cases with extensive fibroid change at the apex or base. Over large, thin-walled cavities at the apex the so-called cracked-pot sound may be obtained. In thin subjects the percussion should be carefully practised in the supraspinous fossæ and the interscapular space, as they correspond to very important areas early involved in the disease. In cases with numerous isolated cavities at the apex, without much fibroid tissue or thickening of the pleura, the percussion note may show little change, and the contrast between the signs obtained on auscultation and percussion is most marked. In the direct percussion of the chest, particularly in thin patients over the pectorals, one frequently sees the phenomenon known as *myoidema,* a local contraction of the muscle causing bulging, which persists for a variable period and gradually subsides. It has no special significance.

(*d*) *Auscultation.*—Feeble breath-sounds are among the most characteristic early signs, since not as much air enters the tubes and vesicles of the affected area. It is well at first always to compare carefully the corresponding points on the two sides of the chest without asking the patient either to draw a deep breath or to cough. With early apical disease the inspiration on quiet breathing may be scarcely audible. Expiration is usually prolonged. On the other hand, there are cases in which the earliest sign is a harsh, rude, respiratory murmur. On deep breathing it is frequently to be noted that inspiration is jerking or wavy, the so-called " cogwheel " rhythm; which, however, is by no means confined to tuberculosis. With extension of the disease the inspiratory murmur is harsh, and, when consolidation occurs, whiffing and bronchial. With these changes in the character of the murmur there are râles, due to the accompanying bronchitis. They may be heard only on deep inspiration or on coughing, and early in the disease are often crackling in character. When softening occurs they are louder and have a bubbling, sometimes a characteristic clicking quality. These " moist sounds," as they are called, when associated with change in the percussion resonance are extremely suggestive. When cavities form, the râles are louder, more gurgling, and resonant in quality. When there is consolidation of any extent the breath-sounds are tubular, and in the large excavations loud and cavernous, or have an amphoric quality. In the unaffected portions of the lobe and in the opposite lung the breath-sounds may be harsh and even puerile. The vocal resonance is usually increased in all stages of the process, and bronchophony and pectoriloquy are met with in the regions of consolidation and over cavities. Pleuritic friction may be present at any stage and, as mentioned before, occurs very early. There are cases in which it is a marked feature throughout. When the lappet of lung over the heart is involved there may be a pleuro-pericardial friction, and when this area is consolidated there may be curious clicking râles synchronous with the heart-beat, due to the compression by the heart of, and the expulsion of air from, this portion. An interesting auscultatory sign, met most commonly in phthisis, is the so-called cardio-respiratory murmur, a whiffing systolic bruit due to the propulsion of air out of the tubes by the impulse of the heart. It is best heard during inspiration and in the antero-lateral regions of the chest.

A systolic murmur is frequently heard in the subclavian artery on either side, the pulsation of which may be very visible. The murmur is in all probability due to pressure on the vessels by the thickened pleura.

The signs of cavity may be here briefly enumerated.

(*a*) When there is not much thickening of the pleura or condensation of the surrounding lung-tissue, the percussion sound may be full and clear, resembling the normal note. More commonly there is defective resonance or a tympanitic quality which may at times be purely amphoric. The pitch of the percussion note changes over a cavity when the mouth is opened or closed (Wintrich's sign), or it may be brought out more clearly on change of position. The cracked-pot sound is only obtainable over tolerably large cavities with thin walls. It is best elicited by a firm, quick stroke, the patient at the time having the mouth open. In those rare instances of almost total excavation of one lung the percussion note may be amphoric in quality. (*b*) On auscultation the so-called cavernous sounds are heard: (1) Various grades of modified breathing—blowing or tubular, cavernous or amphoric. There may be a curiously sharp hissing sound, as if the air was passing from a narrow opening into a wide space. In very large cavities both inspiration and expiration may be typically amphoric. (2) There are coarse bubbling râles which have a resonant quality, and on coughing may have a metallic or ringing character. On coughing they are often loud and gurgling. In very large thin-walled cavities, and more rarely in medium-sized cavities, surrounded by recent consolidation, the râles may have a distinctly amphoric echo, simulating those of pneumothorax. There are dry cavities in which no râles are heard. (3) The vocal resonance is greatly intensified and whispered pectoriloquy is clearly heard. In large apical cavities the heart-sounds are well heard, and occasionally there may be an intense systolic murmur, probably always transmitted to, and not produced as has been supposed, in the cavity itself. In large excavations of the left apex the heart impulse may cause gurgling sounds or clicks synchronous with the systole. They may even be loud enough to be heard at a little distance from the chest wall. A large cavity with smooth walls and thin fluid contents may give the succussion sound when the trunk is abruptly shaken (Walshe), and even the coin sound may be obtained.

Pseudo-cavernous signs may be caused by an area of consolidation near a large bronchus. The condition may be most deceptive—the high-pitched or tympanitic percussion note, the tubular or cavernous breathing, and the resonant râles, simulate closely those of cavity.

4. Complications of Pulmonary Tuberculosis.—(1) In the Respiratory System.—The larynx is rarely spared in chronic pulmonary tuberculosis. The first symptom may be huskiness of the voice. There are pain, particularly in swallowing, and a cough which is often wheezing, and in the later stages very ineffectual. Aphonia and dysphagia are the two most distressing symptoms of the laryngeal involvement. When the epiglottis is seriously diseased and the ulceration extends to the lateral wall of the pharynx, the pain in swallowing may be very intense, or, owing to the imperfect closure of the glottis, there may be coughing spells and regurgitation of food through the nostrils. Bronchitis and tracheitis are almost invariable accompaniments of chronic pulmonary tuberculosis.

Pneumonia is a not infrequent terminal complication of chronic phthisis. It may run a perfectly normal course, while in other instances resolution may be delayed, and one is in doubt, in spite of the abruptness of the onset, as to the presence of a simple or a tuberculous pneumonia.

Emphysema of the uninvolved portions of the lung is a common feature, rarely producing any special symptoms. There are, however, cases of chronic tuberculosis in which emphysema dominates the picture, and in which the condition develops slowly during a period of many years. (General subcutaneous emphysema, which has been met with in a few rare cases, is due either to perforation of the trachea or to the rupture of a cavity closely adherent to the chest wall.)

Gangrene of the lung is an occasional event in chronic pulmonary tuberculosis, due in almost all instances to sphacelus in the walls of the cavity, rarely in the lung-tissue itself.

Complications in the Pleura.—A dry pleurisy is a very common accompaniment of the early stages of tuberculosis. It is always a conservative, useful process. In some cases it is very extensive, and friction murmurs may be heard over the sides and back. The cases with dry pleurisy and adhesions are of course much less liable to the dangers of pneumothorax. Pleurisy with effusion more commonly precedes than develops in the course of pulmonary tuberculosis. Still, it is common enough to meet with cases in which a sero-fibrinous effusion develops in the course of the chronic disease. There are cases in which it is a special feature, and it often, I think, favors chronicity. A patient may during a period of four or five years have signs of local disease at one apex with recurring effusion in the same side. Owing to adhesions in different parts of the pleura, the effusion may be encapsulated. Hæmorrhagic effusions, which are not uncommon in connection with tuberculous pleurisy, are comparatively rare in chronic phthisis. Chyliform or milky exudates are sometimes found. Purulent effusions are not frequent apart from pneumothorax. An empyema, however, may develop in the course of the disease or as a sequence of a sero-fibrinous exudate. Pneumothorax is an extremely common complication of chronic pulmonary tuberculosis. It may occur early in the disease, but more frequently is late. It may prove fatal in twenty-four hours. In other instances a pyo-pneumothorax develops and the patient lingers for weeks or months. In a third group of cases it seems to have a beneficial effect on the course of the disease.

(2) Symptoms referable to other Organs.—(*a*) *Cardio-vascular.*—The retraction of the left upper lobe exposes a large area of the heart. In thin-chested subjects there may be pulsation in the second, third, and fourth interspaces close to the sternum. Sometimes with much retraction of the left upper lobe the heart is drawn up. A systolic murmur over the pulmonary area is common in all stages of phthisis. Apical murmurs are also not infrequent and may be extremely rough and harsh without necessarily indicating that endocarditis is present. The association of heart-disease with phthisis is not, however, very uncommon. As already mentioned, there were 12 instances of endocarditis in 216 autopsies. The arterial tension is usually low in phthisis and the capillary resistance lessened so that the pulse is often full and soft even in the later stages of the disease. The capillary pulse is not infrequently met with, and pulsation of the veins in the back of the hand is occasionally to be seen.

(*b*) *Blood Glandular System.*—The early anæmia has already been noted. It is often more apparent than real, a chloro-anæmia, and the blood-count rarely sinks below two millions per cubic millimetre.

The blood-plates are, as a rule, enormously increased and are seen in the withdrawn blood as the so-called Schultze's granule masses. Without any significance, they are of interest chiefly from the fact that every few years some tyro announces their discovery as a new diagnostic sign of phthisis. The leucocytes are greatly increased, particularly in the later stages.

(*c*) *Gastro-intestinal System.*—The tongue is usually furred, but may be clean and red. Small aphthous ulcers are sometimes distressing. A red line on the gums, a symptom to which at one time much attention was paid as a special feature of phthisis, occurs in other cachectic states. Extensive tuberculous disease of the pharynx, associated with a similar affection of the larynx, may interfere seriously with deglutition and prove a very distressing and intractable symptom.

Of late, special attention has been paid to the gastric symptoms of this affection. Tuberculosis of the stomach is rare. Ulceration may occur as an accidental complication and multiple catarrhal ulcers are not uncommon. Interstitial and parenchymatous changes in the mucosa are common (possibly associated with the venous stasis) and lead to atrophy, but these cannot always be connoted with the symptoms, and they may be found when not expected. On the other hand, when the gastric symptoms have been most persistent the mucosa may show very little change. It is impossible always to refer the anorexia, nausea, and vomiting of consumption to local conditions. The hectic fever and the neurotic influences, upon which Immermann lays much stress, must be taken into account, as they play an important *rôle*. The organ is often dilated, and to muscular insufficiency alone may be due some of the cases of dyspepsia. The condition of the gastric secretion is not constant, and the reports are discordant. In the early stages there may be superacidity; later, a deficiency of acid.

Anorexia is often a marked symptom at the onset; there may be positive loathing of food, and even small quantities cause nausea. Sometimes, without any nausea or distress after eating, the feeding of the patient is a daily battle. When practicable, Debove's forced alimentation is of great benefit in such cases. Nausea and vomiting, though occasionally troublesome at an early period, are more marked in the later stages. The latter may be caused by the severe attacks of coughing. S. H. Habershon refers to four different causes the vomiting in phthisis: (1) central, as from tuberculous meningitis; (2) pressure on the vagi by caseous glands; (3) stimulation from the peripheral branches of the vagus, either pulmonary, pharyngeal, or gastric; and (4) mechanical causes.

Of the *intestinal* symptoms diarrhœa is the most serious. It may come on early, but is more usually a symptom of the later stages, and is associated with ulceration, particularly of the large bowel. Extensive ulceration of the ileum may exist without any diarrhœa. The associated catarrhal condition may account in part for it, and in some instances the amyloid degeneration of the mucous membrane.

(d) *Nervous System.*—(1) Focal lesions due to the development of coarse tubercles and areas of tuberculous meningo-encephalitis. Aphasia, for instance, may result from the growth of meningeal tubercles in the fissure of Sylvius, or even hemiplegia may develop. The solitary tubercles are more common in the chronic phthisis of children. (2) Basilar meningitis is an occasional complication. It may be confined to the brain, though more commonly it is a (3) cerebro-spinal meningitis, which may come on in persons without well-developed local signs in the chest. Twice have I known strong, robust men· brought into hospital with signs of cerebrospinal meningitis, in whom the existence of pulmonary disease was not discovered until the post-mortem. (4) *Peripheral neuritis,* which is not common, may cause an extensor paralysis of the arm or leg, more commonly the latter, with foot-drop. It is usually a late manifestation. (5) Mental symptoms. It was noted, even by the older writers, that consumptives had a peculiarly hopeful temperament, and the *spes phthisica* forms a curious characteristic of the disease. Patients with extensive cavities, high fever, and too weak to move will often make plans for the future and confidently expect to recover.

Apart from tuberculosis of the brain, there is sometimes in chronic phthisis a form of insanity not unlike that which develops in the convalescence from acute affections. The whole question of the mutual relations of insanity and phthisis is dealt with at length in Mickle's Gulstonian lectures.

(e) A remarkable *hypertrophy of the mammary gland* may occur in pulmonary tuberculosis,* most commonly in males. It may be only on the affected side. Two cases came under my notice at the University Hospital, Philadelphia, both in young males. It is a chronic interstitial, non-tuberculous mammitis (Allot).

(f) *Genito-urinary System.*—The urine presents no special peculiarities in amount or constituents. Fever, however, has a marked influence upon it. Albumin is met with frequently and may be associated with the fever, or is the result of definite changes in the kidneys. In the latter case it is more abundant and more curd-like. Amyloid disease of the kidneys is not uncommon. Its presence is shown by albumin and tube-casts, and sometimes by a great increase in the amount of urine. In other instances there is dropsy, and the patients have all the characteristic features of chronic Bright's disease.

Pus in the urine may be due to disease of the bladder or of the pelves of the kidneys. In some instances the entire urinary tract is involved. In pulmonary phthisis,. however, extensive tuberculous disease is rarely found in the urinary organs. Bacilli may occasionally be detected in the pus. Hæmaturia is not a very common symptom. It may occur occasionally as a result of congestion of the kidneys, and pass off leaving the urine albuminous. In other instances it results from disease of the pelvis

---

* Allot, Paris Thesis, 1887.

or of the bladder, and is associated either with early tuberculosis of the mucous membranes or more commonly with ulceration. In any medical clinic the routine inspection of the testes for tubercle will save two or three mistakes a year.

(*g*) *Cutaneous System.*—The skin is often dry and harsh. Local tubercles occasionally develop on the hands. There may be pigmentary staining, the *chloasma phthisicorum*, which is more common when the peritonæum is involved. Upon the chest and back the brown stains of the *pityriasis versicolor* are very frequent. The hair of the head and beard may become dry and lanky. The terminal phalanges, in chronic cases, become clubbed and the nails incurvated—the Hippocratic fingers. A remarkable and unusual complication is general emphysema, which may result from ulceration of an adherent lung or perforation of the larynx.

Diagnosis.—When well advanced there is rarely any doubt as to the existence of tuberculous phthisis, for the sputum gives positive information, and the physical signs of local disease are well marked. The bacilli give an infallible indication of the existence of tuberculosis and may be found in the sputum before the physical signs are at all definite. On the other hand, it must be remembered that there are cases in which, even with tolerably well-defined physical signs, the sputum is extremely scanty and many examinations may be required to detect tubercle bacilli. So essential is the examination of the sputum in the early diagnosis of phthisis that I would earnestly insist upon the more frequent employment of this method. There is no excuse now for its omission, since, if the practitioner has not command of the necessary technique, there are laboratories in many parts of the country at which the examination can be made. *Early detection is of vital importance, as successful treatment depends upon the measures taken before the lungs are extensively involved.*

The presence of elastic fibres in the sputum is an indication of destruction of the lung-tissue. In a large proportion of cases it is indicative, too, of tuberculous disease. It also may be found early, before the physical signs are well marked. Its detection is easy by the above-mentioned method, not requiring high powers of the microscope. In cases of early hæmoptysis, before there is marked constitutional disturbance, or even local signs, it is very important to make a thorough examination of the sputum, from which mucoid and purulent portions may be picked out for examination. With localized and persistent signs in one lung, cough, fever, and loss of flesh, the diagnosis is rarely dubious. It is remarkable, however, to what an extent the local process may sometimes proceed without disturbance of health sufficient to excite the alarm of the physician or friends. There are puzzling cases with localized physical signs at one apex, chiefly moist râles, rarely any percussion changes, perhaps slight fever, and a glairy expectoration containing numerous alveolar cells. I have seen several cases of this kind which have been for a time very obscure, and in which repeated examinations failed to detect either bacilli or elastic tissue. They seem to be instances of local catarrhal trouble in the smaller tubes, some of which clear in a few weeks.

3. Fibroid Phthisis.

In their monograph on Fibroid Diseases of the Lung (1894) Clark Hadley and Chaplin make the following classification: 1. Pure fibroid; fibroid phthisis—a condition in which there is no tubercle. 2. Tuberculo-fibroid disease—a condition primarily tuberculous, but which has run a fibroid course. 3. Fibro-tuberculous disease—a condition primarily fibroid, but which has become tuberculous. The tuberculo-fibroid form may come on gradually as a sequence of a chronic tuberculous broncho-pneumonia, or follow a chronic tuberculous pleurisy. In other instances the process supervenes upon an ordinary ulcerative phthisis. The disease becomes limited to one apex, the cavity is surrounded by layers of dense fibrous tissue, the pleura is thickened, and the lower lobe is gradually invaded by the sclerotic change. Ultimately a picture is produced little if at all different from the condition known as cirrhosis of the lungs. It may even be difficult to say that the process is tuberculous, but in advanced cases the bacilli are usually present in the walls of the cavity at the apex, or old, encapsulated caseous areas exist in the lung, or there may be tubercles at the apex of the other lung and in the bronchial glands. Dilatation of the bronchi is present; the right ventricle, sometimes the entire heart, is hypertrophied.

The disease is chronic, lasting from ten to twenty or more years, during which time the patient may have fair health.

The chief symptoms are cough, which is often paroxysmal in character and most marked in the morning. The expectoration is purulent, and in some instances, when the bronchiectasis is extensive, fetid. There is dyspnœa on exertion, but little or no fever.

The physical signs are very characteristic. The chest is sunken and the shoulder lower on the affected side; the heart is often drawn over and displaced. If the left lung is involved there may be an unusually large area of cardiac pulsation in the third, fourth, and fifth interspaces. Heart-murmurs are common. There is dulness over the affected side and deficient tactile fremitus. At the apex there may be well-marked cavernous sounds; at the base, distant bronchial breathing. The condition may persist indefinitely. In some cases the other lung becomes involved, or the patient has repeated attacks of hæmoptysis, in one of which he dies. As a result of the chronic suppuration, amyloid degeneration of the liver, spleen, and intestines may take place; dropsy frequently supervenes from failure of the right heart.

A more detailed account is found under Cirrhosis of the Lung, with which this form is clinically identical.

Concurrent Infections in Pulmonary Tuberculosis.—It has long been known that in pulmonary tuberculosis organisms other than the specific bacilli are present, particularly the micrococcus lanceolatus, the streptococcus pyogenes, and the staphylococcus aureus; less frequently the bacillus pyocyaneus.

A majority of all cases of pulmonary tuberculosis are combined infections; streptococci and pneumococci may be found in the sputa, and the former have been isolated from the blood. Prudden, who has very carefully studied this question, arrives at the following conclusions: The pulmonary lesions of tuberculosis are subject to variations depending largely on the different modes of distribution of the bacilli, whether by the blood-vessels or through the bronchi, and also whether a concurrent infection with other organisms has taken place. The pneumonia complicating tuberculosis may be the direct result of the tubercle bacillus or its toxines, or it may follow secondary infection with other germs, particularly the streptococcus pyogenes, the micrococcus lanceolatus, and the staphylococcus pyogenes. The frequency of this secondary infection and the relative significance of these germs are not yet fully decided. The introduction of the tubercle bacilli into the lungs of a rabbit through the trachea induces the various phases of pulmonary tuberculosis, but cavity formation is rare. If, on the other hand, into the lungs of a rabbit which are the seat of extensive consolidation the streptococcus pyogenes is introduced, then cavities form rapidly, and the anatomical picture is very similar to that of chronic ulcerative tuberculosis in man. It is very probable that in man, too, the effect of contamination with these pus organisms is a very important one in hastening necrosis and softening, and also in the chronic cases they doubtless produce in large amounts the toxines which are responsible for many of the symptoms of the disease.

Diseases associated with Pulmonary Tuberculosis.—*Lobar pneumonia* is a not uncommon cause of death. It is met with, most frequently indeed, as a terminal event in the chronic cases. It may, however, occur early, and be difficult to distinguish from an acute caseous pneumonia. The sputa in the latter are rarely rusty, while the fever in the former is more continuous and higher, but in many cases it is impossible to differentiate between the two conditions.

Typhoid fever occasionally occurs in persons the subjects of pulmonary tuberculosis. In 4 cases of 80 autopsies in typhoid fever tuberculous lesions were present. There are cases on record also of acute miliary tuberculosis and typhoid fever present in the same subject. There is a widespread opinion that typhoid fever predisposes to tuberculosis, and Wilson Fox in his treatise on diseases of the lungs gives references to a number of cases. In my experience it has been very rare. I have no recollection of an instance in which tuberculosis has developed either during convalescence, or immediately after recovery, from typhoid fever.

Erysipelas not infrequently attacks old *poitrinaires* in hospital wards and almshouses. There are instances in which the attack seems to be beneficial, as the cough lessens and the symptoms ameliorate. It may, however, prove fatal.

The *eruptive fevers*, particularly measles, frequently precede, but rarely develop in the course of pulmonary tuberculosis. In the revaccination of a tuberculous subject the vesicles run a normal course.

Fistula in ano is associated with phthisis in an interesting manner. In a majority of such cases it is a tuberculous process. The general affection may progress rapidly after an operation. The question is considered in tuberculosis of the alimentary canal.

20

Heart-disease.—I have already referred (page 298) to the occurrence of endocarditis in tuberculosis. The antagonism between heart lesions and phthisis, upon which Rokitansky laid stress, is not pronounced. Stenosis of the pulmonary artery and aneurism of the aorta predispose to tuberculosis pulmonum, probably by reducing the activity of the lesser circulation. In mitral stenosis pulmonary tuberculosis is not infrequent, in 9 of 54 cases (Potain). A terminal acute tuberculosis of one or the other of the serous membranes is a very common event in all forms of cardio-vascular disease.

In chronic and arrested phthisis *arterio-sclerosis* and *phlebo-sclerosis* are uncommon. Ormerod noted 30 cases of chronic renal disease in 100 post-mortems.

The association of tuberculosis with *chronic arthritis,* upon which certain writers lay stress, finds its explanation in the lowered resistance of these patients, and the greater liability to infection in the institutions in which so many of them live.

Peculiarities of Pulmonary Tuberculosis at the Extremes of Life.—(*a*) *Old Age.*—It is remarkable how common tuberculosis is in the aged, particularly in institutions. McLachlan noted 145 cases in which tuberculosis was the cause of death in old persons in Chelsea Hospital. All were over sixty years of age. The experience at the Salpêtrière is the same. Laennec met with a case in a person over ninety-nine years of age.

At the Philadelphia Hospital, in the bodies of aged persons sent over from the almshouse it was extremely common to find either old or recent tuberculosis. A patient died under my care at the age of eighty-two with extensive peritoneal tuberculosis. Pulmonary tuberculosis in the aged is usually latent and runs a slow course. The physical signs are often masked by emphysema and by the coexisting chronic bronchitis. The diagnosis may depend entirely upon the discovery of the bacilli and elastic tissue. Contrary to the opinion which was held some years ago, tuberculosis is by no means uncommon with senile emphysema. Some of the cases of tuberculosis in the aged are instances of quiescent disease which may have dated from an early period.

(*b*) *Infants.*—The occurrence of acute tuberculosis in children has already been mentioned, and also the fact that the disease is occasionally congenital. Recent studies, particularly of French writers, have shown that it is a frequent affection in children under two years of age. Leroux has analyzed the statistics of the late Prof. Parrot, embracing 219 cases in children under three years. Of these there were from one day to three months, 23; from three to six months, 35; from six to twelve months, 53 (a total of 111 under one year); and from one to three years, 108. Pulmonary cavities were present in 57 of the cases, and in only 50 was the pulmonary lesion the sole manifestation. At the St. Petersburg Foundling Asylum, in the ten years ending 1884, there were 416 cases of tuberculosis in 16,581 autopsies. The observations of Northrup, at the New York Foundling Hospital, are of special interest in connection with the mode of infection. Of 125 cases of tuberculosis on the records of this institution, in 34 the ravages were extensive, the seat of the primary affection was not clear, and the bronchial glands were large and cheesy. In 20 cases of general tuberculosis there were cheesy masses in the bronchial glands and in the lungs. In 42 cases of general tuberculosis the only cheesy masses were in the bronchial lymph-glands. In 9 cases the tubercles were limited to the bronchial nodes and the lungs; the latter containing only discrete miliary bodies, while the bronchial glands showed advanced caseation. In 13 cases there was tuberculosis of the bronchial nodes only. In most of these cases the patients died of infectious diseases. These figures are very suggestive, and point, as already noted, to infection through the bronchial passages as the most common method, even in children. Of 500 autopsies in children at the Munich Pathological Institute, in 150 (30 per cent) tuberculosis was present and in over 92 per cent the lungs were involved (Müller).

Modes of Death in Pulmonary Tuberculosis. —(a) *By asthenia*, a gradual failure of the strength. The end is usually peaceable and quiet, occasionally disturbed by paroxysms of cough. Consciousness is often retained until near the close.

(b) *By asphyxia*, as in some cases of acute miliary tuberculosis and in acute pneumonic phthisis. In chronic phthisis it is rarely seen, even when pneumothorax develops.

(c) *By syncope.* This is not common. I have known it to happen once or twice in patients who insisted upon going about when in the advanced stages of the disease. There may be, but not necessarily, fatty degeneration of the heart. A rapidly developing syncope may follow hæmorrhage or may be due to thrombosis or embolism of the pulmonary artery, or to pneumothorax.

(d) *From hæmorrhage.* The fatal bleeding in chronic phthisis is due to erosion of a large vessel or rupture of an aneurism in a pulmonary cavity, most commonly the latter. Of 26 cases analyzed by S. West, in 11 the fatal hæmoptysis was due to aneurism, and of 35 cases collected by Percy Kidd, aneurism was present in 30. In a case of Curtin's, at the Philadelphia Hospital, the bleeding proved fatal before hæmoptysis occurred, as the eroded vessel opened into a capacious cavity.

(e) *With cerebral symptoms.* Coma may be due to meningitis, less often to uræmia. Death in convulsions is rare. The hæmorrhagic pachy-meningitis which develops in some cases of phthisis occasionally causes loss of consciousness, but is rarely a direct cause of death. In one of my cases, death resulted from thrombosis of the cerebral sinuses with symptoms of meningitis.

V. Tuberculosis of the Alimentary Canal.

(a) *Lips.*—Tuberculosis of the lip is very rare. It occurs occasionally in the form of an ulcer, either alone or more commonly in association with laryngeal or pulmonary disease. Two cases are reported and the literature is analyzed in Verneuil's Etudes.* The ulcer is usually very sensitive and may be mistaken for a chancre or an epithelioma. The diagnosis may be

---

* Tome iii, Fasc. I.

made in cases of doubt by inoculation or the examination of a portion for tubercle bacilli.

(*b*) *Tongue.*—The disease begins by an aggregation of small granular bodies on the edge or dorsum. Ulceration proceeds, leaving an irregular sore with a distinct but uneven margin, and a rough, often caseous base. The disease extends slowly and may form an ulcer of considerable size. I have known it to be mistaken for epithelioma and the tongue to be excised. It is rarely met with except when other organs are involved. The glands of the angle of the jaw are not enlarged and the sore does not yield to iodide of potassium, which are points of distinction between the tuberculous and the syphilitic ulcer. In doubtful cases the inoculation test should be made, or a portion excised for microscopical examination.

(*c*) The salivary glands belong to that small group of organs of the body which seem to possess an immunity against tuberculous infection— an immunity, however, which in their case is relative, not absolute; a few cases have been reported.

(*d*) Tubercles of the hard or soft *palate* nearly always follow extension of the disease from neighboring parts.

(*e*) *Tuberculosis of the Tonsils.*—In 1884 Strassmann found the tonsils involved in 13 instances out of 21 autopsies. Dmochowski demonstrated tubercle bacilli in the lymphatics between the tonsils and the cervical lymph-glands. The latter observation is interesting in connection with the views of Schlenker, who claims that the majority of the cases of tuberculous cervical glands result from infection with tubercle bacilli which gain admission by way of the tonsil. A large number of his cases of tuberculous cervical adenitis were definitely of a descending variety and associated with tuberculosis of these glands. The majority also had pulmonary tuberculosis, and he regards surface infection of the tonsil by tuberculous food and sputum far more common than infection by way of the circulation. The disease may occur as a superficial ulceration. More commonly there is an infiltration of the tonsil with miliary tubercles, which produces a greater or less hypertrophy which it is practically impossible to distinguish from an ordinary enlarged tonsil without a microscopical examination. Caseous foci occasionally develop.

(*f*) *Pharynx.*—In extensive laryngeal tuberculosis an eruption of miliary granules on the posterior wall of the pharynx is not very uncommon. In chronic phthisis an ulcerative pharyngitis, due to extension of the disease from the epiglottis and larynx, is one of the most distressing of complications, rendering deglutition acutely painful. Adenoids of the nasopharynx may be tuberculous, as shown by Lermoyez. Macroscopically, they do not differ from the ordinary vegetations found in this situation.

(*g*) A few instances occur in the literature of tuberculosis of the *œsophagus*. The condition is a pathological curiosity, except in the slight extension from the larynx, which is not infrequent; but in a case in my wards described by Flexner the ulcer perforated and caused purulent pleurisy. The condition has been fully considered by Claribel Cone, who has described a second case from the Johns Hopkins Hospital (Bulletin, November, 1897).

(*h*) *Stomach.*—Many cases are reported which are doubtful. Primary disease is unknown. Marfan was able to collect only about a dozen authentic cases. Perforation of the stomach occurred six times, thrice by a tuberculous gland. In Oppolzer's case an ulcer of the colon perforated the organ. In Musser's case there was a large tuberculous ulcer $3 \times 1\frac{1}{2}$ inches in extent. Three cases have been described from my wards by Alice Hamilton (J. H. H. Bulletin, April, 1897).

(*i*) *Intestines.*—The tubercles may be (1) primary in the mucous membrane, or more commonly (2) secondary to disease of the lungs, or in rare cases the affection may (3) pass from the peritonæum.

(1) Primary intestinal tuberculosis occurs most frequently in children, in whom it may be associated with enlargement and caseation of the mesenteric glands, or with peritonitis. It may be difficult to say at the time of the autopsy whether the primary lesion has been intestinal or peritoneal. I have already referred to Woodhead's statistics showing the remarkable frequency of infection through the bowel. In adults primary intestinal tuberculosis is rare, occurring in but 1 instance in 1,000 autopsies upon tuberculous adults at the Munich Pathological Institute; but now and then cases occur in which the disease sets in with irregular diarrhœa, moderate fever, and colicky pains. In a few cases hæmorrhage has been the initial symptom. Regarded at first as a chronic catarrh, it is not until the emaciation becomes marked or the signs of disease appear in the lungs that the true nature is apparent. Still more deceptive are the cases in which the tuberculosis begins in the cæcum and there are symptoms of appendicitis—tenderness in the right iliac fossa, constipation, or an irregular diarrhœa and fever. These signs may gradually disappear, to recur again in a few weeks and still further complicate the diagnosis. Fatal hæmorrhage has occurred in several of my cases. Perforation may occur with the formation of a pericæcal abscess, or perforation into the peritonæum may take place, or in very rare instances there is partial healing with great thickening of the walls and narrowing of the lumen.

(2) Secondary involvement of the bowels is very common in chronic pulmonary tuberculosis, e. g., in 566 of the 1,000 Munich autopsies in tuberculosis just referred to. In only three of these cases were the lungs not involved. The lesions are chiefly in the ileum, cæcum, and colon. The affection begins in the solitary and agminated glands or on the surface of or within the mucosa. The caseation and necrosis lead to ulceration, which may be very extensive and involve the greater portion of the mucosa of the large and small bowels. In the ileum the Peyer's patches are chiefly involved and the ulcers may be ovoid, but in the jejunum and colon they are usually round or transverse to the long axis. The tuberculous ulcer has the following characters: (*a*) It is irregular, rarely ovoid or in the long axis, more frequently girdling the bowel; (*b*) the edges and base are infiltrated, often caseous; (*c*) the submucosa and muscularis are usually involved; and (*d*) on the serosa may be seen colonies of young tubercles or a well-marked tuberculous lymphangitis. Perforation and peritonitis are not uncommon events in the secondary ulceration. Stenosis of the bowel from cicatrization may occur; the strictures may be multiple.

Localized chronic tuberculosis of the *ileo-cæcal region* is of great importance. The cæcum frequently presents extensive ulceration of the mucous membrane, which not uncommonly extends into the appendix. As a consequence of the changes produced a definite tumor-like mass develops in the right iliac fossa. This varies in size, is usually elongated in a vertical direction, hard, slightly movable, or bound down by adhesions and very sensitive to pressure. The tumor simulates more or less closely a true neoplasm of this region, particularly carcinoma. The condition is characterized by gradual constriction of the lumen of the bowel, periodic attacks of severe pain, and alternating diarrhœa and constipation. In a few cases extirpation of the cæcum has been performed with fairly successful results. In a second form of this disease, occurring less frequently than the former, there is no definite tumor-mass to be felt, but a general induration and thickening in the right iliac fossa similar to the local changes produced by a recurring appendicitis. In this variety a fistula discharging fecal matter occasionally results. Both forms may be distinguished from the diseases they simulate by the finding of tubercle bacilli in the stools or in the discharge from the fistula when such exists.

Tuberculosis of the *rectum* has a special interest in connection with *fistula in ano*, which, according to Spillman's statistics, occurs in about 3.5 per cent of cases of pulmonary disease. In many instances the lesion has been shown to be tuberculous. It is very rarely primary, but if the tissue on removal contains bacilli and is infective the lungs are almost invariably found to be involved. It is a common opinion that the pulmonary symptoms may develop rapidly after the fistula is cut. This may have some basis if the operation consists in laying the tract open, and not in a free excision.

(3) Extension from the peritonæum may excite tuberculous disease in the bowels. The affection may be primary in the peritonæum or extend from the tubes in women or the mesenteric glands in children. The coils of intestines become matted together, caseous and suppurating foci develop between the folds, and perforation may take place between the coils.

VI. TUBERCULOSIS OF THE LIVER.

This organ is very constantly involved in (*a*) general tuberculosis. The miliary granulation may be very small and in acute cases scarcely perceptible. The liver is pale and often fatty.

(*b*) A remarkable condition of the organ is produced by the development of the tubercles in the finer bile-vessels. They may attain a considerable size and are almost always softened in the centre, resembling small abscesses. The contents are always bile-stained. The organ may be honeycombed with these tuberculous abscesses.

(*c*) Large, coarse caseous masses are occasionally found, sometimes in association with perihepatitis or tuberculous peritonitis. They may attain the size of an orange or may even be larger.

(*d*) Tuberculous cirrhosis. With the eruption of miliary tubercles there may be slight increase in the connective tissue, which is overshadowed by the fatty change. In all the chronic forms of tubercle in this organ there may be fibrous overgrowth. Hanot, who has described several varieties, states that the condition may be primary. Practically it is very rare, except in connection with chronic tuberculous peritonitis and perihepatitis, when the organ may be much deformed by a sclerosis involving the portal canals. In this last group there may be symptoms of ascites; as a rule, tuberculosis of the liver has a purely anatomical interest.

VII. Tuberculosis of the Brain and Cord.

Tuberculosis of the *brain* occurs as (*a*) an acute miliary infection causing meningitis and acute hydrocephalus; (*b*) as a chronic meningo-encephalitis, usually localized, and containing small nodular tubercles; and (*c*) as the so-called solitary tubercle. Between the last two forms there are all gradations, and it is rare to see the meninges uninvolved. The acute variety has already been considered. I shall here consider the chronic form, which develops slowly and has the clinical characters of a tumor.

It is most common in the young. Of 148 cases collected by Pribram 118 were under fifteen years of age. Other organs are usually involved, particularly the lungs, the bronchial glands, or the bones. In rare instances no tubercles are found elsewhere. They occur most frequently in the cerebellum; next in the cerebrum and then in the pons. The growths are often multiple, in 100 out of 183 cases (Gowers). They range in size from a pea to a walnut; larger tumors occasionally occur, and sometimes an entire lobe of the cerebellum is affected. On section the tubercle presents a grayish-yellow, caseous appearance, usually firm and hard, and encircled by a translucent, softer tissue. The centre of the growth may be semi-diffluent. As in other localities the tubercle may calcify. The tumors are as a rule attached to the meninges, often to the pia at the bottom of a sulcus so that they look imbedded in the brain-substance. About the longitudinal fissure there may be an aggregation of the growths, with compression of the sinus, and the formation of a thrombus. The tuberculous tumor not infrequently excites acute meningitis. In localized meningo-encephalitis the pia is thickened, tubercles are adherent to the under surface and grow about the arteries. It is often combined with cerebral softening from interference with the circulation. Several of the most characteristic instances which I have seen were on the meninges covering the insula. This form may develop in pulmonary tuberculosis, causing hemiplegia or aphasia which may persist for months.

The symptoms of tuberculous growths in the brain are those of tumor, and will be considered in the section on the brain.

In the *spinal cord* the same forms are found. The acute tuberculous meningitis has been considered and is almost always cerebro-spinal. The solitary tubercle of the cord is rare. Herter has reported 3 cases and collected 24 from the literature. It was secondary in all save one case. The symptoms are those of spinal tumor or meningitis.

VIII. Tuberculosis of the Genito-urinary System.

The studies of the past few years, and particularly the work of surgeons and gynæcologists, have taught us the great importance of tuberculosis of this tract. Any part of the genito-urinary system may be invaded. The successive involvement of the organs may be so rapid that unless the case has been seen early it may be impossible to state with any degree of certainty which has been the primary seat of infection. There may be simultaneous involvement of various portions of the tract. In tuberculosis of the genito-urinary system one always has to bear in mind the possibility of latent disease elsewhere in the body. As Bollinger says, tubercle bacilli may gain admission at some part of the respiratory tract without producing any lesion at the point of entrance, and finally reach a bronchial gland, where they set up a tuberculous process of extremely slow development without producing any symptoms. From this point bacilli may enter the blood stream and lodge in the epididymis or testicle proper, and produce nodules which are readily discovered, owing to the ease with which these parts are examined. Such a case might be quite easily mistaken for one of primary genital tuberculosis, whereas the true primary tuberculous focus is far distant.

Infection of the genito-urinary tract occurs in various ways:

1. *By Hereditary Transmission.*—It has been met with in the fœtus. The comparative frequency of tuberculosis of the testicle in very young children suggests very strongly that the uro-genital organs may be involved as a result of direct transmission of the disease from the parents.

2. *By infection from areas of tuberculosis already existing in the patient.*

(a) *Infection through the Blood.*—In many cases uro-genital tuberculosis is found at autopsy associated with disease of some distant organ, particularly the lungs, and it would appear most probable that in them infection has been through the blood-vessels. Jani's observations, which were published by Weigert after the author's death, strongly support this theory. In studying sections of the genital organs of patients who died of pulmonary tuberculosis, he found tubercle bacilli in 5 out of 8 cases in the testicle, and in 4 out of 6 cases in the prostate, without in any instance finding microscopical evidences of tubercles in these organs. The bacilli lay, in the testis, partly within and partly close beside the cellular and granular contents of the seminal tubules, while in the prostate they were always situated in the neighborhood of the glandular epithelium.

(b) *Infection from the Peritonæum.*—This source of infection, in both men and women, is much more frequent than is commonly supposed. The intimate relationship between the peritonæum and bladder in both subjects, and with the vesiculæ seminales and vasa deferentia in the male, allows of a ready way of invasion of these organs by direct extension of the disease. The peritonæum is a frequent source of genital tuberculosis in the female. No doubt many cases of tuberculosis of the Fallopian tubes originate from this source. The fact that the fimbriated extremity of the tube is often most seriously involved points rather strongly in this direction, although the fact might be taken as a point in favor of blood infection, favored by its greater vascularity. Various observations go to show that the action of the cilia lining the lumina of the Fallopian tubes tends to attract particles introduced into the peritoneal cavity. Jani's observation is very interesting in this connection, as showing the possibility of tubercle bacilli entering the tubes from the peritoneal cavity without there being any tuberculous peritonitis. He found typical tubercle bacilli in the lumen, in sections of a normal Fallopian tube, in a woman who died of pulmonary and intestinal tuberculosis. The explanation advanced was that the bacilli made their way through the thin peritoneal coat from one of the intestinal ulcers, thus reaching the peritoneal cavity, and thence were attracted into the Fallopian tube by the current produced by the action of the cilia lining the lumen. The intimate relationship between tuberculous peritonitis and tuberculosis of the Fallopian tubes is shown in the fact that the latter are affected in from 30 to 40 per cent of the cases.

(c) *Infection from other Organs by Direct Extension.*—The occurrence of direct extension from the peritonæum has already been mentioned. In tuberculous ulceration of the intestine or rectum adhesions to the bladder in the male or to the uterus and vagina in the female may occur, with resulting fistulæ and a direct extension of the disease. Perirectal tuberculous abscesses may lead to secondary involvement of some portion of the genito-urinary tract. It must not be forgotten that tuberculosis of the vertebræ may be followed by tuberculosis of the kidney as a result of direct extension of the disease.

3. *By Infection from Without.*—Whether uro-genital tuberculosis may occur as a result of the entrance of tubercle bacilli into the urethra or vagina is still a disputed question. That bacilli gain admission to these passages during coitus with a person the subject of uro-genital tuberculosis, or by the use of foul instruments or syringes, seems quite probable. The possibility of genital tuberculosis occurring in the female as a result of coitus with a male the subject of tuberculosis in some portion of the genito-urinary system was first suggested by Cohnheim, who stated, however, that it rarely, if ever, occurred. Gärtner's experiments have been referred to.

In a patient with intestinal tuberculosis the tubercle bacilli might accidentally reach the urethra or vagina from the rectum.

Uro-genital tuberculosis is commonest between the ages of twenty and forty years—that is, during the period of greatest sexual activity. Males are affected much more frequently than females, the proportion being 3 to 1. This great difference is no doubt partly due to the more intimate relationship between the urinary and genital systems in the former than in the latter. In the male the urethra forms the common outlet for the two systems, while in the female there is a separate outlet for each.

Once the uro-genital tract has been invaded, the disease is likely to spread rapidly, and the method of extension is an important one. Quite frequently there is direct extension, as when the bladder is involved secondarily to the kidney by passage of the disease along the ureter, or where the tuberculous process extends along the vas deferens to the vesiculæ seminales. No doubt surface inoculation occurs in some instances, and to this cause may be attributed a certain percentage of cases of vesical and prostatic disease following tuberculosis of the kidney. Although this probability is acknowledged, there is an element of doubt as to the possibility of the kidney becoming affected secondarily to the bladder or prostate by the direct passage of the bacilli up the lumen of one ureter; for in such a case we have to suppose that a non-motile bacillus, contrary to the laws of gravity, ascends against an almost constant current of urine flowing in the opposite direction. The lymphatics may afford a means for the spreading of the disease, but in a greater number of cases than is generally supposed it takes place by way of the blood-vessels. Cystoscopic examinations of the bladder not infrequently show the presence of tubercles beneath the mucous membrane before there is any evidence of superficial ulceration —a fact suggesting strongly a blood infection.

The discovery of tubercle bacilli in the urine and the obtaining of tuberculous lesions in animals as a result of inoculation with the urinary sediment afford us the only positive evidence of genito-urinary tuberculosis. So far there are no authentic accounts of tubercle bacilli having been found in the semen of men with tuberculosis of the testicle or vesiculæ seminales. Owing to the fact that the smegma bacillus has the same staining reaction as the tubercle bacillus, and, morphologically, is practically indistinguishable from it, the greatest care must be used in obtaining the specimen of urine for examination, to eliminate, if possible, all chances of contamination. Thus the urine examined must be a catheterized specimen, and even then one runs the risk of carrying back into the bladder on the end of the catheter a few bacilli which may be washed out in the stream of urine and be mistaken for tubercle bacilli in the sediment.

(*a*) **Tuberculosis of the Kidneys** (*Phthisis renum*).—In general tuberculosis the kidneys frequently present scattered miliary tubercles. In pulmonary tuberculosis it is common to find a few nodules in the substance of the organ, or there may be pyelitis. Primary tuberculosis of the kidneys is not very rare. In a majority of the cases the process involves the pelvis and the ureter as well, sometimes the bladder and prostate. In only 1 of 8 cases was the prostate involved. It may be difficult to say in advanced cases whether the disease has started in the bladder, prostate, or vesicles, and crept up the ureters, or whether it started in the kidneys and proceeded downward. In a majority of cases, I believe, the latter is true, and the infection is through the blood. One kidney alone may be involved, and the disease creeps down the ureter and may only extend a few millimetres on the vesical mucosa. A man with aortic insufficiency, who had no lesions in the lungs, presented a localized patch in the pelvis of the kidney, involving a pyramid, while the ureter, 5 cm. from the bladder and at its orifice, was thickened and tuberculous. The prostate showed an area of caseation. The process is most common in the middle period of life, but it may occur at the extremes of age. It is more frequent in men than in women. In the earliest stage, which may be met with accidentally, the disease is seen to begin in the pyramids and calyces. Necrosis and caseation proceed rapidly, and the colonies of tubercles start throughout the pyramids and extend upon the mucous membrane of the pelvis. As a rule, from the outset it is a tuberculous pyo-nephrosis. The disease may be confined to one kidney, or progress more extensively in one than in the other. At autopsy both organs are usually found enlarged. One kidney may be completely destroyed and converted into a series of cysts containing cheesy substance—a form of kidney which the older writers called scrofulous. In the putty-like contents of these cysts lime salts may be deposited. In other instances the walls of the pelvis are thickened and cheesy, the pyramids eroded, and caseous nodules are scattered through the organ, even to the capsule, which may be thickened and adherent. The other organ is usually less affected, and shows only pyelitis or a superficial necrosis of one or two pyramids. The ureters are usually thickened and the mucous membrane ulcerated and caseous. Involvement of the bladder, vesiculæ seminales, and testes is not uncommon in males.

The *symptoms* are those of pyelitis. The urine may be purulent for years, and there may be little or no distress. Even before the bladder becomes involved micturition is frequent, and many instances are mistaken for cystitis. The condition is for many years compatible with fair health. The curability is shown by the accidental discovery of the so-called scrofulous kidney, converted into cysts containing a putty-like substance. In cases in which the disease becomes advanced and both organs are affected, constitutional symptoms are more marked. There is irregular fever, with chills, and loss of weight and strength. General tuberculosis is common. In only one of my cases were the lungs uninvolved. In a case at the Montreal General Hospital a cyst perforated and caused fatal peritonitis.

Physical examination may detect special tenderness on one side, or the kidney may be palpable in front on deep pressure; but tuberculous pyelonephritis seldom causes a large tumor. Occasionally the pelvis becomes enormously distended; but this is rare in comparison with its frequency in calculous pyelitis. The urine presents changes similar to those of ordinary calculous pyelitis—pus-cells, epithelium, and occasionally definite caseous masses. Albumin is, of course, present. Tubercle bacilli may be demonstrated by the ordinary methods. Tube-casts are not often seen.

To distinguish the condition from calculous pyelitis is often difficult. Hæmorrhage may be present in both, though not nearly so frequently in the tuberculous disease. The diagnosis rests on three points: (1) The detection of some focus of tuberculosis, as in the testes; (2) the presence of tubercle bacilli in the sediment; and (3) the use of tuberculin. In woman the kidney involved is now easily determined by catheterizing the ureters after the plan of my colleague Kelly.

The incidence of renal implication in uro-genital tuberculosis may be gathered from Orth's Göttingen material, analyzed by Oppenheim. Of 60 cases there were 34 in which the kidneys were involved.

Tuberculosis of the suprarenal capsules will be considered under Addison's Disease.

(*b*) **Tuberculosis of the Ureter and Bladder.**—This rarely occurs as a primary affection, but is nearly always secondary to involvement of other parts, particularly the pelvis of the kidney. In the case of uro-genital tuberculosis, above mentioned, in a patient who died of heart-disease, the ureter, just where it enters the bladder, showed a fresh patch of tuberculosis.

Protracted cystitis, which has come on without apparent cause, is always suggestive of tuberculosis. The renal regions, the testes, and the prostate should be examined with care. It may follow a pyelo-nephritis, or be associated with primary disease of the prostate or vesiculæ seminales. Primary tuberculosis of the posterior wall of the bladder may simulate stone.

(c) **Tuberculosis of the Prostate and Vesiculæ Seminales.**—The prostate is frequently involved in tuberculosis of the uro-genital tract. In Krzyincki's cases, of 15 males the prostate was involved in 14 and the vesiculæ seminales in 11. In Orth's cases the prostate was involved in 18 of the 37 cases in males. These parts are much more frequently involved than ordinary post-mortem statistics indicate. *Per rectum* the prostatic lobes are felt to be occupied by hard nodules varying in size from a pea to a bean. There is great irritability of the bladder, and agonizing pain in catheterization. An extremely rare lesion is primary urethral tuberculosis, which may simulate stricture.

(d) **Tuberculosis of the Testes.**—This somewhat common affection may be primary, or, more frequently, is secondary to tuberculous disease elsewhere. Many cases occur before the second year, and it is stated to have been met with in the fœtus. In infants it is serious and usually associated with tuberculous disease in other parts. In 9 cases reported by Hutinel and Deschamps, in every one there was a general affection. In 20 cases reported by Jullien, 6 were under one year, and 6 between one and two years old. In 5 of the cases both testicles were affected. Koplik holds that most of the instances of this kind are congenital, in Baumgarten's sense. In the adult the tubercles begin within the substance of the gland, but in children the tunica albuginea is first affected. The tubercle does not always undergo caseation, but it may present a number of embryonic cells, not unlike a sarcoma.

Tubercle of the testes is most likely to be confounded with syphilis. In the latter the body of the organ is most often affected, there is less pain, and the outlines of the growth are more nodular and irregular. In obscure peritoneal disease the detection of tubercle in a testis has not infrequently led to a correct diagnosis. The association of the two conditions is not uncommon. The lesion in the testis may heal completely, or the disease may become generalized. General infection has followed operation. Too much stress cannot be laid on the importance of a routine examination of the testes in hospital patients.

(e) **Tuberculosis of the Fallopian Tubes, Ovaries, and Uterus.**—The *Fallopian tubes* are by far the most frequent seat of genital tuberculosis. The disease may be primary and produce a most characteristic form of salpingitis, in which the tubes are enlarged, the walls thickened and infiltrated, and the contents cheesy. Adhesion takes place between the fimbriæ and the ovaries, or the uterus may be invaded. The condition is usually bilateral. It may occur in young children. Although, as a rule, very evident to the naked eye, there are specimens resembling ordinary salpingitis, which show on microscopical examination numerous miliary tubercles (Welch and Williams). Tuberculous salpingitis may cause serious local disease with abscess formation, and it may be the starting-point of peritonitis.

Tuberculosis of the *ovary* is always secondary. There may be an eruption of tubercles over the surface in an extensive involvement of the stroma with abscess formation.

Tuberculosis of the *uterus* is very rare. Only three examples have come under my observation, all in connection with pulmonary phthisis. It may be primary. The mucosa of the fundus is thickened and caseous, and tubercles may be seen in the muscular tissue. Occasionally the process extends to the vagina.

IX. Tuberculosis of the Mammary Gland.

Mandry (Bruns's Beiträge, viii) has collected 40 cases, 1 of which was in a male. The disease is most common between the fortieth and sixtieth years. The breast is frequently fistulous, unevenly indurated, and the nipple is retracted. The fistulæ and ulcers present a characteristic tuberculous aspect. There is also a cold tuberculous abscess of the breast. The axillary glands are affected in about two thirds of the cases. The disease runs a chronic course of months or years. The diagnosis can be made by the general appearance of the fistulæ and ulcers, and by the existence of tubercle bacilli. The prognosis is not bad, if total eradication of the disease be possible.

In 1836 Bedor described an hypertrophy of the breast in the subjects of pulmonary tuberculosis. As a rule, if one gland is involved, usually on the side of the affected lung, as already mentioned, the condition is one of chronic interstitial mammitis, and is not tuberculous.

X. Tuberculosis of the Circulatory System.

(a) *Myocardium.*—Scattered miliary tubercles are sometimes met with in the acute disease. Larger caseous tubercles are excessively rare. Alfred Hand, Jr., has reported 2 cases and reviewed 39 instances in the literature.

(b) *Endocardium.*—In 216 autopsies in cases of chronic phthisis I found endocarditis in 12. As a rule, it is a secondary form, the result of a mixed infection, so common in pulmonary tuberculosis. A true tuberculous endocarditis does, however, occur, directly dependent upon infection with the bacillus of Koch. As a rule, it is a vegetative endocarditis, not to be distinguished from that caused by the streptococcus or staphylococcus. In rare cases, however, caseous tubercles develop.

(c) *Arteries.*—Primary tuberculosis of the larger blood-vessels is unknown. The disease may, however, occur in a large artery and not result from external invasion. In a case of chronic tuberculosis Flexner found a fresh tuberculous growth in the aorta, which had no connection with cheesy masses outside the vessel.

In the lungs and other organs attacked by tuberculosis the arteries are involved in an acute infiltration which usually leads to thrombosis, or tubercles may develop in the walls and proceed to caseation and softening frequently with the result of hæmorrhage. By extension into vessels, particularly veins, the bacilli are widely distributed. In meningitis tuberculosis of the arteries plays an important *rôle*.

XI. DIAGNOSIS OF TUBERCULOSIS.

The recognition of the disease usually rests upon the macroscopical and microscopical appearances of the lesions and the presence of the characteristic bacilli. Of late an important additional diagnostic agent has been introduced in the form of Koch's tuberculin. For some years Trudeau has insisted upon the harmlessness of its use in the diagnosis of obscure cases. During the past few years it has been employed extensively at the Johns Hopkins Hospital, both on the medical and surgical sides, with the most satisfactory results, and, so far as I know, without any harmful effects. In obscure internal lesions, in joint cases, and in suspected tuberculosis of the kidneys the use of the tuberculin gives most valuable information. I may mention, for example, an instance of Addison's disease in a young, very muscular man without any sign whatever of visceral tuberculosis. The reaction (as, indeed, might have been expected) was very characteristic. We have used the tuberculin kindly furnished from the Saranac Laboratory, which is made on Koch's original plan. In adults a milligramme is employed, and if this has no reaction a larger dose of two or three milligrammes is employed in two or three days. There is often slight local irritation following the injection, and within from ten to twelve hours the febrile reaction begins, the temperature rising to from 102° to 104°.

XII. THE PROGNOSIS IN TUBERCULOSIS.

Not all persons in whose bodies the bacilli gain a foothold present marked signs of tuberculosis. As will be stated in the next section, local disease is found in a considerable number of all cadavers. Infection does not necessarily mean the establishment of a progressive and fatal disease. In my autopsies, excluding cases dead of pulmonary phthisis, 7.5 per cent presented tuberculous lesions of the lungs—a low percentage in comparison with other records, as I carefully excluded the simple fibroid puckering at the apex, and the solitary cheesy nodules, unless surrounded by colonies of tubercles.

In many cases a natural or spontaneous cure is effected, for the conditions favorable to the development of the disease are not present—in other words, the tissue-soil is unsuitable. Apart from this group, a majority of which probably do not show any sign of disease, there may be spontaneous arrest after the symptoms have become decided. Many years ago Flint called attention to the self-limitation and intrinsic tendency to recovery in well-marked pulmonary tuberculosis. Of his 670 cases, 44 recovered, and in 31 the disease was arrested, spontaneously in 23 of the first group and in 15 of the second. This natural tendency to cure is still more strikingly shown in lymphatic and bone tuberculosis.

The following may be considered favorable circumstances in the prognosis of pulmonary tuberculosis: A good family history, previous good health, a strong digestion, a suitable environment, and an insidious onset, without high fever, and without extensive pneumonic consolidation. Cases beginning with pleurisy seem to run a more protracted and more favorable course. Repeated attacks of hæmoptysis are unfavorable. When well established the course of tuberculosis in any organ is marked by intervals of weeks or months in which the fever lessens, the symptoms subside, and there is improvement in the general health.

In pulmonary cases the duration is extremely variable. Laennec placed the average duration at two years, and for the majority of cases this is perhaps a correct estimate. Pollock's large statistics of over 3,500 cases shows a mean duration of the disease of over two years and a half. Williams's analysis of 1,000 cases in private practice shows a much more protracted course, as the average duration was over seven years.

Under the subject of prognosis comes the question of the marriage of persons who have had tuberculosis, or in whose family the disease prevails. The following brief statements may be made with reference to it:

(a) Subjects with healed lymphatic or bone tuberculosis marry with personal impunity and may beget healthy children. It is undeniable, however, that in such families, scrofula, caries of the bone, arthritis, cerebral and pulmonary tuberculosis are more common. Which is it, "hérédité de graine ou hérédité de terrain," as the French have it, the seed or the soil, or both? We cannot yet say. The risks, however, are such as may properly be taken.

(b) The question of marriage of a person who has arrested or cured lung tuberculosis is more difficult to decide. In a male, the personal risk is not so great; and when the health and strength are good, the external environment favorable, and the family history not extremely bad the experiment—for it is such—is often successful, and many healthy and happy families are begotten under these circumstances. In women the question is complicated with that of child-bearing, which increases the risks enormously. With a localized lesion, absence of hereditary taint, good physique, and favorable environment, marriage might be permitted. When tuberculosis has existed, however, in a girl whose family history is bad, whose chest expansion is slight, and whose physique is below the standard, the physician should, if possible, place his veto upon marriage.

(c) With existing disease, fever, bacilli, etc., marriage should be prohibited. Pregnancy usually hastens the process, though it may be held in abeyance. After parturition the disease advances rapidly. There is much truth, indeed, in the remark of Dubois: "If a woman threatened with phthisis marries, she may bear the first accouchement well; a second, with difficulty; a third, never." Conception may occur in an advanced stage of the disease.

XIII. Prophylaxis in Tuberculosis.

(a) *General.*—The sputa of phthisical patients should be carefully collected and destroyed. Patients should be urged not to spit about carelessly, but always to use a spit-cup and never to swallow the sputa. Several forms of portable flasks have been devised and are now on sale. The destruction of the sputa of consumptives should be a routine measure in both hospital and private practice. Thorough boiling or putting it into the fire is sufficient. In hospitals it is well to have printed directions as to the care of the sputa and also printed cards for out-patients, giving the most important rules. It should be explained to the patient that the only risk, practically, is from this source. The chances of infection are greatest in young children. The nursing and care of consumptives involve very slight risks indeed if proper precautions are taken. The patient should occupy a single bed.

A second important general prophylactic measure relates to the inspection of dairies and slaughter-houses. The possibility of the transmission of tuberculosis by infected milk has been fully demonstrated, and in the interest of public health the state should take measures to stamp out tuberculosis in cattle. Systematic veterinary inspection of dairies, particularly in the large cities, should be made, and full power granted to confiscate and kill suspected animals. The abattoirs should be under skilled veterinary control, and the carcasses of animals with advanced tuberculosis confiscated.

The advisability of placing pulmonary tuberculosis on the list of diseases of which notice must be given, has been much discussed. I am strongly in favor of it. The hardships entailed upon individuals are trifling in comparison with the public good which would follow the adoption of systematic measures of inspection and disinfection.

(b) *Individual.*—A mother with pulmonary tuberculosis should not suckle her child. An infant born of tuberculous parents, or of a family in which consumption prevails, should be brought up with the greatest care and guarded most particularly against catarrhal affections of all kinds. Special attention should be given to the throat and nose, and on the first indication of mouth-breathing, or any obstruction of the naso-pharynx, a careful examination should be made for adenoid vegetations. The child should be clad in flannel and live in the open air as much as possible, avoiding close rooms. It is a good practice to sponge the throat and chest night and morning with cold water. Special attention should be paid to diet and to the mode of feeding. The meals should be at regular hours and the food plain and substantial. From the outset the child should be encouraged to drink freely of milk. Unfortunately, in these cases there seems to be an uncontrollable aversion to fats of all kinds. As the child grows older, systematically regulated exercise or a course of pulmonary gymnastics may be taken. In the choice of an occupation preference should be given to an out-of-door life. Families with a marked predisposition to tuberculosis should, if possible, reside in an equable climate. It would be best for a young man belonging to such a family to remove to

Colorado or Southern California, or to some other suitable climate, before trouble begins.

The trifling ailments of children should be carefully watched. In the convalescence from the fevers, which so frequently prove dangerous, the greatest caution should be exercised to prevent catching cold. Cod-liver oil, the syrup of the iodide of iron, and arsenic may be given. As mentioned, care of the throat in these children is very important. Enlarged tonsils should be removed.

XIV. Treatment of Tuberculosis.

I. The Natural or Spontaneous Cure.—The spontaneous healing of local tuberculosis is an every-day affair. Many cases of adenitis and disease of the bone or of the joints terminate favorably. The healing of pulmonary tuberculosis is shown clinically by the recovery of patients in whose sputa elastic tissue and bacilli have been found; anatomically, by the presence of lesions in all stages of repair. In the granulation products and associated pneumonia a scar-tissue is formed, while the smaller caseous areas become impregnated with lime salts. To such conditions alone should the term healing be applied. When the fibroid change encapsulates but does not involve the entire tuberculous tissue, the tubercle may be termed involuted or quiescent, but is not destroyed. When cavities of any size have formed, healing, in the proper sense of the term, does not occur. I have yet to see a specimen which would indicate that a vomica had cicatrized. Cavities may be greatly reduced in size—indeed, an entire series of them may be so contracted by sclerosis of the tissue about them that an upper lobe, in which this process most frequently occurs, may be reduced to a third of its ordinary dimensions. Laennec understood thoroughly this natural process of cure in tuberculosis, and recognized the frequency with which old tuberculous lesions occurred in the lungs. He described *cicatrices complètes* and *cicatrices fistuleuses*, the latter being the shrunken cavities communicating with the bronchi; and remarked that, as tubercles growing in the glands, which are called scrofula, often heal, why should not the same take place in the lungs?

There is an old German axiom, "*Jedermann hat am Ende ein bischen Tuberculose,*" a statement partly borne out by the statistics showing the proportion of cases in persons dying of all diseases in whom quiescent or tuberculous lesions are found in the lungs. We find at the apices the following conditions, which have been held to signify healed tuberculous processes: (1) Thickening of the pleura, usually at the posterior surface of the apex, with subadjacent induration for a distance of a few millimetres. This has, perhaps, no greater significance than the milky patch on the pericardium. (2) Puckered cicatrices at the apex, depressing the pleura, and on section showing a large pigmented, fibrous scar. The bronchioles in the neighborhood may be dilated, but there are neither tubercles nor cheesy masses. This may sometimes, but not always, indicate a healed tuberculous lesion. (3) Puckered cicatrices with cheesy or cretaceous nodules, and with scattered tubercles in the vicinity. (4) The *cicatrices fistuleuses* of Laennec, in which the fibroid puckering has reduced the size of one or more cavities which communicate directly with the bronchi.

In 1,000 autopsies, excluding the 216 cases dead of phthisis, there were 59 cases (7.5 per cent) which presented undoubted tuberculous lesions in the lungs. I excluded the simple fibroid puckering and the solitary cheesy nodules, unless, in the latter case, there were colonies of tubercles in the vicinity. These 59 cases died of various diseases and at various ages. A majority of them were between forty and sixty. My experience tallies closely with the larger analysis made by Heitler of the Vienna post-mortem records, in which, of 16,562 cases in which the death was not directly caused by phthisis, there were 780 instances of obsolete tubercle—a percentage of 4.7. He excluded, as I have done, the simple fibroid induration. Various observations have been made of late in which the percentage ranges from 27 (Bollinger) to 39 (Massini). In 200 autopsies, in which this point was specially examined, Harris found 38.8 per cent in which there were relics of former active tuberculosis. The statement is made by Bouchard that, of the post-mortems at the Paris morgue—generally upon persons dying suddenly—the percentage found with some evidence of tuberculous lesion, active or obsolete, is as high as 75. These figures show the extraordinary frequency of pulmonary infection and the encouraging fact that in so large a percentage the disease remains local and undergoes a process of arrest or healing.

II. General Measures.—The cure of tuberculosis is a question of nutrition; digestion and assimilation control the situation; make a patient grow fat and the local disease may be left to take care of itself. There are three indications: First, to place the patient in surroundings most favorable for the maintenance of a maximum degree of nutrition; second, to take such measures as, in a local or general way, influence the tuberculous processes; third, to alleviate symptoms.

Open-air Treatment.—The value of fresh air and out-of-door life is well illustrated by an experiment of Trudeau. Inoculated rabbits confined in a dark, damp place rapidly succumbed, while others, allowed to run wild, either recovered or showed slight lesions. It is the same in human tuberculosis. A patient confined to the house—particularly in the close, overheated, stuffy dwellings of the poor, or treated in a hospital ward—is in a position analogous to that of the rabbit confined to a hutch in the cellar; whereas a patient living in the fresh air and sunshine for the greater part of the day has chances comparable to those of the rabbit running wild.

The open-air treatment of tuberculosis may be carried out at home, by change of residence to a suitable climate, or in a sanatorium.

(a) *At Home.*—In a majority of all cases the patient has to be cared for in his own home, and if in the city, under very disadvantageous circumstances. Much, however, may be done even in cities to promote arrest by insisting upon plenty of fresh air. It is often impossible to attempt any systematic open-air treatment in city life, but there are many cases in which it can be done if the physician insists and if he lays down explicit rules. The patient's bed should be in the room with most sunshine. While there is fever he should be at rest in bed, and for the greater part of each day, unless the weather is blustering and rainy, the windows should be open, so that the patient may be exposed freely to the fresh air. Low temperature is not a contraindication. If there is a balcony or a suitable yard, on the brighter days the patient may be wrapped up and put in a reclining chair or on a sofa. The important thing is for the physician to emphasize the fact that neither the cough, fever, night sweats, and not even hæmoptysis contraindicate a full exposure to the fresh air. In country places this can be carried out much more effectively. I always advise to give the patient an almanac, that he can tick off the number of hours of sunshine. In the summer he should be out of doors for at least eleven or twelve hours, and in winter six or eight hours. At night the room should be cool and thoroughly well ventilated. In the early stages of the disease with much fever, it may require several months of this rest treatment in the open air before the temperature falls to normal.

(b) *Treatment in Sanatoria.*—Perhaps the most important advance in the treatment of tuberculosis has been in the establishment in favorable localities of institutions in which patients are made to live according to strict rules. To Brehmer, of Göbersdorf, we owe the successful execution of this plan, which has been followed in Germany with most gratifying results. In this country the zeal, energy, and scientific devotion of Edward L. Trudeau have demonstrated its feasibility, and the Saranac institution has become a model of its kind. We need public sanatoria within easy access of the large cities, in which cases of early tuberculosis could be treated at low rates or at the public cost. Private sanatoria for the well-to-do classes are urgently needed. The results at Göbersdorf, Falkenstein, and Saranac demonstrate the great importance of system and rigid discipline in carrying out a successful treatment of tuberculosis. The establishment of National Sanatoria in Canada, the Sharon Sanatorium near Boston, in charge of Dr. Vincent Y. Bowditch, the new Loomis Sanatorium near New York, and the establishments at Asheville and Aiken indicate that both the profession and the public are beginning to appreciate the supreme importance of this method of treatment. So far as the profession is concerned, they must have implicit confidence in the men in charge of these institutions, in their integrity and in their scientific ability. Burton-Fanning has recently published some interesting observations which show that this open-air plan of treatment can be carried out most effectively in England. (For an interesting description of the method of life at Nordrach in the Black Forest by a physician cured at the sanatorium, see pages 393–396 of Fowler and Godlee's Diseases of the Lungs.)

(c) *Climatic Treatment.*—This, after all, is only a modification of the open-air method. The first question to be decided is whether the patient is fit to be sent from home. In many instances it is a positive hardship. A patient with well-marked cavities, hectic fever, night sweats, and emaciation is much better at home, and the physician should not be too much influenced by the importunities of the sick man or of his friends. The requirements of a suitable climate are a *pure atmosphere*, an *equable temperature* not subject to rapid variations, and a *maximum amount of sunshine*. Given these three factors, and it makes little difference *where* a patient goes, so long as he lives *an outdoor life.* The *purity* of the atmosphere is the first consideration, and it is this requirement that is met so well in the mountains and forests. The different climates may be grouped into the high altitudes, the dry, warm climates, and the moist, warm climates.

In this country of high altitudes, the Colorado resorts are the most important. Of others, those in Arizona and New Mexico have been developing rapidly. The rarefaction of the air in high altitudes is of benefit in increasing the respiratory movements in pulmonary disease, but brings about in time a condition of dilatation of the air-vesicles and a permanent increase in the size of the chest which is a marked disadvantage when such persons attempt subsequently to reside at the sea-level. The great advantage of these western resorts is that they are in progressive, prosperous countries, in which a man may find means of livelihood and live in comfort. In Europe the chief resorts at high altitudes are at Davos, Les Avants, and St. Moritz. Of resorts at a moderate altitude, Asheville and the Adirondacks are the best known in this country. The Adirondack cure has become of late years quite famous. Objections to it are the expense, except in the case of the sanitorium, but for well-to-do people it is by far the most satisfactory place. One very decided advantage is that after arrest of the disease the patient can return to the sea-level without any special risk. The cases most suitable for high altitudes are those in which the disease is limited, without much cavity formation, and without much emaciation. The thin, irritable patients with chronic tuberculosis and a good deal of emphysema are better at the sea-level. The cold winter climate seems to be of decided advantage in tuberculosis, and in the Adirondacks, where the temperature falls sometimes to 20° or even more below zero, the patients are able to lead an out-of-door life throughout the entire winter.

Of the moist, warm climates, in this country Florida and the Bermudas, in Europe the Madeira Islands, and in Great Britain Torquay and Falmouth are the best known.

Of the dry, warm climates, Southern California in this country is the most satisfactory. Many of the health resorts in the Southern States, such as Aiken, Thomasville, and Summerville, are delightful winter climates for tuberculous cases. Egypt, Algiers, and the Riviera are the most satisfactory resorts for patients from Europe. For additional information on the subject of climate, particularly in this country, the reader is referred to Solly's recent work on the subject.

Other considerations which should influence the choice of a locality are good accommodations and good food. Very much is said concerning the choice of locality in the different stages of pulmonary tuberculosis, but when the disease is limited to an apex, in a man of fairly good personal and family history, the chances are that he may fight a winning battle if he lives out of doors in any climate, whether high, dry, and cold or low, moist, and warm. With bilateral disease and cavity formation there is but little hope of permanent cure, and the mild or warm climates are preferable.

III. **Measures which, by their Local or General Action, influence the Tuberculous Process.**—Under this heading we may consider the specific, the dietetic, and the general medicinal treatment of tuberculosis.

(*a*) *Specific Treatment.*—The use of Koch's original tuberculin has been in great part abandoned. Some observers, as Whittaker, have had good success with it. In April, 1897, Koch announced the discovery of new tuberculins, the most important of which is the so-called tuberculin R. It is still under trial. The verdict so far has been not at all favorable, except in lupus.

A very large number of antitoxines of various sorts have been introduced within the past few years. Many of them have been submitted to very searching tests in the Saranac Laboratory by Trudeau and Baldwin, whose careful work has extended over a period of four years. They state briefly that, while one or two of the serums have shown a slight degree of antitoxic power, in all the others the tests were negative. In none could any germicidal or curative influence be demonstrated.

(*b*) *Dietetic Treatment.*—The outlook in tuberculosis depends much upon the digestion. It is rare to see recovery in a case in which there is persistent gastric trouble, and the physician should ever bear in mind the fact that in this disease the *primæ viæ* control the position. The early nausea and loss of appetite in many cases of phthisis are serious obstacles. Many patients loathe food of all kinds. A change of air or a sea voyage may promptly restore the appetite. When either of these is impossible, and if, as is almost always the case, fever is present, the patient should be placed at rest, kept in the open air nearly all day, and fed at stated intervals with small quantities either of milk, buttermilk, or koumyss, alternating if necessary with meat juice and egg albumin. Some cases which are disturbed by eggs and milk do well on koumyss. It may be necessary to resort to Débove's method of over-alimentation or forced feeding. The stomach is first washed out with cold water, and then, through the tube, a mixture is given containing a litre of milk, an egg, and 100 grammes of very finely powdered meat. This is given three times a day. Sometimes the patients will take this mixture without the unpleasant necessity of the stomach-tube, in which case a smaller amount may be given. I can speak of the advantage of this plan in cases in which the gastric symptoms have been obstinate and distressing, and the general expression of opinion is very favorable to this plan of treatment in such instances. In the German sanatoria a very special feature is this overfeeding, even when fever is present.

In many cases the digestion is not at all disturbed and the patient can take an ordinary diet. It is remarkable how rapidly the appetite and digestion improve on the fresh-air treatment, even in cases which have to remain in the city. Care should be taken that the medicines do not disturb the stomach. Not infrequently the sweet syrups used in the cough mixtures, cold-liver oil, creasote, and the hypophosphites produce irritation, and by interfering with digestion do more harm than good. On the other hand, the bitter tonics, with acids, and the various malt preparations are often in these cases most satisfactory. The indications for alcohol in tuberculosis are enfeebled digestion with fever, a weak heart, and rapid pulse. A routine administration is not advisable, and there is no evidence that its persistent use promotes fibroid processes in the tuberculous areas. In the advanced stages, particularly when the temperature is low between eight and ten in the morning, whisky and milk, or whisky, egg, and milk may be given with great advantage. The red wines are also beneficial in moderate quantities.

(c) *General Medical Treatment.*—No medicinal agents have any special or peculiar action upon tuberculous processes. The influence which they exert is upon the general nutrition, increasing the physiological resistance, and rendering the tissues less susceptible to invasion. The following are the most important remedies which seem to act in this manner:

Creasote, which may be administered in capsules, in increasing doses, beginning with 1 minim three times a day and, if well borne, increasing the dose to 8 or 10 minims. It may also be given in solution with tincture of cardamoms and alcohol. It is an old remedy, strongly recommended by Addison, and the reports of Jaccoud, Fraentzel, and many others show that it has a positive value in the disease. Guaiacol may be given as a substitute, either internally or hypodermically. In 101 cases in which it was used at my clinic, by Meredith Reese, the chief action was on the cough and expectoration, which were much lessened, but the remedy had no essential influence on the progress of the disease.

Cod-liver Oil.—In glandular and bone tuberculosis, this remedy is undoubtedly beneficial in improving the nutrition. In pulmonary tuberculosis its action is less certain, and it is scarcely worthy of the unbounded confidence which it enjoyed for so many years. It should be given in small doses, not more than a teaspoonful three times a day after meals. It seems to act better in children than in adults. Fever and gastric irritation are contra-indications to its use. When it is not well borne, a dessertspoonful of rich cream three times a day is an excellent substitute. The clotted or Devonshire cream is preferable.

The Hypophosphites.—These in various forms are useful tonics, but it is doubtful if they have any other action. They certainly exercise no specific influence upon tubercle. They may be given in the form of the syrup of the hypophosphites of calcium, sodium, and potassium of the U. S. P.

Arsenic.—There is no general tonic more satisfactory in cases of tuberculosis of all kinds than Fowler's solution. It may be given in 5-minim doses three times a day and gradually increased; stopping its use whenever unpleasant symptoms arise, and in any case intermitting it every third or fourth week.

One or two special methods of dealing with pulmonary tuberculosis may here be mentioned. The local treatment, by direct injection into the lungs, has been practised since its strong advocacy by Pepper. It has, however, not gained the general support of the profession, and is occasionally followed by serious results. As a rule, it may be practised with impunity, and the injections may be made with a long hypodermic needle into any portion of the lung which is diseased. Iodine, carbolic acid, creasote (3-per-cent solution in almond oil), and iodoform have been used for the purpose. The remarkable results which surgeons have recently obtained in the treatment of joint tuberculosis by injections of iodoform point to this as a remedy which will probably prove of service when injected directly into the lungs.

Treatment by compressed air is in many cases beneficial, and under its use the appetite improves, there is gain in weight, and reduction of the fever. The air may be saturated with creasote.

IV. Treatment of Special Symptoms in Pulmonary Tuberculosis.—(*a*)

The Fever.—There is no more difficult problem in practical therapeutics than the treatment of the pyrexia of tuberculosis. The patient should be at rest, and *in the open air for a definite number of hours daily.* Fever does not contra-indicate an out-of-door life, but it is well for patients with a temperature above 100.5° to be at rest. For the continuous pyrexia or the remittent type of the early stages, quinine, small doses of digitalis, and the salicylates may be tried; but they are uncertain and rarely reliable. Under no circumstances is that priceless remedy, quinine, so much abused as in the fever of tuberculosis. In large doses it has a moderate antipyretic action, but it is just in these efficient doses that it is so apt to disturb the stomach.

Antipyrin and antifebrin may be used cautiously; but it is better, when the fever rises above 103°, to rely upon cold sponging or the tepid bath, gradually cooled. When softening has taken place and the fever assumes the characteristic septic type, the problem becomes still more difficult. As shown by Chart XII (which is not by any means an exceptional one), the pyrexia, at this stage, lasts only for twelve or fifteen hours. As a rule it is not more than from eight to ten hours in which the fever is high enough to demand antipyretic treatment. Sometimes antifebrin, given in 2-grain doses every hour for three or four hours before the rise in temperature takes place, either prevents entirely or limits the paroxysm. If the temperature begins to rise between two and three in the afternoon, the antifebrin may be given at eleven, twelve, one, and, if necessary, at two. It answers better in this way than given in the single doses. Careful sponging of the extremities for from half an hour to an hour during the height of the fever is useful. Quinine is of little benefit in this type of fever; the salicylates are of still less use.

(*b*) *Sweating.*—Atropine, in doses of gr. $\frac{1}{120}-\frac{1}{60}$, and the aromatic sulphuric acid in large doses, are the best remedies. When there are cough and nocturnal restlessness, an eighth of a grain of morphia may be given with the atropine. Muscarin (m v of a 1-per-cent solution), tincture of nux vomica (m xxx), picrotoxin (gr. $\frac{1}{60}$) may be tried. The patient should use light flannel night-dresses, as the cotton night-shirts, when soaked with perspiration, have a very unpleasant cold, clammy feeling.

(*c*) The *cough* is a troublesome, though necessary, feature in pulmonary tuberculosis. Unless very worrying and disturbing sleep at night, or so severe as to produce vomiting, it is not well to attempt to restrict it. When irritative and bronchial in character, inhalations are useful, particularly the tincture of benzoin or preparations of tar, creasote, or turpentine. The throat should be carefully examined, as some of the most irritable and distressing forms of cough in phthisis result from laryngeal erosions. The distressing nocturnal cough, which begins just as the patient gets into bed and is preparing to fall asleep, requires, as a rule, preparations of opium. Codeia, in quarter or half grain doses, or the syrupus codeiæ (ℨ j) may be given. An excellent combination for the nocturnal cough of phthisis is morphia (gr. ⅛–⅙), dilute hydrocyanic acid (♏ ij–iij), and syrup of wild cherry (ℨ j). The spirits of chloroform, B. P., or the mistura chloroformi, U. S. P., or Hoffman's anodyne, given in whisky before going to sleep, are efficacious. Mild counter-irritation, or the application of a hot poultice, will sometimes promptly relieve the cough. The morning cough is often much promoted by taking the first thing in the morning a glass of hot milk or a cup of hot water, to which 15 grains of bicarbonate of soda have been added. In the later stages of the disease, when cavities have formed, the accumulated secretion must be expectorated and the paroxysms of coughing are now most exhausting. The sedatives, such as morphia and hydrocyanic acid, should be given cautiously. The aromatic spirit of ammonia in full doses helps to allay the paroxysm. When the expectoration is profuse, creasote internally, or inhalations of turpentine and iodine, or oil of eucalyptus, are useful. For the troublesome dysphagia a strong solution of cocaine (gr. x) with boric acid (gr. v.) in glycerine and water (ℨ j) may be used locally.

(d) For the *diarrhœa* large doses of bismuth, combined with Dover powder, and small starch enemata, with or without opium, may be given. The acetate of lead and opium pill often acts promptly, and the acid diarrhœa mixture, dilute acetic acid (♏ x–xv), morphia (gr. ⅛), and acetate of lead (gr. j–ij), may be tried.

(e) The treatment of the hæmoptysis will be considered in the section on hæmorrhage from the lungs. Dyspnœa is rarely a prominent symptom except in the advanced stages, when it may be very troublesome and distressing. Ammonia and morphia, cautiously administered, may be used.

If the pleuritic pains are severe, the side may be strapped, or painted with tincture of iodine. The dyspeptic symptoms require careful treatment, as the outlook in individual cases depends much upon the condition of the stomach. Small doses of calomel and soda often allay the distressing nausea of the early stage.

XXXV. LEPROSY.

Definition.—A chronic infectious disease caused by the *bacillus lepræ*, characterized by the presence of tubercular nodules in the skin and mucous membranes (tubercular leprosy) or by changes in the nerves (anæsthetic leprosy). At first these forms may be separate, but ultimately both are combined, and in the characteristic tubercular form there are disturbances of sensation.

History.—The disease appears to have prevailed in Egypt even so far back as three or four thousand years before Christ. The Hebrew writers make many references to it, but, as is evident from the description in Leviticus, many different forms of skin diseases were embraced under the term leprosy. Both in India and in China the affection was also known many centuries before the Christian era. The old Greek and Roman physicians were perfectly familiar with its manifestations. As evidence of a pre-Columbian existence of leprosy in America, Ashmead refers to the old pieces of Peruvian pottery representing deformities suggestive of this disease. Throughout the middle ages leprosy prevailed extensively in Europe, and the number of leper asylums has been estimated at at least 20,000. During the sixteenth century it gradually declined.

The prize essays of the National Leprosy Committee and the recently issued Transactions of the Berlin Leprosy Conference contain an immense body of valuable information relating to every possible aspect of the disease.

Geographical Distribution.—In Europe leprosy prevails in Iceland, Norway and Sweden, parts of Russia, particularly about Dorpat, Riga, and the Caucasus, and in certain provinces of Spain and Portugal. In Great Britain the cases are now all imported.

In the United States there are three important foci: Louisiana, in which the disease has been known since 1785, and has of late increased. The statement that it was introduced by the Acadians does not seem to me very likely, since the records of its existence in Nova Scotia and New Brunswick do not date back to that period. Dr. Dyer reports that on January 12, 1898, he knew of 124 positive living cases, including 25 in the Leper Home in Iberville Parish. He adds that it is justifiable to estimate the number of lepers in the State of Louisiana as between 300 and 500. In California, whither the disease has been imported by the Chinese, cases are not very infrequent. I am informed by D. W. Montgomery that there are (May 1, 1898) 16 cases in the Twenty-sixth Street Hospital, San Francisco. Of these, only 2 are Americans, 10 are Chinese. In Minnesota with the Norwegian colonists about 170 lepers are known to have settled. The disease has steadily decreased. Dr. Bracken, the Secretary of the State Board of Health, writes that all had contracted the disease before coming to America. Four of these are now known to be dead. It is reported that two children of one of the leprous women have shown symptoms of leprosy.

The few cases seen in the large cities of the Atlantic coast are imported.

In the Dominion of Canada there are foci of leprosy in two or three counties of New Brunswick, settled by French Canadians, and in Cape Breton, Nova Scotia. The disease appears to have been imported from Normandy about the end of the last century. The number of cases has gradually lessened. Dr. A. C. Smith, the physician in charge of the lazaretto, at Tracadie, New Brunswick, reports under date of January 17, 1898, that there are 24 lepers at present under his care—18 males and 6 females. Of these, 3 are immigrant Icelanders from Manitoba; 1 is a negro from the West India Islands. Dr. Smith states that segregation is gradually stamping out the disease in New Brunswick. The cases have dwindled from about 40 to half that number. In Cape Breton it has almost disappeared. A few cases are met with among the Icelandic settlers in Manitoba, and with the Chinese the affection has been introduced into British Columbia. Dr. Hannington, of Victoria, writes, January 20, 1898, that there are 8 cases known in this province. They are segregated on Darcy Island.

Leprosy is endemic in the West India Islands. It also occurs in Mexico and throughout the Southern States. In the Sandwich Islands it spread rapidly after 1860, and strenuous attempts have been made to stamp it out by segregating all lepers on the island of Molokai. In 1894 there were 1,152 lepers in the settlement.

In British India, according to the Leprosy Commission, there are 100,000 lepers. This is probably a low estimate. In China leprosy prevails extensively. In South Africa, it has increased rapidly. In Australia, New Zealand, and the Australasian islands it also prevails, chiefly among the Chinese. The essays of Ashburton Thompson and James Cauttie deal fully with leprosy in China, Australia, and the Pacific islands.

Etiology.—The bacillus lepræ, discovered by Hansen, of Bergen, in 1871, is universally recognized as the cause of the disease. It has many points of resemblance to the tubercle bacillus, but can be readily differentiated. It is cultivated with extreme difficulty, and, in fact, there is some doubt as to whether it is capable of growth on artificial media.

Modes of Infection.—(a) *Inoculation.*—While it is highly probable that leprosy may be contracted by accidental inoculation, the experimental evidence is as yet inconclusive. With one possible exception negative results have followed the attempts to reproduce the disease in man. The Hawaiian convict under sentence of death, who was inoculated on September 30, 1884, by Arning, four weeks later had rheumatoid pains and gradual painful swelling of the ulnar and median nerves. The neuritis gradually subsided, but there developed a small lepra tubercle at the site of the inoculation. In 1887 the disease was quite manifest, and the man died of it six years after inoculation. The case is not regarded as conclusive, as he had leprous relatives and lived in a leprous country.

(b) *Heredity.*—For years it was thought that the disease was transmitted from parent to child, but the general opinion, as expressed in the recent Leprosy Congress in Berlin, was decidedly against this view. Of course, the possibility of its transmission cannot be denied, and in this respect leprosy and tuberculosis occupy very much the same position, though men with very wide experience have never seen a new-born leper. The youngest cases are rarely under three or four years of age.

(c) *By Contagion.*—The bacilli are given off from the open sores; they are found in the saliva and expectoration in the cases with leprous lesions in the mouth and throat, and occur in very large numbers in the nasal secretion. Sticker found in 153 lepers, subjects of both forms of the disease, bacilli in the nasal secretion in 128, and herein, he thinks, lies the chief source of danger. Schaffer was able to collect lepra bacilli on clean slides placed on tables and floors near to lepers whom he had caused to read aloud. The bacilli have also been isolated from the urine and the milk of patients. It seems probable that they may enter the body in many ways through the mucous membranes and through the skin. Sticker believes that the initial lesion is in an ulcer above the cartilaginous part of the nasal septum. One of the most striking examples of the contagiousness of leprosy is the following: " In 1860, a girl who had hitherto lived at Holst-fershof, where no leprosy existed, married and went to live at Tarwast with her mother-in-law, who was a leper. She remained healthy, but her three children (1, 2, 3) became leprous, as also her younger sister (4), who came on a visit to Tarwast and slept with the children. The younger sister de-veloped leprosy after returning to Holstfershof. At the latter place a man (5), fifty-two years old, who married. one of the ' younger sister's ' children, acquired leprosy; also a relative (6), thirty-six years old, a tailor by occupation, who frequented the house, and his wife (7), who came from a place where no leprosy existed. The two men last mentioned are at present (1897) inmates of the leper asylum at Dorpat." There is certain evidence to show that the disease may be spread through infected clothing, and the high percentage of washerwomen among lepers is also suggestive.

Conditions influencing Infection.—The disease attacks persons of all ages. We do not yet understand all the conditions necessary. Evidently the closest and most intimate contact is essential. The doctors, nurses, and Sisters of Charity who care for the patients are very rarely attacked. In the lazaretto at Tracadie not one of the Sisters who for more than forty years have so faithfully nursed the lepers has contracted the disease. Father Damian, in the Sandwich Islands, and Father Boglioli, in New Orleans, both fell victims in the discharge of their priestly duties. There has long been an idea that possibly the disease may be associated with some special kind of food, and Jonathan Hutchinson believes that a fish diet is the *tertium quid*, which either renders the patient susceptible or with which the poison may be taken.

Morbid Anatomy.—The leprosy tubercles consist of granuloma-tous tissue made up of cells of various sizes in a connective-tissue matrix. The bacilli in extraordinary numbers lie partly between and partly in the cells. The process gradually involves the skin, giving rise to tuberous out-growths with intervening areas of ulceration or cicatrization, which in the face may gradually produce the so-called *facies leontina.* The mucous membranes, particularly the conjunctiva, the cornea, and the larynx may gradually be involved. In many cases deep ulcers form which result in extensive loss of substance or loss of fingers or toes, the so-called *lepra mutilans.* In anæsthetic leprosy there is a peripheral neuritis due to the development of the bacilli in the nerve-fibres. Indeed, this involvement of the nerves plays a primary part in the etiology of many of the impor-tant features, particularly the trophic changes in the skin and the disturb-ances of sensation.

Clinical Forms.—(*a*) **Tubercular Leprosy.**—Prior to the appear-ance of the nodules there are areas of cutaneous erythema which may be sharply defined and often hyperæsthetic. This is sometimes known as *macular* leprosy. The affected spots in time become pigmented. In some instances this superficial change continues without the development of nodules, the areas become anæsthetic, the pigment gradually disappears, and the skin gets perfectly white—the *lepra alba.* Among the patients at Tracadie it was particularly interesting to see three or four in this early stage presenting on the face and forearms a patchy erythema with slight swelling of the skin. The diagnosis of the condition is perfectly clear, though it may be a long time before any other than sensory changes develop. The eyelashes and eyebrows and the hairs on the face fall out. The mucous membranes finally become involved, particularly of the mouth, throat, and larynx; the voice becomes harsh and finally aphonic. Death results not infrequently from the laryngeal complications and aspiration pneumonia. The conjunctivæ are frequently attacked, and the sight is lost by a leprous keratitis.

(*b*) **Anæsthetic Leprosy.**—This remarkable form has, in characteristic cases, no external resemblance whatever to the other variety. It usually begins with pains in the limbs and areas of hyperæsthesia or of numbness. Very early there may be trophic changes, seen in the formation of small bullæ (Hillis). Maculæ appear upon the trunk and extremities, and after persisting for a variable time gradually disappear, leaving areas of anæsthesia, but the loss of sensation may come on independently of the outbreak of maculæ. The nerve-trunks, where superficial, may be felt to be large and nodular. The trophic disturbances are usually marked. Pemphigus-like bullæ develop in the affected areas, which break and leave ulcers which may be very destructive. The fingers and toes are liable to contractures and to necrosis, so that in chronic cases the phalanges are lost. The course of anæsthetic leprosy is extraordinarily chronic and may persist for years without leading to much deformity. One of the most prominent clergymen on this continent had anæsthetic leprosy for more than thirty years, which did not seriously interfere with his usefulness, and not in the slightest with his career.

Diagnosis.—Even in the early stage the dusky erythematous maculæ with hyperæsthesia or areas of anæsthesia are very characteristic. In an advanced grade neither the tubercular nor anæsthetic forms could possibly be mistaken for any other affection. In a doubtful case the microscopical examination of an excised nodule is decisive.

Treatment.—There are no specific remedies in the disease, and general tonics combined with local treatment meet the only available indications. The gurjun and chaulmoogra oils have been recommended, the former in doses of from 5 to 10 minims, the latter in 2-drachm doses.

The Norwegian method of segregation should be enforced wherever the disease prevails, as in Louisiana and California. It should be compulsory in all cases except where the friends can show that they have ample provision in their own home for the complete isolation and proper care of the patient.

XXXVI. INFECTIOUS DISEASES OF DOUBTFUL NATURE.

(1) FEBRICULA—EPHEMERAL FEVER.

Definition.—Fever of slight duration, probably depending upon a variety of causes.

A febrile paroxysm lasting for twenty-four hours and disappearing completely is spoken of as ephemeral fever. If it persists for three, four, or more days without local affection it is referred to as febricula.

The cases may be divided into several groups:

(*a*) Those which represent mild or abortive types of the infectious diseases. It is not very infrequent, during an epidemic of typhoid, scarlet fever, or measles, to see cases with some of the prodromal symptoms and slight fever, which persist for two or three days without any distinctive features. I have already spoken of these in connection with the abortive type of typhoid fever. Possibly, as Kahler suggests, some of the cases of transient fever are due to the rheumatic poison.

(*b*) In a larger and perhaps more important group of cases the symptoms develop with dyspepsia. In children indigestion and gastro-intestinal catarrh are often accompanied by fever. Possibly some instances of longer duration may be due to the absorption of certain toxic substances. Slight fever has been known to follow the eating of decomposing substances or the drinking of stale beer; but the gastric juice has remarkable antiseptic properties, and the frequency with which persons take from choice articles which are " high," shows that poisoning is not likely to occur unless there is existing gastro-intestinal disturbance.

(*c*) Cases which follow exposure to foul odors or sewer-gas. That a febrile paroxysm may follow a prolonged exposure to noxious odors has long been recognized. The cases which have been described under this heading are of two kinds: an acute severe form with nausea, vomiting, colic, and fever, followed perhaps by a condition of collapse or coma; secondly, a form of low fever with or without chills. A good deal of doubt still exists in the minds of the profession about these cases of so-called sewer-gas poisoning. It is a notorious fact that workers in sewers are remarkably free from disease, and in many of the cases which have been reported the illness may have been only a coincidence. There are instances in which persons have been taken ill with vomiting and slight fever after exposure to the odor of a very offensive post mortem. Whether true or not, the idea is firmly implanted in the minds of the laity that very powerful odors from decomposing matters may produce sickness.

(*d*) Many cases doubtless depend upon slight unrecognized lesions, such as tonsillitis or occasionally an abortive or larval pneumonia. Children are much more frequently affected than adults.

The *symptoms* set in, as a rule, abruptly, though in some instances there may have been preliminary *malaise* and indisposition. Headache, loss of appetite, and furred tongue are present. The urine is scanty and high-colored, the fever ranges from 101° to 103°, sometimes in children it rises higher. The cheeks may be flushed and the patient has the outward manifestations of fever. In children there may be bronchial catarrh with slight cough. Herpes on the lips is a common symptom. Occasionally in children the cerebral symptoms are marked at the outset, and there may be irritation, restlessness, and nocturnal delirium. The fever terminates abruptly by crisis from the second to the fourth day; in some instances it may continue for a week.

The *diagnosis* generally rests upon the absence of local manifestations, particularly the characteristic skin rashes of the eruptive fevers, and most important of all the rapid disappearance of the pyrexia. The cases most readily recognized are those with acute gastro-intestinal disturbance.

The *treatment* is that of mild pyrexia—rest in bed, a laxative, and a fever mixture containing nitrate of potassium and sweet spirits of nitre.

(2) WEIL'S DISEASE.

Acute Febrile Icterus.—In 1886 Weil described an acute infectious disease, characterized by fever and jaundice. Much discussion has taken place concerning the true nature of this affection, but it has not been definitely determined whether it is a specific disease or only a jaundice which may be due to various causes. The majority of the cases have occurred during the summer months. The cases have occurred in groups in different cities. A few cases have been reported in this country (Lanphear). Males are most frequently affected. Many of the cases have been in butchers. The age of the patients has been from twenty-five to forty.

The disease sets in abruptly, usually without prodromes and often with a chill. There are headache, pains in the back, and sometimes intense pains in the legs and muscles, particularly of the cheeks. The fever is characterized by marked remissions. Jaundice appears early. The liver and spleen are usually swollen; the former may be tender. The jaundice may be light, but in many of the cases described it has been of the obstructive form, and the stools have been clay-colored. Gastro-intestinal symptoms are rarely present. The fever lasts from ten to fourteen days; sometimes there are slight recurrences, but a definite relapse is rare.

Albumin is usually present in the urine; hæmaturia has occurred in some cases.

Cerebral symptoms, delirium and coma, may be present.

In the few post-mortems which have been made nothing distinctive has been found. The investigations of Jaeger render it not impossible that this epidemic form of jaundice depends upon infection with a proteus —*bacillus proteus fluorescens.*

(3) MILK-SICKNESS.

This remarkable disease prevails in certain districts of the United States, west of the Alleghany Mountains, and is connected with the affection in cattle known as the *trembles*. It prevailed extensively in the early settlements in certain of the Western States and proved very fatal. The general opinion is that it is communicated to man only by eating the flesh or drinking the milk of diseased animals. The butter and cheese are also poisonous. In animals, cattle and the young of horses and sheep are most susceptible. It is stated that cows giving milk do not themselves show marked symptoms unless driven rapidly, and, according to Graff, the secretion may be infective when the disease is latent. When a cow is very ill, food is refused, the eyes are injected, the animal staggers, the entire muscular system trembles, and death occurs in convulsions, sometimes with great suddenness. Nothing definite is known as to the cause of the disease. It is most frequent in new settlements.

In man the symptoms are those of a more or less acute intoxication. After a few days of uneasiness and distress the patient is seized with pains in the stomach, nausea and vomiting, fever and intense thirst. There is usually obstinate constipation. The tongue is swollen and tremulous, the breath is extremely foul and, according to Graff, is as characteristic of the disease as is the odor in small-pox. Cerebral symptoms—restlessness, irritability, coma, and convulsions—are sometimes marked, and there may gradually be produced a typhoid state in which the patient dies.

The duration of the disease is variable. In the most acute forms death occurs within two or three days. It may last for ten days, or even for three or four weeks. Graff states that insanity occurred in one case. The poisonous nature of the flesh and of the milk has been demonstrated experimentally. An ounce of butter or cheese, or four ounces of the beef, raw or boiled, given three times a day, will kill a dog within six days. No definite pathological lesions are known. Fortunately, the disease has become rare, and the observation of Drake, Yandell, and others, that it gradually disappears with the clearing of the forests and improved tillage, has been amply substantiated. It still prevails in parts of North Carolina.

(4) GLANDULAR FEVER.

Definition.—An infectious disease of children, developing, as a rule, without premonitory signs, and characterized by slight redness of the throat, high fever, swelling and tenderness of the lymph-glands of the neck, particularly those behind the sterno-cleido-mastoid muscles. The fever is of short duration, but the enlargement of the glands persists for from ten days to three weeks.

In children acute adenitis of the cervical and other glands with fever has been noted by many observers, but Pfeiffer in 1889 called special attention to it under the name of *Druesen-Fieber*. He described it as an infectious disease of young children between the ages of five and eight years, characterized by the above-mentioned symptoms. Since Pfeiffer's paper a good deal of work has been done in connection with the subject, and in this country West and Hamill, and in England Dawson Williams, have more particularly emphasized the condition.

Etiology.—It may occur in epidemic form. West, of Bellaire, Ohio, describes an epidemic of 96 cases in children between the ages of seven months and thirteen years. Bilateral swelling of the carotid lymph-glands was a most marked feature. In three fourths of the cases the post-cervical, inguinal, and axillary glands were involved. The mesenteric glands were felt in 37 cases, the spleen was enlarged in 57, and the liver in 87 cases. Coryza was not present, and there were no bronchial or pulmonary symptoms. Cases occurred between the months of October and June. The nature of the infection has not been determined.

Symptoms.—The onset is sudden and the first complaint is of pain on moving the head and neck. There may be nausea and vomiting and abdominal pain. The temperature ranges from 101° to 103°. The tonsils may be a little red and the lymphatic tissues swollen, but the throat symptoms are quite transient and unimportant. On the second or third day the enlarged glands appear, and during the course they vary in size from a pea to a goose-egg. They are painful to the touch, but there is rarely any redness or swelling of the skin, though at times there is some puffiness of the subcutaneous tissues of the neck, and there may be a little difficulty in swallowing. In some instances there has been discomfort in the chest and a paroxysmal cough, indicating involvement of the tracheal and bronchial glands. The swelling of the glands persists for from two to three weeks. Among the serious features of the disease are the termination of the adenitis in suppuration, which seems rare (though Neumann has met with it in 13 cases), and hæmorrhagic nephritis. Acute otitis media and retropharyngeal abscess have also been reported.

The outlook is favorable. West suggests the use of small doses of calomel during the height of the trouble.

(5) MOUNTAIN FEVER—MOUNTAIN SICKNESS.

Several distinct diseases have been described as mountain fever. An important group, the *mountain anæmia*, is associated with the *anchylostoma*, which has not yet been met with in this country. A second group of cases belongs to typhoid fever; and instances of this disease occurring in mountainous regions in the Western States are referred to as mountain fever. The observations of Hoff and Smart, and more recently of Woodruff and of Raymond, show that the disease is typhoid fever.

Recently C. E. Woodruff, of the army, has reported a group of 35 cases at Fort Custer, which, as he says, would certainly have been described as mountain fever, but in which the clinical features and the Widal reaction showed there was no question that they were typhoid. Raymond, too, recently called attention to the existence of typhoid fever in Wyoming among the Indians in the reservation and the soldiers at the post. It would be well, I think, for the use of the term mountain fever to be discontinued.

Mountain sickness comprises the remarkable group of phenomena which develop in very high altitudes. The condition has been very accurately described by Mr. Whymper. In the ascent of Chimborazo they were first affected at a height of 16,664 feet. The symptoms were severe headache, gasping for breath, evidently urgent *besoin de respirer*. The throat was parched, and there was intense thirst, loss of appetite, and of general *malaise*. Mr. Whymper's temperature was 100.4°. The symptoms in his case lasted for nearly three days. In a less aggravated form such symptoms may present themselves at much lower levels, and in the ascent of the railroad at Pike's Peak many persons suffer from distress in breathing. The original cases described by General Fremont were of this nature. A very full description is given by Allbutt in vol. iii of his System.

(6) MILIARY FEVER—SWEATING SICKNESS.

The disease is characterized by fever, profuse sweats, and an eruption of miliary vesicles. It prevailed and was very fatal in England in the fifteenth and sixteenth centuries, but of late years it has been confined entirely to certain districts in France (Picardy) and Italy. An epidemic of some extent occurred in France in 1887. Hirsch gives a chronological account of 194 epidemics between 1718 and 1879, many of which were limited to a single village or to a few localities. Occasionally the disease has become widely spread. Slight epidemics have occurred in Germany and Switzerland. Within the past few years there have been several small outbreaks in Austria. They are usually of short duration, lasting only for three or four weeks—sometimes not more than seven or eight days. As in influenza, a very large number of persons are attacked in rapid succession. In the mild cases there is only slight fever, with loss of appetite, an erythematous eruption, profuse perspiration, and an outbreak of miliary vesicles. The severe cases present the symptoms of intense infection—delirium, high fever, profound prostration, and hæmorrhage. The death-rate at the outset of the disease is usually high, and, as is so graphically described in the account of some of the epidemics of the middle ages, death may occur in a few hours. The most recent and the fullest account of the disease is given in Nothnagel's Handbuch by Immermann.

(7) FOOT AND MOUTH DISEASE—EPIDEMIC STOMATITIS— APHTHOUS FEVER.

Foot and mouth disease is an acute infectious disorder met with chiefly in cattle, sheep, and pigs, but attacking other domestic animals. It is of extraordinary activity, and spreads with "lightning rapidity" over vast territories, causing very serious losses. In cattle, after a period of incubation of three or five days, the animal gets feverish, the mucous membrane of the mouth swells, and little grayish vesicles the size of a hemp seed begin to develop on the edges and lower portion of the tongue, on the gums, and on the mucous membrane of the lips. They contain at first a clear fluid, which becomes turbid, and then they enlarge and gradually become converted into superficial ulcers. There is ptyalism, and the animals lose flesh rapidly. In the cow the disease is also frequently seen about the udder and teats, and the milk becomes yellowish-white in color and of a mucoid consistency.

The transmission to man is by no means uncommon, and of late several important epidemics have been studied in the neighborhood of Berlin. Dr. Salmon informs me that in the United States foot and mouth disease has very rarely occurred, but in 1870, as well as in 1841, it was communicated in a few instances to man. In Zuill's translation of Friedberger and Fröhner's Pathology and Therapeutics of Domestic Animals (Philadelphia, 1895) the disease is thus described: "Transmission of aphthous fever to man is not rare. The veterinarian has oftener occasion to observe it than the physician. The use of milk from aphthous cows contaminates children quite frequently and is fatal to them. This may also happen through ingestion of butter or cheese made of milk coming from aphthous animals, or also directly through wounds of the arms, hands, or by intermediary agents. In man the symptoms are: fever, digestive troubles, and vesicular eruption upon the lips, the buccal and pharyngeal

22

mucous membranes (angina). The disease does not seem to be transmissible through the meat of diseased animals. Perhaps the serious affections of the skin which were observed to develop in children after vaccination (especially in 1883–'84) may have been determined by mistaking the mammary eruption of aphthous fever for cow-pox."

In widespread epidemics there has been sometimes a marked tendency to hæmorrhages. The disease runs, as a rule, a favorable course, but in Siegel's report of a recent epidemic the mortality was 8 per cent.

Several forms of micro-organisms have been described in connection with it. Klein has described a micrococcus.

When epidemics are prevailing in cattle the milk should be boiled, and the proper prophylactic measures taken to isolate both the cattle and the individuals who come in contact with them.

SECTION II.

DISEASES DUE TO ANIMAL PARASITES.

I. PSOROSPERMIASIS.

UNDER this term are embraced several affections produced by the sporozoa. These parasites, belonging to the protozoa, are also known as psorosperms and gregarinidæ. They are extraordinarily abundant in the invertebrates, and are not uncommon in the higher mammals. The entire group of blood parasites, hæmatozoa, which live within the corpuscles, are closely related to them. Psorosperms are, as a rule, parasites of the cells —*Cytozoa*. The commonest and most suitable variety for study is the *Coccidium oviforme* of the rabbit, which produces a disease of the liver in which the organ is studded throughout with whitish nodules, ranging in size from a pin's head to a split pea. On section each nodule is seen to be a dilated portion of a bile-duct; the walls are lined with epithelium in the interior of which are multitudes of ovoid bodies—the coccidia. Another very common form occurs in the muscles of the pig, the so-called Rainey's tube, which is an ovoid body within the sarcolemma containing a number of small, sickle-shaped, unicellular organisms, the *Sarcocystis Miescheri*. Another species, the *S. hominis*, has been described in man.

These bodies probably play a more important *rôle* in human pathology than has hitherto been thought. The cases reported may be grouped under the following divisions: internal and external.

(1) **Internal Psorospermiasis.**—In a majority of the cases of this group the psorosperms have been found in the liver, producing a disease similar to that which occurs in rabbits. In Guebler's case there were tumors which could be felt in the liver during life, and they were determined by Leuckart to be due to coccidia. In W. B. Haddon's case the patient was admitted to St. Thomas's Hospital with slight fever and drowsiness; he gradually became unconscious; death occurred on the fourteenth day of observation. Whitish neoplasms were found upon the peritonæum, omentum, and on the layers of the pericardium; and a few were found in the liver, spleen, and kidneys. A somewhat similar case, though more remarkable, as it ran a very acute course, is reported by Silcott. A woman, aged fifty-three, admitted to St. Mary's Hospital, was thought to be suffering from typhoid fever. She had had a chill six weeks before admission. There were

349

fever of an intermittent type, slight diarrhœa, nausea, tenderness over the liver and spleen, and a dry tongue; death occurred from heart-failure. The liver was enlarged, weighed 83 ounces, and in its substance there were caseous foci, around each of which was a ring of congestion. The spleen weighed 16 ounces and contained similar bodies. The ileum presented six papule-like elevations. The masses resembled tubercles, but on examination coccidia were found.

The parasites are also found in the kidneys and ureters. Cases of this kind have been recorded by Bland Sutton and Paul Eve. In Eve's case the symptoms were hæmaturia and frequent micturition, and death took place on the seventeenth day. The nodules throughout the pelvis and ureters have been regarded as mucous cysts. In a case reported by Joseph Griffiths the tumors in the ureter caused hydronephrosis.

(2) **Cutaneous Psorospermiasis.**—The parasitic nature of the *keratosis follicularis* of White, and of Paget's disease of the nipple, which seemed to have been established, has been called in question, and the bodies described as psorosperms are believed to be the result of epithelial degeneration. So, too, in molluscum contagiosum and in epithelioma, the nature of the structures which lie in and between the epithelial cells, and which have some resemblance to psorosperms, is still unsettled; some claiming that they are truly parasitic, others affirming that they are nothing but altered protoplasm of the epithelial cells.

There are several undoubted instances, however, of parasitic sporozoa producing extensive disease of the skin. In Wernicke's case (from Buenos Ayres) the lesions were scattered over the face, trunk, and left thigh. The sporozoa were found in numbers in the pus of the skin lesions, and also in the inguinal glands, which were excised.

Rixford and Gilchrist describe two cases (Johns Hopkins Hospital Reports, vol. i). In the first case, which was regarded as tuberculosis of the skin, the lesion remained local for nearly eight years. The lymphatic glands then became involved. The affection gradually attacked the nose, cheeks, and other parts of the head, the left hand, the leg, and the left testicle. For seven or eight years the patient had no constitutional symptoms, but after the glands became involved an intermittent fever developed. In the later stages he had a cough with purulent expectoration. The autopsy revealed what appeared to be tuberculosis of the lungs, adrenals, and testis. There were numerous tuberculous-looking nodules in the spleen, on the surface of the liver, and the pleuræ. In all of the lesions enormous numbers of sporozoa were found, especially in the caseous masses. Successful inoculations were made into rabbits and dogs. The second case was similar, but much more acute. There were thirty skin lesions distributed over the body. The patient died within three months after the appearance of the initial lesion. In an excised lymph-gland enormous numbers of sporozoa were found. The cycle of development was readily followed. These bodies differ in all points from those described as protozoa in cancer and in molluscum contagiosum.

Two of the most important protozoön diseases—namely, amœbic dysentery and malaria—have been described.

II. PARASITIC INFUSORIA.

Several flagellates have been found parasitic in man. Among the most common are the *Trichomonas vaginalis,* which measures 15 to 25 μ in length, and has four flagella, which are as long as or longer than the body. It is by no means an uncommon parasite in the acid vaginal mucus.

The *Trichomonas* or *Cercomonas hominis* lives in the intestines, and is met with in the stools under all sorts of conditions. It is probably not pathogenic. I have seen it also in the vomit in a case of chronic gastric catarrh. Trichomonads have been met with also in the urine in several cases, and may be truly pathogenic. In Dock's[*] case the parasites were associated with a hæmorrhagic cystitis without bacteria.

The *Lamblia intestinalis* is another intestinal monad, larger than the common *Trichomonas.* Flagellates have also been found in the expectoration in cases of gangrene of the lung and of bronchiectasis, and in pleurisy.

Among the parasitic *Ciliata* may be mentioned the *Balantidium coli,* which has been found occasionally in the large intestine in forms of dysentery. The parasite is oval in form, 70 to 100 μ long and 50 to 70 μ broad. It is doubtful whether it is pathogenic.

III. DISTOMIASIS.

Several forms of trematodes or flukes are parasitic in man, and when in numbers may cause serious disease.

(1) *Liver Flukes.*—The following species of flukes have been found: The *Fasciola hepatica,* a very common parasite in ruminants, which has a length of from 28 to 32 mm. The *Distomum lanceolatum,* a much smaller form, from 8 to 10 mm. in length, which is also very common in sheep and cattle. The *Distoma buski,* the largest form, measuring from 4 to 8 cm. in length. One or two other less important forms have occasionally been met with. The studies of the Japanese physicians have brought to light the interesting fact that there is a distoma widely endemic in certain provinces in that country. The two forms described as *Distoma endemicum* and *Distoma perniciosum* are identical, and are known now as *Distoma sinense.* According to Baelz, fully 20 per cent of the inhabitants of certain provinces are affected. The *Distoma felineum,* which has been found recently in this country by Ward, of Nebraska, in cats, is a common human parasite in Siberia.

The flukes occupy the bile-passages and the upper portion of the small intestine. When in large numbers they may cause serious and fatal disease of the liver, usually with ascites and jaundice. The liver may be enormously enlarged; in Kichner's case it weighed 11 pounds. The flukes may cause a chronic cholangitis, leading to great thickening or even calcification of the walls of the bile-duct. The ova have been found in the stools. Occasionally the distomes are found under the skin.

---

[*] American Journal of the Medical Sciences, January, 1896.

The endemic fluke disease of Japan is characterized by enlargement of the liver, emaciation, diarrhœa, and frequently ascites.

(2) *The Blood Fluke; Schistosoma hæmatobium* (*Bilharzia hæmatobia*).—This trematode is found in Egypt, southern Africa, and Arabia, and is the cause in these countries of the endemic hæmaturia. The female is about 2 cm. in length, cylindrical, filiform, and about 0.07 mm. in diameter. The parasite lives in the venous system, particularly in the portal vein, and in the veins of the spleen, bladder, kidneys, and mesentery. According to Bilharz, at least 50 per cent of the lower classes in Egypt are infected with it. It is not yet known how the parasite gains entrance to the body. In all probability it is by drinking impure water containing the embryos.

The symptoms are due to changes in the mucous membrane of the urinary organs caused by the presence of the ova in the blood-vessels of these parts. Hæmaturia is the first and most constant symptom, leading gradually to anæmia. There is generally pain during micturition. The blood is not constant in the urine. The ova of the Bilharzia are readily seen under a microscope with a low power. They are ovoid in shape, translucent, with a small spike at one end. They may be widely distributed in the body—in the submucosa of the bowel, in polypoid excrescences in the rectum, in the lungs and elsewhere.

The disease is rarely fatal; a great majority of the cases recover. Children are more commonly attacked than grown persons, and the disease often disappears by the time of puberty.

(3) *Bronchial Fluke; Distomum Westermanni; Parasitic Hæmoptysis.*—In parts of China, Japan, and Formosa there is an epidemic disease, described by Ringer and Manson, characterized by attacks of cough and hæmoptysis associated with the presence of a small fluke in the bronchial tubes.

IV. DISEASES CAUSED BY NEMATODES.

I. ASCARIASIS.

(a) *Ascaris lumbricoides*, the most common human parasite, is found chiefly in children. The female is from 7 to 12 inches in length, the male from 4 to 8 inches. In form it is cylindrical, being pointed at both ends; it has a yellowish-brown, sometimes a slightly reddish color. Four longitudinal bands can be seen, and it is striated transversely. The ova, which are sometimes found in large numbers in the fæces, are small, brownish-red in color, elliptical, and have a very thick covering. They measure 0.075 mm. in length and 0.058 mm. in width. The life history has been demonstrated to be "direct"—i. e., without intermediate host. The parasite occupies the upper portion of the small intestine. Usually not more than one or two are present, but occasionally they occur in enormous numbers. The migrations are peculiar. They may pass into the stomach, whence they may be ejected by vomiting, or they may crawl up the œsophagus and enter the pharynx, from which they may be withdrawn. A child under my care in the small-pox department of the General Hospital, during convalescence, withdrew in this way more than thirty round worms within a few weeks. In other instances the worm reaches the larynx, and has been known to produce fatal asphyxia, or, passing into the trachea, to cause gangrene of the lung. They may go through the Eustachian tube and appear at the external meatus. The most serious migration is into the bile-duct. There is a specimen in the Wistar-Horner Museum of the University of Pennsylvania in which not only the common duct, but also the main branches throughout the liver, are enormously distended and packed with numerous round worms. The bowel may be blocked, or in rare instances an ulcer may be perforated. Even the healthy bowel wall may be penetrated (Apostolides).

A peculiarly irritating substance, often evident to the sense of smell in handling specimens, is formed by the round worms. Peiper and others suggest that the nervous symptoms, sometimes resembling those of meningitis, are due to this poison. Chauffard, Marie, and Tauchon have gone still further, and report a remarkable condition of fever, intestinal symptoms, foul breath, and intermittent diarrhœa in connection with the presence of lumbricoides. They call it typho-lumbricosis. The febrile condition may continue for a month or more. The symptoms are supposed to be excited reflexly, or to be due to the virulence of the ascarides themselves. It does not seem to me a very clearly defined condition, and when one considers the extraordinary frequency of lumbricoid worms and the remarkable number which may be harbored without causing any special trouble, I think we require more evidence before we accept the conclusions of these authors.

The symptoms are not definite. When a few parasites are present they may be passed without causing disturbance. In children there are irritative symptoms usually attributed to worms, such as restlessness, irritability, picking at the nose, grinding of the teeth, twitchings, or convulsions. These symptoms may be marked in very nervous children.

Treatment.—Santonin can be given, mixed with sugar, in doses of from one half to one grain for a child and two to three grains for an adult, followed by a calomel or a saline purge. The dose may be given for three or four days. An unpleasant consequence which sometimes follows the administration of this drug is xanthopsia or yellow vision.

(b) *Oxyuris vermicularis* (*Thread-worm; Pin-worm*).—This common parasite occupies the rectum and colon. The male measures about 4 mm. in length, the female about 10 mm. They produce great irritation and itching, particularly at night, symptoms which become intensely aggravated by the nocturnal migration of the parasites. Occasionally peri-rectal abscesses are formed, containing numbers of the worms.

The patients become extremely restless and irritable, the sleep is often disturbed, and there may be loss of appetite and anæmia. Though most common in children, the parasite occurs at all ages.

The worm is readily detected in the fæces. Infection probably takes place through the water or possibly through salads, such as lettuce and cresses. A person the subject of the worms passes ova in large numbers in the fæces, and the possibility of reinfection must be scrupulously guarded against.

The treatment is simple, though occasionally there are instances in which all forms of medication are resisted. A case is mentioned of a gentleman, aged forty, who had suffered from childhood and had failed to obtain any benefit from prolonged treatment by many helminthologists. I have reported a case of several years' duration. Santonin may be used in small doses, and mild purgatives, particularly rhubarb. Large injections containing carbolic acid, vinegar, quassia, aloes, or turpentine may be employed. In children the use of cold injections of strong salt and water is usually efficacious. They should be repeated for at least ten days. In giving the injection care should be taken to have the hips well elevated, so that the fluid can be retained as long as possible. For the intense itching and irritation at night vaseline may be freely used, or belladonna ointment.

II. Trichiniasis.

The *Trichina spiralis* in its adult condition lives in the small intestine. The disease is produced by the embryos, which pass from the intestines and reach the voluntary muscles, where they finally become encapsulated larvæ—muscle trichinæ. It is in the migration of the embryos (possibly from poisons produced by them) that the group of symptoms known as trichinasis is produced.

Description of the Parasites.—(*a*) Adult or intestinal form. The female measures from 3 to 4 mm.; the male, 1.5 mm., and has two little projections from the hinder end.

(*b*) The larva or muscle trichina is from 0.6 to 1 mm. in length and lies coiled in an ovoid capsule, which is at first translucent, but subsequently opaque and infiltrated with lime salts. The worm presents a pointed head and a somewhat rounded tail.

When flesh containing the trichinæ is eaten by man or by any animal in which the development can take place, the capsules are digested and the trichinæ set free. They pass into the small intestine, and about the third day attain their full growth and become sexually mature. Virchow's experiments have shown that on the sixth or seventh day the embryos are fully developed. The young produced by each female trichina have been estimated at several hundred. Leuckart thinks that various broods are developed in succession, and that as many as a thousand embryos may be produced by a single worm. The time from the ingestion of the flesh containing the muscle trichinæ to the development of the brood of embryos in the intestines is from seven to nine days. The female worm penetrates the intestinal wall and the embryos are probably discharged directly into the lymph spaces (Askanazy), thence into the venous system, and by the blood stream to the muscles, which constitute their seat of election. Dr. J. Y. Graham, of the University of Alabama, has recently reviewed the question of the mode of transmission in an exhaustive monograph, and he gives strong arguments in favor of the transmission through the blood stream. After a preliminary migration in the intermuscular connective tissue they penetrate the primitive muscle-fibres, and in about two weeks develop into the full-grown muscle form. In this process an interstitial myositis is excited and gradually an ovoid capsule develops about the parasite. Two, occasionally three or four, worms may be seen within a single capsule. This process of encapsulation has been estimated to take about six weeks. Within the muscles the parasites do not undergo further development. Gradually the capsule becomes thicker, and ultimately lime salts are deposited within it. This change may take place in man within four or five months. In the hog it may be deferred for many years. The calcification renders the cyst visible, and since first seen by Tiedemann, in 1822, and Hilton, in 1832, these small, opaque, oat-shaped bodies have been familiar objects to demonstrators of normal and morbid anatomy. The trichinæ may live within the muscles for an indefinite period. They have been found alive and capable of developing as late as twenty or even twenty-five years after their entrance into the system. In many instances, however, the worms are completely calcified. The trichina has been found or " raised " in twenty-six different species of animals (Stiles). Medical literature abounds in references to its presence in fish, earthworms, etc., but these parasites belong to other genera. In fæcal examinations for the parasite it is well to remember that the " cell body " of the anterior portion of the intestine is a diagnostic criterion of the *T. spiralis.* It was first found in the hog by the late Joseph Leidy. Experimentally, guinea-pigs and rabbits are readily infected by feeding them with muscle containing the larval form. Dogs are infected with difficulty; cats more readily. Experimentally, animals sometimes die of the disease if large numbers of the parasites have been eaten. In the hog the trichinæ, like the cysticerci, cause few if any symptoms. An animal the muscles of which are swarming with living trichinæ may be well nourished and healthy-looking. An important point also is the fact that in the hog the capsule does not readily become calcified, so that the parasites are not visible as in the human muscles. For a long time the trichina was looked upon as a pathological curiosity, but in 1860 Zenker discovered in a girl in the Dresden Hospital, who had symptoms of typhoid fever, both the intestinal and the muscle forms of the trichinæ, since which time the disease has been thoroughly studied.

Man is infected by eating the flesh of trichinous hogs. The incidence of the disease in swine varies much in different countries. In Germany, where a thorough and systematic microscopic examination of all swine flesh is made, the proportion of trichinous hogs is about 1 in 1,852. At the Berlin abattoir, where the microscopic examination is conducted by a staff of over eighty men and women, two portions are taken from the abdominal muscles, from the diaphragm, and from the intercostal muscles, and one piece from the muscles of the larynx and tongue. A special compressor is used to flatten the fragments of the muscle, and the examination is made with a magnifying power of from 70 to 100 diameters. During the three years ending in 1885 there were 603 trichinous hogs detected, a ratio of 1 to 1,292. Statistics are not available in England. In the United States systematic inspection is unknown, and the statistics are by no means extensive enough. " Taking all the examinations of American pork thus far made, both at home and abroad, and we have a total of 298,782, in which trichinæ were found 6,280 times, being 2.1 per cent, or 1 to 48 " (Salmon, 1884).

In 1883, in conjunction with A. W. Clement, I examined 1,000 hogs at the Montreal abattoir, and found only 4 infected.

Modes of Infection.—The danger of infection depends entirely upon the mode of preparation of the flesh. Thorough cooking, so that all parts of the meat reach the boiling point, destroys the parasites; but in large joints the central portions are often not raised to this temperature. The frequency of the disease in different countries depends largely upon the habits of the people in the preparation of pork. In North Germany, where raw ham and *wurst* are freely eaten, the greatest number of instances have occurred. In South Germany, France, and England cases are rare. In this country the greatest number of persons attacked have been Germans. Salting and smoking the flesh are not always sufficient, and the Havre experiments showed that animals are readily infected when fed with portions of the pickled or the smoked meat as prepared in this country. Carl Fraenkel, however, states that the experiments on this point have been negative, and that it is very doubtful if any cases of trichiniasis in Germany have been caused by American pork. Germany has yet to show a single case of trichiniasis due to pork of unquestioned American origin.

Frequency of Infection.—The dissecting-room and post-mortem statistics show that from one half to two per cent of all bodies contain trichinæ. Of 1,000 consecutive autopsies, of which I have notes, trichinæ were present in 6 instances. I have, in addition, seen them in two dissecting-room cases and in two bodies at the Philadelphia Hospital.

The disease often occurs in epidemics, a large number of persons being infected from a single source. Among the best known of these, one occurred at Hedersleben, in which there were 337 persons affected, and another at Emersleben, in which there were 250 persons attacked. The extensive outbreaks of this sort have been, with few exceptions, in North Germany, and they are a comment on the inefficiency of the inspection. The statistics on the subject in this country have been collected for me by Alfred Mann, by F. A. Packard, of Philadelphia, and more exhaustively by C. W. Stiles, who states that up to 1893 there was a total of 709 cases, since which he says, in a letter of February 7, 1898, there have been 40 or 50 cases reported. He thinks that 900 would cover the total number thus far reported for this country. According to States, New York heads the list with 129 cases; Illinois shows 119; Massachusetts, 115; Iowa, 108. Only rarely are cases diagnosed in hospital practice. With the exception of a typical case in one of Traube's wards, I never recognized an instance of the disease until the past eighteen months, during which time 3 cases have occurred in my service at the Johns Hopkins Hospital.

Symptoms.—The ingestion of trichinous flesh is not necessarily followed by the disease. When a limited number are eaten only a few embryos pass to the muscles and may cause no symptoms. Well-characterized cases present a gastro-intestinal period and a period of general infection.

In the course of a few days after eating the infected meat there are signs of gastro-intestinal disturbance—pain in the abdomen, loss of appetite, vomiting, and sometimes diarrhœa. The preliminary symptoms, however, are by no means constant, and in some of the large epidemics cases have been observed in which they have been absent. In other instances the gastro-intestinal features have been marked from the outset, and the attack has resembled cholera nostras. Pain in different parts of the body, general debility, and weakness have been noted in some of the epidemics.

The invasion symptoms develop between the seventh and the tenth day, sometimes not until the end of the second week. There is fever, except in very mild cases. Chills are not common. The thermometer may register 102° or 104°, and the fever is usually remittent or intermittent. The migration of the parasites into the muscles excites a more or less intense myositis, which is characterized by pain on pressure and movement, and by swelling and tension of the muscles, over which the skin may be œdematous. The limbs are placed in the positions in which the muscles are in least tension. The involvement of the muscles of mastication and of the larynx may cause difficulty in chewing and swallowing. In severe cases the involvement of the diaphragm and intercostal muscles may lead to intense dyspnœa, which sometimes proves fatal. Œdema, a feature of great importance, may be early in the face, particularly about the eyes. Later it develops in the extremities when the swelling and stiffness of the muscles are at their height. Profuse sweats, tingling and itching of the skin, and in some instances urticaria, have been described.

Blood.—A marked leucocytosis, which may reach above 30,000, is present. A special feature is the extraordinary increase in the number of eosinophilic cells, which may comprise more than 50 per cent of all the leucocytes. There have been in my wards within the past two years 5 cases in which this eosinophilia was most pronounced. In 4 of the cases the diagnosis was actually suggested by the great increase in the eosinophiles; in 1 case they reached 68 per cent of the total number of leucocytes.

The general nutrition is much disturbed and the patient becomes emaciated and often anæmic, particularly in the protracted cases. The patellar tendon reflex may be absent. The patients are usually conscious, except in cases of very intense infection, in which the delirium, dry tongue, and tremor give a picture suggesting typhoid fever. In addition to the dyspnœa, present in the severer infections, there may be bronchitis, and in the fatal cases pneumonia or pleurisy. In some epidemics polyuria has been a common symptom. Albuminuria is frequent.

The intensity and duration of the symptoms depend entirely upon the grade of infection. In the mild cases recovery is complete in from ten to fourteen days. In the severe forms convalescence is not established for six or eight weeks, and it may be months before the patient recovers the muscular strength. One case in the Hedersleben epidemic was weak eight years after the attack.

Of 72 fatal cases in the Hedersleben epidemic, the greatest mortality occurred in the fourth and fifth and sixth weeks; namely, 52 cases. Two died in the second week with severe choleraic symptoms.

The mortality has ranged in different outbreaks from 1 or 2 per cent to 30 per cent. In the Hedersleben epidemic 101 persons died. Among the 456 cases reported in this country there were 122 deaths.

The *anatomical changes* are chiefly in the voluntary muscles. The trichinæ enter the primitive muscle bundles, which undergo granular degeneration with marked nuclear proliferation. There is a local myositis, and gradually about the parasite a·cyst wall is formed. These changes, as well as the remarkable alterations in the blood, have been described in full by Dr. Thomas R. Brown.* Cohnheim has described a fatty degeneration of the liver and enlargement of the mesenteric glands. At the time of death in the fourth or fifth week or later the adult trichinæ are still found in the intestines.

The *prognosis* depends much upon the quantity of infected meat which has been eaten and the number of trichinæ which mature in the intestines. In children the outlook is more favorable. Early diarrhœa and moderately intense gastro-intestinal symptoms are, as a rule, more favorable than constipation.

Diagnosis.—The disease should always be suspected when a large birthday party or *Fest* among Germans is followed by cases of apparent typhoid fever. The parasites may be found in the remnants of the ham or sausages used on the occasion. The worms may ·be discovered in the stools. The stools should be spread on a glass plate or black background and examined with a low-power lens, when the trichinæ are seen as small, glistening, silvery threads. In doubtful cases the diagnosis may be made by the removal of a small fragment of muscle. A special harpoon has been devised for this purpose by means of which a small portion of the biceps or of the pectoral muscle may be readily removed. Under cocaine anæsthesia an incision may be made and a small fragment removed. The disease may be mistaken for acute rheumatism, particularly as the pains are so severe on movement, but there is no special swelling of the joints. The great increase in the eosinophiles in the blood is, as mentioned above, a most suggestive point in diagnosis. The tenderness is in the muscles both on pressure and on movement. The intensity of the gastro-intestinal symptoms in some cases has led to the diagnosis of cholera. Many of the former epidemics were doubtless described as typhoid fever, which the severer cases, owing to the prolonged fever, the sweats, the delirium, dry tongue, and gastro-intestinal symptoms, somewhat resemble. The pains in the muscles, with tension and swelling, œdema, particularly about the eyes, and shortness of breath are the most important diagnostic points. Under acute myositis reference has already been made to the cases which closely resemble trichiniasis. The epidemic in 1879 on board the training ship Cornwall presented symptoms similar to those of trichiniasis. One patient died. Two months after burial the body was examined, and living and dead nematode worms were found which, as Bastian showed, were not the trichina, but a rhabditis. They were probably not parasitic, but entered the body of the cadet after burial.

---

* Journal of Experimental Medicine, vol. iii.

Prophylaxis.—It is not definitely known how swine become diseased. It has been thought that they are infected from rats about slaughter-houses, but it is just as reasonable to believe that the rats are infected by eating portions of the trichinous flesh of swine. The swine should, as far as possible, be grain-fed, and not, as is so common, allowed to eat offal. The most satisfactory prophylaxis is the complete cooking of pork and sausages, and to this custom in England, France, South Germany, and particularly in this country, immunity is largely due.

Treatment.—If it has been discovered within twenty-four or thirty-six hours that a large number of persons have eaten infected meat, the indications are to thoroughly evacuate the gastro-intestinal canal. Purgatives of rhubarb and senna may be given, or an occasional dose of calomel. Glycerin has been recommended in large doses in order that by passing into the intestines it may by its hygroscopic properties destroy the worm. Male-fern, kamala, santonin, and thymol have all been recommended in this stage. Turpentine may be tried in full doses. There is no doubt that diarrhœa in the first week or ten days of the infection is distinctly favorable. The indications in the stage of invasion are to relieve the pains, to secure sleep, and to support the patient's strength. There are no medicines which have any influence upon the embryos in their migration through the muscles.

III. ANCHYLOSTOMIASIS.

The *Uncinaria* (*Dochmius, Strongylus*) *duodenalis,* also known as the *Sclerostomum* or *Anchylostomum duodenale,* is the only strongyle harmful to man. It belongs to the same family as the *Sclerostomum equinum,* which causes the verminous aneurism in the horse. The parasites live in the upper portion of the small intestine, chiefly in the jejunum. They are easily seen, the male being from 6 to 10 mm. long, and the female from 10 to 18 mm. The mouth is provided with a series of tooth-like hooks, by means of which the parasite attaches itself to the mucous membrane. The male has a prominent expansion or bursa at the tail end. The existence of the parasite has long been known, but it was not thought to be pathogenic until Griesinger demonstrated its association with the Egyption chlorosis. It has also been shown to be the cause of the anæmia to which miners and brick-makers are subject. Throughout Europe the disease has been widely spread by the employment of Italian and Polish laborers. In certain Italian provinces it is extremely prevalent and serious. It occurs in the Indies, in Brazil, and the West Indies, and has been described in Jamaica (Strachan). Dobson has shown that there is an extraordinary prevalence of the worm even among healthy coolies in India and Assam, amounting to 80 per cent. Dolley states that the parasite was described many years ago by physicians in the Southern States, but no recent observations upon the disease have been made in this country.

Symptoms.—The parasites withdraw blood by suction, and the symptoms result from this slow depletion. That the parasites produce a toxic substance has also been suggested. In the early stage there may only be gastric or gastro-intestinal disturbance, but if the parasites are present in large numbers anæmia is gradually produced and constitutes the characteristic feature of the disease. The Egyptian chlorosis, brick-maker's anæmia, tunnel anæmia, miner's cachexia, and mountain anæmia are due to this cause. The clinical course is variable. In some instances the anæmia develops acutely and reaches a high grade within a short time, causing great shortness of breath and œdema. There is serious disturbance of nutrition, sometimes diarrhœa and colicky pains; but the most pronounced symptom is the pallor and the associated phenomena of chronic anæmia, with debility and wasting. The lesions of the intestines are those of chronic catarrh, and small hæmorrhages occur in the mucosa. The worms are found within 2 metres of the pylorus, often with their heads buried in the mucosa. Dilatation and hypertrophy of the heart have been found in many cases. Sandwith states that in Egypt the disease is most common in peasants who work in the damp earth, many of whom are earth-eaters.

The diagnosis is not difficult. The eggs, which are abundant in the stools, are oval, about 52 μ long by 32 μ broad, and possess a thin, transparent shell. There is no operculum, as in the ovum of the oxyuris, and eggs found in the fæces are in various stages of segmentation. The larvæ develop in moist earth and readily get into the drinking-water, through which infection occurs.

The systematic employment of latrines and the boiling of all water used for drinking purposes are the important prophylactic measures. Thymol, recommended by Bozzolo, is a specific, and should be given in large doses, 2 grammes (in wafers) at 8 A. M. and 2 grammes at 10 A. M. (Sandwith). The diet should be milk and soup. Two hours after the second dose of thymol a purge of castor oil or magnesia is given. If necessary, the treatment may be repeated in a week.

IV. Filariasis.

Zoölogically the *Filaria sanguinis hominis* is as yet *sub judice*. Manson's views are as follows:

Under the general term *Filaria sanguinis hominis* three species of nematodes are included:

1. *Filaria bancrofti,* Cobold, 1877. This is the ordinary blood filaria. The embryos are found in the peripheral circulation only during sleep or at night. The mosquito is the intermediate host. The embryos measure 270 to 340 μ long by 7 to 11 μ broad; tail pointed. The adult male measures 83 mm. long by 0.407 mm. broad; the tail forms two turns of a spiral. The adult female measures 155 mm. long by 0.715 mm. broad; vulva 2.56 mm. from anterior extremity; eggs 38 μ by 14 μ. This is the species to which the hæmatochyluria and elephantiasis are attributed.

2. *Filaria diurna,* Manson, 1891. The larvæ agree with the preceding, except that Manson indicates the absence of granules in the axis of the body. The worms occur in the peripheral circulation only during the day, or when the patient stays awake. Manson suspects that the *Filaria loa* represents the adult stage.

3. *Filaria perstans,* Manson, 1891. Only the embryos are known. These

are much smaller than the preceding—200 μ long, posterior extremity obtuse, anterior extremity with a sort of retractile rostellum.

This is the species to which Manson would attribute the sleeping-sickness of the negroes. He is also inclined to regard the *Filaria perstans* as the cause of *craw-craw*, a papillo-pustular skin eruption of the west coast of Africa, which is probably the same as Nielly's *dermatose parasitaire*, the parasite of which was called by Blanchard *Rhabditis Niellyi*. Manson has shown that in the blood of the aboriginal Indians in British Guiana there are two forms of filarial embryos, which differ somewhat from the ordinary types. Daniels and Ozzard have shown the extraordinary prevalence of these parasites in the aboriginals—fully 58 per cent. Recently Daniels has found the mature filariæ in two subjects in the upper part of the mesentery, near the pancreas and in the subpericardial fat.

The most important of these is the *Filaria bancrofti*, which produces the hæmatochyluria and the lymph-scrotum.

The female produces an extraordinary number of embryos, which enter the blood current through the lymphatics. Each embryo is within its shell, which is elongated, scarcely perceptible, and in no way impedes the movements. They are about the ninetieth part of an inch in length and the diameter of a red blood-corpuscle in thickness, so that they readily pass through the capillaries. They move with the greatest activity, and form very striking and readily recognized objects in a blood-drop under the microscope. A remarkable feature is the periodicity in the occurrence of the embryos in the blood. In the daytime they are almost or entirely absent, whereas at night, in typical cases, they are present in large numbers. If, however, as Stephen Mackenzie has shown, the patient, reversing his habits, sleeps during the day, the periodicity is reversed. The further development of the embryos appears to be associated with the mosquito, which at night sucks the blood and in this way frees them from the body. Some slight development takes place within the body of the mosquito, and it is probable that the embryos are set free in the water after the death of the host. The further development is not known, but it probably occurs in drinking-water. The filariæ may be present in the body without causing any symptoms. In animals blood filariæ are very common and rarely cause inconvenience. It is only when the adult worms or the ova block the lymph channels that certain definite symptoms occur. Manson suggests that it is the ova (prematurely discharged), which are considerably shorter and thicker than the full-grown embryos, which block the lymph channels and produce the conditions of hæmatochyluria, elephantiasis, and lymph-scrotum.

The parasite is widely distributed, particularly in tropical and sub-tropical countries. Guitéras has shown that the disease prevails extensively in the Southern States, and since his paper appeared contributions have been made by Matas, of New Orleans, Mastin, of Mobile, and De Saussure, of Charleston.

The effects produced may be described under the following conditions:

(a) *Hæmatochyluria.*—Without any external manifestations, and in many cases without special disturbance of health, the subject from time to time passes urine of an opaque white, milky appearance, or bloody, or a chylous fluid which on settling shows a slightly reddish clot. The urine may be normal in quantity or increased. The condition is usually intermittent, and the patient may pass normal urine for weeks or months at a time. Microscopically, the chylous urine contains minute molecular fat granules, usually red blood-corpuscles in various amounts. The embryos were first discovered by Demarquay, at Paris (1863), and in the urine by Wucherer, at Bahia, in 1866. It is remarkable for how long the condition may persist without serious impairment of the health. A patient, sent to me by Dawson, of Charleston, has had hæmatochyluria intermittently for eighteen years. The only inconvenience has been in the passage of the blood-clots which collect in the bladder. At times he has also uneasy sensations in the lumbar region. The embryos are present in his blood at night in large numbers. Chyluria is not always due to the filaria. The non-parasitic form of the disease has already been considered.

Opportunities for studying the anatomical condition of these cases rarely occur. In the case described by Stephen Mackenzie the renal and peritoneal lymph plexuses were enormously enlarged, extending from the diaphragm to the pelvis. The thoracic duct above the diaphragm was impervious.

(b) *Lymph-scrotum* and certain forms of *elephantiasis* are also caused by the filaria. In the former the tissues of the scrotum are enormously thickened and the distended lymph-vessels may be plainly seen. A clear, sometimes a turbid, fluid follows puncture of the skin. The parasites are not always to be found. I have examined two typical cases without finding filaria in the exuded fluids or in the blood at night. So also the majority of cases of elephantiasis which occur in this country are non-parasitic. In China it is stated that the parasites occur in all these cases.*

Treatment.—So far as I know, no drug destroys the embryos in the blood. In infected districts the drinking-water should be boiled or filtered. In cases of chyluria the patients should use a dry diet and avoid all excess of fat. The chyle may disappear quite rapidly from the urine under these measures, but it does not necessarily indicate that the case is cured. So long as clots and albumin are present the leak in the lymphoid varix is not healed, although the fat, not being supplied to the chyle, may not be present. A single tumblerful of milk will at once give ocular proof of the patency or otherwise of the rupture in the varix (Manson).

The surgical treatment of some of these cases is most successful, particularly in the removal of the adult filariæ from the enlarged lymph-glands, especially in the groin. Maitland states that during the past seven years 25 operations of this kind have been performed without serious symptoms.

V. DRACONTIASIS (*Guinea-worm Disease*).

The *Filaria* or *Dracunculus medinensis* is a widely spread parasite in parts of Africa and the East Indies. In the United States instances occa-

---

* For full consideration of the subject of congenital occlusion and dilatation of lymph channels, see the work on this subject by Samuel C. Busey, New York, 1878.

sionally occur. Jarvis reports a case in a post chaplain who had lived at Fortress Monroe, Va., for thirty years. Van Harlingen's patient, a man aged forty-seven, had never lived out of Philadelphia, so that the worm must be included among the parasites of this country. A majority of the cases reported in American journals have been imported.

Only the female is known. It develops in the subcutaneous and intermuscular connective tissues and produces vesicles and abscesses. In the large majority of the cases the parasite is found in the leg. Of 181 cases, in 124 the worm was found in the feet, 33 times in the leg, and 11 times in the thigh. It is usually solitary, though there are cases on record in which six or more have been present. It is cylindrical in form, about 2 mm. in diameter, and from 50 to 80 cm. in length.

The worm gains entrance to the system through the stomach, not through the skin, as was formerly supposed. It is probable that both male and female are ingested; but the former dies and is discharged, while the latter after impregnation penetrates the intestine and attains its full development in the subcutaneous tissues, where it may remain quiescent for a long time and can be felt beneath the skin like a bundle of string. The worm contains an enormous number of living embryos, and to enable them to escape she travels slowly downward head first, and, as mentioned, usually reaches the foot or ankle. The head then penetrates the skin and the epidermis forms a little vesicle, which ruptures, and a small ulcer is left, at the bottom of which the head often protrudes. The distended uterus ruptures and the embryos are discharged in a whitish fluid. After getting rid of them the worm will spontaneously leave her host. In the water the embryos develop in the cyclops—a small crustacean—and it seems likely that man is infected by drinking the water containing these developed larvæ.

When the worm first appears it should not be disturbed, as after parturition she may leave spontaneously. When the worm begins to come out a common procedure is to roll it round a portion of smooth wood and in this way prevent the retraction, and each day wind a little more until the entire worm is withdrawn. It is stated that special care must be taken to prevent tearing of the worm, as disastrous consequences sometimes follow, probably from the irritation caused by the migration of the embryos.

The parasite may be excised entire, or killed by injections of bichloride of mercury (1 to 1,000). It is stated that the leaves of the plant called *amarpattee* are almost a specific in the disease. Asafœtida in full doses is said to kill the worm.

In East Africa Kolb states that he found in the abdominal cavity of a recently killed native Massai several large nematode worms believed to be allied to the filaria medinensis. He thinks this parasite is possibly associated with what is known as the Massai disease, characterized by attacks of fever lasting some three days, with tenderness of the abdomen and vomiting. Kolb thinks that in these cases the filariæ which have become encysted about the liver "as a normal event in their life history burst their cysts, the contents escaping into the peritoneal cavity, thereby giving rise to the symptoms." The subject is one which requires further investigation.

23

VI. Other Nematodes.

(*a*) Among less important filarian worms parasitic in man the following may be mentioned: *Filaria loa,* which is a cylindrical worm of about 3 cm. in length and whose habitat is beneath the conjunctiva. It has been found on the West African coast, in Brazil, and in the West Indies. *Filaria lentis,* which has been found in a cataract. Three specimens have been found together. *Filaria labialis,* which has been found in a pustule in the upper lip. *Filaria hominis oris,* which was described by Leidy, from the mouth of a child. *Filaria bronchialis,* which has been found occasionally in the trachea and bronchi. This parasite has been seen in a few cases in the bronchioles and in the lungs. There is no evidence that it ever produces an extensive verminous bronchitis similar to that which I have described in dogs. *Filaria immitis*—the common *Filaria sanguinis* of the dog—of which Bowlby has described two cases in man. In one case with hæmaturia female worms were found in the portal vein, and the ova were present in the thickened bladder wall and in the ureters.

(*b*) *Trichocephalus dispar (Whip-worm).*—This parasite is not infrequently found in the cæcum and large intestine of man. It measures from 4 to 5 cm. in length, the male being somewhat shorter than the female. The worm is readily recognized by the remarkable difference between the anterior and posterior portions. The former, which forms at least three fifths of the body, is extremely thin and hair-like in contrast to the thick hinder portion of the body, which in the female is conical and pointed, and in the male more obtuse and usually rolled like a spring. The eggs are oval, lemon-shaped, 0.05 mm. in length, and each is provided with a button-like projection.

The number of the worms found is variable, as many as a thousand having been counted. It is a widely spread parasite. In parts of Europe it occurs in from 10 to 30 per cent of all bodies examined, but in this country it is not so common. The trichocephalus rarely causes symptoms. It has been thought by certain physicians in the East to be the cause of beri-beri. Several cases have been reported recently in which profound anæmia has occurred in connection with this parasite, usually with diarrhœa. Enormous numbers may be present, as in Rudolphi's case, without producing any symptoms.

The diagnosis is readily made by the examination of the fæces, which contain, sometimes in great abundance, the characteristic lemon-shaped, hard, dark-brown eggs.

(*c*) *Dioctophyme gigas (Eustrongylus gigas).*—This enormous nematode, the male of which measures about a foot in length and the female about three feet, occurs in very many animals and has occasionally been met with in man. It is usually found in the renal region and may entirely destroy the kidney.

(*d*) *Strongyloides intestinalis.*—Under this name are now included the small nematode worms found in the fæces and formerly described as *Anguillula stercoralis, Anguillula intestinalis,* and *Rhabdonema intestinale.* This parasite occurs abundantly in the stools of the endemic diarrhœa of hot countries, and has been specially described by the French in the diarrhœa of Cochin-China. It occurs also in Brazil, and has been found in Italy in connection with the anchylostoma in cases of miners' anæmia. It is stated that the worms occupy all parts of the intestines, and have even been found in the biliary and pancreatic ducts. It is only when they are in very large numbers that they produce severe diarrhœa and anæmia.

ACANTHOCEPHALA (*Thorn-headed Worms*).

The *Gigantorhynchus* or *Echinorhynchus gigas* is a common parasite in the intestine of the hog and attains a large size. The larvæ develop in cockchafer grubs. The American intermediate host is the June bug (Stiles). Lambl found a small *Echinorhynchus* in the intestine of a boy. Welch's specimen, which was found encysted in the intestine of a soldier at Netley, is stated by Cobbold probably not to have been an *Echinorhynchus*. Recently a case of *Echinorhynchus moniliformis* has been described in Italy by Grassi and Calandruccio.

V. DISEASES CAUSED BY CESTODES

(*Tape-worms; Hydatid Disease*).

Man harbors the adult parasites in the small intestine, the larval forms in the muscles and solid organs.

I. INTESTINAL CESTODES; TAPE-WORMS.

(*a*) *Tænia solium*, or pork tape-worm. This is not a common form in this country. It is much more frequent in parts of Europe and Asia. When mature it is from 6 to 12 feet in length. The head is small, round, not so large as the head of a pin, and provided with four sucking disks and a double row of hooklets; hence it is called, in contradistinction to the other form in man, the armed tape-worm. To the head succeeds a narrow, thread-like neck, then the segments, or proglottides, as they are called. The segments possess both male and female generative organs, and about every four hundred and fiftieth becomes mature and contains ripe ova. The worm attains its full growth in from three to three and a half months, after which time the segments are continuously shed and appear in the stools. The segments are about 1 cm. in length and from 7 to 8 mm. in breadth. Pressed between glass plates the uterus is seen as a median stem with about eight to fourteen lateral branches. There are many thousands of ova in each ripe segment, and each ovum consists of a firm shell, inside of which is a little embryo, provided with six hooklets. The segments are continuously passed, and if the ova are to attain further development they must be taken into the stomach, either of a pig, or of man himself. The egg-shells are digested, the six-hooked embryos become free, and passing from the stomach reach various parts of the body (the liver, muscles, brain, or eye), where they develop into the larvæ or cysticerci. A hog under these circumstances is said to be *measled,* and the cysticerci are spoken of as measles or bladder worms.

The *tænia solium* received its name because it was thought to exist as a solitary parasite in the bowel, but two or three or even more worms may occur.

(*b*) *Tænia saginata* or *mediocanellata*—the unarmed or beef tape-worm. This is a longer and larger parasite than the *Tænia solium.* It is certainly the common tape-worm of this country. Of scores of specimens which I have examined almost all were of this variety. According to Bérenger-Férand it has spread rapidly in western Europe, owing probably to the importation of beef and live-stock from the Mediterranean basin. It may attain a length of 15 or 20 feet, or more. The head is large in comparison with that of the *Tænia solium,* and measures over 2 mm. in breadth. It is square-shaped and provided with four large sucking disks, but there are no hooklets. The ripe segments are from 17 to 18 mm. in length, and from 8 to 10 mm. in breadth. The uterus consists of a median stem with from fifteen to thirty-five lateral branches, which are given off more dichotomously than in the *Tænia solium.* The ova are somewhat larger, and the shell is thicker, but the two forms can scarcely be distinguished by their ova. The ripe segments are passed as in the *tænia solium,* and are ingested by cattle, in the flesh or organs of which the eggs develop into the bladder worms or cysticerci. No instance of the cysticercus of the *tænia saginata* has, so far as I know, been reported in man.

Of other forms of tape-worm may be mentioned:

(*c*) *Dipylidium caninum (Tænia elliptica, Tænia cucumerina).* A small parasite very common in the dog and occasionally found in man; the larvæ develop in the lice and fleas of the dog.

(*d*) *Hymenolepsis diminuta (Tænia flavo-punctata).* A small cestode was found in the intestine of a child in Boston, and has since been met with in one or two cases. It is common in rats. The larvæ develop in *Lepidoptera* and in beetles.

(*e*) *Hymenolepsis nana (Tænia nana)* occurs not infrequently in Italy; the *Davainea Madagascariensis (Tænia Madagascariensis)* is a rare form.

(*f*) *Tænia confusa,* a new species described by Ward.

(*g*) *Bothriocephalus latus.* A cestode worm found only in certain districts bordering on the Baltic Sea, in parts of Switzerland, and in Japan. So far as I know, it has not been found in this country except in a few imported cases. The parasite is large and long, measuring from 25 to 30 feet or more. Its head is different from that of the tænia, as it possesses two lateral grooves or pits and has no hooklets. The larvæ develop in the peritonæum and muscles of the pike and other fish, and it has been shown experimentally that they grow into the adult worm when eaten by man.

Symptoms.—These parasites are found at all ages. They are not uncommon in children and are occasionally found in sucklings. W. T. Plant refers to a number of cases in children under two years, and there is one in the literature in which it is stated that the tape-worm was found in an infant five days old.

The parasites may cause no disturbance and are rarely dangerous. A knowledge of the existence of the worm is generally a source of worry and anxiety; the patient may have considerable distress and complain of abdominal pains, nausea, diarrhœa, and sometimes anæmia. Occasionally the appetite is ravenous. In women and in nervous patients the constitutional disturbance may be considerable, and we not infrequently see great mental depression and even hypochondria. Various nervous phenomena, such as chorea, convulsions, or epilepsy, are believed to be caused by the parasites. Such effects, however, are very rare. The *Bothriocephalus* may cause a severe and even fatal form of anæmia, which has been described fully in a recent monograph by Schaumann, of Helsingfors.

The *diagnosis* is never doubtful. The presence of the segments is distinctive. The ova, too, may be recognized in the stools. It makes but little difference as to the form of tape-worm, but the ripe segments of the *Tænia saginata* are larger and broader, and show differences in the generative system as already mentioned.

The *prophylaxis* is most important. Careful attention should be given to three points. First, all tape-worm segments should be burned. They should never be thrown into the water-closet or outside; secondly, careful inspection of meat at the abattoirs; and thirdly, cooking the meat sufficiently to kill the parasites.

In the case of the beef measles, the distribution of the parasites, as given by Ostertag, shows that the muscles of the jaw are much more frequently affected than other parts—360 times, while other organs were infected but 55 times. Sometimes there are instances of general infection. Stiles states that no exact statistics have been published for this country. In Berlin the proportion of cattle infected in 1892–'93 was about 1 to 672. Cold storage kills the cysticercus usually within three weeks. The measles are more readily overlooked in beef than in pork, as they do not present such an opaque white color.

In the examination of hogs for cysticerci " particular stress should be laid upon the tongue, the muscles of mastication, and the muscles of the shoulder, neck, and diaphragm " (Stiles). According to Stiles, statistics for the United States are not available. American hogs are comparatively free. In Prussia one hog is infected in about every 637. Specimens have been found alive twenty-nine days after slaughtering. In the examination of 1,000 hogs in Montreal, Dr. Clement and I found 76 instances of cysticerci. For full details with reference to the inspection of meat for animal parasites, the practitioner is referred to the work of Dr. Stiles in Bulletin No. 19, United States Department of Agriculture, 1898.

Treatment.—For two days prior to the administration of the remedies the patient should take a very light diet and have the bowels moved occasionally by a saline cathartic. The practitioner has the choice of a large number of drugs. As a rule, the male fern acts promptly and well. The ethereal extract, in 2-drachm doses, may be given fasting, and followed in the course of a couple of hours by a brisk purgative. This usually succeeds in bringing away a large portion, but not always the entire worm.

A combination of the remedies is sometimes very effective. An infusion is made of pomegranate root, half an ounce; pumpkin seeds, 1 ounce; powdered ergot, a drachm; and boiling water, 10 ounces. To an emulsion of the male fern (a drachm of ethereal extract), made with acacia powder, 2 minims of croton oil are added. The patient should have had a low diet the previous day and have taken a dose of salts in the evening. The emulsion and infusion are mixed and taken fasting at nine in the morning.

The pomegranate root is a very efficient remedy, and may be given as an infusion of the bark, 3 ounces of which may be macerated in 10 ounces of water and then reduced to one half by evaporation. The entire quantity is then taken in divided doses. It occasionally produces colic, but is a very effective remedy. The active principle of the root, pelletierine, is now much employed. It is given in doses of 6 to 8 or even 10 grains, with a little tannin (grs. v) in sweetened water, and is followed in an hour by a purge.

Pumpkin seeds are sometimes very efficient. Three or 4 ounces should be carefully bruised and then macerated for twelve or fourteen hours and the entire quantity taken and followed in an hour by a purge. Of other remedies, koosso, turpentine in ounce doses in honey, and kamala may be mentioned.

Unless the head is brought away, the parasite continues to grow, and within a few months the segments again appear. Some instances are extraordinarily obstinate. Doubtless almost everything depends upon the exposure of the worm. The head and neck may be thoroughly protected beneath the valvulæ conniventes, in which case the remedies may not act. Owing to its armature the *tænia solium* is more difficult to expel. It is probable that no degree of peristalsis could dislodge the head, and unless the worm is killed it does not let go its extraordinarily firm hold on the mucous membrane. If warm water be put in the commode the worm is less likely to contract and be broken.

II. Visceral Cestodes.

Whereas adult tæniæ may give rise to little or no disturbance, and rarely, if ever, prove directly fatal, the affections caused by the larvæ or immature forms in the solid organs are serious and important. There are two chief cestode larvæ known to frequent man (*a*) the *Cysticercus cellulosæ*, the larva of the *Tænia solium*, and (*b*) the *Echinococcus*, the larva of the *Tænia echinococcus*. The *Cysticercus tæniæ saginatæ* has been found only two or three times in man.

I. **Cysticercus cellulosæ.**—When man accidentally takes into his stomach the ripe ova of *Tænia solium* he is liable to become the intermediate host, a part usually played for this tape-worm by the pig. This accident may occur in an individual the subject of *Tænia solium*, in which case the mature proglottides either themselves wander into the stomach or, what is more likely, are forced into the organ in attacks of prolonged vomiting. Of course the accidental ingestion from the outside of a few ova is quite possible, and the liability of infection should always be borne in mind in handling the segments of the worm.

The symptoms depend entirely upon the number of ova ingested and the localities reached. In the hog the cysticerci produce very little disturbance. The muscles, the connective tissue, and the brain may be swarming with the measles, as they are called, and yet the nutrition is maintained and the animal does not appear to be seriously incommoded. In the invasion period, if large numbers of the parasites are taken, there is, in all probability, constitutional disturbance; certainly this is seen in the calf, when fed with the ripe segments of *Tænia saginata*.

In man a few cysticerci lodged beneath the skin or in the muscles may cause no damage, and in time the larvæ die and become calcified. They are occasionally found in dissection subjects or in post mortems as ovoid white bodies in the muscles or subcutaneous tissue. In this country they are very rare. I have seen but one instance in my post-mortem experience. Depending on the number and the locality specially affected, the symptoms may be grouped into general, cerebro-spinal, and ocular. In 155 cases compiled by Stiles, the parasite in 117 was found in the brain, in 32 in the muscles, in 9 in the heart, in 3 in the lungs, subcutaneously in 5, in the liver in 2.

(1) *General.*—As a rule the invasion of the larvæ in man, unless in very large numbers, does not cause very definite symptoms. It occasionally happens, however, that a striking picture is produced. For instance, a patient was admitted to my wards very stiff and helpless, so much so that he had to be assisted upstairs and into bed. He complained of numbness and tingling in the extremities and general weakness, so that at first he was thought to have a peripheral neuritis. At the examination, however, a number of painful subcutaneous nodules were discovered, which proved on excision to be the cysticerci. Altogether 75 could be felt subcutaneously, and from the soreness and stiffness they probably existed in large numbers in the muscles. There were none in his eyes, and he had no symptoms pointing to brain lesions.

(2) *Cerebro-spinal.*—Remarkable symptoms may result from the presence of the cysticerci in the brain and cord. In the silent region they may be abundant without producing any symptoms. I have in my possession the brain of a pig containing scores of "measles," yet the animal in the few moments in which I saw it just prior to death did not present any symptoms to attract attention. In the ventricles of the brain the cysticerci may attain a considerable size, owing to the fact that in regions in which they are unrestrained in their growth, as in the peritonæum, the bladder-like body grows freely. When in the fourth ventricle, remarkable irritative symptoms may be produced. In 1884 I saw with Friedländer in Berlin a case from Riess's wards in which during life there had been symptoms of diabetes and anomalous nervous symptoms. Post mortem, the cysticercus was found beneath the valve of Vieussens, pressing upon the floor of the fourth ventricle.

(3) *Ocular.*—Since von Graefe demonstrated the presence of the cysticercus in the vitreous humor many cases have been placed on record, and it is a condition easily recognized by oculists.

Except in the eye, the diagnosis can rarely be made; when the cysticerci are subcutaneous, one may be excised. It is possible that when numerous throughout the muscles they may be seen under the tongue, in which situation they may exist in the pig in numbers.

II. **Echinococcus Disease.**—The hydatid worms or echinococci are the larvæ of the *Tænia echinococcus* of the dog. This is a tiny cestode not more than 4 or 5 mm. in length, consisting of only three or four segments, of which the terminal one alone is mature, and has a length of about 2 mm. and a breadth of 0.6 mm. The head is small and provided with four sucking disks and a rostellum with a double row of hooklets. This is an exceedingly rare parasite in the dog. Cobbold states that he has never met with a natural specimen in England. Leidy had not one in his large collection. I have not met with an instance in this country, nor do I know of its ever having been described. The only specimens in my cabinet I procured experimentally by feeding a dog with echinococcus cysts from an ox. The worms are so small that they may be readily overlooked, since they form small white, thread-like bodies closely adherent among the villi of the small intestines. The ripe segment contains about 5,000 eggs, which attain their development in the solid organs of various animals, particularly the hog and ox, more rarely the horse and the sheep. In some countries man is a common intermediate host, owing to the accidental ingestion of the ova.

Development.—The little six-hooked embryo, freed from the eggshell by digestion, burrows through the intestinal wall and reaches the peritoneal cavity or the muscles; it may enter the portal vessels and be carried to the liver. It may enter the systemic vessels, and, passing the pulmonary capillaries, as it is protoplasmic and elastic, may reach the brain or other parts. Once having reached its destination, it undergoes the following changes: The hooklets disappear and the little embryo is gradually converted into a small cyst which presents two distinct layers—an external, laminated, cuticular membrane or capsule, and an internal, granular, parenchymatous layer, the endocyst. The little cyst or vesicle contains a clear fluid. There is more or less reaction in the neighboring tissues, and the cyst in time has a fibrous investment. When this primary cyst or vesicle has attained a certain size, buds develop from the parenchymatous layer, which are gradually converted into cysts, presenting a structure identical with that of the original cyst, namely, an elastic chitinous membrane lined with a granular parenchymatous layer. These secondary or daughter cysts are at first connected with the lining membrane of the primary cyst, but are soon set free. In this way the parent cyst as it grows may contain a dozen or more daughter cysts. Inside these daughter cysts a similar process may occur, and from buds in the walls granddaughter cysts are developed. From the granular layer of the parent and daughter cysts buds arise which develop into brood capsules. From the lining membrane the little outgrowths arise and gradually develop into bodies known as scolices, which represent in reality the head of the *Tænia echinococcus* and present four sucking disks and a circle of hooklets. Each scolex is capable when transferred to the intestines of a dog of developing into an adult tape-worm. The difference between the ovum of an ordinary tape-worm, such as the

Tænia solium, and the *Tænia echinococcus* is in this way very striking. In the former case the ovum develops into a single larva—the *Cysticercus cellulosæ*—whereas the egg of the *Tænia echinococcus* develops into a cyst which is capable of multiplying enormously and from the lining membrane of which millions of larval tape-worms develop. Ordinarily in man the development of the echinococcus takes place as above mentioned and by an endogenous form in which the secondary and tertiary cysts are contained within the primary; but in animals the formation may be different, as the buds from the primary cyst penetrate between the layers and develop externally, forming the exogenous variety. A third form is the multilocular echinococcus, in which from the primary cysts buds develop which are cut off completely and are surrounded by thick capsules of a connective tissue, which join together and ultimately form a hard mass represented by strands of connective tissue enclosing alveolar spaces about the size of peas or a little larger. In these spaces are found the remnants of the echinococcus cyst, occasionally the scolices or hooklets, but they are often sterile.

The fluid of the echinococcus cysts is clear and limpid, and has a specific gravity from 1.005 to 1.009. It does not contain albumin, but may contain traces of sugar. As a rule, the cysts, when not degenerated, contain the hydatid heads or scolices or the characteristic hooklets.

Changes in the Cyst.—It is not known definitely how long the echinococcus remains alive, but it probably lives many years—according to some authors as long as twenty years. The most common change is death and the gradual inspissation of the contents and conversion of the cyst into a mass containing putty-like or granular material which may be partially calcified. Remnants of the chitinous cyst wall or hooklets may be found. These obsolete hydatid cysts are not infrequently found in the liver. A more serious termination is rupture, which may take place into a serous sac, or perforation may take place externally, when the cysts are discharged, as into the bronchi or alimentary canal or urinary passages. More unfavorable are the instances in which rupture occurs into the bile-passages or into the inferior cava. Recovery may follow the rupture and discharge of the hydatids externally. Sudden death has been known to follow the rupture. A third and very serious mode of termination is suppuration, which may occur spontaneously or follow rupture and is found most frequently in the liver. Large abscesses may be formed which contain the hydatid membranes.

Geographical Distribution of the Echinococcus.—The disease prevails most extensively in those countries in which man is brought into close contact with the dog, particularly when, as in Australia, the dogs are used extensively for herding sheep, the animal in which the larval form of the *Tænia echinococcus* is most frequently found. In Iceland the cases are very numerous. In Europe the disease is not uncommon. In this country it is extremely rare and a great majority of all cases are in foreigners. Up to July, 1891, I have been able to find in the literature (and in the museums) only 85 cases in the United States and Canada. In the Icelandic settlements of Manitoba many instances occur. A. H. Ferguson, who has operated on a number of cases at the Winnipeg General Hospital, states that between forty-five and fifty persons with echinococcus disease have been treated in Winnipeg since 1874, the date of the Icelandic immigration.

Distribution in the Body.—Of the 1,862 cases comprised in the statistics of Davaine, Cobbold, Finsen, and Neisser, the parasites existed in the liver in 953, in the intestinal canal in 163, in the lung or pleura in 153, in the kidneys, bladder, and genitals in 186, in the brain and spinal canal in 127, bone 61, heart and blood-vessels 61, other organs 158. Of the 85 cases in this country, the liver was the seat of the disease in 59. Of 50 consecutive cases treated by Mosler at the Greifswald clinic, 36 involved the liver, 10 the lungs, 3 the right kidney, and 1 the spleen.

Symptoms.—(*a*) *Hydatids of the Liver.*—Small cysts may cause no disturbance; large and growing cysts produce signs of tumor of the liver with great increase in the size of the organ. Naturally the physical signs depend much upon the situation of the growth. Near the anterior surface in the epigastric region the tumor may form a distinct prominence and have a tense, firm feeling, sometimes with fluctuation. A not infrequent situation is to the left of the suspensory ligament, forming a tumor which pushes up the heart and causes an extensive area of dulness in the lower sternal and left hypochondriac regions. In the right lobe, if the tumor is on the posterior surface, the enlargement of the organ is chiefly upward into the pleura and the vertical area of dulness in the posterior axillary line is increased. Superficial cysts may give what is known as the hydatid fremitus. If the tumor is palpated lightly with the fingers of the left hand and percussed at the same time with those of the right, there is felt a vibration or trembling movement which persists for a certain time. It is not always present, and it is doubtful whether it is peculiar to the hydatid tumors or is due, as Briançon held, to the collision of the daughter cysts. Very large cysts are accompanied by feelings of pressure or dragging in the hepatic region, sometimes actual pain. The general condition of the patient is at first good and the nutrition little, if at all, interfered with. Unless some of the accidents already referred to occur, the symptoms indeed may be trifling and due only to the pressure or weight of the tumor.

Suppuration of the cyst changes the clinical picture into one of pyæmia. There are rigors, sweats, more or less jaundice, and rapid loss of weight. Perforation may occur into the stomach, colon, pleura, bronchi, or externally, and in some instances recovery has taken place. Perforation into the pericardium and inferior vena cava is fatal. In the latter case the daughter cysts have been found in the heart, plugging the tricuspid orifice and the pulmonary artery. Perforation of the bile-passages causes intense jaundice, and may lead to suppurative cholangitis.

An interesting symptom connected with the rupture of hydatid cysts is the development of urticaria, which may also follow aspiration of the cysts. Brieger has separated a highly toxic material from the fluid, and to it the symptoms of poisoning may be due.

Diagnosis.—Cysts of moderate size may exist without producing symptoms. Large multiple echinococci may cause great enlargement with irregularity of the outline, and such a condition persisting for any time with retention of the health and strength suggests hydatid disease. An irregular, painless enlargement, particularly in the left lobe, or the presence of a large, smooth, fluctuating tumor of the epigastric region is also very suggestive, and in this situation, when accessible to palpation, it gives a sensation of a smooth elastic growth and possibly also the hydatid tremor. When suppuration occurs the clinical picture is really that of abscess, and only the existence of previous enlargement of the liver with good health would point to the fact that the suppuration was associated with hydatids. Syphilis may produce irregular enlargement without much disturbance in the health, sometimes also a very definite tumor in the epigastric region, but this is usually firm and not fluctuating. The clinical features may simulate cancer very closely. In a case which I reported the liver was greatly enlarged and there were many nodular tumors in the abdomen. The post mortem showed enormous suppurating hydatid cysts in the left lobe of the liver which had perforated the stomach in two places and also the duodenum. The omentum, mesentery, and pelvis also contained numerous cysts. As a rule, the clinical course of the disease would suffice to separate it clearly from cancer. Dilatation of the gall-bladder and hydronephrosis have both been mistaken for hydatid disease. In the former the mobility of the tumor, its shape, and the mucoid character of the contents suffice for the diagnosis. In some instances of hydronephrosis only the exploratory puncture could distinguish between the conditions. More frequent is the mistake of confounding a hydatid cyst of the right lobe pushing up the pleura with pleural effusion of the right side. The heart may be dislocated, the liver depressed, and dulness, feeble breathing, and diminished fremitus are present in both conditions. Frerichs lays stress upon the different character of the line of dulness; in the echinococcus cyst the upper limit presents a curved line, the maximum of which is usually in the scapular region. Suppurative pleurisy may be caused by the perforation of the cyst. If adhesions result, the perforation takes place into the lung, and fragments of the cysts or small daughter cysts may be coughed up. For diagnostic purposes the exploratory puncture should be used. As stated, the fluid is usually perfectly clear or slightly opalescent, the reaction is neutral, and the specific gravity varies from 1.005 to 1.009. It is non-albuminous, but contains chlorides and sometimes traces of sugar. Hooklets may be found either in the clear fluid or in the suppurating cysts. They are sometimes absent, however, as the cyst may be sterile.

(b) *Echinococcus of the Respiratory System.*—Of 809 cases of single hydatid cyst collected by Thomas in Australia, the lung was affected in 134 cases. The larvæ may develop primarily in the pleura and attain a large size. The symptoms are at first those of compression of the lung and dislocation of the heart. The physical signs are those of fluid in the pleura and the condition could scarcely be distinguished from ordinary effusion. The line of dulness may be quite irregular. As in the echinococcus of the liver, the general condition of the patient may be excellent in spite of the existence of extensive disease. Pleurisy is rarely excited. The cysts may become inflamed and perforate the chest wall. In a case of D. F. Smith's, of Walkertown, Ontario, a girl, aged twenty, had a running sore in the eighth left intercostal space. This was freely opened, and in the pus which flowed out were a number of well-characterized echinococcus cysts of various sizes. The patient recovered.

Echinococci occur more frequently in the lung than in the pleura. If small, they may exist for some time without causing serious symptoms. In their growth they compress the lung and sooner or later lead to inflammatory processes, often to gangrene, and the formation of cavities which connect with the bronchi. Fragments of membrane or small cysts may be expectorated. Hæmorrhage is not infrequent. Perforation into the pleura with empyema is common. A majority of the cases are regarded during life as either phthisis or gangrene, and it is only the detection of the characteristic membranes or the hooklets which leads to the diagnosis. The condition is usually fatal; only a few cases have recovered. Of the 85 American cases, in 6 the cysts occurred in the lung or pleura.

(c) *Echinococcus of the Kidneys.*—In the collected statistics referred to above the genito-urinary system comes second as the seat of hydatid disease, though here the affection is rare in comparison with that of the liver. Of the 85 American cases, there were only 3 in which the kidneys or bladder were involved. The kidney may be converted into an enormous cyst resembling a hydronephrosis.

The diagnosis is only possible by puncture and examination of the fluid. The cyst may perforate into the pelvis of the kidney, and portions of the membrane or cysts may be discharged with the urine, sometimes producing renal colic. I have reported a case in which for many months the patient passed at intervals numbers of small cysts with the urine. The general health was little if at all disturbed, except by the attacks of colic during the passage of the parasites.

(d) *Echinococcus of the Nervous System.*—In this country very few instances have occurred in the brain. One or two reports indicate clearly that the common cystic disease of the choroidal plexuses has been mistaken for hydatids. Davies Thomas, of Australia, has tabulated 97 cases, including some of the *Cysticercus cellulosæ.* According to his statistics, the cyst is more common on the right than on the left side, and is most frequent in the cerebrum.

The symptoms are very indefinite, as a rule, being those of tumor. Persistent headache, convulsions, either limited or general, and gradually developing blindness have been prominent features in many cases.

Multilocular Echinococcus.—This form merits a brief separate description, as it differs so remarkably from the usual type of the disease. It has been met with only in Bavaria, Würtemberg, the adjacent districts of Switzerland, and in the Tyrol. Possett has reported 13 cases from von Rokitansky's clinic at Innsbruck. In the United States cases are occasionally seen. The patient of Delafield and Prudden was a German, who had been in the country five years. For a year previous to his death he was out of health, jaundiced, and somewhat emaciated. A fluctuating tumor was found in the right lumbar and umbilical regions, apparently connected with the liver. This was opened, and death followed from hæmorrhage. About a fourth of the right lobe of the liver was occupied by an irregular cavity with rough, ragged walls, which in places were from one to two inches in thickness and enclosed irregular small cavities. The lamellated cuticula characteristic of the echinococcus cyst was found lining these cavities. In some instances the tumor bears a striking likeness to colloid cancer, as on section it presents a fibrous stroma with cavities containing gelatinous material. They are often sterile—that is, without the hydatid heads or larvæ. This form is almost exclusively confined to the liver, and the symptoms resemble more those of tumor or cirrhosis. The liver is, as a rule, enlarged and smooth, not irregular as in presence of the ordinary echinococcus. Jaundice is a common symptom. The spleen is usually enlarged, there is progressive emaciation, and toward the close hæmorrhages are common.

Treatment of Echinococcus Disease.—Medicines are of no avail. Post-mortem reports show that in a considerable number of cases the parasite dies and the cyst becomes harmless. Operative measures should be resorted to when the cyst is large or troublesome. The simple aspiration of the contents has been successful in a large number of cases, and as it is not in any way dangerous, it may be tried before the more radical procedure of incision and evacuation of the cysts. Suppuration has occasionally followed the puncture. Injections into the sac should not be practised. With modern methods surgeons now open and evacuate the echinococcus cysts with great boldness, and the Australian records, which are the most numerous and important on this subject, show that recovery is the rule in a large proportion of the cases. Suppurative cysts in the liver should be treated as abscess. Naturally the outlook is less favorable. The practical treatment of hydatid disease has been greatly advanced by Australian surgeons. The works of the Australian physicians James Graham and Thomas may be consulted for interesting details in diagnosis and treatment.

VI. PARASITIC ARACHNIDA.

(1) **Pentastomes.**—(a) *Linguatula rhinaria* (*Pentastoma tænioides*) has a somewhat lancet-shaped body, the female being from 3 to 4 inches in length, the male about an inch in length. The body is tapering and marked by numerous rings. The adult worm infests the frontal sinuses and nostrils of the dog, more rarely of the horse. The larval form, which is known as the *Linguatula serrata* (*Pentastomum denticulatum*), is seen in the internal organs, particularly the liver, but has also been found in the kidney. The adult worm has been found in the nostril of man, but is very rare and seldom occasions any inconvenience. The larvæ are by no means uncommon, particularly in parts of Germany.

(b) The *Porocephalus constrictus* (*Pentastomum constrictum*), which is about the length of half an inch, with twenty-three rings on the abdomen, was found by Aitken in the liver and lungs of a soldier of a West Indian regiment.

The parasite is very rare in this country. Flint refers to a Missouri case in which from 75 to 100 of the parasites were expectorated. The liver was enlarged and the parasites probably occupied this region. In 1869 I saw a specimen which had been passed with the urine by a patient of James H. Richardson, of Toronto.

(2) **Demodex (Acarus) folliculorum** (var. **hominis**).—A minute parasite, from 0.3 mm. to 0.4 mm. in length, which lives in the sebaceous follicles, particularly of the face. It is doubtful whether it produces any symptoms. Possibly when in large numbers they may excite inflammation of the follicles, leading to acne.

(3) **Sarcoptes (Acarus) scabiei** (*Itch Insect*).—This is the most important of the arachnid parasites, as it produces troublesome and distressing skin eruptions. The male is 0.23 mm. in length and 0.19 mm. in breadth; the female is 0.45 mm. in length and 0.35 mm. in width. The female can be seen readily with the naked eye and has a pearly-white color. It is not so common a parasite in the United States and Canada as in Europe.

The insect lives in a small burrow, about 1 cm. in length, which it makes for itself in the epidermis. At the end of this burrow the female lives. The male is seldom found. The chief seat of the parasite is in the folds where the skin is most delicate, as in the web between the fingers and toes, the backs of the hands, the axilla, and the front of the abdomen. The head and face are rarely involved. The lesions which result from the presence of the itch insect are very numerous and result largely from the irritation of the scratching. The commonest is a papular and vesicular rash, or, in children, an ecthymatous eruption. The irritation and pustulation which follow the scratching may completely destroy the burrows, but in typical cases there is rarely doubt as to the diagnosis.

The treatment is simple. It should consist of warm baths with a thorough use of a soft soap, after which the skin should be anointed with sulphur ointment, which in the case of children should be diluted. An ointment of naphthol (drachm to the ounce) is very efficacious.

(4) **Leptus autumnalis** (*Harvest Bug*).—This reddish-colored parasite, about half a millimetre in size, is often found in large numbers in fields and in gardens. They attach themselves to animals and man with their sharp proboscides, and the hooklets of their legs produce a great deal of irritation. They are most frequently found on the legs. They are readily destroyed by sulphur ointment or corrosive-sublimate lotions.

Several varieties of ticks are occasionally found on man—the *Ixodes ricinus* and the *Dermacentor americanus,* which are met with in horses and oxen.

VII. PARASITIC INSECTS.

(1) **Pediculi** (*Phthiriasis; Pediculosis*).—There are three varieties of the body louse, which are found only in persons of uncleanly habits.

Pediculus capitis.—The male is from 1 to 1.5 mm. in length and the female nearly 2 mm. The color varies somewhat with the different races of men. It is light gray with a black margin in the European, and very much darker in the negro and Chinese. They are oviparous, and the female lays about sixty eggs, which mature in a week. The ova are attached to the hairs, and can be readily seen as white specks, known popularly as nits. The symptoms are irritation and itching of the scalp. When numerous the insects may excite an eczema or a pustular dermatitis, which causes crusts and scabs, particularly at the back of the head. In the most extreme cases the hair becomes tangled in these crusts and matted together, forming at the occiput a firm mass which is known as *plica polonica*, as it was not infrequent among the Jewish inhabitants of Poland.

Pediculus corporis (vestimentorum).—This is considerably larger than the head louse. It lives on the clothing, and in sucking the blood causes minute hæmorrhagic specks, which are very common about the neck, back, and abdomen. The irritation of the bites may cause urticaria, and the scratching is usually in linear lines. In long-standing cases, particularly in old dissipated characters, the skin becomes rough and greatly pigmented, a condition which has been termed the vagabond's disease—*morbus errorum* —and which may be mistaken for the bronzing of Addison's disease.

Phthirius pubis differs somewhat from the other forms, and is found in the parts of the body covered with short hairs, as the pubes; more rarely the axilla and eyebrows.

The *taches bleuâtres* are stated by French writers to be excited by the irritation of pediculi.

Treatment.—For the *Pediculus capitis*, when the condition is very bad, the hair should be cut short, as it is very difficult to destroy thoroughly all the nits. Repeated saturations of the hair in coal-oil or in turpentine are usually efficacious, or with lotions of carbolic acid, 1 to 50. Scrupulous cleanliness and care are sufficient to prevent recurrence. In the case of the *Pediculus corporis* the clothing should be placed for several hours in a disinfecting oven. To allay the itching a warm bath containing 4 or 5 ounces of bicarbonate of soda is useful. The skin may be rubbed with a lotion of carbolic acid, 2 drachms to the pint, with 2 ounces of glycerin. For the *Phthirius pubis* white precipitate or ordinary mercurial ointment should be used, and the parts should be thoroughly washed two or three times a day with soft soap and water.

(2) **Cimex lectularius** (*Common Bed-bug*).—This parasite is from 3 to 4 mm. in length and has a reddish-brown color. It lives in the crevices of the bedstead and in the cracks in the floor and in the walls. It is nocturnal in its habits. The peculiar odor of the insect is caused by the secretion of a special gland. The parasite possesses a long proboscis, with which it sucks the blood. Individuals differ remarkably in the reaction to the bite of this insect; some are not disturbed in the slightest by them, in others the irritation causes hyperæmia and often intense urticaria. Fumigation with sulphur or scouring with corrosive-sublimate solution or kerosene destroys them. Iron bedsteads should be used.

(3) **Pulex irritans** (*The Common Flea*).—The male is from 2 to 2.5 mm. in length, the female from 3 to 4 mm. The flea is a transient para-

site on man. The bite causes a circular red spot of hyperæmia in the centre of which is a little speck where the boring apparatus has entered. The amount of irritation caused by the bite is variable. Many persons suffer intensely and a diffuse erythema or an irritable urticaria develops; others suffer no inconvenience whatever.

The *Pulex penetrans* (*sand-flea; jigger*) is found in tropical countries, particularly in the West Indies and South America. It is much smaller than the common flea, and not only penetrates the skin, but burrows and produces an inflammation with pustular or vesicular swelling. It most frequently attacks the feet. It is readily removed with a needle. Where they exist in large numbers the essential oils are used on the feet as a preventive.

VIII. MYIASIS.

Of these, the most important are the larvæ of certain diptera, particularly the flesh flies—*Creophila*. The condition is called myiasis.

The most common form is that in which an external wound becomes *living*, as it is called. This myiasis vulnerum is caused by the larvæ of either the blue-bottle or the common flesh fly. The larvæ of the *Lucilia macellaria*, the so-called screw-worm, have been found in the nose, in wounds, and in the vagina after delivery. They can be removed readily with the forceps; if there is any difficulty, thorough cleansing and the application of an antiseptic bandage is sufficient to kill them. The ova of these flies may be deposited in the nostrils, the ears, or the conjunctiva—the myiasis narium, aurium, conjunctivæ. This invasion rarely takes place unless these regions are the seat of disease. In the nose and in the ear the larvæ may cause serious inflammation.

The cutaneous myiasis may be caused by the larvæ of the *Musca vomitoria*, but more commonly by the bot-flies of the ox and sheep, which occasionally attack man. This condition is rare in temperate climates. Matas has described a case in which œstrus larvæ were found in the gluteal region. In parts of Central America the eggs of another bot-fly, the *Dermatobia*, are not infrequently deposited in the skin and produce a swelling very like the ordinary boil.

A specimen of the *Homalomyia scalaris*, one of the privy flies, was sent to me by Dr. Hartin, of Kaslo City, British Columbia, the larvæ of which were passed in large numbers in the stools of a man aged twenty-four, a native of Louisiana. They were present in the stools from May 1 to July 15, 1897.

Myiasis interna may result from the swallowing of the larvæ of the common house fly or of species of the genus *Anthomyia*. There are many cases on record in which the larvæ of the *Musca domestica* have been discharged by vomiting. Instances in which dipterous larvæ have been passed in the fæces are less common. Finlayson, of Glasgow, has recently reported an interesting case in a physician, who, after protracted constipation and pain in the back and sides, passed large numbers of the larvæ of the flower fly—*Anthomyia canicularis*. Among other forms of larvæ or *gentles,* as they are sometimes called, which have been found in the fæces, are those of the common house fly, the blue-bottle fly, and the *Techomyza fusca.* The larvæ of other insects are extremely rare. It is stated that the caterpillar of the tabby moth has been found in the fæces.

Here may be mentioned among the effects of insects the remarkable *urticaria epidemica,* which is caused in some districts by the procession caterpillars, particularly the species *Cnethocampa.* There are districts in the Kahlberger Schweiz which have been rendered almost uninhabitable by the irritative skin eruptions caused by the presence of these insects, the action of which is not necessarily in consequence of actual contact with them.

In Africa the larvæ of the Cayor fly are not uncommonly found beneath the skin, in little boils.

THE INTOXICATIONS
AND SUN-STROKE.

I. ALCOHOLISM.

(1) **Acute Alcoholism.**—When a large quantity of alcohol is taken, its influence on the nervous system is manifested in muscular incoördination, mental disturbance, and, finally, narcosis. The individual presents a flushed, sometimes slightly cyanosed face, a full pulse, with deep but rarely stertorous respirations. The pupils are dilated. The temperature is frequently below normal, particularly if the patient has been exposed to cold. Perhaps the lowest reported temperatures have been in cases of this sort. An instance is on record in which the patient on admission to hospital had a temperature of 24° C. (ca. 75° F.), and ten hours later the temperature had not risen to 91°. The unconsciousness is rarely so deep that the patient cannot be roused to some extent, and in reply to questions he mutters incoherently. Muscular twitchings may occur, but rarely convulsions. The breath has a heavy alcoholic odor.

The diagnosis is not difficult, yet mistakes are frequently made. Persons are sometimes brought to hospital by the police supposed to be drunk when in reality they are dying from apoplexy. Too great care cannot be exercised, and the patient should receive the benefit of the doubt. In some instances the mistake has arisen from the fact that a person who has been drinking heavily has been stricken with apoplexy. In this condition the coma is usually deeper, stertor is present, and there may be evidence of hemiplegia in the greater flaccidity of the limbs on one side. The subject will be considered in the section upon uræmic coma.

Dipsomania is a form of acute alcoholism seen in persons with a strong hereditary tendency to drink. Periodically the victims go " on a spree," but in the intervals they are entirely free from any craving for alcohol.

(2) **Chronic Alcoholism.**—In moderation, wine, beer, and spirits may be taken throughout a long life without impairing the general health.

According to Payne, the poisonous effects of alcohol are manifested (1) as a functional poison, as in acute narcosis; (2) as a tissue poison, in which its effects are seen on the parenchymatous elements, particularly epithelium and nerve, producing a slow degeneration, and on the blood-vessels, causing thickening and ultimately fibroid changes; and (3) as a checker of tissue oxidation, since the alcohol is consumed in place of the fat. This leads to fatty changes and sometimes to a condition of general steatosis.

The chief effects of chronic alcohol poisoning may be thus summarized.

Nervous System.—Functional disturbance is common. Unsteadiness of the muscles in performing any action is a constant feature. The tremor is best seen in the hands and in the tongue. The mental processes may be dull, particularly in the early morning hours, and the patient is unable to transact any business until he has had his accustomed stimulant. Irritability of temper, forgetfulness, and a change in the moral character of the individual gradually come on. The judgment is seriously impaired, the will enfeebled, and in the final stages dementia may supervene. The relation of chronic alcoholism to insanity has been much discussed. According to Savage, of 4,000 patients admitted to the Bethlehem Hospital, 133 gave drink as the cause of their insanity. Chronic alcoholism is believed by many to be one of the special causes of dementia paralytica, but the opinions of experts on this question are still discordant. Savage states that not more that 7 per cent are caused by alcohol alone. In many cases it is certainly one of the important elements in the strain which leads to this breakdown. Epilepsy may result directly from chronic drinking. It is a hopeful form, and may disappear entirely with a return to habits of temperance.

No characteristic changes are found in the nervous system. Hæmorrhagic pachymeningitis is not very uncommon. Opacity and thickening of the pia-arachnoid membranes, with more or less wasting of the convolutions, generally occur. These are in no way peculiar to chronic alcoholism, but are found in old persons and in chronic wasting diseases. In the very protracted cases there may be chronic encephalo-meningitis with adhesions of the membranes. Finer changes in the nerve-cells, their processes, and the neuroglia have been described by Berkley, Hoch, and others. By far the most striking effect of alcohol on the nervous system is the production of the alcoholic neuritis, which will be considered later.

Digestive System.—Catarrh of the stomach is the most common symptom. The toper has a furred tongue, heavy breath, and in the morning a sensation of sinking at the stomach until he has had his dram. The appetite is usually impaired and the bowels are constipated. In beer-drinkers dilatation of the stomach is common.

Alcohol produces definite changes in the liver, leading ultimately to the various forms of cirrhosis, to be described. In Welch's laboratory J. Friedenwald has caused typical cirrhosis in rabbits by the administration of alcohol. The effect is probably a primary degenerative change in the liver-cells, although many good observers still hold that the poison acts first upon the connective-tissue elements. It is probable that a special vulnerability of the liver-cells is necessary in the etiology of alcoholic cirrhosis. There are cases in which comparatively moderate drinking for a few years has been followed by cirrhosis; on the other hand, the livers of persons who have been steady drinkers for thirty or forty years may show only a moderate grade of sclerosis. For years before cirrhosis develops heavy drinkers may present an enlarged and tender liver, with at times swelling of the spleen. With the gastric and hepatic disorders the facies often becomes very characteristic. The venules of the cheeks and nose are dilated; the latter becomes enlarged, red, and may present the condition known as *acne rosacea*. The eyes are watery, the conjunctivæ hyperæmic and sometimes bile-tinged.

The *heart and arteries* in chronic topers show important degenerative changes. Alcoholism is one of the special factors in causing arterio-sclerosis. Steell has pointed out the frequency of cardiac dilatation in these cases.

Kidneys.—The influence of chronic alcoholism upon these organs is by no means so marked. According to Dickinson the total of renal disease is not greater in the drinking class, and he holds that the effect of alcohol on the kidneys has been much overrated. Formad has directed attention to the fact that in a large proportion of chronic alcoholics the kidneys are increased in size. The Guy's Hospital statistics support this statement, and Pitt notes that in 43 per cent of the bodies of hard drinkers the kidneys were hypertrophied without showing morbid change. The typical granular kidney seems to result indirectly from alcohol through the arterial changes.

It was formerly thought that alcohol was in some way antagonistic to tuberculous disease, but the observations of late years indicate clearly that the reverse is the case and that chronic drinkers are much more liable to both acute and pulmonary tuberculosis. It is probably altogether a question of altered tissue-soil, the alcohol lowering the vitality and enabling the bacilli more readily to develop and grow.

(3) Delirium Tremens (*mania a potu*) is really only an incident in the history of chronic alcoholism, and results from the long-continued action of the poison on the brain. The condition was first accurately described early in this century by Sutton, of Greenwich, who had numerous opportunities for studying the different forms among the sailors. One of the most thorough and careful studies of the disease was made by Ware, of Boston. A spree in a temperate person, no matter how prolonged, is rarely if ever followed by delirium tremens; but in the case of an habitual drinker a temporary excess is apt to bring on an attack. It sometimes develops in consequence of the sudden withdrawal of the alcohol. There are circumstances which in a heavy drinker determine, sometimes with abruptness, the onset of delirium. Such are an accident, a sudden fright or shock, and an acute inflammation, particularly pneumonia. At the outset of the attack the patient is restless and depressed and sleeps badly, symptoms which cause him to take alcohol more freely. After a day or two the characteristic delirium sets in. The patient talks constantly and incoherently; he is incessantly in motion, and desires to go out and attend to some imaginary business. Hallucinations of sight and hearing develop. He sees objects in the room, such as rats, mice, or snakes, and fancies that they are crawling over his body. The terror inspired by these imaginary objects is great, and has given the popular name " horrors " to the disease. The patients need to be watched constantly, for in their delusions they may jump out of the window or escape. Auditory hallucinations are not so common, but the patient may complain of hearing the roar of animals or the threats of imaginary enemies. There is much muscular tremor; the tongue is covered with a thick white fur, and when protruded is tremulous. The pulse is soft, rapid, and readily compressed. There is usually fever, but the temperature rarely registers above 102° or 103°. In fatal cases it may be higher. Insomnia is a constant feature. On the third or fourth day in favorable cases the restlessness abates, the patient sleeps, and improvement gradually sets in. The tremor persists for some days, the hallucinations gradually disappear, and the appetite returns. In more serious cases the insomnia persists, the delirium is incessant, the pulse becomes more frequent and feeble, the tongue dry, the prostration extreme, and death takes place from gradual heart-failure.

Diagnosis.—The clinical picture of the disease can scarcely be confounded with any other. Cases with fever, however, may be mistaken for meningitis. By far the most common error is to overlook some local disease, such as pneumonia or erysipelas, or an accident, as a fractured rib, which in a chronic drinker may precipitate an attack of delirium tremens. In every instance a careful examination should be made, particularly of the lungs. It is to be remembered that in the severer forms, particularly the febrile cases, congestion of the bases of the lungs is by no means uncommon. Another point to be borne in mind is the fact that pneumonia of the apex is apt to be accompanied by delirium similar to *mania a potu*.

Prognosis.—Recovery takes place in a large proportion of the cases in private practice. In hospital practice, particularly in the large city hospitals to which the debilitated patients are taken, the death-rate is higher. Gerhard states that of 1,241 cases admitted to the Philadelphia Hospital 121 proved fatal. Recurrence is frequent, almost indeed the rule, if the drinking is kept up.

Treatment.—Acute alcoholism rarely requires any special measures, as the patient sleeps off the effects of the debauch. In the case of profound alcoholic coma it may be advisable to wash out the stomach, and if collapse symptoms occur the limbs should be rubbed and hot applications made to the body. Should convulsions supervene, chloroform may be carefully administered. In the acute, violent alcoholic mania the hypodermic injection of apomorphia, one eighth or one sixth of a grain, is usually very effectual, causing nausea and vomiting, and rapid disappearance of the maniacal symptoms.

Chronic alcoholism is a condition very difficult to treat, and once fully established the habit is rarely abandoned. The most obstinate cases are those with marked hereditary tendency. Withdrawal of the alcohol is the first essential. This is most effectually accomplished by placing the patient in an institution, in which he can be carefully watched during the trying period of the first week or ten days of abstention. The absence of temptation in institution life is of special advantage. For the sleeplessness the bromides or hyoscine may be employed. Quinine and strychnine in tonic doses may be given. Cocaine or the fluid extract of coca has been recommended as a substitute for alcohol, but it is not of much service. Prolonged seclusion in a suitable institution is in reality the only effectual means of cure. When the hereditary tendency is strongly developed a lapse into the drinking habit is almost inevitable.

In delirium tremens the patient should be confined to bed and carefully watched night and day. The danger of escape in these cases is very great, as the patient imagines himself pursued by enemies or demons. Flint mentions the case of a man who escaped in his night-clothes and ran barefooted for fifteen miles on the frozen ground before he was overtaken. The patient should not be strapped in bed, as this aggravates the delirium; sometimes, however, it may be necessary, in which case a sheet tied across the bed may be sufficient, and this is certainly better than violent restraint by three or four men. Alcohol should be withdrawn at once unless the pulse is feeble.

Delirium tremens is a disease which, in a large majority of cases, runs a course very slightly influenced by medicine. The indications for treatment are to procure sleep and to support the strength. In mild cases half a drachm of bromide of potassium combined with tincture of capsicum may be given every three hours. Chloral is often of great service, and may be given without hesitation unless the heart's action is feeble. Good results sometimes follow the hypodermic use of hyoscine, one one-hundredth of a grain. Opium must be used cautiously. A special merit of Ware's work was the demonstration that on a rational or expectant plan of treatment the percentage of recoveries was greater than with the indiscriminate use of sedatives, which had been in vogue for many years. When opium is indicated it should be given as morphia, hypodermically. The effect should be carefully watched, and if after three or four quarter-grain doses have been given the patient is still restless and excited, it is best not to push it farther. When fever is present the tranquillizing effects of a cold douche or cold bath may be tried, or the cold pack. The large doses of digitalis formerly employed are not advisable.

Careful feeding is the most important element in the treatment of these cases. Milk and concentrated broths should be given at stated intervals. If the pulse becomes rapid and shows signs of flagging alcohol may be given in combination with the aromatic spirits of ammonia.

II. MORPHIA HABIT (*Morphinomania; Morphinism*).

This habit arises from the constant use of morphia—taken at first, as a rule, for the purpose of allaying pain. The craving is gradually engendered, and the habit in this way acquired. The injurious effects vary very much, and in the East, where opium-smoking is as common as tobacco-smoking with us, the ill effects are, according to good observers, not so striking.

The habit is particularly prevalent among women and physicians who use the hypodermic syringe for the alleviation of pain, as in neuralgia or sciatica. The acquisition of the habit as a pure luxury is rare in this country.

The symptoms at first are slight, and moderate doses may be taken for months without serious injury and without disturbance of health. There are exceptional instances in which for a period of years excessive doses have been taken without deterioration of the mental or bodily functions. As a rule, the dose necessary to obtain the desired sensations has gradually to be increased. As the effects wear off the victim experiences sensations of lassitude and mental depression, accompanied often with slight nausea and epigastric distress, symptoms which are relieved by another dose of the drug. The confirmed opium-eater often presents a very characteristic appearance. There is a sallowness of the complexion which is almost pathognomonic, and he becomes emaciated, gray, and prematurely aged. He is restless, irritable, and unable to remain quiet for any time. Itching is a common symptom. The sleep is disturbed, the appetite and digestion are deranged, and except when directly under the influence of the drug the mental condition is one of depression. Occasionally there are profuse sweats, which may be preceded by chills. The pupils, except when under the direct influence of the drug, are dilated, sometimes unequal. Persons addicted to morphia are inveterate liars, and no reliance whatever can be placed upon their statements. In many instances this is not confined to matters relating to the vice. In women the symptoms may be associated with those of pronounced hysteria or neurasthenia. The practice may be continued for an indefinite time, usually requiring increase in the dose until ultimately enormous quantities may be needed to obtain the desired effect. Finally a condition of asthenia is induced, in which the victim takes little or no food and dies from the extreme bodily debility. An increase in the dose is not always necessary, and there are *habitués* who reach the point of satisfaction with a daily amount of 2 or 3 grains of morphia, and who are able to carry on successfully for many years the ordinary business of life.

The *treatment* of the morphia habit is extremely difficult, and can rarely be successfully carried out by the general practitioner. Isolation, systematic feeding, and gradual withdrawal of the drug are the essential elements. As a rule, the patients must be under control in an institution and should be in bed for the first ten days. It is best in a majority of cases to reduce the morphia gradually. The diet should consist of beef-juice, milk, and egg-white, which should be given at short intervals. The sufferings of the patients are usually very great, more particularly the abdominal pains, sometimes nausea and vomiting, and the distressing restlessness. Usually within a week or ten days the opium may be entirely withdrawn. In all cases the pulse should be carefully watched and, if feeble, stimulants should be given, with the aromatic spirits of ammonia and digitalis. For the extreme restlessness a hot bath is serviceable. The sleeplessness is the most distressing symptom, and various drugs may have to be resorted to, particularly hyoscine and sulphonal and sometimes, if the insomnia persist, morphia itself.

It is essential in the treatment of a case to be certain that the patient has no means of obtaining morphia. Even under the favorable circumstances of seclusion in an institution, and constant watching by a night and a day nurse, I have known a patient to practice deception for a period of three months. After an apparent cure the patients are only too apt to lapse into the habit.

The condition is one which has become so common, and is so much on the increase, that physicians should exercise the utmost caution in prescribing morphia, particularly to female patients. Under no circumstances whatever should a patient with neuralgia or sciatica be allowed to use the hypodermic syringe, and it is even safer not to intrust this dangerous instrument to the hands of the nurse.

III. LEAD-POISONING (*Plumbism; Saturnism*).

Etiology.—The disease is widespread, particularly in lead-workers and among plumbers, painters, and glaziers. The metal is introduced into the system in many forms. Miners usually escape, but those engaged in the smelting of lead-ores are often attacked. Animals in the neighborhood of smelting furnaces have suffered with the disease, and even the birds that feed on the berries in the neighborhood may be affected. Men engaged in the white-lead factories are particularly prone to plumbism. Accidental poisoning may come in many ways; most commonly by drinking water which has passed through lead pipes or been stored in lead-lined cisterns. Wines and cider which contain acids quickly become contaminated in contact with lead. It was the frequency of colic in certain of the cider districts of Devonshire which gave the name of Devonshire colic, as the frequency of it in Poitou gave the name *colica Pictonum*. Among the innumerable sources of accidental poisoning may be mentioned milk, various sorts of beverages, hair dyes, false teeth, and thread. A serious outbreak of lead-poisoning, which was investigated by David D. Stewart, occurred recently in Philadelphia, owing to the disgraceful adulteration of a baking-powder with chromate of lead, which was used to give a yellow tint to the cakes. Lead given medicinally rarely produces poisoning.

All ages are attacked, but J. J. Putnam states that children are relatively less liable. The largest number of cases occur between thirty and forty. According to Oliver, from whose recent Gulstonian lectures I here quote, females are more susceptible than males. He states that they are much more quickly brought under its influence, and in a recent epidemic in which a thousand cases were involved the proportion of females to males was four to one.

The lead gains entrance to the system through the lungs, the digestive organs, or the skin. Poisoning may follow the use of cosmetics containing lead. Through the lungs it is freely absorbed. The chief channel, according to Oliver, is the digestive system. It is rapidly eliminated by the kidneys and skin, and is present in the urine of lead-workers. The susceptibility is remarkably varied. The symptoms may be manifest within a month of exposure. On the other hand, Tanquerel (des Planches) met with a case in a man who had been a lead-worker for fifty-two years.

Morbid Anatomy.—Small quantities of lead occur in the body in health. J. J. Putnam's reports show that of 150 persons not presenting symptoms of lead-poisoning traces of lead occurred in the urine of 25 per cent.

In chronic poisoning lead is found in the various organs. The affected muscles are yellow, fatty, and fibroid. The nerves present the features of a peripheral degenerative neuritis. The cord and the nerve-roots are, as a rule, uninvolved. In the primary atrophic form the ganglion cells of the anterior horns are probably implicated. In the acute fatal cases there may be the most intense entero-colitis.

Clinical Forms.—*Acute Poisoning.*—We do not refer here to the accidental or suicidal cases, which present vomiting, pain in the abdomen, and collapse symptoms. In workers in lead there are several manifestations which follow a short time after exposure and set in acutely. There may be, in the first place, a rapidly developing anæmia. Acute neuritis has been described, and convulsions, epilepsy, and a delirium, which may be, as Stephen Mackenzie has noted, not unlike that produced by alcohol. There are also cases in which the gastro-intestinal symptoms are most intense and rapidly prove fatal. There was admitted under my care in the Philadelphia Hospital a painter, aged fifty, suffering with anæmia and severe abdominal pain, which had lasted about a week. He had vomiting, constipation at first, afterward severe diarrhœa and melæna, with distention and tenderness of the abdomen. There were albumin and tube-casts in the urine. The temperature was usually subnormal. Death occurred at the end of the second week. There was found the most intense entero-colitis with hæmorrhages and exudation. These acute forms develop more frequently in persons recently exposed, and, according to Mackenzie, are more frequent in winter than in summer. Da Costa has reported a case of hemiplegia developing after three days' exposure to the poison.

Chronic poisoning presents the following symptoms:

(*a*) *Anæmia*, the so-called saturnine cachexia, which may be profound. As a rule, however, the corpuscles do not sink below 50 per cent. In some of the chronic cases there may be a persistent pallor of the face with a tolerably high blood-count.

(*b*) *Blue line* on the gums, which is a valuable indication, but not invariably present. Two lines must be distinguished: one, at the margin between the gums and teeth, is on, not in the gums, and is readily removed by rinsing the mouth and cleansing the teeth. The other is the well-known characteristic blue-black line at the margin of the gum. The color is not uniform, but being in the papillæ of the gums the line is, as seen with a magnifying-glass, interrupted. The lead is absorbed and converted in the tissues into a black sulphide by the action of sulphuretted hydrogen from the tartar of the teeth. The line may form in a few days after exposure (Oliver) and disappear within a few weeks, or may persist for many months. Philipson has noted the occurrence of a black line in miners, due to the deposition of carbon.

The most important symptoms of chronic lead-poisoning are colic, lead-palsy, and the encephalopathy. Of these, the colic is the most frequent. Of Tanquerel's cases, there were 1,217 of colic, 101 of paralysis, and 72 of encephalopathy.

(c) *Colic* is the most common symptom of chronic lead-poisoning. It is often preceded by gastric or intestinal symptoms, particularly constipation. The pain is over the whole abdomen. The colic is usually paroxysmal, like true colic, and is relieved by pressure. There is often, in addition, between the paroxysms a dull, heavy pain. There may be vomiting. During the attack, as Riegel noted, the pulse is increased in tension and the heart's action is retarded. Attacks of pain with acute diarrhœa may recur for weeks or even for three or four years.

(d) *Lead-palsy.*—This is rarely a primary manifestation. The onset may be acute, subacute, or chronic. It usually develops without fever. In its distribution it may be partial, limited to a muscle or to certain muscle groups, or generalized, involving in a short time the muscles of the extremities and the trunk. Madame Déjerine-Klumpke recognizes the following *localized forms:*

(1) Anti-brachial type, paralysis of the extensors of the fingers and of the wrist. In this the musculo-spiral nerve is involved, causing the characteristic wrist-drop. The supinator longus usually escapes. In the long-continued flexion of the carpus there may be slight displacement backward of the bones, with distention of the synovial sheaths, so that there is a prominent swelling over the wrist. This, which is sometimes known as Gruebler's tumor, though not of any moment, is often very annoying to the patient.

(2) Brachial type, which involves the deltoid, the biceps, the brachialis anticus, and the supinator longus, rarely the pectorals. The atrophy is of the scapulo-humeral form. It is bilateral, and sometimes follows the first form, but it may be primary.

(3) The Aran-Duchenne type, in which the small muscles of the hand and of the thenar and hypothenar eminences are involved, so that we have a paralysis closely resembling that of the early stage of *polio-myelitis anterior chronica.* The atrophy is marked, and may be the first manifestation of the lead-palsy. Möbius has shown that this form is particularly developed in tailors.

(4) The peroneal type. According to Tanquerel, the lower limbs are involved in the proportion of 13 to 100 of the upper limbs. The lateral peroneal muscles, the extensor communis of the toes, and the extensor proprius of the big toe are involved, producing the *steppage* gait.

(5) Laryngeal form. Adductor paralysis has been noted by Morell Mackenzie and others in lead-palsy.

Generalized Palsies.—There may be a slow, chronic paralysis, gradually involving the extremities, beginning with the classical picture of wrist-drop. More frequently there is a rapid generalization, producing complete paralysis in all the muscles of the parts in a few days. It may pursue a course like an ascending paralysis, associated with rapid wasting of all four limbs. Such cases, however, are very rare. Death has occurred by involvement of the diaphragm. Oliver reports a case of Philipson's in which complete paralysis supervened. Déjerine-Klumpke also recognizes a febrile form of general paralysis in lead-poisoning, which may closely resemble the subacute spinal paralysis of Duchenne.

There is also a primary saturnine muscular atrophy in which the weakness and wasting come on together and develop proportionately. It is this form, according to Gowers, which most frequently assumes the Aran-Duchenne type.

The electrical reactions are those of lesions of the lower motor segment, and will be described under diseases of the nerves. The degenerative reaction in its different grades may be present, depending upon the severity of the disease.

Usually with the onset of the paralysis there are pains in the legs and joints, the so-called saturnine arthralgias. Sensation may, however, be unaffected.

(e) The *cerebral symptoms* are numerous. Optic neuritis or neuroretinitis may develop. Hysterical symptoms occasionally occur in girls. Convulsions are not uncommon, and in fits developing in the adult the possibility of lead-poisoning should always be considered. True epilepsy may follow the convulsions. An acute delirium may occur with hallucinations. The patients may have trance-like attacks, which follow or alternate with convulsions. A few cases of lead encephalopathy finally drift into lunatic asylums. Tremor is one of the commonest manifestations of lead-poisoning.

(f) *Arterio-sclerosis.*—Lead-workers are notoriously subject to arteriosclerosis with contracted kidneys and hypertrophy of the heart. The cases usually show distinct gouty deposits, particularly in the big-toe joint; but in this country acute gout in lead-workers is rare. According to Sir William Roberts, the lead favors the precipitation of the crystalline urates of the tissues. Ralfe has shown that lead diminishes the alkalinity of the blood, and so lessens the solubility of the uric acid.

Prognosis.—In the minor manifestations of lead-poisoning this is good. According to Gowers, the outlook is bad in the primary atrophic form of paralysis. Convulsions are, as a rule, serious, and the mental symptoms which succeed may be permanent. Occasionally the wrist-drop persists.

Treatment.—Prophylactic measures should be taken at all lead-works, but, unless employés are careful, poisoning is apt to occur even under the most favorable conditions. Cleanliness of the hands and of the finger-nails, frequent bathing, and the use of respirators when necessary, should be insisted upon. When the lead is in the system, the iodide of potassium should be given in from 5- to 10-grain doses three times a day. For the colic, local applications and, if severe, morphia may be used. An occasional morning purge of sulphate of magnesia may be given. For the anæmia iron should be used. In the very acute cases it is well not to give the iodide, as, according to some writers, the liberation of the lead which has been deposited in the tissues may increase the severity of the symptoms. For the local palsies massage and the constant current should be used.

IV. ARSENICAL POISONING.

Acute poisoning by arsenic is common, particularly by Paris green and such mixtures as "Rough on Rats," which are used to destroy vermin and insects. The chief symptoms are intense pain in the stomach, vomiting, and, later, colic, with diarrhœa and tenesmus; occasionally the symptoms are those of collapse. If recovery takes place, paralysis may follow. The treatment should be similar to that of other irritant poisons—rapid removal with the stomach pump, the promotion of vomiting, and the use of milk and eggs. If the poison has been taken in solution, dialyzed iron may be used in large doses of from 6 to 8 drachms.

Chronic Arsenical Poisoning.—Arsenic is used extensively in the arts, particularly in the manufacture of colored papers, artificial flowers, and in many of the fabrics employed as clothing. The glazed green and red papers used in kindergartens also contain arsenic. It is present, too, in many wall-papers and carpets. Much attention has been paid to this question of late years, as instances of poisoning have been thought to depend upon wall-papers and other household fabrics. The arsenic compounds may be either in the form of solid particles detached from the paper or as a gaseous volatile body. The investigations of Gosio, confirmed by Sanger, have shown that a volatile compound is formed by the action on arsenical organic matter in wall-papers of several moulds, notably penicillum brevicaule, mucor mucedo, etc. In moisture, and at a temperature of from 60° to 95° F., a volatile compound is set free, probably "an organic derivative of arsenic pentoxide" (Sanger). The chronic poisoning from fabrics and wall-papers may be due, according to this author, to the ingestion of minute continued doses of this derivative, "which from its state of oxidation is likely to be accumulated in the system, from which it is slowly eliminated." Arsenic is eliminated in all the secretions, and has been found in the milk. J. J. Putnam, it should be remembered, has shown that it is not uncommon to find traces of arsenic in the urine of many persons in apparent health (30 per cent). The effects of moderate quantities of arsenic are not infrequently seen in medical practice. In chorea and in pernicious anæmia, steadily increasing doses are often given until the patient takes from 15 to 20 drops of Fowler's solution three times a day. Flushing and hyperæmia of the skin, puffiness of the eyelids or above the eyebrows, nausea, vomiting, and diarrhœa are the most common symptoms. Redness and sometimes bleeding of the gums and salivation occur. In the protracted administration of arsenic patients may complain of numbness and tingling in the fingers. Pigmentation of the skin I have seen on several occasions. In chorea neuritis has occurred, and a patient of mine with Hodgkin's disease developed multiple neuritis after taking ℥ iv ℨ j of Fowler's solution in seventy-five days, during which time there were fourteen days on which the drug was omitted.

In the slow poisoning by the absorption of arsenic in minute doses, as from wall-paper and fabrics, the symptoms are varied. J. J. Putnam groups them into the cases in which the symptoms mainly concern the general nutrition without signs of local irritation; those in which the symptoms are due to irritation of the conjunctivæ, mouth, or pharynx; those with symptoms pointing to the digestive tract; cases with marked nervous phenomena; and those in which the nutrition of some special part of the body is involved. The most common symptoms are those of anæmia and debility, perhaps with slight irritation of the mucous membrane, and numbness and tingling, and gastralgia. How far these symptoms are to be attributed to the small quantities of arsenic absorbed from wall-papers and fabrics is by some considered doubtful. That children and adults may take with impunity large doses for months without unpleasant effects, and the fact of the gradual establishment of a toleration which enables Styrian peasants to take as much as 8 grains of arsenious acid in a day, speak strongly against it. On the other hand, as Sanger states, we do not know accurately the effects of many of the compounds in minute and long-continued doses, notably the arsenates.

Arsenical paralysis has the same characteristics as lead-palsy, but the legs are more affected than the arms, particularly the extensors and peroneal group, so that the patient has the characteristic *steppage* gait of peripheral neuritis.

The electrical reaction in the muscles may be disturbed before there is any loss of power, and when the patient is asked to extend the wrist fully and to spread the fingers slight weakness may be detected early.

V. FOOD POISONING. (*Bromatotoxismus : Vaughan*).

There may be " death in the pot " from many causes. Food may contain the specific organisms of disease, as of tuberculosis or trichinosis; milk and other foods may become infected with typhoid bacilli, and so convey the disease.

Animals (or insects, as bees) may feed on substances which cause their flesh or products to be poisonous to man.

The grains used as food may be infected with fungi and cause the epidemics of ergotism, etc.

Foods of all sorts may become contaminated with the bacteria of putrefaction, the products of which may be highly poisonous.

For a full description of food poisoning see Vaughan's section on the subject in vol. xiii of the Twentieth Century Practice.

Among the more common forms are the following:

(1) **Meat Poisoning** (*Kreotoxismus*).—Cases have usually followed the eating of sausages or pork-pie or head-cheese, and also occasionally beef, veal, and mutton. Sausage poisoning, which is known by the name of *botulism* or *allantiasis*, has long been recognized, and there have been numerous outbreaks, particularly in parts of Germany. Similar attacks have been produced by ham and by head-cheese. The precise nature of the kreotoxicons has not yet been determined. Other outbreaks have followed the eating of beef and veal. In the majority of these cases the meat has undergone decomposition, though the change may not have been evident to the

taste. The symptoms of meat poisoning are those of acute gastro-intestinal irritation. Ballard's description of the Wellbeck cases, quoted by Vaughan, holds good for a majority of them:

" A period of incubation preceded the illness. In 51 cases where this could be accurately determined, it was twelve hours or less in 5 cases; between twelve and thirty-six hours in 34 cases; between thirty-six and forty-eight hours in 8 cases; and later than this in only 4 cases. In many cases the first definite symptoms occurred suddenly, and evidently unexpectedly, but in some cases there were observed during the incubation more or less feeling of languor and ill-health, loss of appetite, nausea, or fugitive, griping pains in the belly. In about a third of the cases the first definite symptom was a sense of chilliness, usually with rigors, or trembling, in one case accompanied by dyspnœa; in a few cases it was giddiness with faintness, sometimes accompanied by a cold sweat and tottering; in others the first symptom was headache or pain somewhere in the trunk of the body—e. g., in the chest, back, between the shoulders, or in the abdomen, to which part the pain, wherever it might have commenced, subsequently extended. In one case the first symptom noticed was a difficulty in swallowing. In two cases it was intense thirst. But however the attack may have commenced, it was usually not long before pain in the abdomen, diarrhœa, and vomiting came on, diarrhœa being of more certain occurrence than vomiting. The pain in several cases commenced in the chest or between the shoulders, and extended first to the upper and then to the lower part of the abdomen. It was usually very severe indeed, quickly producing prostration or faintness, with cold sweats. It was variously described as crampy, burning, tearing, etc. The diarrhœal discharges were in some cases quite unrestrainable, and (where a description of them could be obtained) were said to have been exceedingly offensive and usually of a dark color. Muscular weakness was an early and very remarkable symptom in nearly all the cases, and in many it was so great that the patient could only stand by holding on to something. Headache, sometimes severe, was a common and early symptom; and in most cases there was thirst, often intense and most distressing. The tongue, when observed, was described usually as thickly coated with a brown, velvety fur, but red at the tip and edges. In the early stage the skin was often cold to the touch, but afterward fever set in, the temperature rising in some cases to 101°, 103°, and 104° F. In a few severe cases, where the skin was actually cold, the patient complained of heat, insisted on throwing off the bedclothes, and was very restless. The pulse in the height of the illness became quick, counting in some cases 100 to 128. The above were the symptoms most frequently noted. Other symptoms occurred, however, some in a few cases, and some only in solitary cases. These I now proceed to enumerate. Excessive sweating, cramps in the legs, or in both legs and arms, convulsive flexion of the hands or fingers, muscular twitchings of the face, shoulders, or hands, aching pain in the shoulders, joints, or extremities, a sense of stiffness of the joints, prickling or tingling or numbness of the hands lasting far into convalescence in some cases, a sense of general compression of the skin, drowsiness, hallucinations, imperfection of vision, and intolerance of light. In three cases (one that of a medical man) there was observed yellowness of the skin, either general or confined to the face and eyes. In one case, at a late stage of the illness, there was some pulmonary congestion and an attack of what was regarded as gout. In the fatal cases death was preceded by collapse like that of cholera, coldness of the surface, pinched features, and blueness of the fingers and toes and around the sunken eyes. The debility of convalescence was in nearly all cases protracted to several weeks.

" The mildest cases were characterized usually by little remarkable beyond the following symptoms, viz., abdominal pains, vomiting, diarrhœa, thirst, headache, and muscular weakness, any one or two of which might be absent."

Many instances are on record of poisoning by canned goods, particularly meat. Some of these, according to John G. Johnson, have been cases of corrosive poisoning from muriate of zinc and muriate of tin used as an amalgam, but poisonous effects identical with those just described have followed the use of canned meats.

Certain game birds, particularly the grouse, are stated to be poisonous, in special districts and at certain seasons of the year.

(2) **Poisoning by Milk Products.**—(*a*) *Galactotoxismus*, indicating the poisonous effects which follow the drinking of milk infected with saprophytic bacteria, is considered in the section on the diarrhœa of infants.

(*b*) *Cheese Poisoning* (Tyrotoxismus).—Various milk products, ice cream, custard, and cheese may prove highly poisonous. Among the poisons Vaughan now states that the tyrotoxicon " is not the one most frequently present, nor is it the most active one." In one epidemic he and Novy have isolated from cheese a substance belonging to the poisonous albumins, and in an extensive ice-cream epidemic Vaughan and Perkins found in the ice cream a highly pathogenic bacillus, but its toxine has not been separated.

The symptoms are those of acute gastro-intestinal irritation, and are similar to those already detailed by Ballard.

(3) **Poisoning by Shell-fish and Fish.**—(*a*) *Mussel Poisoning* (Mytilotoxismus).—Brieger has separated a ptomaine—mytilotoxin—which exists chiefly in the liver of the mussel. The observations of Schmidtmann and Cameron have shown that the mussel from the open sea only becomes poisonous when placed in filthy waters, as at Wilhelmshafen.

The symptoms of mussel poisoning follow the eating of either raw or cooked mussels. The symptoms are those of an acute poisoning with profound action on the nervous system, and without gastro-intestinal manifestations. There are numbness and coldness, no fever, dilated pupils, and rapid pulse; death occurs sometimes within two hours with collapse symptoms. Poisoning occasionally follows the eating of oysters which are stale or decomposed. The symptoms are usually gastro-intestinal.

(*b*) *Fish Poisoning* (Ichthyotoxismus).—There are two distinct varieties; in one the poison is a physiological product of certain glands of the fish, in the other it is a product of bacterial growth. The salted sturgeon used in parts of Russia has sometimes proved fatal to large numbers of persons. In the middle parts of Europe the barb is stated to be sometimes poisonous, producing the so-called "*barben cholera.*" In China and Japan various species of the *tetrodon* are also toxic, sometimes causing death within an hour, with symptoms of intense disturbance of the nervous system. Beri-beri is thought by some to be due to the consumption of certain kinds of fish.

(4) Grain Poisoning (*Sitotoximus*).

(1) *Ergotism.*—The prolonged use of meal made from grains contaminated with the ergot fungus (*claviceps purpurea*) causes a series of symptoms known as ergotism, epidemics of which have prevailed in different parts of Europe. Two forms of this chronic ergotism are described—the one, gangrenous, is believed to be due to the sphacelinic acid, the other, convulsive, or spasmodic, is due to the cornutin. In the former, mortification affects the extremities—usually the toes and fingers, less commonly the ears and nose. Preceding the onset of the gangrene there are usually anæsthesia, tingling, pains, spasmodic movements of the muscles, and gradual blood stasis in certain vascular territories.

The nervous manifestations are very remarkable. After a prodromal stage of ten to fourteen days, in which the patient complains of weakness, headache, and tingling sensations in different parts of the body, perhaps accompanied with slight fever, symptoms of spasm develop, producing cramps in the muscles and contractures. The arms are flexed and the legs and toes extended. These spasms may last from a few hours to many days and relapses are frequent. In severer cases epilepsy develops and the patient may die in convulsions. Mental symptoms are common, manifested sometimes in a preliminary delirium, but more commonly, in the chronic poisoning, as melancholia or dementia. Posterior spinal sclerosis occurs in chronic ergotism. In the interesting group of 29 cases studied by Tuczek and Siemens, 9 died at various periods after the infection, and four post mortems showed degeneration of the posterior columns. A condition similar to tabes dorsalis is gradually produced by this slow degeneration in the spinal cord.

(2) *Lathyrism* (Lupinosis).—An affection produced by the use of meal from varieties of vetches, chiefly the *Lathyrus sativus* and *L. cicera.* The grain is popularly known as the chick-pea. The grains are usually powdered and mixed with the meal from other cereals in the preparation of bread. As early as the seventeenth century it was noticed that the use of flour with which the seeds of the *Lathyrus* were mixed caused stiffness of the legs. The subject did not, however, attract much attention before the studies of James Irving, in India, who between 1859 and 1868 published several important communications, describing a form of spastic paraplegia affecting large numbers of the inhabitants in certain regions of India and due to the use of meal made from the *Lathyrus* seeds. It also produces a spastic paraplegia in animals. The Italian observers describe a similar form of paraplegia, and it has been observed in Algiers by the French physicians. The condition is that of a spastic paralysis, involving chiefly the legs, which may proceed to complete paraplegia. The arms are rarely, if ever affected. It is evidently a slow sclerosis induced under

the influence of this toxic agent. The precise anatomical condition, so far as I can ascertain, has not yet been determined.

(3) *Pellagra* (Maïdismus).—This is a nutritional disturbance due to the use of altered maize. The disease occurs extensively in parts of Italy, in the south of France, and in Spain. It has not been observed in this country. It prevails extensively among the poorer classes, particularly in the country districts, and appears to be associated in some way with the use of maize which (according to most authorities) is fermented or diseased. In the early stage the symptoms are indefinite, characterized by debility, pains in the spine, insomnia, digestive disturbances, more rarely diarrhœa. The first clear manifestation of the disease is the pellagral erythema, which almost invariably appears in the spring. This is followed by desiccation and exfoliation of the epidermis, which becomes very rough and dry, and occasionally crusts form, beneath which there is suppuration. With these cutaneous manifestations there are digestive troubles—salivation, dyspepsia, and diarrhœa—which may be of a dysenteric nature. After lasting for a few months improvement occurs in the milder cases and convalescence is gradually established. In the more severe and chronic forms there are pronounced nervous symptoms—headache, backache, spasms, and finally paralysis and mental disturbance. The paralytic condition affects the legs and leads gradually to paraplegia. The mental manifestations, which are rarely met with until the third or fourth attack, are melancholia or suicidal mania. Finally, there may be a condition of the most pronounced cachexia.

The anatomical findings are indefinite. Chronic degenerative changes have been found, particularly fatty degeneration and a peculiar pigmentation in the viscera. The measures to be employed are change in diet, removal from the infected district, and, as a prophylaxis, proper preservation of the maize.

VI. SUN-STROKE (*Siriasis*).

(*Heat Exhaustion; Insolation; Thermic Fever; Heat-stroke; Coup de Soleil.*)

Definition.—A condition produced by exposure to excessive heat.

It is one of the oldest of recognized diseases; two instances are mentioned in the Bible. It was long confounded with apoplexy. The Anglo-Indian surgeons gave admirable descriptions of it. In this country the most important contributions have come from the New York Hospital and the Pennsylvania Hospital; from the former, the studies of Swift and Darrach, from the latter, the papers of Gerhard, George B. Wood, the elder Pepper, and Levick. In New Orleans, Bennett Dowler studied the disease and recognized the difference between heat exhaustion and sun-stroke. Two forms are recognized, heat exhaustion and heat-stroke.

Heat Exhaustion.—Prolonged exposure to high temperatures, particularly when combined with physical exertion, is liable to be followed by extreme prostration, collapse, restlessness, and in severe cases by delirium. The surface is usually cool, the pulse small and rapid, and the temperature may be subnormal—as low as 95° or 96°. The individual need not neces-

25

sarily be exposed to the direct rays of the sun, but the condition may come on at night or when working in close, confined rooms. It may also follow exposure to great artificial heat, as in the engine rooms of the Atlantic steamships.

Sun-stroke or Thermic Fever.—The cases are chiefly found in persons who, while working very hard, are exposed to the sun. Soldiers on the march with their heavy accoutrements are particularly liable to attack. In the larger cities of this country the cases are almost exclusively confined to workmen who are much exposed and, at the same time, have been drinking beer and whisky.

Morbid Anatomy and Pathology.—*Rigor mortis* occurs early. Putrefactive changes develop with great rapidity. The venous engorgement is extreme, particularly in the cerebrum. The left ventricle is contracted (Wood), and the right chamber dilated. The blood is usually fluid; the lungs are intensely congested. Parenchymatous changes occur in the liver and kidneys.

According to Wood, "heat exhaustion with lowered temperature represents a sudden vaso-motor palsy, i. e., a condition in which the existing effect of the heat paralyzes the centre in the medulla." On the other hand, thermic fever is held to be due to paralysis under the influence of the extreme external heat of the centre in the medulla which regulates the disposition of the bodily heat. Owing to this disturbance, more heat is produced and less given off than normally.

Sambron has recently (B. M. J., 1898, i) advanced the view that siriasis is an infectious disease. He argues that heat alone cannot cause it, that it occurs in certain localities and in epidemic outbursts, and persons acclimatized have a relative immunity, etc. The question is one worthy of most careful study.

Symptoms.—The patient may be struck down and die within an hour with symptoms of heart-failure, dyspnœa, and coma. This form, sometimes known as the asphyxial, occurs chiefly in soldiers and is graphically described by Parkes. Death indeed may be almost instantaneous, the victims falling as if struck upon the head. The usual form in this latitude comes on during exposure, with pain in the head, dizziness, a feeling of oppression, and sometimes nausea and vomiting. Visual disturbances are common, and a patient may have colored vision. Diarrhœa or frequent micturition may supervene. Insensibility follows, which may be transient or which deepens into a profound coma. The patients are usually admitted to hospital in an unconscious state, with the face flushed, the skin pungent, the pulse rapid and full, and the temperature ranging from 107° to 110°, or even higher, as shown in the accompanying chart. F. A. Packard states that of the 31 cases admitted to the Pennsylvania Hospital in the summer of 1887, in a majority of them the temperature was between 110° and 111°. In one case the temperature was 112°. The breathing is labored and deep, sometimes stertorous. Usually there is complete relaxation of the muscles, but twitchings, jactitation, or very rarely convulsions may occur. The pupils may at first be dilated, but by the time the cases are admitted to hospital they are (in a majority) extremely contracted. Petechiæ may be present upon the skin. In the fatal cases the coma deepens, the cardiac pulsations become more rapid and feeble, the breathing becomes hurried and shallow and of the Cheyne-Stokes type. The fatal termination may occur within twenty-four or thirty-six hours. Favorable indications are the return of consciousness and a fall in the fever. The recovery in these cases may be complete. In other instances there are remarkable after-effects, the most constant of which is a permanent inability to bear high temperatures. Such patients become very uneasy when the thermometer reaches 80° F. in the shade. Loss of the power of mental concentration and failure of memory are more constant and very troublesome sequelæ. Such patients are always worse in the

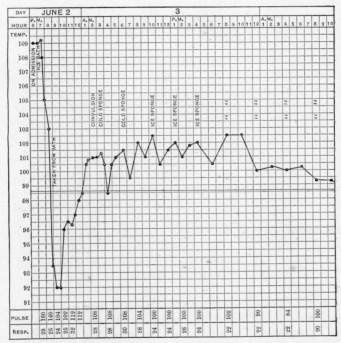

CHART XIII.—Case of sun-stroke treated with the ice-bath; recovery.
(Rectal temperatures).

hot weather. Occasionally convulsions and marked mental disturbance may develop. Dercum has described peripheral neuritis as a sequence, and the patient whose chart is here given developed an acute neuritis in the legs. This is a point in favor of the infectious nature of the disease.

Guitéras has called attention to a form of fever occurring in the South, known in Florida as "Florida fever," in the Carolinas as "country fever," and in tropical countries as *fièvre inflammatoire*. The cases last for a variable time, and are mistaken for malaria or typhoid; but he believes them

to be entirely distinct and due to a prolonged action of the high temperatures. He has called the condition a " continued thermic fever."

The diagnosis of heat exhaustion from thermic fever is readily made,
as the difference between the two conditions is striking. " In solar exhaustion the skin is moist, pale, and cool; the breathing is easy though
hurried; the pulse is small and soft; the vital forces fall into a temporary
collapse; the senses remain entire " (Dowler); whereas in sun-stroke or
heat apoplexy there is usually unconsciousness and pyrexia.

The mode of onset, together with the circumstances under which it
occurs and the high temperature, permits thermic fever to be readily differentiated from apoplexy and coma from other conditions.

Treatment.—In heat exhaustion stimulants should be given freely,
and if the temperature is below normal the hot bath should be used.
Ammonia may be given if necessary. In thermic fever the indications
are to reduce the temperature as rapidly as possible. This may be done
by packing the patient in a bath with ice. Rubbing the body with ice was
practised at the New York Hospital by Darrach in 1857, and is an excellent procedure to lower the temperature rapidly. Ice-water enemata may
also be employed. At the Pennsylvania Hospital in the summer of 1887
the ice-pack was used with great advantage. Of 31 cases only 12 died,
results probably as satisfactory as can be obtained, considering that many
of the patients are almost moribund when brought to hospital. They should
be compared with Swift's statistics, in which of 150 cases 78 died. In the
cases in which the symptoms are those of intense asphyxia, and in which
death may take place in a few minutes, free bleeding should be practised,
a procedure which saved Weir Mitchell when a young man. For the convulsions chloroform should be given at once. Of other remedies, the antipyretics have been employed, and may be given when there is any special
objection to hydrotherapy, for which, however, they cannot be substituted.

CONSTITUTIONAL DISEASES.

I. ARTHRITIS DEFORMANS.

Definition.—A chronic disease of the joints of doubtful etiology, characterized by changes in the cartilages and synovial membranes, with peri-articular formation of bone and great deformity.

Long believed to be intimately associated with gout and rheumatism (whence the names rheumatic gout and rheumatoid arthritis), this close relationship seems now very doubtful, since in a majority of the cases no history of either affection can be determined.

Etiology.—*Age.*—A majority of the cases are between the ages of thirty and fifty. In A. E. Garrod's analysis of 500 cases there were only 25 under twenty years of age.

Sex.—Among Garrod's 500 cases there were 411 in women. In James Stewart's recent report of 40 cases from the Royal Victoria Hospital only 20 were in females. In women its close association with the menopause has been noted. It seems to be more frequent, too, in those who have had ovarian or uterine trouble or who are sterile.

Hereditary Predisposition.—In 216 cases in Garrod's series there was a family history of joint troubles. Two or three children in a family may be affected. It is stated also that the disease is more common in families with a phthisical history.

Rheumatism and Gout.—In nearly a third of Garrod's cases there was a history of gout in the family; of rheumatism in only 64 cases.

Exposure to cold, wet and damp, errors in diet, worry and care, and local injuries are all spoken of as possible exciting causes.

At present there are two chief views prevailing as to the etiology of arthritis deformans—one that it is of nervous origin, the other that it is a chronic infection.

The Relation of Arthritis Deformans to Diseases of the Nervous System.—Our accurate knowledge of arthropathies of nervous origin dates from the papers of J. K. Mitchell, of Philadelphia, in 1831 and 1833, in which he reported cases of inflammation of the joints in connection with caries of the spine and concussion of the cord. Acute and chronic forms of arthritis may occur with gross lesions of the cord; the former are found

399

in acute myelitis, the latter with sclerosis of the posterior columns. The acute spinal arthritis presents anatomically inflammation of the synovial sheaths and of the fibrous investment of the articulations. The chronic arthritis which we see in syringomyelia, tabes, and hemiplegia presents a combination of atrophy and hyperplasia of the bones, with thickening of the ligaments and more or less effusion. Again, there are joint lesions which follow injuries of the nerve trunks themselves, cases of which have been reported by S. Weir Mitchell. The following are the main points urged in favor of the nervous origin of the disease: First, the articular changes are similar to, if not identical with, those of the chronic spinal arthropathies. Secondly, the frequent association in arthritis deformans of dystrophies of the skin (glossy skin), nails, bones, and muscles—changes which are evidently of neurotic origin. In certain cases there is marked and early atrophy of the muscles. Ord, indeed, thinks that this atrophy with the articular lesions forms a dystrophy analogous to progressive muscular atrophy. Thirdly, the symmetrical onset and progress of the disease. Fourthly, the implication of nerve trunks. There may be not only numbness and tingling, but in certain cases excruciating pains. Post mortem, neuritis has been found in several cases, but whether primary or secondary is doubtful. The reflexes are not infrequently increased, in 32 of 50 of Garrod's cases. We need information as to the condition of the spinal cord in these cases of arthritis deformans. Triboulet and Thomas have reported from Déjerine's service a case of a woman with chronic arthritis, in whom the autopsy showed a sclerosis of the posterior columns of the cord in the dorsal region and of the columns of Goll in the cervical region, with degeneration of the posterior roots. The history indicated that the arthritis developed after a puerperal infection.

Arthritis Deformans as a Chronic Infection.—During the past few years the idea has been gaining ground that the disease is of microbic origin. Satisfactory evidence for this view is not yet forthcoming. Schüller, Bannatyne and Blaxall, and several French observers have found micro-organisms in the fluid of the joints. More valuable really is the frequent association of arthritis deformans with previous acute infections; thus in James Stewart's cases there was a history of gonorrhœa in 30 per cent of the males, and in his series of 40 cases 50 per cent had had previously some infectious trouble. Of late years we have learned to recognize cases which have followed directly upon a severe attack of influenza.

The acute mode of onset in some instances is suggestive of an infection. The joints may be red and swollen and painful, and present the clinical picture of an acute infective process.

And, lastly, a consideration of the form in children described by Still lends weight to this view, particularly in the widespread enlargement of the lymph-glands and the swelling of the spleen. A number of the very best students of the disease, as Bäumler, of Freiberg, have accepted the infective theory of the disease, but at present I think the evidence is quite as much in favor of the older neurotic view.

Morbid Anatomy.—The changes in the joints differ essentially from those of gout in the absence of deposits of urate of soda, and from chronic rheumatism in the existence of extensive structural alterations, particularly in the cartilages. We are largely indebted to the magnificent work of Adams for our knowledge of the anatomy of this disease. The changes begin in the cartilages and synovial membranes, the cells of which proliferate. The cartilage covering the joint undergoes a peculiar fibrillation, becomes soft, and is either absorbed or gradually thinned by attrition, thus laying bare the ends of the bone, which become smooth, polished, and eburnated. At the margins, where the pressure is less, the proliferating elements may develop into irregular nodules, which ossify and enlarge the heads of the bones, forming osteophytes which completely lock the joint. The periosteum may also form new bone. There is usually great thickening of the ligaments, and finally complete anchylosis results. This is rarely, however, a true anchylosis, but is caused by the osteophytes and thickened ligaments. There are often hyperostosis and increase in the articular ends of the bone in length and thickness. In long-standing cases and in old persons there may, on the other hand, be great atrophy of the heads of the affected bones. The spongy substance becomes friable, and in the hip-joint the wasting may reach such an extreme grade that the articulating surface lies between the trochanters. This is sometimes called *morbus coxæ senilis*. The anatomical changes may lead to great deformity. The metacarpal joints are enlarged and thickened, and the fingers are deflected toward the ulnar side. The toes often show a similar deflection. The exostoses at the joints are known as Haygarth's nodosities.

The radiographs of arthritis deformans are very instructive. The clear interosseous spaces at the level of the joints disappear early, the hypertrophy and deformity of the articular extremities, and more particularly the exostoses at the margins, give a very distinctive picture of the disease.

The muscles become atrophied, and in some cases the wasting reaches a high grade. Neuritis has been demonstrated in the nerves about the joints.

Symptoms.—Charcot makes a convenient division of the cases into those with Heberden's nodes, the general progressive form, and the partial or mono-articular form.

Heberden's Nodes.—In this form the fingers are affected, and "little hard knobs" develop gradually at the sides of the distal phalanges. They are much more common in women than in men. They begin usually between the thirtieth and fortieth year. The subjects may have had digestive troubles or gout. Heberden, however, says "they have no connection with gout, being found in persons who never had it." In the early stage the joints may be swollen, tender, and slightly red, particularly when knocked. The attacks of pain and swelling may come on in the joints at long intervals or follow indiscretion in diet. The little tubercles at the sides of the dorsal surface of the second phalanx increase in size, and give the characteristic appearance to the affection. The cartilages also become soft, and the ends of the bones eburnated. Urate of soda is never deposited (Charcot). The condition is not curable; but there is this hopeful feature—the subjects of these nodosities rarely have involvement of the larger joints. They have been regarded, too, as an indication of longevity. Charcot states that in women with these nodes cancer seems more frequent.

General Progressive Form.—This occurs in two varieties, acute and chronic. The *acute* form may resemble, at its outset, ordinary articular rheumatism. There is involvement of many joints; swelling, particularly of the synovial sheaths and bursæ; not often redness; but there is moderate fever. Howard describes this condition as most frequent in young women from twenty to thirty years of age, often in connection with recent delivery, lactation, or rapid child-bearing. Acute cases may develop at the menopause. It may also come on in children. " These patients suffer in their general health, become weak, pale, depressed in spirits, and lose flesh. In several cases of this form marked intervals of improvement have occurred; the local disease has ceased to progress, and tolerable comfort has been experienced perhaps until pregnancy, delivery, or lactation again determines a fresh outbreak of the disease."

The *chronic* form is by far the most common. The joints are usually involved symmetrically. The first symptoms are pain on movement and slight swelling, which may be in the joint itself or in the peri-articular sheaths. In some cases the effusion is marked, in others slight. The local conditions vary greatly, and periods of improvement alternate with attacks of swelling, redness, and pain. At first only one or two joints are affected; usually the joints of the hands, then the knees and feet; gradually other articulations are involved, and in extreme cases every joint in the body is affected. Pain is an extremely variable symptom. Some cases proceed to the most extreme deformity without it; in others the suffering is very great, particularly at night and during exacerbations of the disease. There are cases in which pain of an agonizing character is an almost constant symptom, requiring for years the use of morphia.

Gradually the shape of the joints is greatly altered, partly by the presence of osteophytes, partly by the great thickening of the capsular ligaments, and still more by the retraction of the muscles. In moving the affected joint crepitation can be felt, due to the eburnation of the articular surfaces. Ultimately the joints become completely locked, not by a true bony anchylosis, but by the osteophytes which form around the articular surfaces, like ring-bone in horses. There is also a spurious anchylosis, caused by the thickening of the capsular ligaments and fibrous adhesions. The muscles about the joints undergo important changes. Atrophy from disuse gradually supervenes, and contractures tend to flex the thigh upon the abdomen and the leg upon the thigh. There are cases with rapid muscular wasting, symmetrical involvement of the joints, increased reflexes, and trophic changes, which strongly suggest a central origin. Numbness, tingling, pigmentation or glossiness of the skin, and onychia may be present. In extreme cases the patient is completely helpless, and lies on one side with the legs drawn up, the arms fixed, and all the articulations of the extremities locked. Fortunately, it often happens in these severe general cases that the joints of the hand are not so much affected, and the patient may be able to knit or to write, though unable to walk or to use the arms.

It is surprising indeed how much certain patients with advanced arthritis deformans can accomplish. No one who had seen the beautiful models and microscopic preparations of the late H. D. Schmidt, of New Orleans, could imagine that he had been afflicted for years with a most extreme grade of this terrible disease. In many cases, after involving two or three joints, the disease becomes arrested, and no further development occurs. It may be limited to the wrists, or to the knees and wrists, or to the knees and ankles. A majority of the patients finally reach a quiescent stage, in which they are free from pain and enjoy excellent health, suffering only from the inconvenience and crippling necessarily associated with the disease.

Coincident affections are not uncommon. In the active stage the patients are often anæmic and suffer from dyspepsia, which may recur at intervals. There is no tendency to involvement of the heart.

The **partial or mono-articular** form affects chiefly old persons, and is seen particularly in the hip, the knee, the spinal column, or shoulder. It is, in its anatomical features, identical with the general disease. In the hip and shoulder the muscles early show wasting, and in the hip the condition ultimately becomes that already described as *morbus coxæ senilis*. These cases seem not infrequently to follow an injury. They differ from the polyarticular form in occurring chiefly in men and at a later period of life. One of the most interesting forms affects the vertebræ, completely locking the articulations, and producing the condition known as *spondylitis deformans*. When the cervical spine is involved, the head cannot be moved up and down, but is carried stiffly. Usually rotation can be effected. The dorsal and lumbar spines may also be involved, and the body cannot be flexed in the slightest degree. Other joints may not be affected, or with the spine the hip and shoulder joints may be anchylosed. Marie has described this condition as *spondylose rhizomélique*. The smaller joints are not affected. There is a remarkable specimen of it in the museum of the University of Buffalo.

Arthritis Deformans in Children.—A. E. Garrod remarks that all the cases which, on account of their clinical features, are classed as examples of arthritis deformans in children are not truly of that nature. Some examples certainly resemble closely the disease in adults. In others there are very striking differences. A very interesting variety has been differentiated by George F. Still, in which the general enlargement of the joints is associated with swelling of the lymph-glands and of the spleen. He has studied 22 cases of this character. The following are among the more striking peculiarities. The onset is almost always before the second dentition. Girls are more frequently affected than boys. The symptoms complained of are usually slight stiffness in one or two joints; gradually others become involved. The onset may be more acute with fever, or even with chills. The enlargement of the joints is due rather to a general thickening of the soft tissues than to a bony enlargement. There is no bony grating. The limitation of movement may be extreme, owing to the fixation of the joints, and there may be much muscular wasting. The enlargement of the lymph-glands is most striking. In a case at present under my observation the supratrochlear glands are as large as hazel-nuts. The enlargement is general. The edge of the spleen can usually be felt below the costal margin. Sweating is often profuse and there may be anæmia, but heart complications are rare. The children look puny and generally show arrest of development.

Diagnosis.—Arthritis deformans in an advanced stage can rarely be mistaken for either rheumatism or gout. Early cases are difficult or impossible to distinguish from chronic rheumatism. It is important to distinguish from the mono-articular form the local arthritis of the shoulder-joint which is characterized by pain, thickening of the capsule and of the ligaments, wasting of the shoulder-girdle muscles, and sometimes by neuritis. This is an affection which is quite distinct from arthritis deformans, and is, moreover, in a majority of cases curable.

Treatment.—Arthritis deformans is an incurable disease. In many cases, after involvement of two or three joints, the progress is arrested. Too often it invades successively all the articulations, and in ten, fifteen, or twenty years the crippling becomes general and permanent.

The best that can be hoped for is a gradual arrest. It is useless to saturate the patients with iodide of potassium, salicylates, or quinine. Arsenic seems to do good as a general tonic. The improvement may be marked if large doses of it are given. Iron should be used freely, if there is anæmia. An old recipe, called the " Chelsea Pensioner," containing sulphur ℥ j, cream of tartar ℥ j, rhubarb ℈ iv, gum guaiacum ℥ j, honey ℥ xvj (Sig.: ℥ j night and morning in warm wine), was formerly much used. Careful attention to the digestion, plenty of good food, and fresh air are important measures. Hydrotherapy, with carefully performed massage, is best for the alleviation of the pain, and may possibly restrain the progress of the affection. In early cases local improvement and often great gain in the general strength follow a prolonged treatment at the hot mineral baths; but the practitioner should exercise care in recommending this mode of treatment, which is of very doubtful value when the disease is well established. I have repeatedly known cases to be rendered much worse by residence at these institutions. When good results, it is largely from change of scene and climate, and the careful regulation of the diet. The local treatment is of benefit in arresting the progress. When there are much heat and pain the limb should be at rest, cold compresses applied at night, the joints wrapped in oiled silk, and in the morning thoroughly massaged. It is surprising how much can be done by carefully applied friction to reduce the thickening, to promote absorption of effusion, and to restore mobility. Massage is also of special benefit in maintaining the nutrition of the muscles, which early tend to atrophy. In the case of the knees this mode of treatment will sometimes prevent the retraction of the muscles and the gradual flexion of the legs on the thighs. No benefit can be expected from electricity. The hot air treatment, recently introduced, should be given a thorough trial, as it has produced good results in some cases.

In children much may be done surgically in the way of breaking up the fibrous adhesions.

II. CHRONIC RHEUMATISM.

Etiology.—This affection may follow an acute or subacute attack, but more commonly comes on insidiously in persons who have passed the middle period of life. In my experience it is extremely rare as a sequence of acute rheumatism. It is most common among the poor, particularly washer-women, day-laborers, and those whose occupation exposes them to cold and damp.

Morbid Anatomy.—The synovial membranes are injected, but there is usually not much effusion. The capsule and ligaments of the joints are thickened, and the sheaths of the tendons in the neighborhood undergo similar alterations, so that the free play of the joint is greatly impaired. In long-standing cases the cartilages also undergo changes, and may show erosions. Even in cases with the severest symptoms, the joint may be very slightly altered in appearance. Important changes take place in the muscles and nerves adjacent to chronically inflamed joints, particularly in the mono-articular lesions of the shoulder or hip. Muscular atrophy supervenes partly from disuse, partly through nervous influences, either centric or reflex (Vulpian), or as a result of peripheral neuritis. In some cases when the joint is much distended the wasting may be due to pressure, either on the muscles themselves or on the vessels supplying them.

Symptoms.—Stiffness and pain are the chief features of chronic rheumatism. The latter is very liable to exacerbations, especially during changes in the weather. The joints may be tender to the touch and a little swollen, but are seldom reddened. As a rule, many joints are affected; but there are instances in which the disease is confined to one shoulder, knee, or hip. The stiffness and pain are more marked after rest, and as the day advances the joints may, with exertion, become much more supple. The general health may not be seriously impaired. The disease is not immediately dangerous. Anchylosis may occur, and ultimately the joints may become much distorted. In many instances, particularly those in which the pain is severe, the general health may be seriously involved and the subjects become anæmic and very apt to suffer with neuralgia and dyspepsia. Valvular lesions, due to slow sclerotic changes, are not uncommon. They are associated with, not dependent upon, the articular disease.

The *prognosis* is not favorable, as a majority of the cases resist all methods of treatment. It is, however, a disease which persists indefinitely, and does not necessarily shorten life.

Treatment.—Internal remedies are of little service. It is important to maintain the digestive functions and to keep the general health at a high standard. Iodide of potassium, sarsaparilla, and guaiacum are sometimes beneficial. The salicylates are useless.

Local treatment is very beneficial. " Firing " with the Paquelin cautery relieves the pain, and it is perhaps the best form of counter-irritation. Massage, with passive motion, helps to reduce swelling, and prevents anchylosis. It is particularly useful in cases which are associated with atrophy of the muscles. Electricity is not of much benefit. Climatic treatment is very advantageous. Many cases are greatly helped by prolonged residence in southern Europe or Southern California. Rich patients should always winter in the South, and in this way avoid the cold, damp weather.

Hydrotherapeutic measures are specially beneficial in chronic rheumatism. Great relief is afforded by wrapping the affected joints in cold cloths, covered with a thin layer of blanket, and protected with oiled silk. The Turkish bath is useful, but the full benefit of this treatment is rarely seen except at bathing establishments. The hot alkaline waters are particularly useful, and a residence at the Hot Springs of Virginia or Arkansas, or at Banff, in the Rocky Mountains, on the Canadian Pacific Railway, will sometimes cure even obstinate cases.

III. MUSCULAR RHEUMATISM (*Myalgia*).

Definition.—A painful affection of the voluntary muscles and of the fasciæ and periosteum to which they are attached. The affection has received various names, according to its seat, as torticollis, lumbago, pleurodynia, etc.

Etiology.—The attacks follow cold and exposure, the usual conditions favorable to the development of rheumatism. It is by no means certain that the muscular tissues are the seat of the disease. Many writers claim, perhaps correctly, that it is a neuralgia of the sensory nerves of the muscles. Until our knowledge is more accurate, however, it may be considered under the rheumatic affections.

It is most commonly met with in men, particularly those exposed to cold and whose occupations are laborious. It is apt to follow exposure to a draught of air, as from an open window in a railway carriage. A sudden chilling after heavy exertion may also bring on an attack of lumbago. Persons of a rheumatic or gouty habit are certainly more prone to this affection. One attack renders an individual more liable to another. It is usually acute, but may become subacute or even chronic.

Symptoms.—The affection is entirely local. The constitutional disturbance is slight, and, even in severe cases, there may be no fever. Pain is a prominent symptom. It may be constant, or may occur only when the muscles are drawn into certain positions. It may be a dull ache, like the pain of a bruise, or sharp, severe, and cramp-like. It is often sufficiently intense to cause the patient to cry out. Pressure on the affected part usually gives relief. As a rule, myalgia is a transient affection, lasting from a few hours to a few days. Occasionally it is prolonged for several weeks. It is very apt to recur.

The following are the principal varieties:

(1) **Lumbago,** one of the most common and painful forms, affects the muscles of the loins and their tendinous attachments. It occurs chiefly in workingmen. It comes on suddenly, and in very severe cases completely incapacitates the patient, who may be unable to turn in bed or to rise from the sitting posture.

(2) **Stiff neck or torticollis** affects the muscles of the antero-lateral

region of the neck. It is very common, and occurs most frequently in the young. The patient holds the head in a peculiar manner, and rotates the whole body in attempting to turn it. Usually the attack is confined to one side. The muscles at the back of the neck may also be affected.

(3) **Pleurodynia** involves the intercostal muscles on one side, and in some instances the pectorals and serratus magnus. This is, perhaps, the most painful form of the disease, as the chest cannot be at rest. It is more common on the left than on the right side. A deep breath, or coughing, causes very intense pain, and the respiratory movements are restricted on the affected side. There may be pain on pressure, sometimes over a very limited area. It may be difficult to distinguish from intercostal neuralgia, in which affection, however, the pain is usually more circumscribed and paroxysmal, and there are tender points along the course of the nerves. It is sometimes mistaken for pleurisy, but careful physical examination readily distinguishes between the two affections.

(4) Among other forms which may be mentioned are **cephalodynia,** affecting the muscles of the head; **scapulodynia, omodynia,** and **dorsodynia,** affecting the muscles about the shoulder and upper part of the back. Myalgia may also occur in the abdominal muscles and in the muscles of the extremities.

Treatment.—Rest of the affected muscles is of the first importance. Strapping the side will sometimes completely relieve pleurodynia. No belief is more widespread among the public than in the efficacy of porous plasters for muscular pains of all sorts, particularly those about the trunk. If the pain is severe and agonizing, a hypodermic of morphia gives immediate relief. For lumbago acupuncture is, in acute cases, the most efficient treatment. Needles of from three to four inches in length (ordinary bonnet-needles, sterilized, will do) are thrust into the lumbar muscles at the seat of the pain, and withdrawn after five or ten minutes. In many instances the relief is immediate, and I can corroborate fully the statements of Ringer, who taught me this practice, as to its extraordinary and prompt efficacy in many instances. The constant current is sometimes very beneficial. In many forms of myalgia the thermo-cautery gives great relief. In obstinate cases blisters may be tried. Hot fomentations are soothing, and at the outset a Turkish bath may cut short the attack. In chronic cases iodide of potassium may be used, and both guaiacum and sulphur have been strongly recommended. Persons subject to this affection should be warmly clothed, and avoid, if possible, exposure to cold and damp. In gouty persons the diet should be restricted and the alkaline mineral waters taken freely. Large doses of nux vomica are sometimes beneficial.

IV. GOUT (*Podagra*).

Definition.—A nutritional disorder, one factor of which is an excessive formation of uric acid, characterized clinically by attacks of acute arthritis, by the gradual deposition of urate of soda in and about the joints, and by the occurrence of irregular constitutional symptoms.

Etiology.—The precise nature of the disturbance in metabolism is not known. There is probably defective oxidation of the foodstuffs, combined with imperfect elimination of the waste products of the body.

Among important etiological factors in gout are the following:

(*a*) *Hereditary Influences.*—Statistics show that in from 50 to 60 per cent of all cases the disease existed in the parents or grandparents. The transmission is supposed to be more marked from the male side. Cases with a strong hereditary taint have been known to develop before puberty. The disease has been seen even in infants at the breast. Males are more subject to the disease than females. It rarely develops before the thirtieth year, and in a large majority of the cases the first manifestations appear before the age of fifty. (*b*) *Alcohol* is the most potent factor in the etiology of the disease. Fermented liquors favor its development much more than distilled spirits, and it prevails most extensively in countries like England and Germany, which consume the most beer and ale. The lighter beers used in this country are much less liable to produce gout than the heavier English and Scotch ales. (*c*) *Food* plays a *rôle* equal in importance to that of alcohol. Overeating without active bodily exercise is regarded as a very special predisposing cause. A form of gouty dyspepsia has been described. A robust and active digestion is, however, often met in gouty persons. Gout is by no means confined to the rich. In England the combination of poor food, defective hygiene, and an excessive consumption of malt liquors makes the " poor man's gout " a common affection. (*d*) *Lead.* Garrod has shown that workers in lead are specially prone to gout. In 30 per cent of the hospital cases the patients had been painters or workers in lead. The association is probably to be sought in the production by this poison of arterio-sclerosis and chronic nephritis. Chronic lead-poisoning is here frequently associated with arterio-sclerosis and contracted kidneys, but lead-gout is comparatively rare. Gouty deposits are, however, to be found in the big-toe joint and in the kidneys in cases of chronic plumbism.

The nature of gout is unknown. That there is faulty metabolism, associated in some very special way with the chemistry of uric acid, we know, but nothing more. The remainder is theory, awaiting refutation or confirmation. The conditions of life favorable to the development of gout are present in too many of us after the middle period of life—more fuel in the form of meat and drink than the machine needs. G. B. Balfour put it well when he says: " The gouty diathesis is only a comprehensive term for all those changes in the character and composition of the blood induced by the evils of civilization—deficient exercise and excess of nutriment. . . . Gout, on the other hand, is the name given to all those modifications of our metabolism caused by the gouty diathesis, as well as to all the symptoms to which those modifications give rise."

The views regarding uric acid and its relation to gout are very numerous.

Garrod holds that with lessened alkalinity of the blood there is an increase in the uric acid, due chiefly to diminished elimination. He attributes the deposition of the urate of soda to the diminished alkalinity of the plasma, which is unable to hold it in solution. In an acute paroxysm there is an accumulation of the urates in the blood, and the inflammation is caused by their sudden deposit in crystalline form about the joint.

Haig thinks that there is no increased formation of uric acid in gout, but that the blood is less alkaline than normal, and less able to hold the uric acid or its salts in solution.

According to Sir William Roberts, the chalk-like deposits are formed of the crystalline biurate of sodium, and "the arthritic incidents of gout may be said, not improperly, to be simply incidents pertaining to the precipitation of these crystals in the structures of the joints."

Levison (Die Harnsäurediathese, Berlin, 1893) adopts Horbaczewski's views that the uric acid is related especially to the nucleins of the body, and is derived in great part from the destruction of the white blood-corpuscles, the excretion increasing *pari passu* with the intensity of the leucocytosis. While this is true in many diseases, as in pneumonia, Richter, in a careful study, has shown that there are important exceptions.

Ebstein thinks that the first change is a nutritive-tissue disturbance, which leads to necrosis, and in the necrotic areas the urates are deposited —a view which has been modified by von Noorden, who holds that a special ferment leads to the tissue change, to which the deposit of the urates is secondary.

Kolisch believes that the kidneys not only have the function of excreting but also that of forming uric acid. He holds that the graver manifestations of gout only make their appearance when the functions of the kidney become impaired from some cause. In his studies on metabolism in gout, he finds that the total alloxuric bodies (uric acid and xanthin bases) are increased in the urine. This is due to an increase of the alloxuric or xanthin bases and not of the uric acid, which in reality is diminished. In nephritis, Kolisch found that although the total alloxuric bodies were eliminated in normal amount, yet the xanthin bases were markedly increased at the expense of the uric acid excreted. With the kidneys healthy, the greater part of the alloxuric bodies is eliminated as uric acid, but, when diseased, Kolisch holds that the uric acid becomes diminished and the xanthin bases are relatively increased. This leads him to believe that the kidney normally produces uric acid. He demonstrated the toxic effects of the xanthin bases on the kidneys by injecting rabbits and guinea-pigs subcutaneously with hypoxanthin for periods of one to two months. In this way definite parenchymatous degeneration was produced. Having shown that the xanthin bases were also increased in gout, he believes that they are concerned in the production of the kidney affection which precedes the development of gout. Garrod now holds that uric acid is normally formed in the kidneys, and that when it appears in the blood this results from its reabsorption after having been formed in these organs. Luff claims that uric acid under normal conditions is produced only in the kidneys. Latham also is of the opinion that the final formation of uric acid takes place in the kidneys, where it is produced by the union of substances formed in the liver and conveyed to them by the blood current.

Cullen held that gout was primarily an affection of the nervous system. On this nervous theory of gout there is a basic, arthritic stock—a diathetic habit, of which gout and rheumatism are two distinct branches. The gouty diathesis is expressed in (*a*) a neurosis of the nerve-centres, which may be inherited or acquired; and (*b*) " a peculiar incapacity for normal elaboration within the whole body, not merely in the liver or in one or two organs, of food, whereby uric acid is formed at times in excess, or is incapable of being duly transformed into more soluble and less noxious products" (Duckworth). The explosive neuroses and the influence of depressing circumstances, physical or mental, point strongly to the part played by the nervous system in the disease. The recents works of Duckworth and William Ewart may be consulted for a full discussion of the various theories on the nature of gout.

Morbid Anatomy.—The *blood* is stated to have an excess of uric acid. It may be obtained from the blood-serum by the method known as Garrod's uric-acid thread experiment, or from the serum obtained from a blister. To ℥ij of serum add ♍ v–vj of acetic acid in a watch-glass. A thread immersed in this may show in a few hours an incrustation of uric acid. The experiment is rarely successful even in cases of manifest gout. This excess, also, is not peculiar to gout, but occurs in leukæmia and chlorosis.

In 1894 Neusser described a peculiar black granulation over and about the nuclei of the leucocytes in the blood of gouty patients. He termed them " perinuclear basophilic granules," and demonstrated them by using a modified Ehrlich's triacid mixture. They were particularly numerous about the nuclei of the mononuclear leucocytes. He believed that they were of the nature of a nucleo-albumin, and claimed that cases showing them eliminated uric acid in excess. He held that these granules constituted the mother substance from which the uric acid was formed, and that patients showing these granules were suffering from a uratic or gouty diathesis. Subsequent work by Futcher and others seems to have shown that there is no association between the abundance of these granules and the elimination of uric acid or of the total alloxuric bodies.

The important changes are in the articular tissues. The first joint of the great toe is most frequently involved; then the ankles, knees, and the small joints of the hands and wrists. The deposits may be in all the joints of the lower limbs and absent from those of the upper limbs (Norman Moore). If death takes place during an acute paroxysm, there are signs of inflammation, hyperæmia, swelling of the ligamentous tissues, and of effusion into the joint. The primary change, according to Ebstein, is a local necrosis, due to the presence of an excess of urates in the blood. This is seen in the cartilage and other articular tissues in which the nutritional currents are slow. Mordhorst holds that the deposition of the urates is primary, and that the necrosis of the tissues takes place as a result of this deposit. In these areas of coagulation necrosis the reaction is always acid and the neutral urates are deposited in crystalline form, as insoluble acid urates. The articular cartilages are first involved. The gouty deposit may be uniform, or in small areas. Though it looks superficial, the deposit is invariably interstitial and covered by a thin lamina of cartilage. The deposit is thickest at the part most distant from the circulation. The ligaments and fibro-cartilage ultimately become involved and are infiltrated with chalky deposits, the so-called chalk-stones, or tophi. These are usually covered by skin; but in some cases, particularly in the metacarpo-phalangeal articulations, this ulcerates and the chalk-stones appear externally. The synovial fluid may also contain crystals. In very long-standing cases, owing to an excessive deposit, the joint becomes immobile. The marginal outgrowths in gouty arthritis are true exostoses (Wynne). The cartilage of the ear may contain tophi, which are seen as whitish nodules at the margin of the helix. The cartilages of the nose, eyelids, and larynx are less frequently affected.

Of changes in the internal organs, those in the renal and vascular systems are the most important. The kidney changes believed to be characteristic of gout are: (a) A deposit of urates chiefly in the region of the papillæ. This, however, is less common than is usually supposed. Norman Moore found it in only 12 out of 80 cases. The apices of the pyramids show lines of whitish deposit. On microscopical examination the material is seen to be largely in the intertubular tissue. In some instances, however, the deposit seems to be both in the tissue and in the tubules. Ebstein has described and figured areas of necrosis in both cortex and medulla, in the interior of which were crystalline deposits of urate of soda. The presence of these uratic concretions at the apices of the pyramids is not a positive indication of gout. They are not infrequent in this country, in which gout is rare. (b) An interstitial nephritis, either the ordinary " contracted kidney " or the arterio-sclerotic form, neither of which are in any way distinctive. It is not possible to say in a given case that the condition has been due to gout unless marked evidences of the disease coexist.

The metatarso-phalangeal joint of the big toe should be carefully examined, as it may show typical lesions of gout without any outward token of arthritis.

Arterio-sclerosis is a very constant lesion. With it the heart, particularly the left ventricle, is found hypertrophied. According to some authors, concretions of urate of soda may occur on the valves.

Changes in the respiratory system are rare. Deposits have been found in the vocal cords, and uric-acid crystals have been met in the sputa of a gouty patient (J. W. Moore). Emphysema is a very constant condition in old cases.

Symptoms.—Gout is usually divided into acute, chronic, and irregular forms.

Acute Gout.—Premonitory symptoms are common—twinges of pain in the small joints of the hands or feet, nocturnal restlessness, irritability of temper, and dyspepsia. The urine is acid, scanty, and high-colored. It deposits urates on cooling, and there may be, according to Garrod, transient albuminuria. There may be traces of sugar (gouty glycosuria). Before an attack the output of uric acid is low and is also diminished in the early part of the paroxysm. The relation of uric and phosphoric acids to the acute attacks is well represented in Chart XIV,* prepared by Futcher.

---

* The uric acid was determined by the Gowland-Hopkins method and the phosphoric acid by the uranium-nitrate process.

Both were extremely low in the intervals, but reached within normal limits shortly after the onset of the acute symptoms. The phosphoric acid and uric acid show almost parallel curves. The patient was on a very light diet at the time the determinations were made. In some instances the throat

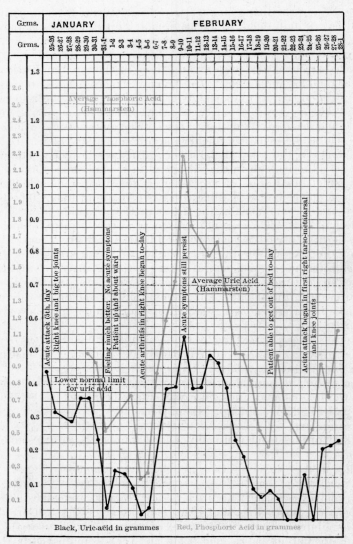

CHART XIV.—Showing uric acid and phosphoric acid output in case of acute gout.

is sore, and there may be asthmatic symptoms. The attack sets in usually in the early morning hours. The patient is aroused by a severe pain in the metatarso-phalangeal articulation of the big toe, and more commonly on the right than on the left side. The pain is agonizing, and, as Sydenham says, "insinuates itself with the most exquisite cruelty among the numerous small bones of the tarsus and metatarsus, in the ligaments of which it is lurking." The joint swells rapidly, and becomes hot, tense, and shiny. The sensitiveness is extreme, and the pain makes the patient feel as if the joint were being pressed in a vice. There is fever, and the temperature may rise to 102° or 103°. Toward morning the severity of the symptoms subsides, and, although the joint remains swollen, the day may be passed in comparative comfort. The symptoms recur the next night, and the fit, as it is called, usually lasts for from five to eight days, the severity of the symptoms gradually abating. Occasionally other joints are involved, particularly the big toe of the opposite foot. The inflammation, however intense, never goes on to suppuration. With the subsidence of the swelling the skin desquamates. After the attack the general health may be much improved. As Aretæus remarks, a person in the interval has won the race at the Olympian games. Recurrences are frequent. Some patients have three or four attacks in a year; others at longer intervals.

The term *retrocedent* or *suppressed* gout is applied to serious internal symptoms, coincident with a rapid disappearance or improvement of the local signs. Very remarkable manifestations may occur under these circumstances. The patient may have severe gastro-intestinal symptoms—pain, vomiting, diarrhœa, and great depression—and death may occur during such an attack. Or there may be cardiac manifestations—dyspnœa, pain, and irregular action of the heart. In some instances in which the gout is said to attack the heart, an acute pericarditis develops and proves fatal. So, too, there may be marked cerebral manifestations—delirium or coma, and even apoplexy—but in a majority of these instances the symptoms are, in all probability, uræmic.

Gout is a comparatively rare disease in America. Among the well-to-do, and even among club-men—a class particularly liable—it is infrequent, in comparison with the prevalence in the corresponding classes in England. Men in large family practice may pass a year or more without seeing a case. It has become more common, however, during the past twenty-five years, and I find a marked increase in hospital practice.

Chronic Gout.—With increased frequency in the attacks, the articular symptoms persist for a longer time, and gradually many joints become affected. Deposits of urates take place, at first in the articular cartilages and then in the ligaments and capsular tissues; so that in the course of years the joints become swollen, irregular, and deformed. The feet are usually first affected, then the hands. In severe cases there may be extensive concretions about the elbows and knees and along the tendons and in the bursæ. The tophi appear in the ears. Finally, a unique clinical picture is produced which cannot be mistaken for that of any other affection. The skin over the tophi may rupture or ulcerate, and about the knuckles the chalk-stones may be freely exposed. Patients with chronic gout are usually dyspeptic, often of a sallow complexion, and show signs of arterio-sclerosis. The pulse tension is increased, the vessels are stiff, and the left ventricle is hypertrophied. The urine is increased in amount, is of low specific grav-

26

ity, and usually contains a slight amount of albumin, with a few hyaline casts. Intercurrent attacks of acute polyarthritis may develop, in which the joints become inflamed, and the temperature ranges from 101° to 103°. There may be pain, redness, and swelling of several joints without fever. Uræmia, pleurisy, pericarditis, peritonitis, and meningitis are common terminal affections. Patients with chronic gout may show remarkable mental and even bodily vigor. Certain of the most distinguished members of our professsion have been terrible sufferers from this disease, notably the elder Scaliger, Jerome Cardan, and Sydenham, whose statement that "more wise men than fools are victims of the affection" still holds good.

Irregular Gout.—This is a motley, ill-defined group of symptoms, manifestations of a condition of disordered nutrition, to which the terms *gouty diathesis* or *lithæmic state* have been given. Cases are seen in members of gouty families, who may never themselves have suffered from the acute disease, and in persons who have lived not wisely but too well, who have eaten and drunk largely, lived sedentary lives, and yet have been fortunate enough to escape an acute attack. It is interesting to note the various manifestations of the disease in a family with marked hereditary disposition. The daughters often escape, while one son may have gouty attacks of great severity, even though he lives a temperate life and tries in every way to avoid the conditions favoring the disorder. Another son has, perhaps, only the irregular manifestations and never the acute articular affection. While the irregular features are perhaps more often met with in the hereditary affection, they are by no means infrequent in persons who appear to have acquired the disease. The tendency in some families is to call every affection gouty. Even infantile complaints, such as scald-head, naso-pharyngeal vegetations, and enuresis, are often regarded, without sufficient grounds, I believe, as evidences of the family ailment. Among the commonest manifestations of irregular gout are the following:

(a) *Cutaneous Eruptions.*—Garrod and others have called special attention to the frequent association of eczema with the gouty habit. The French in particular insist upon the special liability of gouty persons to skin affections, the *arthritides,* as they call them.

(b) *Gastro-intestinal Disorders.*—Attacks of what is termed biliousness, in which the tongue is furred, the breath foul, the bowels constipated, and the action of the liver torpid, are not uncommon in gouty persons. A gouty parotitis is described.

(c) *Cardio-vascular Symptoms.*—With the lithæmia, arterio-sclerosis is frequently associated. The blood tension is persistently high, the vessel walls become stiff, and cardiac and renal changes gradually develop. In this condition the manifestations may be renal, as when the albuminuria becomes more marked, or dropsical symptoms supervene. The manifestations may be cardiac, when the hypertrophy of the left ventricle fails and there are palpitation, irregular action, and ultimately a condition of asystole. Or, finally, the manifestations may be vascular, and thrombosis of the coronary arteries may cause sudden death. Aneurism may develop and prove fatal, or, as most frequently happens, a blood-vessel gives way in the brain, and the patient dies of apoplexy. It makes but little difference whether we regard this condition as primarily an arterio-sclerosis, or as a gouty nephritis; the point to be remembered is that the nutritional disorder with which an excess of uric acid is associated induces in time increased tension, arterio-sclerosis, chronic interstitial nephritis, and changes in the myocardium. Pericarditis is not an infrequent terminal complication of gout.

(d) *Nervous Manifestations.*—Headache and megrim attacks are not infrequent. Haig attributes them to an excess of uric acid. Neuralgias are not uncommon; sciatica and paræsthesias may develop. A common gouty manifestation, upon which Duckworth has laid stress, is the occurrence of hot or itching feet at night. Plutarch mentions that Strabo called this symptom "the lisping of the gout." Cramps in the legs may also be very troublesome. Hutchinson has called attention to hot and itching eyeballs as a frequent sign of masked gout. More serious cerebral manifestations result from a condition of arterio-sclerosis. Apoplexy is a common termination of gout. Meningitis may develop, usually basilar.

(e) *Urinary Disorders.*—The urine is highly acid and high-colored, and may deposit on standing crystals of lithic acid. Transient and temporary increase in this ingredient cannot be regarded as serious. In many cases of chronic gout the amount may be diminished, and only increased at certain periods, forming the so-called uric-acid showers. The chart on page 412 illustrates this very well. Sugar is found intermittently in the urine of gouty persons—gouty glycosuria. It may pass into true diabetes, but is usually very amenable to treatment. Oxaluria may also be present. Gouty persons are specially prone to calculi, Jerome Cardan to the contrary, who reckoned freedom from stone among the chief of the *dona podagræ*. Minute quantities of albumin are very common in persons of gouty dyscrasia, and, when the renal changes are well established, tube-casts. Urethritis, accompanied with a well-marked purulent discharge, may develop, so it is stated, usually at the end of an attack. It may occur spontaneously, or follow a pure connection.

(f) *Pulmonary Disorders.*—There are no characteristic changes, but, as Greenhow has pointed out, chronic bronchitis occurs with great frequency in persons of a gouty habit.

(g) Of eye affections, iritis, glaucoma, hæmorrhagic retinitis, and suppurative panopthalmitis have been described.

Diagnosis.—Recurring attacks of arthritis, limited to the big toe and to the tarsus, occurring in a member of a gouty family, or in a man who has lived too well, leave no question as to the nature of the trouble. There are many cases of gout, however, in which the feet do not suffer most severely. After an attack or two in one toe, other joints may be affected, and it is just in such cases of polyarthritis that the difficulty in diagnosis is apt to arise. We have had of late years several cases admitted for the third or fourth time with involvement of three or more of the larger joints. The presence of tophi has settled the nature of a trouble which in the previous attacks had been regarded as rheumatic. The following are suggestive points in such cases: (1) The patient's habits and occupation. In this country the brewery men and barkeepers are often affected. (2) The presence of tophi. The ears should always be felt in a case of polyarthritis. The diagnosis may rest with a small tophus. The student should learn to recognize on the ear margin Woolner's tip, fibroid nodules, and small sebaceous tumors. The latter are easily recognized microscopically. The urate of soda cystals are distinctive in the tophi. (3) The condition of the urine. As shown in Chart XIV, the uric-acid output is usually very low during the intervals of the paroxysm. There may, indeed, be no excretion whatever. At the height of the attack the elimination, as a rule, is greatly increased. The ratio of the uric acid to the urea excretion is disturbed in gouty cases, and may fall as low as 1 to 60 or 1 to 80. (4) The gouty polyarthritis may be afebrile. A patient with three or four joints red, swollen, and painful in acute rheumatism has fever, and, while pyrexia may be present and often is in gout, its absence is, I think, a valuable diagnostic sign.

Treatment.—*Hygienic.*—Individuals who have inherited a tendency to gout, or who have shown any manifestations of it, should live temperately, abstain from alcohol, and eat moderately. An open-air life, with plenty of exercise and regular hours, does much to counteract an inborn tendency to the disease. The skin should be kept active: if the patient is robust, by the morning cold bath with friction after it; but if he is weak or debilitated the evening warm bath should be substituted. An occasional Turkish bath with active shampooing is very advantageous. The patient should dress warmly, avoid rapid alterations in temperature, and be careful not to have the skin suddenly chilled.

Dietetic.—With few exceptions, persons over forty eat too much, and the first injunction to a gouty person is to keep his appetite within reasonable bounds, to eat at stated hours, and to take plenty of time at his meals. In the matter of food, quantity is a factor of more importance than quality with many gouty persons. As Sir William Roberts well says, " Nowhere perhaps is it more necessary than in gout to consider the man as well as the ailment, and very often more the man than the ailment."

Very remarkable differences of opinion exist as to the most suitable diet in this disease, some urging warmly a vegetable diet, others allowing a very liberal amount of meat. On the one hand, the author just quoted says: " The most trustworthy experiments indicate that fat, starch, and sugar have not the least direct influence on the production of uric acid; but as the free consumption of these articles naturally operates to restrict the intake of the nitrogenous food, their use has indirectly the effect of diminishing the average production of uric acid." On the other hand, W. H. Draper says: " The conversion of azotized food is more complete with a minimum of carbohydrates than it is with an excess of them; in other words, one of the best means of avoiding the accumulation of lithic acid in the blood is to diminish the carbohydrates rather than the azotized foods." The weight of opinion leans to the use of a modified nitrogenous diet, without excess in starchy and saccharine articles of food. Fresh vegetables and fruits may be used freely, but among the latter strawberries and bananas should be avoided.

Ebstein urges strongly the use of fat in the form of good fresh butter, from $2\frac{1}{2}$ to $3\frac{1}{2}$ ounces in the day. He says that stout gouty subjects not only do not increase in weight with plenty of fat in the food, but that they actually become thin and the general condition improves very much. Hot bread of all sorts and the various articles of food prepared from Indian corn should, as a rule, be avoided. Roberts advises gouty patients to restrict as far as practicable the use of common salt with their meals, since the sodium biurate very readily crystallizes out in tissues with a high percentage of sodium salts.

In this matter of diet each individual case must receive separate consideration.

There are very few conditions in the gouty in which stimulants of any sort are required. Whenever indicated, whisky will be found perhaps the most serviceable. While all are injurious to these patients, some are much more so than others, particularly malted liquors, champagne, port, and a very large proportion of all the light wines.

Mineral Waters.—All forms may be said to be beneficial in gout, as the main element is the water, and the ingredients are usually indifferent. Much of the humbuggery in the profession still lingers about mineral waters, more particularly about the so-called lithia waters. For a careful consideration of the question the reader is referred to William Ewart's recent work on Gout and Goutiness.

The question of the utility of alkalies in the treatment of gout is closely connected with this subject of mineral waters. This deep-rooted belief in the profession was rudely shaken a few years ago by Sir William Roberts, who claims to have shown conclusively that alkalescence as such has no influence whatever on the sodium biurate. The sodium salts are believed by this author to be particularly harmful, but, in spite of all the theoretical denunciation of the use of the sodium salts in gout, the gouty from all parts of the world flock to those very Continental springs in which these salts are most predominant.

Of the mineral springs best suited for the gouty may be mentioned, in this country, those of Saratoga, Bedford, and the White Sulphur; Buxton and Bath, in England; in France, Aix-les-Bains and Contrexéville; and in Germany, Carlsbad, Wildbad, and Homburg.

The efficacy in reality is in the water, in the way it is taken, on an empty stomach, and in large quantities; and, as every one knows, the important accessories in the modified diet, proper hours, regular exercise, with baths, douches, etc., play a very important *rôle* in the " cure."

Medicinal Treatment.—In an acute attack the limb should be elevated and the affected joint wrapped in cotton-wool. Warm fomentations, or Fuller's lotion, may be used. The local hot-air treatment may be tried. A brisk mercurial purge is always advantageous at the outset. The wine or tincture of colchicum, in doses of 20 to 30 minims, may be given every four hours in combination with the citrate of potash or the citrate of lithium. The action of the colchicum should be carefully watched. It has, in a majority of the cases, a powerful influence over the symptoms— relieving the pain, and reducing, sometimes with great rapidity, the swelling and redness. It should be promptly stopped so soon as it has relieved the pain. In cases in which the pain and sleeplessness are distressing and do not yield to colchicum, morphia is necessary. The patient should be placed on a diet chiefly of milk and barley-water, but if there is any debility, strong broths may be given, or eggs. It is occasionally necessary to give small quantities of stimulants. During convalescence meats and fish and game may be taken, and gradually the patient may resume the diet previously laid down.

In some of the subacute intercurrent attacks of arthritis in old, deformed joints, the sodium salicylate is occasionally useful, but its administration must be watched in cases of cardiac and renal insufficiency. It is also much advocated by Haig in the uric-acid habit.

The chronic and irregular forms of gout are best treated by the dietetic and hygienic measures already referred to. Iodide of potassium is sometimes useful, and preparations of guaiacum, quinine, and the bitter tonics combined with alkalies are undoubtedly of benefit.

Piperazin has been much lauded as an efficient aid in the solution of uric acid. The clinical results, however, are very discordant. It may be employed in doses of from 15 to 30 grains in the day, and is conveniently given in aërated water containing 5 grains to the tumblerful.

V. DIABETES MELLITUS.*

Definition.—A disorder of nutrition, in which sugar accumulates in the blood and is excreted in the urine, the daily amount of which is greatly increased.

For a case to be considered one of diabetes mellitus it is necessary, according to von Noorden, that the form of sugar eliminated in the urine be grape sugar, that it must be eliminated for weeks, months, or years, and that the excretion of sugar must take place after the ingestion of moderate amounts of carbohydrates.

Etiology.—*Hereditary influences* play an important *rôle*, and cases are on record of its occurrence in many members of the same family. Of the 77 cases which have been treated in the medical wards and dispensary of the Johns Hopkins Hospital, only 2 gave a history of diabetes in relatives (Futcher). There are instances of the coexistence of the disease in man and wife. Schmidt first drew attention to the possibility of diabetes being contagious. Out of his series of 2,320 cases he believed that 26 instances were the result of contagion. In the majority of the cases the wife contracted the disease later than the husband. *Sex.*—Men are more frequently affected than women, the ratio being about three to two. Forty-seven cases of the hospital series were in males and 30 in females. It is a disease of adult life; a majority of the cases occur from the third to the sixth decade. Of the 77 cases, the largest number—24, or 31.1 per cent—occurred between fifty

---

* Since the second edition of this work the literature has been enriched by Pavy's Croonian Lectures, the second edition of Saundby's work, the monographs of von Noorden (2d ed., 1898) and Williamson, and by the magnificent work of Naunyn (1898), which unfortunately arrived too late to be fully utilized for the revision.

and sixty years of age. These figures agree closely with those of Frerichs, Seegen, and Pavy, all of whom found the largest number of cases in the sixth decade, their percentages being 26, 30, and 30.7 respectively. It is rare in childhood, but cases are on record in children under one year of age. Persons of a neurotic *temperament* are often affected. It is a disease of the higher classes. Von Noorden states that the statistics for London and Berlin show that the number of cases in the upper ten thousand exceeds that in the lower hundred thousand inhabitants. *Race.*—Hebrews seem especially prone to it; one fourth of Frerichs' patients were of the Semitic race. I have been much impressed with the frequency of the disease among them. Of the last 16 cases which I have had in private practice, 8 were in Hebrews. Diabetes is comparatively rare in the colored race, but not so uncommon as was formerly supposed. Of the series of 77 cases, 8, or 10.3 per cent, were in negroes (Futcher). The ratio of males to females affected is almost exactly the reverse of that in the white race; 3 of the 8 cases were in males and 5 in females. In a considerable proportion of the cases of diabetes the subjects have been excessively *fat* at the beginning of, or prior to, the onset of the disease. A slight trace of sugar is not very uncommon in obese persons. This so-called lipogenic glycosuria is not of grave significance, and is only occasionally followed by true diabetes. On the other hand, as von Noorden has shown, there may be a " diabetogenous obesity," in which diabetes and obesity develop in early life, and these cases are very unfavorable. There are instances on record in which obesity with diabetes has occurred in three generations. Diabetes is more common in cities than in country districts. Gout, syphilis, and malaria have been regarded as predisposing causes. Burdel and Calmette think that malaria is an important predisposing etiological factor. In only 1 of the 77 cases could malaria be considered more than a possible cause of the diabetes (Futcher). Mental shock, severe nervous strain, and worry precede many cases. In one case the symptoms came on suddenly after the patient had been nearly suffocated by smoke from having been confined in a cell of a burning jail. Shock and the toxic effects of the smoke may both have been factors in this case. The combination of intense application to business, over-indulgence in food and drink, with a sedentary life, seems particularly prone to induce the disease. Glycosuria may set in during pregnancy, and in rare instances may only occur at this period. Trousseau thought that the offspring of phthisical parents were particularly prone to diabetes. *Injury* to or disease of the spinal cord or brain has been followed by diabetes. In the carefully analyzed cases of Frerichs there were 30 instances of organic disease of these parts. The medulla is not always involved. In only 4 of his cases, which showed organic disease, was there sclerosis or other anomaly of this part. An irritative lesion of Bernard's diabetic centre in the medulla is an occasional cause. I saw with Reiss, at the Friedrichshain, Berlin, a woman who had anomalous cerebral symptoms and diabetes, and in whom there was found post mortem a cysticercus in the fourth ventricle. Ebstein has recently recorded 4 cases in which there was a coincident occurrence of epilepsy and diabetes mellitus. He thinks that in the majority of cases the two diseases are dependent on a common cause. He believes that the association would be found much more commonly in Jacksonian epilepsy than has been the case heretofore, if more careful and systematic examinations of the urine were made.

The disease has occasionally followed the *infectious fevers*. Cases have been recorded as occurring during or immediately after diphtheria, influenza, rheumatism, enteric fever, and syphilis. A few cases have followed injury without involvement of the brain or cord.

In comparison with its incidence in European countries diabetes is a rare disease in America. The last census gave only 3.8 per 100,000 of population, against a ratio of from 5 to 14 in the former. The death-rate has been gradually on the increase in Paris during the last three or four decades, reaching 14 to the 100,000 of population in 1891. For the same year the mortality in Malta was 13.1 to the 100,000 of population. The disease is gradually on the increase in the United States. The statistics for 1870 gave 2.1; for 1880, 2.8; and for 1890, 3.8 deaths to the 100,000 population. In this region the incidence of the disease may be gathered from the fact that among 170,000 patients under treatment at the Johns Hopkins Hospital and Dispensary during the nine years since its opening there have been 77 cases. During the nine years 52,000 medical cases were treated, the diabetic patients constituting only 0.14 per cent of these (Futcher). From a study of the statistics of Jefferson College Hospital, Hare concludes that diabetes is becoming more common.

We are ignorant of the nature of the disease. Normally the carbohydrates taken with the food are stored in the liver and in the muscles as glycogen, and then utilized as needed by the system. Glycogen can also be formed from the proteids of the food, and under certain circumstances sugar may be directly formed from the body proteids. Whenever the sugar in the systemic blood exceeds a definite amount (about 0.2 per cent) it is discharged by the kidneys, producing glycosuria. Theoretically diabetes may be supposed to be induced by:

(*a*) The ingestion of a larger quantity of carbohydrates and peptones than can be warehoused, so to speak, in the liver as glycogen, so that part has to pass over into the hepatic blood. Some of the instances of lipogenic or dietetic glycosuria are of this nature.

(*b*) Disturbances of the liver function: (1) Changes in the circulation under nervous influences. Puncture of the medulla, lesions of the cord, and central irritation of various kinds are followed by glycosuria, which is attributed to a vaso-motor paralysis (more rapid blood-flow) induced by these causes. On this view the disease is a neurosis. (2) Instability of the glycogen, owing either to imperfect formation or to conditions in the cells which render it less stable. Phloridzin and other substances which cause diabetes very probably act in this way; phloridzin acts primarily on the renal epithelium, destroying its power of keeping back the sugar. As to the possibility of a renal form of diabetes in man, consult Naunyn, page 106.

(*c*) Defective assimilation of the glucose in the system. How and under what normal circumstances the sugar is utilized we do not yet know. Theoretically faulty metabolism would explain the condition.

Morbid Anatomy.—Saundby (Lectures on Diabetes, 1891) has given a good summary of the anatomical changes:

The *nervous system* shows no constant lesions. In a few instances there have been tumors or sclerosis in the medulla, or, as in the case above mentioned, a cysticercus has pressed on the floor. Cysts have been met with in the white matter of the cerebrum and perivascular changes have been described. Glycogen has been found in the spinal cord. In the peripheral nervous system there are instances in which tumors have been found pressing on the vagus. A secondary multiple neuritis is not rare, and to it the so-called diabetic tabes is probably due. R. T. Williamson has found changes in the posterior columns of the cord similar to those which occur in pernicious anæmia.

In the sympathetic system the ganglia have been enlarged and in some instances sclerosed, but there is nothing peculiar in these changes. The *blood* may contain as high as 0.4 per cent of sugar instead of 0.15 per cent. The plasma is usually loaded with fat, the molecules of which may be seen as fine particles. When drawn, a white creamy layer coats the coagulum, and there may be lipæmic clots in the small vessels. There are no special changes in the red or white corpuscles. The polynuclear leucocytes contain glycogen. Glycogen can occur in normal blood, but it is here extracellular. It has been also found in the polynuclear leucocytes in leukæmia. The *heart* is hypertrophied in some cases. Endocarditis is very rare. Arterio-sclerosis is common. The *lungs* show important changes. Acute broncho-pneumonia or croupous pneumonia (either of which may terminate in gangrene) and tuberculosis are common. The so-called diabetic phthisis is always tuberculous and results from a caseating broncho-pneumonia. In rare cases there is a chronic interstitial pneumonia, non-tuberculous. Fat embolism of the pulmonary vessels has been described in connection with diabetic coma.

The *liver* is usually enlarged; fatty degeneration is common. In the so-called diabetic cirrhosis—the *cirrhose pigmentaire*—the liver is enlarged and sclerotic, and a cachexia develops with melanoderma. Possibly the disease is a separate morbid entity. Dilatation of the stomach is common.

The Pancreas in Diabetes.—Lesions of this organ are met with in about 50 per cent of the cases (Hansemann). Von Mering and Minkowski have shown that extirpation of the gland in dogs is followed by glycosuria, but, if a small portion remains, sugar does not appear in the urine, facts which have been confirmed by Lepine and others. The pancreas, on this view, has, like the liver, a double secretion—an external, which is poured into the intestines, and an internal, which passes into the blood. This latter is supposed to be of the nature of a ferment, in the presence of which alone the normal assimilative processes can take place with the glycogen. Disease of the pancreas causes diabetes by preventing the formation of the glycolytic ferment. Even when, as in a majority of instances of diabetes, the organ is apparently normal, a functional trouble may disturb the formation of this ferment. The fact that if a small portion of the gland is left, in the experiments upon dogs, diabetes does not occur, is analogous to the remarkable circumstance that a small fragment of the thyroid is sufficient to prevent the development of artificial myxœdema.

A patient of W. T. Bull died of diabetes after extirpation of the pancreas. In some instances there is a pigmentary cirrhosis analogous to that which occurs in the liver, and this induration seems to be an important change. Cancer and calculi have been met with; and Longstreth found, in one instance, cystic disease of the pancreas. Fat necrosis of the organ has also been found.

Williamson * examined the pancreas in 23 consecutive cases of diabetes and found pathological changes, chiefly atrophy, in 11. He also analyzed 100 cases of diabetes collected from the literature in which the pancreas was diseased. More than 50 per cent of these showed more or less marked atrophy; fatty degeneration was present in 17, abscess in 3, cancer in 8, and cystic degeneration in 8 cases. Of my series of 77 cases, 46 were treated in medical wards of the Johns Hopkins Hospital, and 17 terminated fatally. Autopsies were obtained in 8 cases, and the pancreas was found more or less atrophied in 6 of them. In only one of his 40 autopsies in diabetes could Naunyn attribute the disease to the condition of the pancreas.

The *kidneys* show usually a diffuse nephritis with fatty degeneration. A hyaline change occurs in the tubal epithelium, particularly of the descending limb of the loop of Henle, and also in the capillary vessels of the tufts.

Symptoms.—*Acute* and *chronic* forms are recognized, but there is no essential difference between them, except that in the former the patients are younger, the course more rapid, and the emaciation more marked. Acute cases may occur in the aged. I saw with Sowers in Washington a man aged seventy-three in whom the entire course of the disease was less than three weeks.

It is also possible to divide the cases into (1) *lipogenic* or *dietetic*, which includes the transient glycosuria of stout persons; (2) *neurotic*, due to injuries or functional disorders of the nervous system; and (3) *pancreatic*, in which there is a lesion of the pancreas. It is, however, by no means easy to discriminate in all cases between these forms. Attempts have been made to separate a clinical variety analogous to experimental pancreatic diabetes. Hirschfeld, from Guttmann's clinic, has described cases running a rapid and severe course usually in young and middle-aged persons. The polyuria is less common or even absent, and there is a striking defect in the assimilation of the albuminoids and fats, as shown by the examination of the fæces and urine. In 4 of 7 cases autopsies were made and the pancreas was found atrophic in two, cancerous in one, and in the fourth exceedingly soft.

The *onset* of the disease is gradual and either frequent micturition or inordinate thirst first attracts attention. Very rarely it sets in rapidly, after a sudden emotion, an injury, or after a severe chill. When fully established the disease is characterized by great thirst, the passage of large

---

* Medical Chronicle, May, 1897.

quantities of saccharine urine, a voracious appetite, and, as a rule, progressive emaciation.

Among the *general symptoms* of the disease *thirst* is one of the most distressing. A very large amount of water is required to keep the sugar in solution and for its excretion in the urine. The amount of water consumed will be found to bear a definite ratio to the quantity excreted. Instances, however, are not uncommon of pronounced diabetes in which the thirst is not excessive; but in such cases the amount of urine passed is never large. The thirst is most intense an hour or two after meals. As a rule, the digestion is good and the appetite inordinate. The condition is sometimes termed *bulimia* or *polyphagia*.

The tongue is usually dry, red, and glazed, and the saliva scanty. The gums may become swollen, and in the later stages aphthous stomatitis is common. Constipation is the rule.

In spite of the enormous amount of food consumed a patient may become rapidly emaciated. This loss of flesh bears some ratio to the polyuria, and when, under suitable diet, the sugar is reduced, the patient may quickly gain in flesh. The skin is dry and harsh, and sweating rarely occurs, except when phthisis coexists. Drenching sweats have been known to alternate with excessive polyuria. The temperature is often subnormal; the pulse is usually frequent, and the tension increased. Many diabetics, however, do not show marked emaciation. Patients past the middle period of life may have the disease for years without much disturbance of the health, and may remain well nourished. These are the cases of the *diabète gras* in contradistinction to *diabète maigre*.

The Urine.—The amount varies from 6 or 8 pints in mild cases to 30 or 40 pints in very severe cases. In rare instances the quantity of urine is not much increased. Under strict diet the amount is much lessened, and in intercurrent febrile affections it may be reduced to normal. The specific gravity is high, ranging from 1.025 to 1.045; but in exceptional cases it may be low, 1.013 to 1.020. The highest specific gravity recorded, so far as I know, is by Trousseau—1.074. Very high specific gravities—1.070 + —suggest fraud. The urine is pale in color, almost like water, and has a sweetish odor and a distinctly sweetish taste. The reaction is acid. Sugar is present in varying amounts. In mild cases it does not exceed $1\frac{1}{2}$ or 2 per cent, but it may reach from 5 to 10 per cent. The total amount excreted in the twenty-four hours may range from 10 to 20 ounces, and in exceptional cases from 1 to 2 pounds. The following are the most satisfactory tests:

Fehling's Test.—The solution consists of sulphate of copper (grs. $90\frac{1}{2}$), neutral tartrate of potassium (grs. 364), solution of caustic soda (fl. ozs. 4), and distilled water to make up 6 ounces. Put a drachm of this in a test-tube and boil (to test the reagent); add an equal quantity of urine and boil again, when, if sugar is present, the yellow suboxide of copper is thrown down. The solution must be freshly prepared, as it is apt to decompose.

Trommer's Test.—To a drachm of urine in a test-tube add a few drops of a dilute sulphate-of-copper solution and then as much *liquor potassæ* as urine. On boiling, the copper is reduced if sugar be present, forming the yellow or orange-red suboxide. There are certain fallacies in the copper tests. Thus, a substance called glycuronic acid is met with in the urine after the use of certain drugs—chloral, phenacetin, morphia, chloroform, etc.—which reduces copper. Homogentisinic, uroleucinic, and glycosuric acids, which are held to be the cause of alcaptonuria, may also prove a source of error (see Alcaptonuria, by T. B. Futcher, N. Y. Med. Jour., 1898, i).

Fermentation Test.—This is free from all doubt. Place a small fragment of yeast in a test-tube full of urine, which is then inverted over a glass vessel containing the same fluid. If sugar is present, fermentation goes on with the formation of carbon dioxide, which accumulates in the upper part of the tube and gradually expels the urine. In doubtful cases a control test should always be used. For laboratory work the polariscope is of great value.

Of other ingredients in the urine, the urea is increased, the uric acid does not show special changes, and the phosphates may be greatly in excess. Ralfe has described a great increase in the phosphates, and in some of these cases, with an excessive excretion, the symptoms may be very similar to those of diabetes, though the sugar may not be constantly present. The term phosphatic diabetes has sometimes been applied to them. *Acetone* and acetone-forming substances are not infrequently present. Lieben's test is as follows: The urine is distilled and a few cubic centimetres of the distillate are rendered alkaline with liquor potassæ. A few drops of Lugol's solution are then added, when, if acetone be present, the distillate assumes a turbid yellow color, due to the formation of iodoform, which is recognized by its odor and by the formation of minute hexagonal and stellate crystals. *Diacetic acid* is sometimes present, and may be recognized from the fact that a solution of the chloride of iron yields a beautiful Bordeaux-red color. Other substances, as formic, carbolic, and salicylic acids, give the same reaction in both fresh and previously boiled urine, while diacetic acid does not give the reaction in urine previously boiled. Munson holds that diacetic acid gives the characteristic " diazo-reaction " of Ehrlich. In testing for diacetic acid perfectly fresh urine should be used, as it rapidly becomes broken up into acetone and carbolic acid. β-oxybutyric acid should be tested for where coma is present. A quantity of the urine is thoroughly fermented, filtered till perfectly clear, and examined with the polariscope. If it be present, the rays of polarized light are deflected to the left. The urine also yields α-crotonic acid crystals by the method recommended by Kulz.

Bremer finds that diabetic urine has the power of dissolving gentian violet, whereas normal urine fails to do so. Unfortunately, the urine in diabetes insipidus and in certain forms of polyuria reacts similarly. Fröhlich has recently devised a test based on the fact that diabetic urine has the property of decolorizing solutions of methylene blue.

Glycogen has also been described as present in the urine.

Albumin is not infrequent. It occurred in nearly 37 per cent of the examinations made by Lippman at Carlsbad.

Pneumaturia, the formation of gas in the urine, due to fermentative processes in the bladder, is occasionally met with.

Fat may be passed in the urine in the form of a fine emulsion (lipuria).

Diabetes in Children.—Stern has analyzed 117 cases in children. They usually occur among the better classes. Six were under one year of age. Hereditary influences were marked. The course of the disease is, as a rule, much more rapid than in adults. The shortest duration was two days. In 7 cases it did not last a month. One case is mentioned of a child apparently born with the glycosuria, who recovered in eight months.

Complications.—(*a*) **Cutaneous.**—Boils and carbuncles are extremely common. Painful onychia may occur. Eczema is also met with, and at times an intolerable itching. In women the irritation of the urine may cause the most intense pruritus pudendi, and in men a balanitis. Rarer affections are xanthoma and purpura. Gangrene is not uncommon, and is associated usually with arterio-sclerosis. William Hunt has analyzed 64 cases. In 50 the localities were as follows: Feet and legs, 37; thigh and buttock, 2; nucha, 2; external genitals, 1; lungs, 3; fingers, 3; back, 1; eyes, 1. Perforating ulcer of the foot may occur. Bronzing of the skin (*diabète bronzé*), a rare feature, is met with in connection with a peculiar type of cirrhosis of the liver. With the onset of severe complications the tolerance of the carbohydrates is much increased.

(*b*) **Pulmonary.**—The patients are not infrequently carried off by *acute pneumonia*, which may be lobar or lobular. *Gangrene* is very apt to supervene, but the breath does not necessarily have the foul odor of ordinary gangrene.

Tuberculous broncho-pneumonia is very common. It was formerly thought, from its rapid course and the limitation of the disease to the lung, that this was not a true tuberculous affection; but in the cases which have come under my notice the bacilli have been present, and the condition is now generally regarded as tuberculous.

(*c*) **Renal.**—*Albuminuria* is a tolerably frequent complication. The amount varies greatly, and, when slight, does not seem to be of much moment. Œdema of the feet and ankles is not an infrequent symptom. General anasarca is rare, however, owing to the marked polyuria. It was present in a marked degree in one of my 77 cases. It is sometimes associated with arterio-sclerosis. It occasionally precedes the development of the diabetic coma. Occasionally cystitis develops.

(*d*) **Nervous System.**—(1) *Diabetic coma*, first studied by Kussmaul, comes on in a considerable proportion of all cases, particularly in the young. Stephen Mackenzie states that of the fatal cases of diabetes collected from the registers of the London Hospital, all under the age of twenty-five, with but one exception, had died in coma. In Frerichs' series coma preceded death in 152 instances out of a total of 250 fatal cases. Of 17 fatal cases at the Johns Hopkins Hospital, coma occurred in 12. It may supervene when diabetes is unsuspected, as in 2 cases reported by Francis Minot. Frerichs recognized three groups of cases: (*a*) Those in which after exertion the patients were suddenly attacked with weakness, syncope, somnolence, and gradually deepening unconsciousness; death occurring in a few hours. (*β*) Cases with preliminary gastric disturbance, such as nausea and vomiting, or some local affection, as pharyngitis, phlegmon, or a pulmonary complication. In such cases the attack begins with headache, delirium, great distress, and dyspnœa, affecting both inspiration and expiration, a condition called by Kussmaul *air-hunger*. Cyanosis may or may not be present. If it is, the pulse becomes rapid and weak and the patient gradually sinks into coma; the attack lasting from one to five days. There may be a very heavy, sweetish odor of the breath, due to the presence of acetone. (γ) Cases in which, without any previous dyspnœa or distress, the patient is attacked with headache and a feeling of intoxication, and rapidly falls into a deep and fatal coma. There are atypical cases in which the coma is due to uræmia, to apoplexy, or to meningitis.

There has been much dispute as to the nature of these symptoms, but our knowledge of the disease is not yet sufficiently advanced to give a rational explanation. The character of the attack and the similarity, in many instances, to uræmia would indicate that it depended upon some toxic agent in the blood. For many years it was almost universally held that this toxic material was acetone, but this theory is no longer tenable, as it has been repeatedly shown experimentally that acetone, when administered to animals, does not produce symptoms resembling those of diabetic coma. It is, however, almost constantly present in the urine and breath of coma patients. Later, the coma was attributed to the presence of diacetic acid in the blood, but this theory in turn gave way to that of Stadelmann, Külz, and Minkowski, who believe that diabetic coma is an autointoxication due to β-oxy-butyric acid in the circulating blood. In 1884 these observers, working independently, almost simultaneously found this acid in the urine of patients with diabetic coma. β-oxy-butyric acid is now believed by most observers to be the exciting cause of the coma. The amount of the acid excreted in the twenty-four hours may be enormous. Külz found in 3 cases 67, 100, and 226 grammes respectively. It is a decomposition product, resulting from the disintegration of the tissue albumins. Acetone and diacetic acid are believed to be derivative from β-oxy-butyric acid.

Saunders and Hamilton have described cases in which the lung capillaries were blocked with fat. They attributed the symptoms to fat embolism, but there are many cases on record in which this condition was not found, though lipæmia is by no means infrequent in diabetes.

The symptoms have been attributed to uræmia, and albuminuria frequently precedes or accompanies the attack.

(2) *Peripheral Neuritis.*—The *neuralgias*, numbness, and tingling, which are not uncommon symptoms in diabetes, are probably minor neuritic manifestations. Herpes zoster may occur. Perforating ulcer of the foot may develop.

Diabetic Tabes (so called).—This is a peripheral neuritis, characterized by lightning pains in the legs, loss of knee-jerk—which may occur without the other symptoms—and a loss of power in the extensors of the feet. The gait is the characteristic *steppage*, as in arsenical, alcoholic, and other forms of neuritic paralysis. Charcot states that there may be atrophy of the optic nerves. Changes in the posterior columns of the cord have been found by Williamson and others.

Diabetic Paraplegia.—This is also in all probability due to neuritis. There are cases in which power has been lost in both arms and legs.

(3) *Mental Symptoms.*—The patients are often morose, and there is a strong tendency to become hypochondriacal. General paralysis has been known to develop. Some patients display an extraordinary degree of restlessness and anxiety.

(4) *Special Senses.*—Cataract is liable to occur, and may develop with rapidity in young persons. Diabetic retinitis closely resembles the albuminuric form. Hæmorrhages are common. Sudden amaurosis, similar to that which occurs in uræmia, may occur. Paralysis of the muscles of accommodation may be present; and lastly, atrophy of the optic nerves. Aural symptoms may come on with great rapidity, either an otitis media, or in some instances inflammation of the mastoid cells.

(5) *Sexual Function.*—Impotence is common, and may be an early symptom. Conception is rare; if it occurs, abortion is apt to follow. A diabetic mother may bear a healthy child; there is no known instance of a diabetic mother bearing a diabetic child. The course of the disease is usually aggravated after delivery.

Course.—In children the disease is rapidly progressive, and may prove fatal in a few days. It may be stated, as a general rule, that the older the patient at the time of onset the slower the course. Cases without hereditary influences are the most favorable. In stout, elderly men diabetes is a much more hopeful disease than it is in thin persons. Middle-aged patients may live for many years, and persons are met with who have had the disease for ten, twelve, or even fifteen years.

Diagnosis.—As stated in the definition, for a case to be considered diabetes the sugar eliminated in the urine must be grape sugar, it should be present for weeks, months, or years, and the excretion of sugar must take place after the ingestion of moderate amounts of carbohydrates. As a rule, there is no difficulty in determining the presence of diabetes. The urine tests already given are distinctive.

Bremer's Blood Test.—This author claims that he is able to make a diagnosis of diabetes from the examination of a drop of the patient's blood, depending on the fact that it reacts differently from normal blood to various aniline dyes.

His latest published method is briefly as follows: Rather thick smears of suspected and normal blood are made on ordinary microscopic slides. They are then heated in a thermostat up to 135° C., and when sufficiently cooled are stained in a one-per-cent aqueous solution of Congo-red for one and a half to two minutes. Slides of the non-diabetic and diabetic blood are placed back to back, so that each will be exposed to the same conditions. The excess of the stain is washed off, and if the suspected patient has diabetes the blood will be unstained, whereas the normal blood takes a distinct Congo-red stain. Bremer obtains this reaction in the prediabetic stage, and also in the intervals when the patient's urine is temporarily free from sugar. He thinks the reaction is due to a qualitative change in the hæmoglobin of the red blood-cells, and not to an excess of grape sugar in the blood. In a number of cases in my wards, in which the test has been performed, the reaction has been repeatedly obtained, but it was not possible to fully confirm Bremer's statement that the reaction was also present when the urine was temporarily free from sugar. According to R. T. Williamson, diabetic blood has the power to decolorize weak alkaline solutions of methylene blue to a yellowish-green or yellow color. He has devised a blood test for diabetes, using definite proportions of blood and the reagent. Williamson has obtained the reaction in every one of 11 cases of diabetes in which the test was tried, but failed to get it in a single instance in the blood of 100 non-diabetic cases. He is inclined to the view that the reaction is due to an excess of sugar in the blood. The reaction was obtained by Futcher in 7 cases in which it was tried in my wards (Phila. Med. Journal, February 12, 1898).

Deception may be practised. A young girl under my care had urine with a specific gravity of 1.065. The reactions were for cane sugar. There is one case in the literature in which, after the cane-sugar fraud was detected, the woman bought grape sugar and put it into her bladder!

Prognosis.—In true diabetes instances of cure are rare. On the other hand, the transient or intermittent glycosuria, met with in stout overfeeders, or in persons who have undergone a severe mental strain, is very amenable to treatment. Not a few of the cases of reputed cures belong to this division. Practically, in cases under forty years of age the outlook is bad; in older persons the disease is less serious and much more amenable to treatment. It is a good plan at the outset to determine whether the urine of a patient contains sugar or not on a diet absolutely free from carbohydrates. In mild cases the sugar disappears; in the severer cases it continues to be formed from the proteids.

Treatment.—In families with a marked predisposition to the disease the use of starchy and saccharine articles of diet should be restricted.

The personal hygiene of a diabetic patient is of the first importance. Sources of worry should be avoided, and he should lead an even, quiet life, if possible in an equable climate. Flannel or silk should be worn next to the skin, and the greatest care should be taken to promote its action. A lukewarm, or if tolerably robust, a cold bath, should be taken every day. An occasional Turkish bath is useful. Systematic, moderate exercise should be taken. When this is not feasible, massage should be given. It is well to study accurately the dietetic capabilities of each case.

Diet.—Our injunctions to-day are those of Sydenham: "Let the patient eat food of easy digestion, such as veal, mutton, and the like, and abstain from all sorts of fruit and garden stuff."

Diabetic patients admitted to the medical wards of the Johns Hopkins Hospital are kept for three or four days on the ordinary ward diet, which contains moderate amounts of carbohydrates, in order to ascertain the amount of sugar excretion. They are then placed on the following standard non-carbohydrate diet, arranged from a diet list recommended by von Noorden:

Breakfast: 7.30, 5 grammes ($\mathfrak{Z}$ i) of tea steeped in 200 cc. ($\mathfrak{Z}$ vi) of water; 150 grammes ($\mathfrak{Z}$ iv) of boiled ham; one egg.

Lunch: 12.30, 200 grammes ($\mathfrak{Z}$ vi) cold roast beef; 60 grammes ($\mathfrak{Z}$ ij) fresh cucumber or celery, with 5 grammes (℥ i) vinegar; 10 grammes (℥ iiss) olive oil, with salt and pepper to taste; 20 cc. (℥ v) whisky, with 400 cc. (℥ iij) water; 60 cc. (℥ iv) coffee, without milk or sugar.

Dinner: 6 p. m., 200 cc. clear bouillon; 250 grammes (℥ viiss) roast beef; 10 grammes (℥ iiss) butter; 80 grammes (℥ ij) green salad, with 10 grammes (℥ iiss) vinegar and 20 grammes (℥ v) olive oil, or three table-spoonsful of some well-cooked green vegetable; three sardines à l'huille; 20 cc. (℥ v) whisky, with 400 cc. (℥ xiij) water.

Supper: 9 p. m., two eggs (raw or cooked); 400 cc. (℥ xiij) water.

This diet contains about 200 grammes of albumin and about 135 grammes of fat. The effect of the diet on the sugar excretion is remarkable. In many cases there is an entire disappearance of the sugar from the urine in three or four days. Chart XV shows very graphically the remarkable drop in the sugar excretion for the first twenty-four hours in a case placed on the standard diet. The sugar failed, however, in this particular case to entirely disappear from the urine except on one day, although he was kept on the diet for over two months. In cases in which the urine becomes free from sugar gradually increasing quantities of starch up to 20, 50, and 100 grammes are added daily. White bread contains fifty-five per cent of starch. The effect of the non-carbohydrate diet, according to von Noorden, is to improve the metabolic functions so that the system can warehouse considerable quantities of carbohydrates without sugar appearing in the urine. He advises that patients should return to the strict non-carbohydrate regimen at intervals of three or four months, so as to increase their power of warehousing carbohydrates.

In cases in which a standard diet is not ordered it is well to begin cutting off article by article until the sugar disappears from the urine. Within a month or two the patient may be allowed a more liberal diet, testing the different kinds of food.

The following is a list of articles which diabetic patients may take:

Liquids: Soups—ox-tail, turtle, bouillon, and other clear soups. Lemonade, coffee, tea, chocolate, and cocoa; these to be taken without sugar, but they may be sweetened with saccharin. Potash or soda water, and Apollinaris, or the Saratoga-Vichy, and milk in moderation, may be used.

Of animal food: Fish of all sorts, including crabs, lobsters, and oysters; salt and fresh butcher's meat (with the exception of liver), poultry, and game. Eggs, butter, buttermilk, curds, and cream cheese.

Of bread: Gluten and bran bread, and almond and cocoanut biscuits.

Of vegetables: Lettuce, tomatoes, spinach, chicory, sorrel, radishes, asparagus, water-cress, mustard and cress, cucumbers, celery, and endives. Pickles of various sorts.

Fruits: Lemons and oranges. Currants, plums, cherries, pears, apples (tart), melons, raspberries and strawberries may be taken in moderation. Nuts are, as a rule, allowable.

Among *prohibited articles* are the following: Thick soups and liver. Ordinary bread of all sorts (in quantity), rye, wheaten, brown, or white. All farinaceous preparations, such as hominy, rice, tapioca, semolina, arrowroot, sago, and vermicelli.

Of vegetables: Potatoes, turnips, parsnips, squashes, vegetable marrow of all kinds, beets, corn, artichokes.

Of liquids: Beer, sparkling wine of all sorts, and the sweet aërated drinks.

In feeding a diabetic patient one of the greatest difficulties is in arranging a substitute for bread. Of the gluten breads, many are very unpalatable; others are frauds.

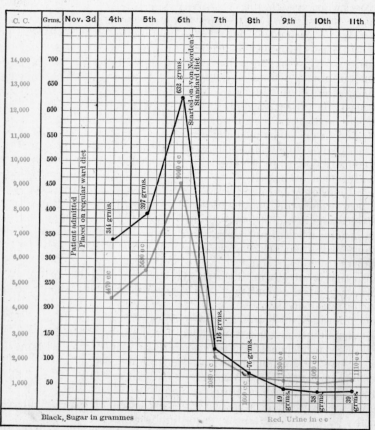

CHART XV.—Illustrating influence of diet on sugar and amount of urine.

A good gluten flour is made by the Battle Creek Sanitarium Company, Michigan. Other substitutes are the almond food, the Aleuronat bread, and soya bread, but these and other substitutes are not satisfactory as a rule. For sweetening purposes saccharin may be used, of which tablets are prepared.

Medicinal Treatment.—This is most unsatisfactory, and no one drug appears to have a directly curative influence. Opium alone stands the test of experience as a remedy capable of limiting the progress of the disease. Diabetic patients seem to have a special tolerance for this drug.

Codeia is preferred by Pavy, and has the advantage of being less consti-
pating than morphia. A patient may begin with half a grain three times
a day, which may be gradually increased to 6 or 8 grains in the twenty-
four hours. Not much effect is noticed unless the patient is on a rigid diet.
When the sugar is reduced to a minimum, or is absent, the opium should
be gradually withdrawn. The patients not only bear well these large doses
of the drug, but they stand its gradual reduction. Potassium bromide is
often a useful adjunct. The arsenite of bromine, a solution of arsenious
acid with bromine in glycerin (dose, 3 to 5 minims after meals), has been
very highly recommended, but it is by no means so certain as opium.
Arsenic alone may be used. Antipyrin may be given in doses of 10 grains
three times a day, and in cases with a marked neurotic constitution is sometimes satisfactory. The salicylates, iodoform, nitroglycerin, jambul, the
lithium salts, strychnine, creasote, and lactic acid have been employed.

Preparations of the pancreas (glycerin extracts of the dried and fresh
gland) have been used in the hope that they would supply the internal secretion necessary to normal sugar metabolism. The success has not, however,
been in any way comparable with that obtained with the thyroid extract in
myxœdema. Lépine has isolated a glycolytic ferment from the pancreas
and also from the malt diastase, and has used it with some success in 4 cases.

Of the complications, the *pruritus* and *eczema* are best treated by cooling lotions of boric acid or hyposulphite of soda (1 ounce; water, 1 quart),
or the use of ichthyol and lanolin ointment.

In the thin, nervous cases the bowels should be kept open and the urine
tested at short intervals for acetone and diacetic acid—the derivatives of
β-oxy-butyric acid.

The *coma* is an almost hopeless complication. Inhalations of oxygen
have been recommended. The use of bicarbonate of soda in very large doses
is recommended to neutralize the acid intoxication. It may be used intra-
venously; as much as 80 grammes have been injected.

The subcutaneous and intravenous injection of physiological salt solution, though rarely curative, has probably given the best results. This
treatment was used in my wards in 10 of the 12 cases in which coma occurred. In 2 cases the patients were restored to complete consciousness,
so that they would have been quite capable of making a will. Both cases
eventually terminated fatally, however. In three instances there was improvement in the pulse, and the respirations were much less labored, though
consciousness never returned. In the remaining 5 cases there was no
appreciable improvement. Reynolds published 2 cases of recovery after
the administration of a dose of castor oil, followed by 30 to 60 grains of
citrate of potassium every hour in copious draughts of water. The bowels
of a diabetic patient should be kept acting freely, as constipation is believed
to predispose to the development of coma.

27

VI. DIABETES INSIPIDUS.

Definition.—A chronic affection characterized by the passage of larg quantities of normal urine of low specific gravity.

The condition is to be distinguished from diuresis or polyuria, whicl is a frequent symptom in hysteria, in Bright's disease, and occasionall in cerebral or other affections. Willis, in 1674, first recognized the distinc tion between a saccharine and non-saccharine form of diabetes.

Etiology.—The disease is most common in young persons. Of th 85 cases collected by Strauss, 9 were under five years; 12 between five an ten years; 36 between ten and twenty-five years. Males are more fre quently attacked than females. The affection may be congenital. A hered itary tendency has been noted in many instances, the most extraordinar of which has been reported by Weil. Of 91 members in four generation 23 had persistent polyuria without any deterioration in health. Injury t the nervous system has been present in certain cases, and the disease ha followed sunstroke, or a violent emotion, such as fright. Traumatisi has occasionally been the exciting cause. The injury may have been t the head, but in other cases it has been to the trunk or to the limbs. Trous seau stated that the parents of children with diabetes insipidus frequentl have glycosuria or albuminuria. Ralfe stated that malnutrition is an im portant predisposing factor in children. The disease has followed rapidl the copious drinking of cold water, or a drinking-bout; or has set in durin the convalescence from an acute disease. Tumors of the brain and lesion of the medulla have been met with in a few instances. Cases of polyuri have been accompanied by paralysis of the sixth nerve. Maguire has seen a instance after meningitis in which paralysis of the sixth pair occurred with it Bernard, it will be remembered, discovered a spot in the floor of the fourtl ventricle of animals which, when punctured, produced polyuria. Lesion of the organs of the abdomen may be associated with an excessive flow o urine, which, however, should not be regarded as true diabetes insipidus Dickenson mentions its occurrence in abdominal tumors; Ralfe, in ab dominal aneurism. I have noted it in several cases of tuberculous peri tonitis. There have been only 2 cases of diabetes insipidus out of a tota of 150,000 patients treated at the Johns Hopkins Hospital and Dispensary

The nature of the disease is unknown. It is, doubtless, of nervou origin. The most reasonable view is that it results from a vaso-motor dis turbance of the renal vessels, due either to local irritation, as in a case o abdominal tumor, to central disturbance in cases of brain-lesion, or t functional irritation of the centre in the medulla, giving rise to continuou renal congestion.

Morbid Anatomy.—There are no constant anatomical lesions. Th *kidneys* have been found enlarged and congested. The *bladder* has beer found hypertrophied. Dilatation of the ureters and of the pelves of th kidneys has been present. Death has not infrequently resulted from chroni pulmonary disease. Very varied lesions have been met with in the nervou system.

Symptoms.—The disease may come on rapidly, as after a fright or an injury. More commonly it develops slowly. According to Ralfe, the patients often complain in the early stages of severe racking pains in the lumbar region shooting down the thighs. A copious secretion of urine, with increased thirst, are the prominent features of the disease. The amount of urine in the twenty-four hours may range from 20 to 40 pints, or even more. Trousseau speaks of a patient who consumed 50 pints of fluid daily and passed about 56 pints of urine in the twenty-four hours. The specific gravity is low, 1.001 to 1.005; the color is extremely pale and watery. The total solid constituents may not be reduced. The amount of urea has sometimes been found in excess. Abnormal ingredients are rare. Muscle-sugar, inosite, has been occasionally found. Albumin is rare. Traces of sugar have been met with. Naturally, with the passage of such enormous quantities of urine, there is a proportionate thirst, and the only inconvenience of the disease is the necessity for frequent micturition and frequent drinking. The appetite is usually good, rarely excessive as in diabetes mellitus; but Trousseau tells of the terror inspired by one of his patients in the keepers of those eating-houses where bread was allowed without extra charge to the extent of each customer's wishes, and says that he was presented with money to prevent him coming back to dine. The patients may be well nourished and healthy-looking. The disease in many instances does not appear to interfere in any way with the general health. The perspiration is naturally slight and the skin is harsh. The amount of saliva is small and the mouth usually dry. Cases have been described in which the tolerance of alcohol has been remarkable, and patients have been known to take a couple of pints of brandy, or a dozen or more bottles of wine, in the day.

The course depends entirely upon the nature of the primary trouble. Sometimes, with organic disease, either cerebral or abdominal, the general health is much impaired; the patient becomes thin, and rapidly loses strength. In the essential or idiopathic cases, good health may be maintained for an indefinite period, and the affection has been known to persist for fifty years. Death usually results from some intercurrent affection. Spontaneous cure may take place.

Diagnosis.—A low specific gravity and the absence of sugar in the urine distinguish the disease from diabetes mellitus. Hysterical polyuria may sometimes simulate it very closely. The amount of urine excreted may be enormous, and only the development of other hysterical manifestations may enable the diagnosis to be made. This condition is, however, always transitory.

In certain cases of chronic Bright's disease a very large amount of urine of low specific gravity may be passed, but the presence of albumin and of hyaline casts, and the existence of heightened arterial tension, stiff vessels, and hypertrophied left ventricle make the diagnosis easy.

Treatment.—The treatment is not satisfactory. No attempt should be made to reduce the amount of liquid. Opium is highly recommended, but is of doubtful service. The preparations of valerian may be tried; either the powdered root, beginning with 5 grains three times a day, and increasing until 2 drachms are taken in the day, or the valerianate of zinc, in 15-grain doses, gradually increased to 30 grains, three times a day. Ergot, ergotin, antipyrin, the salicylates, arsenic, strychnine, turpentine, and the bromides have been recommended. Electricity may be used.

VII. RICKETS (*Rhachitis*).

Definition.—A disease of infants, characterized by impaired nutrition of the entire body and alterations in the growing bones.

Glisson, the anatomist of the liver, accurately described the disease in the seventeenth century. The name is derived from the old English word *wrickken*, to twist. Glisson suggested to change the name to rhachitis, from the Greek, ῥάχις, the spine, as it was one of the first parts affected, and also from the similarity in the sound to rickets.

Etiology.—Rickets exists in all parts of the world, but is particularly marked among the poor of the larger cities, who are badly housed and ill fed. It is much more common in Europe than in America. In Vienna and London from 50 to 80 per cent of all the children at the clinics present signs of rickets. It is a comparatively rare disease in Canada. In the cities of this continent it is very prevalent, particularly among the children of the negro and of the Italian races. Want of sunlight and impure air are important factors. Prolonged lactation and suckling the child during pregnancy are accessory influences in some cases.

There is no evidence that the disease is hereditary.

Rickets affects male and female children equally. It is a disease of the first and second years of life, rarely beginning before the sixth month. Jenner has described a late rickets, in which form the disease may not appear until the ninth or even until the twelfth year. It has been held that rickets is only a manifestation of congenital syphilis (Parrot), but this is certainly not correct. Syphilitic bones rarely, if ever, present the spongy tissue peculiar to rickets, and rachitic bones never show the multiple osteophytes of syphilis. "Syphilis modifies rickets; it does not create it" (Cheadle). A faulty diet is the essential factor in the production of the disease. Like scurvy, rickets may be found in the families of the wealthy under perfect hygienic conditions. It is most common in children fed on condensed milk, the various proprietary foods, cow's milk, and food rich in starches. "An analysis of the foods on which rickets is most frequently and certainly produced shows invariably a deficiency in two of the chief elements so plentiful in the standard food of young animals—namely, animal fat and proteid" (Cheadle). Bland Sutton's interesting experiment with the lion's cubs at the "Zoo" illustrates this point. When milk, pounded bones, and cod-liver oil were added to the meat diet the rickets disappeared, and for the first time in the history of the society the cubs were reared. Associated with the defect in food is a lack of proper assimilation of the lime salts.

Morbid Anatomy.—The bones show the most important changes, particularly the ends of the long bones and the ribs. Between the shaft

and epiphyses a slight bulging is apparent, and on section the zone of proliferation, which normally is represented by two narrow bands, is greatly
thickened, bluish in color, more irregular in outline, and very much softer.
The width of this cushion of cartilage varies from 5 to 15 mm. The line
of ossification is also irregular and more spongy and vascular than normal.
The periosteum strips off very readily from the shaft, and beneath it there
may be a spongioid tissue not unlike decalcified bone. The practical outcome of these changes is a delay in, and imperfect performance of, the
ossification, so that the bone has neither the natural rate of growth nor the
normal firmness. In the cranium there may be large areas, particularly in
the parieto-occipital region, in which the ossification is delayed, producing
the so-called cranio-tabes, so that the bone yields readily to pressure with
the finger. There are localized depressed spots of atrophy, which, on
pressure, give the so-called " parchment crackling." Flat hyperostoses develop from the outer table, particularly on the frontal and parietal bones,
and produce the characteristic broad forehead with prominent frontal eminences, a condition sometimes mistaken for hydrocephalus.

Kassowitz, the leading authority on the anatomy of rickets, regards
the hyperæmia of the periosteum, the marrow, the cartilage, and of the
bone itself as the primary lesion, out of which all the others develop. This
disturbs the normal development of the growing bone and excites changes
in that already formed. The cartilage cells in consequence proliferate,
the matrix is softer, and as a result the bone which is formed from this
unhealthy cartilage is lacking in firmness and solidity. In the bone already
formed this excessive vascularity exaggerates the normal processes of absorption, so that the relation between removal and deposition is disturbed,
absorption taking place too rapidly. The new material is poor in lime salts.
Kassowitz has proved experimentally that hyperæmia of bone results in
defective deposition of lime salts. It is interesting to note that Glisson
attributed rickets to disturbed nutrition by arterial blood, and believed
the changes in the long bones to be due to excessive vascularity.

The chemical analysis of rickety bones shows a marked diminution in
the calcareous salts, which may be as low as 25 or 35 per cent.

The liver and spleen are usually enlarged, and sometimes the mesenteric glands. As Gee suggests, these conditions probably result from the
general state of the health associated with rickets. Beneke has described
a relative increase in the size of the arteries in rickets.

Symptoms.—The disease comes on insidiously about the period of
dentition, before the child begins to walk. Mild grades of it are often overlooked in the families of the well-to-do. In many cases digestive disturbances precede the appearance of the characteristic lesions, and the nutrition
of the child is markedly impaired. There is usually slight fever, the child
is irritable and restless, and sleeps badly. If the child has already walked,
it shows a marked disinclination to do so, and seems feeble and unsteady
in its gait. Sir William Jenner has called attention to three general symptoms of great importance: First, a diffuse soreness of the body, so that
the child cries when an attempt is made to move it, and prefers to keep
perfectly still. This is often a marked and suggestive symptom. Secondly,

slight fever (100° to 101.5°), with nocturnal restlessness, and a tendency to throw off the bedclothes. This may be partly due to the fact that the general sensitiveness is such that even their weight may be distressing. And, thirdly, profuse sweating, particularly about the head and neck, so that in the morning the pillow is found soaked with perspiration.

The tissues become soft and flabby; the skin is pale; and from a healthy, plump condition, the child becomes puny and feeble. The muscular weakness may be marked, particularly in the legs, and paralysis may be suspected. This so-called pseudo-paresis of rickets results in part from the flabby, weak condition of the legs and in part from the pain associated with the movements. Coincident with, or following closely upon, the general symptoms the characteristic skeletal lesions are observed. Among the first of these to appear are the changes in the ribs, at the junction of the bone with the cartilage, forming the so-called rickety rosary. When the child is thin these nodules may be distinctly seen, and in any case can be easily made out by touch. They very rarely appear before the third month. They may increase in size up to the second year, and are rarely seen after the fifth year. The thorax undergoes important changes. Just outside the junction of the cartilages with the ribs there is an oblique, shallow depression extending downward and outward. A transverse curve, sometimes called Harrison's groove, passes outward from the level of the ensiform cartilage toward the axilla and may be deepened at each inspiration. It is rendered more prominent by the eversion and prominence of the costal border. The sternum projects, particularly in its lower half, forming the so-called pigeon or chicken breast. These changes in the thorax are not peculiar, however, to rickets, and are much more commonly associated with hypertrophy of the tonsils, or any trouble which interferes with the free entrance of air into the lungs. The spine is often curved posteriorly, the processes are prominent; lateral curvature is not so common.

The head of a rickety child usually looks large in proportion both to the body and the face, and the fontanelles remain open for a long time. There are areas, particularly in the parieto-occipital regions, in which ossification is imperfect; and the bone may yield to the pressure of the finger, a condition to which the term *cranio-tabes* has been given. The relation of this condition to rickets is still somewhat doubtful, as it is very often associated with syphilis—in 47 of 100 cases studied by George Carpenter. Coincidently with this, hyperplasia proceeds in the frontal and parietal eminences, so that these portions of the skull increase in thickness, and may form irregular bosses. In one type the skull may be large and elongated, with the top considerably flattened. In another, and perhaps more common case, the shape of the skull, when seen from above, is rectangular —the *caput quadratum*. The skull looks large in proportion to the face. The forehead is broad and square, and the frontal eminences marked. The anterior fontanelle is late in closing and may remain open until the third or fourth year. The skin is thin, the veins are full and prominent, and the hair is often rubbed from the back of the skull. In contradistinction to the cranio-tabes is the condition of cranio-sclerosis, which has also been ascribed to rickets.

On placing the ear over the anterior fontanelle, or in the temporal region, a systolic murmur may frequently be heard. This condition, first described by John D. Fisher, of Boston, in 1833, is heard with the greatest frequency in rickets, but its presence and persistence in perfectly healthy infants have been amply demonstrated.* The murmur is rarely heard after the fifth year. A knowledge of the existence of this systolic brain murmur may prevent errors. A case in which it was well marked was reported as an instance of supposed gummy tumor of the brain, in which the murmur was thought to be due to pressure on the vessels at the base.

Changes occur in the bones of the face, chiefly in the maxillæ, which are reduced in size. The normal process of dentition is much disturbed; indeed, late teething is one of the marked features in rickets. The teeth which appear may be small and badly formed.

In the upper limbs changes in the scapulæ are not common. The clavicle may be thickened at the sternal end, and there may be thickening near the attachment of the sterno-cleido muscle. The most noticeable changes are at the lower ends of the radius and ulna. The enlargement is at the junction-area of the shaft and epiphysis. Less evident enlargements may occur at the lower end of the humerus. In severe cases the natural shape of the bones of the arm may be much altered, since they have had to support the weight of the child in crawling on the floor. The changes in the pelvis are of special importance, particularly in female children, as in extreme cases they lead to great deformity and narrowing of the outlet. In the legs, the lower end of the tibia first becomes enlarged; and in slight cases it may alone be affected. In the severe forms the upper end of the bone, the corresponding parts of the fibula, and the lower end of the femur become greatly thickened. If the child walks, slight bowing of the tibiæ inevitably results. In more advanced cases the tibiæ and even the femora may be arched forward. In other instances the condition of knock-knee occurs. Unquestionably the chief cause of these deformities is the weight of the body in walking, but muscular action takes part in it. The green-stick fracture is not uncommon in the soft bones of rickets.

These changes in the skeleton proceed slowly, and the general symptoms vary a good deal with their progress. The child becomes more or less emaciated, though " fat rickets " is by no means uncommon, and a child may be well nourished but " pasty " and flabby. Fever is not constant, but in actively progressing changes in the bone there is usually a slight pyrexia. The abdomen is large, " pot-bellied," due partly to flatulent distention, partly to enlargement of the liver, and in severe cases to diminution of the volume of the thorax. The spleen is often enlarged and readily palpable. The urine is stated to contain an excess of lime salts, but Jacobi and Barlow say this has not been proved. No special or peculiar changes, indeed, have as yet been described. There is usually slight anæmia, the

---

* Osler, On the Systolic Brain Murmur of Children, Boston Medical and Surgical Journal, 1880.

hæmaglobin is absolutely and relatively decreased; a leucocytosis may or may not be present; it is more common with enlargement of the spleen (Morse). Many rickety children show marked nervous symptoms; irritability, peevishness, and sleeplessness are constantly present. Jenner called attention to the close relationship which existed between rickets and infantile convulsions, particularly to the fits which occur after the sixth month. Tetany is by no means uncommon. It involves most frequently the arms and hands; occasionally the legs as well. Laryngismus stridulus is a common complication, and though not, as some state, invariably associated with this disease, yet it is certainly much more frequent in rickety than in other children. Severe rickets interfere seriously with the growth of a child. Extreme examples of rickety dwarfs are not uncommon. The disease known as acute rickets is in reality a manifestation of scurvy and will be described with that disease.

Prognosis.—The disease is never in itself fatal, but the condition of the child is such that it is readily carried off by intercurrent affections, particularly those of the respiratory organs. Spasm of the larynx and convulsions occasionally cause death. In females the deformity of the pelvis is serious, as it may lead to difficulties in parturition.

Treatment.—The better the condition of the mother during pregnancy the less likelihood is there of the development of rickets in the child. Rapidly repeated pregnancies and suckling a child during pregnancy seem important factors in the production of the disease. Of the general treatment, attention to the feeding of the child is the first consideration. If the mother is unhealthy, or cannot from any cause nurse the child, a suitable wet-nurse should be provided, or the child must be artificially fed. Cows' milk, diluted according to the age of the child, should constitute the chief food. Care should be taken to examine the condition of the stools, and if curds are present the child is taking too much, or it is not sufficiently diluted. Barley-water or carefully strained and well-boiled oatmeal gruel form excellent additions to the milk.

The child should be warmly clad and should be in the fresh air and sunshine the greater part of the day. It is a "vulgar error" to suppose that delicate children cannot stand, when carefully wrapped up, an even low temperature. The child should be bathed daily in warm water. Careful friction with sweet oil is very advantageous, and, if properly performed, allays rather than aggravates the sensitiveness. Special care should be taken to prevent deformity. The child should not be allowed to walk, and for this purpose splints applied so as to extend beyond the feet are very effective. Of medicines, phosphorus has been warmly recommended by Kassowitz, and its use is also advised by Jacobi. The child may be given gr. $\frac{1}{120}$ two or three times a day, dissolved in olive oil. Cod-liver oil, in doses of from a half to one teaspoonful, is very advantageous. The syrup of the iodide of iron may be given with the oil. The digestive disturbances, together with the respiratory and nervous complications, should receive appropriate treatment.

VIII. OBESITY.

Corpulence, an excessive development of the bodily fat—an "oily dropsy," in the words of Lord Byron—is a condition for which the physician is frequently consulted, and for which much may be done by a judicious arrangement of the diet. The tendency to polysarcia or obesity is often hereditary, and is particularly apt to be manifest after the middle period of life. It may, however, be seen early, and in this country it is not very uncommon in young girls and young boys.

A very important factor is overeating, a vice which is more prevalent and only a little behind overdrinking in its disastrous effects. A majority of persons over forty years of age habitually eat too much. In some of the most aggravated cases of obesity, however, this plays no part, and the unfortunate victim may be a notoriously small eater. A second element is lack of proper exercise; a third less important factor is the taking largely of alcoholic beverages, particularly beer.

In obesity it is now generally conceded that the carbohydrates, which were so long blamed, are not at fault, since they are themselves converted into water and carbon dioxide. On account, however, of the facility with which they are utilized for the purposes of oxidation, the albuminous elements of the food are less readily oxidized, and not so fully decomposed, and the fat is in reality separated from them. So, too, the fats themselves are not so prone to cause obesity as the carbohydrates, being less readily oxidized and interfering less with the complete metabolism of the albuminous elements.

Many plans are now advised for the reduction of fat, the most important of which are those of Banting, Ebstein, and Oertel. In the Banting method the amount of food is reduced, the liquids are restricted, and the fats and carbohydrates excluded.

Ebstein recommends the use of fat and the rapid exclusion of the carbohydrates. The following is an example of his dietary:

Breakfast (6 A. M. in summer, 7.30 A. M. in winter).—White bread, well toasted (rather less than 2 ounces) and well covered with butter. Tea, without milk or sugar, 8 or 9 ounces.

Dinner, 2 P. M.—Soup made with beef-marrow. Fat meat, with fat sauce, 4 to 5 ounces. A moderate quantity of asparagus, spinach, cabbage, peas, or beans. Two or three glasses of light white wine. After the meal, a large cup of tea without milk or sugar.

Supper, at 7.30 P. M.—An egg, a little roast meat, with fat. About an ounce of bread, well covered with butter. A large cup of tea, without milk or sugar.

Oertel's method will be considered later in connection with the treatment of fatty heart, and is combined with systematic bodily exercise. It is particularly adapted for stout persons with weak hearts.

The so-called Schweninger cure is in reality Oertel's, with the sole modification of the forbidding of any fluid at meals. Liquids must be taken more than two hours after the food.

Yeo, after a full consideration of the various methods, gives the following useful summary:

"The albuminates in the form of animal food should be strictly limited. Farinaceous and all starchy foods should be reduced to a minimum. Sugar should be entirely prohibited. A moderate amount of fats, for the reasons given by Ebstein, should be allowed.

"Only a small quantity of fluid should be permitted at meals, but enough should be allowed to aid in the solution and digestion of the food. Hot water or warm aromatic beverages may be taken freely between meals or at the end of the digestive process, especially in gouty cases, on account of their eliminative action.

"No beer, porter, or sweet wines of any kind to be taken; no spirit, except in very small quantity. It should be generally recognized that the use of alcohol is one of the most common provocatives of obesity. A little Hock, still Moselle, or light claret, with some alkaline table water is all that should be allowed. The beneficial effects of such diet will be aided by abundant exercise on foot and by the free use of saline purgatives, so that we may insure a complete daily unloading of the intestinal canal.

"It is only necessary to mention a few other details. Of animal foods, all kinds of lean meat may be taken, poultry, game, fish (eels, salmon, and mackerel are best avoided), eggs.

"Meat should not be taken more than once a day, and not more than 6 ounces of cooked meat at a time. Two lightly boiled or poached eggs may be taken at one other meal, or a little grilled fish.

"Bread should be toasted in thin slices and completely, not browned on the surface merely.

"Hard captain's biscuits may also be taken.

"Soups should be avoided, except a few tablespoonfuls of clear soup.

"Milk should be avoided, unless skimmed and taken as the chief article of diet. All milk and farinaceous puddings and pastry of all kinds are forbidden. Fresh vegetables and fruit are permitted.

"It is important to bear in mind that the actual quantity of food permitted must have a due relation to the physical development of the individual, and that what would be adequate in one case might be altogether inadequate in the case of another person of larger physique." *

The thyroid extract has been used in obesity, in a few cases with success. It may be tried beginning with small doses, as in myxœdema.

---

* A System of Therapeutics, vol. i, edited by H. A. Hare, Philadelphia, 1891.

SECTION V.

DISEASES OF THE DIGESTIVE SYSTEM.

I. DISEASES OF THE MOUTH.

STOMATITIS.

(1) **Acute Stomatitis.**—Simple or erythematous stomatitis, the commonest form of inflammation of the mouth, results from the action of irritants of various sorts. It is frequent at all ages. In children it is often associated with dentition and with gastro-intestinal disturbance, particularly in ill-nourished, unhealthy subjects. In adults it follows the overuse of tobacco and the use of too hot or too highly seasoned food. It is a frequent concomitant of indigestion, and is met with in the acute specific fevers.

The affection may be limited to the gums and lips or may extend over the whole surface of the mouth and include the tongue. There is at first superficial redness and dryness of the membrane, followed by increased secretion and swelling of the tongue, which is furred, and indented by the teeth. There is rarely any constitutional disturbance, but in children there may be slight elevation of temperature. The condition is sufficient to cause considerable discomfort, sometimes amounting to actual distress and pain, particularly in mastication.

In infants the mouth should be carefully sponged after each feeding. A mouth-wash of borax or the glycerin of borax may be used, and in severe cases, which tend to become chronic, a dilute solution of nitrate of silver (3 or 4 grains to the ounce) may be applied.

(2) **Aphthous Stomatitis.**—This form, also known as *follicular* or *vesicular* stomatitis, is characterized by the presence of small, slightly raised spots, from 2 to 4 mm. in diameter, surrounded by reddened areolæ. The spots appear first as vesicles, which rupture, leaving small ulcers with grayish bases and bright-red margins. They are seen most frequently on the inner surfaces of the lips, the edges of the tongue, and the cheeks. They are seldom present on the mucous membrane of the pharynx. This form is met with most often in children under three years. It may occur either as an independent affection or in association with any one of the febrile diseases of childhood or with an attack of indigestion. The crop

441

of vesicles comes out with great rapidity and the little ulcers may be fully formed within twenty-four hours. The child complains of soreness of the mouth and takes food with reluctance. The buccal secretions are increased, and the breath is heavy, but not foul. The constitutional symptoms are usually those of the disease with which the aphthæ are associated. The disease must not be confounded with thrush. No special parasite has been found in connection with it. It is not a serious condition, and heals rapidly with the improvement of the constitutional state. In severe cases it may extend to the pillars of the fauces and to the pharynx, and produce ulcers which are irritating and difficult to heal.

Each ulcer should be touched with nitrate of silver and the mouth should be thoroughly cleansed after taking food. A wash of chlorate of potassium, or of borax and glycerin, may be used. The constitutional symptoms should receive careful attention.

Here may be mentioned a curious affection which has been observed chiefly in southern Italy, and which is characterized by a pearly-colored membrane with induration, immediately beneath the tongue on the frænum (Riga's disease). There may be much induration and ultimately ulceration. It occurs in both healthy and cachetic children, usually about the time of the eruption of the first teeth. It is sometimes epidemic.

(3) **Ulcerative Stomatitis.**—This form, which is also known by the names of *fetid stomatitis*, or *putrid sore mouth*, occurs particularly in children after the first dentition. It may prevail as a widespread epidemic in institutions in which the sanitary conditions are defective. It has been met with in jails and camps. Insufficient and unwholesome food, improper ventilation, and prolonged damp, cold weather seem to be special predisposing causes. Lack of cleanliness of the mouth, the presence of carious teeth, and the collection of tartar around them favor the development of the disease. The affection spreads like a specific disease, but the microbe has not yet been isolated. It has been held that the disease is the same as the foot-and-mouth disease of cattle, and that it is conveyed by the milk, but there is no positive evidence on these points. Payne suggests that the virus is identical with that of contagious impetigo.

The morbid process begins at the margin of the gums, which become swollen and red, and bleed readily. Ulcers form, the bases of which are covered with a grayish-white, firmly adherent membrane. In severe cases the teeth may become loosened and necrosis of the alveolar process may occur. The ulcers extend along the gum-line of the upper and lower jaws; the tongue, lips, and mucosa of the cheeks are usually swollen, but rarely ulcerated. There is salivation, the breath is foul, and mastication is painful. The submaxillary lymph-glands are enlarged. An exanthem often develops and may be mistaken for measles. The constitutional symptoms are often severe, and in institutions death sometimes results in the case of debilitated children.

In the treatment of this form of stomatitis chlorate of potassium has been found to be almost specific. It should be given in doses of 10 grains, three times a day, to a child, and to an adult double that amount. Locally it may be used as a mouth-wash, or the powdered salt may be applied directly to the ulcerated surfaces. When there is much fetor, a permanganate-of-potash wash may be used, and an application of nitrate of silver may be made to the ulcers.

There are several *other varieties* of ulcerative sore mouth, which differ entirely from this form. Ulcers of the mouth are common in nursing women, and are usually seen on the mucous membrane of the lips and cheeks. They develop from the mucous follicles, and are from 3 to 5 mm. in diameter. They may cause little or no inconvenience; but in some instances they are very painful and interfere seriously with the taking of food and its mastication. As a rule they heal readily after the application of nitrate of silver, and the condition is an indication for tonics, fresh air, and a better diet.

Recurring outbreaks of an herpetic, even pemphigoid, eruption are seen in neurotic individuals (*stomatitis neurotica chronica,* Jacobi). In some cases it is associated with an erythema multiforme.

Parrot describes the occasional appearance in the new-born of small ulcers symmetrically placed on the hard palate on either side of the middle line. They are met with in very debilitated children. The ulcers rarely heal; usually they tend to increase in size, and may involve the bone.

Bednar's aphthæ consist of small patches and ulcers on the hard palate, caused as a rule in young infants by the artificial nipple or the nurse's finger.

(4) **Parasitic Stomatitis** (*Thrush; Soor; Muguet*).—This affection, most commonly seen in children, is dependent upon a fungus, the *saccharomyces albicans,* called by Robin the *oïdium albicans.* It belongs to the order of yeast fungi, and consists of branching filaments, from the ends of which ovoid torula cells develop. The disease does not arise apparently in a normal mucosa. The use of an improper diet, uncleanliness of the mouth, the acid fermentation of remnants of food, or the development, from any cause, of catarrhal stomatitis predispose to the growth of the fungus. In institutions it is frequently transmitted by unclean feeding-bottles, spoons, etc. It is not confined to children, but is met with in adults in the final stages of fever, in chronic tuberculosis, diabetes, and in cachectic states. The parasite develops in the upper layers of the mucosa, and the filaments form a dense felt-work among the epithelial cells. The disease begins on the tongue and is seen in the form of slightly raised, pearly-white spots, which increase in size and gradually coalesce. The membrane thus formed can be readily scraped off, leaving an intact mucosa, or, if the process extends deeply, a bleeding, slightly ulcerated surface. The disease spreads to the cheeks, lips, and hard palate, and may involve the tonsils and pharynx. In very severe cases the entire buccal mucosa is covered by the grayish-white membrane. It may even extend into the œsophagus and, according to Parrot, to the stomach and cæcum. It is occasionally met with on the vocal cords. Robust, well-nourished children are sometimes affected, but it is usually met with in enfeebled, emaciated infants with digestive or intestinal troubles. In such cases the disease may persist for months.

The affection is readily recognized, and must not be confounded with aphthous stomatitis, in which the ulcers, preceded by the formation of vesicles, are perfectly distinctive. In thrush the microscopical examination shows the presence of the characteristic fungus throughout the membrane. In this condition, too, the mouth is usually dry—a striking contrast to the salivation accompanying aphthæ.

Thrush is more readily prevented than removed. The child's mouth should be kept scrupulously clean, and, if artificially fed, the bottles should be thoroughly sterilized. Lime-water or any other alkaline fluid, such as the bicarbonate of soda (a drachm to a tumbler of water), may be employed. When the patches are present these alkaline mouth-washes may be continued after each feeding. A spray of borax or of sulphite of soda (a drachm to the ounce) or the black wash with glycerin may be employed. The permanganate of potassium is also useful. The constitutional treatment is of equal importance, and it will often be found that the thrush persists, in spite of all local measures, until the general health of the infant is improved by change of air or the relief of the diarrhœa, or, in obstinate cases, the substitution of a natural for the artificial diet.

(5) **Gangrenous Stomatitis** (*Cancrum Oris; Noma*).—An affection characterized by a rapidly progressing gangrene, starting on the gums or cheeks, and leading to extensive sloughing and destruction. This terrible, but fortunately rare, disease is seen only in children under very insanitary conditions or during convalescence from the acute fevers. It is more common in girls than in boys. It is met with between the ages of two and five years. In at least one half of the cases the disease has developed during convalescence from measles. Cases have been seen also after scarlet fever and typhoid. The mucous membrane is first affected, usually of the gums or of one cheek. The process begins insidiously, and when first seen there is a sloughing ulcer of the mucous membrane, which spreads rapidly and leads to brawny induration of the skin and adjacent parts. The sloughing extends, and in severe cases the cheek is perforated. The disease may spread to the tongue and chin; it may invade the bones of the jaws and even involve the eyelids and ears. In mild cases an ulcer forms on the inner surface of the cheek, which heals or may perforate and leave a fistulous opening. Naturally in such a severe affection the constitutional disturbance is very great, the pulse is rapid, the prostration extreme, and death usually takes place within a week or ten days. The temperature may reach 103° or 104°. Diarrhœa is usually present, and aspiration pneumonia often develops. H. R. Wharton has described a case in which there was extensive colitis. Bishop and Ryan have isolated an organism which resembles in all points the diphtheria bacillus of reduced virulence.

The treatment of the disease is unsatisfactory. In many cases the onset is so insidious that there is an extensive sloughing sore when the case first comes under observation. Destruction of the sore by the cautery, either the Paquelin or fuming nitric acid, is the most effectual. Antiseptic applications should be made to destroy the fetor. The child should be carefully nourished and stimulants given freely.

(6) **Mercurial Stomatitis** (*Ptyalism*).—An inflammation of the mouth and salivary glands may be caused by mercury. It occurs chiefly in persons

who have a special susceptibility, and rarely now as a result of the excessive use of the drug. It is met with also in persons whose occupation necessitates the constant handling of mercury. It often follows the administration of repeated small doses. Thus, a patient with heart-disease who was ordered an eighth of a grain of calomel every three hours for diuretic purposes had, after taking eight or ten doses, a severe stomatitis, which persisted for several weeks. I have known it to follow the administration of small doses of gray powder. The patient complains first of a metallic taste in the mouth, the gums become swollen, red, and sore, mastication is difficult, and soon there is a great increase in the secretion of the saliva, which flows freely from the mouth. The tongue is swollen, the breath has a foul odor, and, if the affection progresses, there may be ulceration of the mucosa, and, in rare instances, necrosis of the jaw. Although troublesome and distressing, the disease is rarely serious, and recovery usually takes place in a couple of weeks. Instances in which the teeth become loosened or detached or in which the inflammation extends to the pharynx and Eustachian tubes are rarely seen now.

The administration of mercury should be suspended so soon as the gums are "touched." Mild cases of the affection subside within a few days and require only a simple mouth-wash. In severer cases the chlorate of potassium may be given internally, and used to rinse the mouth. The bowels should be freely opened; the patient should take a hot bath every evening and should drink plentifully of alkaline mineral waters. Atropine is sometimes serviceable, and may be given in doses of $\frac{1}{100}$ of a grain twice a day. Iodine is also recommended. When the salivation is severe and protracted, the patient becomes much debilitated, anæmia develops, and a supporting treatment is indicated. The diet is necessarily liquid, for the patient finds the chief difficulty in taking food. If the pain is severe a Dover powder may be given at night.

Here may be appropriately mentioned the influence of stomatitis, particularly the mercurial form, upon the developing teeth of children. The condition known as *erosion*, in which the teeth are honeycombed or pitted owing to defective formation of enamel, is indicative, as a rule, of infantile stomatitis. Such teeth must be distinguished carefully from those of congenital syphilis, which may of course coexist, but the two conditions are distinct. The honeycombing is frequently seen on the incisors; but, according to Jonathan Hutchinson, the test teeth of infantile stomatitis are the first permanent molars, then the incisors, "which are almost as constantly pitted, eroded, and of bad color, often showing the transverse furrow which crosses all the teeth at the same level." Magitot regards these transverse furrows as the result of infantile convulsions or of severe illness during early life. He thinks they are analogous to the furrows on the nails which so often follow a serious disease.

(7) **Eczema of the Tongue** (*Geographical Tongue*).—A remarkable desquamation of the superficial epithelium of the tongue in circinate patches, which spread while the central portions heal. Fusion of patches leads to areas with sinuous outlines. When extensive the tongue may be covered with these areas, like a geographical map. The affection causes a

good deal of itching and heat, and may be a source of much mental worry to the patients, who often dread lest it may be a commencing cancer.

The etiology of the disease is unknown. It occurs in infants and children, and it is not very infrequent in adults. It has been regarded as a gouty manifestation, and transient attacks may accompany indigestion. It is very liable to relapse. In adults it may prove very obstinate, and I know of one instance in which the disease persisted in spite of all treatment for more than two years. Solutions of nitrate of silver give the most satisfactory results in relieving the intense burning.

(8) **Leukoplakia buccalis.**—Samuel Plumbe described the condition as *icthyosis lingualæ*. It has also been called *buccal psoriasis* and *keratosis mucosæ oris*. There are unsymmetrical patches of various shapes, whitish or often pearly white in color, smooth, and without any tendency to ulcerate. They have been called lingual corns. The intensity of the opaque white color depends upon the thickness of the epidermis. The patches may extend and become slightly papillomatous. There are instances in which genuine epithelioma has developed from them. The condition is met with most commonly in heavy smokers, and is sometimes known as the smoker's tongue. An interesting question is the relation to syphilis. While somewhat similar patches develop in infected persons, the true syphilitic glossitis rarely presents the same opaque white, smooth appearance. It is more commonly at the edge and the point of the tongue than on the dorsum, and yields promptly to specific treatment.

Leukoplakia is a very obstinate affection and resists as a rule all forms of treatment. All irritants, such as smoke and very hot food, should be avoided. Local treatment with one-half-per-cent corrosive sublimate or a one-per-cent chromic-acid solution has been recommended. The propriety of active local treatment is doubtful. The appearance of anything like papillomatous outgrowths should be regarded as an indication for surgical intervention.

II. DISEASES OF THE SALIVARY GLANDS.

1. **Supersecretion** (*Ptyalism*).—The normal amount of saliva varies from 2 to 3 pints in the twenty-four hours. The secretion is increased during the taking of food and in the physiological processes of dentition. A great increase, to which the term *ptyalism* is applied, is met with under many circumstances. It occurs occasionally in mental and nervous affections and in rabies. Occasionally it is seen in the acute fevers, particularly in small-pox. It occurs sometimes with disease of the pancreas. It has been met with during gestation, usually early, though it may persist throughout the entire course. It has been known to occur at each menstrual period; and, lastly, it is a common effect of certain drugs. Mercury, gold, copper, the iodine compounds, and (among vegetable remedies) jaborandi, muscarin, and tobacco excite the salivary secretion. Of these we most frequently see the effect of mercury in producing ptyalism. The salivation may be present without any inflammation of the mouth.

2. Xerostomia (*Arrest of the Salivary and Buccal Secretions; Dry Mouth*).—In this condition, first described by Jonathan Hutchinson, the secretions of the mouth and salivary glands are suppressed. The tongue is red, sometimes cracked, and quite dry; the mucous membrane of the cheeks and of the palate is smooth, shining, and dry; and mastication, deglutition, and articulation are very difficult. The condition is not common. A majority of the cases are in women, and in several instances have been associated with nervous phenomena. The general health, as a rule, is unimpaired. Hadden suggests that it is due to involvement of some centre which controls the secretion of the salivary and buccal glands. A well-marked case came under my observation in a man aged thirty-two, who was sent to me by Donald Baynes on account of a peculiar growth in the mouth. This proved to be the remnants of food which, owing to the absence of any salivary or buccal secretions, collected along the gums, became hardened, and adhered to them. The condition lasted for three weeks, and was cured by the galvanic current.

3. Inflammation of the Salivary Glands.

(*a*) *Specific Parotitis*. (See MUMPS.)

(*b*) *Symptomatic parotitis* or *parotid bubo* occurs:

(1) In the course of the infectious fevers—typhus, typhoid, pneumonia, pyæmia, etc. In ordinary practice it occurs oftenest, perhaps, in typhoid fever. It is the result either of septic infection through the blood, or the inflammation, in many cases, passes up the salivary duct, and so reaches the gland. The process is usually very intense and leads rapidly to suppuration. It is, as a rule, an unfavorable indication in the course of a fever. I have seen recently parotitis in secondary syphilis.

(2) In connection with injury or disease of the abdomen or pelvis, a condition to which Stephen Paget has called special attention. Of 101 case of this kind, " 10 followed injury or disease of the urinary tract, 18 were due to injury or disease of the alimentary canal, and 23 were due to injury or disease of the abdominal wall, the peritonæum, or the pelvic cellular tissue. The remaining 50 were due to injury, disease, or temporary derangement of the genital organs." By temporary derangement is meant slight injuries or natural processes—a slight blow on the testis, the introduction of a pessary, menstruation, or pregnancy. The etiology of this form of parotitis is obscure. We have had 3 cases. Many of them are undoubtedly septic.

(3) In association with facial paralysis, as in a case of fatal peripheral neuritis described by Gowers.

In the treatment of parotid bubo the application of half a dozen leeches will sometimes reduce the inflammation and promote resolution. When suppuration seems inevitable hot fomentations should be applied. A free incision should be made *early*.

(*c*) *Chronic parotitis*, a condition in which the glands are enlarged, rarely painful, may follow inflammation of the throat or mumps. Salivation may be present. It may be due to lead or mercury. It occurs also in chronic Bright's disease and in secondary syphilis. Mikulicz has described a remarkable condition of chronic symmetrical enlargement of

28

the salivary and lachrymal glands. The condition may persist for years. The case under my care mentioned in the second edition of this work died subsequently of tuberculosis (Am. Jr. Med. Sci., January, 1898).

(*d*) *Gaseous Tumors of Steno's Duct and of the Parotid Gland.*—In glass-blowers and musicians Steno's duct may become inflated with air and form a tumor the size of a nut or of an egg. Some have contained a mixture of air, saliva, and pus. In rare cases there are gaseous tumors of the glands, which give a sensation of crepitation on palpation.

III. DISEASES OF THE PHARYNX.

(1) Circulatory Disturbances.—(*a*) *Hyperæmia* is a common condition in acute and chronic affections of the throat, and is frequently seen as a result of irritation from tobacco smoke. Venous stasis is seen in valvular disease of the heart, and in mechanical obstruction of the superior vena cava by tumor or aneurism. In aortic insufficiency the capillary pulse may sometimes be seen and the intense throbbing of the internal carotid may be mistaken for aneurism.

(*b*) *Hæmorrhage* is found in association with bleeding from other mucous surfaces, or it is due to local causes in the pharynx itself. In the latter case it may be mistaken for hæmorrhage from the lungs or stomach. The bleeding may come from granulations or vegetations in the naso-pharynx. Sometimes the patient finds the pillow stained in the morning with bloody secretion. The condition is rarely serious, and only requires suitable local treatment of the pharynx. Occasionally a hæmorrhage takes place into the mucosa, producing a pharyngeal hæmatoma. I have thrice seen a condition of the uvula resembling hæmorrhagic infarction. One was in a patient with acute rheumatism, to whom large doses of salicylic acid had been given; the other two were instances of peliosis rheumatica, in both of which partial sloughing of the uvula took place.

(*c*) *Œdema.*—An infiltrated œdematous condition of the uvula and adjacent parts is not very uncommon in conditions of debility, in profound anæmia, and in Bright's disease. The uvula is sometimes from this cause enormously enlarged, whence may arise difficulty in swallowing or in breathing.

(2) Acute Pharyngitis (*Sore Throat; Angina Simplex*).—The entire pharyngeal structures, often with the tonsils, are involved. The condition may follow cold or exposure. In other instances it is associated with constitutional states, such as rheumatism or gout, or with digestive disorders. The patient complains of uneasiness and soreness in swallowing, of a feeling of tickling and dryness in the throat, together with a constant desire to hawk and cough. Frequently the inflammation extends into the larynx and produces hoarseness. Not uncommonly it is only part of a general naso-pharyngeal catarrh. The process may pass into the Eustachian tubes and cause slight deafness. There is stiffness of the neck, the lymph-glands of which may be enlarged and painful. The constitutional symptoms are rarely severe. The disease sets in with a chilly feeling and slight fever; the pulse is increased in frequency. Occasionally the febrile symptoms are more severe, particularly if the tonsils are specially involved. The examination of the throat shows general congestion of the mucous membrane, which is dry and glistening, and in places covered with sticky secretion. The uvula may be much swollen.

Acute pharyngitis lasts only a few days and requires mild measures. If the tonsils are involved and the fever is high, aconite or sodium salicylate may be given. Guaiacum also is beneficial; but in a majority of the cases a calomel purge or a saline aperient and inhalations with steam meet the indications.

(3) **Chronic Pharyngitis.**—This may follow repeated acute attacks. It is very common in persons who smoke or drink to excess, and in those who use the voice very much, such as clergymen, hucksters, and others. It is frequently met with in chronic nasal catarrh. The naso-pharynx and the posterior wall are the parts most frequently affected. The mucous membrane is relaxed, the venules are dilated, and roundish bodies, from 2 to 4 mm. in diameter, reddish in color, project to a variable distance beyond the mucous membrane. These represent the proliferations of lymph tissue about the mucous glands. They may be very abundant, forming elongated rows in the lateral walls of the pharynx. With this there may be a dry glistening state of the pharyngeal mucosa, sometimes known as *pharyngitis sicca.* The pillars of the fauces and the uvula are often much relaxed. The secretion forms at the back of the pharynx and the patient may feel it drop down from the vault, or it is tenacious and adherent, and is only removed by repeated efforts at hawking.

In the *treatment*, special attention must be paid to the general health. If possible, the cause should be ascertained. The condition is almost constant in smokers, and cannot be cured without stopping the use of tobacco. The use of food either too hot or too much spiced should be forbidden. When it depends upon excessive exercise of the voice, rest should be enjoined. In many of these cases change of air and tonics help very much. In the local treatment of the throat gargles, washes, and pastilles of various sorts give temporary relief, but when the hypertrophic condition is marked the spots should be thoroughly destroyed by the galvano-cautery. In many instances this affords great and permanent relief, but in others the condition persists, and as it is not unbearable, the patient gives up all hope of permanent relief.

(4) **Ulceration of the Pharynx.**—(*a*) Follicular. The ulcers are usually small, superficial, and generally associated with chronic catarrh.

(*b*) Syphilitic ulcers are usually painless, and most frequently situated on the posterior wall of the pharynx. They occur in the secondary stage as small, shallow excavations with the mucous patches. In the tertiary stage the ulcers are due to erosion of gummata, and in healing they leave whitish cicatrices.

(*c*) Tuberculous ulceration is not very uncommon in advanced cases of phthisis, and, if extensive, is one of the most distressing features of the later stages of the disease. The ulcers are irregular, with ill-defined edges and grayish-yellow bases. The posterior wall of the pharynx may have an eroded, worm-eaten appearance. These ulcers are, as a rule, intensely painful. Occasionally the primary disease is about the tonsils and the pillars of the fauces.

(*d*) Ulcers occur in connection with pseudo-membranous inflammation, particularly the diphtheritic. In cancer and in lupus ulcers are also present.

(*e*) Ulcers are met with in certain of the fevers, particularly in typhoid.

In many instances the diagnosis of the nature of pharyngeal ulcers is very difficult. The tuberculous and cancerous varieties are readily recognized, but it happens not infrequently that a doubt arises as to the syphilitic character of an ulcer. In many instances the local conditions may be uncertain. Then other evidences of syphilis should be sought for, and the patient should be placed on mercury and iodide of potassium, under which remedies syphilitic ulcers usually heal with great rapidity.

(5) **Acute Infectious Phlegmon of the Pharynx.**—Under this term Senator has described cases in which, along with difficulty in swallowing, soreness of the throat, and sometimes hoarseness, the neck enlarges, the pharyngeal mucosa becomes swollen and injected, the fever is high, the constitutional symptoms are severe, and the inflammation passes on rapidly to suppuration. The symptoms are very intense. The swelling of the pharyngeal tissues early reaches such a grade as to impede respiration. Very similar symptoms may be produced by foreign bodies in the pharynx.

(6) **Retro-pharyngeal abscess** occurs: (1) In healthy children between six months and two years of age. The child becomes restless, the voice changes; it becomes nasal or metallic in tone, and there are pain and difficulty in swallowing. Inspection of the pharynx reveals a projecting tumor in the middle line, or if it be not visible, it is readily felt, on palpation, projecting from the posterior wall. This form has been carefully described by Koplik. (2) As a not infrequent sequel of the fevers, particularly of scarlet fever and diphtheria. (3) In caries of the bodies of the cervical vertebræ.

The diagnosis is readily made, as the projecting tumor can be seen, or felt with the finger on the posterior wall of the pharynx.

(7) **Angina Ludovici** (*Ludwig's Angina; Cellulitis of the Neck*).—In medical practice this is seen as a secondary inflammation in the specific fevers, particularly diphtheria and scarlet fever. It may, however, occur idiopathically or result from trauma. It is probably always a streptococcus infection which spreads rapidly from the glands. The swelling at first is most marked in the submaxillary region of one side. The symptoms are, as a rule, intense, and, unless early and thorough surgical measures are employed, there is great risk of systemic infection. Felix Semon holds that the various acute septic inflammations of the throat—acute œdema of the larynx, phlegmon of the pharynx and larynx, and angina Ludovici— "represent degrees varying in virulence of one and the same process."

IV. DISEASES OF THE TONSILS.

ACUTE TONSILLITIS.

(1) Follicular or Lacunar Tonsillitis.—For practical purposes, under this name may be described the various forms which have been called catarrhal, erythematous, ulcero-membranous, and herpetic.

Etiology.—The disease is met with most frequently in young persons, but in children under ten it is less common than the chronic form. It is rare in infants. Sex has no special influence. Exposure to wet and cold, and bad hygienic surroundings appear to have a direct etiological connection with the disease. In so many instances defective drainage has been found associated with outbreaks of follicular tonsillitis that sewer-gas is regarded as a common exciting cause. One attack renders a patient more liable to subsequent infection. Special stress is laid by some writers upon the coexistence of tonsillitis with rheumatism. Cheadle describes it as one of the phases of rheumatism in childhood with which articular attacks may alternate. I cannot say that, in my experience, the connection between the two affections has been very striking, except in one point, viz., that an attack of acute rheumatism is not infrequently preceded by inflammation of the tonsils. The existence of pains in the limbs is no evidence of the connection of the affection with rheumatism. A disease so common and widespread as acute tonsillitis necessarily attacks many persons in whose families rheumatism prevails or who may themselves have had acute attacks.

Mackenzie gives a table showing that in four successive years more cases occurred in September than in any other month; in October nearly as many, with July, August, and November next. In this country it seems more prevalent in the spring. So many cases develop within a short time that the disease may be almost epidemic. It spreads through a family in such a way that it must be regarded as contagious.

An old notion prevails that there is a definite relation between the tonsils and the testes and ovaries. F. J. Shepherd has called attention to the circumstance that acute tonsillitis is a very common affection in newly married persons. That view is probably correct which regards tonsillitis as a local disease with severe constitutional manifestations, although the fever is often out of proportion to the local symptoms. The commonest organism found in tonsillitis is a streptococcus. Staphylococci also occur. In some cases the *bacillus diphtheriæ* of Loeffler have been found, but it does not always possess the full virulence (see Atypical Forms of Diphtheria).

Morbid Anatomy.—The lacunæ of the tonsils become filled with exudation products, which form cheesy-looking masses, projecting from the orifices of the crypts. Not infrequently the exudations from contiguous lacunæ coalesce. The intervening mucosa is usually swollen, deep-red in color, and may present herpetic vesicles or, in some instances, even membranous exudation, in which case it may be difficult to distinguish the condition from diphtheria. The creamy contents of the crypt are made up of micrococci and epithelial *débris*.

Symptoms.—Chilly feelings, or even a definite chill, and aching pains in the back and limbs may precede the onset. The fever rises rapidly, and in the case of a young child may reach 105° on the evening of the first day. The patient complains of soreness of the throat and difficulty in swallowing. On examination, the tonsils are seen to be swollen and the crypts present the characteristic creamy exudate. The tongue is furred, the breath is heavy and foul, and the urine is highly colored and loaded with urates. In children the respirations are usually very hurried, and the pulse is greatly increased in rapidity. Swallowing is painful, and the voice often becomes nasal. Slight swelling of the cervical glands is present. In severe cases the symptoms increase and the tonsils become still more swollen. The inflammation gradually subsides, and, as a rule, within a week the fever departs and the local condition greatly improves. The tonsils, however, remain somewhat swollen. The prostration and constitutional disturbance are often out of proportion to the intensity of the local disease.

There are complications which occasionally excite uneasiness. Febrile albuminuria is not uncommon, as Haig-Brown has pointed out. Cases of endocarditis or pericarditis have been found. It is to be borne in mind that in children an apex systolic murmur is by no means uncommon at the height of any fever. The disease may extend to the middle ear. The development of paralytic symptoms, local or general, after an attack which has been regarded as follicular tonsillitis indicates an error in diagnosis. A diffuse erythema may develop, simulating that of scarlet fever.

Diagnosis.—It may be difficult to distinguish follicular tonsillitis from diphtheria. It would seem, indeed, as if there were intermediate forms between the mildest lacunar and the severer pseudo-membranous tonsillitis. In the follicular form the individual yellowish-gray masses, separated by the reddish tonsillar tissue, are very characteristic; whereas in diphtheria the membrane is of ashy gray, and uniform, not patchy. A point of the greatest importance in diphtheria is that the membrane is not limited to the tonsils, but creeps up the pillars of the fauces or appears on the uvula. The diphtheritic membrane when removed leaves a bleeding, eroded surface; whereas the exudation of lacunar tonsillitis is easily separated, and there is no erosion beneath it. In all doubtful cases cultures should be made to determine the presence or absence of Loeffler's bacillus.

(2) Suppurative Tonsillitis.

Etiology.—This arises under conditions very similar to those mentioned in the lacunar form. It may follow exposure to cold or wet, and is particularly liable to recur. It is most common in adolescence. The inflammation is here more deeply seated. It involves the stroma, and tends to go on to suppuration.

Symptoms.—The constitutional disturbance is very great. The temperature rises to 104° or 105°, and the pulse ranges from 110 to 130. Nocturnal delirium is not uncommon. The prostration may be extreme. There is no local disease of similar extent which so rapidly exhausts the strength of a patient. Soreness and dryness of the throat, with pain in swallowing, are the symptoms of which the patient first complains. One or both tonsils may be involved. They are enlarged, firm to the touch, dusky red and œdematous, and the contiguous parts are also much swollen. The swelling of the glands may be so great that they meet in the middle line, or one tonsil may even push the uvula aside and almost touch the other gland. The salivary and buccal secretions are increased. The glands of the neck enlarge, the lower jaw is fixed, and the patient is unable to open his mouth. In from two to four days the enlarged gland becomes softer, and fluctuation can be distinctly felt by placing one finger on the tonsil and the other at the angle of the jaw. The abscess points usually toward the mouth, but in some cases toward the pharynx. It may burst spontaneously, affording instant and great relief. Suffocation has followed the rupture of a large abscess and the entrance of the pus into the larynx. When the suppuration is peritonsillar and extensive, the internal carotid artery may be opened; but these are, fortunately, very rare accidents.

Treatment.—In the follicular form aconite may be given in full doses. It acts very beneficially in children. The salicylates, given freely at the outset, are regarded by some as specific, but I have seen no evidence of such prompt and decisive action. At night, a full dose of Dover's powder may be given. The use of guaiacum, in the form of 2-grain lozenges, is warmly recommended. Iron and quinine should be reserved until the fever has subsided. A pad of spongio-piline or thick flannel dipped in ice-cold water may be applied around the neck and covered with oiled silk. More convenient still is a small ice-bag. Locally the tonsils may be treated with the dry sodium bicarbonate. The moistened fingertip is dipped into the soda, which is then rubbed gently on the gland and repeated every hour. Astringent preparations, such as iron and glycerin, alum, zinc, and nitrate of silver, may be tried. To cleanse and disinfect the throat, solutions of borax or thymol in glycerin and water may be used.

In suppurative tonsillitis hot applications in the form of poultices and fomentations are more comfortable and better than the ice-bag. The gland should be felt—it cannot always be seen—from time to time, and should be opened when fluctuation is distinct. The progress of the disease may be shortened and the patient spared several days of great suffering if the gland is scarified early. The curved bistoury, guarded nearly to the point with plaster or cotton, is the most satisfactory instrument. The incision should be made from above downward, parallel with the anterior pillar. There are cases in which, before suppuration takes place, the parenchymatous swelling is so great that the patient is threatened with suffocation. In such instances the tonsil must either be excised or tracheotomy or, possibly, intubation performed. Delavan refers to two cases in which he states that tracheotomy would, under these circumstances, have saved life. Patients with this affection require a nourishing liquid diet, and during convalescence iron in full doses.

CHRONIC TONSILLITIS.

(Chronic Naso-pharyngeal Obstruction; Mouth-Breathing; Aprosexia.)

Under this heading will be considered also hypertrophy of the adenoid tissue in the vault of the pharynx, sometimes known as the pharyngeal tonsil, as the affection usually involves both the tonsils proper and this tissue, and the symptoms are not to be differentiated.

Chronic enlargement of the tonsillar tissues is an affection of great importance, and may influence in an extraordinary way the mental and bodily development of children.

Etiology.—Hypertrophy of the tonsillar structures is occasionally congenital. Cases are perhaps most frequent in children, during the third hemi-decade. The condition also occurs in young adults, more rarely in the middle-aged. The enlargement may follow diphtheria or the eruptive fevers. The frequency of the occurrence of adenoid growths in the nasopharynx has been variously stated. Meyer, to whom the profession is indebted for calling attention to the subject, found them in about one per cent of the children in Copenhagen, while Chappell found 60 cases in the examination of 2,000 children in New York. These figures give a very moderate estimate of the prevalence of the trouble. It occurs equally in boys and girls, according to some writers with greater prevalence in the former.

Morbid Anatomy.—The tonsils proper present a condition of chronic hypertrophy, due to multiplication of all the constituents of the glands. The lymphoid elements may be chiefly involved without much development of the stroma. In other instances the fibrous matrix is increased, and the organ is then harder, smaller, firmer, and is cut with much greater difficulty.

The adenoid growths, which spring from the vault of the pharynx, form masses varying in size from a small pea to an almond. They may be sessile, with broad bases, or pedunculated. They are reddish in color, of moderate firmness, and contain numerous blood-vessels. " Abundant, as a rule, over the vault, on a line with the fossa of the Eustachian tube, the growths may lie posterior to the fossa—namely, in the depression known as the fossa of Rosenmüller, or upon the parts which are parallel to the posterior wall of the pharynx. The growths appear to spring in the main from the mucous membrane covering the localities where the connective tissue fills in the inequalities of the base of the skull " (Harrison Allen). The growths are most frequently papillomatous with a lymphoid parenchyma. Hypertrophy of the pharyngeal adenoid tissue may be present without great enlargement of the tonsils proper. Chronic catarrh of the nose usually coexists.

Symptoms.—The direct effect of chronic tonsillar hypertrophy is the establishment of mouth-breathing. The indirect effects are deformation of the thorax, changes in the facial expression, sometimes marked alteration in the mental condition, and in certain cases stunting of the growth. Woods Hutchinson has suggested that the embryological relation of these structures with the pituitary body may account for the interference with development. The establishment of mouth-breathing is the symptom which first attracts the attention. It is not so noticeable by day, although the child may present the vacant expression characteristic of this condition. At night the child's sleep is greatly disturbed; the respirations are loud and snoring, and there are sometimes prolonged pauses, followed by deep, noisy inspirations. The pulse may vary strangely during these attacks, and in the prolonged intervals may be slow, to increase greatly with the forced inspirations. The alæ nasi should be observed during the sleep of the child as they are sometimes much retracted during inspiration, due to a laxity of the walls, a condition readily remedied by the use of a soft wire dilator. Night terrors are common. The child may wake up in a paroxysm of shortness of breath. Some of these nocturnal attacks may be due to reflex spasm of the glottis. During the day there may be choking fits when eating.

When the mouth-breathing has persisted for a long time definite changes are brought about in the face, mouth, and chest. The facies is so peculiar and distinctive that the condition may be evident at a glance. The expression is dull, heavy, and apathetic, due in part to the fact that the mouth is habitually left open. In long-standing cases the child is very stupid-looking, responds slowly to questions, and may be sullen and cross. The lips are thick, the nasal orifices small and pinched-in looking, the superior dental arch is narrowed and the roof of the mouth considerably raised.

The remarkable alterations in the shape of the chest in connection with enlarged tonsils were first carefully studied by Dupuytren (1828), who evidently fully appreciated the great importance of the condition. He noted " a lateral depression of the parietes of the chest consisting of a depression, more or less great, of the ribs on each side, and a proportionate protrusion of the sternum in front." J. Mason Warren (Medical Examiner, 1839) gave an admirable description of the constitutional symptoms and the thoracic deformities induced by enlarged tonsils. These, with the memoir of Lambron (1861), constitute the most important contributions to our knowledge on the subject. Three types of deformity may be recognized:

(*a*) **The Pigeon or Chicken Breast,** by far the most common form, in which the sternum is prominent and there is a circular depression in the lateral zone (Harrison's groove), corresponding to the attachment of the diaphragm. The ribs are prominent anteriorly and the sternum is angulated forward at the manubrio-gladiolar junction. As a mouth-breather is watched during sleep, one can see the lower and lateral thoracic regions retracted during inspiration by the action of the diaphragm.

(*b*) **Barrel Chest.**—Some children, the subject of chronic naso-pharyngeal obstruction, have recurring attacks of asthma, and the chest may be gradually deformed, becoming rounded and barrel-shaped, the neck short, and the shoulders and back bowed. A child of ten or eleven may have the thoracic conformation of an old man with emphysema.

(*c*) **The Funnel Breast** (*Trichter-brust*).—This remarkable deformity, in which there is a deep depression at the lower sternum, has excited much controversy as to its mode of origin. I believe that in some instances, at least, it is due to the obstructed breathing in connection with adenoid vegetations. I have seen two cases in children, in which the condition was in process of development. During inspiration the lower sternum was forcibly retracted, so much so that at the height the depression corresponded to a well-marked " *trichter-brust.*" While in repose, the lower sternal region was distinctly excavated.

The voice is altered and acquires a nasal quality. The pronunciation of certain letters is changed, and there is inability to pronounce the nasal consonants *n* and *m*. Bloch lays great stress upon the association of mouth-breathing with stuttering.

The hearing is impaired, usually owing to the extension of inflammation along the Eustachian tubes and the obstruction with mucus or the narrowing of their orifices by pressure of the adenoid vegetations. In some instances it may be due to retraction of the drums, as the upper pharynx is insufficiently supplied with air. Naturally the senses of taste and smell are much impaired. With these symptoms there may be little or no nasal catarrh or discharge, but the pharyngeal secretion of mucus is always increased. Children, however, do not notice this, as the mucus is usually swallowed, but older persons expectorate it with difficulty.

Among other symptoms may be mentioned headache, which is by no means uncommon, general listlessness, and an indisposition for physical or mental exertion. Habit-spasm of the face has been described in connection with it. I have known several instances in which permanent relief has been afforded by the removal of the adenoid vegetations. Enuresis is occasionally an associated symptom. The influence upon the mental development is striking. Mouth-breathers are usually dull, stupid, and backward. It is impossible for them to fix the attention for long at a time, and to this impairment of the mental function Guye, of Amsterdam, has given the name *aprosexia.* Headaches, forgetfulness, inability to study without discomfort, are frequent symptoms of this condition in students. There is more than a grain of truth in the aphorism *shut your mouth and save your life,* which is found on the title-page of Captain Catlin's celebrated pamphlet on mouth-breathing.

A symptom specially associated with enlarged tonsils is fetor of the breath. In the tonsillar crypts the inspissated secretion undergoes decomposition and an odor not unlike that of Roquefort or Limburger cheese is produced. The little cheesy masses may sometimes be squeezed from the crypts of the tonsils. Though the odor may not apparently be very strong, yet if the mass be squeezed between the fingers its intensity will at once be appreciated. In some cases of chronic enlargement the cheesy masses may be deep in the tonsillar crypts; and if they remain for a prolonged period lime salts are deposited and a tonsillar calculus in this way produced.

Children with enlarged tonsils are especially prone to take cold and to recurring attacks of follicular disease. They are also more liable to diphtheria, and in them the anginal features in scarlet fever are always more serious. The ultimate results of untreated adenoid hypertrophy are important. In some cases the vegetations disappear, leaving an atrophic condition of the vault of the pharynx. Neglect may also lead to the so-called Thornwaldt's disease, in which there is a cystic condition of the pharyngeal tonsil and constant secretion of muco-pus.

Diagnosis.—The facial aspect is usually distinctive. Enlarged tonsils are readily seen on inspection of the pharynx. There may be no great enlargement of the tonsils and nothing apparent at the back of the throat even when the naso-pharynx is completely blocked with adenoid vegetations. In children the rhinoscopic examination is rarely practicable. Digital examination is the most satisfactory. The growths can then be felt either as small, flat bodies or, if extensive, as velvety, grape-like papillomata.

Treatment.—If the tonsils are large and the general state is evidently influenced by them they should be at once removed. Applications of iodine and iron, or pencilling the crypts with nitrate of silver, are of service in the milder grades, but it is waste of time to apply them in very enlarged glands. There is a condition in which the tonsils are not much enlarged, but the crypts are constantly filled with cheesy secretions and cause a very bad odor in the breath. In such instances the removal of the secretion and thorough pencilling of the crypts with chromic acid may be practised. The galvano-cautery is of great service in many cases of enlarged tonsils when there is any objection to the more radical surgical procedure.

The treatment of the adenoid growths in the pharynx is of the greatest importance, and should be thoroughly carried out. Parents should be frankly told that the affection is serious, one which impairs the mental not less than the bodily development of the child. In spite of the thorough ventilation of this subject by specialists, practitioners do not appear to have grasped as yet the full importance of this disease. They are far too apt to temporize and unnecessarily to postpone radical measures. The child must be etherized, when the growths can be removed either with the finger-nail, which in most instances is sufficient, or with a suitable curette. Considerable hæmorrhage may follow, but it is usually checked quickly. The good effects of the operation are often apparent within a few days, and the child begins to breathe through the nose. In some instances the habit of mouth-breathing persists. As soon as the child goes to sleep the lower jaw drops and the air is drawn into the mouth. In these cases a chin strap can be readily adjusted, which the child may wear at night. In severe cases it may take months of careful training before the child can speak properly.

Throughout the entire treatment attention should be paid to hygiene and diet, and cod-liver oil and the iodide of iron may be administered with benefit.

V. DISEASES OF THE ŒSOPHAGUS.

I. ACUTE ŒSOPHAGITIS.

Etiology.—Acute inflammation occurs (*a*) in the catarrhal processes of the specific fevers; more rarely as an extension from catarrh of the pharynx. (*b*) As a result of intense mechanical or chemical irritation, produced by foreign bodies, by very hot liquids, or by strong corrosives. (*c*) In the form of pseudo-membranous inflammation in diphtheria, and occasionally in pneumonia, typhoid fever, and pyæmia. (*d*) As a pustular inflammation in small-pox, and, according to Laennec, as a result of a prolonged administration of tartar emetic. (*e*) In connection with local disease, particularly cancer either of the tube itself or extension to it from without. And, lastly, acute œsophagitis, occasionally with ulceration, may occur spontaneously in sucklings.

Morbid Anatomy.—It is extremely rare to see redness of the mucosa, except when chemical irritants have been swallowed. More commonly the epithelium is thickened and has desquamated, so that the surface is covered with a fine granular substance. The mucous follicles are swollen and occasionally there may be seen small erosions. In the pseudo-membranous inflammation there is a grayish croupous exudate, usually limited in extent, at the upper portion of the gullet. This must not be confounded with the grayish-white deposit of thrush in children. The pustular disease is very rare in small-pox. In the phlegmonous inflammation the mucous membrane is greatly swollen, and there is purulent infiltration in the submucosa. This may be limited as about a foreign body, or extremely diffuse. It may even extend throughout a large part of the gullet. Gangrene occasionally supervenes. There is a remarkable fibrinous or membranous œsophagitis, which is most frequently met with in the fevers, sometimes also in hysteria, in which long casts of the tube may be vomited.

Symptoms.—Pain in deglutition is always present in severe inflammation of the œsophagus, and in the form which follows the swallowing of strong irritants may prevent the taking of food. A dull pain beneath the sternum is also present. In the milder forms of catarrhal inflammation there are usually no symptoms. The presence of a foreign body is indicated by dysphagia and spasm with the regurgitation of portions of the food. Later, blood and pus may be ejected. It is surprising how extensive the disease may be in the œsophagus without producing much pain or great discomfort, except in swallowing. The intense inflammation which follows the swallowing of corrosives, when not fatal, gradually subsides, and often leads to cicatricial contraction and stricture.

The *treatment* of acute inflammation of the œsophagus is extremely unsatisfactory, particularly in the severer forms. The slight catarrhal cases require no special treatment. When the dysphagia is intense it is best not to give food by the mouth, but to feed entirely by enemata. Fragments of ice may be given, and as the pain and distress subside, demulcent drinks. External applications of cold often give relief.

A *chronic* form of œsophagitis is described, but this results usually from the prolonged action of the causes which produce the acute form.

Ulceration of the Œsophagus.—In many cachectic conditions catarrhal ulceration is found. In a few rare instances ulcers of the œsophagus are met with in typhoid fever. Acute malignant ulceration may perforate the œsophagus and open into the aorta.

Associated with chronic heart-disease and more frequently with the senile and the cirrhotic liver, the œsophageal veins may be enormously distended and varicose, particularly toward the stomach. In these cases the mucous membrane is in a state of chronic catarrh, and the patient has frequent eructations of mucus. Rupture of these œsophageal veins may cause fatal hæmorrhage. Two cases of the kind have occurred in my experience. The blood may pass per rectum alone, as in a case reported by Power, of Baltimore, in 1839.

II. SPASM OF THE ŒSOPHAGUS (*Œsophagismus*).

This so-called spasmodic stricture of the gullet is met with in hysterical patients and hypochondriacs, also in chorea, epilepsy, and especially hydrophobia. It is sometimes associated also with the lodgment of foreign bodies. The idiopathic form is found in females of a marked neurotic habit, but may also occur in elderly men. It may be present only during pregnancy. Of 4 cases which have come under my observation, 2 were in men, one a hypochondriac over sixty years of age who for many months had taken only liquid food, and with great difficulty, owing to a spasm which accompanied every attempt to swallow. The readiness with which the bougie passed and the subsequent history showed the true nature of the case. The patient complains of inability to swallow solid food, and in extreme instances even liquids are rejected. The attack may come on abruptly, and be associated with emotional disturbances and with substernal pain. The bougie, when passed, may be arrested temporarily at the seat of the spasm, which gradually yields, or it may slip through without the slightest effort. The condition is rarely serious. Death has, however, followed it.

The *diagnosis* is not difficult, particularly in young persons with marked nervous manifestations. In elderly persons œsophagismus is almost always connected with hypochondriasis, but great care must be taken to exclude cancer.

In some cases a cure is at once effected by the passage of a bougie. The general neurotic condition also requires special attention.

Paralysis of the œsophagus scarcely demands separate consideration. It is a very rare condition, due most often to central disease, particularly bulbar paralysis. It may be peripheral in origin, as in diphtheritic paralysis. Occasionally it occurs also in hysteria. The essential symptom is dysphagia.

III. STRICTURE OF THE ŒSOPHAGUS.

This results from: (*a*) Congenital narrowing. (*b*) The cicatricial contraction of healed ulcers, usually due to corrosive poisons, occasionally to syphilis, and in rare instances after typhoid fever. (*c*) The growth of tumors in the walls, as in the so-called cancerous stricture. Occasionally polypoid tumors projecting from the mucosa produce great narrowing. (*d*) External pressure by aneurism, enlarged lymph-glands, enlarged thyroid, other tumors, and sometimes by pericardial effusion.

The cicatricial stricture may occur anywhere in the gullet, and in extreme cases may, indeed, involve the whole tube, but in a majority of instances it is found either high up near the pharynx or low down toward the stomach. The narrowing may be extreme, so that only small quantities of food can trickle through, or the obstruction may be quite slight. There is usually no difficulty in making a diagnosis of the cicatricial stricture, as the history of mechanical injury or the swallowing of a corrosive fluid makes clear the nature of the case. When the stricture is low down the œsophagus is dilated and the walls are usually much hypertrophied. When the obstruction is high in the gullet, the food is usually rejected at once, whereas, if it is low, it may be retained and a considerable quantity collects before it is regurgitated. Any doubt as to its having reached the stomach is removed by the alkalinity of the material ejected and the absence of the characteristic gastric odor. Auscultation of the œsophagus may be practised and is sometimes of service. The patient takes a mouthful of water and the auscultator listens along the left of the spine. The normal œsophageal *bruit* may be heard later than seven seconds, the normal time, or there may be heard a loud splashing, gurgling sound. The secondary murmur, heard as the fluid enters the stomach, may be absent. The passage of the œsophageal bougie will determine more accurately the locality. Conical bougies attached to a flexible whalebone stem are the most satisfactory, but the gum-elastic stomach tube may be used; a large one should be tried first. The patient should be placed on a low chair with the head well thrown back. The index finger of the left hand is passed far into the pharynx, and in some instances this procedure alone may determine the presence of a new growth. The bougie is passed beside the finger until it touches the posterior wall of the pharynx, then along it, more to one side than in the middle line, and so gradually pushed into the gullet. It is to be borne in mind that in passing the cricoid cartilage there is often a slight obstruction. Great gentleness should be used, as it has happened more than once that the bougie has been passed through a cancerous ulcer into the mediastinum or through a diverticulum. I have known this accident to happen twice—once in the case of a distinguished surgeon, who performed œsophagotomy and passed the tube, as he thought, into the stomach. The post mortem on the next day showed that the tube had entered a diverticulum and through it the left pleura, in which the milk injected through the tube was found. In the other instance the tube passed through a cancerous ulcer into the lung, which was adherent and inflamed. Fortunately these accidents, sometimes unavoidable, are extremely rare. It is well always, as a precautionary measure before passing the bougie, to examine carefully for aneurism, which may produce all the symptoms of organic stricture. In cases in which the narrowing is extreme there is always emaciation. For treatment, surgical works must be consulted.

IV. CANCER OF THE ŒSOPHAGUS.

This is usually epithelioma. It is not an uncommon disease, and occurs more frequently in males than in females. The common situation is in the upper third of the tube. At first confined to the mucous membrane, the cancer gradually increases and soon ulcerates. The lumen of the tube is narrowed, but when ulceration is extensive in the later stages the stricture may be less marked. Dilatation of the tube and hypertrophy of the walls usually take place above the cancer. The cancerous ulcer may perforate the trachea or a bronchus, the lung, the mediastinum, the aorta or one of its larger branches, the pericardium, or it may erode the vertebral column. In my experience perforation of the lung has been the most frequent, producing, as a rule, local gangrene.

Symptoms.—The earliest symptom is dysphagia, which is progressive and may become extreme, so that the patient emaciates rapidly. Regurgitation may take place at once; or, if the cancer is situated near the stomach, it may be deferred for ten or fifteen minutes, or even longer if the tube is much dilated. The rejected materials may be mixed with blood and may contain cancerous fragments. In persons over fifty years of age persistent difficulty in swallowing accompanied by rapid emaciation usually indicates œsophageal cancer. The cervical lymph-glands are frequently enlarged and may give early indication of the nature of the trouble. Pain may be persistent or be present only when food is taken. In certain instances the pain is very great. I saw an autopsy on a case of cancer of the œsophagus in which the patient gradually became emaciated, but had no special symptoms to call attention to the disease. These latent cases are, however, very rare.

The *prognosis* is hopeless; the patients usually become progressively emaciated, and die either of asthenia or sudden perforation of the ulcer.

In the *diagnosis* of the condition it is important, in the first place, to exclude pressure from without, as by aneurism or other tumor. The history enables us to exclude cicatricial stricture and foreign bodies. The sound may be passed and the presence of the stricture determined. As mentioned above, great care should be exercised. Fragments of carcinomatous tissue may in some instances be removed with the tube. On auscultation along the left side of the spine the primary œsophageal murmur may be much altered in quality.

Treatment.—In most cases milk and liquids can be swallowed, but supplementary nourishment should be given by the rectum. It may be advisable in some instances to pass a tube into the stomach and attempt to feed in this way. When there is difficulty in feeding the patient it is very much better to have gastrotomy performed at once, as it gives the greatest comfort and ease, and prolongs the patient's life.

V. RUPTURE OF THE ŒSOPHAGUS.

This may occur in a healthy organ as a result of prolonged vomiting. Boerhaave described the first case in Baron Wassennar, who " broke asunder the tube of the œsophagus near the diaphragm, so that, after the most excruciating pain, the elements which he swallowed passed, together with the air, into the cavity of the thorax, and he expired in twenty-four hours." Fitz has reported a case and has analyzed the literature on the subject up to 1877. The accident has usually occurred during vomiting after a full meal or when intoxicated. It is, of course, invariably fatal.

Much more common is the post-mortem digestion of the œsophagus, which was first described by King, of Guy's Hospital. It is not very infrequent. In one instance I found the contents of the stomach in the left pleura. The erosion is in the posterior wall, and may be of considerable extent.

VI. DILATATIONS AND DIVERTICULA.

Stenosis of the gullet is followed by secondary dilatation of the tube above the constriction and great hypertrophy of the walls. Primary dilatation is extremely rare. The tube may attain extraordinary dimensions— 30 cm. in circumference in Luschka's case. Regurgitation of food is the most common symptom. There may also be difficulty in breathing from pressure.

Diverticula are of two forms: (a) Pressure diverticula, which are most common at the junction of the pharynx and gullet, on the posterior wall. Owing to weakness of the muscles at this spot, local bulging occurs, which is gradually increased by the pressure of food, and finally forms a saccular pouch. (b) The traction diverticula situated on the anterior wall near the bifurcation of the trachea, result, as a rule, from the extension of inflammation from the lymph-glands with adhesion and subsequent cicatricial contraction, by which the wall of the gullet is drawn out. Diverticula have been successfully extirpated by von Bergmann and by Mixter.

A rare and remarkable condition, of which a case has been recorded by MacLachlan, and of which a second is in attendance at my clinic, is the œsophago-pleuro-cutaneous fistula. In my patient fluids are discharged at intervals through a fistula in the right infra-clavicular region, which appears to communicate with a cavity in the upper part of the pleura or lung. The condition has persisted for more than twenty years.

VI. DISEASES OF THE STOMACH.

I. ACUTE GASTRITIS.

(*Simple Gastritis; Acute Gastric Catarrh; Acute Dyspepsia.*)

Etiology.—Acute gastric catarrh, one of the most common of complaints, occurs at all ages, and is usually traceable to errors in diet. It may follow the ingestion of more food than the stomach can digest, or it may result from taking unsuitable articles, which either themselves irritate the mucosa or, remaining undigested, decompose, and so excite an acute dyspepsia. A frequent cause is the taking of food which has begun to decompose, particularly in hot weather. In children these fermentative processes are very apt to excite acute catarrh of the bowels as well. Another very common cause is the abuse of alcohol, and the acute gastritis which follows a drinking-bout is one of the most typical forms of the disease. The tendency to acute indigestion varies very much in different individuals, and indeed in families. We recognize this in using the expressions a " delicate stomach " and a " strong stomach." Gouty persons are generally thought to be more disposed to acute dyspepsia than others. Acute catarrh of the stomach occurs at the outset of many of the infectious fevers.

Lebert described a special infectious form of gastric catarrh, occurring in epidemic form, and only to be distinguished from mild typhoid fever by the absence of rose spots and swelling of the spleen. Many practitioners still adhere to the belief that there is a form of *gastric fever,* but the evidence of its existence is by no means satisfactory, and certainly a great majority of all cases in this country are examples of mild typhoid.

Morbid Anatomy.—Beaumont's study of St. Martin's stomach showed that in acute catarrh the mucous membrane is reddened and swollen, less gastric juice is secreted, and mucus covers the surface. Slight hæmorrhages may occur or even small erosions. The submucosa may be somewhat œdematous. Microscopically the changes are chiefly noticeable in the mucous and peptic cells, which are swollen and more granular, and there is an infiltration of the intertubular tissue with leucocytes.

Symptoms.—In mild cases the symptoms are those of slight " indigestion "—an uncomfortable feeling in the abdomen, headache, depression, nausea, eructations, and vomiting, which usually gives relief. The tongue is heavily coated and the saliva is increased. In children there are intestinal symptoms—diarrhœa and colicky pains. There is usually no fever. The duration is rarely more than twenty-four hours. In the severer forms the attack may set in with a chill and febrile reaction, in which the temperature rises to 102° or 103°. The tongue is furred, the breath heavy, and vomiting is frequent. The ejected substances, at first mixed with food, subsequently contain much mucus and bile-stained fluids. There may be constipation, but very often there is diarrhœa. The urine presents the usual febrile characteristics, and there is a heavy deposit of urates. The abdomen may be somewhat distended and slightly tender in the epigastric region. Herpes may appear on the lips. The attack may last from one

29

to three days, and occasionally longer. The examination of the vomitus shows, as a rule, absence of the hydrochloric acid, presence of lactic and fatty acids, and marked increase in the mucus.

Diagnosis.—The ordinary afebrile gastric catarrh is readily recognized. The acute febrile form is so similar to the initial symptoms of many of the infectious diseases that it is impossible for a day or two to make a definite diagnosis, particularly in the cases which have come on, so to speak, spontaneously and independently of an error in diet. Some of these resemble closely an acute infection; the symptoms may be very intense, and if, as sometimes happens, the attack sets in with severe headache and delirium the case may be mistaken for meningitis. When the abdominal pains are intense the attack may be confounded with gallstone colic. In discriminating between acute febrile gastritis and the abortive forms of typhoid fever it is to be borne in mind that in the former the temperature rises abruptly, the remissions are slighter and the drop is more sudden. The initial bronchitis, the well-marked splenic enlargement, and the rose spots are not present. It is a very common error to class under gastric fever the mild forms of the various infectious disorders. The gastric crises in locomotor ataxia have in many instances been confounded with a simple acute gastritis, and it is always wise in adults to test the knee-jerks and pupillary reactions.

Treatment.—Mild cases recover spontaneously in twenty-four hours, and require no treatment other than a dose of castor oil in children or of blue mass in adults. In the severer forms, if there is much distress in the region of the stomach, the vomiting should be promoted by warm water or the simple emetics. A full dose of calomel, 8 to 10 grains, should be given, and followed the next morning by a dose of Hunyadi-Janos or Carlsbad water. If there is eructation of acid fluid, bicarbonate of soda and bismuth may be given. The stomach should have, if possible, absolute rest, and it is a good plan in the case of strong persons, particularly in those addicted to alcohol, to cut off all food for a day or two. The patient may be allowed soda water and ice freely. It is well not to attempt to check the vomiting unless it is excessive and protracted. Recovery is usually complete, though repeated attacks may lead to subacute gastritis or to the establishment of chronic dyspepsia.

Phlegmonous Gastritis; Acute Suppurative Gastritis.—This is an excessively rare disease, characterized by the occurrence of suppurative processes in the submucosa. The affection is more common in men than in women. Leith has collected 85 cases, and has given the best account in the literature (Edinburgh Hospital Reports, vol. iv). The cause is seldom obvious. It has been met with as an idiopathic affection, but it has occurred also in puerperal fever and other septic processes, and has occasionally followed trauma. Anatomically there appear to be two forms, a diffuse purulent infiltration and a localized abscess formation, in which case the tumor may reach the size of an egg, and may burst into the stomach or into the peritoneal cavity. In two of the cases I have seen, the abscess was in connection with cancer of the stomach, and it is interesting to note that in both there were recurring chills. In a third case, in a diffuse carcinoma, there was extensive phlegmonous inflammation with vomiting of a horribly fetid material.

The *symptoms* are variable. There are usually pain in the abdomen, fever, dry tongue, and symptoms of a severe infective process, delirium and coma preceding death. Jaundice has been met with in some instances. Occasionally, when the abscess tumor is large, it has been felt externally, in one case forming a mass as large as two fists. There are instances which run a more chronic course, with pains in the abdomen, fever, and chills.

The *diagnosis* is rarely possible, even when with abscess rupture occurs, and the pus is vomited, as it is not possible to differentiate this condition from an abscess perforating into the stomach from without. It is stated, however, that Chvostek made the diagnosis in one of his cases.

Toxic Gastritis.—This most intense form of inflammation of the stomach is excited by the swallowing of concentrated mineral acids or strong alkalies, or by such poisons as phosphorus, corrosive sublimate, ammonia, arsenic, etc. In the non-corrosive poisons, such as phosphorus, arsenic, and antimony, the process consists of an acute degeneration of the glandular elements, and hæmorrhage. In the powerful concentrated poisons the mucous membrane is extensively destroyed, and may be converted into a brownish-black eschar. In the less severe grades there may be areas of necrosis surrounded by inflammatory reaction, while the submucosa is hæmorrhagic and infiltrated. The process is of course more intense at the fundus, but the active peristalsis may drive the poison through the pylorus into the intestine.

The *symptoms* are intense pain in the mouth, throat, and stomach, salivation, great difficulty in swallowing, and constant vomiting, the vomited materials being bloody and sometimes containing portions of the mucous membrane. The abdomen is tender, distended, and painful on pressure. In the most acute cases symptoms of collapse supervene; the pulse is weak, the skin pale and covered with sweat; there is restlessness, and sometimes convulsions. There may be albumin or blood in the urine, and petechiæ may develop on the skin. When the poison is less intense, the sloughs may separate, leaving ulcers, which too often lead, in the œsophagus to stricture, in the stomach to chronic atrophy, and finally to death from exhaustion.

The *diagnosis* of toxic gastritis is usually easy, as inspection of the mouth and pharynx shows, in many instances, corrosive effects, while the examination of the vomit may indicate the nature of the poison.

In poisoning by acids, magnesia should be administered in milk or with egg albumen. When strong alkalies have been taken, the dilute acids should be administered. If the case is seen early, lavage should be used. For the severe inflammation which follows the swallowing of the stronger poisons palliative treatment is alone available, and morphia may be freely employed to allay the pain.

Diphtheritic or Membranous Gastritis.—This condition is met with occasionally in diphtheria, but more commonly as a secondary process in typhus or typhoid fever, pneumonia, pyæmia, small-pox, and occasionally in debilitated children. An instance of it came under my notice in pneumonia. The exudation may be extensive and uniform or in patches. The condition is not recognizable during life, unless, as in a case of John Thomson's, the membranes are vomited.

Mycotic and Parasitic Gastritis.—It occasionally happens that fungi develop in the stomach and excite inflammation. One of the most remarkable cases of the kind is that reported by Kundrat, in which the favus fungus developed in the stomach and intestine.

In cancer and in dilatation of the stomach the sarcinæ and yeast fungi probably aid in maintaining the chronic gastritis. As a rule, the gastric juice is capable of killing the ordinary bacteria. Orth states that the anthrax bacilli, in certain cases, produce swelling of the mucosa and ulceration. Eug. Fraenkel has reported a case of acute emphysematous gastritis probably of mycotic origin. The larvæ of certain insects may excite gastritis, as in the cases reported by Gerhardt, Meschede, and others. In rare instances tuberculosis and syphilis attack the gastric mucosa.

II. CHRONIC GASTRITIS.

(Chronic Catarrh of the Stomach; Chronic Dyspepsia.)

Definition.—A condition of disturbed digestion associated with increased mucous formation, qualitative or quantitative changes in the gastric juice, enfeeblement of the muscular coats, so that the food is retained for an abnormal time in the stomach; and, finally, with alterations in the structure of the mucosa.

Etiology.—The causes of chronic gastritis may be classified as follows: (1) Dietetic. The use of unsuitable or improperly prepared food. The persistent use of certain articles of diet, such as very fat substances or foods containing too much of the carbohydrates. New England pie and the hot breads of the Southern States are responsible for many cases of chronic dyspepsia. The use in excess of tea or coffee, and, above all, of alcohol in its various forms. Under this heading, too, may be mentioned the habits of eating at irregular hours or too rapidly and imperfectly chewing the food. In this country excess in eating does more damage than excess in drinking. A common cause of chronic catarrh is drinking too freely of ice-water during meals, a practice which plays no small part in the prevalence of dyspepsia in America. Another frequent cause is the abuse of tobacco, particularly chewing. (2) Constitutional causes. Anæmia, chlorosis, chronic tuberculosis, gout, diabetes, and Bright's disease are often associated with chronic gastric catarrh. (3) Local conditions: (*a*) of the stomach, as in cancer, ulcer, and dilatation, which are invariably accompanied by catarrh; (*b*) conditions of the portal circulation, causing chronic engorgement of the mucous membrane, as in cirrhosis, chronic heart-disease, and certain chronic lung affections.

Morbid Anatomy.—Anatomically two forms of chronic gastritis may be recognized, the simple and the sclerotic.

(*a*) **Simple Chronic Gastritis.**—The organ is usually enlarged, the mucous membrane pale gray in color, and covered with closely adherent, tenacious mucus. The veins are large, patches of ecchymosis are not infrequently seen, and in the chronic catarrh of portal obstruction and of chronic heart-disease small hæmorrhagic erosions. Toward the pylorus the mucosa is not infrequently irregularly pigmented, and presents a rough, wrinkled, mammillated surface, the *état mammeloné* of the French, a condition which may sometimes be so prominent that writers have described it as *gastritis polyposa*. The membrane may be thinner than normal, and much firmer, tearing less readily with the finger-nail. Ewald thus describes the histological changes: The minute anatomy shows the picture of a parenchymatous and an interstitial inflammation. The gland cells are in part eroded or show cloudy granular swelling or atrophy. The distinction between the principal and marginal cells cannot be recognized, and in many places, particularly in the pyloric region, the tubes have lost their regular form and show in many places an atypical branching, like the fingers of a glove. Individual glands are cut off toward the fundus, but appear at the border of the submucosa as cysts, partly empty, with a smooth membrane, partly filled with remnants of hyaline and refractile epithelium. An abundant small-celled infiltration presses apart the tubules being particularly marked toward the surface of the mucosa, and from the submucosa extensions of the connective tissue may be seen passing between the glands. The mucoid transformation of the cells of the tubules is a striking feature in the process and may extend to the very fundus of the glands.

(*b*) **Sclerotic Gastritis.**—As a final result of the parenchymatous and interstitial changes the mucous membrane may undergo complete atrophy, so that but few traces of secreting substance remain. There appear to be two forms of this sclerotic atrophy—one with thinning of the coats of the stomach, *phthisis ventriculi*, and a retention or even increase of the size of the organ; the other with enormous thickening of the coats and great reduction in the volume of the organ, the condition which is usually described as *cirrhosis ventriculi*. Extreme atrophy of the mucous membrane of the stomach has been carefully studied by Fenwick, Ewald, and others, and we now recognize the fact that there may be such destruction and degeneration of the glandular elements by a progressive development of interstitial tissue that ultimately scarcely a trace of secreting tissue remains. In a characteristic case, studied by Henry and myself, the greater portion of the lining membrane of the stomach was converted into a perfectly smooth, cuticular structure, showing no trace whatever of glandular elements, with enormous hypertrophy of the muscularis mucosæ, and here and there formation of cysts. In the other form, with identical atrophy and cyst formation, there is enormous increase in the connective tissue, and the stomach may be so contracted that it does not hold more than a couple of ounces. The walls may measure from 2 to 3 cm.; the greatest increase in thickness is in the submucosa, but the hypertrophy also extends to the muscular layers. A similar affection may coexist in the cæcum and colon. The condition may be difficult to distinguish from diffuse carcinoma. There may be also proliferative peritonitis, with perihepatitis, perisplenitis, and ascites. While one is not justified in saying that all cases of cirrhosis of the stomach represent a final stage in the history of a chronic catarrh, it is true that in most cases the process is associated with atrophy of the gastric mucosa, while the history indicates the existence of chronic dyspepsia.

Erosions of the Stomach.—Small superficial losses of substance are met with in the stomach under a great variety of conditions, usually in connection with chronic gastritis, diseases of the liver, particularly cirrhosis, and chronic diseases of the heart. Einhorn has described, too, a special condition in which in the washings from the fasting stomach little shreds of gastric mucous membrane are found, and there is tenderness and soreness on passing the tube and a little staining of the water. These are probably the result of passing the tube. True erosions are usually multiple, more common, I think, in the pyloric region, and are usually without any symptoms. The mucosa in the neighborhood of the erosion may be deeply hæmorrhagic. When one sees a large number of erosions, which may be present in some cases, it is difficult to understand why larger ulcers do not form at their site. The only ill effect I know of is the occurrence of profuse or even fatal hæmorrhage.

Symptoms.—The affection persists for an indefinite period, and, as is the case with most chronic diseases, changes from time to time. The appetite is variable, sometimes greatly impaired, at others very good. Among early symptoms are feelings of distress or oppression after eating, which may become aggravated and amount to actual pain. When the stomach is empty there may also be a painful feeling. The pain differs in different cases, and may be trifling or of extreme severity. When localized and felt beneath the sternum or in the præcordial region it is known as heart-burn or sometimes cardialgia. There is pain on pressure over the stomach, usually diffuse and not severe. The tongue is coated, and the patient complains of a bad taste in the mouth. The tip and margin of the tongue are very often red. Associated with this catarrhal stomatitis there may be an increase in the salivary and pharyngeal secretions. Nausea is an early symptom, and is particularly apt to occur in the morning hours. It is not, however, nearly so constant a symptom in chronic gastritis as in cancer of the stomach, and in mild grades of the affection it may not occur at all. Eructation of gas, which may continue for some hours after taking food, is a very prominent feature in cases of so-called flatulent dyspepsia, and there may be marked distention of the intestines. With the gas, bitter fluids may be brought up. Vomiting, which is not very frequent, occurs either immediately after eating or an hour or two later. In the chronic catarrh of old topers a bout of morning vomiting is common, in which a slimy mucus is brought up. The vomitus consists of food in various stages of digestion and slimy mucus, and the chemical examination shows the presence of abnormal acids, such as butyric, or even acetic, in addition to lactic acid, while the hydrochloric acid, if indeed it is present, is much reduced in quantity. The digestion may be much delayed, and on washing out the stomach as late as seven hours after eating, portions of food are still present. The prolonged retention favors decomposition, the stomach becomes distended with gas, and this, with the chronic catarrh, may induce gradually an atony of the muscular walls. The absorption is slow, and iodide of potassium, given in capsules, which should normally reach the saliva within fifteen minutes, may not be evident for more than half an hour.

Constipation is usually present, but in some instances there is diarrhœa, and undigested food passes rapidly through the bowels. The urine is often scanty, high-colored, and deposits a heavy sediment of urates.

Of other symptoms headache is common, and the patient feels constantly out of sorts, indisposed for exertion, and low-spirited. In aggravated cases melancholia may develop. Trousseau called attention to the occurrence of vertigo, a marked feature in certain cases. The pulse is small, sometimes slow, and there may be palpitation of the heart. Fever does not occur. Cough is sometimes present, but the so-called stomach cough of chronic dyspeptics is in all probability dependent upon pharyngeal irritation.

The Gastric Contents.—The fasting stomach may be empty or it may contain much mucus—*gastritis mucipara* of Boas. In the test breakfast, withdrawn in an hour, the HCL is usually diminished, though it may be normal—*gastritis acida*. In other cases the free HCl may be absent—*gastritis anacida*. While in the advanced forms of atrophy of the mucosa there may be neither acids nor ferments—*gastritis atrophicans*.

The motor function of the stomach is not usually much impaired.

The symptoms of atrophy of the mucous membrane of the stomach, with or without contraction of the organ, are very complex, and cannot be said to present a uniform picture. The majority of the cases present the symptoms of an aggravated chronic dyspepsia, often of such severity that cancer is suspected. In one of the cases which I examined, the persistent distress after eating, the vomiting, and the gradual loss of flesh and strength, very naturally led to this diagnosis, but the duration of the disease far exceeded that of ordinary carcinoma. In the cirrhotic form the tumor mass may sometimes be felt. In atrophy of the stomach, whether associated with cirrhosis or not, the clinical picture may be that of pernicious anæmia. As early as 1860, Flint called attention to this connection between atrophy of the gastric tubules and anæmia, an observation which Fenwick and others have amply confirmed.

Diagnosis.—Ewald distinguishes three forms of chronic gastritis: (1) Simple gastritis; (2) mucous (*schleimige*) gastritis; (3) atrophic gastritis.

In (1) the fasting stomach contains only a small quantity of a slimy fluid, while after the test breakfast the HCl is diminished in quantity or may be absent. Lactic acid and the fat acids may be present. After Boas's more rigid test meal the organic acids are rarely found. The pepsin and rennet are always present.

In (2) the acidity is always slight and the condition is distinguished from (1) chiefly by the large amount of mucus present.

In (3) the fasting stomach is generally empty, while after the test breakfast HCl, pepsin, and the curdling ferment are wholly wanting.

The diagnosis of cancer of the stomach from chronic gastritis may be very difficult when a tumor is not present. The cases require most careful study, and it may take several months before a decision can be reached.

Treatment.—When possible the cause in each case should be ascertained and an attempt made to determine the special form of indigestion. Usually there is no difficulty in differentiating the ordinary catarrhal and the nervous varieties. A careful study of the phenomena of digestion in the way already laid down, though not essential in every instance, should certainly be carried out in the more obstinate and obscure forms. Two important questions should be asked of every dyspeptic—first, as to the time taken at his meals; and, second, as to the quantity he eats. Practically a large majority of all cases of disturbed digestion come from hasty and imperfect mastication of the food and from overeating. Especial stress should be laid upon the former point. In some instances it will alone suffice to cure dyspepsia if the patient will count a certain number before swallowing each mouthful. The second point is of even greater importance. People habitually eat too much, and it is probably true that a greater number of maladies arise from excess in eating than from excess in drinking. Particularly is this the case in America, where the average man is abstemious in the matter of alcohol, but imprudent to a degree in all matters relating to food. Moreover, people have not had time to learn the art of cooking, and much of the indigestion, particularly in the country districts, may be charged to the barbarous methods of preparing the food. The treatment may be considered under the headings of dietetic and medicinal.

(a) *General and Dietetic.*—A careful and systematically arranged dietary is the first, sometimes the only essential in the treatment of a case of chronic dyspepsia. It is impossible to lay down rules applicable to all cases. Individuals differ extraordinarily in their capability of digesting different articles of food, and there is much truth in the old adage, " One man's food is another man's poison." The individual preferences for different articles of food should be permitted in the milder forms. Physicians have probably been too arbitrary in this direction, and have not yielded sufficiently to the intimations given by the appetite and desires of the patient.

A rigid milk diet may be tried in obstinate cases. Much depends upon whether the patient is able to take and digest milk properly. In the forms associated with Bright's disease and chronic portal congestion, as well as in many instances in which the dyspepsia is part of a neurasthenic or hysterical trouble, this plan in conjunction with rest is most efficacious. If milk is not digested well it may be diluted one third with soda water or Vichy, or 5 to 10 grains of carbonate of soda, or a pinch of salt may be added to each tumblerful. In many cases the milk from which the cream has been taken is better borne. Buttermilk is particularly suitable, but can rarely be taken for so long a time alone, as patients tire of it much more readily than they do of ordinary milk. Not only can the general nutrition be maintained on this diet, but patients sometimes increase in weight, and the unpleasant gastric symptoms disappear entirely. It should be given at fixed hours and in definite quantities. A patient may take 6 or 8 ounces every three hours. The amount necessary varies a good deal, but at least 3 to 5 pints should be given in the twenty-four hours. This form of diet is not, as a rule, well borne when there is a tendency to dilatation of the stomach. The milk may be previously peptonized, but it is impossible to feed a chronic dyspeptic in this way. The stools should be carefully watched, and if more milk is taken than can be digested it is well to supplement the diet with eggs and dry toast or biscuits.

In a large proportion of the cases of chronic indigestion it is not necessary to annoy the patient with such strict dietaries. It may be quite sufficient to cut off certain articles of food. Thus, if there are acid eructations or flatulency, the farinaceous foods should be restricted, particularly potatoes and the coarser vegetables. A fruitful source of indigestion is the hot bread which, in different forms, is regarded as an essential part of an American breakfast. This, as well as the various forms of pancakes, pies and tarts, with heavy pastry, and fried articles of all sorts, should be strictly forbidden. As a rule, white bread, toasted, is more readily digested than bread made from the whole meal. Persons, however, differ very much in this respect, and the Graham or brown bread is for many people most digestible. Sugar and very sweet articles of food should be taken in great moderation or avoided altogether by persons with chronic dyspepsia. Many instances of aggravated indigestion have come to my notice due to the prevalent practice of eating largely of ice-cream. One of the most powerful enemies of the American stomach in the present day is the soda-water fountain, which has usurped so important a place in the apothecary shop.

Fats, with the exception of a moderate amount of good butter, very fat meats, and thick, greasy soups should be avoided. Ripe fruit in moderation is often advantageous, particularly when cooked. Bananas are not, as a rule, well borne. Strawberries are to many persons a cause of an annual attack of indigestion and sore throat in the spring months.

As stated, in the matter of special articles of food it is impossible to lay down rigid rules, and it is the common experience that one patient with indigestion will take with impunity the very articles which cause the greatest distress to another.

Another detail of importance which may be mentioned in this connection is the general hygienic management of dyspeptics. These patients are often introspective, dwelling in a morbid manner on their symptoms, and much inclined to take a despondent view of their condition. Very little progress can be made unless the physician gains their confidence from the outset. Their fears and whims should not be made too light of or ridiculed. Systematic exercise, carefully regulated, particularly when, as at watering places, it is combined with a restricted diet, is of special service. Change of air and occupation, a prolonged sea voyage, or a summer in the mountains will sometimes cure the most obstinate dyspepsia.

(b) *Medicinal.*—The special therapeutic measures may be divided into those which attempt to replace in the digestive juices important elements which are lacking and those which stimulate the weakened action of the organ. In the first group come the hydrochloric acid and ferments, which are so freely employed in dyspepsia. The former is the most important. It is the ingredient in the gastric juice most commonly deficient. It is not only necessary for its own important actions, but its presence is intimately associated with that of the pepsin, as it is only in the presence of a sufficient quantity that the pepsinogen is converted into the active digestive ferment. It is best given as the dilute acid taken in somewhat larger quantities than are usually advised. Ewald recommends large doses—of from 90 to 100 drops—at intervals of fifteen minutes after the meals. Leube and Riegel advise smaller doses. Probably from 15 to 20 drops is sufficient. The prolonged use of it does not appear to be in any way hurtful. The use, however, should be restricted to cases of neurosis and atrophy of the mucous membrane. In actual gastritis its value is doubtful.

Nitrate of silver is a good remedy in some cases, used in solution in the lavage (1 to 1,500 or 1 to 2,000), or in pill form, one eighth to one fourth of a grain three times a day. For many years Pepper has advocated the more extended use of this drug in chronic gastritis. I have seen an instance of argyria after its protracted use.

The digestive ferments: These are extensively employed to strengthen the weakened gastric and intestinal secretions. The use of pepsin, according to Ewald, may be limited to the cases of advanced mucous catarrh and the instances of atrophy of the stomach, in which it should be given, in doses of from 10 to 15 grains, with dilute hydrochloric acid a quarter of an hour after meals. It may be used in various different forms, either as a powder or in solution or given with the acid. The powder is much more certain. Pepsin wine is generally inert, as there is little of the ferment taken up by alcohol. It is important to use a reliable article. Much that is in the market is valueless.

Pancreatin is of equal or even greater value than the pepsin. Pains should be taken to use a good article, such as that prepared by Merck. It should be given in doses of from 15 to 20 grains, in combination with bicarbonate of soda. It is conveniently administered in tablets, each of which contains 5 grains of the pancreatin and the soda, and of these two or three may be taken fifteen or twenty minutes after each meal. Ptyalin and diastase are particularly indicated when the acid is excessive. The action of the former continues in the stomach during normal digestion. The malt diastase is often very serviceable given with alkalies.

Of measures which stimulate the glandular activity in chronic dyspepsia lavage is by far the most important, particularly in the forms characterized by the secretion of a large quantity of mucus. Luke-warm water should be used, or, if there is much mucus, a 1-per-cent salt solution, or a 3- to 5-per-cent solution of bicarbonate of soda. If there is much fermentation the 3-per-cent solution of boric acid may be used, or a dilute solution of carbolic acid. It is best employed in the morning on an empty stomach, or in the evening some hours after the last meal. It is perhaps preferable in the morning, except in those cases in which there is much nocturnal distress and flatulency. Once a day is, as a rule, sufficient, or, in the case of delicate persons, every second day. The irrigation may be continued until the water which comes away is quite clear. It is not necessary to remove all the fluid after the irrigation.

While perhaps in some hands this measure has been carried to extremes, it is one of such extraordinary value in certain cases that it should be more widely employed by practitioners. When there is an insuperable objection to lavage a substitute may be used in the form of warm alkaline drinks, taken slowly in the early morning or the last thing at night.

Of medicines which stimulate the gastric secretion the most important are the bitter tonics, such as quassia, gentian, calumba, cundurango, ipecacuanha, strychnia, and cardamoms. These are probably of more value in chronic gastritis than the hydrochloric acid. Of these strychnia is the most powerful, though none of them have probably any very great stimulating action on the secretion, and influence rather the appetite than the digestion. Of stomachics which are believed to favorably influence digestion the most important are alcohol and common salt. The former would appear to act in moderate quantities by increasing the acid in the gastric juice, and with it probably the pepsin formation. Others hold that it is not so much the secretory as the motor function of the stomach which the alcohol stimulates. In moderate quantities it has certainly no directly injurious influence on the digestive processes. Special care should be taken, however, in ordering alcohol to dyspeptics. If a patient has been in the habit of taking beer or light wines or stimulants with his meals, the practice may be continued if moderate quantities are taken. Beer, as a rule, is not well borne. A dry sherry or a class of claret is preferable. In the case of women with any form of dyspepsia stimulants should be employed with the greatest caution, and the practitioner should know his patient well before ordering alcohol.

The importance of salt in gastric digestion rests upon the fact that its presence is essential in the formation of the hydrochloric acid. An increase in its use may be advised in all cases of chronic dyspepsia in which the acid is defective.

Treatment of Special Conditions.—Fermentation and flatulency. When the digestion is slow or imperfect, fermentation goes on in the contents, with the formation of gas and the production of lactic, butyric, and acetic acids. For the treatment of this condition careful dieting may suffice, particularly forbidding such articles as tea, pastry, and the coarser vegetables. It is usually combined with pyrosis, in which the acid fluids are brought into the mouth. Bismuth and carbonate of soda sometimes suffice to relieve the condition. Thymol, creasote, and carbolic acid may be employed. For acid dyspepsia Sir William Roberts recommends the bismuth lozenge of the British Pharmacopœia, the antacid properties of which depend on chalk and bicarbonate of soda. It should be taken an hour or two after meals, and only when the pain and uneasiness are present. The burnt magnesia is also a good remedy. Glycerin in from 20- to 60-minim doses, the essential oils, animal charcoal alone or in combination with compound cinnamon powder, may be tried. If there is much pain, chloroform in 20-minim doses or a teaspoonful of Hoffman's anodyne may be used. In obstinate cases lavage is indicated and is sometimes striking in its effects. Alkaline solutions may be used.

Vomiting is not a feature which often calls for treatment in chronic dyspepsia; sometimes in children it is a persistent symptom. Creasote and carbolic acid in drop doses, a few drops of chloroform or of dilute hydrocyanic acid, cocaine, bismuth, and oxalate of cerium may be used. If obstinate, the stomach should be washed out daily.

Constipation is a frequent and troublesome feature of most forms of indigestion. Occasionally small doses of mercury, podophyllin, the laxative mineral waters, sulphur, and cascara may be employed. Glycerin suppositories or the injection of from half a teaspoonful to a teaspoonful of glycerin is very efficacious.

Many cases of chronic dyspepsia are greatly benefited by the use of mineral waters, particularly a residence at the springs with a careful supervision of the diet and systematic exercise. The strict *régime* of certain German Spas is particularly advantageous in the cases in which the chronic dyspepsia has resulted from excess in eating and in drinking. Kissingen, Carlsbad, Ems, and Wiesbaden are to be specially recommended.

III. DILATATION OF THE STOMACH (*Gastrectasis*).

Etiology.—This may occur either as an acute or a chronic condition.

Acute dilatation is rarely seen, though it occurs whenever enormous quantities of food and drink are quickly ingested. Occasionally this leads to extreme paralytic dilatation, and Fagge has described two cases which came on in this way, one of which proved fatal. Allbutt mentions a remarkable instance of acute dilatation of the stomach under the care of Broadbent, in which 8 pints of fluid were siphoned from the stomach. " No sooner, however, was this volume of fluid removed than the stomach began to refill, and was rapidly distended again to its former dimensions."

Chronic dilatation results from: (*a*) Narrowing of the pylorus or of the duodenum by the cicatrization of an ulcer, hypertrophic stenosis of the pylorus (whether cancerous or simple), congenital stricture, or occasionally by pressure from without of a tumor or of a floating kidney. Without any organic disease the pylorus may be tilted up by adhesion to the liver or gall-bladder, or the stomach may be so dilated that the pylorus is dragged down and kinked. (*b*) Relative or absolute insufficiency of the muscular power of the stomach, due on the one hand to repeated overfilling of the organ with food and drink (*Ueberanstrengung des Magens*, Strümpell), and on the other to atony of the coats induced by chronic inflammation or degeneration of impaired nutrition, the result of constitutional affections, as cancer, tuberculosis, anæmia, etc.

It is important to distinguish between a dilated stomach and a displaced organ, which will be considered under the section on enteroptosis.

The most extreme forms are met with in the first group, and most commonly as a sequence of the cicatricial contraction of an ulcer. There may be considerable stenosis without much dilatation, the obstruction being compensated by hypertrophy of the muscular coats. Considerable attention has been directed in Germany by Litten, Ewald, and others to the association of dilatation with dislocation of the right kidney.

In the second group, due to atony of the muscular coats, we must distinguish between instances in which the stomach is simply enlarged and those with actual dilatation, the conditions which Ewald characterized as *megastrie* and *gastrectasis* respectively. The size of the stomach varies greatly in different individuals, and the maximum capacity of a normal organ Ewald places at about 1,600 cc. Measurements above this point indicate absolute dilatation.

Atonic dilatation of the stomach may result from weakness of the coats, due to repeated overdistention or to chronic catarrh of the mucous membrane, or to the general muscular debility which is associated with chronic wasting disorders of all sorts. The combination of chronic gastric catarrh with overfeeding and excessive drinking is one of the most fruitful sources of atonic dilatation, as pointed out by Naunyn. The condition is frequently seen in diabetics, in the insane, and in beer-drinkers. In Germany this form is very common in men employed in the breweries. Possibly muscular weakness of the coats may result in some cases from disturbed innervation. Dilatation of the stomach is most frequent in middle-aged or elderly persons, but the condition is not uncommon in children, especially in association with rickets.

Symptoms.—These are very variable and depend upon the cause and the degree of dilatation. Naturally the features in cancer of the pylorus would be very different from those met with in an excessive drinker. Dyspepsia is present in nearly all cases, and there are feelings of distress and uneasiness in the region of the stomach. The patient may complain much of hunger and thirst and eat and drink freely. The most characteristic symptom is the vomiting at intervals of enormous quantities of liquid and of food, amounting sometimes to four or more litres. The material is often of a dark-grayish color, with a characteristic sour odor due to the organic acids present, and contains mucus and remnants of food. On standing it separates into three layers, the lowest consisting of food, the middle of a turbid, dark-gray fluid, and the uppermost of a brownish froth. The microscopical examination shows a large variety of bacteria, yeast fungi, and the sarcina ventriculi. There may also be cherry stones, plum stones, and grape seeds.

The hydrochloric acid may be absent, diminished, normal, or in excess, depending upon the cause of the dilatation. The fermentation produces lactic, butyric, and, possibly, acetic acid and various gases.

In consequence of the small amount of fluid which passes from the stomach or is absorbed there are constipation, scanty urine, and extreme dryness of the skin. The general nutrition of the patient suffers greatly; there is loss of flesh and strength, and in some cases the most extreme emaciation. A very remarkable symptom which occurs occasionally is tetany, first described by Kussmaul.

Physical Signs—*Inspection.*—The abdomen may be large and prominent, the greatest projection occurring below the navel in the standing posture. In some instances the outline of the distended stomach can be plainly seen, the small curvature a couple of inches below the ensiform cartilage, and the greater curvature passing obliquely from the tip of the tenth rib on the left side, toward the pubes, and then curving upward to the right costal margin. Too much stress cannot be laid on the importance of inspection. In 10 of 13 cases of dilated stomach in my wards during one year the diagnosis was made *de visu*. Active peristalsis may be seen in the dilated organ, the waves passing from left to right. Occasionally anti-peristalsis may be seen. In cases of stricture, particularly of hypertrophic stenosis, as the peristaltic wave reaches the pylorus, the tumor-like thickening can sometimes be distinctly seen through the thin abdominal wall. To stimulate the peristalsis the abdomen may be flipped with a wet towel. Inflation may be practised with carbonic-acid gas. A small teaspoonful of tartaric acid dissolved in an ounce of water is first given, then a rather larger quantity of bicarbonate of soda. In many cases, particularly in thin persons, the outline of the dilated stomach stands out with great distinctness, and waves of peristalsis are seen in it.

Palpation.—The peristalsis may be felt, and usually in stenosis the tumor is evident at the pylorus. The resistance of a dilated stomach is peculiar, and has been aptly compared to that of an air cushion. Bimanual palpation elicits a splashing sound—*clapotage*—which is, of course, not distinctive, as it can be obtained whenever there is much liquid and air in the organ, but which cannot be elicited in a healthy person two or three hours after eating. The splashing may be very loud, and the patient may produce it himself by suddenly depressing the diaphragm, or it may be readily obtained by shaking him. A tube passed into the stomach may be felt externally through the skin, a procedure no longer recommended by Leube, who suggested it. The gurgling of gas through the pylorus may be felt.

Percussion.—The note is tympanitic over the greater portion of a dilated stomach; in the dependent part the note is dull. In the upright position the percussion should be made from above downward, in the left parasternal line, until a change in resonance is reached. The line of this should be marked, and the patient examined in the recumbent position, when it will be found to have altered its level. When this is on a line with the navel or below it, dilatation of the stomach may generally be assumed to exist. The fluid may be withdrawn from the stomach with a tube, and the dulness so made to disappear, or it may be increased by pouring in more fluid. In cases of doubt the organ should be artificially distended with carbonic-acid gas in the manner described above. The most accurate method of determining the size of the stomach is by inflation through a stomach-tube with a Davidson's syringe. Pacanowski has shown that the greatest vertical diameter of gastric resonance in the normal stomach varies from 10 to 14 cm. in the male and is about 10 cm. in the female.

Auscultation.—The *clapotement* or succussion can be obtained readily. Frequently a curious sizzling sound is present, not unlike that heard when the ear is placed over a soda-water bottle when first opened. It can be heard naturally, and is usually evident when the artificial gas is being generated. The heart sounds may sometimes be transmitted with great clearness and with a metallic quality.

Mensuration may be used by passing a hard sound into the stomach until the greater curvature is reached. Normally it rarely passes more than 60 cm., measured from the teeth, but in cases of dilatation it may pass as much as 70 cm.

Diagnosis.—The diagnosis can usually be made without much difficulty. I would like to emphasize again the great value of inspection, particularly in combination with inflation of the stomach with carbonic-acid gas. Curious errors, however, are on record, one of the most remarkable of which was the confounding of dilated stomach with an ovarian cyst; even after tapping and the removal of portions of food and fruit seeds, abdominal section was performed and the dilated stomach opened. I notice the report of a recent case in which the diagnosis of ascites was made and the abdomen was opened. The *prognosis* is bad in cases in which there is stenosis of the pylorus, either simple or cancerous.

Treatment.—In the cases due to atony careful regulation of the diet and proper treatment of the associated catarrh will suffice to effect a cure. Strychnine, ergot, and iron are recommended. Washing out the stomach is of great service, though we do not see such striking and immediate results in this form. In cases of mechanical obstruction the stomach should be emptied and thoroughly washed, either with warm water or with an antiseptic solution. We accomplish in this way three important things: We remove the weight, which helps to distend the organ; we remove the mucus and the stagnating and fermenting material which irritates and inflames the stomach and impedes digestion; and we cleanse the inner surface of the organ by the application of water and medicinal substances. The patient can usually be taught to wash out his own stomach, and in a case of dilatation from simple stricture I have known the practice to be followed daily for three years with great benefit. The rapid reduction in the size of the stomach is often remarkable, the vomiting ceases, the food is taken readily, and in many cases the general nutrition improves rapidly. As a rule, once a day is sufficient, and it may be practised either the first thing in the morning or before going to bed. So soon as the fermentative processes have been checked lukewarm water alone should be used.

The food should be taken in small quantities at frequent intervals, and should consist of scraped beef, Leube's beef solution, and tender meats of all sorts. Fatty and starchy articles of diet are to be avoided. Liquids should be taken sparingly.

When the condition becomes aggravated a resort to surgery is justifiable. Here may be mentioned the recent statistics of gastric surgery. Pyloric stenosis is the common condition. Dreydorff has collected 442 cases—188 cases of pylorectomy, mortality 57.4 per cent; 215 gastro-enterostomies, mortality 43.3 per cent; pyloroplasty, 29 cases, mortality 20.7 per cent. On an average, after pylorectomy the patient remained free from recurrence for a little over a year.

IV. THE PEPTIC ULCER—GASTRIC AND DUODENAL.

The round, perforating, or simple ulcer is usually single, and occurs in the stomach and in the duodenum as far as the papilla biliaria. It follows nutritional disturbance in a limited region of the mucosa, which results in the gradual destruction of this area by the gastric juice. The condition is usually associated with superacidity.

Etiology.—*Incidence in the Post-mortem Room.*—In the extensive records collected by W. H. Welch, ulcer, cicatrized or open, was present in about 5 per cent of persons dying from all causes. Others give percentages as high as 10. The scars are more frequent than the open ulcers. Among the first thousand autopsies at the Johns Hopkins Hospital there were 9 cases of ulcer of the stomach.

Incidence Clinically.—The disease is much less common in some countries than in others, and in some parts of this country. It is certainly less frequently seen in Baltimore than in Massachusetts or in Canada. In nine years there were in my wards only 25 instances with a diagnosis of ulcer.

Sex.—Of 1,699 cases collected from hospital statistics by W. H. Welch and examined post mortem, 40 per cent were in males and 60 per cent were in females.

Age.—In females the largest number of cases occurs between twenty and thirty; in males between thirty and forty. It is by no means uncommon in old people. On the other hand, it is not very rare in children. Goodhart reported a case in an infant thirty hours old; indeed, ulcers of the stomach have been found in the foetus and in the new-born shortly after birth. Of 390 autopsies at the Baby's Hospital in New York, Martha Wollstein found 5 cases.

Heredity appears to play a part in some cases (Dreschfeld).

Occupation.—Servant girls seem particularly prone to the disease. This is to be explained partly by their careless habits in eating, partly in connection with the associated anæmia. The special liability of shoemakers, weavers, and tailors to ulcer is probably connected, as Habershon suggested, with pressure on the stomach.

Trauma.—Ulcers have been known to follow a blow in the region of the stomach. Rasmussen holds that pressure of the costal margin from various causes induces anæmia and atrophy of the mucous membrane, particularly in the region of the smaller curvature.

Associated Diseases.—Anæmia and chlorosis predispose strongly to gastric ulcer, particularly in women and in association with menstrual disorders. A very considerable number of all cases of gastric ulcer occur in chlorotic girls. It has been found also in connection with disease of the heart, arterio-sclerosis, and disease of the liver. The tuberculous and syphilitic ulcers of the stomach have already been considered.

The *duodenal ulcer* is less common than the gastric ulcer, and occurs most frequently in males. The combined statistics of Krauss, Chvostek, Lebert, and Trier give 171 cases in males and 39 in females. In 9 of my cases 7 were in males and 2 in females; one of these was in a lad of twelve.

It has been found in association with tuberculosis, and may follow large superficial burns. Perry and Shaw found it five times in 149 autopsies in cases of burns.

Morbid Anatomy.—Though usually single, the ulcers may be multiple. In none of my cases were there more than five, but there is an instance on record of thirty-four. The ulcer is situated most commonly on the posterior wall of the pyloric portion at or near the lesser curvature. It is not nearly so frequent on the anterior wall. Of 793 cases collected by Welch from hospital statistics, 288 were on the lesser curvature, 235 on the posterior wall, 95 at the pylorus, 69 on the anterior wall, 50 at the cardia, 29 at the fundus, 27 on the greater curvature. The duodenal ulcer is usually situated just outside the ring in the first portion of the gut.

Acute and chronic forms of gastric ulcer may be described. The former is usually small, punched out, the edges clean-cut, the floor smooth, and the peritoneal surface not thickened. The chronic ulcer is of larger size, the margins are no longer sharp, the edges are indurated, and the border is sinuous. The gastric ulcer sometimes reaches an enormous size. The largest of which I have any knowledge is one reported by Peabody, which measured 19 by 10 cm. and involved all of the lesser curvature and spread over a large part of the anterior and posterior walls. It is often distinctly terraced. The floor is formed either by the submucosa, by the muscular layers, or, not infrequently, by the neighboring organs, to which the stomach has become attached. In the healing of the ulcer, if the mucosa is alone involved, the granulation tissue develops from the edges and the floor and the newly formed tissue gradually contracts and unites the margins, leaving a smooth scar. In larger ulcers which have become deep and involved the muscular coat the cicatricial contraction may cause serious changes, the most important of which is narrowing of the pyloric orifice and consequent dilatation of the stomach. In the case of a girdle ulcer, hour-glass contraction of the stomach may be produced. It is probable that large ulcers persist for years without any attempt at healing.

Among the more serious changes which may proceed in an ulcer are the following:

Perforation.—Fortunately, in a majority of the cases, adhesions form between the stomach and adjacent organs, particularly with the pancreas, the left lobe of the liver, and the omental tissues. On the anterior surface of the stomach adhesions do not so readily form, hence the great danger of the ulcer in this situation, which more readily perforates and excites a diffuse and fatal peritonitis. On the posterior wall the ulcer penetrates directly into the lesser peritoneal cavity, in which case it may produce an air-containing abscess with the symptoms of the condition known as subphrenic pyo-pneumothorax. In rare instances adhesions and a gastro-cutaneous fistula form, usually in the umbilical region. Fistulous communication with the colon may also occur, or a gastro-duodenal fistula. The pericardium may be perforated, and even the left ventricle. Perforation into the pleura may also occur. It is to be noted that general emphysema of the subcutaneous tissues occasionally follows perforation of a gastric ulcer.

30

Erosion of Blood-vessels.—The hæmorrhage may occur in the acutely formed ulcer or in the ulceration which takes place at the base of the chronic form; it is in the latter condition that the bleeding is most common. Ulcers on the posterior wall may erode the splenic artery, but perhaps more frequently the bleeding proceeds from the artery of the lesser curve. In the case of duodenal ulcer the pancreatico-duodenal artery may be eroded or (as in one of my cases) fatal hæmorrhage may result from the opening of the hepatic artery, or more rarely the portal vein. Interesting changes occur in the vessels. Embolism of the artery supplying the ulcerated region has been met with in several cases; in others diffuse endarteritis. Small aneurisms have been found in the floor of the ulcers by Douglas Powell, Welch, and others.

Cicatrization.—Superficial ulcers often heal without leaving any serious damage. Stenosis of the pyloric orifice not infrequently follows the healing of an ulcer in its neighborhood. In other instances the large annular ulcer may cause in its cicatrization an hour-glass contraction of the stomach. The adhesion of the ulcer to neighboring parts may subsequently be the cause of much pain. The parts of the mucosa in the neighborhood of the ulcer frequently show signs of chronic gastritis.

The *origin* of the peptic ulcer is still obscure. Ulcers have been produced in animals in many ways, both by artificial emboli and by direct chemical and mechanical irritants applied to the mucosa. The ulcers thus produced heal with great rapidity unless the animals have been rendered anæmic by repeated abstraction of blood. Virchow's view that the process may result from plugging the nutrient artery of the part, either by an embolus or by a thrombus, and that the infarct so produced is destroyed by the gastric juice, has gained general acceptance. It is in conformity with Pavy's well-known experiments and with the anatomical facts already mentioned, particularly with the funnel-like shape of the ulcer, and the actual demonstration, in some cases, of the plugged vessels; but this view scarcely meets all the cases, in many of which the etiology is still obscure. Mere mechanical injury to the mucous membrane is, however, in most cases, insufficient cause for an ulcer, for normally the stomach is perfectly able to withstand such insults. Ewald concludes that certain predisposing causes play an important *rôle* in its development. He points to its frequency in conditions of amenorrhœa, chlorosis, anæmia after confinements, etc., where one may assume that the condition of the blood is not wholly normal, and also to the fact that in the majority of cases of this affection there is a superacidity of the gastric juice. One or both of these predisposing factors seem to be present in most cases, and it has been recently shown that in the various anæmiæ there is an appreciable diminution in the normal alkalinity of the blood, a fact which tends to explain one of the predisposing causes in these affections, and which is in accord with the "alkalescence theory" of Cohnheim. Of late the view has been advanced, particularly by Letulle and by Sydney Martin, that the ulceration is due to a bacterial necrosis of the gastric mucosa, and the latter suggests that the frequency of the ulcer at the pyloric region is associated with the absence of the glands at this part, which form the hydrochloric acid. The duodenal ulcer has an identical origin, but a few cases of acute ulcer, as already mentioned, have a curious relation with superficial burns. Bardeen's researches upon the necroses in the viscera following extensive burns throw an important light upon these cases, showing especially how the gastro-intestinal mucous membrane is implicated in the toxic effects. In one of my cases there was an ulcer in the posterior wall of the duodenum, 1.5 cm. in diameter, with overlapping edges, and not far from it was a cyst-like cavity in the submucosa associated with Brunner's glands, and it is possible that the open ulcer, with undermined edges, resulted from the rupture of one of these cysts.

Symptoms.—The condition may be met with accidentally, post mortem. The first symptoms may be those of perforation. In other cases again, for months and years, the patient has had dyspepsia, and the ulcer may not have been suspected until the occurrence of a sudden hæmorrhage.

The symptoms suggestive of peptic ulcer are: (a) *Dyspepsia,* which may be slight and trifling or of a most aggravated character. In a considerable proportion of all cases nausea and *vomiting* occur, the latter not for two or more hours after eating. The vomitus usually contains a large amount of HCl.

(b) *Hæmorrhage* is present in at least one half of all cases. It may be slight, but more commonly is profuse, and may be in such quantities and brought up so quickly that it is fluid, bright red in color, and quite unaltered. When the blood remains for some time in the stomach and is mixed with food it may be greatly changed, but the vomiting of a large quantity of unaltered blood is very characteristic of ulcer. Syncope or convulsions may follow, or death may directly result from the hæmorrhage. A most extreme grade of anæmia may be produced. I have known hemiplegia to develop after a series of profuse hæmorrhages. In either the gastric or duodenal ulcer, more commonly in the latter, the blood may be passed in the stools and not be vomited. This may occur when the hæmorrhage is slight, but also when it is profuse enough to produce collapse and extreme anæmia. Profuse, even fatal, hæmorrhage may come from small, superficial ulcers, or even from the hæmorrhagic erosions. Probably it is from such that in elderly persons profuse hæmorrhage occurs without previous gastric symptoms.

(c) *Pain* is perhaps the most constant and distinctive feature of ulcer. It varies greatly in character; it may be only a gnawing or burning sensation, which is particularly felt when the stomach is empty, and is relieved by taking food, but the more characteristic form comes on in paroxysms of the most intense gastralgia, in which the pain is not only felt in the epigastrium, but radiates to the back and to the sides. In many cases the two points of epigastric pain and dorsal pain, about the level of the tenth dorsal vertebra, are very well marked. These attacks are most frequently induced by taking food, and they may recur at a variable period after eating, sometimes within fifteen or twenty minutes, at others as late as two or three hours. It is usually stated that when the ulcer is near the cardia the pain is apt to set in earlier, but there is no certainty on this point. In some cases it comes on in the early morning hours. The attacks may occur at intervals with great intensity for weeks or months at a time, so that the patient constantly requires morphia, then again they may disappear entirely for a prolonged period. In the attack the patient is usually bent forward, and finds relief from pressure over the epigastric region; one patient during the attack would lean over the back of a chair; another would lie flat on the floor, with a hard pillow under the abdomen. Pressure is, as a rule, grateful. It has been thought that the posture assumed during the attack would indicate the site of the ulcer, but this is very doubtful.

(d) *Tenderness* on pressure is a common symptom in ulcer, and patients wear the waist-band very low. Pressure should be made with great care, as rupture of an ulcer has been induced by careless manipulation.

(e) In old ulcers with thickened bases an indurated mass can usually be felt in the neighborhood of the pylorus.

(f) Of general symptoms, *loss of weight* results from the prolonged dyspepsia, but it rarely, except in association with cicatricial stenosis of the pylorus, reaches the high grade met with in cancer. The *anæmia* may be extreme, and in one case of duodenal ulcer, which I examined, the blood-count was as low as 700,000 per c. mm. There are instances, such as the one reported by Pepper and Griffith, in which the extreme anæmia cannot be explained by the occurrence of hæmorrhage. In a few cases parotitis occurs. In one of my cases there was a remarkable pigmentation of the face and axillary folds.

(g) *Perforation.*—This occurs in about $6\frac{1}{2}$ per cent of all cases. The acute, perforating forms is much more common in women than in men. The symptoms are those of perforative peritonitis. Particular attention must be given to this accident since it has come so successfully within the sphere of the surgeon. As already mentioned, perforation may take place either into the lesser peritonæum or into the general peritoneal cavity, in both of which cases operation is indicated; in rare instances the ulcer may perforate the pericardium. This was the case in 10 of 28 cases in which the diaphragm was perforated (Pick).

Localized, more frequently subphrenic, abscess may follow perforation.

The course of the disease is, in the majority of cases, chronic. Only a few instances run a very acute course. The following group of clinical forms, described by Welch, indicate the diversity of this affection:

" 1. Latent ulcers, with entire absence of symptoms, and revealed as open ulcers or as cicatrices at the autopsy.

" 2. Acute perforating ulcers. With or without a period of brief gastric disturbance, perforation occurs and causes speedy death.

" 3. Acute hæmorrhagic form of gastric ulcer. After a latent or a brief course of the ulcer, profuse gastrorrhagia occurs, which may terminate fatally or may be followed by the symptoms of chronic ulcer.

" 4. Gastralgic-dyspeptic form. In this, which is the most common form of gastric ulcer, gastralgia, dyspepsia, and vomiting are the symptoms. Sometimes one of the symptoms predominates greatly over the others, so that Lebert distinguishes separately a gastralgic, a dyspeptic, and a vomitive variety. Gastralgia is the most frequent symptom.

" 5. Chronic hæmorrhagic form. Gastrorrhagia is a marked symptom, and occurs usually in combination with the symptoms just mentioned.

" 6. Cachectic form. This usually corresponds only to the final stage of one of the preceding forms, but the cachexia may develop so rapidly and become so marked that the course of the disease closely resembles that of gastric cancer.

" 7. Recurrent form. In this the symptoms of gastric ulcer disappear, and then follow intervals, often of considerable duration, in which there is apparent cure, but the symptoms return, especially after some indiscretion in the mode of living. This intermittent course may continue for many years. In these cases it is probable either that fresh ulcers form or that the cicatrix of an old ulcer becomes ulcerated.

" 8. Stenotic form. By the formation of cicatricial tissue in and around the ulcer, the pyloric orifice becomes obstructed and the symptoms of dilatation of the stomach develop." And to this may be added the form in which cancer develops, which will be referred to later.

The course may be very protracted, and there are cases in which the disease has persisted for over twenty years. I have reported two instances of peptic ulcer, probably duodenal, in which well-marked symptoms were present, in one case for eighteen, and in the other for twelve years. Both were of the chronic hæmorrhagic form.

Diagnosis.—The recognition of gastric ulcer is in many cases easy, as the combination of dyspepsia, gastralgic attacks, and hæmatemesis is very characteristic. Of the symptoms, hæmorrhage with the gastralgic attack is the most characteristic. The distinctions between ulcer and cancer will be given later. The greatest difficulty is offered by certain cases of gastralgia, which may resemble ulcer very closely, as, with the exception of the hæmorrhage, there is no single symptom which may not be present. A difficulty also results from the fact that in many instances gastralgia is one of the symptoms of nervous dyspepsia, and may exist with marked emaciation.

The following points are of value in discriminating between these two conditions:

(*a*) In ulcer the pain is more definitely connected with taking food, though this is not always the case, as in the duodenal form the gastralgic attacks may occur at night when the stomach is empty. Relief of pain after eating is certainly less common in ulcer than in gastralgia, though it is a very uncertain feature, and in certain cases the pain in ulcer is *always* relieved by taking food.

(*b*) In ulcer dyspeptic symptoms are almost invariably present in the intervals between the attacks, and even when pain is absent there is slight distress.

(*c*) Local sensitiveness over a particular spot in the epigastrium is suggestive of ulcer. External pressure usually aggravates the pain in ulcer, and often relieves it in gastralgia. This is, however, a very uncertain feature, as patients writhing with the pains of ulcer may press the abdomen over the back of a chair or place a hard pillow under it.

(*d*) The general condition and history of the patient often give the most trustworthy information. The nutrition is impaired more frequently in ulcer than in gastralgia. In the former we find more commonly (in women) dysmenorrhœa and chlorosis, while in the latter there are associated nervous phenomena—hysterical manifestations or neuralgias in other regions.

(*e*) On examination of the abdomen, not only is pain on pressure much more common in ulcer, but there may also be thickening about the pylorus and, in many cases, signs of dilatation of the stomach.

(*f*) Superacidity and often supersecretion of the gastric juice exists with ulcer.

The *gastric crises* which occur in affections of the spinal cord, particularly in locomotor ataxia, may simulate very closely the gastralgic attacks of ulcer, and as they so often exist in the preataxic stage their true nature may be overlooked; but the occurrence of lightning pains, the ocular symptoms, and the absence of the knee reflex are indications usually sufficient to render the diagnosis clear.

Can the gastric and duodenal ulcer be distinguished clinically? As already stated, they originate in the same way and present the same anatomical characters. In the great majority of cases they cannot be separated during life; as the symptoms produced are identical. Bucquoy has suggested that the duodenal ulcer can be distinguished by the following definite characters: (*a*) Sudden intestinal hæmorrhage in an apparently healthy person, which tends to recur and produce a profound anæmia. Hæmorrhage from the stomach may precede or accompany the melæna. (*b*) Pain in the right hypochondriac region, coming on two or three hours after eating. (*c*) Gastric crises of extreme violence, during which the hæmorrhage is more apt to occur. Certainly the occurrence of sudden intestinal hæmorrhage with gastralgic attacks is extremely suggestive of duodenal ulcer. W. W. Johnston has reported an instance in which he made the diagnosis on these symptoms, and in one of the Montreal cases Palmer Howard suggested correctly the presence of a duodenal ulcer on similar grounds. A patient under my care who had, during eighteen years, frequent attacks of hæmatemesis with gastralgia had melæna repeatedly without vomiting blood; but as a rule in the attacks the blood was vomited first, and did not appear in the stools until later. Occasionally this symptom will be found an important aid in diagnosis. The situation of the pain is too uncertain a factor on which to lay much stress, and the character of the crises is usually identical.

Gall-stone colic may occasionally simulate the pains of gastric ulcer. The sudden onset and as sudden termination, the swelling and tenderness of the liver, the enlargement of the gall-bladder, if present, and the occurrence of jaundice are points to be considered. The experience of surgeons has taught us that a number of cases in which the pains were regarded as gastralgia have in reality been due to gall-stones, with which, as is now well known, jaundice is not necessarily connected.

Treatment.—Post-mortem observations show that a very large number of ulcers heal completely, but the process is slow and tedious, often requiring months, or, in severe cases, years. The following are the important points in treatment:

(a) Absolute rest in bed.

(b) A carefully and systematically regulated diet. While theoretically it is better to give the stomach complete rest by rectal feeding, yet in practice this strict limitation is not found satisfactory. The food should be bland, easily digested, and given at stated intervals. The following dietary will be found useful: At 8 A. M. give 200 cc. of Leube's beef solution; at 12 M., 300 cc. of milk gruel or peptonized milk. The gruel should be made with ordinary flour or arrowroot, and is mixed with an equal quantity of milk. If necessary it may be peptonized. Buttermilk is very well borne by these patients. At 4 P. M. the beef solution again, and at 8 P. M. the milk gruel or the buttermilk.

The stomach in some cases is so irritable that the smallest amount of food is not well borne. In such cases lavage may be practised, if necessary, every morning, with mildly alkaline water, after which the beef solution is given and the feeding supplemented by the rectal injections. Ill effects rarely follow the careful use of the stomach tube in gastric ulcer. There are some cases which do well from the outset on a milk diet, given at regular intervals, 3 or 4 ounces every two hours. When milk is not well borne egg albumen may be substituted, or the whites of eight eggs may be alternated with Leube's beef solution. At the end of a month, if the condition has improved, the patient may be allowed scraped beef or young chicken, perfectly fresh sweet-bread, and farinaceous puddings made with milk and eggs. Local applications, such as warm fomentations, over the abdomen are very useful. The patient should be told that the treatment will take at least three months, and for the greater portion of the time he should be in bed.

(c) Medicinal measures are of very litle value in gastric ulcer, and the remedies employed do not probably benefit the ulcer, but the gastric catarrh. The Carlsbad salts are warmly recommended by von Ziemssen. The artificial preparation (sulphate of sodium, 50; bicarbonate of sodium, 6; chloride of sodium, 3) may be substituted, of which a teaspoonful is taken every morning. Bismuth, in doses of 30 to 60 grains three times a day, and nitrate of silver may be given, but they influence the associated conditions rather than the ulcer.

The pain, if severe, requires opium. Unless the gastralgia is intense morphia should not be given hypodermically, as there is a very serious danger in these cases of establishing the morphia habit. Doses of an eighth of a grain, with the bicarbonate of soda and bismuth, will allay the mild attacks, but the very severe ones require the hypodermic injection of a quarter or often half a grain. Antipyrin and antifebrin may be tried, but, as a rule, are quite ineffectual. In the milder attacks Hoffman's anodyne, or 20 or 30 drops of chloroform, or the spirits of camphor will give relief. Counter-irritation over the stomach with mustard or cantharides is often useful.

When the stomach is intractable, the patient should be fed per rectum. He will sometimes retain food which is passed into the stomach through the tube, and Leube's beef solution or milk may be given in this way. Cracked ice, chloroform, oxalate of cerium, bismuth, hydrocyanic acid, and ingluvin may be tried. When hæmorrhage occurs the patient should be put under the influence of opium as rapidly as possible. No attempt should be made to check the hæmorrhage by administering medicines by the mouth; as the profuse bleeding is always from an eroded artery, frequently from one of considerable size, it is doubtful if acetate of lead, tannic and gallic acids, and the usual remedies have the slightest influence. The essential point is to give rest, which is best obtained by opium. Ergotin may be administered hypodermically in two-grain doses. Nothing should be given by the mouth except small quantities of ice. In profuse bleeding a ligature may be applied around a leg, or a leg and arm. Not infrequently the loss of blood is so great that the patient faints. A fatal result is not, however, very common from hæmorrhage. Transfusion may be necessary, or, still better, the subcutaneous infusion of saline solution.

The patients usually recover rapidly from the hæmorrhage and require iron in full doses, which may, if necessary, be given hypodermically.

Surgical interference in ulcer of the stomach is indicated: (a) When perforation has taken place. The statistics collected by Barling and Mikulicz indicate how successful this operation has become. (b) In very intractable cases which have resisted all treatment, and which are accompanied by attacks of very severe pain and recurring, almost fatal hæmorrhage, the ulcer may be excised. (c) For hæmatemesis. A number of cases have now been successfully operated upon for the recurring bleeding. The surgeon must bear in mind that the very severe, profuse hæmorrhage does not always come from the large round ulcers, but, as Dieulafoy has recently pointed out, from quite small erosions. In a case of this kind the operation was performed successfully. For a full consideration of this question the reader is referred to Keen's Cartwright Lectures on the Surgery of the Stomach, in the Philadelphia Medical Journal for May and June, 1898.

V. CANCER OF THE STOMACH.

Etiology.—*Incidence.*—In an analysis of 30,000 cases of cancer, W. H. Welch found the stomach involved in 21.4 per cent, this organ thus standing next to the uterus in order of frequency. Among 8,464 cases admitted to my wards, there were 150 cases of cancer of the stomach. There were 39 cases among the first 1,000 autopsies in the post-mortem room of the Johns Hopkins Hospital. The disease is more common in some countries. Figures indicate that cancer of the stomach, as of other organs, is increasing in frequency.

Sex.—T. McCrae has analyzed 150 cases from my wards and found that there were 126 males and 24 females. Welch gives the ratio as 5 to 4.

Age.—Of our 150 cases the ages were as follows: Between twenty and thirty, 6; from thirty to forty, 17; forty to fifty, 38; fifty to sixty, 49; sixty to seventy, 36; seventy to eighty, 4. Fifty-eight per cent occurred between the ages of forty and sixty. Of the 6 cases occurring under the thirtieth year, the youngest was twenty-two. Of the large number of cases analyzed by Welch, three fourths occurred between the fortieth and seventieth years. Congenital cancer of the stomach has been described, and cases have been met with in children.

Race.—Among our 150 cases, 131 were white; 19 were negroes.

Heredity.—Of the 150 cases in only 11 was there a positive history of cancer in the family. In some families, as the Bonapartes, the disease seems to prevail. In our series a very much larger number—38—had a family history of tuberculosis.

Previous Diseases, Habits, etc.—A history of dyspepsia was present in only 33 cases; of these, 17 had had attacks at intervals, 11 had had chronic stomach trouble, and 5 had had dyspepsia for one or two years before the symptoms of cancer developed. Napoleon, discussing this interesting point with his physician Autommarchi, said that he had always had a stomach of iron and felt no inconvenience until the onset of what proved to be his fatal illness.

Alcohol.—Seventy-seven of our patients had used it regularly, 65 of these moderately (?), 8 excessively. *Trauma.*—Only one case gave a positive history. In a recent case the cancer developed rapidly after a blow on the stomach, and the patient lost sixty pounds in weight in three months. *Gastric Ulcer.*—Four cases gave a history pointing to ulcer, but there was no instance of ulcus carcinomatosum among the autopsies.

Mental worry and strain were given occasionally as causes of the illness.

Morbid Anatomy.—The most common varieties of gastric cancer are the cylindrical-celled adeno-carcinoma and the encephaloid or medullary carcinoma; next in frequency is scirrhous, and then colloid cancer. With reference to the situation of the tumor, Welch analyzed 1,300 cases, in which the distribution was as follows: Pyloric region, 791; lesser curvature, 148; cardia, 104; posterior wall, 68; the whole or greater part of the stomach, 61; multiple tumors, 45; greater curvature, 34; anterior wall, 30; fundus, 19.

The medullary cancer occurs in soft masses, which involve all the coats of the stomach and usually ulcerate early. The tumor may form villous projections or cauliflower-like outgrowths. It is soft, grayish white in color, and contains much blood. Microscopically it shows a scanty stroma, enclosing alveoli which contain irregular polyhedral and cylindrical cells. The cylindrical-celled epithelioma may also form large irregular masses, but the consistence is usually firmer, particularly at the edges of the cancerous ulcers. Microscopically the section shows elongated tubular spaces filled with columnar epithelium, and the intervening stroma is abundant. Cysts are not uncommon in this form. The scirrhous variety is characterized by great hardness, due to the abundance of the stroma and the limited amount of alveolar structures. It is seen most frequently at the pylorus, where it is a common cause of stenosis. It may be combined with the medullary form. It may be diffuse, involving all parts of the organ, and leading to a condition which cannot be recognized macroscopically from cirrhosis. This form has also been seen in the stomach secondary to cancer of the ovaries. The colloid cancer is peculiar in its widespread invasion of all the coats. It also spreads with greater frequency to the neighboring parts, and it occasionally causes extensive secondary growths of the same nature in other organs. The appearance on section is very distinctive, and even with the naked eye large alveoli can be seen filled with the translucent colloid material. The term alveolar cancer is often applied to this form. Ulceration is not constantly present, and there are instances in which, with most extensive disease, digestion has been but slightly disturbed. There is a specimen in the Warren Museum, at the Harvard Medical School, of the most widespread colloid cancer, in which the stomach contained after death large pieces of undigested beef-steak.

Secondary Cancer of the Stomach.—Of 37 cases collected by Welch, 17 were secondary to cancer of the breast. Among the first 1,000 autopsies at the Johns Hopkins Hospital there were 3 cases of secondary cancer.

Changes in the Stomach.—Cancer at the cardia is usually associated with wasting of the organ and reduction in its size. The œsophagus above the obstruction may be greatly dilated. On the other hand, annular cancer at the pylorus causes stenosis with great dilatation of the organ. In a few rare instances the pylorus has been extremely narrowed without any increase in the size of the stomach. In diffuse scirrhous cancer the stomach may be very greatly thickened and contracted. It may be displaced or altered in shape by the weight of the tumor, particularly in cancer of the pylorus; in such cases it has been found in every region of the abdomen, and even in the true pelvis. The mobility of the tumors is at times extraordinary and very deceptive, and they may be pushed into the right hypochondrium or into the splenic region, entirely beneath the ribs. Adhesions very frequently occur, particularly to the colon, the liver, and the anterior abdominal wall.

Secondary cancerous growths in other organs are very frequent, as shown by the following analysis by Welch of 1,574 cases: Metastasis occurred in the lymphatic glands in 551; in the liver in 475; in the peritonæum, omentum, and intestine in 357; in the pancreas in 122; in the pleura and lung in 98; in the spleen in 26; in the brain and meninges in 9; in other parts in 92. The lymph-glands affected are usually those of the abdomen, but the cervical and inguinal glands are not infrequently attacked, and give an important clue in diagnosis. Secondary metastatic growths occur subcutaneously, either at the navel or beneath the skin in the vicinity, and are of great value in diagnosis. In one instance a patient with jaundice, which had developed somewhat suddenly and was believed to be catarrhal, presented no signs of enlargement of the liver or tumor of the stomach, but a nodular body appeared at the navel, which on removal proved to be typical scirrhus. A second case in the ward at the same time, with an obscure doubtful tumor in the left hypochondrium, developed a painful nodular subcutaneous growth midway between the navel and the left margin of the ribs.

Perforation.—In the extensive ulceration which occurs perforation of the stomach is not uncommon. It occurred into the peritonæum in 17 of the 507 cases of cancer of the stomach collected by Brinton. In our series perforation is recorded in 4 cases. When adhesions form, the most extensive destruction of the walls may take place without perforation into the peritoneal cavity. In one instance which came under my observation a large portion of the left lobe of the liver lay within the stomach. Occasionally a gastro-cutaneous fistula is established. Perforation may occur into the colon, the small bowel, the pleura, the lung, or into the pericardium.

Symptoms.—*Latent Carcinoma.*—The cases are not very infrequent. There may be no symptoms pointing to the stomach, and the tumor may be discovered accidentally after death. In a second group the symptoms of carcinoma are present, not of the stomach, but of the liver or some other organ, or there are subcutaneous nodules, or, as in one of our cases, secondary masses on the ribs and vertebræ. In a third group, seen particularly in elderly persons in institutions, there is gradual asthenia, without nausea, vomiting, or other local symptoms.

Features of Onset.—Of the 150 cases in our series, 48 complained of pain, 44 of dyspepsia, 21 of vomiting, 13 of loss in weight, 3 of difficulty in swallowing, 1 of tumor. In 7 the features of onset suggested pernicious anæmia. In 37 cases there was a history of sudden onset.

General Symptoms.—*Loss of Weight.*—Progressive emaciation is one of the most constant features of the disease. In 79 of our cases in which exact figures were taken: To 30 pounds, 32 cases; 30 to 50 pounds, 36 cases; 50 to 60 pounds, 5 cases; 60 to 70 pounds, 4; over 70 pounds, 1; 100 pounds, a case of cancer at the cardiac end with obstruction to swallowing. The loss in weight is not always progressive. We see increase in weight under three conditions: (*a*) Proper dieting, with treatment of the associated catarrh of the stomach; (*b*) in cases of cancer of the pylorus after relief of the dilatation of the organ by lavage, etc.; (*c*) after a profound mental impression. I have known a gain of ten pounds to follow the visit of an optimistic consultant. In Keen and D. D. Stewart's case there was a gain of seventy pounds after an exploratory operation!

Loss in strength is usually proportionate to the loss in weight. One sees sometimes remarkable vigor almost to the close, but this is exceptional.

Anæmia is present in a large proportion of all cases, and with the emaciation gives the picture of cachexia. There is often a yellow or lemon tint of the skin. In 59 cases careful blood-counts were made, in 3 the red corpuscles were above 6,000,000 per cubic millimetre. This occurs in the concentrated condition of the blood in certain cases of cancer of the pylorus with dilatation of the stomach. The average count in the 59 cases was 3,712,186 per cubic millimetre. In only 8 cases was the count below 2,000,-000, and in none below 1,000,000. The average of the hæmoglobin was 44.9 per cent. In only 9 was it below 30 per cent. In 62 cases in which the leucocytes were counted there were only 18 cases in which they were above 12,000 per cubic millimetre; in only 3 cases were they above 20,000. As mentioned, there were 7 cases in which the features of onset suggested a primary anæmia. To this question we shall return under diagnosis.

Among other general symptoms may be mentioned *fever.* Of our 150 cases, 74 showed some fever. In only 13 of these was the temperature above 101°. In 2 it was above 103°. Fifteen presented fairly constant elevation of temperature. Eight presented sudden rises. Two cases had *chill,* with elevation to 103° and 104°. Chills may be associated with suppuration at the base of the cancer.

Urine.—There may be no changes throughout; in 65 of our cases there were no alterations, in 36 albumin was found, and in 34 albumin with tube-casts. Glycosuria, peptonuria, and acetonuria have been described. Indican is common.

Œdema.—Swelling of the ankles is of frequent occurrence toward the close. In some cases there is even early a general anasarca, usually in combination with extreme anæmia. The cancer is usually overlooked.

The *bowels* are often constipated. In only 12 cases in our series was diarrhœa present. In 2 cases blood was passed per rectum. There are no special *cardiac symptoms;* the pulse becomes progressively weaker. Thrombosis of one femoral vein may occur or, as in one of our cases, widespread thrombosis in the superficial veins of the body.

Symptoms on the part of the nervous system are rare; consciousness is often retained to the end. *Coma* may develop—viz., similar to that seen in diabetes, and is believed to be due to an acid intoxication.

Functional Disturbances.—*Anorexia,* loss of desire for food, is a frequent and valuable symptom, more constant perhaps than any other. *Nausea* is a striking feature in many cases; there is often a sudden repulsion at the sight of food. In exceptional cases the appetite is retained throughout.

Vomiting may come on early, or only after the dyspepsia has persisted for some time. It occurred in 128 cases in our series. At first it is at long intervals, but subsequently it is more frequent, and may recur several times in the day. There are cases in which it comes on in paroxysms and then subsides; in other cases, it sets in early, persists with great violence, and may cause a fatal termination within a few weeks. Vomiting is more frequent when the cancer involves the orifices, particularly the pylorus, in which case it is usually delayed for an hour or more after taking the food. When the cardiac orifice is involved it may follow at a shorter interval. Extensive disease of the fundus or of the anterior or posterior wall may be present without the occurrence of vomiting. The food is sometimes very little changed, even after it has remained in the stomach for twenty-four hours.

Hæmorrhage occurred in 36 of our 150 cases; in 32 the blood was dark and altered, in 3 it was bright red. In 2 cases vomiting of blood was the first symptom. The bleeding is rarely profuse; more commonly there is slight oozing, and the blood is mixed with, or altered by the secretions, and, when vomited, the material is dark brown or black, the so-called " coffee-ground " vomit. The blood can be recognized by the microscope as shadows of the red blood-corpuscles and irregular masses of altered blood pigment. In cases of doubt the spectroscope may be employed or hæmin crystals obtained.

Pain, an early and important symptom, was present in 130 of our cases. It is very variable in situation, and while most common in the epigastrium, it may be referred to the shoulders, the back, or the loins. The pain is described as dragging, burning, or gnawing in character, and very rarely occurs in severe paroxysms of gastralgia, as in gastric ulcer. As a rule, the pain is aggravated by taking food. There is usually marked tenderness on pressure in the epigastric region. The areas of skin tenderness are referred, as Head has shown, to the region between the nipple and the umbilicus in front and behind from the fifth to the twelfth thoracic spine.

Examination of the Stomach Contents.—The vomitus in suspected cases should be carefully studied, particularly as to quantity and character of ingredients. Large amounts brought up at intervals of a few days, with the appearances already described, are characteristic of dilatation of the stomach. Some of the material should be spread in a large glass plate and any suspicious portions picked out for examination. Bacteria in large numbers occur, one, the Oppler-Boas bacillus—an unusually long non-mobile form—is supposed to be of diagnostic value, and to be largely responsible for the formation of lactic acid. The yeast fungus is very commonly found, sarcinæ less frequently than in dilatation from stricture. Blood is a most important ingredient; the persistent presence microscopically of red corpuscles in the early morning washings is always very suspicious. Later, when coffee-ground vomiting takes place, the macroscopic evidence is sufficient. In cases of doubt the spectroscope may be used or the test made for hæmin crystals. Fragments of the new growth may be vomited or may appear in the washings. Positive evidence of cancer may be obtained from them.

Examination of the Test Breakfast.—The Ewald test meal, consisting of a slice of stale bread and a large cup of weak tea without cream or sugar, is given at 7 A. M. and withdrawn at 8 A. M. The Boas test meal, consisting of a gruel made of a tablespoonful of oatmeal flour in a litre of water, is used in the estimation of lactic acid. As an outcome of the enormous number of observations made of late years, it may be said that free HCl is absent in a large proportion of all cases of cancer of the stomach. Of 94 cases in which the contents were examined in 84 free HCl was absent. In 5 undoubted cases the reaction was good; in 2 of these the history suggested previous ulcer. HCl may be absent in chronic gastritis and in atrophy of the gastric mucosa. (For a good discussion of hydrochloric-acid determinations see J. S. Thatcher, Presbyterian Hospital Reports, vol. iii.) The presence of lactic acid after Boas' test meal is regarded as a valuable sign. It is rarely present in chronic catarrhal conditions, but, as Stockton and Jones conclude, it is by no means positive evidence of carcinoma ventriculi.

Physical Examination.—(*a*) *Inspection.*—After a preliminary survey, embracing the facies, state of nutrition, etc., particular direction is given to the abdomen. An all-important matter is to have the patient in a good light. Fulness in the epigastric region, inequality in the infracostal grooves, the existence of peristalsis, a wide area of aortic pulsation, the presence of subcutaneous nodules or small masses about the navel, and, lastly, a well-defined tumor mass—these, together or singly, may be seen on careful inspection. I cannot emphasize too strongly the value of this method of examination. In 62 of the 150 cases a positive tumor could be seen. In 52 the tumor descended with inspiration; in 36 peristalsis was visible; in 3 cases movements were visible in the tumor itself. In 10 cases with visible peristalsis no tumor was seen, but could be felt on palpation. Inflation with carbonic-acid gas may be tried, except when hæmorrhage has been profuse or the cancer is very extensive. The dilatation often renders evident the peristalsis or may bring a tumor into view. The presence of subcutaneous and umbilical nodules is sometimes a very great help. They were found in 5 of our series. *Palpation.*—In 115 cases a tumor could be felt; in 48 in the epigastric region, in 25 in the umbilical, in 18 in the left hypochondriac, in 17 in the right hypochondriac region, while in 7 cases a mass descended in deep inspiration from beneath the left costal margin. These figures illustrate in how large a proportion of the cases the tumor is in evidence. In rare cases examination in the knee-elbow position is of value. *Mobility* in gastric tumor is a point of much importance. First, the change with respiration, already referred to; a mass may descend 3 or 4 inches in deep inspiration; secondly, the communicated pulsation from the aorta, which is often in its extent suggestive; thirdly, the intrinsic movements in the hypertrophied muscularis in the neighborhood of the cancer. This may give a remarkable character to the mass, causing it to appear and disappear, lifting the abdominal wall in the epigastric region; and, fourthly, mechanical movements, with inflation, with change of posture, or communicated with the hand. Tumors of the pylorus are the most movable, and in extreme cases can be displaced to either hypochondrium or pushed far down below the navel (see illustrative cases in my Lectures on the Diagnosis of Abdominal Tumors). Pain on palpation is common; the mass is usually hard, sometimes nodular. Gas can at times be felt gurgling through the tumor at the pyloric region.

Percussion gives less important indications—the note over a tumor is rarely flat, more often a flat tympany. *Auscultation* may reveal the gurgling through the pylorus; sometimes a systolic bruit is transmitted from the aorta, and when a local peritonitis exists a friction may be heard.

Complications.—*Secondary growths* are common. In 44 autopsies in our series there were metastases in 38; in 29 the lymph-glands were involved; in 23 the liver, in 11 the peritonæum, in 8 the pancreas, in 8 the bowel, in 4 the lung, in 3 the pleura, in 4 the kidneys, and in 2 the spleen. In 8 no deposits were found.

Perforation may lead to peritonitis, but in 3 of our 4 cases there was no general involvement. Cancerous ascites is not very uncommon. Dock has called attention to the value of the examination of the fluid in such cases as a help to diagnosis. The cells show mitoses and are very characteristic. Secondary cancer of the *liver* is very common; the enlargement may be very great, and such cases are not infrequently mistaken for primary cancer of the organ. Involvement of the *lymph-glands* may give valuable indications. There may be early enlargement of a gland at the posterior border of the left sterno-cleido-mastoid muscle; later adjacent glands may become affected. This occurs also in uterine cancer. According to Williams, Trosier was the first to describe this condition, which must not be confounded with the *pseudo-lipome sus-claviculaire* of Verneuil.

A very remarkable picture is presented when the cancer *sloughs* or becomes gangrenous; the vomitus has a foul odor, often of a penetrating nature, to be perceived throughout the room. In cases in which the ulcer perforates the colon, the vomiting may be fæcal. I have, however, met with the fæcal odor in a case with incessant vomiting; there was no perforation of the colon at autopsy.

Course.—While usually *chronic* and lasting from a year to eighteen months, *acute* cancer of the stomach is by no means infrequent. Of the 69 cases in which we could determine accurately the duration, 15 lasted under three months, 16 from three to six months, 14 from six to twelve months—a total of 45 under one year. Four cases lasted for two years or over. One case lived for at least two years and a half.

Diagnosis.—In 115 of our 150 cases a tumor existed, and with this the recognition is rarely in doubt. Practically the chief difficulty is in those cases which present gastric symptoms or anæmia, or both, without the presence of tumor. In the one a chronic gastritis is suspected; in the other a primary anæmia. In *chronic gastritis* the history of long-standing dyspepsia, the absence of cachexia, the absence of lactic acid in the test meal, and the less striking blood changes are the important points for consideration. The cases with grave *anæmia* without tumor offer the greatest difficulty. The blood-count is rarely so low as in pernicious anæmia, a point on which F. P. Henry has laid special stress. In only 8 of our 59 cases with careful blood examination was the number below 2,000,000 per cubic millimetre. The lower color index, as in secondary anæmia, the absence of megaloblasts, and a leucocytosis speak for cancer. Some lay stress on the differential count of the leucocytes, but there is not evidence enough to enable us to speak positively on this point. The digestion leucocytosis might be a help in some cases. The chemical findings are of greater value. The constant presence of lactic acid and the absence of HCl have in several of our cases suggested the diagnosis of cancer, which has been verified later on by the development of a tumor.

From *ulcer of the stomach* malignant disease is, as a rule, readily recognized. The *ulcus carcinomatosum* usually presents a well-marked history of ulcer for years. Hemmeter has given a good account of this rare condition in his recent work on the stomach. The greatest difficulty is offered when there is ulcer with tumor due to cicatricial contraction about the pylorus. In 3 such cases we mistook the mass for cancer, and even at operation it may (as in one of them) be impossible to say whether a neoplasm is present. The persistent hyperchlorhydria is the most important single feature of ulcer, and, taken with the gastralgic attacks and the hæmorrhages, rarely leave doubt as to the condition.

Nowadays, when exploratory laparotomy may be advised with such safety, the surgeon often makes the diagnosis.

The practitioner should recognize the fact that there are cases of cancer of the stomach in which a positive diagnosis cannot be reached for weeks or months by any known means at our command.

Treatment.—The disease is incurable and palliative measures are alone indicated. The diet should consist of readily digested substances of all sorts. Many patients do best on milk alone. Washing out of the stomach, which may be done with a soft tube without any risk, is particularly advantageous when there is obstruction at the pylorus, and is by far the most satisfactory means of combatting the vomiting. The excessive fermentation is also best treated by lavage. When the pain becomes severe, particularly if it disturbs the rest at night, morphia must be given. One eighth of a grain, combined with carbonate of soda (gr. v), bismuth (gr. v–x), usually gives prompt relief, and the dose does not always require to be increased. Creasote (℔ j–ij) and carbolic acid are very useful. The bleeding in gastric cancer is rarely amenable to treatment. Operative measures have been advised and practised, and in exceptional instances there are cases in which the limited cancer or even the entire organ has been resected.

Other Forms of Tumor.—*Non-cancerous tumors* of the stomach rarely cause inconvenience. *Polypi* (polyadenomata) are common and they may be numerous; as many as 150 have been reported in one case. There is a form in which the adenoma exists as an extensive area slightly raised above the level of the mucosa—*polyadenome en nappe* of the French. H. B. Anderson has described a case of remarkable multiple *cysts* in the walls of the stomach and small intestine. *Sarcomata* are very rare. *Fibromata* and *lipomata* have been described.

Foreign bodies occasionally produce remarkable tumors of the stomach. The most extraordinary is the *hair tumor*, of which there are 16 cases in the literature. The cases occur in hysterical women who have been in the habit of eating their own hair. A specimen in the medical museum of McGill University is in two sections, which form an exact mould of the stomach. The tumors are large, very puzzling, and are usually mistaken for cancer. Of 7 cases operated upon, 6 recovered; in 9 cases the condition was found post mortem (Schulten).

VI. HYPERTROPHIC STENOSIS OF THE PYLORUS.

(a) *In Adults.*—Any one with a large post-mortem experience has met with instances of dilated stomachs in connection with thickening or hypertrophy of the pylorus, sometimes forming a tumor large enough to be felt, and suggesting the presence of a new growth. Microscopically, however, the condition is found to be very largely hypertrophy of the muscularis and submucosa of the pylorus. It was well described by the older writers. The symptoms are those of dilatation of the stomach. The condition has been fully discussed recently by Boas (Archiv für Verdauungskrankheiten, Bd. 4, I), who reports two interesting cases with successful gastro-enterostomy. The question is whether some of these cases may not really be congenital, as there have been instances reported in girls as early as the twelfth and sixteenth years.

(b) *Congenital Hypertrophy of the Pylorus.*—To this interesting condition much attention has been paid of late. John Thomson, of Edinburgh, Rolleston and Hayne, Meltzer and I. Adler, of New York, have recently reported cases. The average age in 17 cases was five months.

Three cases have been met with in one family. Thomson suggests the name *congenital gastric spasm*, and thinks it is due to nervous incoördination, but the obstruction is usually thought to be mechanical. Histologically the changes appear to be similar to those in the adult. In both Meltzer's and I. Adler's case gastro-enterostomy was performed, but in neither instance with success.

VII. HÆMORRHAGE FROM THE STOMACH (*Hæmatemesis*).

Etiology.—Gastrorrhagia, as this symptom is called, may result from many conditions, some of which are local, others general.

1. In local disease in the stomach itself: (*a*) cancer; (*b*) ulcer; (*c*) disease of the blood-vessels, such as miliary aneurisms of the smaller arteries, and occasionally varicose veins; (*d*) acute congestion, as in gastritis, and possibly in vicarious hæmorrhage, but both of these are extremely rare causes.

2. Passive congestion due to obstruction in the portal system. This may be either (*a*) hepatic, as in cirrhosis of the liver, thrombosis of the portal vein, or pressure upon the portal vein by tumor, and secondarily in cases of chronic disease of the heart and lungs; (*b*) splenic. Gastrorrhagia is by no means an uncommon symptom in enlarged spleen, and is explained by the intimate relations which exist between the vasa brevia and the splenic circulation.

3. Toxic: (*a*) The poisons of the specific fevers, small-pox, measles, yellow fever; (*b*) poisons of unknown origin, as in acute yellow atrophy and in purpura; (*c*) phosphorus.

4. Traumatism: (*a*) Mechanical injuries, such as blows and wounds, and occasionally by the stomach-tube; (*b*) the result of severe corrosive poisons.

5. Certain constitutional diseases: (*a*) Hæmophilia; (*b*) profound anæmias, whether idiopathic or due to splenic enlargements or to malaria; (*c*) cholæmia.

6. In certain nervous affections, particularly hysteria, and occasionally in progressive paralysis of the insane and epilepsy.

7. The blood may not come from the stomach, but flow into it. Thus it may pass from the nose or the pharynx. In hæmoptysis some of the blood may find its way into the stomach. The bleeding may take place from the œsophagus and trickle into the stomach, from which it is ejected. This occurs in the case of rupture of aneurism and of the œsophageal varices. A child may draw blood with the milk from the mother's breast even in considerable quantities and then vomit it.

8. Miscellaneous causes: Aneurism of the aorta or of its branches may rupture into the stomach. There are instances in which a patient has vomited blood once without ever having a recurrence or without developing symptoms pointing to disease of the stomach.

In new-born infants hæmatemesis may occur alone or in connection with bleeding from other mucous membranes.

31

In medical practice, hæmorrhage from the stomach occurs most frequently in connection with cirrhosis of the liver and ulcer of the stomach. It is more frequent in women than in men, owing to the greater prevalence of round ulcer in the former.

Morbid Anatomy.—When death has occurred from the hæmatemesis there are signs of intense anæmia. The condition of the stomach varies extremely. The lesion is evident in cancer and in ulcer of the stomach. It is to be borne in mind that fatal hæmorrhage may come from a small miliary aneurism communicating with the surface by a pin-hole perforation, or the bleeding may be due to the rupture of a submucous vein and the erosion in the mucosa may be small and readily overlooked. It may require a careful and prolonged search to avoid overlooking such lesions. In the large group associated with portal obstruction, whether due to hepatic or splenic disease, the mucosa is usually pale, smooth, and shows no trace of any lesion. In cirrhosis, fatal by hæmorrhage, one may sometimes search in vain for any focal lesion to account for the gastrorrhagia, and we must conclude that it is possible for even the most profuse bleeding to occur by diapedesis. The stomach may be distended with blood and yet the source of the hæmorrhage be not apparent either in the stomach or in the portal system. In such cases the œsophagus should be examined, as the bleeding may come from that source. In toxic cases there are invariably hæmorrhages in the mucous membrane itself.

Symptoms.—In rare instances fatal syncope may occur without any vomiting. In a case of the kind, in which the woman had fallen over and died in a few minutes, the stomach contained between three and four pounds of blood. The sudden profuse bleedings rapidly lead to profound anæmia. When due to ulcer or cirrhosis the bleeding usually recurs for several days. Fatal hæmorrhage from the stomach is met with in ulcer, cirrhosis, enlargement of the spleen, and in instances in which an aneurism ruptures into the stomach or œsophagus. Gastrorrhagia may occur in splenic anæmia or in leukæmia before the condition has aroused the attention of friends or physician.

The vomited blood may be fluid or clotted; it is usually dark in color, but in the basin the outer part rapidly becomes red from the action of the air. The longer blood remains in the stomach the more altered is it when ejected.

The amount of blood lost is very variable, and in the course of a day the patient may bring up three or four pounds, or even more. In a case under the care of George Ross, in the Montreal General Hospital, the patient lost during seven days ten pounds, by measurement, of blood. The usual symptoms of anæmia develop rapidly, and there may be slight fever, and subsequently œdema may occur. Syncope, convulsions, and occasionally hemiplegia occur after very profuse hæmorrhage. An interesting circumstance connected with gastro-intestinal hæmorrhage is the development of amaurosis, the mode of production of which is still under discussion.

Diagnosis.—In a majority of instances there is no question as to the origin of the blood. Occasionally it is difficult, particularly if the case has not been seen during the attack. Examination of the vomit readily determines whether blood is present or not. The materials vomited may be stained by wine, the juice of strawberries, raspberries, or cranberries, which give a color very closely resembling that of fresh blood, while iron and bismuth and bile may produce the blackish color of altered blood. In such cases the microscope will show clearly the presence of the shadowy outlines of the red blood-corpuscles, and, if necessary, spectroscopic and chemical tests may be applied.

Deception is sometimes practised by hysterical patients, who swallow and then vomit blood or colored liquids. With a little care such cases can usually be detected. The cases must be excluded in which the blood passes from the nose or pharynx, or in which infants swallow it with the milk.

There is not often difficulty in distinguishing between hæmoptysis and hæmatemesis, though the coughing and the vomiting are not infrequently combined. The following are points to be borne in mind in the diagnosis:

HÆMATEMESIS.

1. Previous history points to gastric, hepatic, or splenic disease.

2. The blood is brought up by vomiting, prior to which the patient may experience a feeling of giddiness or faintness.

3. The blood is usually clotted, mixed with particles of food, and has an acid reaction. It may be dark, grumous, and fluid.

4. Subsequent to the attack the patient passes tarry stools, and signs of disease of the abdominal viscera may be detected.

HÆMOPTYSIS.

1. Cough or signs of some pulmonary or cardiac disease precedes, in many cases, the hæmorrhage.

2. The blood is coughed up, and is usually preceded by a sensation of tickling in the throat. If vomiting occurs, it follows the coughing.

3. The blood is frothy, bright red in color, alkaline in reaction. If clotted, rarely in such large coagula, and muco-pus may be mixed with it.

4. The cough persists, physical signs of local disease in the chest may usually be detected, and the sputa may be blood-stained for many days.

Prognosis.—Except in the case of rupture of an aneurism or of large veins, hæmatemesis rarely proves fatal. In my experience death has followed more frequently in cases of cirrhosis and splenic enlargement than in ulcer or cancer. In ulcer it is to be remembered that in the chronic hæmorrhagic form the bleeding may recur for years. The treatment of hæmatemesis is considered under gastric ulcer.

VIII. NEUROSES OF THE STOMACH (*Nervous Dyspepsia*).

The studies of Leube, Ewald, Oser, Rosenbach, and many others have shown that serious functional disturbances of the stomach may occur without any discoverable anatomical basis. The cases are met with most frequently in those who have either inherited a nervous constitution or who have gradually, through indiscretions, brought about a condition of nervous prostration. Not infrequently, however, the gastric symptoms stand so far in the foreground that the general neuropathic character of the patient quite escapes notice. Sometimes the gastric manifestations have apparently a reflex origin depending on organic disturbances in remote parts of the body.

The nervous derangements of the stomach may be divided into motor, secretory, and sensory neuroses. These disturbances rarely occur singly; they are usually met with in combined forms. The clinical picture resulting from such a complex of gastric neuroses is known as *nervous dyspepsia*. There, as Leube has pointed out, the sensory disturbances usually play the more important part.

The sufferer from nervous dyspepsia presents a varying picture. All grades occur, from the emaciated skeleton-like patient with anorexia nervosa to the well-nourished, healthy-looking, fresh-complexioned individual whose only complaint is distress and uneasiness after eating. I have followed Riegel's classification as given in his recent exhaustive work on the stomach.

I. Motor Neuroses.—(*a*) *Hyperkinesis or Supermotility.*—An increase in the normal motor activity of the stomach results in too early a discharge of the ingesta into the intestine. It is more commonly a secondary neurosis dependent upon superacidity or supersecretion of the gastric juice; but it may occur primarily, possibly from reflex causes. The diagnosis is to be reached only by means of the stomach-tube. It gives rise to no characteristic clinical symptoms.

(*b*) *Peristaltic Unrest.*—This condition, as described by Kussmaul, is an extremely common and distressing symptom in neurasthenia. Shortly after eating the peristaltic movements of the stomach are increased, and borborygmi and gurgling may be heard, even at a distance. The subjective sensations are most annoying, and it would appear as if in the hyperæsthetic condition of the nervous system the patient felt normal peristalsis, just as in these states the usual beating of the heart may be perceptible to him. A further analogy is afforded by the fact that emotion increases this peristalsis. It may extend to the intestines, particularly to the duodenum, and on palpation over this region the gurgling is most marked. The movement may be anti-peristalsis, in which the wave passes from right to left, a condition which may also extend to the intestines. There are cases on record in which colored enemata or even scybala have been discharged from the mouth.

(*c*) *Nervous Eructations.*—In this condition severe attacks of noisy eructations, following one another often in rapid succession, occur. When violent they last for hours or days. At other times they occur in paroxysms, depending often upon mental excitement. They are more commonly observed in hysterical women and neurasthenics, but also, not infrequently, in children. The hysterical nature of the affection is sometimes testified to by the occurrence, especially in children, of several instances in one household.

The expelled gas in these cases is atmospheric air, which is swallowed or aspirated from without. Sometimes the whole process may be clearly observed, but in other instances the act of swallowing may be almost or quite imperceptible. Bouveret considers the condition due to a spasm of the pharynx which causes involuntary swallowing. Oser has suggested that the air may enter by aspiration, the stomach acting like an elastic rubber bag which tends to fill again after the air is expressed. It is quite possible that in some instances the eructations consist of gas which has never actually reached the stomach, but is brought up from the œsophagus.

(d) *Nervous Vomiting.*—A condition which is not associated with anatomical changes in the stomach or with any state of the contents, but is due to nervous influences acting either directly or indirectly upon the centres presiding over the act of vomiting. The patients are, as a rule, women— usually brunettes—and the subject of more or less marked hysterical manifestations. A special feature of this form is the absence of the preliminary nausea and of the straining efforts of the ordinary act of vomiting. It is rather a regurgitation, and without visible effort and without gagging the mouth is filled with the contents of the stomach, which are then spat out. It comes on, as a rule, after eating, but may occur at irregular intervals. In some cases the nutrition is not impaired, a feature which may give a clew to the true nature of the disease, as there may be no other hysterical manifestation present. As noted by Tuckwell, it may occur in children. Nervous vomiting is rarely serious.

A type of vomiting is that associated with certain diseases of the nervous system—particularly locomotor ataxia—forming part of the gastric crises. Leyden has reported cases of primary periodic vomiting, which he regards as a neurosis.

(e) *Rumination; Merycismus.*—In this remarkable and rare condition the patients regurgitate and chew the cud like ruminants. It occurs in neurasthenic or hysterical persons, epileptics, and idiots. In some patients it is hereditary. There is an instance in which a governess taught it to two children. The habit may persist for years, and does not necessarily impair the health.

(f) *Spasm of the Cardia.*—Spasmodic, usually painful contraction of the circular muscle fibres at the cardiac orifice may follow the introduction of a sound, hasty eating, or the taking of too hot or too cold food. It may occur in tetanus and also in hysterical and neurasthenic individuals, especially in air swallowers, in whom, if it be combined with pyloric spasm, it may result in painful gastric distention—"pneumatosis." Here the spasm may be of considerable duration. The condition is rare and practically not of much moment.

(g) *Pyloric Spasm.*—This is usually a secondary occurrence, following superacidity, supersecretion, ulcer, or the introduction into the stomach of irritating substances. The spasm often causes pain in the region of the pylorus and increased gastric peristalsis. In cases where the spasm is combined with superacidity and supersecretion marked dilatation with atony may follow; it is questionable, however, whether a primary nervous pyloric spasm ever gives rise to serious results. I have already referred to John

Thomson's views of pyloric spasm in association with the congenital form of hypertrophic stenosis of the pylorus.

(*h*) *Atony of the Stomach.*—Motor insufficiency of the stomach is generally due to injudicious feeding, to organic disease of the stomach itself, or to general wasting processes. In some otherwise normal individuals of neurotic temperaments an atony may, however, occur which possibly deserves to be classed among the neuroses. The symptoms are usually those of a moderate dilatation, and are often associated with marked sensory disturbances—feelings of weight and pressure, distention, eructations, and so forth.

Great care must be taken in the diagnosis to rule out all other possible causes.

(*i*) *Insufficiency or Incontinence of the Pylorus.*—This condition was described first by de Séré and later by Ebstein. It may be recognized by the rapid passing of gas from the stomach into the bowel on attempts at inflation of the former, as well as by the presence of bile and intestinal contents in the stomach. There are no distinctive clinical symptoms.

(*j*) *Insufficiency of the Cardia.*—This condition is only recognized by the occurrence of eructations or in rumination.

II. **Secretory Neuroses.**—(*a*) *Hyperacidity; Superacidity; Hyperchlorhydria.*—Nervous dyspepsia with hyperacidity of the gastric juices. The symptoms depend upon the secretion of an abnormally acid gastric juice at the time of digestion. This is a common form of dyspepsia in young and neurotic individuals. Osswald has pointed out its remarkable frequency in chlorotic girls. The symptoms are very variable. They do not, as a rule, immediately follow the ingestion of food, but occur one to three hours later, at the height of digestion. There is a sense of weight and pressure, sometimes of burning in the epigastrium, commonly associated with acid eructations. If vomiting occurs, the pain is relieved. The patient is usually relatively well nourished, and the appetite is often good, though the sufferer may be afraid to eat on account of the anticipated pain. Its association with ulcer has been referred to. There is commonly constipation.

(*b*) *Supersecretion, Intermittent and Continuous.*—This is a form of dyspepsia which has been long recognized, but of late has been specially studied by Reichmann and others. The increased flow of the gastric juice may be intermittent or continuous. The secretion under such circumstances is usually superacid, though this is not always the case. The periodical form— the *gastroxynsis* of Rossbach—may be quite independent of the time of digestion. Great quantities of highly acid gastric juice may be secreted in a very small space of time. Such cases are rare, and are especially associated either with profound neurasthenia or with locomotor ataxia. The attack may last for several days. It usually sets in with a gnawing, unpleasant sensation in the stomach, severe headache, and shortly after the patient vomits a clear, watery secretion of such acidity that the throat is irritated and made raw and sore. As mentioned, the attacks may be quite independent of food. *Continuous supersecretion* is more common. The constant presence of fluid in the stomach, together with the pyloric spasm, which commonly results from the irritation of the overacid gastric juice, are followed by a more or less extensive dilatation. Digestion of the starches is retarded, and there are eructations of acid fluid and gastric distress. This secretion of highly acid gastric juice may continue when the stomach is free from food. In these cases pain, burning acid eructations, and even vomiting, occurring during the night and early in the morning, are rather characteristic.

(c) *Nervous Subacidity or Inacidity; Achylia Gastrica Nervosa.*—Lack of the normal amount of acid is found in chronic catarrh, and particularly in cancer. As Leube has shown, a reduction in the normal amount of acid may exist with the most pronounced symptoms of nervous dyspepsia and yet the stomach will be free from food within the regular time. A condition in which free acid is absent in the gastric juice may occur in cancer, in extreme sclerosis of the mucous membrane, as a nervous manifestation of hysteria, and occasionally of tabes. In most of these cases, though there be no free acid, yet the other digestive ferments—pepsin and the curdling ferments—or their zymogens are to be demonstrated in the gastric juice. There may, however, be a complete absence of the gastric secretion. To these cases Einhorn has given the name of *achylia gastrica*. This condition was at first thought to occur only in cases of total atrophy of the gastric mucosa, but recent observations have shown that it may occur as a neurosis. In a case of Einhorn's the gastric secretions returned after five years of total *achylia gastrica*.

The symptoms of subacidity, or even of *achylia gastrica*, vary greatly in intensity; they may be almost or quite absent in cases of advanced atrophy of the mucosa, and, as a rule, are not marked so long as the motor activity of the stomach remains good. If atony, however, develop and abnormal fermentative processes arise, severe gastric and intestinal symptoms may follow. In the cases associated with hysteria and neurasthenia, even though the food may be well taken care of by the intestines, there are very commonly grave sensory disturbances in the region of the stomach, in addition to the general nervous symptoms.

III. **Sensory Neuroses.**—(a) *Hyperæsthesia.*—In this condition the patients complain of fulness, pressure, weight, burning, and so forth, during digestion, just such symptoms as accompany a variety of organic diseases of the stomach, and yet in all other respects the gastric functions appear quite normal. Sometimes these distressing sensations are present even when the stomach is empty. These symptoms are usually associated with other manifestations of hysteria and neurasthenia. The pain often follows particular articles of food. An hysterical patient may apparently suffer excruciating pain after taking the smallest amount of food of any sort, while anything prescribed as a medicine may be well borne. In severe cases the patient may be reduced to an extreme degree of starvation.

(b) *Gastralgia; Gastrodynia.*—Severe pains in the epigastrium, paroxysmal in character, occur (a) as a manifestation of a functional neurosis, independent of organic disease, and usually associated with other nervous symptoms (it is this form which will here be described); (b) in chronic disease of the nervous system, forming the so-called gastric crises; and (c) in organic disease of the stomach, such as ulcer or cancer.

The functional neurosis occurs chiefly in women, very commonly in connection with disturbed menstrual function or with pronounced hysterical symptoms. The affection may set in as early as puberty, but it is more common at the menopause. Anæmic, constipated women who have worries and anxieties at home are most prone to the affection. It is more frequent in brunettes than in blondes. Attacks of it sometimes occur in robust, healthy men. More often it is only one feature in a condition of general neurasthenia or a manifestation of that form of nervous dyspepsia in which the gastric juice or hydrochloric acid is secreted in excess. I am very sceptical as to the existence of a gastralgia of purely malarial origin.

The symptoms are very characteristic; the patient is suddenly seized with agonizing pains in the epigastrium, which pass toward the back and around the lower ribs. The attack is usually independent of the taking of food, and may recur at definite intervals, a periodicity which has given rise to the supposition in some cases that the affection is due to malaria. The most marked periodicity, however, may be in the gastralgic attacks of ulcer. They frequently come on at night. Vomiting is rare; more commonly the taking of food relieves the pain. To this, however, there are striking exceptions. Pressure upon the epigastrium commonly gives relief, but deep pressure may be painful. It seems scarcely necessary to separate the forms, as some have done, into irritative and depressive, as the cases insensibly merge into each other. Stress has been laid upon the occurrence of painful points, but they are so common in neurasthenia that very little importance can be attributed to them.

The *diagnosis* offers many difficulties. Organic disease either of the stomach or of the nervous system, particularly the gastric crises of locomotor ataxia, must be excluded. In the case of ulcer or cancer this is not always easy. The fact that the pain is most marked when the stomach is empty and is relieved by the taking of food is sometimes regarded as pathognomonic of simple gastralgia, but to this there are many exceptions, and in cancer the pains may be relieved on eating. The prolonged intervals between the attacks and their independence of diet are important features in simple gastralgia; but in many instances it is less the local than the general symptoms of the case which enable us to make the diagnosis. It is to be remembered that in gall-stone colic jaundice is frequently absent, and in any long-standing case of gastralgia, in which the attacks recur at intervals for years, the question of cholelithiasis should be considered.

(*c*) *Anomalies of the Sense of Hunger and Repletion; Bulimia.*—Abnormally excessive hunger coming on often in paroxysmal attacks, which cause the patient to commit extraordinary excesses in eating. This condition may occur in diabetes mellitus and sometimes in gastric disorders, particularly those associated with supersecretion. It is, however, more commonly seen in hysteria and in psychoses. It may occur in cerebral tumors, in Graves' disease, and in epilepsy.

The attacks often begin suddenly at night, the patient waking with a feeling of faintness and pain, and an uncontrollable desire for food. Sometimes such attacks occur immediately after a large meal. The attack may be relieved by a small quantity of food, while at other times enormous quantities may be taken. In obstinate cases gastritis, atony, and dilatation frequently result from the abuse of the stomach.

Akoria.—An absence of the sense of satiety. This condition is commonly associated with bulimia and polyphagia, but not always. The patient always feels "empty." There are usually other well-marked manifestations of hysteria or neurasthenia.

Anorexia Nervosa.—This condition, which is a manifestation of a neurotic temperament, is discussed subsequently under the general heading of Hysteria.

Treatment of Neuroses of the Stomach.—The most important part of the treatment of nervous dyspepsia is often that directed toward the improvement of the general physical and mental condition of the patient. The possibility that the symptoms may be of reflex origin should be borne in mind. A large proportion of cases of nervous dyspepsia are dependent upon mental and physical exhaustion or worry, and a vacation or a change of scene will often accomplish what years of treatment at home have failed to do. The manner of life of the patient should be investigated and a proper amount of physical exercise in the open air insisted upon. This alone will in some cases be sufficient to cause the disappearance of the symptoms.

Many cases of nervous dyspepsia with marked neurasthenic or hysterical symptoms do well on the Weir-Mitchell treatment, and in obstinate forms it should be given a thorough trial. The most striking results are perhaps seen in the case of anorexia nervosa, which will be referred to subsequently. It is also of value in nervous vomiting.

In *cardiac spasm* care should be taken to eat slowly, to avoid swallowing too large morsels or irritating substances. The methodical introduction of thick sounds may be of value.

The treatment in *atony* of the stomach should be similar to that adopted in moderate dilatation—the administration of small quantities of food at frequent intervals; the limitation of the fluids, which should also be taken in small amounts at a time; lavage. Strychnine in full doses may be of value.

In the distressing cases of *hyperacidity*, in addition to the treatment of the general neurotic condition, alkalies must be employed either in the form of magnesia or bicarbonate of soda. These should be given in large doses and at the *height of digestion*. The burning acid eructations may be relieved in this way. The diet should be mainly albuminous, and should be administered in a non-irritating form. Stimulating condiments and alcohol should be avoided. Starches should be sparingly allowed, and only in most digestible forms. Fats are fairly well borne.

Limiting the patient to a strictly meat diet is a valuable procedure in many cases of dyspepsia associated with hyperacidity. The meat should be taken either raw or, if an insuperable objection exists to this, very slightly cooked. It is best given finely minced or grated on stale bread. An ample dietary is 3¼ ounces (100 grammes) of meat, two medium slices of stale bread, and an ounce (30 grammes) of butter. This may be taken three times a day with a glass of Apollinaris water, soda water, or, what is just as satisfactory, spring water. The fluid should not be taken too cold. Special care should be taken in the examination of the meat to guard against tape-worm infection, but suitable instructions on this point can be given. This is sufficient for an adult man, and many obstinate cases yield satisfactorily to a month or six weeks of this treatment, after which time the less readily digested articles of food may be gradually added to the dietary.

In *supersecretion* the use of the stomach-tube is of the greatest value. In the periodical form it should be used as soon as the attack begins. The stomach may be washed with alkaline solutions or solutions of nitrate of silver, 1 to 1,000, may be used. Where this is impracticable the taking of albuminous food may give relief. One of my patients used to have two hard-boiled eggs by his bedside, by the eating of which nocturnal attacks were alleviated. Alkalies in large doses are also indicated.

In cases of *continued supersecretion* there is usually atony and dilatation. The diet here should be much as in superacidity, but should be administered in smaller quantities at frequent intervals. Lavage with alkaline solutions or with nitrate of silver is of great value. To relieve pain large quantities of bicarbonate of soda or magnesia should be given at the height of digestion.

In *subacidity* a carefully regulated, easily digestible mixed diet, not too rich in albuminoids, is advisable. Bitter tonics before meals are sometimes of value. In *achylia gastrica* the use of predigested foods and of hydrochloric acid in full doses may be of assistance.

In marked *hyperæsthesia*, beside the treatment of the general condition, nitrate of silver in doses of gr. $\frac{1}{3}-\frac{1}{2}$, taken in $\text{\small ʒ}$ iij–$\text{\small ʒ}$ iv of water on an empty stomach, is advised by Rosenheim.

In some instances rectal feeding may have to be resorted to.

The gastralgia, if very severe, requires morphia, which is best administered subcutaneously in combination with atropia. In the milder attacks the combination of morphia (gr. $\frac{1}{3}$) with cocaine and belladonna is recommended by Ewald. The greatest caution should, however, be exercised in these cases in the use of the hypodermic syringe. It is preferable, if opium is necessary, to give it by the mouth, and not to let the patient know the character of the drug. Chloroform, in from 10- to 20-drop doses, or Hoffman's anodyne will sometimes allay the severe pains. The general condition should receive careful attention, and in many cases the attacks recur until the health is restored by change of air with the prolonged use of arsenic. If there is anæmia iron may be given freely. Nitrate of silver in doses of gr. $\frac{1}{4}$ to $\frac{1}{2}$ in a large claret-glass of water taken on an empty stomach is useful in some cases.

There are forms of nervous dyspepsia occurring in women who are often well nourished and with a good color, yet who suffer—particularly at night —with flatulency and abdominal distress. The sleep may be quiet and undisturbed for two or three hours, after which they are aroused with painful sensations in the abdomen and eructations. The appetite and digestion may appear to be normal. Constipation is, however, usually present. In many of these patients the condition seems rather intestinal dyspepsia, and the distress is due to the accumulation of gases, the result of excessive putrefaction. The fats, starches, and sugars should be restricted. A diastase ferment is sometimes useful. The flatulency may be treated by the methods above mentioned. Naphthalin, salicylate of bismuth, and salol have been recommended. Some of these cases obtain relief from thorough irrigation of the colon at bedtime.

The treatment of *anorexia nervosa* is described subsequently.

VII. DISEASES OF THE INTESTINES.

I. DISEASES OF THE INTESTINES ASSOCIATED WITH DIARRHŒA.

CATARRHAL ENTERITIS; DIARRHŒA.

In the classification of catarrhal enteritis the anatomical divisions of the bowel have been too closely followed, and a duodenitis, jejunitis, ileitis, typhlitis, colitis, and proctitis have been recognized; whereas in a majority of cases the entire intestinal tract, to a greater or lesser extent, is involved, sometimes the small most intensely, sometimes the large bowel; but during life it may be quite impossible to say which portion is specially affected.

Etiology.—The causes may be either *primary* or *secondary*. Among the causes of *primary* catarrhal enteritis are: (a) Improper food, one of the most frequent, especially in children, in whom it follows overeating, or the ingestion of unripe fruit. In some individuals special articles of diet will always produce a slight diarrhœa, which may not be due to a catarrh of the mucosa, but to increased peristalsis induced by the offending material. (b) Various toxic substances. Many of the organic poisons, such as those produced in the decomposition of milk and articles of food, excite the most intense intestinal catarrh. Certain inorganic substances, as arsenic and mercury, act in the same way. (c) Changes in the weather. A fall in the temperature of from twenty to thirty degrees, particularly in the spring or autumn, may induce—how, it is difficult to say—an acute diarrhœa. We speak of this as a catarrhal process, the result of cold or of chill. On the other hand, the diarrhœal diseases of children are associated in a very special way with the excessive heat of summer months. (d) Changes in the constitution of the intestinal secretions. We know too little about the *succus entericus* to be able to speak of influences induced by change in its quantity or quality. It has long been held that an increase in the amount of bile poured into the bowel might excite a diarrhœa; hence the term bilious diarrhœa, so frequently used by the older writers. Possibly there are conditions in which an excessive amount of bile is poured into the intestine, increasing the peristalsis, and hurrying on the contents; but the opposite state, a scanty secretion, by favoring the natural fermentative processes, much more commonly causes an intestinal catarrh. Absence of the pancreatic secretion from the intestine has been associated in certain cases with a fatty diarrhœa. (*e*) Nervous influences. It is by no means clear how mental states act upon the bowels, and yet it is an old and trustworthy observation, which every-day experience confirms, that the mental state may profoundly affect the intestinal canal. These influences should not properly be considered under catarrhal processes, as they result simply from increased peristalsis or increased secretion, and are usually described under the heading *nervous diarrhœa*. In children it frequently follows fright. It is common, too, in adults as a result of emotional disturbances. Canstatt mentions a surgeon who always before an important operation had watery diarrhœa. In hysterical women it is seen as an occasional occurrence, due to transient excitement, or as a chronic, protracted diarrhœa, which may last for months or even years.

Among the *secondary* causes of intestinal catarrh may be mentioned: (*a*) Infectious diseases. Dysentery, cholera, typhoid fever, pyæmia, septicæmia, tuberculosis, and pneumonia are occasionally associated with intestinal catarrh. In dysentery and typhoid fever the ulceration is in part responsible for the catarrhal condition, but in cholera it is probably a direct influence of the bacilli or of the toxic materials produced by them. (*b*) The extension of inflammatory processes from adjacent parts. Thus, in peritonitis, catarrhal swelling and increased secretion are always present in the mucosa. In cases of invagination, hernia, tuberculous or cancerous ulceration, catarrhal processes are common. (*c*) Circulatory disturbances cause a catarrhal enteritis, usually of a very chronic character. This is common in diseases of the liver, such as cirrhosis, and in chronic affections of the heart and lungs—all conditions, in fact, which produce engorgement of the terminal branches of the portal vessels. (*d*) In the cachectic conditions met with in cancer, profound anæmia, Addison's disease, and Bright's disease intestinal catarrh may develop, and may terminate life.

Morbid Anatomy.—Changes in the mucous membrane are not always visible, and in cases in which, during life, the symptoms of intestinal catarrh have been marked, neither redness, swelling, nor increased secretion—the three signs usually laid down as characteristic of catarrhal inflammation—may be present post mortem. It is rare to see the mucous membrane injected; more commonly it is pale and covered with mucus. In the upper part of the small intestine the tips of the valvulæ conniventes may be deeply injected. Even in extreme grades of portal obstruction intense hyperæmia is not often seen. The entire mucosa may be softened and infiltrated, the lining epithelium swollen, or even shed, and appearing as large flakes among the intestinal contents. This is, no doubt, a post-mortem change. The lymph follicles are almost always swollen, particularly in children. The Peyer's patches may be prominent and the solitary follicles in the large and small bowel may stand out with distinctness and present in the centres little erosions, the so-called follicular ulcers. This may be a striking feature in the intestine in all forms of catarrhal enteritis in children, quite irrespective of the intensity of the diarrhœa.

When the process is more chronic the mucosa is firmer, in some instances thickened, in others distinctly thinned, and the villi and follicles present a slaty pigmentation.

Symptoms.—Acute and chronic forms may be recognized. The important symptom of both is diarrhœa, which, in the majority of instances, is the sole indication of this condition. It is not to be supposed that diarrhœa is invariably caused by, or associated with, catarrhal enteritis, as it may be produced by nervous and other influences. It is probable that catarrh of the jejunum may exist without any diarrhœa; indeed, it is a very common circumstance to find post mortem a catarrhal state of the small bowel in persons who have not had diarrhœa during life. The stools vary extremely in character. The color depends upon the amount of bile with which they are mixed, and they may be of a dark or blackish brown, or of a light-yellow, or even of a grayish-white tint. The consistence is usually very thin and watery, but in some instances the stools are pultaceous like thin gruel. Portions of undigested food can often be seen (lienteric diarrhœa), and flakes of yellowish-brown mucus. Microscopically there are innumerable micro-organisms, epithelium and mucous cells, crystals of phosphate of lime, oxalate of lime, and occasionally cholesterin and Charcot's crystals.

Pain in the abdomen is usually present in the acute catarrhal enteritis, particularly when due to food. It is of a colicky character, and when the colon is involved there may be tenesmus. More or less tympanites exists, and there are gurgling noises or borborygmi, due to the rapid passage of fluid and gas from one part to another. In the very acute attacks there may be vomiting. Fever is not, as a rule, present, but there may be a slight elevation of one or two degrees. The appetite is lost, there is intense thirst, and the tongue is dry and coated. In very acute cases, when the quantity of fluid lost is great and the pain excessive, there may be collapse symptoms. The number of evacuations varies from four or five to twenty or more in the course of the day. The attack lasts for two or three days, or may be prolonged for a week or ten days.

Chronic catarrh of the bowels may follow the acute form, or may develop gradually as an independent affection or as a sequence of obstruction in the portal circulation. It is characterized by diarrhœa, with or without colic. The dejections vary; when the small bowel is chiefly involved the diarrhœa is of a lienteric character, and when the colon is affected the stools are thin and mixed with much mucus. A special form of mucous diarrhœa will be subsequently described. The general nutrition in these chronic cases is greatly disturbed; there may be much loss of flesh and great pallor. The patients are inclined to suffer from low spirits, or hypochondriasis may develop.

Diagnosis.—It is important, in the first place, to determine, if possible, whether the large or small bowel is chiefly affected. In catarrh of the small bowel the diarrhœa is less marked, the pains are of a colicky character, borborygmi are not so frequent, the fæces usually contain portions of food, and are more yellowish-green or grayish-yellow and flocculent and do not contain much mucus. When the large intestine is at fault there may be no pain whatever, as in the catarrh of the large intestine associated with tuberculosis and Bright's disease. When present, the pains are most intense and, if the lower portion of the bowel is involved, there may be marked tenesmus. The stools have a uniform soupy consistence; they are grayish in color and granular throughout, with here and there flakes of mucus, or they may contain very large quantities of mucus.

There are no positive symptoms by which the diagnosis of duodenitis can be made. It is usually associated with acute gastritis and, if the process extends into the bile-duct, with jaundice. Neither jejunitis nor ileitis can be separated from general intestinal catarrh.

ENTERITIS IN CHILDREN.

We may recognize three forms: (1) The acute dyspeptic diarrhœa; (2) cholera infantum; and (3) acute entero-colitis.

General Etiology of the Diarrhœas of Children.—The disease is most frequent in artificially fed children, and the greatest number of cases occur between the ages of six and eighteen months. A popular and well-founded belief ascribes special danger to the second summer of the infant. Infantile diarrhœa is very prevalent among the poorer classes in the large cities. It attacks, however, children with the most favorable surroundings. Two factors influence the disease, diet and temperature. An immense majority of all fatal cases are artificially fed. Of 1,943 fatal cases in Holt's statistics, only three per cent were exclusively breast fed. Among the poor the bowel complaint in children begins with the artificial feeding. The relation of temperature to the prevalence of diarrhœal diseases in children has long been recognized. The mortality curve begins to rise in May, increases in June, reaches the maximum in July, and gradually sinks through August and September. The maximum corresponds closely with the highest mean temperature; yet we cannot regard the heat itself as the direct agent, but only as one of several factors. Thus the mean temperature of June is only four or five degrees lower than that of July, and yet the mortality is not more than one third. Seibert, who has carefully analyzed the mortality and the temperature, month by month, in New York, for ten years, fails to find a constant relation between the degree of heat and the number of cases of diarrhœa. Neither barometric pressure nor humidity appears to have any influence.

Relation of Bacteria.—The healthy fæces of sucklings contain a number of bacteria and micrococci, the most important of which are the *bacterium lactis aerogenes* and the *bacterium coli commune*. The former is only present in the intestine after a milk diet, the milk sugar appearing to furnish the materials necessary for its growth. It occurs rather in the upper portion of the bowel, and in this region excites the fermentative processes in the milk. The *bacterium coli commune* is found more abundantly in the lower portion of the small intestine and in the colon, and excites fermentative changes which are probably associated with certain phases of digestion. The observations of Escherich show the remarkable simplicity of this bacterial vegetation in the healthy fæces of milk-fed children, as these two organisms alone develop and are constant. In infantile diarrhœa the number of bacteria which may be isolated from the stools is remarkable. Booker has discriminated forty varieties, the greatest number of which were found in the cases of cholera infantum. The two constant forms noted above do not disappear in the diarrhœal stools. No forms have been found to bear a constant or specific relation to the diarrhœal fæces, such as the two above mentioned do to the healthy milk fæces. The bacteria of the *proteus* group are most frequent, and possess pathogenic properties. All the varieties develop and produce important changes in the milk, which have been dealt with very fully by Booker in his exhaustive monograph (Johns Hopkins Hospital Reports, vol. vi). This author concludes that in the diarrhœa of infants " not one specific kind, but many different kinds of bacteria are concerned, and that their action is manifested more in the alteration of the food and intestinal contents and in the production of injurious products than in a direct irritation upon the intestinal wall." With these agree the conclusions of Jeffries and Baginsky regarding cholera infantum.

Morbid Anatomy.—We find most frequently a catarrhal swelling of the mucosa of both small and large bowel with enlargement of the lymph follicles. In more chronic cases the latter show small erosions or follicular ulcers; more rarely there is croupous enteritis affecting the lower part of the ileum and the colon. The changes in the other organs are neither numerous nor characteristic. Broncho-pneumonia occurs in many cases. The spleen may be swollen. Brain lesions are rare; the membranes and substance are often anæmic, but meningitis or thrombosis is very uncommon.

Clinical Forms.—Acute Dyspeptic Diarrhœa.—The child may appear in its usual health, but has an increase in the number of stools, without fever or special disturbance except slight restlessness at night. After persisting for a day or two the stools become more frequent and contain undigested food and curds, and are very offensive. In other cases the disease sets in abruptly with vomiting, griping pains, and fever, which may rise rapidly and reach 104° or 105°. There may be convulsions at the outset. The abdomen is sensitive, and the child lies with the legs drawn up. The stools consist of grayish or greenish-yellow fæces mixed with gas, curds, and portions of food. In children over two years of age such attacks not infrequently follow eating freely of unripe fruit or the drinking of milk which has been tainted. With judicious treatment the children improve in a few days; but relapses are not uncommon, and in the hot weather the attack may be the starting point of a severe entero-colitis. In a debilitated child a mild attack may prove fatal. This dyspeptic diarrhœa is distinguished sharply from cholera infantum by the character of the stools, which never have a watery, serous character. In many instances this form precedes the onset of the specific fevers, particularly during the hot weather.

Cholera Infantum.—This is by no means so common as the ordinary dyspeptic diarrhœa of children, and, according to Holt, occurs only in two or three per cent of the cases of summer diarrhœa. It prevails in the hot weather and in children artificially fed or who have had previously some slight dyspeptic derangement. It is characterized by vomiting, uncontrollable diarrhœa, and collapse. The disease sets in with vomiting, which is incessant and is excited by an attempt to take food or drink. The stools are profuse and frequent; at first fæcal in character, brown or yellow in color, and finally thin, serous, and watery. The stools first passed are very offensive; subsequently they are odorless. The thin, serous stools are alkaline. There is fever, but the axillary temperature may register three or more degrees below that of the rectum. From the outset there is marked prostration; the eyes are sunken, the features pinched, the fontanelle depressed, and the skin has a peculiar ashy pallor. At first restless and excited, the child subsequently becomes heavy, dull, and listless. The tongue is coated at the onset, but subsequently becomes red and dry. As in all choleraic conditions, the thirst is insatiable; the pulse is rapid and feeble, and toward the end becomes irregular and imperceptible. Death may occur within twenty-four hours, with symptoms of collapse and great elevation of the internal temperature. Before the end the diarrhœa and vomiting may cease. In other instances the intense symptoms subside, but the child remains torpid and semi-comatose with fingers clutched, and there may be convulsions. The head may be retracted and the respirations interrupted, irregular, and of the Cheyne-Stokes type. The child may remain in this condition for some days without any signs of improvement. It was to this group of symptoms in infantile diarrhœa that Marshall Hall gave the term "hydrencephaloid" or spurious hydrocephalus. As a rule, no changes in the brain or other organs are found, and the condition is no doubt caused by the toxic agents absorbed from the intestine. A remarkable condition of sclerema is described as a sequel of cholera infantum. The skin and subcutaneous tissues become hard and firm and the appearance has been compared to that of a half-frozen cadaver.

No constant organism has been found in these cases. Baginsky considers the disease the result of the action on the system of the poisonous products of decomposition encouraged by the various bacteria present—a *Fäulniss* disease. The clinical picture is that produced by an acute bacterial infection, as in Asiatic cholera.

The *diagnosis* is readily made. There is no other intestinal affection in children for which it can be mistaken. The constant vomiting, the frequent watery discharges, the collapse symptoms, and the elevated temperature make an unmistakable clinical picture. The outlook in the majority of cases is bad, particularly in children artificially fed. Hyperpyrexia, extreme collapse, and incessant vomiting are the most serious symptoms.

Acute Entero-colitis.—In this form the ileum and colon are most affected, chiefly in the lymph follicles, hence the term follicular enteritis or follicular dysentery. Catarrhal ulceration is a common sequence. It occurs most frequently in warm weather, in artificially fed children; but it may set in at any season of the year, and is the form of enteritis most common as a secondary complication in the specific fevers of childhood.

The attack may follow the ordinary dyspeptic diarrhœa. The temperature increases, the stools change in character and contain traces of blood and mucus, the former usually only in streaks. The fæces are passed without any pain. The abdomen is distended and tender along the line of the colon. Vomiting may be present at the outset, but is not a characteristic feature, as in cholera infantum. The diarrhœa may be gradually checked and convalescence is established in two or three weeks; in other instances the disease becomes subacute, the fever subsides, but the diarrhœa persists and the general health of the child rapidly deteriorates. The case may drag on for five or six weeks, when improvement gradually occurs or the child is carried off by a severe intercurrent attack. In a third form of acute entero-colitis, in which anatomically the lesions are those already mentioned—namely, an intense follicular inflammation—the symptoms are of a more severe character, and the affection is sometimes spoken of as acute dysentery. It attacks children up to the third or fourth year or even older. The onset is sudden, with high fever, vomiting, frequent stools, which at first contain remnants of food and fæces and subsequently much mucus and some blood. There is incessant pain, which may be more severe than in any intestinal affection of childhood. The prostration is very great and the fatal termination may occur within forty-eight hours. More commonly the case lasts for a week or longer.

The Cœliac Affection.—Under this heading Gee has described an intestinal disorder, most commonly met with in children between the ages of one and five, characterized by the occurrence of pale, loose stools, not unlike gruel or oatmeal porridge. They are bulky, not watery, yeasty, frothy, and extremely offensive. The affection has received various names, such as *diarrhœa alba* or *diarrhœa chylosa*. It is not associated with tuberculous or other hereditary disease. It begins insidiously and there are progressive wasting, weakness, and pallor. The belly becomes doughy and inelastic. There is often flatulency. Fever is usually absent. The disease is lingering and a fatal termination is common. So far nothing is known of the pathology of the disease. Ulceration of the intestines has been met with, but it is not constant. *falling out of the hair*

Sprue or Psilosis.—A remarkable disease of the tropics, characterized by " a peculiar, inflamed, superficially ulcerated, exceedingly sensitive condition of the mucous membrane of the tongue and mouth; great wasting and anæmia; pale, copious, and often loose, frequent, and frothy fermenting stools; very generally by more or less diarrhœa; and also by a marked tendency to relapse " (Manson).

It is very prevalent in India, China, and Java. Nothing definite is known as to its cause.

When fully established the chief symptoms are a disturbed condition of the bowels, pale, yeasty-looking stools, a raw, bare, sore condition of the tongue, mouth, and gullet, sometimes with actual superficial ulceration. With these gastro-intestinal symptoms there are associated anæmia and general wasting. It is very chronic, with numerous relapses. There are no characteristic anatomical changes. There are usually ulcers in the colon, and the French think it is a form of dysentery.

Manson recommends rest and a milk diet as curative in a large proportion of the cases. The recent monograph by Thin and the article by Manson in Allbutt's System give very full descriptions of the disease.

32

DIPHTHERITIC OR CROUPOUS ENTERITIS.

A croupous or diphtheritic inflammation of the mucosa of the small and large intestines occurs (a) most frequently as a secondary process in the infectious diseases—pneumonia, pyæmia in its various forms, and typhoid fever; (b) as a terminal process in many chronic affections, such as Bright's disease, cirrhosis of the liver, or cancer; and (c) as an effect of certain poisons—mercury, lead, and arsenic.

There are three different anatomical pictures. In one group of cases the mucosa presents on the top of the folds a thin grayish-yellow diphtheritic exudate situated upon a deeply congested base. In some cases all grades may be seen between the thinnest film of superficial necrosis and involvement of the entire thickness of the mucosa. In the colon similar transversely arranged areas of necrosis are seen situated upon hyperæmic patches, and it may be here much more extensive and involve a large portion of the membrane. There may be most extensive inflammation without any involvement of the solitary follicles of the large or small bowel.

In a second group of cases the membrane has rather a croupous character. It is grayish white in color, more flake-like and extensive, limited, perhaps, to the cæcum or to a portion of the colon; thus, in several cases of pneumonia I found this flaky adherent false membrane, in one instance forming patches 1 to 2 cm. in diameter, which were not unlike in form to rupia crusts.

In a third group the affection is really a follicular enteritis, involving the solitary glands, which are swollen and capped with an area of diphtheritic necrosis or are in a state of suppuration. Follicular ulcers are common in this form. The disease may run its course without any symptoms, and the condition is unexpectedly met with post mortem. In other instances there are diarrhœa, pain, but not often tenesmus or the passage of blood-stained mucus. In the toxic cases the intestinal symptoms may be very marked, but in the terminal colitis of the fevers and of constitutional affections the symptoms are often trifling.

The ulcerative colitis of chronic disease may be only a terminal event in these diphtheritic processes.

PHLEGMONOUS ENTERITIS.

As an independent affection this is excessively rare, even less frequent than its counterpart in the stomach. It is seen occasionally in connection with intussusception, strangulated hernia, and chronic obstruction. Apart from these conditions it occurs most frequently in the duodenum, and leads to suppuration in the submucosa and abscess formation. Except when associated with hernia or intussusception the affection cannot be diagnosed. The symptoms usually resemble those of peritonitis.

ULCERATIVE ENTERITIS.

In addition to the specific ulcers of tuberculosis, syphilis, and typhoid fever, the following forms of ulceration occur in the bowels:

(a) *Follicular Ulceration.*—As previously mentioned, this is met with very commonly in the diarrhœal diseases of children, and also in the secondary or terminal inflammations in many fevers and constitutional disorders. The ulcers are small, punched out, with sharply cut edges, and they are usually limited to the follicles. With this form may be placed the catarrhal ulcers of some writers.

(*b*) *Stercoral ulcers*, which occur in long standing cases of constipation. Very remarkable indeed are the cases in which the sacculi of the colon become filled with rounded small scybala, some of which produce distinct ulcers in the mucous membrane. The fæcal masses may have lime salts deposited in them, and thus form little enteroliths.

(*c*) *Simple Ulcerative Colitis.*—This affection, which clinically is characterized by diarrhœa, is often regarded wrongly as a form of dysentery. It is not a very uncommon affection, and is most frequently met with in men above the middle period of life. The ulceration may be very extensive, so that a large proportion of the mucosa is removed. The lumen of the colon is sometimes greatly increased, and the muscular walls hypertrophied. There are instances in which the bowel is contracted. Frequently the remnants of the mucosa are very dark, even black, and there may be polypoid outgrowths between the ulcers.

These cases rarely come under observation at the outset, and it is difficult to speak of the mode of origin. They are characterized by diarrhœa of a lienteric rather than of a dysenteric character. There is rarely blood or pus in the stools. Constipation may alternate with the diarrhœa. There is usually great impairment of nutrition, and the patients get weak and sallow. Perforation occasionally occurs.

The disease may prove fatal, or it may pass on and become chronic. The affection was not very infrequent at the Philadelphia Hospital, and though the disease bears some resemblance to dysentery, it is to be separated from it. Some of the cases which we have learned to recognize as amœbic dysentery resemble this form very closely. An excellent description of it is given by Hale White in Allbutt's System. The ulcerative colitis met with in institutions, such as that described by Gemmel, of the Lancaster Asylum, in a recent monograph, seems to be a true dysentery. Dickinson has described what he calls albuminuric ulceration of the bowels in cases of contracted kidney.

(*d*) *Ulceration from External Perforation.*—This may result from the erosion of new growths or, more commonly, from localized peritonitis with abscess formation and perforation of the bowel. This is met with most frequently in tuberculous peritonitis, but it may occur in the abscess which follows perforation of the appendix or suppurative or gangrenous pancreatitis. Fatal hæmorrhage may result from the perforation.

(*e*) *Cancerous Ulcers.*—In very rare instances of multiple cancer or sarcoma the submucous nodules break down and ulcerate. In one case the ileum contained eight or ten sarcomatous ulcers secondary to an extensive sarcoma in the neighborhood of the shoulder-joint.

(*f*) Occasionally a *solitary ulcer* is met with in the cæcum or colon, which may lead to perforation. Two instances of ulcer of the cæcum, both with perforation, have come under my observation, and in one instance a simple ulcer of the colon perforated and led to fatal peritonitis.

Diagnosis of Intestinal Ulcers.—As a rule, diarrhœa is present in all cases, but exceptionally there may be extensive ulceration, particularly in the small bowel, without diarrhœa. Very limited ulceration in the colon may be associated with frequent stools. The character of the dejections is of great importance. Pus, shreds of tissue, and blood are the most valuable indications. Pus occurs most frequently in connection with ulcers in the large intestine, but when the bowel alone is involved the amount is rarely great, and the passage of any quantity of pure pus is an indication that it has come from without, most commonly from the rupture of a pericæcal abscess, or in women of an abscess of the broad ligament. Pus may also be present in cancer of the bowel, or it may be due to local disease in the rectum. A purulent mucus may be present in the stools in cases of ulcer, but it has not the same diagnostic value. The swollen, sago-like masses of mucus which are believed by some to indicate follicular ulceration are met with also in mucous colitis. Hæmorrhage is an important and valuable symptom of ulcer of the bowel, particularly if profuse. It occurs under so many conditions that taken alone it may not be specially significant, but with other coexisting circumstances it may be the most important indication of all.

Fragments of tissue are occasionally found in the stools in ulcer, particularly in the extensive and rapid sloughing in dysenteric processes. Definite portions of mucosa, shreds of connective tissue, and even bits of the muscular coat may be found. Pain occurs in many cases, either of a diffuse, colicky character, or sometimes, in the ulcer of the colon, very limited and well defined.

Perforation is an accident liable to happen when the ulcer extends deeply. In the small bowel it leads to a localized or general peritonitis. In the large intestine, too, a fatal peritonitis may result, or if perforation takes place in the posterior wall of the ascending or descending colon, the production of a large abscess cavity in the retro-peritonæum. In a case at the University Hospital, Philadelphia, there was a perforation at the splenic flexure of the colon with an abscess containing air and pus—a condition of subphrenic pyo-pneumothorax.

Treatment of the Previous Conditions.

(a) **Acute Dyspeptic Diarrhœa.**—All solid food should be withheld. If vomiting is present ice may be given, and small quantities of milk and soda water may be taken. If the attack has followed the eating of large quantities of undigestible material, castor oil or calomel is advisable, but is not necessary if the patient has been freely purged. If the pain is severe, 20 drops of laudanum and a drachm of spirits of chloroform may be given, or, if the colic is very intense, a hypodermic of a quarter of a grain of morphia. It is not well to check the diarrhœa unless it is profuse, as it usually stops spontaneously within forty-eight hours. If persistent, the aromatic chalk powder or large doses of bismuth (30 to 40 grains) may be given. A small enema of starch (2 ounces) with 20 drops of laudanum, every six hours, is a most valuable remedy.

(b) **Chronic diarrhœa,** including chronic catarrh and ulcerative enteritis. It is important, in the first place, to ascertain, if possible, the cause and whether ulceration is present or not. So much in treatment depends upon the careful examination of the stools—as to the amount of mucus, the presence of pus, the occurrence of parasites, and, above all, the state of digestion of the food—that the practitioner should pay special attention to them. Many cases simply require rest in bed and a restricted diet. Chronic diarrhœa of many months' or even of several years' duration may be sometimes cured by strict confinement to bed and a diet of boiled milk and albumen water.

In that form in which immediately after eating there is a tendency to loose evacuations it is usually found that some one article of diet is at fault. The patient should rest for an hour or more after meals. Sometimes this alone is sufficient to prevent the occurrence of the diarrhœa. In those forms which depend upon abnormal conditions in the small intestine, either too rapid peristalsis or faulty fermentative processes, bismuth is indicated. It must be given in large doses—from half a drachm to a drachm three times a day. The smaller doses are of little use. Naphthalin preparations here do much good, given in doses of from 10 to 15 grains (in capsule) four or five times a day. Larger doses may be needed. Salol and the salicylate of bismuth may be tried.

An extremely obstinate and intractable form is the diarrhœa of hysterical women. A systematic rest cure will be found most advantageous, and if a milk diet is not well borne the patient may be fed exclusively on egg albumen. The condition seems to be associated in some cases with increased peristalsis, and in such the bromides may do good, or preparations of opium may be necessary. There are instances which prove most obstinate and resist all forms of treatment, and the patient may be greatly reduced. A change of air and surroundings may do more than medicines.

In a large group of the chronic diarrhœas the mischief is seated in the colon and is due to ulceration. Medicines by the mouth are here of little value. The stools should be carefully watched and a diet arranged which shall leave the smallest possible residue. Boiled or peptonized milk may be given, but the stools should be examined to see whether there is an excess of food or of curds. Meat is, as a rule, badly borne in these cases. The diarrhœa is best treated by enemata. The starch and laudanum should be tried, but when ulceration is present it is better to use astringent injections. From 2 to 4 pints of warm water, containing from half a drachm to a drachm of nitrate of silver, may be used. In the chronic diarrhœa which follows dysentery this is particularly advantageous. In giving large injections the patient should be in the dorsal position, with the hips elevated, and it is best to allow the injection to flow in gradually from a siphon bag. In this way the entire colon can be irrigated and the patient can retain the injection for some time. The silver injections may be very painful, but they are invaluable in all forms of ulcerative colitis. Acetate of lead, boracic acid, sulphate of copper, sulphate of zinc, and salicylic acid may be used in 1-per-cent solutions.

In the intense forms of choleraic diarrhœa in adults associated with constant vomiting and frequent watery discharges the patient should be given at once a hypodermic of a quarter of a grain of morphia, which should be repeated in an hour if the pains return or the purging persists. This gives prompt relief, and is often the only medicine needed in the attack. The patient should be given stimulants, and, when the vomiting is allayed by suitable remedies, small quantities of milk and lime water.

(c) **The Diarrhœa of Children.**—*Hygienic management* is of the first importance. The effect of a change from the hot, stifling atmosphere of a town to the mountains or the sea is often seen at once in a reduction in the number of stools and a rapid improvement in the physical condition. Even in cities much may be done by sending the child into the parks or for daily excursions on the water. However extreme the condition, fresh air is indicated. The child should not be too thickly clad. Many mothers, even in the warm weather, clothe their children too heavily. Bathing is of value in infantile diarrhœa, and when the fever rises above 102.5° the child should be placed in a warm bath, the temperature of which may be gradually reduced, or the child is kept in the bath for twenty minutes, by which time the water is sufficiently cooled. Much relief is obtained by the application of ice-cold cloths or of the ice-cap to the head. Irrigation of the colon with ice-cold water is sometimes favorable, but it has not the advantage of the general bath, the beneficial effect of which is seen, not only in the reduction of the temperature, but in a general stimulation of the nervous system of the child.

Dietetic Treatment.—In the case of a hand-fed child it is important, if possible, to get a wet-nurse. While fever is present, digestion is sure to be much disturbed, and the amount of food should be restricted. If water or barley water be given the child will not feel the deprivation of food so much. When the vomiting is incessant it is much better not to attempt to give milk or other articles of food, but let the child take the water whenever it will.

In the dyspeptic diarrhœas of infants, practically the whole treatment is a matter of artificial feeding, and there is no subject in medicine on which it is more difficult to lay down satisfactory rules. The studies of Rotch on modified milk have revolutionized the artificial feeding of infants, and the establishment of the Walker-Gordon laboratories in various cities has been a great boon to the public and the profession. No doubt within a few years the study of the bacterial processes going on in the intestines of the child will give us most important suggestions. From his observations Escherich lays down the following rules, recognizing two well-defined forms of intestinal fermentation—the acid and the alkaline: If there is much decomposition, with foul, offensive stools, the albuminous articles should be withheld from the diet and the carbohydrates given, such as dextrin foods, sugar, and milk, which, on account of its sugar, ranks with the carbohydrates. If there is acid fermentation, with sour but not fetid stools, an albuminous diet is given, such as broths and egg albumen. It is, however, by no means certain whether the reaction of the stools, upon which this author relies, is a sufficient test of the nature of the intestinal fermentation. In the dyspeptic diarrhœas of artificially fed infants it is best, as a rule, to withhold milk and to feed the child, for the time at least, on egg albumen, broths, and beef juices. To prepare the egg albumen, the whites of two or three eggs may be stirred in a pint of water and a tea-spoonful of brandy and a little salt mixed with it. The child will usually take this freely, and it is both stimulating and nourishing. It is some-times remarkable with what rapidity a child which has been fed on artificial food and milk will pick up and improve on this diet alone. Beef-juice is obtained by pressing with a lemon-squeezer fresh steak, previously minced and either uncooked or slightly broiled. This may be given alternately with the egg albumen or it may be given alone. Mutton or chicken broth will be found equally serviceable, but it is prepared with greater difficulty and contains more fat. In the preparation, a pound of mutton, chicken, or beef, carefully freed from fat, is minced and placed in a pint of cold water and allowed to stand in a glass jar on ice for three or four hours. It should then be cooked over a slow fire for at least three hours, and, after being strained, allowed to cool; the fat is then skimmed off and sufficient salt added; it may then be given either warm or cold. These naturally prepared albumin foods are very much to be preferred to the various artificial sub-stances. There is no form of nourishment so readily assimilated and apt to cause so little disturbance as egg albumen or the simple beef juices. The child should be fed every two hours, and in the intervals water may be freely given. It cannot be expected that, with the digestion seriously impaired, as much food can be taken as in health, and in many instances we see the diarrhœa aggravated by persistent over feeding. When the child's stomach is quieted and the diarrhœa checked there may be a gradual return to the milk diet. The milk should be sterilized, and in institutions and in cities this simple prophylactic measure is of the very first importance and is readily carried out by means of the Arnold steam sterilizer. The milk should be at first freely diluted—four parts of water to one of milk, which is perhaps the preferable way—or it may be peptonized. The stools should be examined daily, as important indications may be obtained from them. Milk-whey and forms of fermented milk are sometimes useful and may be employed when the stomach is very irritable. These general directions as to food also hold good in cholera infantum.

Medicinal Treatment.—The first indication in the dyspeptic diarrhœa of children is to get rid of the decomposing matter in the stomach and in-testines. The diarrhœa and vomiting partially effect this, but it may be more thoroughly accomplished, so far as the stomach is concerned, by irri-gation. It may seem a harsh procedure in the case of young infants, but in reality, with a large-sized soft-rubber catheter, it is practised without any difficulty. By means of a funnel, lukewarm water is allowed to pass in and out until it comes away quite clear. I can speak in the very warmest man-ner of the good results obtained by this simple procedure in cases of the most obstinate gastro-intestinal catarrh in children. In most cases the warm water is sufficient. In some hands this method has probably been carried to excess, but that does not detract from its great value in suitable cases. To remove the fermenting substances from the intestines, doses of calomel or gray powder may be administered. The castor oil is equally efficacious, but is more apt to be vomited. Irrigation of the large bowel is useful, and not only thoroughly removes fermenting substances, but cleanses the mucosa. The child should be placed on the back with the hips elevated. A flexible catheter is passed for from 6 to 8 inches and from a pint to 2 pints of water allowed to flow in from a fountain syringe. A pint will thoroughly irrigate the colon of a child of six months and a quart that of a child of two years. The water may be lukewarm, but when there is high fever ice-cold water may be used. In cases of entero-colitis there may be injections with borax, a drachm to the pint, or dilute nitrate of silver, which may be either given in large injections, as in the adult, or in injections of 3 or 4 ounces with 3 grains of nitrate of silver to the ounce. These often cause very great pain, and it is well in such cases to follow the silver injection with irrigations of salt solution, a drachm to a pint.

We are still without a reliable intestinal antiseptic. Neither naphthalin, salol, resorcin, the salicylates, nor mercury meets the indications. As in the diarrhœa of adults, bismuth in large doses is often very effective, but practitioners are in the habit of giving it in doses which are quite insufficient. To be of any service it must be used in large doses, so that an infant a year old will take as much as 2 drachms in the day. The gray powder has long been a favorite in this condition and may be given in half-grain doses every hour. It is perhaps preferable to calomel, which may be used in small doses of from one tenth to one fourth of a grain every hour at the onset of the trouble. The sodium salicylate (in doses of 2 or 3 grains every two hours to a child a year old) has been recommended.

In cholera infantum serious symptoms may develop with great rapidity, and here the incessant vomiting and the frequent purging render the administration of remedies extremely difficult. Irrigation of the stomach and large bowel is of great service, and when the fever is high ice-water injections may be used or a graduated bath. As in the acute choleraic diarrhœa of adults, morphia hypodermically is the remedy which gives greatest relief, and in the conditions of extreme vomiting and purging, with restlessness and collapse symptoms, this drug alone commands the situation. A child of one year may be given from $\frac{1}{100}$ to $\frac{1}{80}$ of a grain, to be repeated in an hour, and again if not better. When the vomiting is allayed, attempts may be made to give gray powder in half-grain doses with $\frac{1}{10}$ of Dover's powder. Starch ($\mathfrak{Z}$ ij) and laudanum ($\mathfrak{M}$ ij–iij) injections, if retained, are soothing and beneficial. The combination of bismuth with Dover's powder will also be found beneficial. No attempt should be made to give food. Water may be allowed freely, even when ejected at once by vomiting. Small doses of brandy or champagne, frequently repeated and given cold, are sometimes retained. When the collapse is extreme, hypodermic injections of 1-per-cent saline solution may be used as recommended in Asiatic cholera, and hypodermic injections of ether and brandy may be tried. The convalescence requires very careful management, as many cases pass on into the condition of entero-colitis. When the intense symptoms have subsided, the food should be gradually given, beginning with teaspoonful doses of egg albumen or beef-juice. It is best to withhold milk for several days, and when used it should be at first completely peptonized or diluted with gruel. A teaspoonful of raw, scraped meat three or four times a day is often well borne.

II. APPENDICITIS.

Inflammation of the vermiform appendix is the most important of acute intestinal disorders. Formerly the "iliac phlegmon" was thought to be due to disease of the cæcum—*typhlitis*—and of the peritonæum covering it—*perityphlitis;* but we now know that with rare exceptions the cæcum itself is not affected, and even the condition formerly described as stercoral typhlitis is in reality appendicitis. The recognition of the importance of appendicitis is due largely to the work of the American physicians and surgeons—to Pepper, who described in 1883 the relapsing form; to Fitz, whose exhaustive article in 1886 served to put the whole question on a rational basis; to Willard Parker, who was the first to advocate early operation; and to Sands, Bull, McBurney, Weir, Morton, Keen, Senn, J. William White, Deaver, and others, who have done so much to improve the operative measures for its relief. Treves, of London, has been foremost in advocating the proper surgical treatment of the disease. The interest attached to the subject is manifest from the appearance within a few years of a number of special monographs by Kelynack, Talamon, Fowler, Sonnenberg, Hawkins, Deaver, and Mynter.

Anatomy.—The appendix veriformis is a functionless relic of a large ancestral cæcum. It measures usually about 3 inches in length, but it may be scarcely an inch. The diameter is about one fourth of an inch. In a majority of instances it has a triangular-shaped meso-appendix, usually shorter than the tube, which thus becomes a little curled or bent upon itself. There is often a small lymph-gland just at the root of its mesentery. The position of the appendix is very variable. The most common direction it assumes is upward and inward, the tip pointing toward the spleen. The position next in frequency is behind the cæcum, and next passing over the pelvic brim. It may be met with, however, in almost every region of the abdomen, and adherent to almost every organ in it. I have seen it in close contact with the bladder, adherent to one ovary and the broad ligament; in the central portion of the abdomen close to the navel; in contact with the gall-bladder, passing out at right angles and adherent to the sigmoid flexure to the left of the middle line of the abdomen; and in one case it entered with the cæcum the inguinal canal, curved upon itself, re-entered the abdomen, and was adherent to the wall of an abscess cavity just to the right of the promontory of the sacrum. The structure of the appendix is almost identical with that of the cæcum; it is particularly rich in lymphoid tissue. The blood supply is derived from a small artery which passes along the free edge of its mesentery.

Morbid Anatomy and Etiology.—The following are the most common morbid conditions:

(*a*) **Fæcal Concretions.**—The lumen of the appendix may contain a mould of fæces, which can readily be squeezed out. Even while soft the contents of the tube may be moulded in two or three sections with rounded ends. Concretions—enteroliths, coproliths—are also common. The mode of formation is not very clear. Possibly, as with gall-stones, the micro-organisms may have a favoring influence. They were present in 38 cases in 400 autopsies (Ribbert), and in 179 of 459 autopsies in perityphlitis collected by Renvers. The enteroliths often resemble in shape date-stones. The importance of these concretions is shown by the great frequency with which they are found in all acute inflammations of the appendix.

(*b*) **Foreign bodies** are by no means so frequently met with—only 12 per cent in 152 cases of appendicitis collected by Fitz. Only two instances came under my observation in ten years' pathological work in Montreal; in one there were eight snipe-shot and in another five apple-pits. The stones and seeds of various fruits, bits of bone, and pins have been found. It is well to bear in mind that some of the concretions bear a very striking resemblance to cherry and date stones.

(*c*) **Obliterative Appendicitis.**—The entire tube is thickened, the peritoneal surface smooth or injected, and either with adhesions from slight circumscribed peritonitis, or perfectly free. The mucosa may show nothing more than a shedding of epithelium with infiltration of leucocytes in the submucosa, while in more chronic cases there is almost complete denudation of the mucosa, which is replaced by granulation tissue. The muscular coats are thickened throughout, and the entire tube is firm and stiff, as if in a state of erection. When laid open longitudinally it at once assumes a rolled form in the reverse direction.

The term *catarrhal*, which has been applied to this condition, is scarcely appropriate, since the changes are diffuse throughout the whole tube. In the majority of instances the term *appendicitis obliterans*, used by Senn, is in reality more appropriate. As Hawkins remarks, this condition is probably a fertile source of local peritonitis, and one may see in this stage fresh adhesions on the peritoneal surface or more extensive circumscribed peritonitis. It may, however, be, as he says, the precursor of complete immunity from such attacks. "For if by the pressure of the surrounding parts the opposed granulating surfaces are brought into contact, and if the whole organ remains at rest, union may take place, and the appendix as a source of disease then ceases to exist. In other cases obliteration of the lumen cannot take place on account of the rigid incollapsible character of the walls, and it is this condition of chronic appendicitis which may lead to recurrences of attacks of colic and local symptoms in the right iliac fossa."

McBurney lays great stress upon the narrowing of the lumen as preventing normal drainage of the tube and establishing conditions favorable for the development of septic processes.

Obliterative appendicitis is met with in about 2 per cent of all subjects. When the stricture occurs at the cæcal end of the tube the lumen may become greatly dilated, forming a cystic appendix which may reach the size of the thumb, or even that of an ordinary sausage. The contents of the cyst are either clear fluid or pus. Ulceration and perforation are very apt to occur. Obliterative appendicitis may go on as an ordinary involution process without causing any symptoms, but in many instances there are attacks of pain—appendicular colic; in others, exacerbations of

fever with pain and swelling; while in others again ulceration and perforation may take place.

(d) **Ulcerative Appendicitis.**—Local ulceration in the appendix is met
with as a result of the presence of concretions or of foreign bodies, or as
the result of the action of certain micro-organisms, either those normally
inhabiting the cæcum or, under certain circumstances, the typhoid and
tubercle bacilli. Fæcal concretions and foreign bodies are met with in the
appendix without apparently causing the slightest abrasion of its mucosa.
In other cases the enterolith has caused atrophy of the mucous membrane
with which it is in contact. In other cases again, the concretion or foreign
body may be pocketed in an ulcer at the tip of the appendix, from which
it may be shelled out. These conditions may be present without adhesions and without reddening of the serous surface, but one not infrequently
sees thickening of the peritonæum with adhesions to the adjacent parts in
ulcerative appendicitis.

Tuberculosis of the appendix is by no means uncommon. Ulceration
in typhoid fever is also frequently met with; in a series of 80 autopsies
there were 3 instances of perforation of the appendix by a typhoid ulcer.
An actinomycotic ulcer has also been described.

(e) **Necrosis and Sloughing of the Appendix—Acute Infective Appendicitis.**—Following upon the conditions described under (c) and (d), necrosis
and sloughing may take place either in a limited portion of the appendix
with perforation, or *en masse* without perforation, in both cases leading to
the most intense peritonitis, localized or general. Most commonly the gangrene is localized to one spot, either at the tip or in some portion of the
tube. Usually the organ is swollen; the color may be reddish brown, black,
or greenish yellow. Necrosis may occur *en masse*, and the entire appendix
may indeed slough off from the cæcum and lie free in an abscess cavity.
In one remarkable case operated upon by my colleague, Halsted, the appendix, between 4 and 5 inches in length, was shrunken, blackish brown in
color, sphacelated throughout, and looked like a desiccated earthworm.

These active processes leading to ulceration and necrosis are due to the
action of micro-organisms, and much work has been done to determine
their character. Hodenpyl showed that the bacillus coli cummunis was
present in a very large number of cases of appendicitis. In 61 cases of
peritoneal inflammation consequent upon disease of the appendix the bacillus coli communis was found in 57, and in 50 of these it was the only
organism present. The streptococcus pyogenes and the staphylococcus
pyogenes aureus, the proteus and bacillus pyocyaneus have also been found.
The streptococcus infection is the most virulent. Probably too much stress
has been laid upon the bacillus coli communis as a cause of infective processes in and about the appendix. In many cases, with slight fresh adhesion and a little sero-fibrin, the cultures are negative. As Welch remarks,
"There is reason to believe that the highly resistant colon bacillus may
survive in an inflamed part after the primary organism which started the
trouble has died out, or has been crowded out by the invader." The proneness of the appendix to infective inflammation of this sort lies " in that
subtle structure which determines the degree of resistance of a tissue to dis-

ease. One man differs from another in his power of resistance; the more degenerate the man the less resistance can he exert. In like manner, one organ in a man differs from another. And in the appendix we are dealing with an organ which is degenerate and functionless from first to last, and its scanty power of resistance to bacterial invasion is but another way of expressing this fact " (Hawkins).

It has been urged that the anatomical relations of the meso-appendix and the adjacent peritoneal folds are such that distention of the cæcum, or of the lower portion of the ileum, may cause dragging with torsion and interfere seriously with the blood supply of the tube. The swelling of the mucosa so induced may be an important factor in the infection of its tissues.

Fowler suggests, and brings a case in support, that in some of these cases the necrosis is due to the thrombosis of a large arterial branch.

Immediate Effects of the Perforation. (*a*) Acute General Peritonitis.— If the appendix is free, without adhesions, the perforation may lead at once to a widespread peritonitis. The inflammation varies much in virulence, depending apparently upon the infecting organism. The worst cases are those in which the streptococcus pyogenes is present. A general peritonitis is more common in the acute infective appendicitis than in the other forms. It probably results less frequently from direct perforation, or sloughing of the appendix, than from extension of inflammation from a local peri-appendicular abscess.

(*b*) **Localized Peritonitis, with Abscess.**—Perforation leads usually to the formation of a circumscribed intra-peritoneal abscess cavity, which varies in situation with the position of the appendix, and in size from a walnut to a cocoanut. Perhaps the most common situation is on the psoas muscle, just at the angle between the ileum and the cæcum. The perforated appendix, however, may be within the pelvis, or upon the promontory of the sacrum, or lie between the coils of small bowel in the neighborhood of the umbilicus. A common situation for the large circumscribed intra-peritoneal abscess is in the iliac region midway between the navel and the anterior superior spine. Perforation, adhesive peritonitis, and the production of a localized abscess may proceed without causing any serious symptoms, and the condition may be found when death has resulted from accident or from some intercurrent affection. The contents of the abscess may be a grayish yellow, thick pus, usually with a strong fæcal odor; but in the old, limited, small abscesses it is usually dark gray in color, and horribly offensive. The appendix may be found free in the localized abscess; in other instances it is so covered with pus and inflammatory exudate that it is impossible to find it. While in a majority of all instances the abscess cavity, even when large, is intra-peritoneal, there may be—

(*c*) **Extensive Extra-Peritoneal Suppuration.**—When an appendix perforates, it lies, of course, in immediate contact with the peritonæum; if on the iliac fascia, or the wall of the pelvis, or behind the cæcum, the adhesion may take place in such a way that the perforation occurs into the retroperitoneal tissue. In these days of operation we do not so often see the extensive retro-peritoneal abscesses due to appendix disease. The pus may pass beneath the iliac fascia and appear at Poupart's ligament, in which situation external perforation may occur and recovery take place. The pus may be chiefly in the retro-peritoneal tissue in the flank, forming a large perinephritic abscess. In a case under the care of Gardner, of Montreal, an enormous abscess cavity developed in this situation, which contained air, pushed up the diaphragm nearly to the second rib, and produced the symptoms of pneumothorax. Perforation of the pleura may occur in these cases, forming a fæcal pleural fistula. The pus may extend along the psoas muscle and may perforate the hip joint, or pass to the neighborhood of the rectum, or produce multiple abscesses of the scrotum; or, passing through the obturator foramen, form a large gluteal abscess. Both the intra- and extra-peritoneal appendix abscess may perforate into the bladder or into the bowel, and recovery may follow, though there is greater danger in perforation into the latter. The appendix has been discharged *per anum.*

Remote Effects.—The remote effects of perforative appendicitis are interesting. Hæmorrhage may occur. In one of my cases the appendix was adherent to the promontory of the sacrum, and the abscess cavity had perforated in two places into the ileum. Death resulted from profuse hæmorrhage. Cases are on record in which the internal iliac artery or the deep circumflex iliac artery has been opened. Suppurative pylephlebitis may result from inflammation of the mesenteric veins near the perforated appendix. Two instances of it have come under my notice; in one there was a small localized abscess which had resulted from the perforation of a typhoid ulcer of the appendix. In the other case, which I saw with Machell, of Toronto, the symptoms were those of septicæmia and of suppuration of the liver. The abscess of the appendix was small and had not produced symptoms. In the healing of extensive inflammation about the margin of the pelvis the iliac veins may be greatly compressed, and one of my patients had for months œdema of the right leg, which is now permanently enlarged.

The appendix may perforate in a hernial sac. Several instances of this have been recorded. In a case which came under my care at the University Hospital, Philadelphia, there was a hernia of the cæcum in the inguinal canal. The proximal orifice of the appendix was at the extreme end of the hernia in the inguinal canal. The tube then curved upon itself, passed into the abdomen, and the terminal three fourths of an inch had sloughed in a small circumscribed sac situated close to the promontory of the sacrum.

The following additional facts may be mentioned, bearing on the etiology:

Age.—Appendicitis is a disease of young persons. According to Fitz's statistics, more than 50 per cent of the cases occur before the twentieth year; according to Einhorn's, 60 per cent between the sixteenth and thirtieth years. It has been met with as early as the seventh week, but it is rarely seen prior to the third year.

Sex.—It is much more common in males than in females, 80 per cent of the former in the table of Fitz. In Hawkins' series, 161 were males and 63 females. Contrary to the general experience, the Munich figures given by Einhorn indicate a relatively greater number of women at-tacked.

Occupation.—Persons whose work necessitates the lifting of heavy weights seem more prone to the disease. Trauma plays a very definite *rôle*, and in a number of cases the symptoms have followed very closely a fall or a blow.

Indiscretions in diet are very prone to bring on an attack, particularly in the recurring form of the disease, in which pain in the appendix region not infrequently follows the eating of indigestible articles of food. I have been impressed, too, with the number of cases in boys in which there has been a history of gorging with peanuts.

Symptoms.—In a large proportion of all cases of acute appendicitis the following symptoms are present: (1) Sudden pain in the abdomen, usu-ally referred to the right iliac fossa; (2) fever, often of moderate grade; (3) gastro-intestinal disturbance—nausea, vomiting, and frequently consti-pation; (4) tenderness or pain on pressure in the appendix region.

Such a group of symptoms in a young person, particularly following an indiscretion in diet or an injury or strain, in the absence of signs of hernia, indicate the existence of appendicitis; they do not suggest in any way the nature of the lesion, whether obliterative, ulcerative, or an acute necrotic appendicitis. We may first consider more fully these general symptoms of the disease.

Pain.—A sudden, violent pain in the abdomen is, according to Fitz, the most constant, first, decided symptom of perforating inflammation of the appendix, and occurred in 84 per cent of the cases analyzed by him. In fully half of the cases it is localized in the right iliac fossa, but it may be central, diffuse, or indeed in almost any region of the abdo-men. Even in the cases in which the pain is at first not in the appendix region, it is usually felt here within thirty-six or forty-eight hours. It may extend toward the perinæum or testicle. It is sometimes very sharp and colic-like, and cases have been mistaken for nephritic or for biliary colic. Some patients speak of it as a sharp, intense pain—serous-mem-brane pain; others as a dull ache—connective-tissue pain. While a very valuable symptom, pain is at the same time one of the most misleading. Some of the forms of recurring pain in the appendix region Talamon has called appendicular colic. The condition is believed to be due to partial occlusion of the lumen, leading to violent and irregular peristal-tic action of the circular and longitudinal muscles in the expulsion of the mucus.

Fever.—A rise in the temperature follows rapidly upon the pain, and is one of the most valuable of the symptoms of the early stage of appendi-citis. An initial chill is very rare. The fever may be moderate, from 100° to 102°; sometimes in children at the very outset the thermometer may register above 103.5°. The thermometer is one of the most trust-worthy guides in the diagnosis of acute appendicitis. Appendicular colic of great severity may occur without fever. When a localized abscess has formed, and in some very virulent cases of general peritonitis, the tempera-ture may be normal, but at this stage there are other symptoms which indicate the gravity of the situation. The pulse is quickened in proportion to the fever.

Gastro-intestinal Disturbance.—The tongue is usually furred and moist, seldom dry. Nausea and vomiting are symptoms which may be absent, but which are commonly present in the acute perforative cases. The vomiting rarely persists beyond the second day in favorable cases. Constipation is the rule, but the attack may set in with diarrhœa, particularly in children.

Local Signs.—Inspection of the abdomen is at first negative; there is no distention, and the iliac fossæ look alike. On palpation there are usually from the outset two important signs—namely, great tension of the right rectus muscle, and tenderness or actual pain on deep pressure. The muscular rigidity may be so great that a satisfactory examination cannot be made without an anæsthetic. McBurney has called attention to the value of a localized point of tenderness on deep pressure, which is situated at the intersection of a line drawn from the navel to the anterior superior spine of the ilium, with a second, vertically placed, corresponding to the outer edge of the right rectus muscle. Firm, deep, continuous pressure with one finger at this spot causes pain, often of the most exquisite character. In addition to the tenderness, rigidity, and actual pain on deep pressure, there is to be felt, in a majority of the cases, an induration or swelling. In some cases this is a boggy, ill-defined mass in the situation of the cæcum; more commonly the swelling is circumscribed and definite, situated in the iliac fossa, two or three fingers' breadth above Poupart's ligament. Some have been able to feel and roll beneath the fingers the thickened appendix. The later the case comes under observation the greater the probability of the existence of a well-marked tumor mass. It is not to be forgotten that there may be neither tumor mass nor induration to be felt in some of the most intensely virulent cases of perforative appendicitis.

In addition may be mentioned great irritability of the bladder, which I have known to lead to the diagnosis of cystitis. It may be a very early symptom. The urine is scanty and often contains albumin and indican. Peptonuria is of no moment. The attitude is somewhat suggestive, the decubitis is dorsal, and the right leg is semi-flexed. Examination *per rectum* in the early stages rarely gives any information of value, unless the appendix lies well over the brim of the pelvis, or unless there is a large abscess cavity.

There are three possibilities in any case of appendicitis presenting the above symptoms: (1) Gradual recovery, (2) the formation of a local abscess, and (3) the development of a general peritonitis.

Recovery is the rule. Out of 264 cases at St. Thomas's Hospital with the above-mentioned clinical characters, 190 recovered. In one instance the appendix was removed, and in two, attempts were made to remove it (Hawkins). There are surgeons who claim that the getting well in these cases does not mean much; that the patients have recurrences and are constantly liable to the graver accidents of the disease. This, I feel sure, is an unduly dark picture.

In a case which is proceeding to recovery the pain lessens at the end of the third or fourth day, the temperature falls, the tongue becomes cleaner, the vomiting ceases, the local tenderness is less marked, and the bowels are moved. By the end of a week the acute symptoms have subsided. The entire attack may not last more than ten days. In other instances slight fever persists, and it may be two or three weeks before convalescence is established. An induration or an actual small tumor mass from the size of a walnut to that of an egg may persist—a condition which leaves the patients very liable to a recurrence.

In these cases there is either a chronic appendicitis without perforation or involvement of the serous surface, or there is involvement of the peritoneal surface, usually from perforation, with a sero-fibrinous exudate and an agglutination of the contiguous parts. In the cases with a well-defined tumor, whether large or small, there is almost always pus formation.

Local Abscess Formation.—As a result of ulceration and perforation, sometimes following the necrosis, rarely as a sequence of the diffuse appendicitis, the patient has the train of symptoms above described; but at the end of the first week the local features persist or become aggravated. The course of the disease may be indeed so acute that by the end of the fourth or fifth day there is an extensive area of induration in the right iliac fossa, with great tenderness, and operations have shown that even at this very early date an abscess cavity may have formed. Though as a rule the fever becomes aggravated with the onset of suppuration, this is not always the case. The two most important elements in the diagnosis of abscess formation are the gradual increase of the local tumor and the aggravation of the general symptoms. Nowadays, when operation is so frequent, we have opportunities of seeing the abscess in various stages of development. Quite early the pus may lie between the cæcum and the coils of the ileum, with the general peritonæum shut off by fibrin, or there is a sero-fibrinous exudate with a slight amount of pus between the lower coils of the ileum. The abscess cavity may be small and lie on the psoas muscle, or at the edge of the promontory of the sacrum, and never reach a palpable size. The sac, when larger, may be roofed in by the small bowel and present irregular processes and pockets leading in different directions. In larger collections in the iliac fossa the roof is generally formed by the abdominal wall. Some of the most important of the localized abscesses are those which are situated entirely within the pelvis. The various directions and positions into which the abscess may pass or perforate have already been referred to under morbid anatomy, but it may be here mentioned again that, left alone, they may discharge externally, or burrow in various directions, or discharge through the rectum, vagina, or bladder. Death may be caused by septicæmia, by perforation into an artery or vein, or by pylephlebitis.

General Peritonitis.—This may be caused by direct perforation of the appendix and general infection of the peritonæum before any delimiting inflammation is excited. In a second group of cases there has been an attempt at localizing the infective process, but it fails, and the general peritonæum becomes involved. In a third group of cases a localized focus of suppuration exists about an inflamed appendix, and from this perforation takes place.

Death in appendicitis is due usually to general peritonitis.

We see at operations all grades of the affection, from the mildest, in which the serous surface is injected, turbid, and sticky, but without lymph or effusion, except in the immediate neighborhood of the perforated appendix. In other cases there is a fibrinous exudate gluing the coils together and a variable amount of turbid serous fluid. In other instances, as the abdomen is opened, pus wells out, and there is a diffuse purulent inflammation of the peritonæum. It is interesting, however, to note the comparative rarity of fatal peritonitis from appendix disease in general medical work. In 450 consecutive autopsies on patients dead in my wards there was not a single instance of general peritonitis from appendix disease. On the surgical side there have been admitted during the same period 10 cases of diffuse peritonitis from this cause. Eight were operated upon; all died. In 9 cases there was found a perforated and more or less gangrenous appendix, with little or no attempt at localization; in 1 case rupture of an abscess caused the general peritonitis.

The gravity of appendix disease lies in the fact that from the very outset the peritonæum may be infected; the initial symptoms of pain, with nausea and vomiting, fever, and local tenderness, present in all cases, may indicate a widespread infection of this membrane. The onset is usually sudden, the pain diffuse, not always localized in the right iliac fossa, but it is not so much the character as the greater intensity of the symptoms from the outset that makes one suspicious of a general peritonitis. Abdominal distention, diffuse tenderness, and absence of abdominal movements are the most trustworthy local signs, but they are not really so trustworthy as the general symptoms. The initial nausea and vomiting persist, the pulse becomes more rapid, the tongue is dry, the urine scanty. In very acute cases, by the end of twenty-four hours the abdomen may be distended. By the third and fourth days the classical picture of a general peritonitis is well established—a distended and motionless abdomen, a rapid pulse, a dry tongue, dorsal decubitus with the knees drawn up, and an anxious, pinched, Hippocratic facies.

Fever is an uncertain element. It is usually present at first, but if the physician does not see the case until the third or fourth day he should not be deceived by a temperature below 100.5°. The pulse is really a better indication than the temperature. One rarely has any doubt on the third or fourth day whether or not peritonitis exists, but it must be acknowledged that there are exceptions which trouble the judgment not a little. While on the one hand, without suggestive symptoms, a laparotomy has disclosed an unexpected general peritonitis, on the other, with severe constitutional symptoms and apparently characteristic local signs, the peritonæum has been found smooth.

Relapsing Appendicitis.—Pepper, in 1883, called attention to the remarkable liability to relapse in perityphlitis. The patient gets well and all trace of induration and tenderness disappears; then in three or four months, or earlier, he again has fever, pain, and local signs of trouble.

33

The attacks may recur for years. The cases which recover with the persistence of an induration or tumor mass are most prone to relapse. There are more severe cases in which the intervals between the attacks are very short, and the patient becomes a chronic invalid. After repeated attacks, however, recovery may be perfect. The frequency of recurrence is difficult to estimate. Fitz places it at 44 per cent, Hawkins at 23.6 per cent. The recent statistics of operations given by Deaver, Murphy, and others indicate how common must be this type of the disease. Bull has collected 442 operations in chronic relapsing appendicitis by eighty surgeons, with a mortality of 1.8 per cent, but he thinks that 5 or 6 per cent would be a fairer estimate.

The morbid condition in this form is either a simple obliterative appendicitis with or without adhesions, or an adherent, perhaps perforated appendix with a small localized abscess circumscribed by dense fibroid tissue.

Diagnosis.—Appendicitis is by far the most common inflammatory condition, not only in the cæcal region, but in the abdomen generally in persons under thirty. The surgeons have taught us that, almost without exception, sudden pain in the right iliac fossa, with fever and localized tenderness, with or without tumor, means appendix disease. There are certain diseases of the abdominal organs characterized by pain which are apt to be confounded with appendicitis. Biliary colic, kidney colic, and the colicky pains at the menstrual period in women have in some cases to be most carefully considered. I have not met with an instance of either renal or hepatic calculus causing any difficulty in diagnosis, but a patient was admitted to my wards with a history of very sudden onset of severe pain three days previously in the right side of the abdomen, and with an ill-defined tumor mass low in the right flank. Fortunately, she was transferred at once to the surgical side for operation, and the condition proved to be an acutely distended and inflamed gall-bladder almost on the point of perforating. A second very similar case has since occurred.

Diseases of the tubes and pelvic peritonitis may simulate appendicitis very closely, but the history and the local examination under ether should in most cases enable the practitioner to reach a diagnosis. I have seen several cases supposed to be recurring appendicitis which proved to be tubo-ovarian disease.

The Dietl's crises in floating kidney have been mistaken for appendicitis.

Both intussusception and internal strangulation may present very similar symptoms, and if the patient is only seen at the later stages, when there is diffuse peritonitis and great tympany, the features may be almost identical. Fæcal vomiting, which is common in obstruction, is never seen in appendicitis, and in children the marked tenesmus and bloody stools are important signs of intussusception. It is not often difficult to decide when the cases are seen early and when the history is clear, but mistakes have been made by surgeons of the first rank.

Acute hæmorrhagic pancreatitis may also produce symptoms very like those of appendicitis with general peritonitis. Typhoid fever has been mistaken for appendicitis. I was told of a case recently in one of the large hospitals of this country in which the fever, the presence of a tender induration in the right iliac fossa, seemed to indicate so clearly appendix disease that an operation was performed, but the induration was found to be the swollen ileum and adjacent glands. In a person who had had previous appendicitis the diagnosis might be extremely difficult, as in a case mentioned by Da Costa. Late in the convalescence of typhoid fever symptoms of appendicitis may develop, due to the perforation of an unhealed ulcer.

There is a well-marked appendicular hypochondriasis. Through the pernicious influence of the daily press, appendicitis has become a sort of fad, and the physician has often to deal with patients who have a sort of fixed idea that they have the disease. The worst cases of this class which I have seen have been in members of our profession, and I know of at least one instance in which a perfectly normal appendix was removed. The question really has its ludicrous side. A well-known physician in a Western city having one night a bellyache, and feeling convinced that his appendix had perforated, summoned a surgeon, who quickly removed the supposed offender!

Hysteria may of course simulate appendicitis very closely, and it may require a very keen judgment to make a diagnosis.

Mucous colitis with enteralgia in nervous women is sometimes mistaken for appendicitis. In two instances of the kind I have prevented proposed operation, and I have heard of cases in which the appendix has been removed.

Perinephritic and pericæcal abscess from perforation of ulcer, either simple or cancerous, and circumscribed peritonitis in this region from other causes, can rarely be differentiated until an exploratory incision is made.

Chronic obliterative appendicitis cannot always be differentiated from the perforative form, and in intensity of pain, severity of symptoms, and, in rare instances, even in the production of peritonitis, the two may be identical.

Briefly stated, localized pain in the right iliac fossa, with or without induration or tumor, the existence of McBurney's tender point, fever, furred tongue, vomiting, with constipation or diarrhœa, indicate appendicitis. The occurrence of general peritonitis is suggested by increase and diffusion of the abdominal pain, tympanites (as a rule), marked aggravation of the constitutional symptoms, particularly elevation of fever and increased rapidity of the pulse. Obliteration of hepatic dulness is rarely present, as the peritonæum in these cases does not often contain gas.

Prognosis. —While we cannot overestimate the gravity of certain forms of appendicitis, it is well to recognize that a large proportion of all cases recover. It is the element of *uncertainty* in individual cases which has given such an impetus to the surgical treatment of the disease. That an inflamed appendix may heal perfectly, even after perforation, is shown by instances (post mortem) of obliterated tubes firmly imbedded in old scar tissue. Formerly we had not a full knowledge of the natural history of the disease. As J. William White remarked in an address at the College of Physicians, Philadelphia, "We are in special need of reliable medical statistics as to this point." These have now been supplied in the admirable monograph of Hawkins (London, 1895), in which he has analyzed the cases at St. Thomas's Hospital, 264 in number. The work is to be commended particularly to surgeons, since, while written from the standpoint of the physician and pathologist, the author is fully alive to the surgical aspects of the disease, and does ample justice to the work of American operators. His figures are as follows: (a) Peritonitis, limited to the right iliac fossa and not proceeding to the formation of pus, 190 cases, no deaths; (b peritonitis, similarly localized, but ending in the formation of pus (perityphlitic abscess), 38 cases, with 10 deaths; (c) general peritonitis, 36 cases, with 27 deaths. This gives a total mortality of 14 per cent. Fifty-nine of the 264 patients had had one or more previous attacks; 45 of these had simple "perityphlitis," and all recovered; of 7 with abscess formation, 3 died; of 7 with general peritonitis, 3 died. These figures compare very favorably with those collected by Porter: Removal of appendix during the attack, 19.7 per cent mortality; incision and drainage of abscess, 18.18 per cent of deaths. The statistics of individual operators give a much more favorable showing, and we may say that in acute cases without generalized peritonitis, and in the localized appendicular abscess, the percentage of deaths in the hands of good surgeons is now very much lower.

Treatment.—So impressed am I by the fact that we physicians lose lives by temporizing with certain cases of appendicitis, that I prefer, in hospital work, to have the suspected cases admitted directly to the surgical side. The general practitioner does well to remember—whether his leanings be toward the conservative or the radical methods of treatment—that the surgeon is often called too late, never too early.

There is no medicinal treatment of appendicitis. There are remedies which will allay the pain, but there are none capable in any way of controlling the course of the disease. Rest in bed, a light diet, measures directed to allay the vomiting—upon these all are agreed. There are two points on which the profession is very much divided, namely, the use of opium and of saline purges. The practice of giving opium in some form in appendicitis and peritonitis is almost universal with physicians. Surgeons, on the other hand, almost unanimously condemn the practice, as obscuring the clinical picture and tending to give a false sense of security; and since they control the situation, I think we should—deferring in this matter to their judgment—give less opium, and trust to the persistent use of ice locally to relieve the pain.

The use of saline purges early in the disease, which is advocated by some surgeons, is, I believe, a most injurious practice. In any given case the pain and tenderness at the outset may mean perforation of the appendix, and the life of the patient may depend upon whether a limiting adhesive inflammation is set up. Under these circumstances, anything that will stimulate active peristalsis of the bowel wall throughout its extent is certainly contra-indicated. Surgery, too, has taught us that the cæcum is rarely, if ever, filled with hardened fæces, so that it is really on theoretical grounds that a saline is urged to clear this part of the bowel. I am glad to see, too, that some surgeons of the largest experience, as McBurney, state that they never employ purgatives. They are also contra-indicated, I think, when there are signs of the formation of a local abscess. If useful at all, it is when general peritonitis has been established, but then, as a rule, the mischief is done, and purgatives cannot influence the result.

Operation is indicated in all cases of acute inflammatory trouble in the cæcal region, whether tumor is present or not, when the general symptoms are severe, and *when by the third day the features of the case point to a progressive lesion.* The mortality from early operation under these circumstances is very slight.

In recurring appendicitis, when the attacks are of such severity and frequency as seriously to interrupt the patient's occupation, the figures already given show how slight the mortality is in the hands of capable operators. Unfortunately, in hospital practice too many cases are brought in with general peritonitis—a condition in which operation is rarely successful.

Post-operative Features in Appendicitis.—Unfortunately, the operation does not always finish the victim's troubles. I have been consulted by several patients with severe pain following the operation, and the literature contains a number of reports of recurrence of the pain in the right iliac fossa. There have been instances, indeed, in which an indurated cord has been felt, and might have readily been mistaken for the appendix had it not been previously removed. In some instances a second operation has been successful in freeing the adhesions which have caused the pain.

III. INTESTINAL OBSTRUCTION.

Intestinal obstruction may be caused by strangulation, intussusception, twists and knots, strictures and tumors, and by abnormal contents.

Etiology and Pathology.—(*a*) **Strangulation.**—This is the most frequent cause of acute obstruction, and occurred in 34 per cent of the 295 cases analyzed by Fitz,* and in 35 per cent of the 1,134 cases of Leichtenstern.† Of the 101 cases of strangulation in Fitz's table, which has the special value of having been carefully selected from the literature since 1880, the following were the causes: Adhesions, 63; vitelline remains, 21; adherent appendix, 6; mesenteric and omental slits, 6; peritoneal pouches and openings, 3; adherent tube, 1; peduncular tumor, 1. The bands and adhesions result, in a majority of cases, from former peritonitis. A number of instances have been reported following operations upon the pelvic organs in women. The strangulation may be recent and due to adhesion of the bowel to the abdominal wound or a coil may be caught between the pedicle of a tumor and the pelvic wall. Such cases are only too common. Late occlusion after recovery from the operation is due to bands and adhesions.

---

* Transactions of the Congress of American Physicians and Surgeons, vol. i, 1889. The percentages of his tables are used throughout this section.
† Von Ziemssen's Encyclopædia of Practical Medicine.

The vitelline remains are represented by Meckel's diverticulum, which forms a finger-like projection from the ileum, usually within eighteen inches of the ileo-cæcal valve. It is a remnant of the omphalo-mesenteric duct, through which, in the early embryo, the intestine communicated with the yolk-sac. The end, though commonly free, may be attached to the abdominal wall near the navel, or to the mesentery, and a ring is thus formed through which the gut may pass.

Seventy per cent of the cases of obstruction from strangulation occur in males; 40 per cent of all the cases occur between the ages of fifteen and thirty years. In 90 per cent of the cases of obstruction from these causes the site of the trouble is in the small bowel; the position of the strangulated portion was in the right iliac fossa in 67 per cent of the cases, and in the lower abdomen in 83 per cent.

(b) **Intussusception.**—In this condition one portion of the intestine slips into an adjacent portion, forming an invagination or intussusception. The two portions make a cylindrical tumor, which varies in length from a half-inch to a foot or more. The condition is always a descending intussusception, and as the process proceeds, the middle and inner layers increase at the expense of the outer layer. An intussusception consists of three layers of bowel: the outermost, known as the intussuscipiens, or receiving layer; a middle or returning layer; and the innermost or entering layer. The student can obtain a clear idea of the arrangement by making the end of a glove-finger pass into the lower portion. The actual condition can be very clearly studied in the post-mortem invaginations which are so common in the small bowel of children. In the statistics of Fitz, 93 of 295 cases of acute intestinal obstruction were due to this cause. Of these, 52 were in males and 27 in females. The cases are most common in early life, 34 per cent under one year and 56 per cent under the tenth year. Of 103 cases in children, nearly 50 per cent occurred in the fourth, fifth, and sixth months (Wiggin). No definite causes could be assigned in 42 of the cases; in the others diarrhœa or habitual constipation had existed.

The site of the invagination varies. We may recognize (1) an *ileo-cæcal*, when the ileo-cæcal valve descends into the colon. There are cases in which this is so extensive that the valve has been felt per rectum. This form occurred in 75 per cent of the cases; in 89 per cent of Wiggin's collected cases. In the *ileo-colic* the lower part of the ileum passes through the ileo-cæcal valve. (2) The *ileal*, in which the ileum is alone involved. (3) The *colic*, in which it is confined to the large intestine. And (4) *colico-rectal*, in which the colon and rectum are involved.

Irregular peristalsis is the essential cause of intussusception. Nothnagel found in the localized peristalsis caused by the faradic current that it was not the descent of one portion into the other, but the drawing up of the receiving layer by contraction of the longitudinal coat. Invagination may follow any limited, sudden, and severe peristalsis.

In the post-mortem examination, in a case of death from intussusception, the condition is very characteristic. Peritonitis may be present or an acute injection of the serous membrane. When death occurs early, as it may do from shock, there is little to be seen. The portion of bowel affected is large and thick, and forms an elongated tumor with a curved outline. The parts are swollen and congested, owing to the constriction of the mesentery between the layers. The entire mass may be of a deep livid-red color. In very recent processes there is only congestion, and perhaps a thin layer of lymph, and the intussusception can be reduced, but when it has lasted for a few days, lymph is thrown out, the layers are glued together, and the entering portion of the gut cannot be withdrawn.

The anatomical condition accounts for the presence of the tumor, which exists in two thirds of all cases; and the engorgement, which results from the compression of the mesenteric vessels, explains the frequent occurrence of blood in the discharges, which has so important a diagnostic value. If the patient survives, necrosis and sloughing of the invaginated portion may occur, and if union has taken place between the middle and outer layer, the calibre of the gut may be restored and a cure in this way effected. Many cases of the kind are on record. In the Museum of the Medical Faculty of McGill University are 17 inches of small intestine, which were passed by a lad who had had symptoms of internal strangulation, and who made a complete recovery.

(c) **Twists and Knots.**—Volvulus or twist occurred in 42 of the 295 cases. Sixty-eight per cent were in males. It is most frequent between the ages of thirty and forty. In the great majority of all cases the twist is axial and associated with an unusually long mesentery. In 50 per cent of the cases it was in the sigmoid flexure. The next most common situation is about the cæcum, which may be twisted upon its axis or bent upon itself. As a rule, in volvulus the loop of bowel is simply twisted upon its long axis, and the portions at the end of the loop cross each other and so cause the strangulation. It occasionally happens that one portion of the bowel is twisted about another.

(d) **Strictures and Tumors.**—These are very much less important causes of acute obstruction, as may be judged by the fact that there are only 15 instances out of the 295 cases, in 14 of which the obstruction occurred in the large intestine. On the other hand, they are common causes of chronic obstruction.

The obstruction may result from: (1) *Congenital stricture.* These are exceedingly rare. Much more commonly the condition is that of complete occlusion, either forming the imperforate anus or the congenital defect by which the duodenum is not united to the pylorus. (2) *Simple cicatricial stenosis*, which results from ulceration, tuberculous or syphilitic, more rarely from dysentery, and most rarely of all from typhoid ulceration. (3) *New growths.* The malignant strictures are due chiefly to cylindrical epithelioma, which forms an annular tumor, most commonly met with in the large bowel, about the sigmoid flexure, or the descending colon. Of benign growths, papillomata, adenomata, lipomata, and fibromata occasionally induce obstruction. (4) *Compression and traction.* Tumors of neighboring organs, particularly of the pelvic viscera, may cause obstruction by adhesion and traction; more rarely, a coil, such as the sigmoid flexure, filled with fæces, compresses and obstructs a neighboring coil. In the healing of tuberculous peritonitis the contraction of the thick exudate may cause compression and narrowing of the coils.

(e) **Abnormal Contents.**—Foreign bodies, such as fruit stones, coins, pins, needles, or false teeth, are occasionally swallowed accidentally, or by lunatics on purpose. Round worms may become rolled into a tangled mass and cause obstruction. In reality, however, the majority of foreign bodies, such as coins, buttons, and pins, swallowed by children, cause no inconvenience whatever, but in a day or two are found in the stools. Occasionally such a foreign body as a pin will pass through the œsophagus and will be found lodged in some adjacent organ, as in the heart (Peabody), or a barley ear may reach the liver (Dock).

Medicines, such as magnesia or bismuth, have been known to accumulate in the bowels and produce obstruction, but in the great majority of the cases the condition is caused by fæces, gall-stones, or enteroliths. Of 44 cases, in 23 the obstruction was by gall-stones, in 19 by fæces, and in 2 by enteroliths. Obstruction by fæces may happen at any period of life. As mentioned when speaking of dilatation of the colon, it may occur in young children and persist for weeks. In fæcal accumulation the large bowel may reach an enormous size and the contents become very hard. The retained masses may be channeled, and small quantities of fæcal matter are passed until a mass too large enters the lumen and causes obstruction. There may be very few symptoms, as the condition may be borne for weeks or even for months.

Obstruction by gall-stones is not very infrequent, as may be gathered from the fact that 23 cases were reported in the literature in eight years. Eighteen of these were in women and 5 in men. In six sevenths of the cases it occurred after the fiftieth year. The obstruction is usually in the ileo-cæcal region, but it may be in the duodenum. These large solitary gall-stones ulcerate through the gall-bladder, usually into the small intestine, occasionally into the colon. In the latter case they rarely cause obstruction Courvoisier has collected 131 cases in the literature.

Enteroliths may be formed of masses of hair, more commonly of the phosphates of lime and magnesia, with a nucleus formed of a foreign body or of hardened fæces. Nearly every museum possesses specimens of this kind. They are not so common in men as in ruminants, and, as indicated in Fitz's statistics, are very rare causes of obstruction.

Symptoms.—(a) **Acute Obstruction.**—Constipation, pain in the abdomen, and vomiting are the three important symptoms. Pain sets in early and may come on abruptly while the patient is walking or, more commonly, during the performance of some action. It is at first colicky in character, but subsequently it becomes continuous and very intense. Vomiting follows quickly and is a constant and most distressing symptom. At first the contents of the stomach are voided, and then greenish, bile-stained material, and soon, in cases of acute and permanent obstruction, the material vomited is a brownish-black liquid, with a distinctly fæcal odor. This sequence of gastric, bilious, and, finally, stercoraceous vomiting is perhaps the most important diagnostic feature of acute obstruction. The constipation may be absolute, without the discharge of either fæces or gas. Very often the contents of the bowel below the stricture are discharged. Distention of the abdomen usually occurs, and when the large bowel is involved it is extreme. On the other hand, if the obstruction is high up in the small intestine, there may be very slight tympany. At first the abdomen is not painful, but subsequently it may become acutely tender.

The constitutional symptoms from the outset are severe. The face is pallid and anxious, and finally collapse symptoms supervene. The eyes become sunken, the features pinched, and the skin is covered with a cold, clammy sweat. The pulse becomes rapid and feeble. There may be no fever; the axillary temperature is often subnormal. The tongue is dry and parched and the thirst is incessant. The urine is high-colored, scanty, and there may be suppression, particularly when the obstruction is high up in the bowel. This is probably due to the constant vomiting and the small amount of liquid which is absorbed. The case terminates as a rule in from three to six days. In some instances the patient dies from shock or sinks into coma.

(*b*) **Symptoms of Chronic Obstruction.**—When due to fæcal impaction, there is a history of long-standing constipation. There may have been discharge of mucus, or in some instances the fæcal masses have been channeled, and so have allowed the contents of the upper portion of the bowel to pass through. In elderly persons this is not infrequent; but examination, either *per rectum* or externally, in the course of the colon, will reveal the presence of hard scybalous masses. There may be retention of fæces for weeks without exciting serious symptoms. In other instances there are vomiting, pain in the abdomen, gradual distention, and finally the ejecta become fæcal. The hardened masses may excite an intense colitis or even peritonitis.

In stricture, whether cicatricial or cancerous, the symptoms of obstruction are very diverse. Constipation gradually comes on, is extremely variable, and it may be months or even years before there is complete obstruction. There are transient attacks, in which from some cause the fæces accumulate above the stricture, the intestine becomes greatly distended, and in the swollen abdomen the coils can be seen in active peristalsis. In such attacks there may be vomiting, but it is very rarely of a fæcal character. In the majority of these cases the general health is seriously impaired; the patient gradually becomes anæmic and emaciated, and finally, in an attack in which the obstruction is complete, death occurs with all the features of acute occlusion or the case may be prolonged for ten or twelve days.

Diagnosis.—(*a*) **The Situation of the Obstruction.**—Hernia must be excluded, which is by no means always easy, as fatal obstruction may occur from the involvement of a very limited portion of the gut in the external ring or in the obturator foramen. Mistakes from both of these causes have come under my observation; they were cases in which it was impossible to make a diagnosis other than acute obstruction. Timely operation would have saved both lives. A thorough rectal and, in women, a vaginal examination should be made, which will give important information as to the condition of the pelvic and rectal contents, particularly in cases of intussusception, in which the descending bowel can sometimes be felt. In cases of obstruction high up the empty coils sink into the pelvis and can there be detected. Rectal exploration with the entire hand is of doubtful value. In the inspection of the abdomen there are important indications, as the special prominence in certain regions, the occurrence of indefinite, well-defined masses, and the presence of hypertrophied coils in active peristalsis. John Wyllie has recently called attention to the great value in diagnosis of the "patterns of abdominal tumidity." * In obstruction of the lower end of the large intestine not only may the horseshoe of the colon stand out plainly, when the bowel is in rigid spasm, but even the pouches of the gut may be seen. When the cæcum or lower end of the ileum is obstructed the tumidity is in the lower central region, and during spasm the coils of the small bowel may stand out prominently, one above the other, either obliquely or transversely placed—the so-called "ladder pattern." In obstruction of the duodenum or jejunum there may only be slight distention of the upper part of the abdomen, associated usually with rapid collapse and anuria.

In the ileum and cæcum the distention is more in the central portion of the abdomen; the vomiting is distinctly fæcal and occurs early. In obstruction of the colon, tympanites is much more extensive and general. Tenesmus is more common, with the passage of mucus and blood. The course is not so quick, the collapse does not supervene so rapidly, and the urinary secretion is not so much reduced.

In obstruction from stricture or tumor the situation can in some cases be accurately localized, but in others it is very difficult. Digital examination of the rectum should first be made. The rectal tube may then be passed, but it is impossible to get beyond the sigmoid flexure. In the use of the rigid tube there is danger of perforation of the bowel in the neighborhood of a stricture. The quantity of fluid which can be passed into the large intestine should be estimated. The capacity of the large bowel is about six quarts. Wiggin advises about a pint and a half from a height of three feet for an infant. To thoroughly irrigate the bowel the patient should be chloroformed and should lie on the back or on the side—best on the back, with the hips elevated. Treves suggests that the cæcal region should be auscultated during the passage of the fluid. For diagnostic purposes the rectum may be inflated, either by the bellows or by the use of bicarbonate of soda and tartaric acid. In certain cases these measures give important indications as to the situation of the obstruction in the large bowel.

(b) **Nature of the Obstruction.**—This is often difficult, not infrequently impossible, to determine. *Strangulation* is not common in very early life. In many instances there have been previous attacks of abdominal pain, or there are etiological factors which give a clew, such as old peritonitis or operation on the pelvic viscera. Neither the onset nor the character of the pain gives us any information. In rare instances nausea and vomiting

* Edinburgh Hospital Reports, vol. ii.

may be absent. The vomiting usually becomes fæcal from the third to the fifth day. A tumor is not common in strangulation, and was present in only one fifth of the cases. Fever is not of diagnostic value.

Intussusception is an affection of childhood, and is of all forms of internal obstruction the one most readily diagnosed. The presence of tumor, bloody stools, and tenesmus are the important factors. The tumor is usually sausage-shaped and felt in the region of the transverse colon. It existed in 66 of 93 cases. It was present on the first day in more than one third of the cases, on the second day in more than one fourth, and on the third day in more than one fifth. Blood in the stools occurs in at least three fifths of the cases, either spontaneously or following the use of an enema. The blood may be mixed with mucus. Tenesmus is present in one third of the cases. Fæcal vomiting is not very common and was present in only 12 of the 93 instances. Abdominal tympany is a symptom of slight importance, occurring in only one third of the cases.

Volvulus can rarely be diagnosed. The frequency with which it involves the sigmoid flexure is to be borne in mind. The passage of a flexible tube or injecting fluids might in these cases give valuable indications. An absolute diagnosis can probably be made only by an abdominal section.

In fæcal obstruction the condition is usually clear, as the fæces can be felt per rectum and also in the distended colon. Fæcal vomiting, tympany, abdominal pain, nausea, and vomiting are late and are not so constant. In obstruction by gall-stone a few of the cases gave a previous history of gall-stone colic. Jaundice was present in only 2 of the 23 cases. Pain and vomiting, as a rule, occur early and are severe, and fæcal vomiting is present in two thirds of the cases. A tumor is rarely evident.

(*c*) **Diagnosis from other Conditions.**—Acute enteritis with great relaxation of the intestinal coils, vomiting, and pain may be mistaken for obstruction. In an autopsy on a case of this kind the small and large bowels were intensely inflamed, relaxed, sodden, and enormously distended. The symptoms were those of acute obstruction, but the intestine was free from duodenum to rectum. Of late years many instances have been reported in which peritonitis following disease of the appendix has been mistaken for acute obstruction. The intense vomiting, the general tympany and abdominal tenderness, and in some instances the suddenness of the onset are very deceptive, and in two cases which have come under my notice the symptoms pointed very strongly to internal strangulation. In appendix disease the temperature is more frequently elevated, the vomiting is never fæcal, and in many cases there is a history of previous attacks in the cæcal region. Acute hæmorrhagic pancreatitis may produce symptoms which simulate closely intestinal obstruction. A boy was admitted to the Johns Hopkins Hospital with a history of obstinate vomiting, intense abdominal pain, gradually increasing tympany, and no passage for several days. His condition seemed serious and he was transferred at once to the surgical wards. At the operation the coils were found uniformly distended and covered in places with the thinnest film of lymph. No obstruction existed, but there was a tumor-like mass surrounding the pancreas, firm, hard, and deeply infiltrated with blood. The patient improved after the operation and recovered completely.

Treatment.—Purgatives should not be given. For the pain hypodermic injections of morphia are indicated. To allay the distressing vomiting, the stomach should be washed out. Not only is this directly beneficial, but Kussmaul claims that the abdominal distention is relieved, the pressure in the bowel above the seat of obstruction is lessened, and the violent peristalsis is diminished. It may be practised three or four times a day, and in some instances has proved beneficial; in others curative. Thorough irrigation of the large bowel with injections should be practised, the warm fluid being allowed to flow in from a fountain syringe, and the amount carefully estimated. Jonathan Hutchinson recommends that the patient be placed under an anæsthetic, the abdomen thoroughly kneaded, and a copious enema given while in the inverted position. Then, with the aid of three or four strong men, the patient is to be thoroughly shaken, first with the abdomen held downward, and subsequently in the inverted position.

Inflation may also be tried, by forcing the air into the rectum with the bellows or with a Davidson's syringe. It is a measure not without risk, as instances of rupture of the bowel have been reported. Fitz's figures show that in the first eight years of the last decade there were 33 cases of recovery after injection or inflation in cases of certain or probable intussusception, and 11 deaths. Of 39 cases in children treated by inflation or enemata 16 recovered (Wiggin). In cases of acute obstruction, if these means do not prove successful by the third day, surgical measures should be resorted to, and when the obstruction seems persistent and the condition serious, laparotomy should be performed at once. Of 64 cases in which laparotomy was performed, 21 recovered. The youngest case operated upon was only three days old.

For the tympanites turpentine stupes and hot applications may be applied; if extreme, the bowel may be punctured with a small aspirator needle. In cases of chronic obstruction the diet must be carefully regulated, and opium and belladonna are useful for the paroxysmal pains. Enemata should be employed, and if the obstruction becomes complete, resort must be had to surgical measures.

IV. CONSTIPATION (*Costiveness*).

Definition.—Retention of fæces from any cause.

Constipation in Adults.—The causes are varied and may be classed as general and local.

General Causes.—(*a*) Constitutional peculiarities: Torpidity of the bowels is often a family complaint and is found more often in dark than in fair persons. (*b*) Sedentary habits, particularly in persons who eat too much and neglect the calls of nature. (*c*) Certain diseases, such as anæmia, neurasthenia and hysteria, chronic affections of the liver, stomach, and intestines, and the acute fevers. Under this heading may appropriately be placed that most injurious of all habits, *drug-taking*. (*d*) Either a coarse diet, which leaves too much residue, or a diet which leaves too little, may be a cause of costiveness.

Local Causes.—Weakness of the abdominal muscles in obesity or from overdistention in repeated pregnancies. Atony of the large bowel from chronic disease of the mucosa; the presence of tumors, physiological or pathological, pressing upon the bowel; enteritis; foreign bodies, large masses of scybala, and strictures of all kinds. An important local cause is atony of the colon, particularly of the muscles of the sigmoid flexure by which the fæces are propelled into the rectum. By far the most obstinate form is that associated with a contracted state of the bowel, which is sometimes spoken of as spasmodic constipation. This may be met with in three conditions: First, as a sequence of chronic dysentery or ulcerative colitis; secondly, in protracted cases of hysteria and neurasthenia in women, particularly in association with uterine disease; and, thirdly, in very old persons often without any definite cause. It may be that the sigmoid flexure and lower colon are in a condition of contraction and spasm, while the transverse and ascending parts are in a state of atony and dilatation. The most characteristic sign of this variety is the presence of hard, globular masses, or more rarely small and sausage-like fæces.

Symptoms.—The most persistent constipation for weeks or even months may exist with fair health. All kinds of evils have been attributed to poisoning by the resorption of noxious matters from the retained fæces —copræmia—but it is not likely that this takes place to any extent. Chlorosis, which Sir Andrew Clark attributes to fæcal poisoning, is not always associated with constipation, and if due to this cause should be in men, women, and children the most common of all disorders. Debility, lassitude, and a mental depression are frequent symptoms in constipation, particularly in persons of a nervous temperament. Headache, loss of appetite, and a furred tongue may also occur. Individuals differ extraordinarily in this matter: one feels wretched all day without the accustomed evacuation; another is comfortable all the week except on the day on which by purge or enema the bowels are relieved.

When persistent, the accumulation of fæces leads to unpleasant, sometimes serious symptoms, such as piles, ulceration of the colon, distention of the sacculi, perforation, enteritis, and occlusion. In women, pressure may cause pain at the time of menstruation and a sensation of fulness and distention in the pelvic organs. Neuralgia of the sacral nerves may be caused by an overloaded sigmoid flexure. The fæces collect chiefly in the colon. Even in extreme grades of constipation it is rare to find dry fæces in the cæcum. The fæces may form large tumors at the hepatic or splenic flexures, or a sausage-like, doughy mass above the navel, or an irregular lumpy tumor in the left inguinal region. In old persons the sacculi of the colon become distended and the scybala may remain in them and undergo calcification, forming enteroliths.

In cases with prolonged retention the fæcal masses become channelled and diarrhœa may occur for days before the true condition is discovered by rectal or external examination. In women who have been habitually constipated, attacks of diarrhœa with nausea and vomiting should excite suspicion and lead to a thorough examination of the large bowel. Fever may occur in these cases, and Meigs has reported an instance in which the condition simulated typhoid fever.

Constipation in infants is a common and troublesome disorder. The causes are congenital, dietetic, and local. There are instances in which the child is constipated from birth and may not have a natural movement for years and yet thrive and develop. An instance of the kind was in my ward recently in which a baby of seven months had never had a movement without preliminary injections. The abdomen became swollen every day, but subsided after an injection and the passage of a long catheter. No stricture could be felt. There are cases of enormous dilatation of the large bowel with persistent constipation. The condition appears sometimes to be a congenital defect. In some of these patients there may be constricting bands, or, as in a case of Cheever's, a congenital stricture.

Dietetic causes are more common. In sucklings it often arises from an unnatural dryness of the small residue which passes into the colon, and it may be very difficult to decide whether the fault is in the mother's milk or in the digestion of the child. Most probably it is in the latter, as some babies may be persistently costive on natural or artificial foods. Deficiency of fat in the milk is believed by some writers to be the cause. In older children it is of the greatest importance that regular habits should be enjoined. Carelessness on the part of the mother in this matter often lays the foundation of troublesome constipation in after life. Impairment of the contractility of the intestinal wall in consequence of inflammation, disturbance in the normal intestinal secretions, and mechanical obstruction by tumors, twists, and intussusception are the chief local causes.

Treatment.—Much may be done by systematic habits, particularly in the young. The desire to go to stool should always be granted. Exercise in moderation is helpful. In stout persons and in women with pendulous abdomens the muscles should have the support of a bandage. Friction or regularly applied massage is invaluable in the more chronic cases. A good substitute is a metal ball weighing from four to six pounds, which may be rolled over the abdomen every morning for five or ten minutes. The diet should be light, with plenty of fruit and vegetables, particularly salads and tomatoes. Oatmeal is usually laxative, though not to all; brown bread is better than that made from fine white flour. Of liquids, water and aërated mineral waters may be taken freely. A tumblerful of cold water on rising, taken slowly, is efficacious in many cases. A glass of hot water at night may also be tried alone. A pipe or a cigar after breakfast is with many men an infallible remedy.

When the condition is not very obstinate it is well to try to relieve it by hygienic and dietetic measures. If drugs must be used they should be the milder saline laxatives or the compound liquorice powder. Enemata are often necessary, and it is much perferable to employ them early than to constantly use purgative pills. Glycerin either in the form of suppository or as a small injection is very valuable. Half a drachm of boric acid placed within the rectum is sometimes efficacious. The injections of tepid water, with or without soap, may be used for a prolonged period with good effect and without damage. The patient should be in the dorsal position with the hips elevated, and it is best to let the fluid flow in slowly from a fountain syringe.

The usual remedies employed are often useless in the constipation associated with contracted bowel. A very satisfactory measure is the olive-oil injection as recommended by Kussmaul. The patient lies on the back with the hips elevated, and with a cannula and tube from 15 to 20 ounces of pure oil are allowed to flow slowly (or are injected) into the bowel. The operation should take at least fifteen minutes. This may be repeated every day until the intestine is cleared, and subsequently a smaller injection every few days will suffice.

There are various drugs which are of special service, particularly the combination of ipecacuanha, nux vomica, or belladonna, with aloes, rhubarb, colocynth, or podophyllin. Meigs recommends particularly the combination of extract of belladonna (gr. $\frac{1}{12}$), extract of nux vomica (gr. $\frac{1}{4}$), and extract of colocynth (gr. ij), one pill to be taken three times a day. In anæmia and chlorosis, a sulphur confection taken in the morning, and a pill of iron, rhubarb, and aloes throughout the day, are very serviceable.

In children the indications should be met, as far as possible, by hygienic and dietetic measures. In the constipation of sucklings a change in the diet of the mother may be tried, or from one to three teaspoonfuls of cream may be given before each nursing. In artificially fed children the top milk with the cream should be used. Drinking of water, barley water, or oatmeal water will sometimes obviate the difficulty. If laxatives are required, simple syrup, manna, or olive oil may be sufficient. The conical piece of soap, so often seen in nurseries, is sometimes efficacious. Massage along the colon may be tried. Small injections of cold water may be used. Large injections should be avoided, if possible. If it is necessary to give a laxative by the mouth, castor oil or the fluid magnesia is the best. If there are signs of gastro-intestinal irritation, rhubarb and soda or gray powder may be given. In older children the diet should be carefully regulated.

V. ENTEROPTOSIS (*Glénard's Disease*).

Definition.—" Dropping of the viscera," visceroptosis, is not a disease, but a symptom group characterized by looseness of the mesenteric and peritoneal attachments, so that the stomach, the intestines, particularly the transverse colon, the liver, the kidneys, and the spleen occupy an abnormally low position in the abdominal cavity.

Symptoms and Physical Signs.—It is important to recognize two groups of cases. In one the splanchnoptosis follows the loss of normal support of the abdominal wall in consequence of repeated pregnancies or recurring ascites. The condition may be extreme without the slightest distress on the part of the patient.

The second and most important group occurs usually in young persons, who present, with splanchnoptosis, the features of more or less marked neurasthenia.

In the first group inspection of the abdomen shows a very relaxed abdominal wall, and as a rule the lineæ albicantes of recurring pregnancies. Peristalsis of the intestines may be seen, and in extreme cases the outlines of the stomach itself with its waves of peristalsis. On inflating the stomach with carbonic-acid gas the organ stands out with great prominence, and the lesser and greater curvatures are seen, the latter extending perhaps a hand's breadth below the level of the navel. The waves of peristalsis are feeble and without the vigor and force of those seen in the stomach dilated from stricture of the pylorus. The condition of descensus ventriculi with atony is best studied in this group of cases. An important point to remember is that it may exist in an extreme grade without symptoms.

In the other group is embraced a somewhat motley series of cases, in which, with a pronounced nervous, or, as we call it now, neurasthenic basis, there are displacements of the viscera *with symptoms*. The patients are usually young, more frequently women than men, and of spare habit. The condition may follow an acute illness with wasting. They complain, as a rule, of dyspepsia, throbbing in the abdomen, and dragging pains or weakness in the back, and inability to perform the usual duties of life. A very considerable proportion of all the cases of neurasthenia present the local features of enteroptosis. When preparing for the examination one notices usually an erythematous flushing of the skin; the scratch of the nail is followed instantly by a line of hyperæmia, less often of marked pallor. The pulsation of the abdominal aorta is readily seen.

On examination of the viscera one finds the following: The stomach is below the normal level, and in women who have laced it may be vertically placed. The splashing or clapotage is unusually distinct. After inflation with carbonic-acid gas the outlines of the stomach are seen through the thin abdominal walls. In extreme cases there may be great dilatation of the stomach, in consequence of obstruction of the pylorus by pressure of the displaced right kidney.

Nephroptosis, or displacement of the kidney, is one of the most constant phenomena in enteroptosis. It is well, perhaps, to distinguish between the kidney which one can just touch on deep inspiration—palpable kidney, one which is freely movable, and which on deep inspiration descends so that one can put the fingers of the palpating hand above it and hold it down, and, thirdly, a floating kidney, which is entirely outside the costal arch, is easily grasped in the hand, readily moved to the middle line, and low down toward the right iliac fossa. It is held by some that the designation floating kidney should be restricted to the cases in which there is a meso-nephron, but this is excessively rare, while extreme grades of renal mobility are common. Some of the more serious sequences of movable kidney, namely, Dietl's crises and intermittent hydronephrosis, will be considered with diseases of the kidney.

Displacement of the liver is very much less common. In thin women who have laced the organ is often tilted forward, so that a very large surface of the lobes comes in contact with the abdominal wall; it is a very common mistake under these circumstances to think that the organ is enlarged. Dislocation of the liver itself will be considered later.

Mobility of the spleen is sometimes very marked in enteroptosis. In an extreme grade it may be found in almost any region of the abdomen. It is very frequently mistaken for a fibroid or ovarian tumor. A considerable proportion of the cases come first under the care of the gynecologist.

There is usually much relaxation of the mesentery and of the peritoneal folds which support the intestines. The colon is displaced downward (coloptosis), with consequent kinking at the flexures. The descent may be so low that the transverse colon is at the brim of the pelvis. It may indeed be fixed or bent in the form of a V. It is frequently to be felt, as Glénard states, as a firm cord crossing the abdomen at or below the level of the navel. This kinking may take place not only in the colon, but at the pylorus, where the duodenum passes into the jejunum, and where the ileum enters the cæcum.

The explanation of the phenomena accompanying enteroptosis is by no means easy. It has been suggested by Glénard and others that the vascular disturbances in the abdominal viscera in consequence of displacements and kinking account for the feelings of exhaustion and general nervousness. In a large proportion of the cases, however, no symptoms develop until after an illness or some protracted nervous strain.

Treatment.—In a majority of all cases four indications are present: To treat the existing neurasthenia, to relieve the nervous dyspepsia, to overcome the constipation, and to afford mechanical support to the organs. Three of these are considered under their appropriate sections. In cases in which the enteroptosis has followed loss in weight after an acute illness or worries and cares, an important indication is to fatten the patient.

A well adapted abdominal bandage is one of the most important measures in enteroptosis. In many of the milder grades it alone suffices. I know of no single simple measure which affords relief to distressing symptoms in so many cases as the abdominal bandage. It is best made of linen, should fit snugly, and should be arranged with straps so that it cannot ride up over the hips. A special form must be used, as will be mentioned later, for movable kidney. Some of the more aggravated types of enteroptosis are combined with such features of neurasthenia that a rigid Weir Mitchell treatment is indicated. In a few very refractory cases surgical interference may be called for. Treves, in Allbutt's System, records two cases, one in which the laparotomy was resorted to as a medical measure with perfect results. In the other the liver was stitched in place, and complete recovery followed.

And lastly, the physician must be careful in dealing with the subjects of enteroptosis not to lay too much stress on the disorder. It is well never to tell the patient that a kidney is movable; the symptoms may date from a knowledge of the existence of the condition.

34

VI. MISCELLANEOUS AFFECTIONS.

I. MUCOUS COLITIS.

This affection is known by various names, such as *membranous enteritis,* *tubular diarrhœa,* and *mucous colic.* It is a remarkable disease, to which much attention has been paid for several centuries. An exhaustive description of it is given by Woodward, in vol. ii of the Medical and Surgical Reports of the Civil War. It is an affection of the large bowel, characterized by the production of a very tenacious adherent mucus, which may be passed in long strings or as a continuous, tubular membrane. I have twice had opportunities of seeing this membrane *in situ,* closely adherent to the mucosa of the colon, but capable of separation without any lesion of the surface. Judging from the statement of English authors as to its rarity, it would appear to be a more frequent disease in this country, in which it has been carefully studied by Da Costa, Edwards, and others. According to Edwards, 80 per cent of the recorded adult cases have been in women. It occurs occasionally in children. Of 111 cases 6 were under the age of ten. The cases are almost invariably seen in nervous or hysterical women or in men with neurasthenia. All grades of the affection occur, from the passage of a slimy mucus, like frog-spawn, to large tubular casts a foot or more in length. Microscopically the casts are, as shown by Sir Andrew Clark, not fibrinous, but mucoid, and even the firmest consist of dense, opaque, transformed mucus. The nature of the disease has been much discussed. It is probably not an enteritis, but a secretion neurosis. In favor of this view is the large proportion of cases in neurotic women.

Symptoms.—The disease persists for years, varying extremely from time to time, and is characterized by paroxysms of pain in the abdomen, tenderness, occasionally tenesmus, and the passage of flakes or long strings of mucus, sometimes of definite casts of the bowel. There is frequently a spot of great tenderness just between the navel and the left costal border. The attacks last for a day or, in some instances, for ten days or two weeks. Mental emotions and worry of any sort seem particularly apt to bring on an attack. Occasionally errors in diet or dyspepsia precede an outbreak. Membranes are not passed with every paroxysm, even when the pains and cramps are severe. There are instances in which the morphia habit has been contracted on account of the severity of the pain. There may be marked nervous symptoms, and authors mention hysterical outbreaks, hypochondriasis, and melancholia. Blood may be passed in rare instances. The condition may persist for years and lead to great emaciation and chronic invalidism. Constipation is a special feature in many cases. Herringham states that he knew of three cases of mucous colitis in which death had suddenly occurred, in all with great pain in the left side of the abdomen. In another case there was an abscess in the region of the descending colon.

The *diagnosis* is rarely doubtful, but it is important not to mistake the membranes for other substances; thus, the external cuticle of asparagus and undigested portions of meat or sausage-skins sometimes assume forms not unlike mucous casts, but the microscopical examination will quickly differentiate them. Twice I have known mucous colitis with severe pain to be mistaken for appendicitis.

The *treatment* is very unsatisfactory. Drugs are of doubtful benefit. Measures directed to the nervous condition are perhaps most important. Sometimes local treatment with Kelly's long rectal tubes is beneficial. Hale White recommends in very obstinate cases in which life is a burden right inguinal colotomy. This has been performed with success now in several cases. The artificial anus should remain open for some time.

II. DILATATION OF THE COLON.

Hale White, in Allbutt's System, recognizes four groups of cases. In the first the distention is entirely gaseous, and occurs not infrequently as a transient condition. In many cases it has an important influence, inasmuch as it may be extreme, pushing up the diaphragm and seriously impairing the action of the heart and lungs. H. Fenwick has called attention to this as occasionally a cause of sudden heart-failure.

In the second group are the cases in which the distention of the colon is caused by solid substances, as fæcal matter, occasionally by foreign bodies introduced from without, and more rarely by gall-stones.

In a third group are embraced the cases in which the dilatation is due to an organic obstruction in front of the dilated gut. Under these circumstances the colon may reach a very large size. These cases are common enough in malignant tumors and sometimes in volvulus. Dilatation of the sigmoid flexure occurs particularly when this portion of the bowel is congenitally very long. In such cases the bowel may be so distended that it occupies the greater part of the abdomen, pushing up the liver and the diaphragm. An acute condition is sometimes caused by a twist in the meso-colon.

Fourthly, there are the cases of so-called *idiopathic dilatation of the colon.* The condition has been very carefully studied by Rolleston, C. F. Martin, and others. I have had four well-marked instances under my care. Treves suggests that the condition is always due to a narrowing low down in the colon. This proved to be true in Case II of my series, a boy who died at the age of about two and a half years. There was a distinct stricture in the sigmoid flexure. In the idiopathic chronic form the gut reaches an enormous size. The coats may be hypertrophied without evidence of any special organic change in the mucosa. The most remarkable instance has been reported by Formad. The patient, known as the " balloon-man," aged twenty-three years at the time of his death, had had a distended abdomen from infancy. Post mortem the colon was found as large as that of an ox, the circumference ranging from 15 to 30 inches. The weight with the contents was 47 pounds. The condition is incurable, and surgical interference should be probably the only measure. In one of my cases good results followed the establishment of an artificial anus, but the most brilliant case is that reported recently by Treves, who excised the greater part of the colon, with recovery.

III. INTESTINAL SAND.

" *Sable Intestinal.*"—Biliary gravel may be passed in large amount, and the seeds of raspberries, etc., may occur in the fæces in extraordinary numbers. Delépine, Shattock, and others have described in the fæces saburrous matter consisting of spheroidal aggregations of vegetable sclerenchymatous cells, such as occur in pears. In Shattock's patient the discharge was intermittent, but it could always be brought away by an aperient. I have recently seen a case in which the patient on two occasions passed a considerable quantity of sand. The sample which he brought consisted of small grains, some of a beautiful garnet color. They proved to be vegetable matter.

IV. AFFECTIONS OF THE MESENTERY.

There are various diseases of the structure embraced in the mesentery, which are of more or less importance.

(1) **Hæmorrhage** (*hæmatoma*).—Instances in which the bleeding is confined to the mesenteric tissues are rare; more commonly the condition is associated with hæmorrhagic infiltration of the pancreas and with retroperitoneal hæmorrhage. It occurs in ruptures of aneurisms, either of the abdominal aorta or of the superior mesenteric artery, in malignant forms of the infectious fevers, as small-pox, and, lastly, in individuals in whom no predisposing conditions exist. In 1887, at the Philadelphia Hospital, there was a patient in the ward of my colleague, Bruen, who had obscure abdominal symptoms for several days with great pain and prostration. I found at the post mortem the greater portion of the mesentery and the retro-peritoneal tissues infiltrated with large blood-clots. There was no disease of the aorta or of the branches of the cœliac axis or of the mesenteric vessels. Isambard Owen has reported a case of sudden death in a woman aged sixty-seven from hæmorrhage in the transverse meso-colon.

(2) **Affections of the Mesenteric Arteries.**—(*a*) *Aneurism* (see under Arteries).

(*b*) *Embolism and Thrombosis—Infarction of the Bowel.*—When the mesenteric vessels are blocked by emboli or thrombi the condition of infarction follows in the territory supplied. Probably the occlusion of small vessels does not produce any symptoms, and the circulation may be reestablished. If the superior mesenteric artery is blocked, a serious and fatal condition follows. Three instances have come under my observation. In one, a woman aged fifty-five was seized with nausea and vomiting, which persisted for more than a week. There was pain in the abdomen, tympanites, and toward the close the vomiting was incessant and fæcal. The autopsy showed great congestion, with swelling and infiltration of the jejunum and ileum. The superior mesenteric artery was blocked at its orifice by a firm thrombus. In the second case, a woman aged seventy-five was seized with severe abdominal pain and frequent vomiting. At first there was diarrhœa; subsequently the symptoms pointed to obstruction, with great distention of the abdomen. The post mortem showed the small bowel, with the exception of the first foot of the jejunum and the last six inches of the ileum, greatly distended and deeply infiltrated with blood. The mesentery was also congested and infiltrated. The superior mesenteric artery contained a firm brownish-yellow clot. There were many recent warty vegetations on the mitral valve. In the third case, a man aged forty was suddenly seized with intense pain in the abdomen, became faint, fell to the ground, and vomited. For a week he had persistent vomiting, severe diarrhœa, tympanites, and great pain in the abdomen. The stools were thin and at times blood-tinged. The autopsy showed an aneurism involving the aorta at the diaphragm. The superior mesenteric artery, half an inch from its origin on the sac, was blocked by a portion of the fibrinous clot of the aneurism. Watson has analyzed the symptoms in 27 cases; in 18 there was pain, usually colicky and violent; diarrhœa occurred in 14; vomiting in 14; and abdominal distention in 12. In a majority of the cases the heart or the abdominal aorta was diseased. In one sixth of the cases the lesion was limited enough to have permitted the successful resection of the bowel. J. W. Elliot has operated upon two cases of infarction of the bowel, in one of which (thrombosis of the mesenteric veins) he successfully resected forty-eight inches. In the horse, infarction of the intestine is extremely common in connection with the verminous aneurisms of the mesenteric arteries, and is the usual cause of colic in this animal.

(3) **Diseases of the Mesenteric Veins.**—Dilatation and sclerosis occur in cirrhosis of the liver. In instances of prolonged obstruction there may be large saccular dilatations with calcification of the intima, as in a case of obliteration of the vena portæ described by me. Suppuration of the mesenteric veins is not rare, and occurs usually in connection with pylephlebitis. The mesentery may be much swollen and is like a bag of pus, and it is only on careful dissection that one sees that the pus is really within channels representing extremely dilated mesenteric veins. Two of the three cases I have seen were in connection with local appendix abscess.

(4) **Disorders of the Chyle Vessels.**—Varicose, cavernous, and cystic chylangiomata are met with in the mucosa and submucosa of the small intestine, occasionally of the stomach. Extravasation of chyle into the mesenteric tissue is sometimes seen. Chylous cysts are found. I saw one the size of an egg at the root of the mesentery. Bramann records a case in a man aged sixty-three, in which a cyst of this kind the size of a child's head was healed by operation. There is an instance on record of a congenital malformation of the thoracic duct, in which the receptaculum formed a flattened cyst which discharged into the peritonæum, and a chylous ascitic fluid was withdrawn on several occasions. Homans, of Boston, reports an extraordinary case of a girl, who from the third to the thirteenth year had an enlarged abdomen. Laparotomy showed a series of cysts containing clear fluid. They were supposed to be dilated lymph vessels connected with the intestines.

(5) **Cysts of the Mesentery.**—Much attention has been directed of late years to the occurrence of mesenteric cysts, and the literature which is fully given by Delmez (Paris Thesis, 1891) is already extensive. They may be either dermoid, hydatid, serous, sanguineous, or chylous. They

occur at any portion of the mesentery, and range from a few inches in diameter to large masses occupying the entire abdomen. They are frequently adherent to the neighboring organs, to the liver, spleen, uterus, and sigmoid flexure.

The symptoms usually are those of a progressively enlarging tumor in the abdomen. Sometimes a mass develops rapidly, particularly in the hæmorrhagic forms. Colic and constipation are present in some cases. The general health, as a rule, is well maintained in spite of the progressive enlargement of the abdomen, which is most prominent in the umbilical region. Mesenteric cysts may persist for many years, even ten or twenty.

The diagnosis is extremely uncertain, and no single feature is in any way distinctive. Augagneur gives three important signs: the great mobility, the situation in the middle line, and the zone of tympany in front of the tumor. Of these, the second is the only one which is at all constant, as when the tumors are large the mobility disappears, and at this stage the intestines, too, are pushed to one side. It is most frequently mistaken for ovarian tumor. Movable kidney, hydronephrosis, and cysts of the omentum have also been confused with it. In certain instances puncture may be made for diagnostic purposes, but it is better to advise laparotomy for the purpose of drainage, or, if possible, enucleation may be practised.

VIII. DISEASES OF THE LIVER.

I. JAUNDICE (*Icterus*).

Definition.—Jaundice or icterus is a condition characterized by coloration of the skin, mucous membranes, and fluids of the body by the bile-pigment.

For a full consideration of the theories of jaundice the reader is referred to William Hunter's article in Allbutt's System of Medicine. The cases with icterus may be divided into two great groups.

1. OBSTRUCTIVE JAUNDICE.

The following classification of the causes of obstructive jaundice is given by Murchison: (1) Obstruction by foreign bodies within the ducts, as gall-stones and parasites; (2) by inflammatory tumefaction of the duodenum or of the lining membrane of the duct; (3) by stricture or obliteration of the duct; (4) by tumors closing the orifice of the duct or growing in its interior; (5) by pressure on the duct from without, as by tumors of the liver itself, of the stomach, pancreas, kidney, or omentum; by pressure of enlarged glands in the fissures of the liver, and, more rarely, of abdominal aneurism, fæcal accumulation, or the pregnant uterus.

To these causes some add lowering of the blood pressure in the portal system so that the tension in the smaller bile-ducts is greater than in the blood-vessels. For this view, however, there is no positive evidence. In this class may perhaps be placed the cases of jaundice from mental shock or depressed emotions, which "may conceivably cause spasm and reversed peristalsis of the bile-duct" (W. Hunter).

General Symptoms of Obstructive Jaundice.—(1) Icterus, or tinting of the skin and conjunctivæ. The color ranges from a lemon-yellow in catarrhal jaundice to a deep olive-green or bronzed hue in permanent obstruction. In some instances the color of the skin is greenish black, the so-called "black jaundice."

(2) Of the other cutaneous symptoms, pruritus in the more chronic forms may be intense and cause the greatest distress. It may precede the onset of the jaundice, but as a rule it is not very marked except in cases of prolonged obstruction. Sweating is common, and may be curiously localized to the abdomen or to the palms of the hands. Lichen, urticaria, and boils may develop, and the skin disease known as xanthelasma or vitiligoidea. The jaundice may be due to the extension of the xanthomata to the bile-passages. The visceral localization of this disorder has been chiefly observed when there are numerous punctate tubercles on the limbs (Hallopeau). In very chronic cases telangiectases develop in the skin, sometimes in large numbers over the body and face, occasionally on the mucous membrane of the tongue and lips, forming patches of a bright red color from 1 to 2 cm. in breadth.

(3) The secretions are colored with bile-pigment. The sweat tinges the linen; the tears and saliva and milk are rarely stained. The expectoration is not often tinted unless there is inflammation, as when pneumonia coexists with jaundice. The urine may contain the pigment before it is apparent in the skin or conjunctiva. The color varies from light greenish yellow to a deep black-green. Gmelin's test is made by allowing five or six drops of urine and a similar amount of common nitric acid to flow together slowly on the flat surface of a white plate. A play of colors is produced—various shades of green, yellow, violet, and red. In cases of jaundice of long standing or great intensity the urine usually contains albumin and always bile-stained tube-casts.

(4) No bile passes into the intestine. The stools therefore are of a pale drab or slate-gray color, and usually very fetid and pasty. There may be constipation; in many instances, owing to decomposition, there is diarrhœa.

(5) Slow pulse. The heart's action may fall to 40, 30, or even to 20 per minute. It is particularly noticeable in the cases of catarrhal jaundice, and is not as a rule an unfavorable symptom. The respirations may fall to 10 or even to 7 per minute.

(6) Hæmorrhage. The tendency to bleeding in chronic icterus is a serious feature in some cases. It has been shown that the blood coagulation time may be much retarded, and instead of from three minutes and a half to four minutes and a half we have found it in some cases as late as eleven or twelve minutes. This is a point which should be taken account of by surgeons, inasmuch as incontrollable hæmorrhage is a well-recognized accident in operating upon patients with chronic obstructive jaundice. Purpura, large subcutaneous extravasations, more rarely hæmorrhages from the

mucous membranes, occur in protracted jaundice, and in the more severe forms.

(7) Cerebral symptoms. Irritability, great depression of spirits, or even melancholia may be present. In any case of persistent jaundice special nervous phenomena may develop and rapidly prove fatal—such as sudden coma, acute delirium, or convulsions. Usually the patient has a rapid pulse, slight fever, and a dry tongue, and he passes into the so-called "typhoid state." These features are not nearly so common in obstructive as in febrile jaundice, but they not infrequently terminate a chronic icterus in whatever way produced. The group of symptoms has been termed *cholæmia* or, on the supposition that cholesterin is the poison, *cholesteræmia;* but its true nature has not yet been determined. In some of the cases the symptoms may be due to uræmia.

2. Toxæmic Jaundice.

In this form there is no obstruction in the bile-passages, but the jaundice is associated with toxic states of the blood, dependent upon various poisons which either act directly on the blood itself or in some cases on the liver-cells as well. The term hæmatogenous jaundice was formerly applied to this group in contradistinction to the hepatogenous jaundice, associated with obstructive changes in the bile-passages. Hunter groups the causes as follows:

1. Jaundice produced by the action of poisons, such as toluylendiamin, phosphorus, arsenic, snake-venom.

2. Jaundice met with in various specific fevers and conditions, such as yellow fever, malaria (remittent and intermittent), pyæmia, relapsing fever, typhus, enteric fever, scarlatina.

3. Jaundice met with in various conditions of unknown but more or less obscure infective nature, and variously designated as epidemic, infectious, febrile, malignant jaundice, icterus gravis, Weil's disease, acute yellow atrophy.

The symptoms of toxic jaundice are not nearly so striking as in the obstructive variety. The bile is usually present in the stools, sometimes in excess, causing very dark movements. The skin has in many cases only a light lemon tint. In the severer forms, as in acute yellow atrophy, the color may be more intense, but in malaria and pernicious anæmia the tint is usually light. In these mild cases the urine may contain little or no bile-pigment, but the urinary pigments are considerably increased. In many cases of the toxic variety the constitutional disturbance is very profound, and there are high fever, delirium, convulsions, suppression of urine, black vomit, and cutaneous hæmorrhages.

In connection with the various fevers, malaria, yellow fever, and Weil's disease jaundice has been described. Two special affections may here receive consideration, the icterus of the new-born and acute yellow atrophy.

II. ICTERUS NEONATORUM.

New-born infants are liable to jaundice, which in some instances rapidly proves fatal. A mild and a severe form may be recognized.

The *mild or physiological icterus* of the new-born is a common disease in foundling hospitals, and is not very infrequent in private practice. In 900 consecutive births at the Sloane Maternity, icterus was noted in 300 cases (Holt). The discoloration appears early, usually on the first or second day, and is of moderate intensity. The urine may be bile-stained and the fæces colorless. The nutrition of the child is not usually disturbed, and in the majority of cases the jaundice disappears within two weeks. This form is never fatal. The cause of this jaundice is not at all clear. Some have attributed it to stasis in the smaller bile-ducts, which are compressed by the distended radicals of the portal vein. Others hold that the jaundice is due to the destruction of a large number of red blood-corpuscles during the first few days after birth.

The *severe form* of icterus in the new-born may depend upon (*a*) congenital absence of the common or hepatic duct, of which there are several instances on record; (*b*) congenital syphilitic hepatitis; and (*c*) septic poisoning, associated with phlebitis of the umbilical vein. This is a severe and fatal form, in which also hæmorrhage from the cord may occur.

III. ACUTE YELLOW ATROPHY. (*Malignant Jaundice; Icterus Gravis*).

Definition.—Jaundice associated with marked cerebral symptoms and characterized anatomically by extensive necrosis of the liver-cells with reduction in volume of the organ.

Etiology.—This is a rare disease. No case has been admitted to the Johns Hopkins Hospital in the nine years of its work. Hunter has collected only 50 cases between 1880 and 1894 (inclusive), which brings up the total number of recorded cases to about 250. In a somewhat varied post-mortem and clinical experience no instance has fallen under my observation. On the other hand, a physician may see several cases within a few years, or even within a few months, as happened to Reiss, who saw five cases within three months at the Charité, in Berlin. The disease seems to be rare in this country. It is more common in women than in men. Of the 100 cases collected by Legg, 69 were in females; and of Thierfelder's 143 cases, 88 were in women. There is a remarkable association between the disease and pregnancy, which was present in 25 of the 69 women in Legg's statistics, and in 33 of the 88 women in Thierfelder's collection. It is most common between the ages of twenty and thirty, but has been met with as early as the fourth day and the tenth month. It has followed fright or profound mental emotion. In hypertrophic cirrhosis the symptoms of a profound icterus gravis may develop, with all the clinical features of acute yellow atrophy, including the presence of leucin and tyrosin in the urine, and convulsions. I have seen two such cases; in both there were extensive necroses in the liver-cells. Though the symptoms produced by phosphorus poisoning closely simulate those of acute yellow atrophy, the two conditions are not identical.

Morbid Anatomy.—The liver is greatly reduced in size, looks thin and flattened, and sometimes does not reach more than one half or even one third of its normal weight. It is flabby and the capsule is wrinkled. On section the color is of a yellowish brown, yellowish red, or mottled, and the outlines of the lobules are indistinct. The yellow and dark-red portions represent different stages of the same process—the yellow an earlier, the red a more advanced stage. The organ may cut with considerable firmness. Microscopically the liver-cells are seen in all stages of necrosis, and in spots appear to have undergone complete destruction, leaving a fatty, granular *débris* with pigment grains and crystals of leucin and tyrosin. The bile-ducts and gall-bladder are empty. Hunter concludes that it is a toxæmic catarrh of the finer bile-ducts, similar to that which is found after poisoning by toluylendiamin or phosphorus.

The other organs show extensive bile-staining, and there are numerous hæmorrhages. The kidneys may show marked granular degeneration of the epithelium, and usually there is fatty degeneration of the heart. In a majority of the cases the spleen is enlarged.

Symptoms.—In the initial stage there is a gastro-duodenal catarrh, and at first the jaundice is thought to be of a simple nature. In some instances this lasts only a few days, in others two or three weeks. Then severe symptoms set in—headache, delirium, trembling of the muscles, and, in some instances, convulsions. Vomiting is a constant symptom, and blood may be brought up. Hæmorrhages occur into the skin or from the mucous surfaces; in pregnant women abortion may occur. With the development of the head symptoms the jaundice usually increases. Coma sets in and gradually deepens until death. The body temperature is variable; in a majority of the cases the disease runs an afebrile course, though sometimes just before death there is an elevation. In some instances, however, there has been marked pyrexia. The pulse is usually rapid, the tongue coated and dry, and the patient is in a " typhoid state."

The urine is bile-stained and often contains tube-casts. Leucin and tyrosin are not constantly present; of 23 recent cases collected by Hunter, in 9 neither was found; in 10 both were present; in 3 tyrosin only; in 1 leucin only. The leucin occurs as rounded disks, the tyrosin in needle-shaped crystals, arranged either in bundles or in groups. The tyrosin may sometimes be seen in the urine sediment, but it is best first to evaporate a few drops of urine on a cover-glass. In the majority of cases no bile enters the intestines, and the stools are clay-colored. The disease is almost invariably fatal. In a few instances recovery has been noted. I saw in Leube's clinic, at Würzburg, a case which was convalescent.

Diagnosis.—Jaundice with vomiting, diminution of the liver volume, delirium, and the presence of leucin and tryosin in the urine, form a characteristic and unmistakable group of symptoms. Leucin and tyrosin are not, however, distinctive. They may be present in cases of afebrile jaundice with slight enlargement of the liver.

It is not to be forgotten that any severe jaundice may be associated with intense cerebral symptoms.   The clinical features in certain cases of hypertrophic cirrhosis are almost identical, but the enlargement of the liver, the more constant occurrence of fever, and the absence of leucin and tyrosin are distinguishing signs.   Phosphorus poisoning may closely simulate acute yellow atrophy, particularly in the hæmorrhages, jaundice, and the diminution in the liver volume, but the gastric symptoms are usually more marked, and leucin and tyrosin are stated not to occur in the urine.

No known remedies have any influence on the course of the disease.

IV. AFFECTIONS OF THE BLOOD-VESSELS OF THE LIVER.

(1) **Anæmia.**—On the post-mortem table, when the liver looks anæmic, as in the fatty or amyloid organ, the blood-vessels, which during life were probably well filled, can be readily injected.   There are no symptoms indicative of this condition.

(2) **Hyperæmia.**—This occurs in two forms.   (a) *Active hyperæmia.* After each meal the rapid absorption by the portal vessels induces transient congestion of the organ, which, however, is entirely physiological; but it is quite possible that in persons who persistently eat and drink too much this active hyperæmia may lead to functional disturbance or, in the case of drinking too freely of alcohol, to organic change.   In the acute fevers an acute hyperæmia may be present.

The *symptoms* of active hyperæmia are indefinite.   Possibly the sense of distress or fulness in the right hypochondrium, so often mentioned by dyspeptics and by those who eat and drink freely, may be due to this cause. There are probably diurnal variations in the volume of the liver.   In cirrhosis with enlargement the rapid reduction in volume after a copious hæmorrhage indicates the important part which hyperæmia plays even in organic troubles.   It is stated that suppression of the menses or suppression of a hæmorrhoidal flow is followed by hyperæmia of the liver.   Andrew H. Smith has described a case of periodical enlargement of the liver.

(b) *Passive Congestion.*—This is much more common and results from an increase of pressure in the efferent vessels or sub-lobular branches of the hepatic veins.   Every condition leading to venous stasis in the right heart at once affects these veins.

In chronic valvular disease, in emphysema, cirrhosis of the lung, and in intrathoracic tumors mechanical congestion occurs and finally leads to very definite changes.   The liver is enlarged, firm, and of a deep-red color; the hepatic vessels are greatly engorged, particularly the central vein in each lobule and its adjacent capillaries.   On section the organ presents a peculiar mottled appearance, owing to the deeply congested hepatic and the anæmic portal territories; hence the term *nutmeg* which has been given to this condition.   Gradually the distention of the central capillaries reaches such a grade that atrophy of the intervening liver-cells is induced.   Brown pigment is deposited about the centre of the lobules and the connective tissue is greatly increased. In this cyanotic induration or cardiac liver the organ is large in the early stage, but later it may become contracted. Occasionally in this form the connective tissue is increased about the lobules as well, but the process usually extends from the sublobular and central veins.

The symptoms of this form are not always to be separated from those of the associated conditions. Gastro-intestinal catarrh is usually present and hæmatemesis may occur. The portal obstruction in advanced cases leads to ascites, which may precede the development of general dropsy. There is often slight jaundice, the stools may be clay-colored, and the urine contains bile-pigment.

On examination the organ is found to be increased in size. It may be a full hand's breadth below the costal margin and tender on pressure. It is in this condition particularly that we meet with pulsation of the liver. We must distinguish the communicated throbbing of the heart, which is very common, from the heaving, diffuse impulse due to regurgitation into the hepatic veins, in which, when one hand is upon the ensiform cartilage and the other upon the right side at the margin of the ribs, the whole liver can be felt to dilate with each impulse.

The indications for *treatment* in passive hyperæmia are to restore the balance of the circulation and to unload the engorged portal vessels. In cases of intense hyperæmia 18 or 20 ounces of blood may be directly aspirated from the liver, as advised by George Harley and practised by many Anglo-Indian physicians. Good results sometimes follow this hepato-phlebotomy. The prompt relief and marked reduction in the volume of the organ which follow an attack of hæmatemesis or bleeding from piles suggests this practice. Salts administered by Matthew Hay's method deplete the portal system freely and thoroughly. As a rule, the treatment must be that of the condition with which it is associated.

(3) **Diseases of the Portal Vein.**—(*a*) *Thrombosis; Adhesive Pylephlebitis.*—Coagulation of blood in the portal vein is met with in cirrhosis, in syphilis of the liver, invasion of the vein by cancer, proliferative peritonitis involving the gastro-hepatic omentum, perforation of the vein by gall-stones, and occasionally follows sclerosis of the walls of the portal vein or of its branches (Borrmann). In rare instances a complete collateral circulation is established, the thrombus undergoes the usual changes, and ultimately the vein is represented by a fibrous cord, a condition which has been called *pylephlebitis adhesiva*. In a case of this kind which I dissected the portal vein was represented by a narrow fibrous cord; the collateral circulation, which must have been completely established for years, ultimately failed, ascites and hæmatemesis supervened and rapidly proved fatal.* The diagnosis of obstruction of the portal vein can rarely be made. A suggestive symptom, however, is a *sudden* onset of the most intense engorgement of the branches of the portal system, leading to hæmatemesis, melæna, ascites, and swelling of the spleen.

Emboli in the branches of the portal vein do not, as a rule, produce infarction, for blood reaches the lobular capillary plexus, as shown by

---

* Journal of Anatomy and Physiology, vol. xvii.

Cohnheim and Litten, through the free anastomosis with a hepatic artery. In rare instances, however, a condition resembling infarction does occur, sometimes in small areas, at others in quite extensive territories. Septic emboli, on the other hand, may induce suppuration.

(b) *Suppurative pylephlebitis* will be considered in the section on abscess.

(4) **Affections of the hepatic vein** are extremely rare. Dilatation occurs in cases of chronic enlargement of the right heart, from whatever cause produced. Emboli occasionally pass from the right auricle into the hepatic veins. A rare and unusual event is stenosis of the orifices of the hepatic veins, which I met in a case of fibroid obliteration of the inferior vena cava and which was associated with a greatly enlarged and indurated liver.[*]

(5) **Hepatic Artery.**—Enlargement of this vessel is seen in cases of cirrhosis of the liver. It may be the seat of extensive sclerosis. Aneurism of the hepatic artery is rare, but instances are on record, and will be referred to in the section on arteries.

V. DISEASES OF THE BILE-PASSAGES AND GALL-BLADDER.

(a) ACUTE CATARRH OF THE BILE-DUCTS (*Catarrhal Jaundice*).

Definition.—Jaundice due to swelling and obstruction of the terminal portion of the common duct.

Etiology.—General catarrhal inflammation of the bile-ducts is usually associated with gall-stones. The catarrhal process now under consideration is probably always an extension of a gastro-duodenal catarrh, and the process is most intense in the *pars intestinalis* of the duct, which projects into the duodenum. The mucous membrane is swollen, and a plug of inspissated mucus fills the diverticulum of Vater, and the narrower portion just at the orifice, completely obstructing the outflow of bile. It is not known how widespread this catarrh is in the bile-passages, and whether it really passes up the ducts. It would, of course, be possible to have a catarrh of the finer ducts within the liver, which some French writers think may initiate the attack, but the evidence for this is not strong, and it seems more likely that the terminal portion of the duct is always first involved. In the only instance which I have had an opportunity to examine post mortem the orifice was plugged with inspissated mucus, the common and hepatic ducts were slightly distended and contained a bile-tinged, not a clear, mucus, and there were no observable changes in the mucosa of the ducts.

This catarrhal or simple jaundice results from the following causes: (1) Duodenal catarrh, in whatever way produced, most commonly following an attack of indigestion. It is most frequently met with in young persons, but may occur at any age, and may follow not only errors in diet, but also cold, exposure, and malaria, as well as the conditions associated with portal obstruction, chronic heart-disease, and Bright's disease. (2)

---

[*] Journal of Anatomy and Physiology, vol. xvi.

Emotional disturbances may be followed by jaundice, which is believed to be due to catarrhal swelling. Cases of this kind are rare and the anatomical condition is unknown. (3) Simple or catarrhal jaundice may occur in epidemic form. (4) Catarrhal jaundice is occasionally seen in the infectious fevers, such as pneumonia, and typhoid fever. The nature of acute catarrhal jaundice is still unknown. It may possibly be an acute infection. In favor of this view are the occurrence in epidemic form and the presence of slight fever. The spleen, however, is not often enlarged. In only 4 out of 23 cases was it palpable.

Symptoms.—There may be neither pain nor distress, and the patient's friends may first notice the yellow tint, or the patient himself may observe it in the looking-glass. In other instances there are dyspeptic symptoms and uneasy sensations in the hepatic region or pains in the back and limbs. In the epidemic form, the onset may be more severe, with headache, chill, and vomiting. Fever is rarely present, though the temperature may reach 101°, sometimes 102°. All the signs of obstructive jaundice already mentioned are present, the stools are clay-colored, and the urine contains bile-pigment. The jaundice has a bright-yellow tint; the greenish, bronzed color is never seen in the simple form. The pulse may be normal, but occasionally it is remarkably slow, and may fall to 40 or 30 beats in the minute, and the respirations to as low as 8 per minute. Sleepiness, too, may be present. The liver may be normal in size, but is usually slightly enlarged, and the edge can be felt below the costal margin. Occasionally the enlargement is more marked. As a rule the gall-bladder cannot be felt. The spleen may be increased in size. The duration of the disease is from four to eight weeks. There are mild cases in which the jaundice disappears within two weeks; on the other hand, it may persist for three months. The stools should be carefully watched, for they give the first intimation of removal of the obstruction.

The *diagnosis* is rarely difficult. The onset in young, comparatively healthy persons, the moderate grade of icterus, the absence of emaciation or of evidences of cirrhosis or cancer, usually make the diagnosis easy. Cases which persist for two or three months cause uneasiness, as the suspicion is aroused that it may be more than simple catarrh. The absence of pain, the negative character of the physical examination, and the maintenance of the general nutrition are the points in favor of simple jaundice. There are instances in which time alone can determine the true nature of the case. The possibility of Weil's disease must be borne in mind in anomalous types.

Treatment.—As a rule the patient can keep on his feet from the outset. Measures should be used to allay the gastric catarrh, if it is present. A dose of calomel may be given, and the bowels kept open subsequently by salines. The patient should not be violently purged. Bismuth and bicarbonate of soda may be given, and the patient should drink freely of the alkaline mineral waters, of which Vichy is the best. Irrigation of the large bowel with cold water may be practised. The cold is supposed to excite peristalsis of the gall-bladder and ducts, and thus aid in the expulsion of the mucus.

(*b*) Chronic Catarrhal Angiocholitis.

This may possibly occur also as a sequel of the acute catarrh. I have never met with an instance, however, in which a chronic, persistent jaundice could be attributed to this cause. A chronic catarrh always accompanies obstruction in the common duct, whether by gall-stones, malignant disease, stricture, or external pressure. There are two groups of cases:

(1) *With Complete Obstruction of the Common Duct.*—In this form the bile-passages are greatly dilated, the common duct may reach the size of the thumb or larger, there is usually dilatation of the gall-bladder and of the ducts within the liver. The contents of the ducts and of the gall-bladder are a clear, colorless mucus. The mucosa may be everywhere smooth and not swollen. The clear mucus is usually sterile. The patients are the subjects of chronic jaundice, usually without fever.

(2) *With Incomplete Obstruction of the Duct.*—There is pressure on the duct or there are gall-stones, single or multiple, in the common duct or in the diverticulum of Vater. The bile-passages are not so much dilated, and the contents are a bile-stained, turbid mucus. The gall-bladder is rarely much dilated. In a majority of all cases stones are found in it.

The symptoms of this type of catarrhal angiocholitis are sometimes very distinctive. With it is associated most frequently the so-called hepatic intermittent fever, recurring attacks of chills, fever, and sweats. We need still further information about the bacteriology of these cases. In all probability the febrile attacks are due distinctly to infection. I cannot too strongly emphasize the point that the recurring attacks of intermittent fever do not necessarily mean suppurative angiocholitis. The question will be referred to again under gall-stones.

(*c*) Suppurative and Ulcerative Angiocholitis.

The condition is a diffuse, purulent angiocholitis involving the larger and smaller ducts. In a large proportion of all cases there is associated suppurative disease of the gall-bladder.

Etiology.—It is the most serious of the sequels of gall-stones. Occasionally a diffuse suppurative angiocholitis follows the acute infectious cholecystitis; this, however, is rare, since fortunately in the latter condition the cystic duct is usually occluded. Cancer of the duct, foreign bodies, such as lumbricoids or fish bones, are occasional causes. And lastly there may be extension from a suppurative pylephlebitis.

The common duct is greatly dilated and may reach the size of the index finger or the thumb; the walls are thickened, and there may be fistulous communications with the stomach, colon, or duodenum. The hepatic ducts and their extensions in the liver are dilated and contain pus mixed with bile. On section of the liver small abscesses are seen, which correspond to the dilated suppurating ducts. The gall-bladder is usually distended, full of pus, and with adhesions to the neighboring parts, or it may have perforated.

Symptoms.—The symptoms of suppurative cholangitis are usually very severe. A previous history of gall-stones, the development of a septic fever, the swelling and tenderness of the liver, the enlargement of the gall-bladder, and the leucocytosis are suggestive features. Jaundice is always present, but is variable. In some cases it is very intense, in others it is slight. There may be very little pain. There is progressive emaciation and loss of strength. In a recent case parotitis developed on the left side, which subsided without suppuration.

Ulceration, stricture, perforation, and fistulæ of the bile-passages will be considered with gall-stones.

(*d*) Acute Infectious Cholecystitis.

Etiology.—Acute inflammation of the gall-bladder is usually due to bacterial invasion, with or without the presence of gall-stones. Three varieties or grades may be recognized: The catarrhal, the suppurative, and the phlegmonous. The condition is very serious, difficult to diagnose, often fatal, and may require for its relief prompt surgical intervention. The cases associated with gall-stones have of course long been recognized, but we now know that an acute infection of the gall-bladder leading to suppuration, gangrene, or perforation is by no means infrequent. For an interesting series of cases the reader is referred to a paper by Maurice H. Richardson in the American Journal of the Medical Sciences, 1898, I. In 10 of his 59 operations upon the gall-bladder acute cholecystitis was present without known pre-existing disease!

Acute non-calculus cholecystitis is a result of bacterial invasion. The colon bacillus, the typhoid bacillus, the pneumococcus and staphylococci and streptococci have been the organisms most often found. The frequency of gall-bladder infection in the fevers is a point already referred to, particularly in typhoid fever. Two instances of acute cholecystitis have occurred within the past year at the Johns Hopkins Hospital in which typhoid bacilli were isolated from pure culture, and the Widal reaction was present in the patient's blood, without, so far as could be ascertained, any history of typhoid fever (see Cushing, Typhoid Cholecystitis, J. H. H. Bulletin, May, 1898).

Condition of the Gall-bladder.—The organ is usually distended and the walls tense. Adhesions may have formed with the colon or the omentum. In other instances perforation has taken place and there is a localized abscess, or in the more fulminant forms general peritonitis. The contents of the organ are usually dark in color, muco-purulent, purulent, or hæmorrhagic. In the cases with acute phlegmonous inflammation there may be a very foul odor. As Richardson remarks, the cystic duct is often found closed even when no stone is impacted. It should be borne in mind that in the acutely distended gall-bladder the elongation and enlargement may take place chiefly upward and inward, toward the foramen of Winslow.

Symptoms.—Severe paroxysmal pain is, as a rule, the first indication, most commonly in the right side of the abdomen in the region of the liver. It may be in the epigastrium or low down in the region of the appendix. " Nausea, vomiting, rise of pulse and temperature, prostration, distention of the abdomen, rigidity, general tenderness becoming localized " usually follow (Richardson). In this form, without gall-stones, jaundice is not often present. The local tenderness is extreme, but it may be deceptive in its situation. Associated probably with the adhesion and inflammatory processes between the gall-bladder and the bowel are the intestinal symptoms, and there may be complete stoppage of gas and fæces; indeed, the operation for acute obstruction has been performed in several cases. The distended gall-bladder may sometimes be felt.

The *diagnosis* is by no means easy. The symptoms may not indicate the section of the abdomen involved. In two of our cases and in three of Richardson's appendicitis was diagnosed; in two of his cases acute intestinal obstruction was suspected. This was the diagnosis in a case of acute phlegmonous cholecystitis which I reported in 1881. The history of the cases is often a valuable guide. Occurring during the convalescence from typhoid fever, after pneumonia, or in a patient with previous cholecystitis, such a group of symptoms as mentioned would be highly suggestive. The differentiation of the variety of the cholecystitis cannot be made. In the acute suppurative and phlegmonous forms the symptoms are usually more severe, perforation is very apt to occur, with local or general peritonitis, and unless operated upon death ensues.

There is an acute cholecystitis, probably an infective form, in which the patient has recurring attacks of pain in the region of the gall-bladder. The diagnosis of gall-stones is made, but an operation shows simply an enlarged gall-bladder filled with mucus and bile, and the mucous membrane perhaps swollen and inflamed. In some of these cases gall-stones may have been present and have passed before the operation.

(e) CANCER OF THE BILE-PASSAGES.

The subject has been very thoroughly studied of late years by Zenker, Musser, Ames, Rolleston, and Kelynack. Females suffer in the proportion of 3 to 1 (Musser), or 4 to 1 (Ames). In cases of primary cancer of the bile-duct, on the other hand, men and women appear to be about equally affected. In Musser's series 65 per cent of the cases occurred between the ages of forty and seventy. The association of malignant disease of the gall-bladder with gall-stones has long been recognized. The fact is well put by Kelynack as follows: " While gall-stones are found in from 6 to 12 per cent of all general cases (that is, coming to autopsy), they occur in association with cancer of the gall-bladder in from 90 to 100 per cent."

The exact nature of the association is not very clear, but it is usually regarded as an effect of the chronic irritation. On the other hand, it is urged that the presence of the malignant disease may itself favor the production of gall-stones. Histologically, " carcinoma of the gall-bladder varies much, both in the form of the cells and in their structural arrangement; it may be either columnar or spheroidal-celled " (Rolleston). The fundus is usually first involved in the gall-bladder, and in the ducts the ductus communis choledochus.

When the disease involves the *gall-bladder*, a tumor can be detected extending diagonally downward and inward toward the navel, variable in

35

size, occasionally very large, due either to great distention of the gall-bladder or to involvement of contiguous parts. It is usually very firm and hard.

Among the important symptoms are jaundice, which was present in 69 per cent of Musser's cases; pain, often of great severity and paroxysmal in character. The pain and tenderness on pressure persist in the intervals between the paroxysmal attacks. In one of my three cases, which Ames reported, there was a very profound anæmia, but an absence of jaundice throughout. Gall-stones were present in two of the cases, and a history of gall-stone attacks was obtained from the third.

Primary malignant disease in the *bile-ducts* is less common, and rarely forms tumors that can be felt externally. Kelynack (Medical Chronicle, November, 1897) gives very fully a number of important points in the differential diagnosis between tumors in the duct and tumors in the gall-bladder. There is usually an early, intense, and persistent jaundice. The gall-bladder is much dilated. At best the diagnosis is very doubtful, unless cleared up by an exploratory operation. A very interesting form of malignant disease of the ducts is that which involves the diverticulum of Vater. Busson has collected eleven cases. A few months ago an elderly woman was admitted under my care with jaundice of some months duration, without pain, with progressive emaciation, and a greatly enlarged gall-bladder. My colleague, Halsted, operated and found obstruction at the orifice of the common duct. He opened the duodenum, removed a cylindrical-celled epithelioma of the ampulla of Vater, and stitched the common duct to another portion of the duodenum. The patient made an uninterrupted recovery, and now, fourteen weeks after the operation, has gained twenty-five pounds in weight and is passing bile with the fæces.

(f) Stenosis and Obstruction of the Bile-ducts.

Stenosis or complete occlusion may follow ulceration, most commonly after the passage of a gall-stone. In these instances the obstruction is usually situated low down in the common duct. Instances are extremely rare. Foreign bodies, such as the seeds of various fruits, may enter the duct, and occasionally round worms crawl into it. In the Wistar-Horner Museum of the University of Pennsylvania there is a remarkable specimen showing the common and hepatic ducts enormously distended and densely packed with a dozen or more lumbricoid worms. Similar specimens exist in one of the Paris museums, and at the Royal Victoria Hospital, Netley. Liver-flukes and echinococci are rare causes of obstruction in man.

Obstruction by *pressure* from without is more frequent. Cancer of the head of the pancreas, less often a chronic interstitial inflammation, may compress the terminal portion of the duct; rarely, cancer of the pylorus. Secondary involvement of the lymph-glands of the liver is a common cause of occlusion of the duct, and is met with in many cases of cancer of the stomach and other abdominal organs. Rare causes of obstruction are aneurism of a branch of the cœliac axis of the aorta, and pressure of very large abdominal tumors.

The symptoms produced are those of chronic obstructive jaundice. At first, the liver is usually enlarged, but in chronic cases it may be reduced in size, and be found of a deeply bronzed color. The hepatic intermittent fever is not often associated with complete occlusion of the duct from any cause, but it is most frequently met with in chronic obstruction by gall-stones. Permanent occlusion of the duct terminates in death. In a majority of the cases the conditions which lead to the obstruction are in themselves fatal. The liver, which is not necessarily enlarged, presents a moderate grade of cirrhosis. Cases of cicatricial occlusion may last for years. A patient under my care, who was permanently jaundiced for nearly three years, had a fibroid occlusion of the duct.

The *diagnosis* of the nature of the occlusion is often very difficult. A history of colic, jaundice of varying intensity, paroxysms of pain, and intermittent fever point to gall-stones. In cancerous obstruction the tumor mass can sometimes be felt in the epigastric region. In cases in which the lymph-glands in the transverse fissure are cancerous, the primary disease may be in the pelvic organs or the rectum, or there may be a limited cancer of the stomach, which has not given any symptoms. In these cases the examination of the other lymphatic glands may be of value. In a case who came under observation with a jaundice of seven weeks' duration, believed to be catarrhal (as the patient's general condition was good and he was not said to have lost flesh), a small nodular mass was detected at the navel, which on removal proved to be scirrhus. Involvement of the clavicular groups of lymph-glands may also be serviceable in diagnosis. The gall-bladder is usually enlarged in obstruction of the common duct, except in the cases of gall-stones (Courvoisier's law). Great and progressive enlargement of the liver with jaundice and moderate continued fever is more commonly met with in cancer.

Congenital obliteration of the ducts is an interesting condition, of which there are some 60 or 70 cases on record. It may occur in several members of one family. Spontaneous hæmorrhages are frequent, particularly from the navel. The subjects may live for three or even eight weeks. For a recent careful consideration of the subject, see John Thomson's article in Allbutt's System of Medicine.

VI. CHOLELITHIASIS.

No chapter in medicine is more interesting than that which deals with the question of gall-stones. Few affections present so many points for study—chemical, bacteriological, pathological, and clinical. The past few years have seen a great advance in our knowledge in two directions: First, as to the mode of formation of the stones, and, secondly, as to the surgical treatment of the cases. The recent study of the origin of stones dates from Naunyn's work in 1891. Marion Sims's suggestion that gall-stones came within the sphere of the surgeon has been most fruitful. Lawson Tait, Langenbuch, Mayo Robson, Riedel, Kehr, and in this country Keen, Fenger, Murphy, Lange, and Halsted have not only revolutionized the treatment of cholelithiasis, but from their work we physicians have gathered much of the greatest moment in symptomatology and diagnosis.

Origin of Gall-stones.—Two important points with reference to the formation of calculi in the bile-passages were brought out by Naunyn: (*a*) The origin of the cholesterin of the bile, as well as of the lime salts from the mucous membrane of the biliary passages, particularly when inflamed; and (*b*) the remarkable association of micro-organisms with gall-stones. It is stated that Bristowe first noticed the origin of cholesterin in the gall-bladder itself, but Naunyn's observations showed that both the cholesterin and the lime were in great part a production of the mucosa of the gall-bladder and of the bile-ducts, particularly when in a condition of catarrhal inflammation excited by the presence of microbes. According to the views of this author, the lithogenous catarrh (which, by the way, is quite an old idea) modifies materially the chemical constitution of the bile and favors the deposition about epithelial *débris* and bacteria of the insoluble salts of lime in combination with the bilirubin. Welch and others have demonstrated the presence of micro-organisms in the centre of gall-stones. Three additional points of interest may be referred to:

First, the demonstration that the gall-bladder is a peculiarly favorable habitat for micro-organisms. The colon bacilli, staphylococci, streptococci, pneumococci, and the typhoid bacilli have all been found here under varying conditions of the bile. A remarkable fact is the length of time which they may live in the gall-bladder, as was first demonstrated by Blachstein in Welch's laboratory. The typhoid bacillus has been isolated in pure culture seven years after an attack.

Secondly, the experimental production of gall-stones has been successfully accomplished by Gilbert and Fournier by injecting micro-organisms into the gall-bladder of animals.

Thirdly, the association of gall-stones with the specific fevers. Bernheim, in 1889, first called attention to the frequency of gall-stone attacks after typhoid. Since that time Dufort has collected a series of cases, and Chiari, Mason, and Osler have called attention to the great frequency of gall-bladder complications during and after this disease.

While it is probable that a lithogenous catarrh, induced by micro-organisms, is the most important single factor, there are other accessory causes of great moment.

Age.—Nearly 50 per cent of all the cases occur in persons above forty years of age. They are rare under twenty-five. They have been met with in the new-born, and in infants (John Thomson).

Sex.—Three fourths of the cases occur in women. Pregnancy has an important influence. Naunyn states that 90 per cent of women with gall-stones have borne children.

All conditions which favor *stagnation of bile* in the gall-bladder predispose to the formation of stones. Among these may be mentioned corsetwearing, enteroptosis, nephroptosis, and occupations requiring a "leaning forward" position. Lack of exercise, sedentary occupations, particularly when combined with over-indulgence in food, constipation, depressing mental emotions are also to be regarded as favoring circumstances. The belief prevailed formerly that there was a lithiac diathesis closely allied to that of gout.

Physical Characters of Gall-stones.—They may be single, in which case the stone is usually ovoid and may attain a very large size. Instances are on record of gall-stones measuring more than 5 inches in length. They may be extremely numerous, ranging from a score to several hundreds or even several thousands, in which case the stones are very small. When moderately numerous, they show signs of mutual pressure and have a polygonal form, with smooth facets; occasionally, however, five or six gall-stones of medium size are met with in the bladder which are round or ovoid and without facets. They are sometimes mulberry-shaped and very dark, consisting largely of bile-pigments. Again there are small, black calculi, rough and irregular in shape, and varying in size from grains of sand to small shot. These are sometimes known as gall-sand. On section, a calculus contains a nucleus, which consists of bile-pigment, rarely a foreign body. The greater portion of the stone is made up of cholesterin, which may form the entire calculus and is arranged in concentric laminæ showing also radiating lines. Salts of lime and magnesia, bile acids, fatty acids, and traces of iron and copper are also found in them. A majority of gall-stones consist of from 70 to 80 per cent of cholesterin, in either the amorphous or the crystalline form. As above stated, it is sometimes pure, but more commonly it is mixed with the bile-pigment. The outer layer of the stone is usually harder and brownish in color, and contains a larger proportion of lime salts.

The Seat of Formation.—Within the liver itself calculi are occasionally found, but are here usually small and not abundant, and in the form of ovoid, greenish-black grains. A large majority of all calculi are formed within the gall-bladder. The stones in the larger ducts have usually had their origin in the gall-bladder.

Symptoms.—In a majority of the cases, gall-stones cause no symptoms. The gall-bladder will tolerate the presence of large numbers for an indefinite period of time, and post-mortem examinations show that they are present in 25 per cent of all women over sixty years of age (Naunyn).

The French writers have suggested recently a useful division of the symptoms of cholelithiasis into (1) the aseptic, mechanical accidents in consequence of migration of the stone or of obstruction, either in the ducts or in the intestines; (2) the septic, infectious accidents, either local (the angiocholitis and cholecystitis with empyema of the gall-bladder, and the fistulæ and abscess of the liver and infection of the neighboring parts) or general, the biliary fever and the secondary visceral lesions.

It will be better, perhaps, to consider cholelithiasis under the following headings: The symptoms produced by the passage of a stone through the ducts—biliary colic; the effects of permanent plugging of the cystic duct; of the stone in the common duct; and the more remote effects, due to ulceration, perforation, and the establishment of fistulæ.

1. **Biliary Colic.**—Gall-stones may become engaged in the cystic or the common duct without producing pain or severe symptoms. More commonly the passage of a stone excites the violent symptoms known as biliary colic. The attack sets in abruptly with agonizing pain in the right hypo-

chondriac region, which radiates to the shoulder, or is very intense in the epigastric and in the lower thoracic regions. It is often associated with a rigor and a rise in temperature from 102° to 103°. The pain is usually so intense that the patient rolls about in agony. There are vomiting, profuse sweating, and great depression of the circulation. There may be marked tenderness in the region of the liver, which may be enlarged, and the gall-bladder may become palpable and very tender. In other cases the fever is more marked. The spleen is enlarged (Naunyn) and the urine contains albumin with red blood-corpuscles. Ortner holds that *cholecystitis acuta*, occurring in connection with gall-stones, is a septic (bacterial) infection of the bile-passages. The symptoms of acute infectious cholecystitis and those of what we call gall-stone colic are very similar, and surgeons have frequently performed cholecystotomy for the former condition, believing calculi were present. In a large number of the cases jaundice develops, but it is not a necessary symptom. Of course it does not occur during the passage of the stone through the cystic duct, but only when it becomes lodged in the common duct. The pain is due (*a*) to the slow progress in the cystic duct, in which the stone takes a rotary course owing to the arrangement of the Heisterian valve; (*b*) to the acute inflammation which usually accompanies an attack; and (*c*) to the stretching and distention of the gall-bladder by retained secretions.

The attack varies in duration. It may last for a few hours, several days, or even a week or more. If the stone becomes impacted in the orifice of the common duct, the jaundice becomes intense; much more commonly it is a slight transient icterus. The attack of colic may be repeated at intervals for some time, but finally the stone passes and the symptoms rapidly disappear.

Occasionally accidents occur, such as rupture of the duct with fatal peritonitis. Fatal syncope during an attack, and the occurrence of repeated convulsive seizures have come under my observation. These are, however, rare events. Palpitation and distress about the heart may be present, and occasionally a mitral murmur develops during the paroxysm; but the cardiac conditions described by some writers as coming on acutely in biliary colic are possibly pre-existent in these patients.

The *diagnosis* of acute hepatic colic is generally easy. The pain is in the upper abdominal and thoracic regions, whereas the pain in nephritic colic is in the lower abdomen. A chill, with fever, is much more frequent in biliary colic than in gastralgia, with which it is liable, at times, to be confounded. A history of previous attacks is an important guide, and the occurrence of jaundice, however slight, determines the diagnosis. To look for the gall-stones, the stools should be thoroughly mixed with water and carefully filtered through a narrow-meshed sieve. Pseudo-biliary colic is not infrequently met with in nervous women, and the diagnosis of gall-stones made. This nervous hepatic colic may be periodical; the pain may be in the right side and radiating; sometimes associated with other nervous phenomena, often excited by emotion, tire, or excesses. The liver may be tender, but there are neither icterus nor inflammatory conditions. The combination of colic and jaundice, so distinctive of gall-stones, is not always present.

The pains may be not colicky, but more constant and dragging in character. Of 50 cases operated upon by Riedel, 10 had not had colic, only 14 presented a gall-bladder tumor, while a majority had not had jaundice. A remarkable xanthoma of the bile-passages has been found in association with hepatic colic. I have already spoken of the diagnosis of acute cholecystitis from appendicitis and obstruction of the bowels. Recurring attacks of pain in the region of the liver may follow adhesions between the gall-bladder and adjacent parts.

2. **Obstruction of the Cystic Duct.**—The effects may be thus enumerated:

(*a*) Dilatation of the gall-bladder—hydrops vesicæ felleæ. In acute obstruction the contents are bile mixed with much mucous or muco-purulent material. In chronic obstruction the bile is replaced by a clear fluid mucus. This is an important point in diagnosis, particularly as a dropsical gall-bladder may form a very large tumor. The reaction is not always constant. It is either alkaline or neutral; the consistence is thin and mucoid. Albumin is usually present. A dilated gall-bladder may reach an enormous size, and in one instance Tait found it occupying the greater part of the abdomen. In such cases, as is not unnatural, it has been mistaken for an ovarian tumor. I have described a case in which it was attached to the right broad ligament. The dilated gall-bladder can usually be felt below the edge of the liver, and in many instances it has a characteristic outline like a gourd. An enlarged and relaxed organ may not be palpable, and in acute cases the distention may be upward toward the hilus of the liver. The dilated gall-bladder usually projects directly downward, rarely to one side or the other, though occasionally toward the middle line. It may reach below the navel, and in persons with thin walls the outline can be accurately defined. Riedel has called attention to a tongue-like projection of the anterior margin of the right lobe in connection with enlarged gall-bladder. It is to be remembered that distention of the gall-bladder may occur without jaundice; indeed, the greatest enlargement has been met with in such cases.

Gall-stone crepitus may be felt when the bladder is very full of stones and its walls not very tense. It is rarely well felt unless the abdominal walls are much relaxed. It may be found in patients who have never had any symptoms of cholelithiasis.

(*b*) Acute cholecystitis. The simple form is common, and to it are due probably very many of the symptoms of the gall-stone attack. Phlegmonous cholecystitis is rare; only seven instances are found in the enormous statistics of Courvoisier. It is, however, much more common than these figures indicate. Perforation may occur with fatal peritonitis.

(*c*) Suppurative cholecystitis, empyema of the gall-bladder, is much more common, and in the great majority of cases is associated with gall-stones—41 in 55 cases (Courvoisier). There may be enormous dilatation, and over a litre of pus has been found. Perforation and the formation of abscesses in the neighborhood are not uncommon.

(*d*) Calcification of the gall-bladder is commonly a termination of the previous condition. There are two separate forms: incrustation of the mucosa with lime salts and the true infiltration of the wall with lime, the so-called ossification. A remarkable example of the latter, sent to me by Groves, of Carp, is now in the McGill Medical Museum.

(e) Atrophy of the gall-bladder. This is by no means uncommon. The organ shrinks into a small fibroid mass, not larger, perhaps, than a good-sized pea or walnut, or even has the form of a narrow fibrous string; more commonly the gall-bladder tightly embraces a stone. This condition is usually preceded by hydrops of the bladder.

Occasionally the gall-bladder presents diverticula, which may be cut off from the main portion, and usually contain calculi.

(3) **Obstruction of the Common Duct.**—There may be a single stone tightly wedged in the duct in any part of its course, or a series of stones, sometimes extending into both hepatic and cystic ducts, or a stone lies in the diverticulum of Vater. There are three groups of cases: (a) In rare instances a stone tightly corks the common duct, causing *permanent occlusion;* or it may partly rest in the cystic duct, and may have caused thickening of the junction of the ducts; or a big stone may compress the hepatic or upper part of the common duct. The jaundice is deep and enduring, and there are no septic features. The pains, the previous attacks of colic, and the absence of enlarged gall-bladder help to separate the condition from obstruction by new growths, although it cannot be differentiated with certainty. The ducts are usually much dilated and everywhere contain a clear mucoid fluid.

(b) *Incomplete obstruction, with infective cholangitis.*

There may be a series of stones in the common duct, a single stone which is freely movable, or a stone (ball-valve stone) in the diverticulum of Vater. These conditions may be met with at autopsy, without the subjects having had symptoms pointing to gall-stones; but in a majority of cases there are very characteristic features.

The common duct may be as large as the thumb; the hepatic duct and its branches through the liver may be greatly dilated, and the distention may even be apparent beneath the liver capsule. Great enlargement of the gall-bladder is rare. The mucous membrane of the ducts is usually smooth and clear, and the contents consist of a thin, slightly turbid bile-stained mucus.

Naunyn has given the following as the distinguishing signs of stone in the common duct: " (1) The continuous or occasional presence of bile in the fæces; (2) distinct variations in the intensity of the jaundice; (3) normal size or only slight enlargement of the liver; (4) absence of distention of the gall-bladder; (5) enlargement of the spleen; (6) absence of ascites; (7) presence of febrile disturbance; and (8) duration of the jaundice for more than a year."

In connection with the ball-valve stone, which is most commonly found in the diverticulum of Vater, though it may be in the common duct itself, I have tried to separate a special symptom group: (a) Ague-like paroxysms, chills, fever, and sweating; the *hepatic intermittent fever* of Charcot; (b) jaundice of varying intensity, which persists for months or even years, and deepens after each paroxysm; (c) at the time of the paroxysms, pains in the region of the liver with gastric disturbance. These symptoms may continue on and off for three or four years, without the development of suppurative cholangitis. In one of my cases the jaundice and recurring hepatic intermittent fever existed from July, 1879, until August, 1882; the patient recovered and still lives. The condition has lasted from eight months to three years. The rigors are of intense severity, and the temperature rises to 103° or 105°. The chills may recur daily for weeks, and present a tertian or quartan type, so that they are often attributed to malaria, with which, however, they have no connection. The jaundice is variable, and deepens after each paroxysm. The itching may be most intense. Pain, which is sometimes severe and colicky, does not always occur. There may be marked vomiting and nausea. As a rule there is no progressive deterioration of health. In the intervals between the attacks the temperature is normal.

The clinical history and the post-mortem examinations in my cases show conclusively that this condition may persist for years without a trace of suppuration within the ducts. There must, however, be an infection, such as may exist for years in the gall-bladder, without causing suppuration. It is probable that the toxic symptoms only develop when a certain grade of tension is reached.

An interesting and valuable diagnostic point is the absence of dilatation of the gall-bladder in cases of obstruction from stone—Courvoisier's rule. Ecklin, who has recently reviewed this point, finds that of 172 cases of obstruction of the common duct by calculus in 34 the gall-bladder was normal, in 110 it was contracted, and in 28 it was dilated. Of 139 cases of occlusion of the common duct from other causes the gall-bladder was normal in 9, shrunken in 9, and dilated in 121.

(c) *Incomplete obstruction, with suppurative cholangitis.*

When suppurative cholangitis exists the mucosa is thickened, often eroded or ulcerated; there may be extensive suppuration in the ducts throughout the liver, and even empyema of the gall-bladder. Occasionally the suppuration extends beyond the ducts, and there is localized liver abscess, or there is perforation of the gall-bladder with the formation of abscess between the liver and stomach.

Clinically it is characterized by a fever which may be intermittent, but more commonly is remittent and without prolonged intervals of apyrexia. The jaundice is rarely so intense, nor do we see the deepening of the color after the paroxysms. There is usually greater enlargement of the liver and tenderness and more definite signs of septicæmia. The cases run a shorter course, and recovery never takes place.

(4) **The More Remote Effects of Gall-stones.**—(a) *Biliary Fistulæ.* These are not uncommon. There may, for instance, be abnormal communication between the gall-bladder and the hepatic duct or the gall-bladder and a cavity in the liver itself. More rarely perforation occurs between the common duct and the portal vein. Of this there are at least four instances on record, among them the celebrated case of Ignatius Loyola. Perforation into the abdominal cavity is not uncommon; 119 cases exist in the literature (Courvoisier), in 70 of which the rupture occurred directly into the peritoneal cavity; in 49 there was an encapsulated abscess. Per-

foration may take place from an intrahepatic branch or from the hepatic, common, or cystic ducts. Perforation from the gall-bladder is the most common.

Fistulous communications between the bile-passages and the gastro-intestinal canal are frequent. Openings into the stomach are rare. Between the duodenum and bile-passages they are much more common. Courvoisier has collected 10 instances of communication between the ductus communis and the duodenum, and 73 cases between the gall-bladder and the duodenum. Communication with the ileum and jejunum is extremely rare. Of fistulous opening into the colon 39 cases are on record. These communications can rarely be diagnosed; they may be present without any symptoms whatever. It is probably by ulceration into the duodenum or colon that the large gall-stones escape.

Occasionally the urinary passages may be opened into and the stones may be found in the bladder. Many instances are on record of fistulæ between the bile-passages and the lungs. Courvoisier has collected 24 cases, to which list J. E. Graham has added 10, including 2 cases of his own. (Trans. of Assoc. of Am. Physicians, xiii.) Bile may be coughed up with the expectoration, sometimes in considerable quantities.

Of all fistulous communications the external or cutaneous is the most common. Courvoisier's statistics number 184 cases, in 50 per cent of which the perforation took place in the right hypochondrium; in 29 per cent in the region of the navel. The number of stones discharged varied from one or two to many hundreds. Recovery took place in 78 cases; some with, some without operation.

(b) *Obstruction of the Bowel by Gall-stones.*—Reference has already been made to this; its frequency appears from the fact that of 295 cases of obstruction, occurring during eight years, analyzed by Fitz, 23 were by gall-stone. Courvoisier's statistics give a total number of 131 cases, in 6 of which the calculi had a peculiar situation, as in a diverticulum or in the appendix. Of the remaining 125 cases, in 70 the stone was spontaneously passed, usually with severe symptoms. The post-mortem reports show that in some of these cases even very large stones have passed *per viam naturalem,* as the gall-duct has been enormously distended, its orifice admitting the finger freely. This, however, is extremely rare. The stones have been found most commonly in the ileum.

Treatment of Gall-stones and their Effects.—In an attack of biliary colic the patient should be kept under morphia, given hypodermically, in quarter-grain doses. In an agonizing paroxysm it is well to give a whiff or two of chloroform until the morphia has had time to act. Great relief is experienced from the hot bath and from fomentations in the region of the liver. The patient should be given laxatives and should drink copiously of alkaline mineral waters. Olive oil has proved useless in my hands. When taken in large quantities, fatty concretions are passed with the stools, which have been regarded as calculi; and concretions due to eating pears have been also mistaken, particularly when associated with colic attacks. Since the days of Durande, whose mixture of ether and turpentine is still largely used in France, various remedies have been advised to dissolve the stones within the gall-bladder, none of which are efficacious.

The diet should be regulated, the patient should take regular exercise and avoid, as much as possible, the starchy and saccharine foods. The soda salts recommended by Prout are believed to prevent the concentration of the bile and the formation of gall-stones. Either the sulphate or the phosphate may be taken in doses of from 1 to 2 drachms daily. For the intolerable itching McCall Anderson's dusting powder may be used; starch, an ounce; camphor, a drachm and a half; and sulphate of zinc, half an ounce. Some of this should be finely dusted over the skin with a powder-puff. Powdering with starch, strong alkaline baths (hot), pilocarpin hypodermically (gr. $\frac{1}{8}$–$\frac{1}{6}$), and antipyrin (gr. viij), may be tried. Ichthyol and lanolin ointment sometimes gives relief.

Exploratory puncture, as practised by the elder Pepper, in 1857, in a case of empyema of the gall-bladder, and by Bartholow in 1878 is not now often done. Aspiration is usually a safe procedure, though a fatal result has followed.

The surgical treatment of gall-stones has of late years made rapid progress. The operation of cholecystotomy, or opening the gall-bladder and removing the stones, which was advised by Sims, has been remarkably successful. The removal of the gall-bladder, cholecystectomy, has also been practised with success. The indications for operation are: (a) Repeated attacks of gall-stone colic. The operation is now attended with such slight risk that the patient is much safer in the hands of a surgeon than when left to Nature, with the feeble assistance of drugs and mineral waters. (b) The presence of a distended gall-bladder, associated with attacks of pain or with fever. (c) When a gall-stone is permanently lodged in the common duct, and the group of symptoms above described are present, the question, then, of advising operation depends largely upon the personal methods and success of the surgeon who is available. The operation, necessarily much more serious and difficult than that upon the gall-bladder, is now remarkably successful even in desperate cases of years' duration.

VII. THE CIRRHOSES OF THE LIVER.

General Considerations.—The many forms of cirrhoses of the liver have one feature in common—an increase in the connective tissue of the organ. In fact, we use the term cirrhosis (by which Lannec characterized the tawny, yellow color of the common atrophic form) to indicate similar changes in other organs.

The cirrhoses may be classified, etiologically, according to the supposed causation; anatomically, according to the structure primarily involved; or clinically, according to certain special symptoms.

Etiological Classification.—1. *Toxic Cirrhoses.*—Alcohol is the chief cause of cirrhosis of the liver. Other poisons, such as lead and the toxic products of faulty metabolism in gout, diabetes, rickets, and indigestion, play a minor *rôle*.

2. *Infectious Cirrhoses.*—With many of the specific fevers necrotic changes occur in the liver which, when widespread, may be followed by cirrhosis. Possibly the hypertrophic cirrhosis of Hanot and other forms met with in early life are due to infection. The malarial cirrhosis is a well-recognized variety. The syphilitic poison produces a very characteristic form.

3. *Cirrhosis from chronic congestion of the blood-vessels* in heart-disease —the cardiac liver.

4. *Cirrhosis from chronic obstruction of the bile-ducts*, a form of very slight clinical interest. In anthracosis the carbon pigment may reach the liver in large quantities and be deposited in the connective tissue about the portal canal, leading to cirrhosis (Welch).

Anatomical Classification.—1. *Vascular cirrhoses*, in which the new growth of connective tissue has its starting point about the finer branches the portal or hepatic veins.

2. *Biliary cirrhoses*, in which the process is supposed to begin about the finer bile-ducts, as in the hypertrophic cirrhosis of Hanot and in the form from obstruction of the larger ducts.

3. *Capsular cirrhoses*, a perihepatitis leading to great thickening of the capsule and reduction in the volume of the liver.

Clinical Classification.—For practical purposes we may recognize the following varieties of cirrhosis of the liver:

1. The alcoholic cirrhosis of Laennec, including with this the fatty cirrhotic liver.

2. The hypertrophic cirrhosis of Hanot.

3. Syphilitic cirrhosis.

4. Capsular cirrhosis—chronic perihepatitis.

Other forms, of slight clinical interest, are considered elsewhere under diabetes, malaria, tuberculosis, and heart-disease. The cirrhosis from malaria, upon which the French writers lay so much stress (one describes thirteen varieties!), is excessively rare. In our large experience with malaria during the past nine years not a single case of advanced cirrhosis due to this cause has been seen in the wards or autopsy-room of the Johns Hopkins Hospital.

I. ALCOHOLIC CIRRHOSIS.

Etiology.—The disease occurs most frequently in middle-aged males who have been addicted to drink. Whiskey, gin, and brandy are more potent to cause cirrhoses than beer. It is more common in countries in which strong spirits are used than in those in which malt liquors are taken. Among 1,000 autopsies in my colleague Welch's department of the Johns Hopkins Hospital there were 63 cases of small atrophic liver, and 8 cases of the fatty cirrhotic organ. Lancereaux claims that the *vin ordinaire* of France is a common cause of cirrhosis. Of 210 cases, excess in wine alone was present in 68 cases. He thinks it is the sulphate of potash in the plaster of Paris used to give the " dry " flavor which damages the liver.

Cirrhosis of the liver in young children is not very rare. Palmer Howard collected 63 cases, to which Hatfield added 93. In a certain number of the cases there is an alcoholic history, in others syphilis has been present, while a third group, due to the poisons of the infectious diseases, embraces a certain number of the cases of Hanot's hypertrophic cirrhosis.

Morbid Anatomy.—Practically on the post-mortem table we see alcoholic cirrhosis in two well-characterized forms:

The Atrophic Cirrhosis of Laennec.—The organ is greatly reduced in size and may be deformed. The weight is sometimes not more than a pound or a pound and a half. It presents numerous granulations on the surface; is firm, hard, and cuts with great resistance. The substance is seen to be made up of greenish-yellow islands, surrounded by grayish-white connective tissue. This yellow appearance of the liver induced Laennec to give to the condition the name of cirrhosis.

The Fatty Cirrhotic Liver.—Even in the atrophic form the fat is increased, but in typical examples of this variety the organ is not reduced in size, but is enlarged, smooth or very slightly granular, anæmic, yellowish white in color, and resembles an ordinary fatty liver. It is, however, firm, cuts with resistance, and microscopically shows a great increase in the connective tissue. This form occurs most frequently in beer-drinkers.

The two essential elements in cirrhosis are destruction of liver-cells and obstruction to the portal circulation.

In an autopsy on a case of atrophic cirrhosis the peritonæum is usually found to contain a large quantity of fluid, the membrane is opaque, and there is chronic catarrh of the stomach and of the small intestines. The spleen is enlarged, in part, at least, from the chronic congestion, possibly due in part to a " vital reaction," to a toxic influence (Parkes Weber). The kidneys are sometimes cirrhotic, the bases of the lungs may be much compressed by the ascitic fluid, the heart often shows marked degeneration, and arterio-sclerosis is usually present. A remarkable feature is the association of acute tuberculosis with cirrhosis. In seven cases of my series the patients died with either acute tuberculous peritonitis or acute tuberculous pleurisy. Pitt states that 22½ per cent of the cases of cirrhosis dying in Guy's Hospital during twelve years had acute tuberculosis. Of 121 autopsies at the Manchester Royal Infirmary in cirrhosis, about 23 per cent gave evidence of tuberculous infection. Twelve of these had tuberculosis of the peritonæum, and 12 died directly from the tuberculous infection (Kelynack).

The compensatory circulation is usually readily demonstrated. It is carried out by the following set of vessels: (1) The accessory portal system of Sappey, of which important branches pass in the round and suspensory ligaments and unite with the epigastric and mammary systems. These vessels are numerous and small. Occasionally a large single vein, which may attain the size of the little finger, passes from the hilus of the liver, follows the round ligament, and joins the epigastric veins at the navel. Although this has the position of the umbilical vein, it is usually, as Sappey showed, a para-umbilical vein—that is, an enlarged vein by the side of the obliterated umbilical vessel. There may be produced about the navel a large bunch of varices, the so-called caput Medusæ. Other branches of this system occur in the gastro-epiploic omentum, about the gall-bladder, and, most important of all, in the suspensory ligament. These latter form large branches, which anastomose freely with the diaphragmatic veins, and so unite with the vena azygos. (2) By the anastomosis between the œsophageal and gastric veins. The veins at the lower end of the œsophagus may be enormously enlarged, producing varices which project on the mucous membrane. (3) The communications between the hæmorrhoidal and the inferior mesenteric veins. The freedom of communication in this direction is very variable, and in some instances the hæmorrhoidal veins are not much enlarged. (4) The veins of Retzius, which unite the radicles of the portal branches in the intestines and mesentery with the inferior vena cava and its branches. To this system belong the whole group of retroperitoneal veins, which are in most instances enormously enlarged, particularly about the kidneys, and which serve to carry off a considerable proportion of the portal blood.

Symptoms.—The most extreme grade of atrophic cirrhosis may exist without symptoms. *So long as the compensatory circulation is maintained* the patient may suffer little or no inconvenience. The remarkable efficiency of this collateral circulation is well seen in those rare instances of permanent obliteration of the portal vein. The symptoms may be divided into two groups—obstructive and toxic.

Obstructive.—The overfilling of the blood-vessels of the stomach and intestine lead to chronic catarrh, and the patients suffer with nausea and vomiting, particularly in the morning; the tongue is furred and the bowels are irregular. Hæmorrhage from the stomach may be an early symptom; it is often profuse and liable to recur. It seldom proves fatal. The amount vomited may be remarkable, as in a case already referred to, in which ten pounds were ejected in seven days. Following the hæmatemesis melæna is common; but hæmorrhages from the bowels may occur for several years without hæmatemesis. The bleeding very often comes from the œsophageal varices already described (p. 459). Enlargement of the spleen, usually regarded as a sign of the passive congestion, may, as Parkes Weber suggests, be due to a toxemia. The organ can usually be felt. Evidences of the establishment of the collateral circulation are seen in the enlarged epigastric and mammary veins, more rarely in the presence of the caput Medusæ and in the development of hæmorrhoids. The distended venules in the lower thoracic zone along the line of attachment of the diaphragm are not specially marked in cirrhosis. The most striking feature of failure in the compensatory circulation is ascites, the effusion of serous fluid into the peritoneal cavity. The conditions under which this occurs are still obscure. The abdomen gradually distends, may reach a large size, and contain as much as 15 or 20 litres. Œdema of the feet may precede or develop with the ascites. The dropsy rarely becomes general.

Jaundice is usually slight, and was present in only 35 of 130 cases of cirrhosis reported by Fagge. The skin has frequently a sallow, slightly icteroid tint. The urine is often reduced in amount, contains urates in abundance, often a slight amount of albumin, and, if jaundice is intense, tube-casts. The disease may be afebrile throughout, but in many cases, as shown by Carrington, there is slight fever, from 100° to 102.5°.

Examination at an early stage of the disease may show an enlarged and painful liver. Dreschfeld, Foxwell, and others in England have of late years called particular attention to the fact that in very many of the cases of alcoholic cirrhosis the organ is " enlarged at all stages of the disease, and that whether enlarged or contracted the clinical symptoms and course are much the same " (Foxwell). The patient may first come under observation for dyspepsia, hæmatemesis, slight jaundice, or nervous symptoms. Later in the disease, the patient has an unmistakable hepatic facies; he is thin, the eyes are sunken, the conjunctivæ watery, the nose and cheeks show distended venules, and the complexion is muddy or icteroid. On the enlarged abdomen the vessels are distended, and a bunch of dilated veins may surround the navel. When much fluid is in the peritonæum it is impossible to make a satisfactory examination, but after withdrawal the area of liver dulness is found to be diminished, particularly in the middle line, and on deep pressure the edge of the liver can be detected, and occasionally the hard, firm, and even granular surface. The spleen can be felt in the left hypochondriac region. Examination of the anus may reveal the presence of hæmorrhoids.

Toxic Symptoms.—At any stage of atrophic cirrhosis the patient may develop cerebral symptoms, either a noisy, joyous delirium, or stupor, coma, or even convulsions. The condition is not infrequently mistaken for uræmia. The nature of the toxic agent is not yet settled. The symptoms may develop without jaundice, and cannot be attributed to cholæmia, and they may come on in hospital when the patient has not had alcohol for weeks.

The fatty cirrhotic liver may produce symptoms similar to those of the atrophic form, but it more frequently is latent and is found accidentally in topers who have died from various diseases. The greater number of the cases clinically diagnosed as cirrhosis with enlargement come in this division.

Diagnosis.—With ascites, a well-marked history of alcoholism, the hepatic facies, and hæmorrhage from the stomach or bowels, the diagnosis is rarely doubtful. If, after withdrawal of the fluid, the spleen is found to be enlarged and the liver either not palpable or, if it is enlarged, hard and regular, the probabilities in favor of cirrhosis are very great. In the early stages of the disease, when the liver is increased in size, it may be impossible to say whether it is a cirrhotic or a fatty liver. The differential diagnosis between common and syphilitic cirrhosis can sometimes be made. A marked history of syphilis or the existence of other syphilitic lesions, with great irregularity in the surface or at the edge of the liver, are the points in favor of the latter. Thrombosis or obliteration of the portal vein can rarely be differentiated. In a case of fibroid transformation of the portal vein which came under my observation, the collateral circulation had been established for years, and the symptoms were simply those of extreme portal obstruction, such as occur in cirrhosis. Thrombosis of the portal vein is frequent in cirrhosis and may be characterized by a rapidly developing ascites.

Prognosis.—The prognosis is bad. When the collateral circulation is fully established the patient may have no symptoms whatever. Three cases of advanced atrophic cirrhosis have died under my observation of other affections without presenting during life any symptoms pointing to disease of the liver. There are instances, too, of enlargement of the liver, slight jaundice, cerebral symptoms, and even hæmatemesis, in which the liver becomes reduced in size, the symptoms disappear, and the patient may live in comparative comfort for many years. There are cases, too, possibly syphilitic, in which, after one or two tappings, the symptoms have disappeared and the patients have apparently recovered. Ascites is a very serious event in ordinary cirrhosis. Of 34 cases with ascites 10 died before tapping was necessary; 14 were tapped, and the average duration of life after the swelling was first noticed was only eight weeks; of 10 cases the diagnosis was wrong in 4, and in the remaining 6, who were tapped oftener than once, chronic peritonitis and perihepatitis were present (Hale White).

II. HYPERTROPHIC CIRRHOSIS (*Hanot*).

This well-characterized form was first described by Requin in 1846, but our accurate knowledge of the condition dates from the work of the lamented Hanot (1875), whose name in France it bears—*maladie de Hanot*.

Cirrhosis with enlargement occurs in the early stage of atrophic cirrhosis; there is an enlarged fatty and cirrhotic liver of alcoholics, a pigmentary form in diabetes has been described, and in association with syphilis the organ is often very large. The hypertrophic cirrhosis of Hanot is easily distinguished from these forms.

Etiology.—Males are more often affected than females—in 22 of Schachmann's 26 cases. The subjects are young; some of the cases in children probably belong to this form. Of four recent cases under my care the ages were from twenty to thirty-five. Two were brothers. Alcohol plays a minor part. Not one of the four cases referred to had been a heavy drinker. The absence of all known etiological factors is a remarkable feature in a majority of the cases.

Morbid Anatomy.—The organ is enlarged, weighing from 2,000 to 4,000 grammes. The form is maintained, the surface is smooth, or presents small granulations; the color in advanced cases is of a dark olive green; the consistence is greatly increased. The section is uniform, greenish yellow in color, and the liver lobules may be seen separated by connective tissue. The bile-passages present nothing abnormal. In a case without much jaundice exploratory operation showed a very large red organ, with a slightly roughened surface. Microscopically the following characteristics are described by French writers: The cirrhosis is mono- or multilobular, with a connective tissue rich in round cells. The bile-vessels are the seat of an angiocholitis, catarrhal and productive, and there is an extraordinary development of new biliary canaliculi. The liver-cells are neither fatty nor pigmented, and may be increased in size and show karyokinetic figures. From the supposed origin about the bile-vessels it has been called biliary cirrhosis, but the histological details have not yet been worked out fully, and the separation of this as a distinct form should, for the present at least, rest

upon clinical rather than anatomical grounds.   The spleen is greatly enlarged and may weigh 600 or more grammes.

Symptoms.—Hanot's hypertrophic cirrhosis presents the following
very characteristic group of symptoms.   As previously stated, the cases
occur in young persons; there is not, as a rule, an alcoholic history, and
males are usually affected: (*a*) A remarkably chronic course of from four
to six, or even ten years.   (*b*) Jaundice, usually slight, often not more than
a lemon tint, or a tinging of the conjunctivæ.   At any time during the
course an *icterus gravis*, with high fever and delirium, may develop.   There
is bile in the urine; the stools are not clay-colored as in obstructive jaundice,
but may be very dark and " bilious."   (*c*) Attacks of pain in the region of the
liver, which may be severe and associated with nausea and vomiting.   The
pain may be slight and dragging, and in some cases is not at all a prominent symptom.   The jaundice may deepen after attacks of pain.   (*d*)
Enlarged liver.   A fulness in the upper abdominal zone may be the first
complaint.   On inspection the enlargement may be very marked.   In one
of my cases the left lobe was unusually prominent and stood out almost
like a tumor.   An exploratory operation showed only an enlarged, smooth
organ without adhesions.   On palpation the hypertrophy is uniform, the
consistence is increased, and the edge distinct and hard.   The gall-bladder
is not enlarged.   The vertical flatness is much increased and may extend
from the sixth rib to the level of the navel.   (*e*) The spleen is enlarged, easily palpable, and very hard.   (*f*) Certain negative features are of moment—
absence of ascites and of dilatation of the subcutaneous veins of the abdomen.   Among other symptoms may be mentioned hæmorrhages.   One of
my cases had bleeding at the gums for a year; another had had for years
most remarkable attacks of purpura with urticaria.   Pruritus, xanthoma,
lichen, and telangiectasies may be present in the skin.   In one of my cases
the skin became very bronzed, almost as deeply as in Addison's disease.
Slight fever may be present, which increases during the crises of pain.
There may be a marked leucocytosis.   A curious attitude of the body has
been seen, in which the right shoulder and right side look dragged down.
The patients die with the symptoms of icterus gravis, from hæmorrhage,
from an intercurrent infection, or in a profound cachexia.   Certain of the
cases of cirrhosis of the liver in children are of this type; the enlargement
of the spleen may be very pronounced.

III. SYPHILITIC CIRRHOSIS.

This has already been considered in the section on syphilis (p. 249).   I
refer to it again to emphasize (1) its frequency; (2) the great importance of
its differentiation from the alcoholic form; (3) its curability in many cases;
and (4) the tumor formations in connection with it.

IV. CAPSULAR CIRRHOSIS—PERIHEPATITIS.

Local capsulitis is common in many conditions of the liver.   The form
of disease here described is characterized by an enormous thickening of the
entire capsule, with great contraction of the liver, but not necessarily with

36

special increase in the connective tissue of the organ itself. Our chief knowledge of the disease we owe to the Guy's Hospital physicians, particularly to Hilton Fagge and to Hale White, who has collected from the records 22 cases. The liver substance itself was "never markedly cirrhotic; its tissue was nearly always soft." Chronic capsulitis of the spleen and a chronic proliferative peritonitis are almost invariably present. In 19 of the 22 cases the kidneys were granular. Hale White regards it as a sequel of interstitial nephritis. The youngest case in his series was twenty-nine. The symptoms are those of atrophic cirrhosis—ascites, often recurring and requiring many tappings. Jaundice is not often present. I have met with two groups of cases—the one in adults usually with ascites and regarded as ordinary cirrhosis. I have never made a diagnosis in such a case. Signs of interstitial nephritis, recurring ascites, and absence of jaundice are regarded by Hale White as important diagnostic points. In the second group of cases the perihepatitis, perisplenitis, and proliferative peritonitis are associated with adherent pericardium and chronic mediastinitis. In one such case the diagnosis of capsular hepatitis was very clear, as the liver could be grasped in the hand and formed a rounded, smooth organ resembling the spleen. The child was tapped 121 times (Archives of Pædiatrics, 1896).

Treatment of the Cirrhoses.—Ordinary cirrhosis of the liver is an incurable disease. Many writers, speaking of the curability of certain forms, show a lack of appreciation of the essential conditions upon which the symptoms depend. So far as we have any knowledge, no remedies at our disposal can alter or remove the cicatricial connective tissue which constitutes the *materia peccans* in ordinary cirrhosis. On the other hand, we know that extreme grades of contraction of the liver may persist for years without symptoms when the compensatory circulation exists. The so-called cure of cirrhosis means the re-establishment of this compensation; and it would be as unreasonable to speak of healing a chronic valvular lesion when with digitalis we have restored the circulatory balance as it is to speak of curing cirrhosis of the liver, when by tapping and other measures the compensation has in some way been restored.

The patient should abstain entirely from alcohol, and, if possible, should take a milk diet, which has been highly recommended by Semmola. In any case, the diet should be nutritious, but not too rich. Measures should be employed to reduce the gastro-intestinal catarrh, and the patient should lead a quiet, out-of-door life and keep the skin active, the bowels regular, and the urine abundant. In non-syphilitic cases it is useless to give either mercury or iodide of potassium. When a well-marked history of syphilis exists these remedies should be used, but neither of them has any more influence upon the development of a new growth of connective tissue in the liver than it has upon the progressive development of a scar tissue in a keloid or in an ordinary developing cicatrix. The ascites should be tapped early, and the operation may be repeated so soon as the distention becomes distressing. The continuous drainage with a Southey's tube may be employed. It is much better to resort to tapping early if after a few days' trial the fluid does not subside rapidly under the use of saline purges.

from half an ounce to an ounce and a half of sulphate of magnesia may be given in as little water as possible half an hour before breakfast. Elaterium, the compound jalap powder, or the bitartrate of potash may also be employed. Digitalis and squills are often useful. Surgical treatment has been advocated of late. The fluid is thoroughly drained and the surface of the liver and spleen and the parietal peritonæum is then firmly scrubbed, so as to promote adhesions, in which compensatory vessels could develop. Of three cases recently treated in my wards in this way one has recovered. In the syphilitic cases, or when syphilis is suspected, iodide of potassium may be given in doses of from 15 to 30 drops of the saturated solution three times a day, and mercury, which is conveniently given with squills and digitalis in the form of Addison's or Niemeyer's pill. A patient of well-marked syphilitic cirrhosis with recurring ascites, in which tapping was resorted to on eight or ten occasions, took this pill at intervals for a year with the greatest benefit and subsequently had four years of tolerably good health.

VIII. ABSCESS OF THE LIVER.

Etiology.—Suppuration within the liver, either in the parenchyma or in the blood or bile passages, occurs under the following conditions:

(1) The tropical abscess. In hot climates this form may develop idiopathically, but more commonly follows dysentery. It frequently occurs among Europeans in India, particularly those who drink alcohol freely and are exposed to great heat. The relation of this form of abscess to dysentery is still under discussion, and Anglo-Indian practitioners are by no means unanimous on the subject. Certainly cases may develop without a history of previous dysentery, and there have been fatal cases without any affection of the large bowel. In this country the large solitary tropical abscess also occurs, oftenest in the Southern States. In Baltimore it is not very infrequent.

The relation of this form of abscess to the *amœba coli* has been carefully studied by Kartulis and exhaustively considered in a monograph by Councilman and Lafleur. The descriptions and illustrations of these authors are most convincing as to the direct etiological association of this organism with liver abscess. Clinically the patient may have *amœbæ coli* in the stools and well-marked signs of liver abscess without marked symptoms of dysentery and even with the fæces well formed.

(2) Traumatism is an occasional cause. The injury is generally in the hepatic region. Two instances have come under my notice of it in brakemen who were injured while coupling cars. Injury to the head is not infrequently followed by liver abscess.

(3) Embolic or pyæmic abscesses are the most numerous, and may develop in a general pyæmia from any cause or follow foci of suppuration in the territory of the portal vessels. The infective agents may reach the liver through the hepatic artery, as in those cases in which the original focus of infection is in the area of the systemic circulation; though it may happen occasionally that the infective agent, instead of passing through

the lungs, reaches the liver through the inferior vena cava and the hepatic veins. A remarkable instance of multiple abscesses of arterial origin was afforded by the case of aneurism of the hepatic artery reported by Ross and myself. Infection through the portal vein is much more common. It results from dysentery and other ulcerative affections of the bowels, appendicitis, occasionally after typhoid fever, in rectal affections, and in abscesses in the pelvis. In these cases the abscesses are multiple and, as a rule, within the branches of the portal vein—suppurative pylephlebitis.

(4) A not uncommon cause of suppuration is inflammation of the bile-passages caused by gall-stones, more rarely by parasites—suppurative cholangitis.

In some instances of tuberculosis of the liver the affection is chiefly of the bile-ducts, with the formation of multiple tuberculous abscesses containing a bile-stained pus.

(5) Foreign bodies and parasites. In rare instances foreign bodies, such as a needle, may pass from the stomach or gullet, lodge in the liver, and excite an abscess, or, as in several instances which have been reported, a foreign body, such as a needle or a fish-bone, has perforated a branch or the portal vein itself and induced extensive pylephlebitis. Echinococcus cysts frequently cause suppuration; the penetration of round worms into the liver less commonly; and most rarely of all the liver-fluke.

Morbid Anatomy.—(a) *Of the Solitary or Tropical Abscess.*—This is not always single; there may be two or even more large abscess cavities, ranging in size from an orange to a child's head. The largest-sized abscess may contain from 3 to 6 litres of pus and involve more than three fourths of the entire organ. In Waring's statistics, 62 per cent of the cases were single. The abscess in nearly 70 per cent of the cases was in the right lobe, more toward the convexity than the concave side. In long-standing cases the abscess-wall may be firm and thick, but, as a rule, the cavity possesses no definite limiting membrane, and section of the wall shows an internal layer grayish in color, shreddy, and made up of necrotic liver substance, pus-cells, and amœbæ; a middle layer, brownish red in color; and an external zone of hyperæmic liver tissue. The pus is often reddish brown in color, closely resembling anchovy sauce. In other instances it is grayish white, mucoid, and may be quite creamy. The odor is at times very peculiar. In one instance it had the sour smell of chyme, though no connection with the stomach was found. In amœbic dysentery there may also be multiple miliary abscesses in the liver, containing amœbæ.

The bacteriological examination of the contents show either a sterile pus or, in some cases, staphylococci, streptococci, or the colon bacillus. The termination of this form of abscess may be as follows, as noted in Waring's 300 cases: Remained intact, 56 per cent; opened by operation, 16 per cent; perforated the right pleura, nearly 5 per cent; ruptured into the right lung, 9 per cent; ruptured into the peritonæum, 5 per cent; ruptured into the colon, nearly 3 per cent; and there were, in addition, instances which ruptured into the hepatic and bile-vessels and into the gall-bladder. Flexner has reported two cases of perforation into the inferior vena cava. For a full consideration of the subject of amœbic abscess of the liver the reader is referred to Lafleur's article in Allbutt's System of Medicine.

(b) *Of Septic and Pyæmic Abscesses.*—These are usually multiple, though occasionally, following injury, there may be a large solitary collection of pus.

In suppurative pylephlebitis the liver is uniformly enlarged. The capsule may be smooth and the external surface of the organ of normal appearance. In other instances, numerous yellowish-white points appear beneath the capsule. On section there are isolated pockets of pus, either having a round outline or in some places distinctly dendritic, and from these the pus may be squeezed. They look like small, solitary abscesses, but, on probing, are found to communicate with the portal vein and to represent its branches, distended and suppurating. The entire portal system within the liver may be involved; sometimes territories are cut off by thrombi. The suppuration may extend into the main branch or even into the mesenteric and gastric veins. The pus may be fetid and is often bile-stained; it may, however, be thick, tenacious, and laudable. In suppurative cholangitis there is usually obstruction by gall-stones, the ducts are greatly distended, the gall-bladder enlarged and full of pus, and the branches within the liver are extremely distended, so that on section there is an appearance not unlike that described in pylephlebitis.

Suppuration about the echinococcus cysts may be very extensive, forming enormous abscesses, the characters of which are at once recognized by the remnants of the cysts.

Symptoms.—(a) *Of the Large Solitary Abscess.*—In the tropics there are instances in which the abscess appears to be latent and to run a course without definite symptoms; death may occur suddenly from rupture.

Fever, pain, enlargement of the liver, and the development of a septic condition are the important symptoms of hepatic abscess. The temperature is elevated at the outset and is of an intermittent or septic type. It is irregular, and may remain normal or even subnormal for a few days; then the patient has a rigor and the temperature rises to 103° or higher. Owing to this intermittent character of the fever the cases are usually, in this latitude, mistaken for malaria. The fever may rise every afternoon without a rigor. Profuse sweating is common, particularly when the patient falls asleep. In chronic cases there may be little or no fever. One of my patients, with a liver abscess which had perforated the lung, coughed up pus after his temperature had been normal for weeks. The pain is variable, and is usually referred to the back or shoulder; or there is a dull aching sensation in the right hypochondrium. When turned on the left side, the patient often complains of a heavy, dragging sensation, so that he usually prefers to lie on the right side; at least, this has been the case in a majority of the instances which have come under my observation. Pain on pressure over the liver is usually present, particularly on deep pressure at the costal margin in the nipple line.

The enlargement of the liver is most marked in the right lobe, and, as the abscess cavity is usually situated more toward the upper than the under surface, the increase in volume is upward and to the right, not downward, as in cancer and the other affections producing enlargement. Percussion in the mid-sternal and parasternal lines may show a normal limit. At the nipple-line the curve of liver dulness begins to rise, and in the mid-axillary it may reach the fifth rib, while behind, near the spine, the area of dulness may be almost on a level with the angle of the scapula. Of course there are instances in which this characteristic feature is not present, as when the abscess occupies the left lobe. The enlargement of the liver may be so great as to cause bulging of the right side, and the edge may project a hand's-breadth or more below the costal margin. In such instances the surface is smooth. Palpation is painful, and there may be fremitus on deep inspiration. In some instances fluctuation may be detected. Adhesions may form to the abdominal wall and the abscess may point below the margin of the ribs, or even in the epigastric region. In many cases the appearance of the patient is suggestive. The skin has a sallow, slightly icteroid tint, the face is pale, the complexion muddy, the conjunctivæ are infiltrated, and often slightly bile-tinged. There is in the facies and in the general appearance of the patient a strong suggestion of the existence of abscess. There is no internal affection associated with suppuration which gives, I think, just the same hue as certain instances of abscess of the liver. Marked jaundice is rare. Diarrhœa may be present and may give an important clew to the nature of the case, particularly if amœbæ are found in the stools. Constipation may occur.

Remarkable and characteristic symptoms arise when the abscess invades the lung. The extension may occur through the diaphragm, without actual rupture, and with the production of a purulent pleurisy and invasion of the lung. The patients gradually develop a severe cough, usually of an aggravated and convulsive character, there are signs of involvement at the base of the right lung, defective resonance, feeble tubular breathing, and increase in the tactile fremitus; but the most characteristic feature is the presence of a reddish-brown expectoration of a brick-dust color, resembling anchovy sauce. This, which was noted originally by Budd, was present in our cases, and in addition Reese and Lafleur found the *amœbæ coli* identical with those which exist in the liver abscess and in the stools. They are present in variable numbers and display active amœboid movements. The brownish tint of the expectoration is due to blood-pigment and blood-corpuscles, and there may be orange-red crystals or hæmatoidin.

The abscess may perforate externally, as mentioned already, or into the stomach or bowel; occasionally into the pericardium. The duration of this form is very variable. It may run its course and prove fatal in six or eight weeks or may persist for several years.

The prognosis is serious, as the mortality is more than 50 per cent. The death-rate has been lowered of late years, owing to the greater fearlessness with which surgeons now attack these cases.

(b) *Of the Pyæmic Abscess and Suppurative Pylephlebitis.*—Clinically these conditions cannot be separated. Occurring in a general pyæmia, no special features may be added to the case. When there is suppuration within the portal vein the liver is uniformly enlarged and tender, though pain may not be a marked feature. There is an irregular, septic fever, and the complexion is muddy, sometimes distinctly icteroid. The features are indeed those of pyæmia, plus a slight icteroid tinge, and an enlarged and painful liver. The latter features alone are peculiar. The sweats, chills, prostration, and fever have nothing distinctive.

Diagnosis.—Abscess of the liver may be confounded with intermittent fever, a common mistake in malarial regions. Practically an intermittent fever which resists quinine is not malarial. Laveran's organisms are also absent from the blood. When the abscess bursts into the pleura a right-sided empyema is produced and perforation of the lung usually follows. When the liver abscess has been latent and dysenteric symptoms have not been marked, the condition may be considered empyema or abscess of the lung. In such cases the anchovy-sauce-like color of the pus and the presence of the amœbæ will enable one to make a definite diagnosis, as has been done in cases by Lafleur. Perforation externally is readily recognized, and yet in an abscess cavity in the epigastric region it may be difficult to say whether it has proceeded from the liver or is in the abdominal wall. When the abscess is large, and the adhesions are so firm that the liver does not descend during inspiration, the exploratory needle does not make an up-and-down movement during aspiration. In an instance of this kind which I saw with Hearn at the Philadelphia Hospital, all the features, local and general, seemed to point to abscess in the abdominal wall, but the operation revealed a large perforating abscess cavity in the left lobe of the liver. The diagnosis of suppurating echinococcus cyst is rarely possible, except in Australia and Iceland, where hydatids are so common.

Perhaps the most important affection from which suppuration within the liver is to be separated is the intermittent hepatic fever associated with gall-stones. Of the cases reported a majority have been considered due to suppuration, and in two of my cases the liver had been repeatedly aspirated. Post-mortem examinations have shown conclusively that the high fever and chills may recur at intervals for years without suppuration in the ducts. The distinctive features of this condition are paroxysms of fever with rigors and sweats—which may occur with great regularity, but which more often are separated by long intervals—the deepening of the jaundice after the paroxysms, the entire apyrexia in the intervals, and the maintenance of the general nutrition. The time element also is important, as in some of these cases the disease has lasted for several years. Finally, it is to be remembered that abscess of the liver, in temperate climates at least, is invariably secondary, and the primary source must be carefully sought for, either in dysentery, slight ulceration of the rectum, suppurating hæmorrhoids, ulcer of the stomach, or in suppurative diseases of other parts of the body, particularly in the skull or in the bones.

The presence of a leucocytosis is the most important feature in all forms of suppuration of the liver.

In suspected cases, whether the liver is enlarged or not, exploratory aspiration may be performed without risk. The needle may be entered in the anterior axillary line in the lowest interspace, or in the seventh interspace in the mid-axillary line, or over the centre of the area of dulness behind. The patient should be placed under ether, for it may be necessary to make several deep punctures. It is not well to use too small an aspirator. No ill effects follow this procedure, even though blood may leak into the peritoneal cavity. Extensive suppuration may exist, and yet be missed in the aspiration, particularly when the branches of the portal vein are distended with pus.

Treatment.—Pyæmic abscess and suppurative pylephlebitis are invariably fatal. Treves, however, reports a case of pyæmic abscess following appendicitis in which the patient recovered after an exploratory operation. Surgical measures are not justified in these cases, unless an abscess shows signs of pointing. As the abscesses associated with dysentery are often single, they afford a reasonable hope of benefit from operation. If, however, the patient is expectorating the pus, if the general condition is good and the hectic fever not marked, it is best to defer operation, as many of these instances recover spontaneously. The large single abscesses are the most favorable for operation. The general medical treatment of the cases is that of ordinary septicæmia.

IX. NEW GROWTHS IN THE LIVER.

These may be cancer, either primary or secondary, sarcoma, or angioma.

Etiology.—Cancer of the liver is third in order of frequency of internal cancer. It is rarely primary, usually secondary to cancer in other organs. It is a disease of late adult life. According to Leichtenstern, over 50 per cent of the cases occur between the fortieth and the sixtieth years. It occasionally occurs in children. Women are attacked less frequently than men. It is stated by some authors that secondary cancer is more common in women, owing to the frequency of cancer of the uterus. Heredity is believed to have an influence in from 15 to 20 per cent.

In many cases trauma is an antecedent, and cancer of the bile-passages is associated in many instances with gall-stones. Cancer is stated to be less common in the tropics. Its relative proportion to other diseases may be judged from the fact that among the first 3,000 patients admitted to the wards of the Johns Hopkins Hospital there were seven cases of cancer of the liver.

Morbid Anatomy.—The following forms of new growths occur in the liver and have a clinical importance:

Cancer.—(1) *Primary cancer*, of which three forms may be recognized.[*]

(*a*) The *massive cancer*, which causes great enlargement and on section shows a uniform mass of new growth, which occupies a large portion of the organ. It is grayish white, usually not softened, and is abruptly outlined from the contiguous liver substance.

(*b*) *Nodular cancer*, in which the liver is occupied by nodular masses, some large, some small, irregularly scattered throughout the organ. Usually in one region there is a larger, perhaps firmer, older-looking mass, which indicates the primary seat, and the numerous nodules are secondary to it.

---

[*] Hanot and Gilbert, Études sur les Maladies du Foie, Paris, 1888.

This form is much like the secondary cancerous involvement, except that it seldom reaches a large size.

(*c*) The third is the remarkable and rare variety, *cancer with cirrhosis*, which forms an anatomical picture perfectly unique and at first very puzzling. The liver is not much enlarged, rarely weighing more than $2\frac{1}{2}$ or 3 kilogrammes. The surface is grayish yellow, studded over with nodular yellowish masses, resembling the projections in an ordinary cirrhotic liver. On section the cancerous nodules are seen scattered throughout the entire organ, varying in diameter from 3 to 10 or more millimetres and surrounded with fibrous tissue.

Histologically, the primary cancers are epitheliomata—alveolar and trabecular. The character of the cells varies greatly. In some varieties they are polymorphous; in others small polyhedral; in others, again, giant cells are found. In rare instances, as in one described by Greenfield, the cells are cylindrical. The trabecular form of epithelioma is also known as adenoma or adeno-carcinoma.

(2) *Secondary Cancer.*—The organ is usually enormously enlarged, and may weigh 20 pounds or more. The cancerous nodules project beneath the capsule, and can be felt during life or even seen through the thin abdominal walls. They are usually disseminated equally, though in rare instances they may be confined to one lobe. The consistence of the nodules varies; in some cases they are firm and hard and those on the surface show a distinct umbilication, due to the shrinking of the fibrous tissue in the centre. These superficial cancerous masses are still sometimes spoken of as " Farre's tubercles." More frequently the masses are on section grayish white in color, or hæmorrhagic. Rupture of blood-vessels is not uncommon in these cases. In one specimen there was an enormous clot beneath the capsule of the liver, together with hæmorrhage into the gall-bladder and into the peritonæum. The secondary cancer shows the same structure as the initial lesion, and is usually either an alveolar or cylindrical carcinoma. Degeneration is common in these secondary growths; thus the hyaline transformation may convert large areas into a dense, dry, grayish-yellow mass. Extensive areas of fatty degeneration may occur, sclerosis is not uncommon, and hæmorrhages are frequent. Suppuration sometimes follows.

(3) *Cancer of the bile-passages* which has been already considered.

Sarcoma.—Of primary sarcoma of the liver very few cases have been reported. Secondary sarcoma is more frequent, and many examples of lympho-sarcoma and myxo-sarcoma are on record, less frequently glio-sarcoma or the smooth or striped myoma.

The most important form is the melano-sarcoma, which develops in the liver secondarily to sarcoma of the eye or of the skin. Very rarely melano-sarcoma develops primarily in the liver. Of the reported cases Hanot excludes all but one. In this form the liver is greatly enlarged, is either uniformly infiltrated with the cancer, which gives the cut surface the appearance of dark granite, or there are large nodular masses of a deep black or marbled color. There are usually extensive metastases, and in some instances every organ of the body is involved. Nodules of melano-sarcoma of the skin may give a clew to the diagnosis. Hamburger (J. H. H. Bulletin, 1898) has reported the cases which have been in my wards.

Other Forms of Liver Tumor.—One of the commonest tumors in the liver is the angioma, which occurs as a small, reddish body the size of a walnut, and consists simply of a series of dilated vessels. Occasionally in children angiomata have developed and produced large tumors.

Cysts are occasionally found in the liver, either single, which are not very uncommon, or multiple, when they usually coexist with congenital cystic kidneys.

Symptoms.—It is often impossible to differentiate primary and secondary cancer of the liver unless the primary seat of the disease is evident, as in the case of scirrhus of the breast, or cancer of the rectum, or of a tumor in the stomach, which can be felt. As a rule, cancer of the liver is associated with progressive enlargement; but there are cases of primary nodular cancer, and in the cancer with cirrhosis the organ may not be enlarged. Gastric disturbance, loss of appetite, nausea, and vomiting are frequent. Progressive loss of flesh and strength may be the first symptoms. Pain or a sensation of uneasiness in the right hypochondriac region may be present, but enormous enlargement of the liver may occur without the slightest pain. Jaundice, which is present in at least one half of the cases, is usually of moderate extent, unless the common duct is occluded. Ascites is rare, except in the form of cancer with cirrhosis, in which the clinical picture is that of the atrophic form. Pressure by nodules on the portal vein or extension of the cancer to the peritonæum may also induce ascites.

Inspection shows the abdomen to be distended, particularly in the upper zone. In late stages of the disease, when emaciation is marked, the cancerous nodules can be plainly seen beneath the skin, and in rare instances even the umbilications. The superficial veins are enlarged. On palpation the liver is felt, a hand's-breadth or more below the costal margin, descending with each inspiration. The surface is usually irregular, and may present large masses or smaller nodular bodies, either rounded or with central depressions. In instances of diffuse infiltration the liver may be greatly enlarged and present a perfectly smooth surface. The growth is progressive, and the edge of the liver may ultimately extend below the level of the navel. Although generally uniform and producing enlargement of the whole organ, occasionally, when the tumor develops from the left lobe, it may form a solid mass, which occupies the epigastric region. By percussion the outline can be accurately limited and the progressive growth of the tumor estimated. The spleen is rarely enlarged. Pyrexia is present in many cases, usually a continuous fever, ranging from 100° to 102°; it may be intermittent, with rigors. This may be associated with the cancer alone, or, as in one of my cases, with suppuration. Œdema of the feet, from anæmia, usually supervenes. Cancer of the liver kills in from three to fifteen months. One patient lived for more than two years.

Diagnosis.—The diagnosis is easy when the liver is greatly enlarged and the surface nodular. The smoother forms of diffuse carcinoma may at first be mistaken for fatty or amyloid liver, but the presence of jaundice, the rapid enlargement, and the more marked cachexia will usually suffice to differentiate it. Perhaps the most puzzling conditions occur in the rare cases of enlarged amyloid liver with irregular gummata. The large echinococcus liver may present a striking similarity to carcinoma, but the projecting nodules are usually softer, the disease lasts much longer, and the cachexia is not marked.

Hypertrophic cirrhosis may at first be mistaken for carcinoma, as the jaundice is usually deep and the liver very large; but the absence of a marked cachexia and wasting, and the painless, smooth character of the enlargement are points against cancer. When in doubt in these cases, aspiration may be safely performed, and positive indication may be gained from the materials so obtained. In large, rapidly growing secondary cancers the superficial rounded masses may almost fluctuate and these soft tumor-like projections may contain blood. The form of cancer with cirrhosis can scarcely be separated from atrophic cirrhosis itself. Perhaps the wasting is more extreme and more rapid, but the jaundice and the ascites are identical. Melano-sarcoma causes great enlargement of the organ. There are frequently symptoms of involvement of other viscera, as the lungs, kidneys, or spleen. Secondary tumors may develop on the skin. A very important symptom, not present in all cases, is melanuria, the passage of a very dark-colored urine, which may, however, when first voided, be quite normal in color. The existence of a melano-sarcoma of the eye, or the history of blindness in one eye, with subsequent extirpation, may indicate at once the true nature of the hepatic enlargement. The secondary tumors may develop some time after the extirpation of the eye, as in a case under the care of J. C. Wilson, at the Philadelphia Hospital, or, as in a case under Tyson at the same institution, the patient may have a sarcoma of the choroid which had never caused any symptoms.

The *treatment* must be entirely symptomatic—allaying the pain, relieving the gastric disturbance, and meeting other symptoms as they arise.

X. FATTY LIVER.

Two different forms of this condition are recognized—the fatty infiltration and fatty degeneration.

Fatty infiltration occurs, to a certain extent, in normal livers, since the cells always contain minute globules of oil.

In fatty degeneration, which is a much less common condition, the protoplasm of the liver-cells is destroyed and the fat takes its place, as seen in cases of malignant jaundice and in phosphorus poisoning.

Fatty liver occurs under the following conditions: (a) In association with general obesity, in which case the liver appears to be one of the storehouses of the excessive fat. (b) In conditions in which the oxidation processes are interfered with, as in cachexia, profound anæmia, and in phthisis. The fatty infiltration of the liver in heavy drinkers is to be attributed to the excessive demand made by the alcohol upon the oxygen. (c) Certain poisons, of which phosphorus is the most characteristic, produce an intense fatty degeneration with necrosis of the liver-cells. The poison of acute yellow atrophy, whatever its nature, acts in the same way.

The fatty liver is uniformly increased in size. The edge may reach below the level of the navel. It is smooth, looks pale and bloodless; on section it is dry, and renders the surface of the knife greasy. The liver may weigh many pounds, and yet the specific gravity is so low that the entire organ floats in water.

The symptoms of fatty liver are not definite. Jaundice is never present; the stools may be light-colored, but even in the most advanced grades the bile is still formed. Signs of portal obstruction are rare. Hæmorrhoids are not very infrequent. Altogether, the symptoms are ill-defined, and chiefly those of the disease with which the degeneration is associated. In cases of great obesity, the physical examination is uncertain; but in phthisis and cachectic conditions, the organ can be felt to be greatly enlarged, though smooth and painless. Fatty livers are among the largest met with at the bedside.

XI. AMYLOID LIVER.

The waxy, lardaceous, or amyloid liver occurs as part of a general degeneration, associated with cachexias, particularly when the result of long-standing suppuration.

In practice, it is found oftenest in the prolonged suppuration of tuberculous disease, either of the lungs or of the bones. Next in order of frequency are the cases associated with syphilis. Here there may be ulceration of the rectum, with which it is often connected, or chronic disease of the bone, or it may be present when there are no suppurative changes. It is found occasionally in rickets, in prolonged convalescence from the infectious fevers, and in the cachexia of cancer.

The amyloid liver is large, and may attain dimensions equalled only by those of the cancerous organ. Wilks speaks of a liver weighing fourteen pounds. It is solid, firm, resistant, on section anæmic, and has a semitranslucent, infiltrated appearance. Stained with a dilute solution of iodine, the areas infiltrated with the amyloid matter assume a rich mahogany-brown color. The precise nature of this change is still in question. It first attacks the capillaries, usually of the median zone of the lobules, and subsequently the interlobular vessels and the connective tissue. The cells are but little if at all affected.

There are no characteristic *symptoms* of this condition. Jaundice does not occur; the stools may be light-colored, but the secretion of bile persists. The physical examination shows the organ to be uniformly enlarged and painless, the surface smooth, the edges rounded, and the consistence greatly increased. Sometimes the edge, even in very great enlargement, is sharp and hard. The spleen also may be involved, but there are no evidences of portal obstruction.

The *diagnosis* of the condition is, as a rule, easy. Progressive and great enlargement in connection with suppuration of long standing or with syphilis, is almost always of this nature. In rare instances, however, the amyloid liver is reduced in size.

In *leukæmia* the liver may attain considerable size and be smooth and uniform, resembling, on physical examination, the fatty organ. The blood condition at once indicates the true nature of the case.

XII. ANOMALIES IN FORM AND POSITION OF THE LIVER.

In transposition of the viscera the right lobe of the organ may occupy the left side. A common and important anomaly is the tilting forward of the organ, so that the long axis is vertical, not transverse. Instead of the edge of the right lobe presenting just below the costal margin, a considerable portion of the surface of the lobe is in contact with the abdominal parietes, and the edge may be felt as low, perhaps, as the navel. This anteversion is apt to be mistaken for enlargement of the organ.

The "lacing" liver is met with in two chief types. In one, the anterior portion, chiefly of the right lobe, is greatly prolonged, and may reach the transverse navel line, or even lower. A shallow transverse groove separates the thin extension from the main portion of the organ. The peritoneal coating of this groove may be fibroid, and in rare instances the deformed portion is connected with the organ by an almost tendinous membrane. The liver may be compressed laterally and have a pyramidal shape, and the extreme left border and the hinder margin of the left lobe may be much folded and incurved. The projecting portion of the liver, extending low in the right flank, may be mistaken for a tumor, or more frequently for a movable right kidney. Its continuity with the liver itself may not be evident on palpation or on percussion, as coils of intestine may lie in front. It descends, however, with inspiration, and usually the margin can be traced continuously with that of the left lobe of the liver. The greatest difficulty arises when this anomalous lappet of the liver is either naturally very thick and united to the liver by a very thin membrane, or when it is swollen in conditions of great congestion of the organ.

The other principal type of lacing liver is quite different in shape. It is thick, broader above than below, and lies almost entirely above the transverse line of the cartilages. There is a narrow groove just above the anterior border, which is placed more transversely than normal.*

Movable Liver.—This rare condition has received much attention of late, and J. E. Graham, in a recent paper, has collected 70 reported cases from the literature. In a very considerable number of these there has been a mistaken diagnosis. A slight grade of mobility of the organ is found in the pendulous abdomen of enteroptosis, and after repeated ascites.

The organ is so connected at its posterior margin with the inferior vena cava and diaphragm that any great mobility from this point is im-

---

* See P. Hertz, Abnormitäten in der Lage und Form der Bauchorgane, Berlin, 1894.

possible, except on the theory of a meso-hepar or congenital ligamentous union between these structures. The ligaments, however, may show an extreme grade of relaxation (the suspensory 7.5 cm., and the triangular ligament 4 cm., in one of Leube's cases); and when the patient is in the erect posture the organ may drop down so far that its upper surface is entirely below the costal margin. The condition is rarely met with in men; 56 of the cases were in women.

IX. DISEASES OF THE PANCREAS.

The importance of diseases of the pancreas has been emphasized, particularly through studies made in this country by F. W. Draper on hæmorrhage and by Fitz on acute pancreatitis, while those of Senn have created a surgery of the gland. An additional interest has been given to the organ by the work of v. Mering and Minkowski on pancreatic diabetes. The works of Claessen (1842) and of Ancelet (1866) give the older literature. The modern study of the subject dates from Senn's paper in the American Journal of the Medical Sciences, 1885, and Fitz's Middleton Goldsmith Lecture for 1889. In rewriting this section I have drawn freely on Körte's recent monograph.

I. HÆMORRHAGE.

Both Spiess (1866) and Zenker (1874) were acquainted with hæmorrhage into the pancreas as a cause of sudden death, but the great medico-legal importance of the subject was first fully recognized by F. W. Draper, of Boston, whose townsmen, Harris, Fitz, Whitney, and others have contributed additional studies. In 4,000 autopsies Draper met with 19 cases of pancreatic hæmorrhage, in 9 or 10 of which no other cause of death was found. When the bleeding is extensive the entire tissue of the gland is destroyed and the blood invades the retro-peritoneal tissue. In other instances the peritoneal covering is broken and the blood fills the lesser peritonæum (see hæmo-peritonæum). The hæmorrhage may be in connection with an acute pancreatitis or with necrotic inflammation of the gland. In an instance in which there was a small growth in the tail of the pancreas I found hæmorrhage into the gland and into the retro-peritonæum, forming a blood sac which surrounded the left kidney.

Zenker suggests that the sudden death in these cases is due to shock through the solar plexus.

The *symptoms* are thus briefly summarized by Prince: " The patient, who has previously been perfectly well, is suddenly taken with the illness which terminates his life. . . . When the hæmorrhage occurs the patient may be quietly resting or pursuing his usual occupation. The pain which ushers in the attack is usually very severe and located in the upper part of the abdomen. It steadily increases in severity, is sharp or perhaps colicky in character. It is almost from the first accompanied by nausea and vomiting; the latter becomes frequent and obstinate, but gives no relief. The patient soon becomes anxious, restless, and depressed; he tosses about, and only with difficulty can he be restrained in bed. The surface is cold and the forehead is covered with a cold sweat. The pulse is weak, rapid, and sooner or later imperceptible. The abdomen becomes tender, the tenderness being located in the upper part of the abdomen or epigastrium. Tympanites is sometimes marked. The temperature in most cases is either normal or below normal. The bowels are apt to be constipated. These symptoms continue without relief, those which are most striking being the pain, vomiting, anxiousness, restlessness, and the state of collapse into which the patient soon falls."

It has been suggested in such cases to open the abdomen, expose the pancreas, and relieve the tension, since the fatal result is often due to the pressure and not to the loss of blood.

II. ACUTE PANCREATITIS.

(a) **Acute Hæmorrhagic Pancreatitis.**—In this form the inflammation is combined with hæmorrhage, and it is difficult to separate clearly the two processes.

Etiology.—Körte has collected 41 instances, of which only 4 were in women. A large majority of the cases occur in adult males. McPhedran has reported one in a nine months' old child. Many of the patients had been addicted to alcohol; others had suffered occasionally with severe pains and vomiting.

Morbid Anatomy.—The pancreas is found enlarged, and the interlobular tissue infiltrated with blood, and perhaps with clots. In some instances the contiguous tissues may also be hæmorrhagic, and the whole may form a large, firm mass, situated at the upper and back part of the abdominal cavity. The root of the mesentery, the mesocolon, and the omentum may also show hæmorrhages; the other organs may be practically normal. As a rule there can be seen about the lobules areas of opaque white tissue, and upon the omentum and mesentery similar opaque, white specks, which will be referred to subsequently as the fatty necrosis of Balser. In spots the gland-cells may also be found necrotic, while there may be cases showing a marked increase in the fibrous tissue.

Symptoms.—One of the most characteristic features is the suddenness of the onset, usually with violent colicky pain in the upper part of the abdomen. Nausea and vomiting follow, with collapse symptoms, more or less severe according to the intensity of the attack. The abdomen becomes swollen and tense and there is constipation. The temperature at first may be low; subsequenly fever sets in, sometimes initiated by a chill. There may be early delirium. Collapse symptoms supervene, and death occurs usually from the second to the fourth day, or even earlier. The swelling and infiltration in the region of the pancreas necessarily involve the coeliac plexus, and the stretching of the nerves may account for the agonizing pain and the sudden collapse. In a case which I have reported the semilunar ganglia were swollen, the nerve-cells indistinct, and there was an interstitial infiltration of round cells. The Pacinian corpuscles in the neighborhood of the pancreas were enormously swollen and œdematous.

Deep pressure on the upper part of the abdomen may give evidence of circumscribed resistance.

Diagnosis.—Intestinal obstruction or acute perforating peritonitis is usually suspected. Now that the condition has become better known the diagnosis *intra viram* has been made (by Fitz and by Thayer). "Acute pancreatitis is to be suspected when a previously healthy person or a sufferer from occasional attacks of indigestion is suddenly seized with a violent pain in the epigastrium followed by vomiting and collapse, and in the course of twenty-four hours by a circumscribed epigastric swelling, tympanitic or resistant, with slight elevation of temperature. Circumscribed tenderness in the course of the pancreas and tender spots throughout the abdomen are valuable diagnostic signs" (Fitz). An interesting case admitted to the Johns Hopkins Hospital illustrates a common mistake. The young man had had symptoms of obstruction of the bowels for three or four days. The abdomen was distended, tender, and very painful. I saw him on admission, agreed in the diagnosis of probable obstruction, and ordered him to be transferred at once to the operating-room. Halsted found no evidence of obstruction, but in the region of the pancreas and at the root of the mesentery there was a dense, thick, indurated mass, and there were areas of fat-necrosis in both mesentery and omentum. Oddly enough this patient returned four years afterward with another attack, but he refused to be operated upon and was taken away by his friends.

(*b*) **Acute Suppurative Pancreatitis—Pancreatic Abscess.**—Fitz, in his monograph in 1889, reported 22 cases. To this list Körte has added 24. Of the cases, 32 were in males.

The *etiology* in a majority of cases is doubtful. Dyspeptic disturbances and trauma have preceded the onset in some instances. In 24 cases there was a single abscess; in 14 there were numerous small abscesses. In other instances there was a diffuse purulent infiltration. Some of the sequels are peri-pancreatic abscess, perforation into the stomach, the duodenum, or the peritonæum, and thrombosis of the portal vein.

The *symptoms* of suppurative pancreatitis are not always well defined. In one case in my wards Thayer made a correct diagnosis. The patient, aged thirty-four, had had occasional attacks of severe pain and vomiting. This was followed by fever and delirium. A deep-seated mass was felt in the median line just above the umbilicus. Finney operated and found disseminated fat-necrosis and a deep-seated abscess with necrotic pancreatic tissue. The patient recovered. The course of the suppurative form is much more chronic. Icterus, fatty diarrhœa, and sugar in the urine have been met with in some cases. The presence of a tumor mass in the epigastrium is of the greatest moment.

(*c*) **Gangrenous Pancreatitis.**—Complete necrosis of the gland, or part of it, may follow either hæmorrhage, acute inflammation, or suppurative infiltration, and in exceptional cases may occur after injury or the perforation of an ulcer of the stomach. In Fitz's monograph 15 cases are reported. Körte has increased this number to 40. Symptoms of hæmorrhagic pancreatitis may precede or be associated with it. Death usually follows in from ten to twenty days, with symptoms of collapse.

Anatomically the pancreas may present a dry necrotic appearance, but as a rule the organ is converted into a dark slaty-colored mass lying nearly free in the omental cavity or attached by a few shreds. In other instances the totally or partially sequestrated organ may lie in a large abscess cavity, forming a palpable tumor in the epigastric region. In two cases, reported by Chiari, the necrotic pancreas was discharged per rectum, with recovery.

Relation of Fat-necrosis to Pancreatic Disease.—In connection with all forms of pancreatic disease small yellowish areas, to which Balser first directed attention, may be found in the interlobular pancreatic tissue, in the mesentery, in the omentum, and in the abdominal fatty tissue generally. In slight grades they may be present without other changes, and they have been seen in the living without any disease of the gland being discovered. They are most frequently in the hæmorrhagic and necrotic forms of pancreatitis, less common in the suppurative. In the pancreas the lobules are seen to be separated by a dead-white necrotic tissue, which gives a remarkable appearance to the section. In the abdominal fat the areas are usually not larger than a pin's head; they at once attract attention, and may be mistaken, on superficial examination, for miliary tubercles or neoplasms. They may be larger; instances have been reported in which they were the size of a hen's egg. On section they have a soft, tallowy consistence. Langerhans has shown that this substance is a combination of lime with certain fatty acids. They may be crusted with lime, and in a man, aged eighty, who died of Bright's disease, I found the lobules of the pancreas entirely isolated by areas of fatty necrosis with extensive deposition of lime salts. There is no necessary etiological relation between disease of the pancreas and disseminated fatty necroses of the abdomen at the time the latter are discovered. Cases have been found accidentally in laparotomy for ovarian tumor and in instances in which the pancreas has been normal. They may be present in thin persons or in association with gall-stones. The *bacterium coli commune* was present in two instances, with diphtheritic colitis, examined by Welch, though in most cases the areas of necrosis are sterile. Langerhans produced fat-necrosis by injecting extract of pancreas into the peri-renal fatty tissue of a dog; and Hildebrand and Williams have shown experimentally that the fat-necroses are caused by certain constituents of the pancreatic juice, but not by trypsin. Flexner has demonstrated by chemical tests the existence of the fat-splitting ferment in peritoneal fat-necroses in recent human and experimental cases. The ferment (steapsin) disappears after five or six days in experimental necroses, and cannot be demonstrated in the lime-incrusted human ones. H. U. Williams has produced similar lesions in the subcutaneous fat by inserting bits of sterile pancreas beneath the skin. In their experimental studies Hildebrand, Williams, and Flexner, while they were able to produce fat-necroses by tying the veins of and sometimes lacerating the pancreas, never actually succeeded in reproducing the picture of hæmorrhagic and necrotic pancreatitis. This has recently been

37

accomplished by Hlava and Flexner by injecting artificial gastric juice and dilute solutions of hydrochloric acid into the duct of Wirsung. The very acutely developing cases in dogs may result fatally within twenty-four hours. The fat-necroses in these cases are caused not by the acids but by the fat-splitting ferment (Flexner).

It is well for surgeons to remember that in two cases at least the most serious symptoms of acute pancreatic disease have been found in association with only widespread fat-necrosis of the gland. In a case reported by Stockton and Williams a man, on his return journey from Europe, was seized with vomiting and pain, without fever, but with a very small pulse. The patient died soon after his arrival in America. The post mortem showed a pancreas 18 cm. long, at first sight normal, but showing on section most extensive fatty infiltration with fat-necrosis.

III. CHRONIC PANCREATITIS.

Dieckhoff recognizes two forms: (1) The most common, a chronic inflammation which extends from the ducts, and is met with in association with chronic catarrhal processes in the stomach and duodenum and in the bile-passages; (2) a chronic pancreatitis of hæmatogenous origin, resulting from toxic materials in the blood, particularly from alcohol and lues. The organ may be reduced in size and very hard, as in the atrophic sclerosis seen not infrequently in diabetes. Occasionally it is larger than normal, and may form a tumor readily palpable in the upper part of the abdomen. In connection with the diabetic form there may be pigmentary changes in association with a similar condition in the liver. The sclerosis may follow pancreatic calculi, and occasionally interstitial lipomatosis causes great wasting of the tissue of the gland.

The interest in atrophy of the pancreas relates *first* to the association with it of diabetes, which has been already considered; and *secondly* to the possibility of a chronic interstitial pancreatitis, particularly at the head of the organ, blocking the terminal part of the common bile-duct. Riedel refers to severe cases in which he found during operation for gall-stones the head of the pancreas enlarged and hard as stone, so that he dreaded the possibility of new growth; but two of his patients recovered and were well for years, and in the third the post mortem showed that the condition was one of chronic pancreatitis. In one of Körte's cases a small nodule of the gland involved in a chronic pancreatitis had pressed directly upon the ductus communis choledochus and caused the jaundice.

IV. PANCREATIC CYSTS.

Of 121 cases operated upon by surgeons 60 were in males and 56 in females; in 5 the sex was not given (Körte). Sixty-six of the cases occurred in the fourth decade. T. C. Railton's case (which is not in Körte's series), an infant aged six months, and Shattuck's case in a child of thirteen and a half months, are the youngest in the literature. According to the origin Körte recognizes three varieties.

(1) **Traumatic Cases.**—In this list of 33 cases 30 were in men and only 3 in women. Blows on the abdomen or constantly repeated pressure are the most common forms of trauma. One case followed severe massage. Usually with the onset there are inflammatory symptoms, pain, and vomiting, sometimes suggestive of peritonitis. The contents of the cyst are usually bloody, though in 13 of the traumatic cases it was clear or yellowish.

(2) **Cysts following Inflammatory Conditions.**—In 51 cases the trouble began gradually after attacks of dyspepsia with colic, simulating somewhat that of gall-stones. Occasionally the attack set in with very severe symptoms, suggestive of obstruction of the bowel. In this group the tumor appeared in 19 cases soon after the onset of the pain; in others it was delayed for a period of from a few weeks to two or three years. McPhedran has reported a remarkable instance in which the tumor developed in the epigastrium with signs of severe inflammation. It was opened and drained and believed to be a hydrops of the lesser peritoneal cavity. Three months later a second cyst developed, which appeared to spring directly from the pancreas.

(3) **Cysts without any Inflammatory or Traumatic Etiology.**—Of 33 cases in this group 26 were in women. A remarkable feature is the prolonged period of their existence—in one case for forty-seven years, in one for between sixteen and twenty years, in others for sixteen, nine, and eight years, in the majority for from two to four years.

Anatomically Körte recognizes (1) *retention cysts* due to plugging of the main duct; (2) *proliferation cysts* of the pancreatic tissue—the cysto-adenoma; (3) *retention cysts* arising from the alveoli of the gland and of the smaller ducts, which become cut off and dilate in consequence of chronic interstitial pancreatitis; (4) *pseudo-cysts* following inflammatory or traumatic affections of the pancreas, usually the result of injury, causing hæmorrhage and hydrops of the lesser peritonæum.

Situation.—In its growth the cyst may (1) develop in the lesser peritonæum, push the stomach upward, and reach the abdominal wall between the stomach and the transverse colon; (2) more rarely the cyst appears above the lesser curvature and pushes the stomach downward; in both of these cases the situation of the tumor is high in the abdomen, but in (3) it may develop between the leaves of the transverse meso-colon and lie below both the colon and the stomach. The relation of these two organs to the tumor is variable, but in the majority of cases the stomach lies above and the transverse colon below the cyst. Occasionally, too, as in T. C. Railton's case, the cyst may develop from the tail of the pancreas and project far over in the left hypochondrium in the position of the spleen or of a renal tumor.

General Symptoms.—Apart from the features of onset already referred to, the patient may complain of no trouble whatever, particularly in the very chronic cases, unless the cyst reaches a very large size. Painful colicky attacks, with nausea and vomiting and progressive enlargement of the abdomen, have frequently been noted. Fatty diarrhœa from disturbance of the function of the pancreas is rare. Sugar in the urine has been present in a number of cases. Increased secretion of the saliva, the so-called pancreatic salivation, is also rare. Pressure of the cyst may sometimes cause jaundice, and in rare instances dyspnœa. Very marked loss of flesh has been present in a number of cases. A remarkable feature often noticed has been the transitory disappearance of the cyst. In one of Halsted's cases the girth of the abdomen decreased from 43 to 31 inches in ten days with profuse diarrhœa. Sometimes the disappearance has followed blows.

Diagnosis.—The cyst occupies the upper abdomen, usually forming a semicircular bulging in the median line, rarely to either side. In 16 cases Körte states that the chief projection was below the navel. In one case operated upon by Halsted the tumor occupied the greater part of the abdomen. The cyst is immobile, respiration having little or no influence on it. As already mentioned, the stomach, as a rule, lies above it and the colon below.

In a majority of the cases the fluid is of a reddish or dark-brown color, and contains blood or blood coloring matter, cell detritus, fat granules, and sometimes cholesterin. The consistence of the fluid is usually mucoid, rarely thin. The reaction is alkaline, the specific gravity from 1.010 to 1.020. In 22 cases Körte states that the fluid was not hæmorrhagic.

The existence of ferments is important. In 54 cases they were present in the fluid or in the material from the fistula. In 20 cases only one ferment was present, in 20 cases two, and in 14 cases all three of the pancreatic ferments were found. As diastatic and fat emulsifying ferments occur widely in various exudates the most important and only positive signs in the diagnosis of the pancreatic secretion is the digestion of fibrin and albumin.

Results.—Körte states of 101 cases in which the cyst was opened and drained 4 deaths followed the operation directly; 1 resulted from infection of the fistula. In 14 cases the cyst was extirpated; of these 12 recovered.

V. TUMORS OF THE PANCREAS.

Of new growths in the organ carcinoma is the most frequent. Sarcoma, adenoma, and lymphoma are rare.

Frequency.—At the General Hospital in Vienna in 18,069 autopsies there were 22 cases of cancer of the pancreas (Biach). In 11,472 postmortems at Milan, Segré found 132 tumors of the pancreas, 127 of which were carcinomata, 2 sarcomata, 2 cysts, and 1 syphiloma. In 6,000 autopsies at Guy's Hospital there were only 20 cases of primary malignant disease of the organ (Hale White). In the first 1,000 autopsies at the Johns Hopkins Hospital there were 5 cases of adeno-carcinoma, and 1 doubtful case in which the exact origin could not be stated. There were 5 cases of secondary malignant disease of the pancreas. The head of the gland is most commonly involved, but the disease may be limited to the body or to the tail. The majority of the patients are in the middle period of life.

Symptoms.—The diagnosis is not often possible. The following are the most important and suggestive features: (*a*) Epigastric pains, often occurring in paroxysms. (*b*) Jaundice, due to pressure of the tumor in the head of the pancreas on the bile-duct. The jaundice is intense and permanent, and associated with dilatation of the gall-bladder, which may reach a very large size. (*c*) The presence of a tumor in the epigastrium. This is very variable. In 137 cases Da Costa found the tumor present in only 13. Palpation under anæsthesia with the stomach empty would probably give a very much larger percentage. As the tumor rests directly upon the aorta there is usually a marked degree of pulsation, sometimes with a bruit. There may be pressure on the portal vein, causing thrombosis and its usual sequels. (*d*) Symptoms due to loss of function of the pancreas are less important. Fatty diarrhœa is not very often present. In consequence of the absence of bile the stools are usually very clay-colored and greasy. Diabetes also is not common. (*e*) A very rapid wasting and cachexia. Of other symptoms nausea and vomiting are common. In some instances the pylorus is compressed and there is great dilatation of the stomach. In a few cases there has been profuse salivation.

The points of greatest importance in the diagnosis are the intense and permanent jaundice, with dilatation of the gall-bladder, rapid emaciation, and the presence of a tumor in the epigastric region. Of less importance are features pointing to disturbance of the function of the gland.

Of other new growths sarcoma and lymphoma have been occasionally found. Miliary tubercle is not very uncommon in the gland. Syphilis may occur as rather a chronic interstitial inflammation, or in the form of gummous tumors.

The outlook in tumors of the pancreas is, as a rule, hopeless. However, of 10 cases operated upon of late years, 6 recovered (Körte).

VI. PANCREATIC CALCULI.

Pancreatic lithiasis is comparatively rare. In 1883 George W. Johnston collected 35 cases in the literature. In 1,000 autopsies at the Johns Hopkins Hospital there were 2 cases.

The stones are usually numerous, either round in shape or rough, spinous and coral-like. The color is opaque white. They are composed chiefly of carbonate of lime. The effects of the stones are: (1) A chronic interstitial inflammation of the gland substance with dilatation of the duct; sometimes there is cystic dilatation of the gland; (2) acute inflammation with suppuration; (3) the irritation of the stones, as in the gall-bladder, may lead to carcinoma.

Symptoms.—Pepper in 1882 made a diagnosis of calculus of the pancreas, of which, however, there was no confirmation either by the passage of the stone or by autopsy. Minnich has reported a case in which, after an attack of colic, calculi composed of calcic carbonate and phosphate were passed in the stools. Lichtheim, in a case with severe colic, diabetes, and fatty diarrhœa, made the diagnosis of pancreatic calculi, which was afterward confirmed by autopsy.

X. DISEASES OF THE PERITONÆUM.

I. ACUTE GENERAL PERITONITIS.

Definition.—Acute inflammation of the peritonæum.

Etiology.—The condition may be primary or secondary.

(*a*) **Primary, Idiopathic Peritonitis.**—Considering how frequently the pleura and pericardium are primarily inflamed the rarity of idiopathic inflammation of the peritonæum is somewhat remarkable. It may follow cold or exposure and is then known as rheumatic peritonitis. No instance of the kind has come under my notice. In Bright's disease, gout, and arterio-sclerosis acute peritonitis may develop as a terminal event. Of 102 cases of peritonitis which came to autopsy at the Johns Hopkins Hospital, 12 were of this form. In these there was some pre-existing chronic disease (Flexner).

(*b*) **Secondary peritonitis** is due to extension of inflammation from, or perforation of one of the organs covered by the peritonæum. Peritonitis from extension may follow inflammation of the stomach or intestines, extensive ulceration in these parts, cancer, acute suppurative inflammations of the spleen, liver, pancreas, retroperitoneal tissues, and the pelvic viscera.

Perforative peritonitis is the most common, following external wounds, perforation of ulcer of the stomach or bowels, perforation of the gall-bladder, abscess of the liver, spleen, or kidneys. Two important causes are appendicitis and suppurating inflammation about the Fallopian tubes and ovaries. There are instances in which peritonitis has followed rupture of an apparently normal Graafian follicle.

Of the above 102 cases, 56 originated in an extension from some diseased abdominal viscus. The remaining 34 followed surgical operations upon the peritonæum or the contained organs.

The peritonitis of septicæmia and pyæmia is almost invariably the result of a local process. An exceedingly acute form of peritonitis may be caused by the development of tubercles on the membrane.

Morbid Anatomy.—In recent cases, on opening the abdomen the intestinal coils are distended and glued together by lymph, and the peritonæum presents a patchy, sometimes a uniform injection. The exudation may be: (*a*) Fibrinous, with little or no fluid, except a few pockets of clear serum between the coils. (*b*) Sero-fibrinous. The coils are covered with lymph, and there is in addition a large amount of a yellowish, sero-fibrinous fluid. In instances in which the stomach or intestine is perforated this may be mixed with food or fæces. (*c*) Purulent, in which the exudate is either thin and greenish yellow in color, or opaque white and creamy. (*d*) Putrid. Occasionally in puerperal and perforative peritonitis, particularly when the latter has been caused by cancer, the exudate is thin, grayish green in color, and has a gangrenous odor. (*e*) Hæmorrhagic. This is sometimes found as an admixture in cases of acute peritonitis following wounds, and occurs in the cancerous and tuberculous forms. (*f*) A rare form occurs in which the injection is present, but almost all signs of exudation are wanting. Close inspection may be necessary to detect a slight dulling of the serous surfaces. The bacteriological examination reveals large numbers of bacteria.

The amount of the effusion varies from half a litre to 20 or 30 litres. There are probably essential differences between the various kinds of peritonitis.

Bacteriology of Acute Peritonitis.—Much work has been done lately upon the subject. Flexner has analyzed 102 cases of peritonitis, in which bacteriological studies were made, which came to autopsy in the Johns Hopkins Hospital. He makes three classes. The first class embraces the primary or idiopathic form, of which 12 cases were found. These were with one exception mono-infections. The prevailing micro-organism was the streptococcus pyogenes (five times), the remaining ones being the staphylococcus aureus, micrococcus lanceolatus, bacillus proteus, pyocyaneus, and coli communis. The second class followed operations upon the peritonæum, excepting operations upon the intestine. The majority of these cases were examples of wound infection. They were 33 in number. In 25 of these mono-infections, in 8 mixed infections existed. The prevailing micro-organism was the staphylococcus aureus, which was present alone in 12 and combined in 2 cases. The streptococcus occurred 5 times uncombined and 4 times combined. The bacillus coli was found 5 times in all, being unassociated in 3 cases. Other organisms found were the micrococcus lanceolatus, staphylococcus albus, bacillus pyocyaneus, and ærogenes capsulatus. The remaining 56 cases, forming the third class, were instances of intestinal infection. These comprised 23 mono- and 33 polyinfections. The predominating micro-organism was the bacillus coli communis which occurred in 43 cases, 8 times alone and 35 in association. The streptococcus was present in 37 cases, being alone in 7. The staphylococci, pneumococcus, bacillus proteus, pyocyaneus, typhosus, and aerogenes capsulatus occurred in a smaller number of instances.

Among the micro-organisms thus far found rarely in peritonitis, may be mentioned the gonococcus, the anthrax bacillus, the proteus bacillus, and the typhoid bacillus. As illustrating the importance of the gonococcus, I may state that as I write there are two young girls both of whom were admitted to my wards with diffuse peritonitis arising from fresh gonorrhœal salpingitis. Both were operated upon by Cushing successfully. Welch has found the bacillus coli communis in peritonitis due to ulceration of the intestines without perforation.

Symptoms.—In the perforative and septic cases the onset is marked by chilly feelings or an actual rigor with intense pain in the abdomen. In typhoid fever, when the sensorium is benumbed, the onset may not be noticed. The pain is general, and is usually intense and aggravated by movements and pressure. A position is taken which relieves the tension of the abdominal muscles, so that the patient lies on the back with the thighs drawn up and the shoulders elevated. The greatest pain is usually below the umbilicus, but in peritonitis from perforation of the stomach pain may be referred to the back, the chest, or the shoulder. The respiration is superficial—costal in type—as it is painful to use the diaphragm. For the same reason the action of coughing is restrained, and even the movements necessary for talking are limited. In this early stage the sensitiveness may be great and the abdominal muscles are often rigidly contracted. If the patient is at perfect rest the pain may be very slight, and there are instances in which it is not at all marked, and may, indeed, be absent.

The abdomen gradually becomes distended and tense and is tympanitic on percussion. The pulse is rapid, small, and hard, and often has a peculiar wiry quality. It ranges from 110 to 150. The temperature may rise rapidly after the chill and reach 104° or 105°, but the subsequent elevation is moderate. In some very severe cases there may be no fever throughout. The tongue at first is white and moist, but subsequently becomes dry and often red and fissured. Vomiting is an early and prominent feature and causes great pain. The contents of the stomach are first ejected, then a yellowish and bile-stained fluid, and finally a greenish and, in rare instances, a brownish-black liquid with slight fæcal odor. The bowels may be loose at the onset and then constipation may follow. Frequent micturition may be present, less often retention. The urine is usually scanty and high-colored, and contains a large quantity of indican.

The appearance of the patient when these symptoms have fully developed is very characteristic. The face is pinched, the eyes are sunken, and the expression is very anxious. The constant vomiting of fluids causes a wasted appearance, and the hands sometimes present the washer-woman's skin. Except in cholera, we see the Hippocratic facies more frequently in this than in any other disease—"*a sharp nose, hollow eyes, collapsed temples; the ears cold, contracted, and their lobes turned out; the skin about the forehead being rough, distended, and parched; the color of the whole face being brown, black, livid, or lead-colored.*" There are one or two additional points about the abdomen. The tympany is usually excessive, owing to the great relaxation of the walls of the intestines by inflammation and exudation. The splenic dulness may be obliterated, the diaphragm pushed up, and the apex beat of the heart dislocated to the fourth interspace. The liver dulness may be greatly reduced, or may, in the mammary line, be obliterated. It has been claimed that this is a distinctive feature of perforative peritonitis, but on several occasions I have been able to demonstrate that the liver dulness in the middle and mammary line was obliterated by tympanites alone. In the axillary line, on the other hand, the liver dulness, though diminished, may persist. Pneumo-peritonæum following perforation more certainly obliterates the hepatic dulness. In such cases the fluid effused produces a dulness in the lateral region; but with gas in the peritonæum, if the patient is turned on the left side, a clear note is heard beneath the seventh and eighth ribs. Acute peritonitis may present a flat, rigid abdomen throughout its course.

Effusion of fluid—ascites—is usually present except in some acute rapidly fatal cases. The flanks are dull on percussion. The dulness may be movable, though this depends altogether upon the degree of adhesions. There may be considerable effusion without either movable dulness or fluctuation. A friction-rub may be present, as first pointed out by Bright, but it is not nearly so common in acute as in chronic peritonitis.

Course.—The acute diffuse peritonitis usually terminates in death. The most intense forms may kill within thirty-six to forty-eight hours; more commonly death results in four or five days, or the attack may be prolonged to eight or ten days. The pulse becomes irregular, the heart-sounds weak, the breathing shallow; there are lividity with pallor, a cold skin with high rectal temperature—a group of symptoms indicating profound failure of the vital functions for which Gee has revived the old term *lipothymia*. Occasionally death occurs with great suddenness, owing, possibly, to paralysis of the heart.

Diagnosis.—In typical cases the severe pain at onset, the distention of the abdomen, the tenderness, the fever, the gradual development of effusion, collapse symptoms, and the vomiting give a characteristic picture. Careful inquiries should at once be made concerning the previous condition, from which a clew can often be had as to the starting-point of the trouble. In young adults a considerable proportion of all cases depends upon perforating appendicitis, and there may be an account of previous attacks of pain in the iliac region, or of constipation alternating with diarrhœa. In women the most frequent causes are suppurative processes in the pelvic viscera, associated with salpingitis, abscesses in the broad ligaments, or acute puerperal infection. Perforation of gastric ulcer is a more common factor in women than in men. It is not always easy to determine the cause. Many cases come under observation for the first time with the abdomen distended and tender, and it is impossible to make a satisfactory examination. In such instances the pelvic organs should be examined with the greatest care. In typhoid fever, if the patient is conscious, the sudden onset of pain, the development of great meteorism, and the aggravation of the general symptoms indicate clearly what has happened. When the patient is in deep coma, on the other hand, the perforation may be overlooked. The following conditions are most apt to be mistaken for acute peritonitis:

(*a*) *Acute Entero-colitis.*—Here the pain and distention and the sensitiveness on pressure may be marked. The pain is more colicky in character, the diarrhœa is more frequent, and the collapse is more extreme.

(*b*) *The So-called Hysterical Peritonitis.*—This has deceived the very elect, as almost every feature of genuine peritonitis, even the collapse, may be simulated. The onset may be sudden, with severe pain in the abdomen, tenderness, vomiting, diarrhœa, difficulty in micturition, and the characteristic decubitus. Even the temperature may be elevated. There may be recurrence of the attack. A case has been reported by Bristowe in which four attacks occurred within a year, and it was not until special hysterical symptoms developed that the true nature of the trouble was suspected.

(*c*) *Obstruction of the bowel*, as already mentioned, may simulate peritonitis, both having pain, vomiting, tympanites, and constipation in common. It may for a couple of days really be impossible to make a diagnosis in the absence of a satisfactory history.

(*d*) *Rupture of an abdominal aneurism or embolism of the superior mesenteric artery* may cause symptoms which simulate peritonitis. In the latter, sudden onset with severe pain, the collapse symptoms, frequent vomiting, and great distention of the abdomen may be present.

(*e*) I have already referred to the fact that acute hæmorrhagic pancreatitis may be mistaken for peritonitis. Lastly, a ruptured tubal pregnancy may resemble acute peritonitis.

II. PERITONITIS IN INFANTS.

Peritonitis may occur in the fœtus as a consequence of syphilis, and may lead to constriction of the bowel by fibrous adhesions.

In the new-born a septic peritonitis may extend from an inflamed cord. Distention of the abdomen, slight swelling and redness about the cord, and not infrequently jaundice are present. It is an uncommon event, and existed in only 4 of 51 infants dying with inflammation of the cord and septicæmia (Runge).

During childhood peritonitis develops from causes similar to those affecting the adult. Perforative appendicitis is common. Peritonitis following blows or kicks on the abdomen occurs more frequently at this period. In boys injury while playing foot-ball may be followed by diffuse peritonitis. A rare cause in children is extension through the diaphragm from an empyema. There are on record instances of peritonitis occurring in several children at the same school, and it has been attributed to sewer-gas poisoning. It was in investigating an epidemic of this kind at the Wandsworth school, in London, that Anstie received the post-mortem wound of which he died.

III. LOCALIZED PERITONITIS.

1. Subphrenic Peritonitis.—The general peritonæum covering the right and left lobes of the liver may be involved in an extension from the pleura of suppurative, tuberculous, or cancerous processes. In various affections of the liver—cancer, abscess, hydatid disease, and in affections of the gall-bladder—the inflammation may be localized to the peritonæum covering the upper surface of the organ. These forms of localized subphrenic peritonitis in the greater sac are not so important in reality as those which occur in the lesser peritonæum. The anatomical relations of this structure are as follows: It lies behind and below the stomach, the gastro-hepatic omentum, and the anterior layer of the great omentum. Its lower limit forms the upper layer of the transverse meso-colon. On either side it reaches from the hepatic to the splenic flexure of the colon, and from the foramen of Winslow to the hilus of the spleen. Behind it covers and is tightly adherent to the front of the pancreas. Its upper limit is formed by the transverse fissure of the liver, and by that portion of the diaphragm which is covered by the lower layer of the right lateral ligament of the liver; the lobus Spigelii lies bare in the cavity. The foramen of Winslow, through which the lesser communicates with the greater peritonæum, is readily closed by inflammation.

Inflammatory processes, exudates, and hæmorrhages may be confined entirely to the lesser peritonæum. The exudate of tuberculous peritonitis may be confined to it. Perforations of certain parts of the stomach, of the duodenum, and of the colon may excite inflammation in it alone; and in various affections of the pancreas, particularly trauma and hæmorrhage, the effusion into the sac has often been confounded with cyst of this organ. " Pathological distention of the lesser peritonæum gives rise to a tumor in the left hypochondriac, epigastric, and umbilical regions of a somewhat characteristic shape, but which appears to vary from time to time in form and size, according to the conditions of the overlying stomach; for when the viscus is full of liquid contents it increases the area of the tumor's dulness, while it makes its outlines less definable by palpation, and if the stomach is distended with gas the dull area becomes resonant and apparently the tumor may disappear altogether. The colon always lies below the tumor and never in front of or above it, as is the case in kidney enlargement " (Jordan Lloyd).

Special mention must be made of the remarkable form of subphrenic abscess containing air, which may simulate closely pneumothorax, and hence was called by Leyden *Pyo-pneumothorax subphrenicus*. The affection has been thoroughly studied of late years by Scheurlen, Mason, Meltzer, and Lee Dickinson. In 142 out of 170 recorded cases the cause was known. In a few instances, as in one reported by Meltzer, the subphrenic abscess seemed to have followed pneumonia. Pyothorax is an occasional cause. By far the most frequent condition is gastric ulcer, which occurred in 80 of the cases. Duodenal ulcer was the cause in 6 per cent. In about 10 per cent of the cases the appendix was the starting-point of the abscess. Cancer of the stomach is an occasional cause. Other rare causes are trauma, which was present in one of my cases, perforation of an hepatic or a renal abscess, lesions of the spleen, abscess, and cysts of the pancreas.

In a majority of all the cases in which the stomach or duodenum is perforated—sometimes, indeed, in the cases following trauma, as in *Case 3* of my series—the abscess contains air.

The symptoms of subphrenic abscess vary very considerably, depending a good deal upon the primary cause. The onset, as a rule, is abrupt, particularly when due to perforation of a gastric ulcer. There are severe pain, vomiting, often of bilious or of bloody material; respiration is embarrassed, owing to the involvement of the diaphragm; then the constitutional symptoms develop associated with suppuration, chills, irregular fever, and emaciation. Subsequently perforation may take place into the pleura or into the lung, with severe cough and abundant purulent expectoration.

The conditions are so obscure that the diagnosis of subphrenic abscess is not often made. The perihepatic abscess beneath the arch of the diaphragm, whether to the right or left of the suspensory ligament, when it does not contain air, is almost invariably mistaken for empyema. When a pus collection of any size is in the lesser peritonæum, the tumor is formed which has the characters already mentioned in a quotation from Mr. Jordan Lloyd.

The most remarkable features are those which are superadded when the abscess cavity contains air. Here, on the right side, when the abscess is in the greater peritonæum, above the right lobe of the liver, the diaphragm may be pushed up to the level of the second or third rib, and the physical signs on percussion and auscultation are those of pneumothorax, particularly the tympanitic resonance and the movable dulness. The liver is usually greatly depressed and there is bulging on the right side. Still more obscure are the cases of air-containing abscesses due to perforation of the stomach or duodenum, in which the gas is contained in the lesser peritonæum. Here the diaphragm is pushed up and there are signs of pneumothorax on the left side. In a large majority of all the cases which follow perforation of a gastric ulcer the effusion lies between the diaphragm above, and the spleen, stomach, and the left lobe of the liver below.

The prognosis in subphrenic abscess is not very hopeful. Of the cases on record about 20 per cent only have recovered. Of the five cases which have come under my observation, three recovered after operation.

2. **Appendicular.**—The most frequent cause in the male of localized peritonitis is inflammation of the appendix vermiformis. The situation varies with the position of this extremely variable organ. The adhesion, perforation, and intraperitoneal abscess cavity may be within the pelvis, or to the left of the median line in the iliac region, in the lower right quadrant of the umbilical region—a not uncommon situation—or, of course, most frequently in the right iliac fossa. In the most common situation the localized abscess lies upon the psoas muscle, bounded by the cæcum on the right and the terminal portion of the ileum and its mesentery in front and to the left. In many of these cases the limitation is perfect, and post-mortem records show that complete healing may take place with the obliteration of the appendix in a mass of firm scar tissue.

3. **Pelvic Peritonitis.**—The most frequent cause is inflammation about the uterus and Fallopian tubes. Puerperal septicæmia, gonorrhœa, and tuberculosis are the usual causes. The tubes are the starting-point in a majority of the cases. The fimbriæ become adherent and closely matted to the ovary, and there is gradually produced a condition of thickening of the parts, in which the individual organs are scarcely recognizable. The tubes are dilated and filled with cheesy matter or pus, and there may be small abscess cavities in the broad ligaments. Rupture of one of these may cause general peritonitis, or the membrane may be involved by extension, as in tuberculosis of these parts.

IV. CHRONIC PERITONITIS.

The following varieties may be recognized: (*a*) **Local adhesive peritonitis,** a very common condition, which occurs particularly about the spleen, forming adhesions between the capsule and the diaphragm, about the liver, less frequently about the intestines and mesentery. Points of thickening or puckering on the peritonæum occur sometimes with union of the coils or with fibrous bands. In a majority of such cases the condition is met accidentally post mortem. Two sets of symptoms may, however, be caused by these adhesions. When a fibrous band is attached in such a way as to form a loop or snare, a coil of intestine may pass through it. Thus, of the 295 cases of intestinal obstruction analyzed by Fitz, 63 were due to this cause. The second group is less serious and comprises cases with persistent abdominal pain of a colicky character, sometimes rendering life miserable. Instances of this kind have been successfully operated upon by Homans and H. A. Kelly.

(b) **Diffuse Adhesive Peritonitis.**—This is a consequence of an acute inflammation, either simple or tuberculous. The peritonæum is obliterated. On cutting through the abdominal wall, the coils of intestines are uniformly matted together and can neither be separated from each other nor can the visceral and parietal layers be distinguished. There may be thickening of the layers, and the liver and spleen are usually involved in the adhesions.

(c) **Proliferative Peritonitis.**—Apart from cancer and tubercle, which produce typical lesions of chronic peritonitis, the most characteristic form is that which may be described under this heading. The essential anatomical feature is great thickening of the peritoneal layers, usually without much adhesion. The cases are sometimes seen with sclerosis of the stomach. In one instance I found it in connection with a sclerotic condition of the cæcum and the first part of the colon. In the inspection of a case of this kind there is usually moderate effusion, more rarely extensive ascites. The peritonæum is opaque-white in color, and everywhere thickened, often in patches. The omentum is usually rolled and forms a thickened mass transversely placed between the stomach and the colon. The peritonæum over the stomach, intestines, and mesentery is sometimes greatly thickened. The liver and spleen may simply be adherent, or there is a condition of chronic perihepatitis or perisplenitis, so that a layer of firm, almost gristly connective tissue of from one fourth to half an inch in thickness encircles these organs. Usually the volume of the liver is in consequence greatly reduced. The gastro-hepatic omentum may be constricted by this new growth and the calibre of the portal vein much narrowed. A serous effusion may be present. On account of the adhesions which form, the peritonæum may be divided into three or four different sacs, as is more fully described under the tuberculous peritonitis. In these cases the intestines are usually free, though the mesentery is greatly shortened. There are instances of chronic peritonitis in which the mesentery is so shortened by this proliferative change that the intestines form a ball not larger than a cocoa-nut situated in the middle line, and after the removal of the exudation can be felt as a solid tumor. The intestinal wall is greatly thickened and the mucous membrane of the ileum is thrown into folds like the valvulæ conniventes. This proliferative peritonitis is found frequently in the subjects of chronic alcoholism. In cases of long-continued ascites the serous surfaces generally become thickened and present an opaque, dead-white color. This condition is observed especially in hepatic cirrhosis, but attends tumors, chronic passive congestions, etc.

In all forms of chronic peritonitis a friction may be felt usually in the upper zone of the abdomen.

In some instances of chronic peritonitis the membrane presents numerous nodular thickenings, which may be mistaken for tubercles. They may be scattered in numbers on the membranes, and it may be extremely difficult, without the most careful microscopical examination, to determine their nature. J. F. Payne has described a case of this sort associated with disseminating growths throughout the liver which were not cancerous. It has been suggested that some of the cases of tuberculous peritonitis cured by operation have been of this nature, but histological examination would, as a rule, readily determine between the conditions. Miura, in Japan, has reported a case in which these nodules contained the ova of a parasite. One case has been reported in which the exciting cause was regarded as cholesterin plates, which were contained within the granulomatous nodules.

(d) **Chronic Hæmorrhagic Peritonitis.**—Blood-stained effusions in the peritonæum occur particularly in cancerous and tuberculous disease. There is a form of chronic inflammation analogous to the hæmorrhagic pachymeningitis of the brain. It was described first by Virchow, and is localized most commonly in the pelvis. Layers of new connective tissue form on the surface of the peritonæum with large wide vessels from which hæmorrhage occurs. This is repeated from time to time with the formation of regular layers of hæmorrhagic effusion. It is rarely diffuse, more commonly circumscribed.

V. NEW GROWTHS IN THE PERITONÆUM.

(a) **Tuberculous Peritonitis.**—This has already been considered.

(b) **Cancer of the Peritonæum.**—Although, as a rule, secondary to disease of the stomach, liver, or pelvic organs, cases of primary cancer have been described. It is probable that the so-called primary cancers of the serous membranes are endotheliomata and not carcinomata. Secondary malignant peritonitis occurs in connection with all forms of cancer. It is usually characterized by a number of round tumors scattered over the entire peritonæum, sometimes small and miliary, at other times large and nodular, with puckered centres. The disease most commonly starts from the stomach or the ovaries. The omentum is indurated, and, as in tuberculous peritonitis, forms a mass which lies transversely across the upper portion of the abdomen. Primary malignant disease of the peritonæum is extremely rare. Colloid is said to have occurred, forming enormous masses, which in one case weighed over 100 pounds. Cancer of this membrane spreads, either by the detachment of small particles which are carried in the lymph currents and by the movements to distant parts, or by contact of opposing surfaces. It occurs more frequently in women than in men, and more commonly at the later period of life.

The *diagnosis* of cancer of the peritonæum is easy with a history of a local malignant disease; as when it occurs with ovarian tumor or with cancer of the pylorus. In cases in which there is no evidence of a primary lesion the diagnosis may be doubtful. The clinical picture is usually that of chronic ascites with progressive emaciation. There may be no fever. If there is much effusion nothing definite can be felt on examination. After tapping, irregular nodules or the curled omentum may be felt lying transversely across the upper portion of the abdomen. Unfortunately, this tumor upon which so much stress is laid occurs as frequently in tuberculous peritonitis and may be present in a typical manner in the chronic proliferative form, so that in itself it has no special diagnostic value. Multiple nodules, if large, indicate cancer, particularly in persons above middle life. Nodular tuberculous peritonitis is most frequent in children. The presence about the navel of secondary nodules and indurated masses is more common in cancer. Inflammation, suppuration, and the discharge of pus from the navel rarely occurs except in tuberculous disease. Considerable enlargement of the inguinal glands may be present in cancer. The nature of the fluid in cancer and in tubercle may be much alike. It may be hæmorrhagic in both; more often in the latter. The histological examination in cancer may show large multinuclear cells or groups of cells—the sprouting cell-groups of Foulis—which are extremely suggestive. The colloid cancer may produce a totally different picture; instead of ascitic fluid, the abdomen is occupied by the semi-solid gelatinous substance, and is firm, not fluctuating.

And, lastly, there are instances of echinococci in the peritonæum which may simulate cancer very closely. I have reported a case of this kind, in which the enlarged liver and the innumerable nodular masses in the peritonæum naturally led to this diagnosis.

VI. ASCITES (*Hydro-peritonæum*).

Definition.—The accumulation of serous fluid in the peritoneal cavity.

Etiology.—(1) **Local Causes.**—(*a*) Chronic inflammation of the peritonæum, either simple, cancerous, or tuberculous. (*b*) Portal obstruction in the terminal branches within the liver, as in cirrhosis and chronic passive congestion, or by compression of the vein in the gastro-hepatic omentum, either by proliferative peritonitis, by new growths, or by aneurism. (*c*) Tumors of the abdomen. The solid growths of the ovaries may cause considerable ascites, which may completely mask the true condition. The enlarged spleen in leukæmia, less commonly in malaria, may be associated with recurring ascites.

(2) **General Causes.**—The ascites is part of a general dropsy, the result of mechanical effects, as in heart-disease, chronic emphysema, and sclerosis of the lung. In cardiac lesions the effusion is sometimes confined to the peritonæum, in which case it is due to secondary changes in the liver, or it has been suggested to be connected with a failure of the suction action of this organ, by which the peritonæum is kept dry. Ascites occurs also in the dropsy of Bright's disease, and in hydræmic states of the blood.

Symptoms.—A gradual uniform enlargement of the abdomen is the characteristic symptom of ascites. The physical signs are usually distinctive. (*a*) *Inspection.*—According to the amount of fluid the abdomen is protuberant and flattened at the sides. With large effusions, the skin is tense and may present the lineæ albicantes. Frequently the navel itself and the parts about it are very prominent. In many cases the superficial veins are enlarged and a plexus joining the mammary vessels can be seen. Sometimes it can be determined by pressure on these veins that the current is from below upward. In some instances, as in thrombosis or obliteration of the portal vein, these superficial abdominal vessels may be extensively varicose. About the navel in cases of cirrhosis there is occasionally a large bunch of distended veins, the so-called caput Medusæ.

(*b*) *Palpation.*—Fluctuation is obtained by placing the fingers of one hand upon one side of the abdomen and by giving a sharp tap on the opposite side with the other hand, when a wave is felt to strike as a definite shock against the applied fingers. Even comparatively small quantities of fluid may give this fluctuation shock. When the abdominal walls are thick or very fat, an assistant may place the edge of the hand or a piece of cardboard in the front of the abdomen. A different procedure is adopted in palpating for the solid organs in case of ascites. Instead of placing the hand flat upon the abdomen, as in the ordinary method, the pads of the fingers only are placed lightly upon the skin, and then by a sudden depression of the fingers the fluid is displaced and the solid organ or tumor may be felt. By this method of " dipping " or displacement, as it is called, the liver may be felt below the costal margin, or the spleen, or sometimes solid tumors of the omentum or intestine.

(*c*) *Percussion.*—In the dorsal position with a moderate quantity of fluid in the peritonæum the flanks are dull, while the umbilical and epigastric regions, into which the intestines float, are tympanitic. This area of clear resonance may have an oval outline. Having obtained the lateral limit of the dulness on one side, if the patient turns on the opposite side, the fluid gravitates to the dependent part and the uppermost flank is now tympanitic. In moderate effusions this movable dulness changes greatly in the different postures. Small amounts of fluid, probably under a litre, would scarcely give movable dulness, as the pelvis and the renal regions hold a considerable quantity. In such cases it is best to place the patient in the knee-elbow position, when a dull note will be determined at the most dependent portion. By careful attention to these details mistakes are usually avoided.

The following are among the conditions which may be mistaken for dropsy: *Ovarian tumor*, in which the sac develops, as a rule, unilaterally, though when large it is centrally placed. The dulness is anterior and the resonance is in the flanks, into which the intestines are pushed by the cyst. Examination *per vaginam* may give important indications. In those rare instances in which gas develops in the cyst the diagnosis may be very difficult. Succussion has been obtained in such cases. A *distended bladder* may reach above the umbilicus. In such instances some urine dribbles away, and suspicion of ascites or a cyst is occasionally entertained. I once saw a trochar thrust into a distended bladder, which was supposed to be an ovarian cyst, and it is stated that John Hunter tapped a bladder, supposing it to be ascites. Such a mistake should be avoided by careful catheterization prior to any operative procedures. And lastly, there are large pancreatic or hydatid cysts in the abdomen which may simulate ascites.

Nature of the Ascitic Fluid.—Usually this is a clear serum, light yellow in the ascites of anæmia and Bright's disease, often darker in color in cirrhosis of the liver. The specific gravity is low, seldom more than 1.010 or 1.015, whereas in the fluid of ovarian cysts the specific gravity is high, 1,020 or over. It is albuminous and sometimes coagulates spontaneously. Dock has called attention to the importance of the study of the cells in the exudate. In cancer very characteristic forms, with nuclear figures, may be found. Hæmorrhagic effusion usually occurs in cancer and tuberculosis, and occasionally in cirrhosis. I have already referred to the instances of hæmorrhagic effusion in connection with ruptured tubal pregnancy. A chylous, milky exudate is occasionally found. Busey has collected 33 cases from the literature. There are, as Quincke has pointed out, two distinct varieties, a fatty and a chylous, which may be distinguished by the microscope, as in the former there are distinct fat-globules. These cases have been sometimes connected with peritoneal or mesenteric cancer. In the true chylous ascites the fluid is turbid and milky. In some of the cases, as in Whitla's, a perforation of the thoracic duct has been found. The condition does not necessarily follow obliteration of the thoracic duct. Mild grades of chylous ascites, which are occasionally found clinically, may be due to the fact that the patient upon a milk diet has a permanent lipæmia, such as is present in young animals and in diabetics, in whom the liquor sanguinis is always fatty. Under such circumstances an exudate may contain enough of the molecular base of the chyle to produce turbidity of the fluid. Some of the cases have been associated with filariasis. In a recent case in my clinic N. McL. Harris isolated the bacillus diphtheriæ from the chylous fluid.

Treatment of the Previous Conditions.—(*a*) **Acute Peritonitis.**—Rest is enjoined upon the patient by the severe pain which follows the slightest movement, and he should be propped in the position which gives him greatest relief. For the pain morphia should be injected hypodermically in full doses. In an adult it is better to give a third or half a grain at once, and subsequently at intervals repeat it in smaller doses, when necessary. The action of the drug should be carefully watched and the patient should not be allowed to pass into such a degree of unconsciousness that he cannot be aroused. The respiration and the condition of the pupils also give valuable information. The amount of opium which has been given in certain instances is remarkable, and indicates a tolerance of the drug. The doses given by the late Alonzo Clark, of New York, may be truly termed heroic. Austin Flint notes that a patient under the care of this physician took " in the first twenty-four hours, of opium and the sulphate of morphia, a quantity equivalent to 106 grains of opium; in the second twenty-four hours she took 472 grains; on the third day, 236 grains; on the fourth day, 120 grains; on the fifth day,

38

54 grains; on the sixth day, 22 grains; on the seventh day, 18 grains; after which the treatment was suspended." It is unnecessary to use these enormous doses, as, even when the pain is most intense, from a third to a half grain of morphia every few hours will usually keep the patient thoroughly under the influence of the drug. In a robust, strong patient, seen at the outset, twenty leeches applied over the abdomen will give great relief.

Local applications—either hot turpentine stupes or cloths wrung out of ice-water—may be laid upon the abdomen. The patients sometimes declare that they are greatly relieved by the latter.

The question of the use of purgatives in peritonitis has of late been warmly discussed. Lawson Tait and other gynæcologists have used the saline purges with the greatest benefit in post-operation peritonitis. Theoretically it appears correct to give salines in concentrated form, which cause a rapid and profuse exosmosis of serum from the intestinal vessels, relieving the congestion and reducing the œdema, which is one important factor in causing the meteorism. It is also urged that the increased peristalsis prevents the formation of adhesions. In reading the reports of these successful cases, one is not always convinced, however, that peritonitis actually existed. Still, in cases of acute peritonitis due to extension or following operation or in septic conditions the judgment of many careful men is decidedly in favor of the use of salines. I cannot speak from personal experience on this question. The majority of cases of peritonitis which come under the care of the physician follow lesions of the abdominal viscera or are due to perforation of ulcer of the stomach, the ileum, or the appendix. In such cases, particularly in the large group of appendix cases, to give saline purgatives is, to say the least, most injudicious treatment. The safety of the patient lies in the restriction of the peristalsis and the localization of the inflammation, for which purpose opium alone is of service. In these instances rectal injections should be employed to relieve the large bowel. No symptom in acute peritonitis is more serious than the tympanites, and none is more difficult to meet. The use of the long tube and injections containing turpentine may be tried. Drugs by the mouth cannot be retained.

For the vomiting, ice and small quantities of soda water may be employed. The patient should be fed on milk, but if the vomiting is distressing it is best not to attempt to give food by the mouth, but to use small nutrient enemata. In all cases of peritonitis it is best to have a surgeon in consultation early in the disease, as the question of operation may come up at any moment. I have already mentioned the conditions under which laparotomy is indicated in perforative appendicitis. The acute purulent cases, particularly those in which the streptococci occur, usually die; but the results of operative interference even in this form are steadily improving. In the acute forms of tuberculous peritonitis operative measures appear to be more hopeful, but they are not always successful.

(*b*) **Chronic Peritonitis.**—For the cases of chronic proliferative peritonitis very little can be done. The treatment is practically that of ascites. In all these forms, when the distention becomes extreme, tapping is indicated. The treatment of tuberculous peritonitis has fallen largely into the hands of the surgeons, and the results in many cases are very good. According to the statistics of Maurange,* of 71 cases, 28 survived the operation for more than a year. Of 26 additional cases which I have collected,† 14 were dead at the time of the report. Within two years and three months there were 6 operations performed at the Johns Hopkins Hospital in tuberculous peritonitis, with 4 recoveries.

(c) **Ascites.**—The treatment depends somewhat on the nature of the case. In cirrhosis early and repeated tapping may give time for the establishment of the collateral circulation, and temporary cures have followed this precedure. Permanent drainage with Southey's tube, incision, and washing out the peritonæum have also been practised. In the ascites of cardiac and renal disease the cathartics are most satisfactory, particularly the bitartrate of potash, given alone or with jalap, and the large doses of salts given an hour before breakfast with as little water as possible. These sometimes cause rapid disappearance of the effusion, but they are not so successful in ascites as in pleurisy with effusion. The stronger cathartics may sometimes be necessary. The ascites forming part of the general anasarca of Bright's disease will receive consideration under another section.

---

* Paris Thesis, 1889.

† On Tuberculous Peritonitis, Johns Hopkins Hospital Reports, 1890.

SECTION VI.

DISEASES OF THE RESPIRATORY SYSTEM.

I. DISEASES OF THE NOSE.

I. ACUTE CORYZA.

ACUTE catarrhal inflammation of the upper air-passages, popularly known as a " catarrh " or a " cold," is usually an independent affection, but may precede the development of another disease.

Etiology.—It prevails most extensively in the changeable weather of the spring and early winter, and may occur in epidemic form, many cases developing in a community within a few weeks. These outbreaks are very like, though less intense than the epidemic influenza, cases of which may begin with symptoms of ordinary coryza. The disease probably depends upon a micro-organism. Irritating fumes, such as those of iodine or ammonia, also may cause an acute catarrh of the nose.

Symptoms.—The patient feels indisposed, perhaps chilly, has slight headache, and sneezes frequently. In severe cases there are pains in the back and limbs. There is usually slight fever, the temperature rising to 101°. The pulse is quick, the skin is dry, and there are all the features of a feverish attack. At first the mucous membrane of the nose is swollen, " stuffed up," and the patient has to breathe through the mouth. A thin, clear, irritating secretion flows, and makes the edges of the nostrils sore. The mucous membrane of the tear-ducts is swollen, so that the eyes weep and the conjunctivæ are injected. The sense of smell and, in part, the sense of taste is lost. With the nasal catarrh there is slight soreness of the throat and stiffness of the neck; the pharynx looks red and swollen, and sometimes the act of swallowing is painful. The larynx also may be involved, and the voice becomes husky or is even lost. If the inflammation extends to the Eustachian tubes there may be impairment of the hearing. In more severe cases there are bronchial irritation and cough. Occasionally there is an outbreak of labial or nasal herpes. Usually within thirty-six hours the nasal secretion becomes turbid and more profuse, the swelling of the mucosa subsides, the patient gradually becomes able to breathe through the nostrils, and within four or five days the symptoms disapppear, with the exception of the increased discharge from the nose

610

and upper pharynx. There are rarely any bad effects from a simple coryza. When the attacks are frequently repeated the disease may become chronic.

The *diagnosis* is always easy, but caution must be exercised lest the initial catarrh of measles or severe influenza should be mistaken for the simple coryza.

Treatment.—Many cases are so mild that the patients are able to be about and to attend to their work. If there are fever and constitutional disturbance, the patient should be kept in bed and should take a simple fever mixture, and at night a drink of hot lemonade and a full dose of Dover's powder. Many persons find great benefit from the Turkish bath. For the distressing sense of tightness and pain over the frontal sinuses, cocaine is very useful and sometimes gives immediate relief. The 4-percent solution may be injected into the nostrils, or cotton-wool soaked in it may be inserted into them. Later, the snuff recommended by Ferrier is advantageous, composed, as it is, of morphia (gr. ij), bismuth ($\mathfrak{Z}$ iv), acacia powder ($\mathfrak{Z}$ ij). This may occasionally be blown or snuffed into the nostrils. The fluid extract of hamamelis, "snuffed" from the hand every two or three hours, is much better.

II. CHRONIC NASAL CATARRH.

(*Rhinitis; Rhinitis hypertrophica; Rhinitis atrophica*).

In *simple chronic catarrh* there is increased irritability of the mucous membrane, particularly of the erectile tissue on the septum and turbinated bones. There is a tendency to frequent stoppage of one or both nostrils and the patient very easily catches cold. The secretion is at first clear and afterward thick and tenacious. The sense of smell is not specially disturbed at this stage. With the mirror the mucous membrane looks congested and swollen and the veins may be distended.

In *hypertrophic rhinitis*, which is usually a sequel of the former condition, the nasal passages are obstructed, chiefly by enlargement of the lower turbinated bodies and swelling of the mucous membrane of the septum. Very often there is hypertrophy of the adenoid tissue in the vault of the pharynx and of the mucous membrane about the orifices of the Eustachian tubes. The two conditions frequently go together as expressed in the designation, chronic naso-pharyngeal catarrh. The symptoms of this hypertrophic rhinitis may be local or general.

The most important local symptom is the obstruction of the passage of air through the nostrils, so that the patients become mouth-breathers. During the day this may not be very distressing, but at night the mouth and throat get extremely dry and the sleep is disturbed. The voice becomes nasal in quality and in advanced cases, when the Eustachian tubes are obstructed, there may be deafness. It should ever be borne in mind by the practitioner that a very large proportion of all cases of deafness originate in chronic naso-pharyngeal catarrh. The general symptoms have been considered more fully under chronic pharyngeal catarrh and mouth-breathing.

Atrophic rhinitis, which is also known under the names coryza fetida and ozæna, may be a sequence of the hypertrophic form. Ozæna is only a symptom, and is met with in many ulcerative conditions of the nostrils, particularly as a result of syphilis, foreign bodies, caries and necrosis of the bones, and glanders. Fortunately, the atrophic form by no means necessarily follows the hypertrophic stage. The cases are much more frequent in women than in men, and usually occur early in life. The mucous membrane is thin and covered with grayish crusts which, when removed, show a slightly excoriated surface, but true ulcers are rarely seen. The erectile tissue is completely atrophied by a process of slow connective-tissue growth, or, as J. N. Mackenzie calls it, a cirrhosis. The mucous membrane of the pharynx is usually dry and glazed.

The symptoms are most distinctive, owing to the horrible odor which comes from the nose, and of which, fortunately, the patient is himself unconscious, because the sense of smell is lost. The secretion, which is puriform, dries and forms large crusts, which are dislodged by picking or which gradually fall off. The cause of the offensive odor has been much discussed—whether it is due to a special organism or to specially favorable conditions for the growth and development of the germs of putrefaction. Probably the latter view is correct.

The *treatment* of hypertrophic rhinitis consists in the thorough cleansing of the nasal passages, the removal of the pharyngeal growths, and the reduction of the hypertrophied nasal mucosa. It is best to use a simple douche, in order to keep the membrane absolutely clean. The Birmingham nasal douche is the most simple and satisfactory, and may be filled with alkaline and antiseptic or deodorizing solutions. One of the most satisfactory is the bicarbonate of soda (1½ drachm), listerine (6 drachms), and water (1 ounce). Operative procedures are necessary in a majority of the cases, and the practitioner should early call to his assistance the specialist. It is sad to think of the misery which has been entailed upon thousands of people owing to neglect of naso-pharyngeal catarrh by parents and physicians.

The treatment of atrophic rhinitis comes more properly under the special monographs.

III. AUTUMNAL CATARRH (*Hay Fever*).

An affection of the upper air-passages, often associated with asthmatic attacks, due to the action of certain stimuli upon a hypersensitive mucous membrane.

This affection was first described in 1819 by Bostock, who called it *catarrhus æstivus.* Morrill Wyman, of Cambridge, Mass., wrote a monograph on the subject, and described two forms, the "June cold," or "rose cold," which comes on in the spring, and the autumnal form which, in this country, does not develop until August and September, and never persists after a severe frost. Blakely studied its connection with the pollen of various grasses and flowers. The late George M. Beard made many careful observations on the disease. Until recently this form of catarrh was believed to result exclusively from the action of certain irritants on the mucous membrane of the nose, particularly the pollen of plants, which, as the experiments of Blakeley showed, play an important *rôle* in the disease. Other emanations also may induce an attack, as in the case of the late Austin Flint, who was liable to coryza, or even asthma, if he slept on a certain sort of feather pillow. This, however, is only one factor in the disease. A second, most important one, was discovered in the condition of the nasal mucous membrane in these cases. Voltolini, of Breslau, in 1871, observed the cure of a case of asthma by the removal of a nasal polypus. Since that date the observations of Hack, in Germany, and particularly of Daly, of Pittsburg, Roe, of Rochester, John N. Mackenzie, of Baltimore, and Harrison Allen, of Philadelphia, have demonstrated the association of asthmatic attacks with nasal disease. Daly discovered that in a large proportion of the cases of hay asthma there was local disease of the mucous membrane of the nose, the cure of which rendered the patient insusceptible to conditions previously exciting the attacks. This has been abundantly confirmed. Still identical lesions exist in many people who never suffer with the disease, so that there must be a third factor, a neurotic constitution. In the etiology of hay fever, then, these three elements prevail—a nervous constitution, an irritable nasal mucosa, and the stimulus.

The disease affects certain families, particularly, it is said, those with a neurotic taint. The peculiarity may occur through several generations. It is certainly more common in the United States than in Europe, and much more common in the United States than in Canada. The United States Hay Fever Association now numbers thousands of members.

Dwellers in cities are more subject than residents in the country. The structural peculiarities of the nasal mucous membrane are those of hypertrophic rhinitis. Harrison Allen states that the inferior turbinated bones lie well above the floor of the nostrils, which renders the mucous membrane more liable to irritation from inhaled substances. Deflection of the septum, hypertrophy of the soft parts, and excessive hyperæsthesia, so that the mere touch with a probe may be sufficient to induce an attack, are common conditions.

Symptoms.—These are, in a majority of the cases, very like those of ordinary coryza. There may, however, be much more headache and distress, and some patients become very low-spirited. Cough is a common symptom and may be very distressing. Paroxysms of asthma may develop, so like as to be indistinguishable from the ordinary bronchial form. The two conditions may indeed alternate, the patient having at one time an attack of common hay fever and at another, under similar circumstances, an attack of bronchial asthma. Of the immediate exciting causes of the attack, unquestionably in a majority of the cases coming on in the autumn there is an association with the presence of pollen in the atmosphere, but this is only one of a host of exciting causes. In certain persons the paroxysms may develop at any season from sudden changes in the temperature. An attack may even come on through association of ideas. The well-known experiment of J. N. Mackenzie, of inducing an attack in a susceptible person by offering her an artificial rose to smell, strikingly illustrates the neurotic element in the disease.

Treatment.—This may be comprised under three heads: First, since the disease appears in many instances to be a form of chronic neurosis, remedies which improve the stability of the nervous system may be employed—such as arsenic, phosphorus, and strychnia. Second, climatic. Dwellers in the cities of the Atlantic seaboard and of the Central States enjoy complete immunity in the Adirondacks and White Mountains. As a rule the disease is aggravated by residence in agricultural districts. The dry mountain air is unquestionably the best; there are cases, however, which do well at the seaside. Third, the thorough local treatment of the nose, particularly the destruction of the vessels and sinuses over the sensitive areas.

IV. EPISTAXIS.

Etiology.—Bleeding from the nose may result from local or constitutional conditions. Among local causes may be mentioned traumatism, small ulcers, picking or scratching the nose, new growths, and the presence of foreign bodies. In chronic nasal catarrh bleeding is not infrequent. The blood may come from one or both nostrils. The flow may be profuse after an injury.

Among general conditions with which nose-bleeding is associated, the following are the most important: It occurs with great frequency in growing children, particularly about the age of puberty; more frequently in the delicate than in the strong and vigorous. I have seen two cases of chronic recurring epistaxis in adults associated with remarkable telangiectases of the skin and visible mucous membranes.

Epistaxis is a very common event in persons of so-called plethoric habit. It is stated sometimes to precede, or to indicate a liability to, apoplexy, but this is very doubtful.

In venous engorgement, due to heart or pulmonary disease, epistaxis is not common and there may be a most extreme grade of cyanosis without its occurrence. In balloon and mountain ascensions, in the very rarefied atmosphere, hæmorrhage from the nose is a common event. In hæmophilia the nose ranks first of the mucous membranes from which bleeding arises. It occurs in all forms of chronic anæmias. It precedes the onset of certain fevers, more particularly typhoid, with which it seems associated in a special manner. Vicarious epistaxis has been described in cases of suppression of the menses. Lastly, it is said to be brought on by certain psychical impressions, but the observations on this point are not trustworthy. The blood in epistaxis results from capillary oozing or diapedesis. The mucous membrane is deeply congested and there may be small ecchymoses. The bleeding area is usually in the respiratory portion of one nostril and upon the cartilaginous septum.

Symptoms.—Slight hæmorrhage is not associated with any special features. When the bleeding is protracted the patients have the more serious manifestations of loss of blood. In the slow dripping which takes place in some instances of hæmophilia, there may be formed a remarkable blood tumor projecting from one nostril and extending even below the mouth.

Death from ordinary epistaxis is very rare. The more blood is lost, the greater is the tendency to clotting with spontaneous cessation of the bleeding.

The *diagnosis* is usually easy. One point only need be mentioned; namely, that bleeding from the posterior nares occasionally occurs during sleep and the blood trickles into the pharynx and may be swallowed. If vomited, it may be confounded with hæmatemesis; or, if coughed up, with hæmoptysis.

Treatment.—In a majority of the cases the bleeding ceases of itself. Various simple measures may be employed, such as holding the arms above the head, the application of ice to the nose, or the injection of cold or hot water into the nostrils. Astringents, such as zinc, alum, or tannin, may be used; and the old-fashioned and sometimes successful remedy, a cobweb, may be introduced into the nostrils. If the bleeding comes from an ulcerated surface, an attempt should be made to apply chromic acid or to cauterize. If the bleeding is at all severe and obstinate, the posterior nares should be plugged. Ergot may be given internally or hypodermically. The inhalation of carbonic-acid gas may be tried or a solution of gelatine injected into the nostril.

II. DISEASES OF THE LARYNX.

I. ACUTE CATARRHAL LARYNGITIS.

This may come on as an independent affection or in association with general catarrh of the upper respiratory passages.

Etiology.—Many cases are due to catching cold or to overuse of the voice; others develop in consequence of the inhalation of irritating gases. It may occur in the general catarrh associated with influenza and measles. Very severe laryngitis is excited by traumatism, either injuries from without or the lodgment of foreign bodies. It may be caused by the action of very hot liquids or corrosive poisons.

Symptoms.—There is a sense of tickling referred to the larynx; the cold air irritates and, owing to the increased sensibility of the mucous membrane, the act of inspiration may be painful. There is a dry cough, and the voice is altered. At first it is simply husky, but soon phonation becomes painful, and finally the voice may be completely lost. In adults the respirations are not increased in frequency, but in children dyspnœa is not uncommon and may occur in spasmodic attacks. If much œdema accompanies the inflammatory swelling, there may be urgent dyspnœa.

The laryngoscope shows a swollen and tumefied mucous membrane of the larynx, particularly the ary-epiglottidean folds. The vocal cords have lost their smooth and shining appearance and are reddened and swollen. Their mobility also is greatly impaired, owing to the infiltration of the adjoining mucous membrane and of the muscles. A slight mucoid exudation covers the parts. The constitutional symptoms are not severe. There is rarely much fever, and in many cases the patient is not seriously ill. Occasionally cases come on with greater intensity, the cough is very distressing, deglutition is painful, and there may be urgent dyspnœa.

Diagnosis.—There is rarely any difficulty in determining the nature of a case if a satisfactory laryngoscopic examination can be made. The severer forms may simulate œdema of the glottis. When the loss of voice is marked, the case may be mistaken for one of nervous aphonia, but the laryngoscope would decide the question at once. Much more difficult is the diagnosis of acute laryngitis in children, particularly in the very young, in whom it is so hard to make a proper examination. From ordinary laryngismus it is to be distinguished by the presence of fever, the mode of onset, and particularly the coryza and the previous symptoms of hoarseness or loss of voice. Membranous laryngitis may at first be quite impossible to differentiate, but in a majority of cases of this affection there are patches on the pharynx and early swelling of the cervical glands. The symptoms, too, are much more severe.

Treatment.—Rest of the larynx should be enjoined, so far as phonation is concerned. In cases of any severity the patient should be kept in bed. The room should be at an even temperature and the air saturated with moisture. Early in the disease, if there is much fever, aconite and citrate of potash may be given, and for the irritating painful cough a full dose of Dover's powder at night. An ice-bag externally often gives great relief.

II. CHRONIC LARYNGITIS.

Etiology.—The cases usually follow repeated acute attacks. The most common causes are overuse of the voice, particularly in persons whose occupation necessitates shouting in the open air. The constant inhalation of irritating substances, as tobacco-smoke, may also cause it.

Symptoms.—The voice is usually hoarse and rough and in severe cases may be almost lost. There is usually very little pain; only the unpleasant sense of tickling in the larynx, which causes a frequent desire to cough. With the laryngoscope the mucous membrane looks swollen, but much less red than in the acute condition. In association with the granular pharyngitis, the mucous glands of the epiglottis and of the ventricles may be involved.

Treatment.—The nostrils should be carefully examined, since in some instances chronic laryngitis is associated with and even dependent upon obstruction to the free passage of air through the nose. Local application must be made directly to the larynx, either with a brush or by means of a spray. Among the remedies most recommended are the solutions of nitrate of silver, chlorate of potash, perchloride of zinc, and tannic acid. Insufflations of bismuth are sometimes useful.

Among directions to be given are the avoidance of heated rooms and loud speaking, and abstinence from tobacco and alcohol. The throat should not be too much muffled, and morning and evening the neck should be sponged with cold water.

III. ŒDEMATOUS LARYNGITIS.

Etiology.—Œdema of the glottis, or, more correctly, of the structures which form the glottis, is a very serious affection which is met with (a) As a rare sequence of ordinary acute laryngitis. (b) In chronic diseases of the larynx, as syphilis or tubercle. (c) In severe inflammatory diseases like diphtheria, in erysipelas of the neck, and in various forms of cellulitis. (d) Occasionally in the acute infectious diseases—scarlet fever, typhus, or typhoid. In Bright's disease, either acute or chronic, there may be a rapidly developing œdema. (e) In angio-neurotic œdema.

Symptoms.—There is dyspnœa, increasing in intensity, so that within an hour or two the condition becomes very serious. There is sometimes marked stridor in respiration. The voice becomes husky and disappears. The laryngoscope shows enormous swelling of the epiglottis, which can sometimes be felt with the finger or even seen when the tongue is strongly depressed with a spatula. The ary-epiglottidean folds are the seat of the chief swelling and may almost meet in the middle line. Occasionally the œdema is below the true cords.

The diagnosis is rarely difficult, inasmuch as even without the laryngoscope the swollen epiglottis can be seen or felt with the finger. The disease is very fatal.

Treatment.—An ice-bag should be placed on the larynx, and the patient given ice to suck. If the symptoms are urgent, the throat should be sprayed with a strong solution of cocaine, and the swollen epiglottis scarified. If relief does not follow, tracheotomy should immediately be performed. The high rate of mortality is due to the fact that this operation is as a rule too long delayed.

IV. SPASMODIC LARYNGITIS (*Laryngismus stridulus*).

Spasm of the glottis is met with in many affections of the larynx, but there is a special disease in children which has received the above-mentioned and other names.

Etiology.—A purely nervous affection, without any inflammatory condition of the larynx, it occurs in children between the ages of six months and three years, and is most commonly seen in connection with rickets. As Escherich has shown, the disease has close relations with tetany and may display many of the accessory phenomena of this disease. Often the attack comes on when the child has been crossed or scolded. Mothers sometimes call the attacks "passion fits" or attacks of "holding the breath." It was supposed at one time that they were associated with enlargement of the thymus, and the condition therefore received the name of *thymic asthma.*

The actual state of the larynx during a paroxysm is a spasm of the adductors, but the precise nature of the influences causing it is not yet known, whether centric or reflex from peripheral irritation. The disease is not so common in America as in England.

Symptoms.—The attacks may come on either in the night or in the day; often just as the child awakes. There is no cough, no hoarseness, but the respiration is arrested and the child struggles for breath, the face gets congested, and then, with a sudden relaxation of the spasm, the air is drawn into the lungs with a high-pitched crowing sound, which has given to the affection the name of "child-crowing." Convulsions may occur during an attack or there may be carpo-pedal spasms. Death may, but rarely does, occur during the attack. With the cyanosis the spasm relaxes and respiration begins. The attacks may recur with great frequency throughout the day.

Treatment.—The gums should be carefully examined and, if swollen and hot, freely lanced. The bowels should be carefully regulated, and as these children are usually delicate or rickety, nourishing diet and cod-liver oil should be given. By far the most satisfactory method of treatment is the cold sponging. In severe cases, two or three times a day the child should be placed in a warm bath and the back and chest thoroughly sponged for a minute or two with cold water. Since learning this practice from Ringer, at the University Hospital, I have seen many cases in which it proved successful. It may be employed when the child is in a paroxysm, though if the attack is severe and the lividity is great it is much better to dash cold water into the face. Sometimes the introduction of the finger far back into the throat will relieve the spasm.

Spasmodic croup, believed to be a functional spasm of the muscles of the larynx, is an affection seen most commonly between the ages of two and five years. According to Trousseau's description, the child goes to bed well, and about midnight or in the early morning hours awakes with oppressed breathing, harsh, croupy cough, and perhaps some huskiness of voice. The oppression and distress for a time are very serious, the face is congested, and there are signs of approaching cyanosis. The attack passes off abruptly, the child falls asleep and awakes the next morning feeling perfectly well. These attacks may be repeated for several nights in succession, and usually cause great alarm to the parents. Whether this is entirely a functional spasm is, I think, doubtful. There are instances in which the child is somewhat hoarse throughout the day, and has slight catarrhal symptoms and a brazen, croupy cough. There is probably slight catarrhal laryngitis with it. These cases are not infrequently mistaken for true croup, and parents are sometimes unnecessarily disturbed by the serious view which the physician takes of the case. Too often the poor child, deluged with drugs, is longer in recovering from the treatment than he would be from the disease. To allay the spasm a whiff of chloroform may be administered, which will in a few moments give relief, or the child may be placed in a hot bath. A prompt emetic, such as zinc or wine of ipecac, will usually relieve the spasm, and is specially indicated if the child has overloaded the stomach through the day.

V. TUBERCULOUS LARYNGITIS.

Etiology.—Tubercles may develop primarily in the laryngeal mucosa, but in the great majority of cases the affection is secondary to pulmonary tuberculosis, in which it is met with in a variable proportion of from 18 to 30 per cent. Laryngitis may occur very early in pulmonary tuberculosis. There may be well-marked involvement of the larynx with signs of very limited trouble at one apex. These are cases which, in my experience, run a very unfavorable course.

Morbid Anatomy.—The mucosa is at first swollen and presents scattered tubercles, which seem to begin in the neighborhood of the blood-vessels. By their fusion small tuberculous masses arise, which caseate and finally ulcerate, leaving shallow irregular losses of substance. The ulcers are usually covered with a grayish exudation, and there is a general thickening of the mucosa about them, which is particularly marked upon the arytenoids. The ulcers may erode the true cords and finally destroy them, and passing deeply may cause perichondritis with necrosis and occasionally exfoliation of the cartilages. The disease may extend laterally and involve the pharynx, and downward over the mucous membrane, covering the cricoid cartilage toward the œsophagus. Above, it may reach the posterior wall of the pharynx, and in rare cases extend to the fauces and tonsils. The epiglottis may be entirely destroyed. There are rare instances in which cicatricial changes go on to such a degree that stenosis of the larynx is induced.

Symptoms.—The first indication is slight huskiness of the voice, which finally deepens to hoarseness, and in advanced stages there may be complete loss of voice. There is something very suggestive in the early hoarseness of tuberculous laryngitis. My attention has frequently been directed to the lungs simply by the quality of the voice.

The cough is in part due to involvement of the larynx. Early in the disease it is not very troublesome, but when the ulceration is extensive it becomes husky and ineffectual. Of the symptoms of laryngeal tuberculosis, none is more aggravating than the dysphagia, which is met with particularly when the epiglottis is involved, and when the ulceration has extended to the pharynx. There is no more distressing or painful complication in phthisis. In instances in which the epiglottis is in great part destroyed, with each attempt to take food there are distressing paroxysms of cough, and even of suffocation.

With the laryngoscope there is seen early in the disease a pallor of the mucous membrane, which also looks thickened and infiltrated, particularly that covering the arytenoid cartilages. The tuberculous ulcers are very characteristic. They are broad and shallow, with gray bases and ill-defined outlines. The vocal cords are infiltrated and thickened, and ulceration is very common.

The diagnosis of tuberculous laryngitis is rarely difficult, as it is usually associated with well-marked pulmonary disease. In case of doubt some of the secretion from the base of an ulcer should be removed and examined for bacilli.

Treatment.—Physicians pay scarcely sufficient attention to the laryngeal complications of consumption. The ulcers should be sprayed and kept thoroughly cleansed. Solutions of tannic acid, nitrate of silver, or sulphide of zinc may be employed. The insufflation, two or three times a day, of a powder of iodoform, with morphia, after thoroughly cleansing the ulcers with a spray, relieves the pain in a majority of the cases. Cocaine (4-percent solution) applied with the atomizer will often enable the patient to swallow his food comfortably. There are, however, distressing cases of extensive laryngeal and pharyngeal ulceration in which even cocaine loses its good effects. When the epiglottis is lost the difficulty in swallowing becomes very great. Wolfenden states that this may be obviated if the patient hangs his head over the side of the bed and sucks milk through a rubber tubing from a mug placed on the floor.

VI. SYPHILITIC LARYNGITIS.

Syphilis attacks the larynx with great frequency. It may result from the inherited disease or be a secondary or tertiary manifestation of the acquired form.

Symptoms.—In secondary syphilis there is occasionally erythema of the larynx, which may go on to definite catarrh, but has nothing characteristic. The process may proceed to the formation of superficial whitish ulcers, usually symmetrically placed on the cords or ventricular bands. Mucous patches and condylomata are rarely seen. The symptoms are practically those of slight loss of voice with laryngeal irritation, as in the simple catarrhal form.

The tertiary laryngeal lesions are numerous and very serious. True gummata, varying in size from the head of a pin to a small nut, develop in the submucous tissue, most commonly at the base of the epiglottis. They go through the changes characteristic of these structures and may either break down, producing extensive and deep ulceration, or—and this is more characteristic of syphilitic laryngitis—in their healing form a fibrous tissue which shrinks and produces stenosis. The ulceration is apt to extend deeply and involve the cartilage, inducing necrosis and exfoliation, and even hæmorrhage from erosion of the arteries. Œdema may suddenly prove fatal. The cicatrices which follow the sclerosis of the gummata or the healing of the ulcers produce great deformity. The epiglottis, for instance, may be tied down to the pharyngeal wall or to the epiglottic folds, or even to the tongue; and eventually a stenosis results, which may necessitate tracheotomy.

The laryngeal symptoms of inherited syphilis have the usual course of these lesions and appear either early, within the first five or six months, or after puberty; most commonly in the former period. Of 76 cases, J. N.

Mackenzie found that 63 occurred within the first year. The gummatous infiltration leads to ulceration, most commonly of the epiglottis and in the ventricles, and the process may extend deeply and involve the cartilage. Cicatricial contraction may also occur.

The diagnosis of syphilis of the larynx is rarely difficult, since it occurs most commonly in connection with other symptoms of the disease.

Treatment.—The administration of constitutional remedies is the most important, and under mercury and iodide of potassium the local symptoms may rapidly be relieved. The tertiary laryngeal manifestations are always serious and difficult to treat. The deep ulceration is specially hard to combat, and the cicatrization may necessitate tracheotomy, or the gradual dilatation, as practised by Schroetter.

III. DISEASES OF THE BRONCHI.

I. ACUTE BRONCHITIS.

Acute catarrhal inflammation of the bronchial mucous membrane is a very common disease, rarely serious in healthy adults, but very fatal in the old and in the young, owing to associated pulmonary complications. It is bilateral and affects either the larger and medium sized tubes or the smaller bronchi, in which case it is known as capillary bronchitis.

We shall speak only of the former, as the latter is part and parcel of broncho-pneumonia.

Etiology.—Acute bronchitis is a common sequel of catching cold, and is often nothing more than the extension downward of an ordinary coryza. It occurs most frequently in the changeable weather of early spring and late autumn. Its association with cold is well indicated by the popular expression "cold on the chest." It may prevail as an epidemic apart from influenza, of which it is an important feature.

Acute bronchitis is associated with many other affections, notably measles. It is by no means rare at the onset of typhoid fever and malaria. It is present also in asthma and whooping-cough. The subjects of spinal curvature are specially liable to the disease. The bronchitis of Bright's disease, gout, and heart-disease is usually a chronic form. It attacks persons of all ages, but most frequently the young and the old. There are individuals who have a special disposition to bronchial catarrh, and the slightest exposure is apt to bring on an attack. Persons who live an out-of-door life are usually less subject to the disease than those who follow sedentary occupations.

The affection is probably microbic, though we have as yet no definite evidence upon this point.

Morbid Anatomy.—The mucous membrane of the trachea and bronchi is reddened, congested, and covered with mucus and muco-pus, which may be seen oozing from the smaller bronchi, some of which are dilated. The finer changes in the mucosa consist in desquamation of the ciliated epithelium, swelling and œdema of the submucosa, and infiltration of the tissue with leucocytes. The mucous glands are much swollen.

Symptoms.—The symptoms of an ordinary "cold" accompany the onset of an acute bronchitis. The coryza extends to the tubes, and may also affect the larynx, producing hoarseness, which in many cases is marked. A chill is rare, but there is invariably a sense of oppression, with heaviness and languor and pains in the bones and back. In mild cases there is scarcely any fever, but in severer forms the range is from 101° to 103°. The bronchial symptoms set in with a feeling of tightness and rawness beneath the sternum and a sensation of oppression in the chest. The cough is rough at first, and often of a ringing character. It comes on in paroxysms which rack and distress the patient extremely. During the severe spells the pain may be very intense beneath the sternum and along the attachments of the diaphragm. At first the cough is dry and the expectoration scanty and viscid, but in a few days the secretion becomes muco-purulent and abundant, and finally purulent. With the loosening of the cough great relief is experienced. The sputum is made up largely of pus-cells, with a variable number of the large round alveolar cells, many of which contain carbon grains, while others have undergone the myelin degeneration.

Physical Signs.—The respiratory movements are not greatly increased in frequency unless the fever is high. There are instances, however, in which the breathing is rapid and when the smaller tubes are involved there is dyspnœa. On palpation the bronchial fremitus may often be felt. On auscultation in the early stage, piping sibilant rales are everywhere to be heard. They are very changeable, and appear and disappear with coughing. With the relaxation of the bronchial membranes and the greater abundance of the secretion, the rales change and become mucous and bubbling in quality. The bases of the lungs should be carefully examined each day, particularly in children and the aged.

The *course* of the disease depends on the conditions under which it develops. In healthy adults, by the end of a week the fever subsides and the cough loosens. In another week or ten days convalescence is fully established. In young children the chief risk is in the extension of the process downward. In measles and whooping-cough, the ordinary bronchial catarrh is very apt to descend to the finer tubes, which become dilated and plugged with muco-pus, inducing areas of collapse, and finally bronchopneumonia. This extension is indicated by changes in the physical signs. Usually at the base the rales are subcrepitant and numerous and there may be areas of defective resonance and of feeble or distant tubular breathing. In the aged and debilitated there are similar dangers if the process extends from the larger to the smaller tubes. In old age the bronchial mucosa is less capable of expelling the mucus, which is more apt to sag to the dependent parts and induce dilatation of the tubes with extension of the inflammation to the contiguous air-cells.

The *diagnosis* of acute bronchitis is rarely difficult. Although the mode of onset may be brusque and perhaps simulate pneumonia, yet the absence of dulness and blowing breathing, and the general character of the bronchial inflammation, render the diagnosis simple. About once a year I see a case of typhoid fever, in which the diagnosis at first has been acute bronchitis. The complication of broncho-pneumonia is indicated by the greater severity of the symptoms, particularly the dyspnœa, the changed color, and the physical signs.

Treatment.—In mild cases, household measures suffice. The hot foot-bath, or the warm bath, a drink of hot lemonade, and a mustard plaster on the chest will often give relief. For the dry, racking cough, the symptom most complained of by the patient, Dover's powder is the best remedy. It is a popular belief that quinine, in full doses, will check an oncoming cold on the chest, but this is doubtful. It is a common custom when persons feel the approach of a cold to take a Turkish bath, and though the tightness and oppression may be relieved by it, there is in a majority of the cases great risk. Some of the severest cases of bronchitis which I have seen have followed this initial Turkish bath. No doubt, if the person could go to bed directly from the bath, its action would be beneficial, but there is great risk of catching additional " cold " in going home from the bath. Relief is obtained from the unpleasant sense of rawness by keeping the air of the room saturated with moisture, and in this dry stage the old-fashioned mixture of the wines of antimony and ipecacuanha with liquor ammonii acetatis and nitrous ether is useful. If the pulse is very rapid, tincture of aconite may be given, particularly in the case of children. For the cough, when dry and irritating, opium should be freely used in the form of Dover's powder. Of course, in the very young and the aged care must be exercised in the use of opium, particularly if the secretions are free; but for the distressing, irritative cough, which keeps the patient awake, no remedy can take its place. As the cough loosens and the expectoration is more abundant, the patient becomes more comfortable. In this stage it is customary to ply him with expectorants of various sorts. Though useful occasionally, they should not be given as a matter of routine. A mixture of squills, ammonia, and senega is a favorite one with many practitioners at this stage.

In the acute bronchitis of children, if the amount of secretion is large and difficult to expectorate, or if there is dyspnœa and the color begins to get dusky, an emetic (a tablespoonful of ipecac wine) should be given at once and repeated if necessary.

II. CHRONIC BRONCHITIS.

Etiology.—This affection may follow repeated attacks of acute bronchitis, but it is most commonly met with in chronic lung affections, heart-disease, aneurism of the aorta, gout, and renal disease. It is frequent in the aged; the young rarely are affected. Climate and season have an important influence. It is the winter cough of the old man, which recurs with regularity as the weather gets cold and changeable.

Morbid Anatomy.—The bronchial mucosa presents a great variety of changes, depending somewhat upon the disease with which chronic

39

bronchitis is associated. In some cases the mucous membrane is very thin, so that the longitudinal bands of elastic tissue stand out prominently. The tubes are dilated, the muscular and glandular tissues are atrophied, and the epithelium is in great part shed.

In other instances the mucosa is thickened, granular, and infiltrated. There may be ulceration, particularly of the mucous follicles. Bronchial dilatations are not uncommon and emphysema is a constant accompaniment.

Symptoms.—In the form met with in old men, associated with emphysema, gout, or heart-disease, the chief symptoms are as follows: Shortness of breath, which may not be noticeable except on exertion. The patients " puff and blow " on going up hill or up a flight of stairs. This is due not so much to the chronic bronchitis itself as to associated emphysema or even to cardiac weakness. They complain of no pain. The cough is variable, changing with the weather and with the season. During the summer they may remain free, but each succeeding winter the cough comes on with severity and persists. There may be only a spell in the morning, or the chief distress is at night. The sputum in chronic bronchitis is very variable. In cases of the so-called dry catarrh there is no expectoration. Usually, however, it is abundant, muco-purulent, or distinctly purulent in character. There are instances in which the patient coughs up for years a thin fluid sputum. There is rarely fever. The general health may be good and the disease may present no serious features apart from the liability to induce emphysema and bronchiectasy. In many cases it is an incurable affection. Patients improve and the cough disappears in the summer time only to return during the winter months.

Physical Signs.—The chest is usually distended, the movements are limited, and the condition is often that which we see in emphysema. The percussion note is clear or hyperresonant. On auscultation, expiration is prolonged and wheezy and rhonchi of various sorts are heard—some high-pitched and piping, others deep-toned and snoring. Crepitation is common at the bases.

Clinical Varieties.—The description just given is of the ordinary chronic bronchitis which occurs in connection with emphysema and heart-disease and in many elderly men. There are certain forms which merit special description: (a) On several occasions I have met with a form of *chronic bronchitis*, particularly in women, which comes on between the ages of twenty and thirty and may continue indefinitely without serious impairment of the health.

(b) *Bronchorrhœa.*—Excessive bronchial secretion is met with under several conditions. It must not be mistaken for the profuse expectoration of bronchiectasy. The secretion may be very liquid and watery—*bronchorrhœa serosa*, and in extraordinary amount. More commonly, it is purulent though thin, and with greenish or yellow-green masses. It may be thick and uniform. This profuse bronchial secretion is usually a manifestation of chronic bronchitis and may lead to dilatation of the tubes and ultimately to fetid bronchitis. In the young the condition may persist for years without impairment of health and without apparently damaging the lungs.

(c) *Putrid Bronchitis.*—Fetid expectoration is met with in connection with bronchiectasis, gangrene, abscess, or with decomposition of secretions within phthisical cavities and in an empyema which has perforated the lung. There are instances in which, apart from any of these states, the expectoration has a fetid character. The sputa are abundant, usually thin, grayish-white in color, and they separate into an upper fluid layer capped with frothy mucus and a thick sediment in which may sometimes be found dirty yellow masses the size of peas or beans—the so-called Dittrich's plugs. The affection is very rare apart from the above-mentioned conditions. In severe cases it leads to changes in the bronchial walls, pneumonia, and often to abscess or gangrene. Metastatic brain abscess has followed putrid bronchitis in a certain number of cases.

(d) *Dry Catarrh.*—The *catarrhe sec* of Laennec, a not uncommon form, is characterized by paroxysms of coughing of great intensity, with little or no expectoration. It is usually met with in elderly persons with emphysema, and is one of the most obstinate of all varieties of bronchitis.

In England the damp cold of the unwarmed houses is responsible in great part for the prevalence of chronic bronchitis among the aged and weak. An equable, warm temperature is of the first importance to all persons prone to the disease.

Treatment.—By far the most satisfactory method of treating the recurring winter bronchitis is change of climate. Removal to a southern latitude may prevent the onset. Southern France, southern California, and Florida furnish winter climates in which the subjects of chronic bronchitis live with the greatest comfort. All cases of prolonged bronchial irritation are benefited by change of air.

The first endeavor in treating a case of chronic bronchitis is to ascertain, if possible, whether there are constitutional or local affections with which it is associated. In many instances the urine is found to be highly acid, perhaps slightly albuminous, and the arteries are stiff. In the form associated with this condition, sometimes called gouty bronchitis, the attacks seem related to the defective renal elimination, and to this condition the treatment should be first directed. In other instances there are heart-disease and emphysema. In the form occurring in old men much may be done in the way of prophylaxis. Septuagenarians should read Oliver Wendell Holmes's * " De Senectute " with reference to the care of the health. There is no doubt that with prudence even in our changeable winter weather much may be done to prevent the onset of chronic bronchitis. Woollen undergarments should be used and especial care should be taken in the spring months not to change them for lighter ones before the warm weather is established.

Cure is seldom effected by medicinal remedies. There are instances in which iodide of potassium acts with remarkable benefit, and it should always be given a trial in cases of paroxysmal bronchitis of obscure origin. For the morning cough, bicarbonate of sodium (gr. xv), chloride of sodium (gr. v), spirits of chloroform (♏v) in anise water and taken with an equal

---

* Over the Tea-cups, Boston, 1890.

amount of warm water will be found useful (Fowler). When there is much sense of tightness and fulness of the chest, the portable Turkish bath may be tried. When the secretion is excessive muriate of ammonia and senega are useful. Stimulating expectorants are contraindicated. When the heart is feeble, the combination of digitalis and strychnia is very beneficial. Turpentine, the old-fashioned remedy so warmly recommended by the Dublin physicians, has in many quarters fallen undeservedly into disuse. Preparations of tar, creasote, and terebene are sometimes useful. Of other balsamic remedies, sandal-wood, the compound tincture of benzoin, copaiba, balsam of Peru or tolu may be used. Inhalations of eucalyptus and of the spray of ipecacuanha wine are often very useful. If fetor be present, carbolic acid in the form of spray (10 to 20 per cent solution) will lessen the odor, or thymol (1 to 1,000). For urgent dyspnœa with cyanosis, bleeding from the arm gives most relief.

III. BRONCHIECTASIS.

Etiology.—Dilatation of the bronchi occurs under the following conditions: (1) As a congenital defect or anomaly. Such cases are extremely rare, commonly unilateral. Grawitz has described the condition as *bronchiectasis universalis*. Welch has met an instance in a young girl. (2) In connection with inflammation of the bronchi, particularly when this leads to weakness of the walls with the accumulation of secretion. I have seen an instance after influenza. Under this category comes the dilatation met with in chronic bronchitis and emphysema, the dilated bronchi in chronic phthisis, in the catarrhal pneumonias of children, and particularly the dilatation which results from the presence of foreign bodies in the air-tubes or from pressure, as of an aneurism on one bronchus. (3) In extreme contraction of the lung tissue, whether due to interstitial pneumonia or to compression by pleural adhesions, bronchial dilatation is a common though not a constant accompaniment.

Unquestionably the weakening of the bronchial wall is the most important, probably the essential, factor in inducing bronchiectasy, since the wall is then not able to resist the pressure of air in severe spells of coughing and in straining. In some instances the mere weight of the accumulated secretion may be sufficient to distend the terminal tubules, as is seen in compression of a bronchus by aneurism.

Morbid Anatomy.—Two chief forms are recognized—the *cylindrical* and the *saccular*—which may exist together in the same lung. The condition may be general or partial. Universal bronchiectasis is always unilateral. It occurs in rare congenital cases and is occasionally seen as a sequence of interstitial pneumonia. The entire bronchial tree is represented by a series of sacculi opening one into the other. The walls are smooth and possibly without ulceration or erosion except in the dependent parts. The lining membrane of the sacculi is usually smooth and glistening. The dilatations may form large cysts immediately beneath the pleura. Intervening between the sacculi is a dense cirrhotic lung tissue. The partial dilatations—the saccular and cylindrical—are common in chronic phthisis, particularly at the apex, in chronic pleurisy at the base, and in emphysema. Here the dilatation is more commonly cylindrical, sometimes fusiform. The bronchial mucous membrane is much involved and sometimes there is a narrowing of the lumen. Occasionally one meets with a single saccular bronchiectasy in connection with chronic bronchitis or emphysema. Some of these look like simple cysts, with smooth walls, without fluid contents. A form of acute bronchiectasis in children has been described by Sharkey, Carr, and others. A good account of it is given in Fowler and Godlee's work on the lungs.

Histologically the bronchi which are the seat of dilatation show important changes. In the large, smooth dilatations the cylindrical is replaced by a pavement epithelium. The muscular layer is stretched, atrophied, and the fibres separated; the elastic tissue is also much stretched and separated. In the large saccular bronchiectases and in some of the cylindrical forms, due to retained secretions, the lining membrane is ulcerated. The contents of some of the larger bronchiectatic cavities are horribly fetid.

Symptoms.—In the limited dilatations of phthisis, emphysema, and chronic bronchitis, the symptoms are in great part those of the original disease, and the condition often is not suspected during life.

In extensive saccular bronchiectasy the characters of the cough and expectoration are distinctive. The patient will pass the greater part of the day without any cough and then in a severe paroxysm will bring up a large quantity of sputum. Sometimes change of the position will bring on a violent attack, probably due to the fact that some of the secretion flows from the dilatation to a normal tube. The daily spell of coughing is usually in the morning. The expectoration is in many instances very characteristic. It is grayish or grayish brown in color, fluid, purulent, with a peculiar acid, sometimes fetid, odor. Placed in a conical glass, it separates into a thick granular layer below and a thin mucoid intervening layer above, which is capped by a brownish froth. Microscopically it consists of pus-corpuscles, often large crystals of fatty acids, which are sometimes in enormous numbers over the field and arranged in bunches. Hæmatoidin crystals are sometimes present. Elastic fibres are seldom found except when there is ulceration of the bronchial walls. Tubercle bacilli are not present. In some cases the expectoration is very fetid and has all the characters of that described under fetid bronchitis. Nummular expectoration, such as comes from phthisical cavities, is not common. Hæmorrhage occurred in 14 out of 35 cases analyzed by Fowler. Abscess of the brain has in a few instances followed the bronchiectasis. Rheumatoid affections may develop, and it is one of the conditions with which the pulmonary osteo-arthropathy is commonly associated.

The *diagnosis* is not possible in a large number of the cases. In the extensive sacculated forms, unilateral and associated with interstitial pneumonia or chronic pleurisy, the diagnosis is easy. There is contraction of the side, which in some instances is not at all extreme. The cavernous signs may be chiefly at the base and may vary according to the condi-

tion of the cavity, whether full or empty. There may be the most exquisite amphoric phenomena and loud resonant rales. The condition
persists for years and is not inconsistent with a tolerably active life. The
patients frequently show signs of marked embarrassment of the pulmonary circulation. There is cyanosis on exertion, the finger-tips are
clubbed, and the nails incurved. A condition very difficult to distinguish from bronchiectasy is a limited pleural cavity communicating with a
bronchus.

Treatment.—Medical treatment is not satisfactory, since it is impossible to heal the cavity. I have practised the injection of antiseptic fluids
in some instances with benefit. Intratracheal injections have been very
warmly recommended of late. With a suitable syringe a drachm may be
injected twice a day of the following solution: Menthol 10 parts, guaiacol 2 parts, olive oil 88 parts. The creasote vapor bath may be given in a
small room. The patient's eyes must be protected with well-fitting goggles,
and the nostrils stuffed with cotton-wool. Commercial creasote is poured
into a metal saucer on a tripod and the saucer heated by a spirit lamp. At
first the vapor is very irritating and disagreeable, but the patient gets used
to it. The bath should be taken at first every other day for fifteen minutes, then gradually increased to an hour daily. The treatment should
be continued for three months. Fowler states that he has known the
fetor to disappear. In suitable cases drainage of the cavities may be attempted, particularly if the patient is in fairly good condition. For the
fetid secretion turpentine may be given, or terebene, and inhalations used
of carbolic acid or thymol.

IV. BRONCHIAL ASTHMA.

Asthma is a term which has been applied to various conditions associated with dyspnœa—hence the names cardiac and renal asthma—but its
use should be limited to the affection known as bronchial or spasmodic
asthma.

Etiology.—All writers agree that there is in a majority of cases of
bronchial asthma a strong neurotic element. Many regard it as a neurosis in which, according to one view, spasm of the bronchial muscles, according to the other turgescence of the mucosa, results from disturbed innervation, pneumogastric or vaso-motor. Of the numerous theories the
following are the most important:

(1) That it is due to spasm of the bronchial muscles, a theory which
has perhaps the largest number of adherents. The original experiments
of C. J. B. Williams, upon which it is largely based, have not, however,
been confirmed of late years.

(2) That the attack is due to swelling of the bronchial mucous membrane—fluctionary hyperæmia (Traube), vaso-motor turgescence (Weber),
diffuse hyperæmic swelling (Clark).

(3) That in many cases it is a special form of inflammation of the
smaller bronchioles—*bronchiolitis exudativa* (Curschmann). Other theo-

ries which may be mentioned are that the attack depends on spasm of the diaphragm or on reflex spasm of all the inspiratory muscles.

As already mentioned, the so-called hay fever is an affection which has many resemblances to bronchial asthma, with which the attacks may alternate. In the suddenness of onset and in many of their features these diseases have the same origin and differ only in site, as suggested by Sir Andrew Clark and now generally acknowledged by specialists. Making due allowance for anatomical differences, if the structural changes occurring in the nasal mucous membrane during an attack of hay fever were to occur also in various parts of the bronchial mucosa, their presence there would afford a complete and adequate explanation of the facts observed during a paroxysm of bronchial asthma (Clark). With this statement I fully agree, but the observations of Curschmann have directed attention to a feature in asthma which has been neglected; namely, that in a majority of the cases it is associated with an exudation, such as might be supposed to come from a turgescent mucosa and which is of a very characteristic and peculiar character. The hyperæmia and swelling of the mucosa and the extremely viscid, tenacious mucus explain well the hindrance to inspiration and expiration and also the quality of the rales. An œdema of the angio-neurotic type has been described in the hands and arms in asthma (J. S. Billings, Jr.).

Some general facts with reference to etiology may be mentioned. The affection sometimes runs in families, particularly those with irritable and unstable nervous systems. The attack may be associated with neuralgia or, as Salter mentions, even alternate with epilepsy. Men are more frequently affected than women. The disease often begins in childhood and sometimes lasts until old age. It may follow an attack of whooping-cough. One of its most striking peculiarities is the *bizarre* and extraordinary variety of circumstances which at times induce a paroxysm. Among these local conditions climate or atmosphere are most important. A person may be free in the city and invariably suffer from an attack when he goes into the country, or into one special part of the country. Such cases are by no means uncommon. Breathing the air of a particular room or a dusty atmosphere may bring on an attack. Odors, particularly of flowers and of hay, or emanations from animals, as the horse, dog, or cat, may at once cause an outbreak. Fright or violent emotion of any sort may bring on a paroxysm. Uterine and ovarian troubles were formerly thought to induce attacks and may do so in rare instances. Diet, too, has an important influence, and in persons subject to the disease severe paroxysms may be induced by overloading the stomach, or by taking certain articles of food. Chronic cases, in which the attacks recur year after year, gradually become associated with emphysema, and every fresh " cold " induces a paroxysm. And lastly, many cases of bronchial asthma are associated with affections of the nose, particularly with hypertrophic rhinitis and nasal polypi. According to some specialists of large experience, all cases of bronchial asthma have some affection of the upper air-passages, but I am convinced from personal observation that this is erroneous. Still physicians must acknowledge the debt which we owe to Voltolini, Hack, Daly, Roe, and others who have shown the close connection which exists between affections of the naso-pharynx and many cases of bronchial asthma.

Briefly stated then, bronchial asthma is a neurotic affection, character-ized by hyperæmia and turgescence of the mucosa of the smaller bronchial tubes and a peculiar exudate of mucin. The attacks may be due to direct irritation of the bronchial mucosa or may be induced reflexly, by irritation of the nasal mucosa, and indirectly, too, by reflex influences, from stomach, intestines, or genital organs.

Symptoms.—Premonitory sensations precede some attacks, such as chilly feelings, a sense of tightness in the chest, flatulence, the passage of a large quantity of urine, or great depression of spirits. Nocturnal attacks are common. After a few hours' sleep, the patient is aroused with a dis-tressing sense of want of breath and a feeling of great oppression in the chest. Soon the respiratory efforts become violent, all the accessory mus-cles are brought into play, and in a few minutes the patient is in a paroxysm of the most intense dyspnœa. The face is pale, the expression anxious, speech is impossible, and in spite of the most strenuous inspiratory efforts very little air enters the lungs. Expiration is prolonged and also wheezy. The number of respirations, however, is not much increased. The asth-matic fit may last from a few minutes to several hours. When severe, the signs of defective aëration soon appear, the face becomes bedewed with sweat, the pulse is small and quick, the extremities get cold, and just as the patient seems to be at his worst, the breathing begins to get easier, and often with a paroxysm of coughing relief is obtained and he sinks ex-hausted to sleep. The relief may be but temporary and a second attack may soon come on. In a majority of the cases even in the intervals be-tween the asthmatic fits the respiration is somewhat embarrassed. The cough is at first very tight and dry and the expectoration is expelled with the greatest difficulty.

The physical signs during an attack are very characteristic. On in-spection the thorax looks enlarged, barrel-shaped, and is fixed, the amount of expansion being altogether disproportionate to the intensity of the in-spiratory movements. The diaphragm is lowered and moves but slightly. Inspiration is short and quick, expiration prolonged. Percussion may not reveal any special difference, but there is sometimes marked hyperreso-nance, particularly in cases which have had repeated attacks.

On auscultation, with inspiration and expiration, there are innumer-able sibilant and sonorous rales of all varieties, piping and high-pitched, low-pitched and grave. Later in the attack there are moist rales.

The *sputum* in bronchial asthma is quite distinctive, unlike that which occurs in any other affection. Early in the attack it is brought up with great difficulty and is in the form of rounded gelatinous masses, the so-called *" perles "* of Laennec. Though ball-like, they can be unfolded and really represent moulds in mucus of the smaller tubes. The entire expec-toration may be made up of these somewhat translucent-looking pellets, floating in a small quantity of thin mucus. Some of them are opaque. Often with a naked eye a twisted spiral character can be seen, particularly if the sputum is spread on a glass with a black background. Microscopically, many of these pellets have a spiral structure, which renders them among the most remarkable bodies met with in sputum. It is not a little curious that they should have been practically overlooked until described a few years ago by Curschmann. Under the microscope the spirals are of two forms. In one there is simply a twisted, spirally arranged mucin, in which are entangled leucocytes, the majority of which are eosinophiles. The twist may be loose or tight. The second form is much more peculiar. In the centre of a tightly coiled skein of mucin fibrils with a few scattered cells is a filament of extraordinary clearness and translucency, probably composed of transformed mucin. As Curschmann suggests, these spirals are doubtless formed in the finer bronchioles and constitute the product of an acute bronchiolitis. It is difficult to explain their spiral nature. I do not know of any observations upon the course of the currents produced by the ciliated epithelium in the bronchi, but it is quite possible that their action may be rotatory, in which case, particularly when combined with spasm of the bronchial muscles, it is possible to conceive that the mucus formed in the tube might be compelled to assume a spiral form. Within two or three days the sputum changes entirely in character; it becomes muco-purulent and Curschmann's spirals are no longer to be found. They occur in all instances of true bronchial asthma in the early period of the attack. I have never seen the true spirals either in bronchitis or pneumonia. There are, in addition, in many cases, the pointed, octahedral crystals described by Leyden and sometimes called asthma crystals. They are identical with the crystals found in the semen and in the blood in leukæmia. At one time they were supposed, by their irritating character, to induce the paroxysms. Eosinophiles in the blood are enormously increased in asthma—to 25 or 35 per cent of the leucocytes, or even to 53.6 per cent in one case (J. S. Billings, Jr.).

The *course* of the disease is very variable. In severe attacks the paroxysms recur for three or four nights or even more, and in the intervals and during the day there may be wheezing and cough. Early in the disease the patient may be free in the morning, without cough or much distress, and the attacks may appear at first to be of a purely nervous character. In the long-standing cases emphysema almost invariably develops, and while the pure asthmatic fits diminish in frequency the chronic bronchitis and shortness of breath become aggravated.

We have no knowledge of the morbid anatomy of true asthma. Death during the attack is unknown. In long-standing cases the lesions are those of chronic bronchitis and emphysema.

Treatment.—The asthmatic attack usually demands immediate and prompt treatment, and remedies should be administered which experience has shown are capable of relieving the condition of the bronchial mucosa. A few whiffs of chloroform will produce prompt though temporary relaxation. In a child with very severe attacks, resisting all the usual remedies, the treatment by chloroform gave immediate and finally permanent relief. Hypodermic injections of pilocarpin (gr. $\frac{1}{8}$) will sometimes relax the mucosa in the profuse sweating. Perles of nitrite of amyl may be broken on the handkerchief or from two to five drops of the solution may be placed upon cotton-wool and inhaled. Strong stimulants given hot or a dose of spirits of chloroform in hot whisky will sometimes induce relaxation. More permanent relief is given by the hypodermic injection of morphia or of morphia and cocaine combined. In obstinate and repeatedly recurring attacks this has proved a very satisfactory plan. The sedative antispasmodics, such as belladonna, henbane, stramonium, and lobelia, may be given in solution or used in the form of cigarettes. Nearly all the popular remedies either in this form or in pastilles contain some plant of the order *solanaceæ*, with nitrate or chlorate of potash. Excellent cigarettes are now manufactured and asthmatics try various sorts, since one form benefits one patient, another form another patient. Nitre paper made with a strong solution of nitrate of potash is very serviceable. Filling the room with the fumes of this paper prior to retiring will sometimes ward off a nocturnal attack. I have known several patients to whom tobacco smoke inhaled was quite as potent as the prepared cigarettes.

The use of compressed air in the pneumatic cabinet is very beneficial; oxygen inhalations may also be tried. In preventing the recurrence of the attacks there is no remedy so useful as iodide of potassium, which sometimes acts like a specific. From 10 to 20 grains three times a day is usually sufficient.

Particular attention should be paid to the diet of asthmatic patients. A rule which experience generally compels them to make is to take the heavy meals in the early part of the day and not retire to bed before gastric digestion is completed. As the attacks are often induced by flatulency, the carbohydrates should be restricted. Coffee is a more suitable drink than tea. In respect to climate it is very difficult to lay down rules for asthmatics. The patients are often much better in the city than in the country. The high and dry altitudes are certainly more beneficial than the sea-shore; but in protracted cases, with emphysema as a secondary complication, the rarefied air of high altitudes is not advantageous. In young persons I have known a residence for six months in Florida or southern California to be followed by prolonged freedom from attacks.

V. FIBRINOUS BRONCHITIS.

An acute or chronic affection, characterized by the formation in certain of the bronchial tubes of fibrinous casts, which are expelled in paroxysms of dyspnœa and cough.

In several diseases fibrinous moulds of the bronchi are formed, as in diphtheria and croup (with extension into the trachea and bronchi), in pneumonia, and occasionally in phthisis—conditions which, however, have nothing to do with true fibrinous bronchitis. These casts are not to be confounded with the blood-casts which occur occasionally in hæmoptysis.

Etiology.—Nothing is known of its causation. It occurs more frequently in males. It is met with at all periods of life, but is more common between the ages of twenty and forty. It has been known to attack several members of the same family. Instances have been described occurring together as if due to some endemic influence (Pichini). The cases are rare, particularly in hospital practice. The attacks occur most commonly in the spring months. An association with tuberculosis has been frequently noted. Model, in an article from Bäumler's clinic, states that tuberculosis was present in ten of twenty-one post mortems. It has been met with also in connection with skin-diseases, such as pemphigus, impetigo, and herpes. The attacks appeared to be related in some cases to the menstrual period. Several instances have been described with heart-disease, but it seems probable that in all these conditions the connection was not causal.

Symptoms.—Acute cases are rare. They may set in with high fever, rigors, severe paroxysms of cough, and perhaps with hæmoptysis. The clinical picture resembles that of acute bronchitis, and only the expulsion of the membranous casts gives the characteristic features to the case. It is much more serious than the chronic form and fatal termination is not uncommon. N. S. Davis has reported two fatal cases. In some of the acute cases there has been affection of the tonsils, and it is possible that the disease may have been truly diphtheritic in character and due to extension of the membrane into the trachea and bronchi. The casts in these cases are not only more extensive, but they also do not present the laminated structure characteristic of true plastic bronchitis.

A patient may have a single attack without any recurrence, but in the chronic form the attacks come on at varying intervals and the disease may last for ten or even twenty years. Instances are on record in which the paroxysms have occurred at definite intervals for many months. The attacks may recur weekly or a period of a year or more may intervene. The onset is marked by bronchitic symptoms, not necessarily with fever. The cough becomes distressing and paroxysmal in character; the sputa may be blood-stained and the patient brings up rounded, ball-like masses, which, when disentangled, are found to be moulds of bronchi; the hæmorrhage may be profuse. In one of the two cases which I have seen it invariably accompanied the attack, and the whitish dendritic casts of the tubes were always entangled in the blood and clots. Urgent dyspnœa and cyanosis may be present in severe attacks. The *physical* signs are those of a severe bronchitis. It may occasionally be possible to determine the weakened or suppressed breath sounds in the affected territory and there may be deficient expansion or even retraction of the chest wall in a corresponding area, but this is in reality very difficult, and twice prior to the expulsion of the casts I failed to determine by physical examination the affected region.

As mentioned, the casts are usually rolled up and mixed with mucus or blood. When unravelled in water they present a complete mould of a secondary or tertiary bronchus with its ramifications. The size of the cast may vary with different attacks, but, as has often been noticed, the form and size may be identical at each attack as if precisely the same bronchial area was involved each time. The casts are hollow, laminated, the size of the lumen varying with the number and thickness of the laminæ. Sometimes they are almost solid. Transverse sections show a beautiful concentric arrangement. The casts have been determined by Grandy to be composed of mucus and not of fibrin. He regards the process as analogous to the mucous colitis. The mucin appears in places to retain its fibrillary structure; in others, as in diphtheritic membrane, it has undergone the hyaline transformation. Leucocytes are imbedded in the meshes. In the centre, particularly in the smaller casts, it is not uncommon to see alveolar epithelium with numerous carbon particles. Leyden's crystals are sometimes found and occasionally Curschmann's spirals.

The pathology of the disease is obscure. The membrane is identical with that to which the term croupous is applied, and the obscurity relates not so much to the mechanism of the production, which is probably the same as in other mucous surfaces, as to the curious limitation of the affection to certain bronchial territories and the remarkable recurrence at stated or irregular intervals throughout a period of many years.

In the acute cases the *treatment* should be that of ordinary acute bronchitis. We know of nothing which can prevent the recurrence of the attacks in the chronic form. In the uncomplicated cases there is rarely any danger during the paroxysm, even though the symptoms may be most distressing and the dyspnœa and cough very severe. Inhalations of ether, steam, or atomized lime-water aid in the separation of the membranes. Pilocarpine might be useful, as in some instances it increases the bronchial secretion. The employment of emetics may be necessary, and in some cases they are effective in promoting the removal of the casts.

IV. DISEASES OF THE LUNGS.

I. CIRCULATORY DISTURBANCES IN THE LUNGS.

Congestion.—There are two forms of congestion of the lungs—active and passive.

(1) *Active Congestion of the Lungs.*—Much doubt and confusion still exist on this subject. French writers, following Woillez, regard it as an independent primary affection (*maladie de Woillez*), and in their dictionaries and text-books allot much space to it. English and American authors more correctly regard it as a symptomatic affection. Active fluxion to the lungs occurs with increased action of the heart, and when very hot air or irritating substances are inhaled. In diseases which interfere locally with the circulation the capillaries in the adjacent unaffected portions may be greatly distended. The importance, however, of this collateral fluxion, as it is called, is probably exaggerated. In a whole series of pulmonary affections there is this associated congestion—in pneumonia, bronchitis, pleurisy, and tuberculosis.

The symptoms of active congestion of the lungs are by no means definite. The description given by Woillez and by other French writers is of an affection which is difficult to recognize from anomalous or larval forms of pneumonia. The chief symptoms described are initial chill, pain in the side, dyspnœa, moderate cough, and temperature from 101° to 103°. The physical signs are defective resonance, feeble breathing, sometimes bronchial in character, and fine rales. A majority of clinical physicians would undoubtedly class such cases under inflammation of the lung. In many epidemics the abnormal and larval forms are specially prevalent. This is no doubt the condition to which Porcher, of Charleston, called attention a short time ago as a " hitherto undescribed affection of the lungs."

The occurrence of an intense and rapidly fatal congestion of the lung, following extreme heat or cold or sometimes violent exertion, is recognized by some authors. Renforth, the oarsman, is said to have died from this cause during the race at Halifax. Leuf has described cases in which, in association with drunkenness, exposure, and cold, death occurred suddenly, or within twenty-four hours, the only lesion found being an extreme, almost hæmorrhagic, congestion of the lungs. It is by no means certain that in these cases death really occurs from pulmonary congestion in the absence of specific statements with reference to the coronary arteries. Several times in sudden death from disease of these vessels I have seen great engorgement of the lungs though not the extreme grade mentioned by Leuf. I have no personal knowledge of cases such as he describes.

(2) *Passive Congestion.*—Two forms of this may be recognized, the mechanical and the hypostatic.

(*a*) Mechanical congestion occurs whenever there is an obstacle to the return of the blood to the heart. It is a common event in many affections of the left heart. The lungs are voluminous, russet brown in color, cutting and tearing with great resistance. On section they show at first a brownish-red tinge, and then the cut surface, exposed to the air, becomes rapidly of a vivid red color from oxidation of the abundant hæmoglobin. This is the condition known as *brown induration* of the lung. Histologically it is characterized by (*a*) great distention of the alveolar capillaries; (*β*) increase in the connective-tissue elements of the lung; (*γ*) the presence in the alveolar walls of many cells containing altered blood-pigment; (*δ*) in the alveoli numerous epithelial cells containing blood-pigment in all stages of alteration, which are also found in great numbers in the sputum.

It occasionally happens that this mechanical hyperæmia of the lung results from pressure by tumors. So long as compensation is maintained the mechanical congestion of the lung in heart-disease does not produce any symptoms, but with enfeebled heart action the engorgement becomes marked and there are dyspnœa, cough, and expectoration, with the characteristic alveolar cells.

(*b*) Hypostatic congestion. In fevers and adynamic states generally, it is very common to find the bases of the lungs deeply congested, a condition induced partly by the effect of gravity, the patient lying recumbent in one posture for a long time, but chiefly by weakened heart action. That it is not an effect of gravity alone is shown by the fact that a healthy person may remain in bed an indefinite time without its occurrence. The term hypostatic congestion is applied to it. The posterior parts of the lung are dark in color and engorged with blood and serum; in some instances to such a degree that the alveoli no longer contain air and portions of the lung sink in water. The term *splenization* and hypostatic pneumonia have been given to these advanced grades. It is a common affection in protracted cases of typhoid fever and in long debilitating illnesses. In ascites, meteorism, and abdominal tumors the bases of the lungs may be compressed and congested. In this connection must be mentioned the form of passive congestion met with in injury to, and organic disease of, the brain. In cerebral apoplexy the bases of the lungs are deeply engorged, not quite airless, but heavy, and on section drip with blood and serum. I have twice seen this condition in an extreme grade throughout the lungs in death from morphia poisoning. In some instances the lung tissue has a blackish, gelatinous, infiltrated appearance, almost like diffuse pulmonary apoplexy. Occasionally this congestion is most marked in, and even confined to, the hemiplegic side. In prolonged coma the hypostatic congestion may be associated with patches of consolidation, due to the aspiration of portions of food into the air-passages.

The symptoms of hypostatic congestion are not at all characteristic, and the condition has to be sought for by careful examination of the bases of the lungs, when slight dulness, feeble, sometimes blowing, breathing and liquid rales can be detected.

The *treatment* of congestion of the lungs is usually that of the condition with which it is associated. In the intense pulmonary engorgement, which may possibly occur primarily, and which is met with in heart-disease and emphysema, free bleeding should be practised. From 20 to 30 ounces of blood should be taken from the arm, and if the blood does not flow freely and the condition of the patient is desperate, aspiration of the right auricle may be performed.

Œdema.—In all forms of intense congestion of the lungs there is a transudation of serum from the engorged capillaries chiefly into the air-cells, but also into the alveolar walls. Not only is it very frequent in congestion, but also with inflammation, with new growths, infarcts, and tubercles. When limited to the neighborhood of an affected part, the name collateral œdema is sometimes applied to it. General œdema occurs under conditions very similar to those met with in congestion. It is very often, no doubt, a terminal event, occurring with the death agony. It is seen in typical form in the cachexias, in death from anæmia, also in chronic Bright's disease, disease of the heart, and cerebral affections.

The œdematous lung is heavy, looks watery, pits on pressure, and from the cut surface a large quantity of clear and, in cases of congestion, bloody serum flows freely; the tissue may even have a gelatinous, infiltrated appearance. The condition is much more common at the bases, but it may exist throughout the entire lung. The pathology of pulmonary œdema is not always clear. Two factors usually prevail in extreme cases—increased tension within the pulmonary system and a diluted blood plasma. The increased tension alone is not capable of producing it. The experiments of Welch seem to indicate that the essential factor lies in a disproportionate weakness of the left ventricle, so that the blood accumulates in the lung capillaries until transudation occurs, a view which satisfactorily explains certain cases, particularly the terminal œdemas.

The *symptoms* of œdema of the lungs are often only an aggravation of those already existing, and are due to the primary disease, whether cardiac, renal, or general. There are usually increasing dyspnœa and cough, and on examination there may be defective resonance and large liquid rales at the bases. There are cases in which the œdema comes on with great suddenness, and in chronic Bright's disease it may prove rapidly fatal.

In the cases of so-called inflammatory œdema fever is always present, and there are often signs, more or less marked, of pneumonia.

The *treatment* of œdema of the lung is practically that of the conditions with which it is associated. In the acute cases active catharsis, and, if there is cyanosis, free venesection should be resorted to.

Pulmonary Hæmorrhage.—This occurs in two forms—*broncho-pulmonary hæmorrhage*, sometimes called bronchorrhagia, in which the blood is poured out into the bronchi and is expectorated, and *pulmonary apoplexy* or pneumorrhagia, in which the hæmorrhage takes place into the air-cells and the lung tissue.

1. *Broncho-pulmonary Hæmorrhage; Hæmoptysis.*—Spitting of blood, to which the term hæmoptysis should be restricted, results from a variety of conditions, among which the following are the most important: (*a*) In young healthy persons hæmoptysis may occur without warning, and after continuing for a few days disappear and leave no ill traces. There may be at the time of the attack no physical signs indicating pulmonary disease. In such cases good health may be preserved for years and no further trouble occur. These cases are not very uncommon. In Ware's important contribution to this subject,* of 386 cases of hæmoptysis noted in private practice 62 recovered and pulmonary disease did not subsequently develop in them. I know three professional men who had hæmoptysis as students, and who now, at periods of from fifteen to eighteen years subsequently, remain in perfect health. (*b*) Hæmoptysis in pulmonary tuberculosis, which is considered in pages 302–304. (*c*) In connection with certain diseases of the lung, as pneumonia (in the initial stage) and cancer, occasionally in gangrene, abscess, and bronchiectasis, hæmoptysis occurs. (*d*) Hæmoptysis is met with in many heart affections, particularly mitral lesions. It may be profuse and recur at intervals for years. (*e*) In ulcerative affections of the larynx, trachea, or bronchi. Sometimes the hæmorrhage is profuse and rapidly fatal, as when an ulcer erodes a large branch of the pulmonary artery, an accident which I have known to happen in a case of chronic bronchitis with emphysema. (*f*) Aneurism is an occasional cause of hæmoptysis. It may be sudden and rapidly fatal when the sac bursts into the air-passages. Slight bleeding may continue for weeks or even longer, due to pressure on the mucous membrane or erosion of the lung; or in some cases the sac " weeps " through the exposed laminæ of fibrin. (*g*) Vicarious hæmorrhage, which occurs in rare instances in cases of interrupted menstruation. The instances are well authenticated. Flint mentions a case which he had had under observation for four years, and Hippocrates refers to it in the aphorism, " Hæmoptysis in a woman is removed by an eruption of the menses." Periodical hæmoptysis has also been met with after the removal of both ovaries. Even fatal hæmorrhage has oc-

---

* On Hæmoptysis as a Symptom, by John Ware, M. D.

curred from the lung during menstruation when no lesion was found to acount for it. (*h*) There is a form of recurring hæmoptysis in arthritic subjects to which Sir Andrew Clark has called special attention and which also is described by French writers. The cases occur in persons over fifty years of age who usually present signs of the arthritic diathesis. It rarely leads to fatal issue and subsides without inducing pulmonary changes. (*i*) Hæmoptysis recurs sometimes in malignant fevers and in purpura hæmorrhagica. Lastly, there is endemic hæmoptysis, due to the *Distomum westermanni* in the bronchial tubes, an affection which is confined to parts of China and Japan.

Symptoms.—Hæmoptysis sets in as a rule suddenly. Often without warning the patient experiences a warm, saltish taste as the mouth fills with blood. Coughing is usually induced. There may be only an ounce or so brought up before the hæmorrhage stops, or the bleeding may continue for days, the patient bringing up small quantities. In other instances, particularly when a large vessel is eroded or an aneurism bursts, the amount is large, and the patient after a few attempts at coughing shows signs of suffocation and death is produced by inundation of the bronchial system. Fatal hæmorrhage may even occur into a large cavity in a patient debilitated by phthisis without the production of hæmoptysis. I dissected a case of this kind at the Philadelphia Hospital. The blood from the lungs generally has characters which render it readily distinguishable from the blood which is vomited. It is alkaline in reaction, frothy, and mixed with mucus, and when coagulation occurs air-bubbles are present in the clot. Blood-moulds of the smaller bronchi are sometimes seen. Patients can usually tell whether the blood has been brought up by coughing or by vomiting, and in a majority of cases the history gives important indications. In paroxysmal hæmoptysis connected with menstrual disturbances the practitioner should see that the blood is actually coughed up, since deception may be practised. The spurious hæmoptysis of hysteria is considered with that disease. Naturally, the patient is at first alarmed at the occurrence of bleeding, but, unless very profuse, as when due to rupture of an aortic aneurism in a pulmonary cavity, the danger is rarely immediate. The attacks, however, are apt to recur for a few days and the sputa may remain blood-tinged for a longer period. In the great majority of cases the hæmorrhage ceases spontaneously. It should be remembered that some of the blood may be swallowed and produce vomiting, and, after a day or two, the stools may be dark in color. It is not well during an attack of hæmoptysis to examine the chest. It was formerly thought that hæmorrhage exercised a prejudicial effect and excited inflammation of the lungs, but this is not often the case.

(2) *Pulmonary Apoplexy; Hœmorrhagic Infarct.*—In this condition the blood is effused into the air-cells and interstitial tissue. It is rarely indeed diffuse, the parenchyma being broken, as is the brain tissue in cerebral apoplexy. Sometimes, in disease of the brain, in septic conditions, and in the malignant forms of fevers, the lung tissue is uniformly infiltrated with blood and has, on section, a black, gelatinous appearance.

As a rule, the hæmorrhage is limited and results from the blocking of a branch of the pulmonary artery either by a thrombus or an embolus. The condition is most common in chronic heart-disease. Although the pulmonary arteries are terminal ones, blocking is not always followed by infarction; partly because the wide capillaries furnish sufficient anastomosis, and partly because the bronchial vessels may keep up the circulation. The infarctions are chiefly at the periphery of the lung, usually wedge-shaped, with the base of the wedge toward the surface. When recent, they are dark in color, hard and firm, and look on section like an ordinary blood-clot. Gradual changes go on, and the color becomes a reddish brown. The pleura over an infarct is usually inflamed. A microscopical section shows the air-cells to be distended with red blood-corpuscles, which may also be in the alveolar walls. The infarcts are usually multiple and vary in size from a walnut to an orange. Very large ones may involve the greater part of a lobe. In the artery passing to the affected territory a thrombus or an embolus is found. The globular thrombi, formed in the right auricular appendix, play an important part in the production of hæmorrhagic infarction. In many cases the source of the embolus cannot be discovered, and the infarct may have resulted from thrombosis in the pulmonary artery, but, as before mentioned, it is not infrequent to find total obstruction of a large branch of a pulmonary artery without hæmorrhage into the corresponding lung area. The further history of an infarction is variable. It is possible that in some instances the circulation is re-established and the blood removed. More commonly, if the patient lives, the usual changes go on in the extravasated blood and ultimately a pigmented, puckered, fibroid patch results. Sloughing may occur with the formation of a cavity. Occasionally gangrene results. In a case at the University Hospital, Philadelphia, a gangrenous infarct ruptured and produced fatal pneumothorax.

The *symptoms* of pulmonary apoplexy are by no means definite. The condition may be suspected in chronic heart-disease when hæmoptysis occurs, particularly in mitral stenosis, but the bleeding may be due to the extreme engorgement. When the infarcts are very large, and particularly in the lower lobe, in which they most commonly occur, there may be signs of consolidation with blowing breathing.

Treatment of Pulmonary Hæmorrhage.—In the treatment of hæmoptysis it is important to remember the condition of the pulmonary circulation and the nature of the lesions associated with the hæmorrhage.

The pressure within the pulmonary artery is considerably less than that in the aortic system. We have as yet very imperfect knowledge of the circumstances which influence the lesser circulation in man. Researches, particularly those of Bradford, indicate that the system is under vasomotor control, but our knowledge of the mutual relations of pressure in the aorta and in the pulmonary artery, under varying conditions, is still very imperfect. Experiments with drugs seem to show that there may be an influence on systemic blood-pressure without any on the pulmonary, and the pressure in the one may rise while it falls in the other, or it may rise and fall in both together. In Andrew's Harveian Oration these rela-

40

tions are thoroughly described, and a statement is made, based on Brad-ford's experiments, as to the action on the pulmonary blood-pressure of many of the drugs employed in hæmoptysis. Thus ergot, the remedy perhaps most commonly used, causes a distinct rise in the pulmonary blood-pressure, while aconite produces a definite fall.

The anatomical condition in hæmoptysis is either hyperæmia of the bronchial mucosa (or of the lung tissue) or a perforated artery. In the latter case the patient often passes rapidly beyond treatment, though there are instances of the most profuse hæmorrhage, which must have come from a perforated artery or a ruptured aneurism, in which recovery has occurred. Practically, for treatment, we should separate these cases, as the remedies which would be applicable in a case of congested and bleeding mucosa would be as much out of place in a case of hæmorrhage from ruptured aneurism as in a cut radial artery. When the blood is brought up in large quantities, it is almost certain either that an aneurism has ruptured or a vessel has been eroded. In the instances in which the sputa are blood-tinged or when the blood is in smaller quantities, bleeding comes by diapedesis from hyperæmic vessels. In such cases the hæmorrhage may be beneficial in relieving the congested blood-vessels.

The indications are to reduce the frequency of the heart-beats and to lower the blood-pressure. By far the most important measure is absolute quiet of body, such as can only be secured by rest in bed and seclusion. In the majority of cases of mild hæmoptysis this is sufficient. Even when the patient insists upon going about, the bleeding may stop spon-taneously. The diet should be light and unstimulating. Alcohol should not be used. The patient may, if he wishes, have ice to suck. Small doses of aromatic sulphuric acid may be given, but unless the bleeding is protracted styptic and astringent medicines are not indicated. For cough, which is always present and disturbing, opium should be freely given, and is of all medicines most serviceable in hæmoptysis. Digitalis should not be used, as it raises the blood-pressure in the pulmonary artery. Aconite, as it lowers the pressure, may be used when there is much vascu-lar excitement. Ergot, tannic acid, and lead, which are so much em-ployed, have little or no influence in hæmoptysis; ergot probably does harm. One of the most satisfactory means of lowering the blood-pressure is purga-tion, and when the bleeding is protracted salts may be freely given. In profuse hæmoptysis, such as comes from erosion of an artery or the rup-ture of an aneurism, a fatal result is common, and yet post-mortem evi-dence shows that thrombosis may occur with healing in a rupture of con-siderable size. The fainting induced by the loss of blood is probably the most efficient means of promoting thrombosis, and it was on this principle that formerly patients were bled from the arm, or from both arms, as in the case of Laurence Sterne. Ligatures, or Esmarch's bandages, placed around the legs may serve temporarily to check the bleeding. The ice-bag on the sternum is of doubtful utility. In a protracted case Cayley in-duced pneumothorax, but without effect.

Briefly, then, we may say that cases of hæmorrhage from rupture of aneurism or erosion of a blood-vessel usually prove fatal. The fainting induced by the loss of blood is beneficial, and, if the patient can be kept alive for twenty-four hours, a thrombus of sufficient strength to prevent further bleeding may form. The chief danger is the inundation of the bronchial system with the blood, so that while the hæmorrhage is profuse the cough should be encouraged. Opium should not then be used, and stimulants should be given with caution.

In the other group, in which the hæmorrhage comes from a congested area and is limited, the patient gets well if kept absolutely quiet, and fatal hæmorrhage probably never occurs from this source. Rest, reduction of the blood-pressure by minimum diet, purging, if necessary, and the administration of opium to allay the cough are the main indications.

II. BRONCHO-PNEUMONIA (*Capillary Bronchitis*).

This is essentially an inflammation of the terminal bronchus and the air-vesicles which make up a pulmonary lobule, whence the term broncho-pneumonia. It is also known as lobular, in contradistinction to lobar pneumonia. The term catarrhal is less applicable. The process begins usually with an inflammation of the capillary bronchi, which is a condition rarely, if ever, found without involvement of the lobular structures, so that it is now customary to consider the affections together. All forms of broncho-pneumonia depend upon invasion of the lung with microbes, and it would have been more consistent to place them with lobar pneumonia among the infectious disorders, but it is well perhaps to defer this until the bacteriology of the different varieties has been more fully worked out.

Etiology.—Broncho-pneumonia occurs either as a primary or as a secondary affection. The relative frequency in 443 cases is thus given by Holt: Primary, without previous bronchitis, 154; secondary (*a*) to bronchitis of larger tubes, 41; to measles, 89; to whooping-cough, 66; to diphtheria, 47; to scarlet fever, 7; to influenza, 6; to varicella, 2; to erysipelas, 2; and to acute ileo-colitis, 19. The proportion of primary to secondary forms as shown in this list is probably too low.

Primary acute broncho-pneumonia, like the lobar form, attacks children in good health, usually under two years. The etiological factors are very much those of ordinary pneumonia, and probably the pneumococcus is more often associated with it.

Secondary broncho-pneumonia occurs in two great groups: 1. As a sequence of the infectious fevers—measles, diphtheria, whooping-cough, scarlet fever, and, less frequently, small-pox, erysipelas, and typhoid fever. In children it forms the most serious complication of these diseases, and in reality causes more deaths than are due directly to the fevers. In large cities it ranks next in fatality to infantile diarrhœa. Following, as it does, the contagious diseases which principally affect children, we find that a large majority of cases occur during early life. According to Morrill's Boston statistics, it is most fatal during the first two years of life. The number of cases in a community increases or decreases with the prevalence of measles, scarlet fever, and diphtheria. It is most prevalent in the winter and spring months. In the febrile affections of adults broncho-pneumonia is not very common. Thus in typhoid fever it is not so frequent as lobar pneumonia, though isolated areas of consolidation at the bases are by no means rare in protracted cases of this disease. In old people it is an extremely common affection, following debilitating causes of any sort, and supervening in the course of chronic Bright's disease and various acute and chronic maladies.

2. In the second division of this affection are embraced the cases of so-called aspiration or deglutition pneumonia. Whenever the sensitiveness of the larynx is benumbed, as in the coma of apoplexy or uræmia, minute particles of food or drink are allowed to pass the *rima*, and, reaching finally the smaller tubes, excite an intense inflammation similar to the vagus pneumonia which follows the section of the pneumogastrics in the dog. Cases are very common after operations about the mouth and nose, after tracheotomy, and in cancer of the larynx and œsophagus. The aspirated particles in some instances induce such an intense broncho-pneumonia that suppuration or even gangrene supervenes. The ether pneumonia, already described (p. 129), is often lobular in type.

An aspiration broncho-pneumonia may follow hæmoptysis (which has been already considered), the aspiration of material from a bronchiectatic cavity, and occasionally the material from an empyema which has ruptured into the lung.

A common and fatal form of broncho-pneumonia is that excited by the tubercle bacillus, which has already been considered.

Among general predisposing causes may be mentioned age. As just noted, it is prone to attack infants, and a majority of cases of pneumonia in children under five years of age are of this form. Of 370 cases in children under five years of age, 75 per cent were broncho-pneumonia (Holt). At the opposite extreme of life it is also common, in association with various debilitating circumstances and with the chronic diseases incident to the old. In children, rickets and diarrhœa are marked predisposing causes, and broncho-pneumonia is one of the most frequent post-mortem-room lesions in infants' homes and foundling asylums. The disease prevails most extensively among the poorer classes.

Morbid Anatomy.—On the pleural surfaces, particularly toward the base, are seen depressed bluish or blue-brown areas of collapse, between which the lung tissue is of a lighter color. Here and there are projecting portions over which the pleura may be slightly turbid or granular. The lung is fuller and firmer than normal, and, though in great part crepitant, there can be felt in places throughout the substance solid, nodular bodies. The dark depressed areas may be isolated or a large section of one lobe may be in the condition of collapse or atelectasis. Gradual inflation by a blow-pipe inserted in the bronchus will distend a great majority of these collapsed areas. On section, the general surface has a dark reddish color and usually drips blood. Projecting above the level of the section are lighter red or reddish-gray areas representing the patches of broncho-pneumonia. These may be isolated and separated from each other by tracts of uninflamed tissue or they may be in groups; or the greater part of a lobe may be involved. Study of a favorable section of an isolated patch shows: (*a*) A dilated central bronchiole full of tenacious purulent mucus. A fortunate section parallel to the long axis may show a racemose arrangement—the alveolar passages full of muco-pus. (*b*) Surrounding the bronchus for from 3 to 5 mm. or even more, an area of grayish-red consolidation, usually elevated above the surface and firm to the touch. Unlike the consolidation of lobar pneumonia, it may present a perfectly smooth surface, though in some instances it is distinctly granular. In a late stage of the disease small grayish-white points may be seen, which on pressure may be squeezed out as purulent droplets. A section in the axis of the lobule may present a somewhat grape-like arrangement, the stalks and stems representing the bronchioles and alveolar passages filled with a yellowish or grayish-white pus, while surrounding them is a reddish-brown hepatized tissue. (*c*) In the immediate neighborhood of this peribronchial inflammation the tissue is dark in color, smooth, airless, at a somewhat lower level than the hepatized portion, and differs distinctly in color and appearance from the other portions of the lung. This is the condition to which the term *splenization* has been given. It really represents a tissue in the early stage of inflammation, and it perhaps would be as well to give up the use of this term and also that of *carnification*, which is only a more advanced stage. The condition of collapse probably always precedes this, and it is difficult in some instances to tell the difference, as one shades into the other. In fact, collapse, splenization, and carnification are but preliminary steps in broncho-pneumonia.

While, in many cases, the areas of broncho-pneumonia present a reddish-brown color and are indistinctly granular, in others, particularly in adults, the nodules may resemble more closely gray hepatization and the air-cells are filled with a grayish, muco-purulent material. Minute hæmorrhages are sometimes seen in the neighborhood of the inflamed areas or on the pleural surfaces. Emphysema is commonly seen at the anterior borders and upper portions of the lung or in lobules adjacent to the inflamed ones. In many cases following diphtheria and measles the process is so extensive that the greater part of a lobe is involved, and it looks like a case of lobar hepatization. It has not, however, the uniformity of this affection, and collapsed dark strands may be seen between extensive areas of hepatized tissue.

There are three groups of cases: (1) Those in which the bronchitis and bronchiolitis are most marked, and in which there may be no definite consolidation, and yet on microscopical examination many of the alveolar passages and adjacent air-cells appear filled with inflammatory products. (2) The disseminated broncho-pneumonia, in which there are scattered areas of peribronchial hepatization with patches of collapse, while a considerable proportion of the lobe is still crepitant. This is by far the most common condition. (3) The pseudo-lobar form, in which the greater portion of the lobe is consolidated, but not uniformly, for intervening strands of dark congested lung tissue separate the groups of hepatized lobules.

Microscopically, the centre of the bronchus is seen filled with a plug of exudation, consisting of leucocytes and swollen epithelium. Section in the long axis may show irregular dilatations of the tube. The bronchial wall is swollen and infiltrated with cells. Under a low power it is readily seen that the air-cells next the bronchus are most densely filled, while toward the periphery of the focus the alveolar exudation becomes less. The contents of the air-cells are made up of leucocytes and swollen endothelial cells in varying proportions. Red corpuscles are not often present and a fibrin network is rarely seen, though it may be present in some alveoli. In the swollen walls are seen distended capillaries and numerous leucocytes. As Delafield has pointed out, the interstitial inflammation of the bronchi and alveolar walls is the special feature of broncho-pneumonia.

The histological changes in the aspiration or deglutition broncho-pneumonia differ from the ordinary post-febrile form in a more intense infiltration of the air-cells with leucocytes, producing suppuration and foci of softening; even gangrene may be present.

Bacteriology of Broncho-pneumonia.—The organisms most commonly found in broncho-pneumonia are the *micrococcus lanceolatus*, the *streptococcus pyogenes* (either alone or with the pneumococcus), the *staphylococcus aureus et albus*, and Friedländer's *bacillus pneumoniæ*. The Klebs-Loeffler bacillus is not infrequently found in the secondary lesions of diphtheria. Except the pneumococcus these microbes are rarely found in pure cultures. In the lobular type the streptococcus is the most constant organism, in the pseudo-lobar the pneumococcus. Mixed infections are almost the rule in broncho-pneumonia.

M. Wollstein, in 17 primary cases, found the *micrococcus lanceolatus* alone in 9, with the streptococcus in 7. Of 14 secondary cases the *micrococcus lanceolatus* was found alone in 2 and with other organisms in 9. The primary form is the result of infection with the pneumococcus, the secondary most often with the streptococcus.

Terminations of Broncho-pneumonia.—(1) In *resolution*, which when it once begins goes on more rapidly than in fibrinous pneumonia. Broncho-pneumonia of the apices, in a child, persisting for three or more weeks, particularly if it follows measles or diphtheria, is often tuberculous. In these instances, when resolution is supposed to be delayed, caseation has in reality taken place. (2) In *suppuration*, which is rarely seen apart from the aspiration and deglutition forms, in which it is extremely common. (3) In *gangrene*, which occurs under the same conditions. (4) In *fibroid changes*—chronic broncho-pneumonia—a rare termination in the simple, a common sequence of the tuberculous, disease. Formerly it was thought that one of the most common changes in broncho-pneumonia, particularly in children, was caseation; but this is really a tuberculous process, the natural termination of an originally specific broncho-pneumonia. It is of course quite possible that a broncho-pneumonia, simple in its origin, may subsequently be the seat of infection by the *bacillus tuberculosis*.

Symptoms.—The *primary* form sets in abruptly with a chill or a convulsion. The child has not had a previous illness, but there may have been slight exposure. The temperature rises rapidly and is more constant; the physical signs are more local and there is not the widespread diffuse catarrh of the smaller tubes. Many cases are mistaken for lobar pneumonia. In others the pulmonary features are in the background or are overlooked in the intensity of the general or cerebral symptoms. The termination is often by crisis, and the recovery is prompt. The mortality of this form is slight. S. West has recently (British Medical Journal, 1898, i) called attention to the importance of recognizing these primary cases and to their resemblance in clinical features with acute lobar pneumonia. The *secondary* form begins usually as a bronchitis of the smaller tubes. Much confusion has arisen from the description of capillary bronchitis as a separate affection, whereas it is only a part, though a primary and important one, of broncho-pneumonia. At the outset it may be said that if in convalescence from measles or in whooping-cough a child has an accession of fever with cough, rapid pulse, and rapid breathing, and if, on auscultation, fine rales are heard at the bases, or widely spread throughout the lungs, even though neither consolidation nor blowing breathing can be detected, the diagnosis of broncho-pneumonia may safely be made. I have never seen in a fatal case after diphtheria or measles a capillary bronchitis as the sole lesion. The onset is rarely sudden, or with a distinct chill; but after a day or so of indisposition the child gets feverish and begins to cough and to get short of breath. The fever is extremely variable; a range of from 102° to 104° is common. The skin is very dry and pungent. The cough is hard, distressing, and may be painful. Dyspnœa gradually becomes a prominent feature. Expiration may be jerky and grunting. The respirations may rise as high as 60 or even 80 per minute. Within the first forty-eight hours the percussion resonance is not impaired; the note, indeed, may be very full at the anterior borders of the lungs. On auscultation, many rales are heard, chiefly the fine subcrepitant variety, with sibilant rhonchi. There may really be no signs indicating that the parenchyma of the lung is involved, and yet even at this early stage, within forty-eight hours of the onset of the pulmonary symptoms, I have repeatedly, after diphtheria, found scattered nodules of lobular hepatization. Northrup, in a case in which death occurred within the first twenty-four hours, in addition to the extensive involvement of the smaller bronchi, found the intralobular tissue also involved in places. The dyspnœa is constant and progressive and soon signs of deficient aëration of the blood are noted. The face becomes a little suffused and the finger-tips bluish. The child has an anxious expression and gradually enters upon the most distressing stage of asphyxia. At first the urgency of the symptoms is marked, but soon the benumbing influence of the carbon dioxide on the nerve-centres is seen and the child no longer makes strenuous efforts to breathe. The cough subsides and, with a gradual increase in lividity and a drowsy restlessness, the right ventricle becomes more and more distended, the bronchial rales become more liquid as the tubes fill with mucus, and death occurs from heart paralysis. These are symptoms of a severe case of broncho-pneumonia, or what the older writers called *suffocative catarrh*.

The *physical signs* may at first be those of capillary bronchitis, as indicated by the absence of dulness, the presence of fine subcrepitant and whistling rales. In many cases death takes place before any definite pneumonic signs are detected. When these exist they are much more frequent at the bases, where there may be areas of impaired resonance or even of positive dulness. When numerous foci involve the greater part of a lobe the breathing may become tubular, but in the scattered patches of ordinary broncho-pneumonia, following the fevers, the breathing is more commonly harsh than blowing. In grave cases there is retraction of the base of the sternum and of the lower costal cartilages during inspiration, pointing to deficient lung expansion.

Diagnosis.—With lobar pneumonia it may readily be confounded if the areas of consolidation are large and merged together. It is to be remembered, as Holt's figures well show, that broncho-pneumonia occurs chiefly in children under one year, whereas lobar pneumonia is more common after the third year. No writer has so clearly brought out the difference between pneumonia at these periods as Gerhard,* of Philadelphia, whose papers on this subject, though published nearly sixty years ago, have the freshness and accuracy which characterize all the writings of that eminent physician. Between lobar pneumonia and the secondary form of broncho-pneumonia the diagnosis is easy. The mode of onset is essentially different in the two infections, the one developing insidiously in the course or at the conclusion of another disease, the other setting in abruptly in a child in good health. In lobar pneumonia the disease is almost always unilateral, in broncho-pneumonia bilateral. The chief trouble arises in cases of primary broncho-pneumonia, which by aggregation of the foci involves the greater part of one lobe. Here the difficulty is very great, and the physical signs may be practically identical, but in broncho-pneumonia it is much more likely that a lesion, however slight, will be found on the other side.

A still more difficult question to decide is whether an existing broncho-pneumonia is simple or tuberculous. In many instances the decision cannot be made, as the circumstances under which the disease occurs, the mode of onset, and the physical signs may be identical. It has often been my experience that a case has been sent down from the children's ward to the dead-house with the diagnosis of post-febrile broncho-pneumonia in which there was no suspicion of the existence of tuberculosis; but on section there were found tuberculous bronchial glands and scattered areas of broncho-pneumonia, some of which were distinctly caseous, while others showed signs of softening. I have already spoken fully of this in the section on tuberculosis, but it is well to emphasize the fact that there are many cases of broncho-pneumonia in children which time alone enables us to distinguish from tuberculosis. The existence of extensive disease at the apices or central regions is a suggestive indication, and signs of softening may be detected. In the vomited matter, which is brought up after severe spells of coughing, sputum may be picked out and elastic tissue and bacilli detected.

It is a superfluous refinement to make a diagnosis between capillary bronchitis and catarrhal pneumonia, for the two conditions are part and parcel of the same disease. In simple bronchitis involving the larger tubes urgent dyspnœa and pulmonary distress are rarely present and the rales

---

* American Journal of the Medical Sciences, vols. xiv and xv.

are coarser and more sibilant. It must not be forgotten that, as in lobar pneumonia, cerebral symptoms may mask the true nature of the disease, and may even lead to the diagnosis of meningitis. I recall more than one instance in which it could not be satisfactorily determined whether the infant had tuberculous meningitis or a cerebral complication of an acute pulmonary affection.

Prognosis.—In the primary form the outlook is good. In children enfeebled by constitutional disease and prolonged fevers broncho-pneumonia is terribly fatal, but in cases coming on in connection with whooping-cough or after measles recovery may take place in the most desperate cases. It is in this disease that the truth of the old maxim is shown—"Never despair of a sick child." The death-rate in children under five has been variously estimated at from 30 to 50 per cent. After diphtheria and measles thin, wiry children seem to stand broncho-pneumonia much better than fat, flabby ones. In adults the aspiration or deglutition pneumonia is a very fatal disease.

Prophylaxis.—Much can be done to reduce the probability of attack after febrile affections. Thus, in the convalescence from measles and whooping-cough, it is very important that the child should not be exposed to cold, particularly at night, when the temperature of the room naturally falls. In a nocturnal visit to the nursery—sometimes, too, I am sorry to say, to a children's hospital—how often one sees children almost naked, having kicked aside the bedclothes and having the night-clothes up about the arms! The use of light flannel "combinations" obviates this nocturnal chill, which is, I am sure, an important factor in the colds and pulmonary affections of young children, both in private houses and in institutions. The catarrhal troubles of the nose and throat should be carefully attended to, and during fevers the mouth should be washed two or three times a day with an antiseptic solution.

Treatment.—The frequency and the seriousness of broncho-pneumonia render it a disease which taxes to the utmost the resources of the practitioner. There is no acute pulmonary affection over which he at times so greatly despairs. On the other hand, there it not one in which he will be more gratified in saving cases which have seemed past all succor. The general arrangements should receive special attention. The room should be kept at an even temperature—about 65° to 68°—and the air should be kept moist with vapor.

At the outset the bowels should be opened by a mild purge, either castor oil or small doses of calomel, one twelfth to one sixth of a grain hourly until a movement is obtained, and care should be taken throughout the attack to secure a daily movement. The common saline fever mixture of citrate of potash, liquor ammonii acetatis, and aromatic spirits of ammonia may be given every two or three hours. If the disease comes on abruptly with high fever, minim or minim and a half doses of the tincture of aconite may be given with it. The pain, the distressing symptoms, and the incessant cough often demand opium, which must of course be used with care and judgment in the case of young children, but which is certainly not contra-indicated and may be usefully given in the form of

Dover's powder. Blisters are now rarely if ever employed, and even the jacket poultice has gone out of fashion. For the latter, however, I confess to a strong prejudice, and when lightly made and frequently changed it undoubtedly gives great relief. Much more commonly we now see, both in private and in hospital practice, the jacket of cotton-batting. Ice-poultices to the chest I have seen used apparently with great benefit, and they are warmly recommended by many German physicians as well as by Goodhart and others in England. The diet should consist of milk, broths, and egg albumen. Milk often curds and is disagreeable. Egg-white is particularly suitable and very acceptable when given in cold water with a little sugar. It forms, indeed, an excellent medium for the administration of the stimulants. If the pulse shows signs of failing, it is best to begin early with brandy. As in all febrile affections of children, cold water should be constantly at the bedside, and the child should be encouraged to drink freely. With these measures, in many cases the disease progresses to a favorable termination, but too often other and more serious symptoms arise. Cough becomes more distressing, dyspnœa increases, the ominous rattling of the mucus can be heard in the tubes, the child's color is not so good, and there is greater restlessness. Under these circumstances stimulant expectorants—ammonia, squills, and senega—should be given. Together they make a very disagreeable dose for a young child, particularly with the carbonate of ammonia. The aromatic spirits of ammonia is somewhat better. If the carbonate is employed, it must be given in small doses, not more than a grain to an infant of eighteen months. If the child has increasing difficulty in getting up the mucus, an emetic should be given—either the wine of ipecac or, if necessary, tartar emetic. There is no necessity, however, to keep the child constantly nauseated. Enough should be given to cause prompt emesis, and the benefit results in the expulsion of mucus from the larger tubes. In this stage, too, strychnine is undoubtedly helpful in stimulating the depressed respiratory centre. With commencing cyanosis, inhalations of oxygen may be employed, sometimes with great benefit.

With rapid failure of the heart, loud mucous rattles in the throat, and increasing lividity, every measure should be used to arouse the child and excite coughing. Alternate douches of hot and cold water, electricity, which I have seen applied with good results at Wiederhofer's clinic in Vienna, and hypodermic injections of ether may be tried. For the reduction of temperature, particularly if cerebral symptoms are prominent, there is nothing so satisfactory as the wet pack or the cold bath. In the case of children, when the latter is used it should be graduated, beginning with a temperature which is pleasantly warm and gradually reducing it to 75° or 80°. Even when the temperature is not high, the cerebral symptoms are greatly relieved by the bath or the pack.

III. CHRONIC INTERSTITIAL PNEUMONIA

(*Cirrhosis of the Lung—Fibroid Phthisis*).

This consists in the gradual substitution to a greater or less extent of connective tissue for the normal lung. It is a fibroid change which may have its starting-point in the tissue about the bronchi and blood-vessels, the interlobular septa, the alveolar walls, or in the pleura. So diverse are the different forms and so varied the conditions under which this change occurs that a proper classification is extremely difficult. We may recognize, however, two chief forms—the *local,* which involves only a limited area of the lung substance, and the *diffuse,* invading either both lungs or an entire organ.

Etiology.—*Local* fibroid change in the lungs is common. It is a constant accompaniment of tubercle and in every case of phthisis the chronic interstitial changes play a very important *rôle.* In tumors, abscess, gummata, hydatids, and emphysema it also occurs. Fibroid processes are frequently met with at the apices of the lung and may be due either to a limited healed tuberculosis, to fibroid induration in consequence of pigment, or, in a few instances, may result from thickening of the pleura. They have been described at page 331.

Diffuse interstitial pneumonia is met with under the following circumstances: 1. As a sequence of acute fibrinous pneumonia. Although extremely rare, this is recognized as a possible termination. From unknown causes resolution fails to take place. A gradual process of organization goes on in the fibrinous plugs within the air-cells and the alveolar walls become greatly thickened by a new growth, first of nuclear and subsequently of fibrillated connective tissue. Macroscopically there is produced a smooth, grayish, homogeneous tissue which has the peculiar translucency of all new-formed connective tissue. This has been called gray induration. A majority of the cases terminate within a few months, and instances which have been followed from the outset are very rare.

2. *Chronic Broncho-Pneumonia.*—The relation of broncho-pneumonia to cirrhosis of the lung has been specially studied by Charcot, who states that it may follow the acute or subacute form of this disease, particularly in children. The fibrosis extends from the bronchi, which are usually found dilated. Bronchiectasis itself may be followed by fibrosis of the lung. The alveolar walls are thickened and the lobules converted into firm grayish masses, in which there is no trace of normal lung tissue. This process may go on and involve an entire lobe or even the whole lung. Many of these cases are tuberculous from the outset.

3. *Pleurogenous Interstitial Pneumonia.*—Charcot applies this term to that form of cirrhosis of the lung which follows invasion from the pleura. Doubt has been expressed by some writers whether this really occurs. While Wilson Fox is probably correct in questioning whether an entire lung can become cirrhosed by the gradual invasion from the pleura, there can be no doubt that there are instances of primitive dry pleurisy, which,

as Sir Andrew Clark has pointed out, gradually compresses the lung and at the same time leads to interstitial cirrhosis. This may be due in part to the fibroid change which follows prolonged compression. In some cases there seems to be a distinct connection between the greatly thickened pleura and the dense strands of fibrous tissue passing from it into the lung substance. Instances occur in which one lobe or the greater part of it presents, on section, a mottled appearance, owing to the increased thickness of the interlobar septa—a condition which may exist without a trace of involvement of the pleura. In many other cases, however, the extension seems to be so definitely associated with pleurisy that there is no doubt as to the causal connection between the two processes. In these instances the lung is removed with great difficulty, owing to the thickness and close adhesion of the pleura to the chest wall.

4. *Chronic interstitial pneumonia,* due to inhalation of dust, which is considered in a separate section.

5. *Syphilis* of the lung presents the features of a chronic fibrosis of the organ (see p. 247).

6. Indurative changes in the lung may follow the compression by aneurism or new growth or the irritation of a foreign body in a bronchus.

Morbid Anatomy.—There are two chief forms, the massive or lobar and the insular or broncho-pneumonic form. In the massive type the disease is unilateral; the chest of the affected side is sunken, deformed, and the shoulder much depressed. On opening the thorax the heart is seen drawn far over to the affected side. The unaffected lung is emphysematous and covers the greater portion of the mediastinum. It is scarcely credible in how small a space, close to the spine, the cirrhosed lung may lie. The adhesions between the pleural membranes may be extremely dense and thick, particularly in the pleurogenous cases; but when the disease has originated in the lung there may be little thickening of the pleura. The organ is airless, firm, and hard. It strongly resists cutting, and on section shows a grayish fibroid tissue of variable amount, through which pass the blood-vessels and bronchi. The latter may be either slightly or enormously dilated. There are instances in which the entire lung is converted into a series of bronchiectatic cavities and the cirrhosis is apparent only in certain areas or at the root. The tuberculous cases can usually be differentiated by the presence of an apical cavity, not bronchiectatic, and often large; and the other lung almost invariably shows tuberculous lesions. Pulmonary aneurisms are not infrequent in the cavities. The other lung is always greatly enlarged and emphysematous. The heart is hypertrophied, particularly the right ventricle, and there may be marked atheromatous changes in the pulmonary artery. An amyloid condition of the viscera is found in some cases.

In the broncho-pneumonic form the areas are smaller, often centrally placed, and most frequently in the lower lobes. They are deeply pigmented, show dilated bronchi, and when multiple are separated by emphysematous lung tissue.

A *reticular form* of fibrosis of the lung has been described by Percy

Kidd and W. McCollum, in which the lungs are intersected by grayish fibroid strands following the lines of the interlobular septa.

Symptoms and Course.—The disease is essentially chronic, extending over a period of many years, and when once the condition is established the health may be fairly good. In a well-marked case the patient complains only of his chronic cough, perhaps a slight shortness of breath. In other respects he is quite well, and is usually able to do light work. The cases are commonly regarded as phthisical, though there may be scarcely a symptom of that affection except the cough. There are instances, however, of fibroid phthisis which cannot be distinguished from cirrhosis of the lung except by the presence of tubercle bacilli in the expectoration. As the bronchi are usually dilated, the symptoms and physical signs may be those of bronchiectasis. The cough is paroxysmal and the expectoration is generally copious and of a muco-purulent or sero-purulent nature. It is sometimes fetid. Hæmorrhage is by no means infrequent, and occurred in more than one half of the cases analyzed by Bastian. Walking on the level and in the ordinary affairs of life the patient may show no shortness of breath, but in the ascent of stairs and on exertion there may be dyspnœa.

Physical Signs.—*Inspection.*—The affected side is immobile, retracted, and shrunken, and contrasts in a striking way with the voluminous sound side. The intercostal spaces are obliterated and the ribs may even overlap. The shoulder is drawn down and from behind it is seen that the spine is bowed. The heart is greatly displaced, being drawn over by the shrinkage of the lung to the affected side. When the left lung is affected there may be a large area of visible impulse in the second, third, and fourth interspaces. Mensuration shows a great diminution in the affected side, and with the saddle-tape the expansion may be seen to be negative. The *percussion* note varies with the condition of the bronchi. It may be absolutely flat, particularly at the base or at the apex. In the axilla there may be a flat tympany or even an amphoric note over a large sacculated bronchus. On the opposite side the percussion note is usually hyperresonant. On *auscultation* the breath-sounds have either a cavernous or amphoric quality at the apex, and at the base are feeble, with mucous, bubbling rales. The voice-sounds are usually exaggerated. Cardiac murmurs are not uncommon, particularly late in the disease, when the right heart fails. These are, of course, the physical signs of the disease when it is well established. They naturally vary considerably, according to the stage of the process. The disease is essentially chronic, and may persist for fifteen or twenty years. Death occurs sometimes from hæmorrhage, more commonly from gradual failure of the right heart with dropsy, and occasionally from amyloid degeneration of the organs.

The *diagnosis* is never difficult. It may be impossible to say, without a clear history, whether the origin is pleuritic or pneumonic. Between cases of this kind and fibroid phthisis it is not always easy to discriminate, as the conditions may be almost identical. When tuberculosis is present, however, even in long-standing cases, bacilli are usually present in the sputa, and there may be signs of disease in the other lung.

Treatment.—It is only for an intercurrent affection or for an aggravation of the cough that the patient seeks relief. Nothing can be done for the condition itself. When possible the patient should live in a mild climate, and should avoid exposure to cold and damp. A distressing feature in some cases is the putrefaction of the contents of the dilated tubes, for which the same measures may be used as in fetid bronchitis.

IV. PNEUMONOKONIOSIS.

Under this term, introduced by Zenker, are embraced those forms of fibrosis of the lung due to the inhalation of dusts in various occupations. They have received various names, according to the nature of the inhaled particles—*anthracosis*, or coal-miner's disease; *siderosis*, due to the inhalation of metallic dusts, particularly iron; *chalicosis*, due to the inhalation of mineral dusts, producing the so-called stone-cutter's phthisis, or the "grinder's rot" of the Sheffield workers.

The dust particles inhaled into the lungs are dealt with extensively by the ciliated epithelium and by the phagocytes, which exist normally in the respiratory organs. The ordinary mucous corpuscles take in a large number of the particles, which fall upon the trachea and main bronchi. The cilia sweep the mucus out to a point from which it can be expelled by coughing. It is doubtful if the particles ever reach the air-cells, but the swollen alveolar cells (in which they are in numbers) probably pick them up on the way. The mucous and the alveolar cells are the normal respiratory scavengers. In dwellers in the country, in which the air is pure, they are able to prevent the access of dust particles to the lung tissue, so that even in adults these organs present a rosy tint, very different from the dark, carbonized appearance of the lungs of dwellers in cities. When the impurities in the air are very abundant, a certain proportion of the dust particles escapes these cells and penetrates the mucosa, reaching the lymph spaces, where they are attacked at once by the cells of the connective-tissue stroma, which are capable of ingesting and retaining a large quantity. In coal-miners, coal-heavers, and others whose occupations necessitate the constant breathing of a very dusty atmosphere even these forces are insufficient. Many of the particles enter the lymph stream and, as Arnold has shown in his beautiful researches, are carried (1) to the lymph nodules surrounding the bronchi and blood-vessels; (2) to the interlobular septa beneath the pleura, where they lodge in and between the tissue elements; and (3) along the larger lymph channels to the substernal, bronchial and tracheal glands, in which the stroma cells of the follicular cords dispose of them permanently and prevent them from entering the general circulation. Occasionally in anthracosis the carbon grains do reach the general circulation, and the coal dust is found in the liver and spleen. As Weigert has shown, this occurs when the densely pigmented bronchial glands closely adhere to the pulmonary veins, through the walls of which the carbon particles pass to the general circulation. The lung tissue has a remarkable tolerance for these particles, probably because a large proportion of them is warehoused, so to speak, in protoplasmic cells. By constant exposure a limit is reached, and there is brought about a very definite pathological condition, an interstitial sclerosis. In coal-miners this may occur in patches, even before the lung tissue is uniformly infiltrated with the dust. In others it appears only after the entire organs have become so laden that they are dark in color, and an ink-like juice flows from the cut surface. The lungs of a miner may be black throughout and yet show no local lesions and be everywhere crepitant.

As already mentioned, the particles are deposited in large numbers in the follicular cords of the tracheal and bronchial glands and of the peri-bronchial and peri-arterial lymph nodules, and in these they finally excite proliferation of the connective-tissue elements. It is by no means uncommon to find in persons whose lungs are only moderately carbonized the bronchial glands sclerosed and hard. In anthracosis the fibroid changes usually begin in the peri-bronchial lymph tissue, and in the early stage of the process the sclerosis may be largely confined to these regions. A Nova Scotian miner, aged thirty-six, died under my care, at the Montreal General Hospital, of black small-pox, after an illness of a few days. In his lungs (externally coal-black) there were round and linear patches ranging in size from a pea to a hazel-nut, of an intensely black color, airless and firm, and surrounded by a crepitant tissue, slate-gray in color. In the centre of each of these areas was a small bronchus. Many of them were situated just beneath the pleura, and formed typical examples of limited fibroid broncho-pneumonia. In addition there is usually thickening of the alveolar walls, particularly in certain areas. By the gradual coalescence of these fibroid patches large portions of the lung may be converted into firm grayish-black, in the case of the coal-miner—steel-gray, in the case of the stone-worker—areas of cirrhosis. In the case of a Cornish miner, aged sixty-three, who died under my care, one of these fibroid areas measured 18 by 6 cm. and 4.5 cm. in depth.

A second important factor in these cases is chronic bronchitis, which is present in a large proportion and really causes the chief symptoms. A third is the occurrence of emphysema, which is almost invariably associated with long-standing cases of pneumonokoniosis. With the changes so far described, unless the cirrhotic area is unusually extensive, the case may present the features of chronic bronchitis with emphysema, but finally another element comes into play. In the fibroid areas softening occurs, probably a process of necrosis similar to that by which softening is produced in fibro-myomata of the uterus. At first these are small and contain a dark liquid. Charcot calls them *ulcères du poumon*. They rarely attain a large size unless a communication is formed with the bronchus, in which case they may become converted into suppurating cavities. The question has been much discussed of late as to what part the tubercle bacillus plays in these cases of pneumonokoniosis with cavity formation. In some instances there is certainly a tuberculous process ingrafted, but that large excavations may occur, or in other instances bronchiectasis without the presence of bacilli, I have convinced myself by the examination of several characteristic specimens.

The *siderosis* induced by the oxide of iron causes an interstitial pneumonia similar to anthracosis. Workers in brass and in bronze are liable to a like affection.

Chalicosis, due to the deposit of particles of silex and alumina, is found in the makers of mill-stones, particularly the French mill-stones, and also in knife and axe grinders and stone-cutters. Anatomically, this form is characterized by the production of nodules of various sizes, which are cut with the greatest difficulty and sometimes present a curious grayish, even glittering, crystalloid appearance.

Workers in flax and in cotton, and grain-shovellers are also subject to these chronic interstitial changes in the lungs. In all these occupations, as shown by Greenhow, to whose careful studies we owe so much of our knowledge of these diseases, the condition of the lung may ultimately be almost identical.

The *symptoms* do not come on until the patient has worked for a variable number of years in the dusty atmosphere. As a rule there are cough and failing health for a prolonged period of time before complete disability. The coincident emphysema is responsible in great part for the shortness of breath and wheezy condition of these patients. The expectoration is usually muco-purulent, often profuse; in a case of anthracosis, very dark in color—the so-called " black spit " ; in a case of chalicosis there may be seen under the microscope the bright angular particles of silica.

Even when there are physical signs of cavity, tubercle bacillus are not necessarily, and indeed in my experience they are not usually present. It is remarkable for how long a time a coal-miner may continue to bring up sputum laden with coal particles even when there are only signs of a chronic bronchitis. Many of the particles are contained in the cells of the alveolar epithelium. In these instances it appears that an attempt is made by the leucocytes to rid the lungs of some of the carbon grains.

The *diagnosis* of the condition is rarely difficult; the expectoration is usually characteristic. It must always be borne in mind that chronic bronchitis and emphysema form essential parts of the process and that in late stages there may be tuberculous infection.

The *treatment* of the condition is practically that of chronic bronchitis and emphysema.

V. EMPHYSEMA.

Definition.—The condition in which the infundibular passages and the alveoli are dilated and the alveolar walls atrophied.

A practical division may be made into compensatory, hypertrophic, and atrophic forms, the acute vesicular emphysema, and the interstitial forms. The last two do not in reality come under the above definition, but for convenience they may be considered here.

I. Compensatory Emphysema.

Whenever a region of the lung does not expand fully in inspiration, either another portion of the lung must expand or the chest wall sink in order to occupy the space. The former almost invariably occurs. We have already mentioned that in broncho-pneumonia there is a vicarious distention of the air-vesicles in the adjacent healthy lobules, and the same happens in the neighborhood of tuberculous areas and cicatrices. In general pleural adhesions there is often compensatory emphysema, particularly at the anterior margins of the lung. The most advanced example of this form is seen in cirrhosis, when the unaffected lung increases greatly in size, owing to distention of the air-vesicles. A similar though less marked condition is seen in extensive pleurisy with effusion and in pneumothorax.

At first, this distention of the air-vesicles is a simple physiological process and the alveolar walls are stretched but not atrophied. Ultimately, however, in many cases they waste and the contiguous air-cells fuse, producing true emphysema.

II. Hypertrophic Emphysema.

The large-lunged emphysema of Jenner, also known as substantive or idiopathic emphysema, is a well-marked clinical affection, characterized by enlargement of the lungs, due to distention of the air-cells and atrophy of their walls, and clinically by imperfect aëration of the blood and more or less marked dyspnœa.

Etiology.—Emphysema is the result of persistently high intra-alveolar tension acting upon a congenitally weak lung tissue. If the mechanical views as to its origin, which have prevailed so long, were true, the disease would certainly be much more common; since violent respiratory efforts, believed to be the essential factor, are performed by a majority of the working classes. Strongly in favor of the view, that the nutritive change in the air-cells is the primary factor, is the markedly hereditary character of the disease and the frequency with which it starts early in life. These are two points upon which scarcely sufficient stress has been laid. To James Jackson, Jr., of Boston, we owe the first observations on the hereditary character of emphysema. Working under Louis' directions, he found that in 18 out of 28 cases one or both parents were affected.

I have been impressed by the frequency of its origin in childhood. It may follow recurring asthmatic attacks due to adenoid vegetations. It may develop, too, in several members of the same family. We are still ignorant as to the nature of this congenital pulmonary weakness. Cohnheim thinks it probably due to a defect in the development of the elastic-tissue fibres—a statement which is borne out by Eppinger's observations.

Heightened pressure within the air-cells may be due to forcible inspiration or expiration. Much discussion has taken place as to the part played by these two acts in the production of the disease. The inspiratory

41

theory was advanced by Laennec and subsequently modified by Gairdner, who held that in chronic bronchitis areas of collapse were induced, and compensatory distention took place in the adjacent lobules. This unquestionably does occur in the vicarious or compensatory emphysema, but it probably is not a factor of much moment in the form now under consideration. The expiratory theory, which was supported by Mendelssohn and Jenner, accounts for the condition in a much more satisfactory way. In all straining efforts and violent attacks of coughing, the glottis is closed and the chest walls are strongly compressed by muscular efforts, so that the strain is thrown upon those parts of the lung least protected, as the apices and the anterior margins, in which we always find the emphysema most advanced. The sternum and costal cartilages gradually yield to the heightened intrathoracic pressure and are, in advanced cases, pushed forward, giving the characteristic rotundity to the thorax. The cartilages gradually become calcified. One theory of the disease is that there is a gradual enlargement of the thorax and the lungs increase in volume to fill up the space.

Of other etiological factors occupation is the most important. The disease is met with in players on wind instruments, in glass-blowers, and in occupations necessitating heavy lifting or straining. Whooping-cough and bronchitis play an important *rôle*, not so much in the changes which they induce in the bronchi as in consequence of the prolonged attacks of coughing.

Morbid Anatomy.—The thorax is capacious, usually barrel-shaped, and the cartilages are calcified. On removal of the sternum, the anterior mediastinum is found completely occupied by the edges of the lungs, and the pericardial sac may not be visible. The organs are very large and have lost their elasticity, so that they do not collapse either in the thorax or when placed on the table. The pleura is pale and there is often an absence of pigment, sometimes in patches, termed by Virchow *albinism* of the lung. To the touch they have a peculiar, downy, feathery feel, and pit readily on pressure. This is one of the most marked features. Beneath the pleura greatly enlarged air-vesicles may be readily seen. They vary in size from $\frac{1}{2}$ to 3 mm., and irregular bullæ, the size of a walnut or larger, may project from the free margins. The best idea of the extreme rarefaction of the tissue is obtained from sections of a lung distended and dried. At the anterior margins the structure may form an irregular series of air-chambers, resembling the frog's lung. On careful inspection with the hand-lens, remnants of the interlobular septa or even of the alveoli may be seen on these large emphysematous vesicles. Though general throughout the organs, the distention is more marked, as a rule, at the anterior margins, and is often specially developed at the inner surface of the lobe near the root, where in extreme cases air-spaces as large as an egg may sometimes be found. Microscopically there is seen atrophy of the alveolar walls, by which is produced the coalescence of neighboring air-cells. In this process the capillary network disappears before the walls are completely atrophied. The loss of the elastic tissue is a special feature. It is stated, indeed, that in certain cases there is a congenital defect in the development of this tissue.   The epithelium of the air-cells undergoes a fatty change, but the large distended air-spaces retain a pavement layer.

The bronchi show important changes.   In the larger tubes the mucous membrane may be rough and thickened from chronic bronchitis; often the longitudinal lines of submucous elastic tissue stand out prominently.   In the advanced cases many of the smaller tubes are dilated, particularly when, in addition to emphysema, there are peri-bronchial fibroid changes. Bronchiectasis is not, however, an invariable accompaniment of emphysema, but, as Laennec remarks, it is difficult to understand why it is not more common.   Of associated morbid changes the most important are found in the heart.   The right chambers are dilated and hypertrophied, the tricuspid orifice is large, and the valve segments are often thickened at the edges.   In advanced cases the cardiac hypertrophy is general.   The pulmonary artery and its branches may be wide and show marked atheromatous changes.

The changes in the other organs are those commonly associated with prolonged venous congestion.

Symptoms.—The disease may be tolerably advanced before any special symptoms develop.   A child, for instance, may be somewhat short of breath on going up-stairs or may be unable to run and play as other children without great discomfort; or, perhaps, has attacks of slight lividity. Doubtless much depends upon the completeness of cardiac compensation. When this is perfect, there may be no special interruption of the pulmonary circulation and, except with violent exertion, there is no interference with the aëration of the blood.   In well-developed cases the following are the most important symptoms: *Dyspnœa*, which may be felt only on slight exertion, or may be persistent, and aggravated by intercurrent attacks of bronchitis.   The respirations are often harsh and wheezy, and expiration is distinctly prolonged.

Cyanosis of an extreme grade is more common in emphysema than in other affections with the exception of congenital heart-disease.   So far as I know it is the only disease in which a patient may be able to go about and even to walk into the hospital or consulting-room with a lividity of startling intensity.   The contrast between the extreme cyanosis and the comparative comfort of the patient is very striking.   In other affections of the heart and lungs associated with a similar degree of cyanosis the patient is invariably in bed and usually in a state of orthopnœa.   One condition must be here referred to, viz., the extraordinary cyanosis in cases of poisoning by aniline products, which is in most part due to the conversion of the hæmoglobin into methæmoglobin.

Bronchitis with associated cough is a frequent symptom and often the direct cause of the pulmonary distress.   The contrast between emphysematous patients in the winter and summer is marked in this respect. In the latter they may be comfortable and able to attend to their work, but with the cold and changeable weather they are laid up with attacks of bronchitis.   Finally, in fact, the two conditions become inseparable and the patient has persistently more or less cough.   The acute bronchitis may produce attacks not unlike asthma. In some instances this is true spasmodic asthma, with which emphysema is frequently associated.

As age advances, and with successive attacks of bronchitis, the condition gets slowly worse. In hospital practice it is common to admit patients over sixty with well-marked signs of advanced emphysema. The affection can generally be told at a glance—the rounded shoulders, barrel chest, the thin yet oftentimes muscular form, and sometimes, I think, a very characteristic facial expression.

There is another group, however, of younger patients from twenty-five to forty years of age who, winter after winter, have attacks of intense cyanosis in consequence of an aggravated bronchial catarrh. On inquiry we find that these patients have been short-breathed from infancy, and they belong, I believe, to a category in which there has been a primary defect of structure in the lung tissue.

Physical Signs.—*Inspection.*—The thorax is markedly altered in shape; the antero-posterior diameter is increased and may be even greater than the lateral, so that the chest is barrel-shaped. The appearance is somewhat as if the chest was in a permanent inspiratory position. The sternum and costal cartilages are prominent. The lower zone of the thorax looks large and the intercostal spaces are much widened, particularly in the hypochondriac regions. The sternal fossa is deep, the clavicles stand out with great prominence, and the neck looks shortened from the elevation of the thorax and the sternum. A zone of dilated venules may be seen along the line of attachment of the diaphragm. Though this is common in emphysema, it is by no means peculiar to it or indeed to any special affection. Andrew, of Bartholomew's Hospital, and, according to Duckworth, Laycock called attention to it.

The curve of the spine is increased and the back is remarkably rounded, so that the scapulæ seem to be almost horizontal. Mensuration shows the rounded form of the chest and the very slight expansion on deep inspiration. The respiratory movements, which may look energetic and forcible, exercise little or no influence. The chest does not expand, but there is a general elevation. The inspiratory effort is short and quick; the expiratory movement is prolonged. There may be retraction instead of distention in the upper abdominal region during inspiration, and there is sometimes seen a transverse curve crossing the abdomen at the level of the twelfth rib. The apex beat of the heart is not visible, and there is usually marked pulsation in the epigastric region. The cervical veins stand out prominently and may pulsate.

Palpation.—The vocal fremitus is somewhat enfeebled but not lost. The apex beat can rarely be felt. There is a marked shock in the lower sternal region and very distinct pulsation in the epigastrium. *Percussion* gives greatly increased resonance, full and drum-like—what is sometimes called hyperresonance. The note is not often distinctly tympanitic in quality. The percussion note is greatly extended, the heart dulness may be obliterated, the upper limit of liver dulness is greatly lowered, and the resonance may extend to the costal margin. Behind, a clear percussion note extends to a much lower level than normal. The level of splenic dulness, too, may be lowered.

On *auscultation* the breath-sounds are usually enfeebled and may be masked by bronchitic rales. The most characteristic feature is the prolongation of the expiration, and the normal ratio may be reversed—4 to 1 instead of 1 to 4. It is often wheezy and harsh and associated with coarse rales and sibilant rhonchi. It is said that in interstitial emphysema there may be a friction sound heard, not unlike that of pleurisy. The heart-sounds are usually clear; but in advanced cases, when there is marked cyanosis, a tricuspid regurgitant murmur may be heard. Accentuation of the pulmonary second sound is present.

The *course* of the disease is slow but progressive, the recurring attacks of bronchitis aggravating the condition. Death may occur from intercurrent pneumonia, either lobar or lobular, and dropsy may supervene from cardiac failure. Occasionally death results from overdistention of the heart, with extreme cyanosis. Duckworth has called attention to the occasional occurrence of fatal hæmorrhage in emphysema. In an old emphysematous patient at the Montreal General Hospital death followed the erosion of a main branch of the pulmonary artery by an ulcer near the bifurcation of the trachea.

Treatment.—Practically, the measures mentioned in connection with bronchitis should be employed. In children with asthma and developing emphysema the nose should be carefully examined. No remedy is known which has any influence over the progress of the condition itself. Bronchitis is the great danger of these patients, and therefore when possible they should live in an equable climate. In consequence of the venous engorgement they are liable to gastric and intestinal disturbance, and it is particularly important to keep the bowels regulated and to avoid flatulency which often seriously aggravates the dyspnœa. Patients who come into the hospital in a state of urgent dyspnœa and lividity, with great engorgement of the veins, particularly if they are young and vigorous, should be bled freely. On more than one occasion I have saved the lives of persons in this condition by venesection. Inhalation of oxygen may be used and the remedies given already mentioned in connection with bronchitis. Strychnine will be found specially useful.

III. Atrophic Emphysema.

This is really a senile change and is called by Sir William Jenner small-lunged emphysema. It is really a primary atrophy of the lung, coming on in advanced life, and scarcely constitutes a special affection. It occurs in " withered-looking old persons " who may perhaps have had a winter cough and shortness of breath for years. In striking contrast to the essential or hypertrophic emphysema, the chest in this form is small. The ribs are obliquely placed, the decrease in the diameter being due to greatly increased obliquity in the position of the ribs. The thoracic muscles are usually atrophied. In advanced cases of this affection the lung presents a remarkable appearance, being converted into a series of large vesicles, on the walls of which the remnants of air-cells may be seen. It is a condition for which nothing can be done.

IV. ACUTE VESICULAR EMPHYSEMA.

When death occurs from bronchitis of the smaller tubes, or from cyanosis when strong inspiratory efforts have been made, the lungs are large in volume and the air-cells are much distended. Clinically, this condition may develop rapidly in cases of cardiac asthma and angina pectoris. The lungs are voluminous, the area of pulmonary resonance is much increased, and on auscultation there are heard everywhere piping rales and prolonged expiration. It is the condition to which von Basch has given the names *Lungenschwellung* and *Lungenstarrheit*. A similar condition may follow pressure on the vagi.

V. INTERSTITIAL EMPHYSEMA.

In this form beads of air are seen in the interlobular and subpleural tissue; sometimes they form large bullæ beneath the pleura. A rare event is rupture close to the root of the lung, and the passage of air along the trachea into the subcutaneous tissues of the neck. After tracheotomy just the reverse may occur and the air may pass from the tracheotomy wound along the wind-pipe and bronchi and appear beneath the surface of the pleura. From this interstitial emphysema spontaneous pneumothorax may arise in healthy persons.

VI. GANGRENE OF THE LUNG.

Etiology.—Gangrene of the lung is not an affection *per se*, but occurs in a variety of conditions when necrotic areas undergo putrefaction. It it not easy to say why sphacelus should occur in one case and not in another, as the germs of putrefaction are always in the air-passages, and yet necrotic territories rarely become gangrenous. Total obstruction of a pulmonary artery, as a rule, causes infarction, and the area shut off does not often, though it may, sphacelate. Another factor would seem to be necessary—probably a lowered tissue resistance, the result of general or local causes. It is met with (1) as a sequence of lobar pneumonia. This rarely occurs in a previously healthy person—more commonly in the debilitated or in the diabetic subject. (2) Gangrene is very prone to follow the aspiration pneumonia, since the foreign particles rapidly undergo putrefactive changes. Of a similar nature are the cases of gangrene due to perforation of cancer of the œsophagus into the lung or into a bronchus. (3) The putrid contents of a bronchiectatic, more commonly of a tuberculous, cavity may excite gangrene in the neighboring tissues. The pressure bronchiectasis following aneurism or tumor may lead to extensive sloughing. (4) Gangrene may follow simple embolism of the pulmonary artery. More commonly, however, the embolus is derived from a part which is mortified or comes from a focus of bone disease. In typhus and in typhoid fever gangrene of the lung may follow thrombosis of one of the larger branches of the pulmonary artery. A case occurred in my wards in October, 1897, in connection with a typhoid septicæmia. Typhoid bacilli were isolated from the lung. Lastly, gangrene of the lung may occur in conditions of debility during convalescence from protracted fever—occasionally, indeed, without our being able to assign any reasonable cause.

Morbid Anatomy.—Laennec, who first accurately described pulmonary gangrene, recognized a diffuse and a circumscribed form. The former, though rare, is sometimes seen in connection with pneumonia, more rarely after obliteration of a large branch of the pulmonary artery. It may involve the greater part of a lobe, and the lung tissue is converted into a horribly offensive greenish-black mass, torn and ragged in the centre. In the circumscribed form there is well-marked limitation between the gangrenous area and the surrounding tissue. The focus may be single or there may be two or more. The lower lobe is more commonly affected than the upper, and the peripheral more than the central portion of the lung. A gangrenous area is at first uniformly greenish brown in color; but softening rapidly takes place with the formation of a cavity with shreddy, irregular walls and a greenish, offensive fluid. The lung tissue in the immediate neighborhood shows a zone of deep congestion, often consolidation, and outside this an intense œdema. In the embolic cases the plugged artery can sometimes be found. When rapidly extending, vessels may be opened and a copious hæmorrhage ensue. Perforation of the pleura is not uncommon. The irritating decomposing material usually excites the most intense bronchitis. Embolic processes are not infrequent. There is a remarkable association in some cases between circumscribed gangrene of the lung and abscess of the brain. It has been referred to under the section on bronchiectasis.

Symptoms and Course.—Usually definite symptoms of local pulmonary disease precede the characteristic features of gangrene. These, of course, are very varied, depending on the nature of the trouble. The sputum is very characteristic. It is intensely fetid—usually profuse—and, if expectorated into a conical glass, separates into three layers—a greenish-brown, heavy sediment; an intervening thin liquid, which sometimes has a greenish or a brownish tint; and, on top, a thick, frothy layer. Spread on a glass plate, the shreddy *débris* of lung tissue can readily be picked out. Even large fragments of lung may be coughed up. Robertson, of Onancock, Va., sent me one several centimetres in length, which had been expectorated by a lad of eighteen, who had severe gangrene and recovered. Microscopically, elastic fibres are found in abundance, with granular matter, pigment grains, fatty crystals, bacteria, and leptothrix. It is stated that elastic tissue is sometimes absent, but I have never met with such an instance. The peculiar plugs of sputum which occur in bronchiectasy are not found. Blood is often present, and, as a rule, is much altered. The sputum has, in a majority of the cases, an intensely fetid odor, which is communicated to the breath and may permeate the entire room. It is much more offensive than in fetid bronchitis or in abscess of the lung. The fetor is particularly marked when there is free communication between the gangrenous cavities and the bronchi. On several occasions I have found, post mortem, localized gangrene, which had been unsuspected during life, and in which there had been no fetor of the breath.

The physical signs, when extensive destruction has occurred, are those of cavity, but the limited circumscribed areas may be difficult to detect. Bronchitis is always present.

Among the general symptoms may be mentioned fever, usually of moderate grade; the pulse is rapid, and very often the constitutional depression is severe. But the only special features indicative of gangrene are the sputa and the fetor of the breath. The patient generally sinks from exhaustion. Fatal hæmorrhage may ensue.

Treatment.—The treatment of gangrene is very unsatisfactory. The indications, of course, are to disinfect the gangrenous area, but this is often impossible. An antiseptic spray of carbolic acid may be employed. A good plan is for the patient to use over the mouth and nose an inhaler, which may be charged with a solution of carbolic acid or with guaiacol; the latter drug has also been used hypodermically, with, it is said, happy results in removing the odor. If the signs of cavity are distinct an attempt should be made to cleanse it by direct injections of an antiseptic solution. If the patient's condition is good and the gangrenous region can be localized, surgical interference may be indicated. Successful cases have been reported. The general condition of the patient is always such as to demand the greatest care in the matter of diet and nursing.

VII. ABSCESS OF THE LUNG.

Etiology.—Suppuration occurs in the lung under the following conditions: (1) As a sequence of inflammation, either lobar or lobular. Apart from the purulent infiltration this is unquestionably rare, and even in lobar pneumonia the abscesses are of small size and usually involve, as Addison remarked, several points at the same time. On the other hand, abscess formation is extremely frequent in the deglutition and aspiration forms of lobular pneumonia. After wounds of the neck or operations upon the throat, in suppurative disease of the nose or larynx, occasionally even of the ear (Volkmann), infective particles reach the bronchial tubes by aspiration and excite an intense inflammation which often ends in abscess. Cancer of the œsophagus, perforating the root of the lung or into the bronchi, may produce extensive suppuration. The abscesses vary in size from a walnut to an orange, and have ragged and irregular walls, and purulent, sometimes necrotic, contents.

(2) Embolic, so-called metastatic, abscesses, the result of infectious emboli, are extremely common in a large proportion of all cases of pyæmia. They may occur in enormous numbers and present very definite characters. As a rule they are superficial, beneath the pleura, and often wedge-shaped. At first firm, grayish red in color, and surrounded by a zone of intense hyperæmia, suppuration soon follows with the formation of a definite abscess. The pleura is usually covered with greenish

lymph, and perforation sometimes takes place with the production of pneumothorax.

(3) Perforation of the lung from without, lodgment of foreign bodies, and, in the right lung, perforation from abscess of the liver or a suppurating echinococcus cyst are occasional causes of pulmonary abscess.

(4) Suppurative processes play an important part in chronic pulmonary tuberculosis, many of the symptoms of which are due to them.

Symptoms.—Abscess following pneumonia is easily recognized by an aggravation of the general symptoms and by the physical signs of cavity and the characters of the expectoration. Embolic abscesses cannot often be recognized, and the local symptoms are generally masked in the general pyæmic manifestations. The characters of the sputum are of great importance in determining the presence of abscess. The odor is offensive, yet it rarely has the horrible fetor of gangrene or of putrid bronchitis. In the pus fragments of lung tissue can be seen, and the elastic tissue may be very abundant. The presence of this with the physical signs rarely leaves any question as to the nature of the trouble. Embolic cases usually run a fatal course. Recovery occasionally occurs after pneumonia. In a case following typhoid fever which I saw at the Garfield Hospital, Kerr removed two ribs and found free in the pus of a localized empyema a sequestrated piece of lung, the size of the palm of the hand, which had sloughed off clearly from the lower lobe. The patient made a good recovery.

Medicinal treatment is of little avail in abscess of the lung. When well defined and superficial, an attempt should always be made to open and drain it. A number of successful cases have already been treated in this way.

VIII. NEW GROWTHS IN THE LUNGS.

Etiology and Morbid Anatomy.—While primary tumors are rare, secondary growths are not uncommon.

The primary growths of the lung are either encephaloid, scirrhus or epithelioma. Recent observations show that the last is the most common form. Sarcoma also is occasionally found as a primary growth, and still more rarely enchondroma.

The secondary growths may be of various forms. Most commonly they follow tumors in the digestive or genito-urinary organs; not infrequently also tumors of the bone. There may be encephaloid, scirrhus, epithelioma, colloid, melano-sarcoma, enchondroma, or osteoma.

Primary cancer or sarcoma usually involves only one lung. The secondary growths are distributed in both. The primary growth generally forms a large mass, which may occupy the greater part of a lung. Occasionally the secondary growths are solitary and confined chiefly to the pleura. The metastatic growths are nearly always disseminated. Occasionally they occupy a large portion of the pulmonary tissue. In a case of colloid cancer secondary to cancer of the pancreas, I found both lungs voluminous, heavy only slightly crepitant, and occupied by circular translucent masses, varying in size from a pea to a large walnut.

There are numerous accessory lesions in the pulmonary new growths. There may be pleurisy, either cancerous or sero-fibrinous. The effusion may be hæmorrhagic, but in 200 cases of cancer, primary or secondary, of the lungs and pleura analyzed by Moutard-Martin, hæmorrhagic effusion occurred in only 12 per cent. The tracheal and bronchial glands are usually affected, the cervical glands not infrequently, and occasionally even the inguinal.

The disease is most common in the middle period of life. The primary form affects the sexes equally, but secondary cancer is much more frequent in women than in men. The conditions which predispose to it are quite unknown. It is a remarkable fact that the workers in the Schneeberg cobalt mines are very liable to primary cancer of the lungs. It is stated that in this region a considerable proportion of all deaths in persons over forty are due to this disease.

Symptoms.—The clinical features of neoplasms of the lungs are by no means distinctive, particularly in the case of primary growths. The patient may, indeed, as noted by Walshe, present no symptoms pointing to intrathoracic disease. Among the more important symptoms are pain, particularly when the pleura is involved; dyspnœa, which is apt to be paroxysmal when due to pressure upon the trachea; cough, which may be dry and painful and accompanied by the expectoration of a dark mucoid sputum. This so-called prune-juice expectoration, which was present 10 times in 18 cases of primary cancer of the lung, was thought by Stokes to be of great diagnostic value.

In many instances there are signs of compression of the large veins, producing lividity of the face and upper extremities, or occasionally of only one arm. Compression of the trachea and bronchi may give rise to urgent dyspnœa. The heart may be pushed over to the opposite side. The pneumogastric and recurrent laryngeal nerves are occasionally involved in the growth.

Physical Signs.—The patient, according to Walshe, usually lies on the affected side. On inspection this side may be enlarged and immobile and the intercostal spaces are obliterated. This is more commonly due to the effusion than to the growth itself. The external lymph-glands may be enlarged, particularly the clavicular. The signs, on percussion and auscultation, are varied, depending much upon the presence or absence of fluid. Signs of consolidation are, of course, present; the tactile fremitus is absent and the breath-sounds are usually diminished in intensity. Occasionally there is typical bronchial breathing. Among other symptoms may be mentioned fever, which is present in a certain number of cases. Emaciation is not necessarily extreme. The duration of the disease is from six to eight months. Occasionally it runs a very acute course, as noted by Carswell. Cases are reported in which death occurred in a month or six weeks, and in one instance (Jaccoud) the patient died in a week from the onset of the symptoms.

Diagnosis.—In secondary growths this is not difficult. The development of pulmonary symptoms within a year or two after the removal of a cancer of the breast, or after the amputation of a limb for osteo-sarcoma, or the onset of similar symptoms in connection with cancer of the liver, or of the uterus, or of the rectum, would be extremely suggestive. In primary cases the unilateral involvement, the anomalous character of the physical signs, the occurrence of prune-juice expectoration, the progressive wasting, and the secondary involvement of the cervical glands are the important points in the diagnosis.

New growths are occasionally primary in the pleura (Harris, Journal of Pathology, vol. ii).

V. DISEASES OF THE PLEURA.

I. ACUTE PLEURISY.

Anatomically, the cases may be divided into dry or adhesive pleurisy and pleurisy with effusion. Another classification is into primary or secondary forms. According to the course of the disease, a division may be made into *acute* and *chronic* pleurisy, and as it is impossible, at present, to group the various forms etiologically, this is perhaps the most satisfactory division. The following forms of acute pleurisy may be considered:

I. FIBRINOUS OR PLASTIC PLEURISY.

In this the pleural membrane is covered by a sheeting of lymph of variable thickness, which gives it a turbid, granular appearance, or the fibrin may exist in distinct layers. It occurs (1) as an independent affection, following cold or exposure. This form of acute plastic pleurisy without fluid exudate is not common in perfectly healthy individuals. Cases are met with, however, in which the disease sets in with the usual symptoms of pain in the side and slight fever, and there are the physical signs of pleurisy as indicated by the friction. After persisting for a few days, the friction murmur disappears and no exudation occurs. Union takes place between the membranes, and possibly the pleuritic adhesions which are found in such a large percentage of all bodies examined after death originate in these slight fibrinous pleurisies.

Fibrinous pleurisy occurs (2) as a secondary process in acute diseases of the lung, such as pneumonia, which is always accompanied by a certain amount of pleurisy, usually of this form. Cancer, abscess, and gangrene also cause plastic pleurisy when the surface of the lung becomes involved. This condition is specially associated in a large number of cases with tuberculosis. Pleural pain, stitch in the side, and a dry cough, with marked friction sounds on auscultation are the initial phenomena in many instances of phthisis. The signs are usually basic, but Burney Yeo has recently called attention to the frequency with which they occur at the apex.

II. Sero-fibrinous Pleurisy.

In a majority of cases of inflammation of the pleura there is, with the fibrin, a variable amount of fluid exudate, which produces the condition known as pleurisy with effusion.

Etiology.—For generations physicians have considered cold the potent factor in inducing pleurisy. This may be true in many cases, but modern views of serous inflammations scarcely recognize cold as anything more than a predisposing agent, which permits the action of various micro-organisms. We have not yet, however, brought all the acute pleurisies into the category of microbic affections, and the fact remains that pleurisy does follow with great rapidity a sudden wetting or a chill. Of late years an attempt has been made, particularly by French writers, to show that the majority of acute pleurisies are tuberculous. In this connection the following facts may be admitted: (1) In a large number of cases of pleurisy coming on abruptly in healthy persons the disease has been shown—(a) by post-mortem, in cases of accidental or sudden death, (b) by the subsequent history—to be tuberculous; (2) in a larger proportion of those cases which come on insidiously in persons who have been in failing health or who are delicate the disease is tuberculous from the outset; (3) the acute pleurisy, which occurs as a secondary, often a terminal, event in chronic affections, such as cirrhosis of the liver, Bright's disease, and cancer, is very frequently tuberculous. I confess that the more carefully I have studied the question the larger does the proportion appear to be of primary pleurisies of tuberculous origin. The subsequent history of cases of acute pleurisy forces us to conclude that in at least two thirds of the cases it is a curable affection. This may well be so, according to our present ideas of local tuberculous disease. Several years ago I looked over the post-mortem records of 101 successive cases which had died in my wards with pleurisy—fibrinous, sero-fibrinous, hæmorrhagic, or purulent. Of these, there were only 32 in which the pleurisy was definitely tuberculous. One of the most interesting contributions to this question has been made from the records of Henry I. Bowditch, of Boston, to whom we are indebted for so many important additions to our knowledge of pleurisy.* Of 90 cases of acute pleurisy which had been under observation between 1849 and 1879, 32 died of or had phthisis—a percentage large enough to indicate what an important *rôle* tuberculosis plays in the etiology of this disease.

Bacteriology of Acute Pleurisy.—From a bacteriological standpoint we may recognize three groups of cases of acute pleurisy: the tuberculous, the pneumococcus, and the streptococcus.

The *bacillus tuberculosis* is present in a very large proportion of all cases of primary or so-called idiopathic pleurisy. The exudate is usually sterile on cover-slips or in the culture and inoculation tests made in the ordinary way, as the bacilli are very scanty. It has been demonstrated clearly that a large amount of the exudate must be taken to make the test complete, either in cultures or in the inoculation of animals. Eichhorst

---

* Vincent Y. Bowditch, in Boston Medical and Surgical Journal, 1889.

found that more that 62 per cent were demonstrated as tuberculous when as much as 15 cc. of the exudate was inoculated into test animals, while less than 10 per cent of the cases showed tuberculosis when only 1 cc. of the exudate was used.   This is a point to which observers should pay very special attention. Le Damany has recently in 55 primary pleurisies demonstrated the tuberculous character of all but 4. He has used large quantities of the fluid for his inoculation experiments.

The pneumococcus pleurisy is almost always secondary to a focus of inflammation in the lung. It may, however, be primary. The exudate is usually purulent and the outlook is very favorable.

The streptococcus pleurisy is the typical septic form which may occur either from direct infection of the pleura through the lung in bronchopneumonia, or in cases of streptococcus pneumonia; in other instances it follows infection of more distant parts. The acute streptococcus pleurisy is the most serious and fatal of all forms.

Among other bacilli which have been found are the staphylococcus, Friedländer's bacillus, the typhoid bacillus, and the diphtheria bacillus.

Morbid Anatomy.—In sero-fibrinous pleurisy the serous exudate is abundant and the fibrin is found on the pleural surfaces and scattered through the fluid in the form of flocculi. The proportion of these constituents varies a great deal. In some instances there is very little membranous fibrin; in others it forms thick, creamy layers and exists in the dependent part of the fluid as whitish, curd-like masses. The fluid of sero-fibrinous pleurisy is of a lemon color, either clear or slightly turbid, depending on the number of formed elements. In some instances it has a dark-brown color. The microscopical examination of the fluid shows leucocytes, occasional swollen cells, which may possibly be derived from the pleural endothelium, shreds of fibrillated fibrin, and a variable number of red blood-corpuscles. On boiling, the fluid is found to be rich in albumin. Sometimes it coagulates spontaneously. Its composition closely resembles that of blood-serum. Cholesterin, uric acid, and sugar are occasionally found. The amount of the effusion varies from $\frac{1}{2}$ to 4 litres.

The lung in acute sero-fibrinous pleurisy is more or less compressed. If the exudation is limited the lower lobe alone is atelectatic; but in an extensive effusion which reaches to the clavicle the entire lung will be found lying close to the spine, dark and airless, or even bloodless—i. e., carnified.

In large exudations the adjacent organs are displaced. In large right-sided pleurisies the liver is much depressed. Rather varying statements are made with reference to the position of the heart and as to whether or not it rotates on its axis. In a number of post-mortems I have carefully studied its position, both in pneumothorax and in large effusions, and can speak with some degree of certainty on the following points: (1) Even in the most extensive left-sided exudation there is no rotation of the apex of the heart, which in no case was to the right of the mid-sternal line; (2) the relative position of the apex and base is usually maintained; in some instances the apex is lifted, in others the whole heart lies more transversely; (3) the right chambers of the heart occupy the greater portion of the front, so that the displacement is rather a definite dislocation of the mediastinum, with the pericardium, to the right, than any special twisting of the heart itself; (4) the kink or twist in the inferior vena cava described by Bartels was not present in any of the cases.

Symptoms.—Prodromes are not uncommon, but the disease may set in abruptly with a chill, followed by fever and a severe pain in the side. In very many cases, however, the onset is insidious. Washbourn has called attention to the frequency with which the pneumococcus pleurisy sets in with the features of pneumonia. The pain in the side is the most distressing symptom, and is usually referred to the nipple or axillary regions. It must be remembered, however, that pleuritic pain may be felt in the abdomen or low down in the back, particularly when the diaphragmatic surface of the pleura is involved. It is lancinating, sharp, and severe, and is aggravated by cough. At this early stage, on auscultation, sometimes indeed on palpation, a dry friction rub can be detected. The fever rarely rises so rapidly as in pneumonia, and does not reach the same grade. A temperature of from 102° to 103° is an average pyrexia. It may drop to normal at the end of a week or ten days without the appearance of any definite change in the physical signs, or it may persist for several weeks. The temperature of the affected is higher than that of the sound side. Cough is an early symptom in acute pleurisy, but is rarely so distressing or so frequent as in pneumonia. There are instances in which it is absent. The expectoration is usually slight in amount, mucoid in character, and occasionally streaked with blood.

At the outset there may be dyspnœa, due partly to the fever and partly to the pain in the side. Later it results from the compression of the lung, particularly if the exudation has taken place rapidly. When, however, the fluid is effused slowly, one lung may be entirely compressed without inducing shortness of breath, except on exertion, and the patient will lie quietly in bed without evincing the slightest respiratory distress. When the effusion is large the patient usually prefers to lie upon the affected side.

Physical Signs.—*Inspection* shows some degree of immobility on the affected side, depending upon the amount of exudation, and in large effusions an increase in volume, which may appear to be much more than it really is as determined by mensuration. The intercostal spaces are obliterated. In right-sided effusions the apex beat may be lifted to the fourth interspace or be pushed beyond the left nipple, or may even be seen in the axilla. When the exudation is on the left side, the heart's impulse may not be visible; but if the effusion is large it is seen in the third and fourth spaces on the right side, and sometimes as far out as the nipple, or even beyond it.

Palpation enables us more successfully to determine the deficient movements on the affected side, and the obliteration of the intercostal spaces, and more accurately to define the position of the heart's impulse. In simple sero-fibrinous effusion there is rarely any œdema of the chest walls. It is scarcely ever possible to obtain fluctuation. Tactile fremitus is greatly diminished or abolished. If the effusion is slight there may be only enfeeblement. The absence of the voice vibrations in effusions of any size constitutes one of the most valuable of physical signs. In children there may be much effusion with retention of fremitus. In rare cases the vibrations may be communicated to the chest walls through localized pleural adhesions.

Mensuration.—With the cyrtometer, if the effusion is excessive, a difference of from half an inch to an inch, or even, in large effusions, an inch and a half, may be found between the two sides. Allowance must be made for the fact that the right side is naturally larger than the left. With the saddle-tape the difference in expansion between the two sides can be conveniently measured.

Percussion.—Early in the disease, when the pain in the side is severe and the friction murmur evident, there may be no alteration, but with the gradual accumulation of the fluid the resonance becomes defective, and finally gives place to absolute flatness. From day to day the gradual increase in height of the fluid may be studied. In a pleuritic effusion rising to the fourth rib in front, the percussion signs are usually very suggestive. In the subclavicular region the attention is often aroused at once by a tympanitic note, the so-called Skoda's resonance, which is heard perhaps more commonly in this situation with pleural effusion than in any other condition. It shades insensibly into a flat note in the lower mammary and axillary regions. Skoda's resonance may be obtained also behind, just above the limit of effusion. The dulness has a peculiarly resistant, wooden quality, differing from that of pneumonia and readily recognized by skilled fingers. It has long been known that when the patient is in the erect posture the upper line of dulness is not horizontal, but is higher behind than it is in front, forming a parabola. The curve marking the intersection of the plane of contact of lung and fluid with the chest wall has been variously described. The " Ellis line of flatness," which Garland has verified clinically and by animal experiments, is perhaps the most characteristic. With medium-sized effusions " this line begins lowest behind, advances upward and forward in a letter-S curve to the axillary region, whence it proceeds in a straight decline to the sternum." Such a curve is present only when the patient is in the erect position, when the lung is in fairly normal condition, since then by its elastic tension it controls the position and shape of the mass of fluid, even supporting the entire weight of a considerable exudate, and when the pleuræ are free from adhesions. With larger exudates the curve flattens much, but the S can be detached with the fluid as high as the third rib. Garland emphasizes that the line can be accurately determined only by light percussion. (Garland's exhaustive work on Pneumo-dynamics.)

On the right side the dulness passes without change into that of the liver. On the left side in the nipple line it extends to and may obliterate Traube's semilunar space. If the effusion is moderate, the phenomenon of movable dulness may be obtained by marking carefully, in the sitting posture, the upper limit in the mammary region, and then in the recumbent posture, noting the change in the height of dulness. This infallible sign of fluid cannot always be obtained. In very copious exudation the dulness may reach the clavicle and even extend beyond the sternal margin of the opposite side.

Auscultation.—Early in the disease a friction rub can usually be heard, which disappears as the fluid accumulates. It is a to-and-fro dry rub, close to the ear, and has a leathery, creaking character. There is another pleural friction sound which closely resembles, and is scarcely to be distinguished from, the fine crackling crepitus of pneumonia. This may be heard at the commencement of the disease, and also, as pointed out in 1844 by Mac-Donnell, Sr., of Montreal, when the effusion has receded and the pleural layers come together again.

With even a slight exudation there is weakened or distant breathing. Often inspiration and expiration are distinctly audible, though distant, and have a tubular quality. Sometimes only a puffing tubular expiration is heard, which may have a metallic or amphoric quality. Loud resonant rales accompanying this may forcibly suggest a cavity. These pseudo-cavernous signs are met with more frequently in children, and often lead to error in diagnosis. Above the line of dulness the breath-sounds are usually harsh and exaggerated, and may have a tubular quality.

The vocal resonance is usually diminished or absent. The whispered voice is said to be transmitted through a serous and not through a purulent exudate (Baccelli's sign). This author advises direct auscultation in the antero-lateral region of the chest. There may, however, be intensification—bronchophony. The voice sometimes has a curious nasal, squeaking character, which was termed by Laennec *ægophony*, from its supposed resemblance to the bleating of a goat. In typical form this is not common, but it is by no means rare to hear a curious twang-like quality in the voice, particularly at the outer angle of the scapula.

In the examination of the heart in cases of pleuritic effusion it is well to bear in mind that when the apex of the heart lies beneath the sternum there may be no impulse. The determination of the situation of the organ may rest with the position of maximum loudness of the sounds. Over the displaced organ a systolic murmur may be heard. When the lappet of lung over the pericardium is involved on either side there may be a pleuro-pericardial friction. A leucocytosis is usually present.

The *course* of acute sero-fibrinous pleurisy is very variable. After persisting for a week or ten days the fever subsides, the cough and pain disappear, and a slight effusion may be quickly absorbed. In cases in which the effusion reaches as high as the fourth rib recovery is usually slower. Many instances come under observation for the first time, after two or three weeks' indisposition, with the fluid at a level with the clavicle. The fever may last from ten to twenty days without exciting anxiety, though, as a rule, in ordinary pleurisy from cold, as we say, the temperature in cases of moderate severity is normal within eight or ten days. Left to itself the natural tendency is to resorption; but this may take place very slowly. With the absorption of the fluid there is a redux-friction crepitus, either leathery and creaking or crackling and rale-like, and for months, or even longer, the defective resonance and feeble breathing are heard at the base. Rare modes of termination are perforation and discharge through the lung, and externally through the chest wall, examples of which have been recorded by Sahli.

A sero-fibrinous exudate may persist for months without change, particularly in tuberculous cases, and will sometimes reaccumulate after aspiration and resist all treatment. After persistence for more than twelve months, in spite of repeated tapping, a serous effusion was cured by incision without deformity of the chest (S. West). The change of the exudate into pus will be spoken of in connection with empyema. Death is a rare termination of sero-fibrinous effusion. When one pleura is full and the heart is greatly dislocated, the condition, although in a majority of cases producing remarkably little disturbance, is not without risk. *Sudden death* may occur, and its possibility under these circumstances should always be considered. I have seen two instances—one in right and the other in left sided effusion—both due, apparently, to syncope following slight exertion, such as getting out of bed. In neither case, however, was the amount of fluid excessive. Weil, who has studied carefully this accident, concludes as follows: (1) That it may be due to thrombosis or embolism of the heart or pulmonary artery, œdema of the opposite lung, or degeneration of the heart muscle; (2) such alleged causes as mechanical impediment to the circulation, owing to dislocation of the heart or twisting of the great vessels, require further investigation. Death may occur without any premonitory symptoms.

III. Purulent Pleurisy (*Empyema*).

Etiology.—Pus in the pleura is met with under the following conditions: (*a*) As a sequence of acute sero-fibrinous pleurisy. It is not always easy to say why, in certain cases, the exudate becomes purulent. It rarely does so in the acute pleurisies of healthy individuals. In children many cases are probably purulent from the onset. Aspiration, which is said to favor the occurrence of empyema, in my experience does so very rarely. (*b*) Purulent pleurisy is common as a secondary inflammation in various infectious diseases, among which scarlet fever takes the first place. It has long been known that the pleurisy supervening in the convalescence of this disease is almost always purulent. It should be remembered that it is latent in its onset, and that there may be no pulmonary symptoms. The pleurisy following typhoid fever is also usually purulent. Other infectious diseases —measles and whooping-cough—are more rarely followed by this complication. Of late years especial attention has been paid to the connection of pneumonia with empyema, and it has been shown that very many cases come on insidiously either in the course of or during convalescence from this disease; and, lastly, a limited number of tuberculous pleurisies early become purulent. (*c*) Empyema results from local causes—fracture of the rib, penetrating wounds, malignant disease of the lung or œsophagus, and, perhaps most frequently of all, the perforation of the pleura by tuberculous cavities.

The bacteriology of empyema is of great importance. A sterile exudate suggests tuberculosis. In many cases the pneumococci are present, and these cases, as a rule, run a very favorable course. The streptococci are found

42

most commonly in the secondary cases in connection with septic processes. In a few instances psorosperms have been present.

Morbid Anatomy.—On opening an empyema post mortem, we usually find that the effusion has separated into a clear, greenish-yellow serum above and the thick, cream-like pus below. The fluid may be scarcely more than turbid, with flocculi of fibrin through it. In the pneumococcus empyema the pus is usually thick and creamy. It usually has a heavy, sweetish odor, but in some instances—particularly those following wounds —it is fetid. In cases of gangrene of the lung or pleura the pus has a horribly stinking odor. Microscopically it has the characters of ordinary pus. The pleural membranes are greatly thickened, and present a grayish-white layer from 1 to 2 mm. in thickness. On the costal pleura there may be erosions, and in old cases fistulous communications are common. The lung may be compressed to a very small limit, and the visceral pleura also may show perforations.

Symptoms.—Purulent pleurisy may begin abruptly, with the symptoms already described. More frequently it comes on insidiously in the course of other diseases or follows an ordinary sero-fibrinous pleurisy. There may be no pain in the chest, very little cough, and no dyspnœa, unless the side is very full. Symptoms of septic infection are rarely wanting. If in a child, there is a gradually developing pallor and weakness; sweats occur, and there is irregular fever. A cough is by no means constant. The leucocytes are usually much increased; in one fatal case they numbered 115,-000 per cubic millimetre.

Physical Signs.—Practically they are those already considered in pleurisy with effusion. There are, however, one or two additional points to be mentioned. In empyema, particularly in children, the disproportion between the sides may be extreme. The intercostal spaces may not only be obliterated, but may bulge. Not infrequently there is œdema of the chest walls. The network of subcutaneous veins may be very distinct. It must not be forgotten that in children the breath-sounds may be *loud and tubular* over a purulent effusion of considerable size. Whispered pectoriloquy is usually not heard in empyema (Baccelli's sign). The dislocation of the heart and the displacement of the liver are more marked in empyema than in sero-fibrinous effusion—probably, as Senator suggests, owing to the greater weight of the fluid.

A curious phenomenon associated generally with empyema, but which may occur in the sero-fibrinous exudate, is *pulsating pleurisy*, first described by MacDonnell, Sr., of Montreal. Of 42 cases 39 occurred on the left side. In all but one case the fluid was purulent. Pneumothorax may be present. There are two groups of cases, the intrapleural pulsating pleurisy and the pulsating *empyema necessitatis*, in which there is an external pulsating tumor. No satisfactory explanation has been offered how the heart impulse is thus forcibly communicated through the effusion.

Empyema is a chronic affection, which in a few instances terminates naturally in recovery, but a majority of cases, if left alone, end in death. The following are some modes of natural cure: (*a*) By absorption of the fluid. In small effusions this may take place gradually. The chest wall sinks. The pleural layers become greatly thickened and enclose between them the inspissated pus, in which lime salts are gradually deposited. Such a condition may be seen once or twice a year in the post-mortem room of any large hospital. (*b*) By perforation of the lung. Although in this event death may take place rapidly, by suffocation, as Aretæus says, yet in cases in which it occurs gradually recovery may follow. Since 1873, when I saw a case of this kind in Traube's clinic, and heard his remarks on the subject, I have seen a number of instances of the kind and can corroborate his statement as to the favorable termination of many of them. Empyema may discharge either by opening into the bronchus and forming a fistula, or, as Traube pointed out, by producing necrosis of the pulmonary pleura, sufficient to allow the soakage of the pus through the spongy lung tissue into the bronchi. In the first way pneumothorax usually, though not always, develops. In the second way the pus is discharged without formation of pneumothorax. Even with a bronchial fistula recovery is possible. (*c*) By perforation of the chest wall—*empyema necessitatis*. This is by no means an unfavorable method, as many cases recover. The perforation may occur anywhere in the chest wall, but is, as Cruveilhier remarked, more common in front. It may be anywhere from the third to the sixth interspace, usually, according to Marshall, in the fifth. It may perforate in more than one place, and there may be a fistulous communication which opens into the pleura at some distance from the external orifice. The tumor, when near the heart, may pulsate. The discharge may persist for years. In Copeland's Dictionary is mentioned an instance of a Bavarian physician who had a pleural fistula for thirteen years and enjoyed fairly good health.

An empyema may perforate the neighboring organs, the œsophagus, peritonæum, pericardium, or the stomach. Very remarkable cases are those which pass down the spine and along the psoas into the iliac fossa, and simulate a psoas or lumbar abcess.

IV. Tuberculous Pleurisy.

This has already been considered (p. 284), and the symptoms and physical signs do not require any description other than that already given in connection with the sero-fibrinous and purulent forms.

V. Other Varieties of Pleurisy.

Hæmorrhagic Pleurisy.—A bloody effusion is met with under the following conditions: (*a*) In the pleurisy of asthenic states, such as cancer, Bright's disease, and occasionally in the malignant fevers. It is interesting to note the frequency with which hæmorrhagic pleurisy is found in cirrhosis of the liver. It occurred in the very patient in whom Laennec first accurately described this disease. While this may be a simple hæmorrhagic pleurisy, in a majority of the cases which I have seen it has been tuberculous. (*b*) Tuberculous pleurisy, in which the bloody effusion may result from the rupture of newly formed vessels in the soft exudate accompanying the eruption of miliary tubercles, or it may come from more slowly formed tubercles in a pleurisy secondary to extensive pulmonary disease. (c) Cancerous pleurisy, whether primary or secondary, is frequently hæmorrhagic. (d) Occasionally hæmorrhagic exudation is met with in perfectly healthy individuals, in whom there is not the slightest suspicion of tuberculosis or cancer. In one such case, a large, able-bodied man, the patient was to my knowledge healthy and strong eight years afterward. And, lastly, it must be remembered that during aspiration the lung may be wounded and blood in this way get mixed with the sero-fibrinous exudate. The condition of hæmorrhagic pleurisy is to be distinguished from hæmothorax, due to the rupture of aneurism or the pressure of a tumor on the thoracic veins.

Diaphragmatic Pleurisy.—The inflammation may be limited partly or chiefly to the diaphragmatic surface. This is often a dry pleurisy, but there may be effusion, either sero-fibrinous or purulent, which is circumscribed on the diaphragmatic surface. In these cases the pain is low in the zone of the diaphragm and may simulate that of acute abdominal disease. It may be intensified by pressure at the point of insertion of the diaphragm at the tenth rib. The diaphragm is fixed and the respiration is thoracic and short. Andral noted in certain cases severe dyspnœa and attacks simulating angina. As mentioned, the effusion is usually plastic, not serous. Serous or purulent effusions of any size limited to the diaphragmatic surface are extremely rare. Intense subjective with trifling objective features are always suggestive of diaphragmatic pleurisy.

Encysted Pleurisy.—The effusion may be circumscribed by adhesions or separated into two or more pockets or loculi, which communicate with each other. This is most common in empyema. In these cases there have usually been, at different parts of the pleura, multiple adhesions by which the fluid is limited. In other instances the recent false membranes may encapsulate the exudation on the diaphragmatic surface, for example, or the part of the pleura posterior to the mid-axillary line. The condition may be very puzzling during life, and present special difficulties in diagnosis. In some cases the tactile fremitus is retained along certain lines of adhesion. The exploratory needle should be freely used.

Interlobar Pleurisy forms an interesting and not uncommon variety. In nearly every instance of acute pleurisy the interlobular serous surfaces are also involved and closely agglutinated together, and sometimes the fluid is encysted between them. In this position tubercles are to be carefully looked for. In a case of this kind following pneumonia there was between the lower and upper and middle lobes of the right side an enormous purulent collection, which looked at first like a large abscess of the lung. These collections may perforate the bronchi, and the cases present special difficulties in diagnosis.

Diagnosis of Pleurisy.—Acute plastic pleurisy is readily recognized. In the diagnosis of pleuritic effusion the first question is, Does a fluid exudate exist? the second, What is its nature? In large effusions the increase in the size of the affected side, the immobility, the absence of tactile fremitus, together with the displacement of organs, give infallible indications of the presence of fluid. The chief difficulty arises in effusions of moderate extent, when the dulness, the presence of bronchophony, and, perhaps, tubular breathing may simulate *pneumonia.* The chief points to be borne in mind are: (*a*) Differences in the onset and in the general characters of the two affections, more particularly the initial chill, the higher fever, more urgent dyspnœa, and the rusty expectoration, which characterize pneumonia. As already mentioned, some of the cases of pneumococcus pleurisy set in like pneumonia. (*b*) Certain physical signs—the more wooden character of the dulness, the greater resistance, and the marked diminution or the absence of tactile fremitus in pleurisy. The auscultatory signs may be deceptive. It is usually, indeed, the persistence of tubular breathing, particularly the high-pitched, even amphoric expiration, heard in some cases of pleurisy, which has raised the doubt. The intercostal spaces are more commonly obliterated in pleuritic effusion than in pneumonia. As already mentioned, the displacement of organs is a very valuable sign. Nowadays with the hypodermic needle the question is easily settled. A separate small syringe with a capacity of two drachms should be reserved for exploratory purposes, and the needle should be longer and firmer than in the ordinary hypodermic instrument. With careful preliminary disinfection the instrument can be used with impunity, and in cases of doubt the exploratory puncture should be made without hesitation. Pneumothorax is an occasional sequence. The hypodermic needle is especially useful in those cases in which there are pseudo-cavernous signs at the base. In cases, too, of massive pneumonia, in which the bronchi are plugged with fibrin, if the patient has not been seen from the outset, the diagnosis may be impossible without it.

On the left side it may be difficult to differentiate a very large pericardial from a pleural effusion. The retention of resonance at the base, the presence of Skoda's resonance toward the axilla, the absence of dislocation of the heart-beat to the right of the sternum, the feebleness of the pulse and of the heart-sounds, and the urgency of the dyspnœa, out of all proportion to the extent of the effusion, are the chief points to be considered. Unilateral hydrothorax, which is not at all uncommon in heart-disease, presents signs identical with those of sero-fibrinous effusion. Certain tumors within the chest may simulate pleural effusion. It should be remembered that many intrathoracic growths are accompanied by exudation. Malignant disease of the lung and of the pleura and hydatids of the pleura produce extensive dulness, with suppression of the breath-sounds, simulating closely effusion.

On the right side, abscess of the liver and hydatid cysts may rise high into the pleura and produce dulness and enfeebled breathing. Often in these cases there is a friction sound, which should excite suspicion, and the upper outline of the dulness is sometimes plainly convex. In a case of cancer of the kidney the growth involved the diaphragm very early, and for months there were signs of pleurisy before our attention was directed to the kidney. In all these instances the exploratory puncture should be made.

The second question, as to the nature of the fluid, is quickly decided by the use of the needle. The persistent fever, the occurrence of sweats, a leucocytosis, and the increase in the pallor suggest the presence of pus. In children the complexion is often sallow and earthy. In protracted cases, even in children, when the general symptoms and the appearance of the patient has been most strongly suggestive of pus, the syringe has withdrawn clear fluid. On the other hand, effusions of short duration may be purulent, even when the general symptoms do not suggest it. The following statement may be made with reference to the prognostic import of the bacteriological examination of the aspirated fluid: The presence of the pneumococcus is of favorable significance, as such cases usually get well rapidly, even with a single aspiration. The streptococcus empyema is the most serious form, and even after a free drainage the patient may succumb to a general septicæmia. A sterile fluid indicates in a majority of instances a tuberculous origin.

Treatment.—At the onset the severe pain may demand leeches, which usually give relief, but a hypodermic of morphia is more effective. The Paquelin cautery may be lightly but freely applied. It is well to administer a mercurial or saline purge. Fixing the side by careful strapping with long strips of adhesive plaster, which should pass well over the middle line, drawn tightly and evenly, gives great relief, and I can corroborate the statement of F. T. Roberts as to its efficacy. Cupping, wet or dry, is now seldom employed. Blisters are of no special service in the acute stages, although they relieve the pain. The ice-bag may be used as in pneumonia. The general treatment at the early stage should be rest in bed and a liquid diet. Medicines are rarely required. A Dover's powder may be given at night. Mercurials are not indicated.

When the effusion has taken place, mustard plasters or iodine, producing slight counter-irritation, appear useful, particularly in the later stages. The following rational plan is successful in some cases. It is based upon the idea that if the blood serum is depleted or if it is kept concentrated, the liquid will be absorbed from the lymph spaces, of which the pleura is one, to equalize the loss. To do this the patient should have the daily amount of liquid food greatly restricted. If there is no fever, a meat diet, with an egg and dry bread and 8 to 10 ounces of liquid in the form of milk or water, should be given. Salt articles of food may be used, but I do not think it necessary to give, as some do, doses of salt. The second element in the treatment is the active depletion of blood serum, which is effected in the way introduced by Matthew Hay. Every morning, if the patient is robust, otherwise every second morning, from half an ounce to an ounce and a half of Epsom salts is given an hour before breakfast, in as concentrated a form as is possible. This produces copious liquid discharges. I have seen large exudations disappear rapidly when this plan was followed. By acting upon the skin and kidneys, the same end may be obtained, but with much less certainty. The vapor or hot bath may be used and an occasional dose of pilocarpin. Diuretics, such as digitalis, squills, and acetate of potash, may sometimes be required. I rarely resort, however, to diuretics or diaphoretics in the treatment of pleurisy with effusion. Iodide of potassium is of doubtful benefit. By some the salicylates are believed to be of special efficacy.

Aspiration of the fluid is the most thorough and satisfactory method and should be resorted to whenever the effusion becomes large or if it resists the ordinary methods of treatment. The credit of introducing aspiration in pleuritic effusions is due to Morrill Wyman, of Cambridge, Mass., and Henry I. Bowditch, of Boston. Years prior to Dieulafoy's work, aspiration was in constant use at the Massachusetts General Hospital and was advocated repeatedly by Bowditch. As the question is one of some historical interest, I give Bowditch's conclusions concerning aspiration, expressed nearly fifty years ago, and which practically represent the opinion of to-day: " (1) The operation is perfectly simple, but slightly painful, and can be done with ease upon any patient in however advanced a stage of the disease. (2) It should be performed forthwith in *all* cases in which there is complete filling up of one side of the chest. (3) He had determined to use it in *any* case of even *moderate* effusion lasting more than a few weeks and in which there should seem to be a disposition to resist ordinary modes of treatment. (4) He urged this practice upon the profession as a very important measure in practical medicine; believing that by this method death may frequently be prevented from ensuing either by sudden attack of dyspnœa or subsequent phthisis, and, finally, from the gradual wearing out of the powers of life or inability to absorb the fluid. (5) He believed that this operation would sometimes prevent the occurrence of those tedious cases of spontaneous evacuation of purulent fluid and those great contractions of the chest which occur after long-continued effusion and the subsequent discharge or absorption of a fluid."

There is scarcely anything to be added to-day to these observations. When the fluid reaches to the clavicle the indication for aspiration is imperative, even though the patient be comfortable and present no signs of pulmonary distress. The presence of fever is not a contra-indication; indeed, sometimes with serous exudates the temperature falls after aspiration.

The operation is extremely simple and is practically without risk. The spot selected for puncture should be either in the seventh interspace in the mid-axilla or at the outer angle of the scapula in the eighth interspace. The arm of the patient should be brought forward with the hand on the opposite shoulder, so as to widen the interspaces. The needle should be thrust in close to the upper margin of the rib, so as to avoid the intercostal artery, the wounding of which, however, is an excessively rare accident. The fluid should be withdrawn slowly. The amount will depend on the size of the exudate. If the fluid reaches to the clavicle a litre or more may be withdrawn with safety. In chronic cases of serous pleurisy after repeated tappings S. West has shown the great value of free incision and drainage. He has reported cases of recovery after effusions of fifteen and eighteen months' standing.

Symptoms and Accidents during Paracentesis.—*Pain* is usually complained of after a certain amount of fluid has been withdrawn; it is sharp and cutting in character. *Coughing* occurs toward the close, and may be severe and paroxysmal. *Pneumothorax* may follow an exploratory puncture with a hypodermic needle; it is rare during aspiration. *Subcutaneous emphysema* may develop from the point of puncture, without the production of pneumothorax. *Albuminous expectoration* is a remarkable phenomenon described by French writers. It usually develops after the tapping, is associated with dyspnœa, and many prove suddenly fatal. *Cerebral symptoms.*—Faintness is not uncommon. Epileptic convulsions may occur either during the withdrawal or while irrigating the pleura. I have seen but a single instance. They are very difficult to explain and are regarded by most authors as of reflex origin; and lastly *sudden death* may occur either from syncope or during the convulsions.

Empyema is really a surgical affection, and I shall make only a few general remarks upon its treatment. When it has been determined by exploratory puncture that the fluid is purulent, aspiration should not be performed, except as preliminary to operation or as a temporary measure. Perhaps it is better not to have an exception to this rule, although the empyemas of children and the pneumonic empyema occasionally get well rapidly after a single tapping. It is sad to think of the number of lives which are sacrificed annually by the failure to recognize that empyema should be treated as an ordinary abscess, by free incision. The operation dates from the time of Hippocrates and is by no means serious. A majority of the cases get well, providing that free drainage is obtained, and it makes no difference practically what measures are followed so long as this indication is met. The good results in any method depend upon the thoroughness with which the cavity is drained. Irrigation of the cavity is rarely necessary unless the contents are fetid. In the subsequent treatment a point of great importance in facilitating the closure of the cavity is the distention of the lung on the affected side. This may be accomplished by the method advised by Ralston James, which has been practised with great success in the surgical wards of the Johns Hopkins Hospital. The patient daily, for a certain length of time, increasing gradually with the increase of his strength, transfers by air-pressure water from one bottle to another. The bottles should be large, holding at least a gallon each, and by the arrangement of tubes, as in the Wolff's bottle, an expiratory effort of the patient forces the water from one bottle into the other. In this way expansion of the compressed lung is systematically practised. The abscess cavity is gradually closed, partly by the falling in of the chest wall and partly by the expansion of the lung. In some instances it is necessary to resect portions of one or more ribs.

The physician is often asked, in cases of empyema with emaciation, hectic and feeble rapid pulse, whether the patient could stand the operation. Even in the most desperate cases the surgeon should never hesitate to make a free incision.

II. CHRONIC PLEURISY.

This affection occurs in two forms: (1) *Chronic pleurisy with effusion,* in which the disease may set in insidiously or may follow an acute serofibrinous pleurisy. There are cases in which the liquid persists for months or even years without undergoing any special alteration and without becoming purulent. Such cases have the characters which we have described under pleurisy with effusion. (2) *Chronic dry pleurisy.* The cases are met with (*a*) as a sequence of ordinary pleural effusion. When the exudate is absorbed and the layers of the pleura come together there is left between them a variable amount of fibrinous material which gradually undergoes organization, and is converted into a layer of firm connective tissue. This process goes on at the base, and is represented clinically by a slight grade of flattening, deficient expansion, defective resonance on percussion, and enfeebled breathing. After recovery from empyema the flattening and retraction may be still more marked. In both cases it is a condition which can be greatly benefited by pulmonary gymnastics. In these firm, fibrous membranes calcification may occur, particularly after empyema. It is not very uncommon to find between the false membranes a small pocket of fluid forming a sort of pleural cyst. In the great majority of these cases the condition is one which need not cause anxiety. There may be an occasional dragging pain at the base of the lung or a stitch in the side, but patients may remain in perfectly good health for years. The most advanced grade of this secondary dry pleurisy is seen in those cases of empyema which have been left to themselves and have perforated and ultimately healed by a gradual absorption or discharge of the pus, with retraction of the side of the chest and permanent carnification of the lung. Traumatic lesions, such as gunshot wounds, may be followed by an identical condition. Post mortem, it is quite impossible to separate the layers of the pleura, which are greatly thickened, particularly at the base, and surround a compressed, airless, fibroid lung. Bronchiectasis may gradually develop, and in one remarkable case which I have seen on several occasions with Dr. Blackader, of Montreal, not only on the affected side, but also in the lower lobe of the other lung.

(*b*) *Primitive dry pleurisy.* This condition may directly follow the acute plastic pleurisy already described; but it may set in without any acute symptoms whatever, and the patient's attention may be called to it by feeling the pleural friction. A constant effect of this primitive dry pleurisy is the adhesion of the layers. This is probably an invariable result, whether the pleurisy is primary or secondary. The organization of the thin layer of exudation in a pneumonia will unite the two surfaces by delicate bands. Pleural adhesions are extremely common, and it is rare to examine a body entirely free from them. They may be limited in extent or universal. Thin fibrous adhesions do not produce any alteration in the percussion characters, and, if limited, there is no special change heard on auscultation. When, however, there is general synechia on both sides the expansile movement of the lung is considerably impaired. We should naturally think that universal adhesions would interfere materially with the function of the lungs, but practically we see many instances in which there has not been the slightest disturbance. The physical signs of total adhesion are by no means constant. It has been stated that there is a marked disproportion between the degree of expansion of the chest walls and the intensity of the vesicular murmur, but the latter is a very variable factor, and under perfectly normal conditions the breath-sounds, with very full chest expansion, may be extremely feeble. The diaphragm phenomenon—Litten's sign—is absent.

Is there a primitive dry pleurisy which gradually leads to great thickening of the membranes, and which ultimately may invade the lung and induce cirrhotic change? Upon this question neither pathologists nor clinicians agree. I think that Sir Andrew Clark, in his Lumleian lectures at the Royal College of Physicians (1885), has made good his claim that such a disease does exist. Clinically the cases are of great interest, and should, I think, be separated, on the one hand, from the condition which follows a healed empyema or old pleurisy with effusion, and, on the other, from the rare instances of primitive cirrhosis of the lung. However, in all three states there may ultimately be an almost identical clinical picture. Anatomically in these pleuritic cases the pleura, particularly that surrounding the lower lobe, sometimes the entire membrane, is thickened, the two layers are intimately united, and fibrinous bands passing from the pleura traverse the lung tissue, sometimes dividing it in a remarkable way into sections. The bronchi may present marked dilatations, though this is not always the case, and the lung tissue is more or less sclerosed. The cases belong to the group of chronic pneumonias called by Charcot pleurogenous.

Lastly, there is a primitive dry pleurisy of tuberculous origin. In it both parietal and costal layers are greatly thickened—perhaps from 2 to 3 mm. each—and present firm fibroid, caseous masses and small tubercles, while uniting these two greatly thickened layers is a reddish-gray fibroid tissue, sometimes infiltrated with serum. This may be a local process confined to one pleura, or it may be in both. These cases are sometimes associated with a similar condition in the pericardium and peritonæum.

Occasionally remarkable vaso-motor phenomena occur in chronic pleurisy, whether simple or in connection with tuberculosis of an apex. Flushing or sweating of one cheek or dilatation of the pupil are the common manifestations. They appear to be due to involvement of the first thoracic ganglion at the top of the pleural cavity.

III. HYDROTHORAX.

Hydrothorax is a transudation of simple non-inflammatory fluid into the pleural cavities, and occurs as a secondary process in many affections. The fluid is clear, without any flocculi of fibrin, and the membranes are smooth. It is met with more particularly in connection with general dropsy, either renal, cardiac, or hæmic. It may, however, occur alone, or with only slight œdema of the feet. A child was admitted to the Montreal General Hospital with urgent dyspnœa and cyanosis, and died the night after admission. She had extensive bilateral hydrothorax, which had come on early in the nephritis of scarlet fever. In renal disease hydrothorax is almost always bilateral, but in heart affections one pleura is more commonly involved. The physical signs are those of pleural effusion, but the exudation is rarely excessive. In kidney and heart-disease, even when there is no general dropsy, the occurrence of dyspnœa should at once direct attention to the pleura, since many patients are carried off by a rapid effusion. Post-mortem records show the frequency with which this condition is overlooked. The saline purges will in many cases rapidly reduce the effusion, but, if necessary, aspiration should repeatedly be practised.

IV. PNEUMOTHORAX (*Hydro-Pneumothorax and Pyo-Pneumothorax*).

Air alone in the pleural cavity, to which the term pneumothorax is strictly applicable, is an extremely rare condition. It is almost invariably associated with a serous fluid—hydro-pneumothorax, or with pus—pyo-pneumothorax.

Etiology.—There exists normally within the pleural cavity of an adult a negative pressure of several millimetres of mercury, due to the recoil of the distended, perfectly elastic, lung. Hence through any opening connecting the pleural cavity with the external air we should expect air to rush in until this negative pressure is relieved. To explain the absence of pneumothorax in a few cases in which it would be expected, S. West has assumed the existence of a cohesion between the pleuræ which overcomes the tendency of the chest to this condition, but this force has not as yet been satisfactorily demonstrated.

In a case of pneumothorax, if the opening causing it remain patent, the intrathoracic pressure will be that of the atmosphere, the lung will be found to have collapsed by virtue of its own elastic tension, the intercostal grooves obliterated, the heart displaced to the other side, and the diaphragm lower than normal, because the negative pressure by reason of which these organs are retained in their ordinary position has been relieved. If the opening becomes closed the intrathoracic pressure may rise above the atmospheric and the above-mentioned displacements be much increased. Some of the reasons for this rise of pressure are, the valvular action of the opening during violent expiratory efforts, the rise of temperature of the imprisoned gas, and the compression of the air by the usual effusion into the cavity.

Pneumothorax arises: (1) In perforating wounds of the chest, in which case it is sometimes associated with extensive cutaneous emphysema. It has followed exploratory puncture. Herman Biggs has reported two cases and I have seen it twice. Pneumothorax rarely follows fracture of the rib, even though the lung may be torn. (2) In perforation of the pleura through the diaphragm, usually by malignant disease of the stomach or colon. The pleura may also be perforated in cases of cancer of the œsophagus. (3) When the lung is perforated. This is by far the most common cause, and may occur: (*a*) In a normal lung from rupture of the air-vesicles during straining or even when at rest. Special attention has been called to this accident by S. West and De H. Hall. The air may be absorbed and no ill effect follows. It does not necessarily excite pleurisy, as pointed out many years ago by Gairdner, but inflammation and effusion are the usual result. In a recent case the condition developed as the patient was going down-stairs; no effusion followed; he did not react to tuberculin. (*b*) From perforation due to local disease of the lung, either the softening of a caseous focus or the breaking of a tuberculous cavity. According to S. West, 90 per cent of all the cases are due to this cause. Less common are the cases due to septic broncho-pneumonia and to gangrene. A rare cause is the breaking of a hæmorrhagic infarct in chronic heart-disease, of which I met an instance a few years ago. (*c*) Perforation of the lung from the pleura, which arises in certain cases of empyema and produces a pleuro-bronchial fistula. (*d*) Spontaneously, by the development in pleural exudates of the gas bacillus (*B. aërogenes capsulatus* Welch).

Pneumothorax occurs chiefly in adults, though cases are met with in very young children. It is more frequent in males than in females.

Morbid Anatomy.—If a trocar or blow-pipe is inserted between the ribs, there may be a jet of air of sufficient strength to blow out a lighted match. On opening the thorax the mediastinum and pericardium are seen to be pushed, or rather, as Douglas Powell pointed out, drawn over to the opposite side; but, as before mentioned, the heart is not rotated, and the relation of its parts is maintained much as in the normal condition. A serous or purulent fluid is usually present, and the membranes are inflamed. The cause of the pneumothorax can usually be found without difficulty. In the great majority of instances it is the perforation of a tuberculous cavity or a breaking of a superficial caseous focus. The orifice of rupture may be extremely small. In chronic cases there may be a fistula of considerable size communicating with the bronchi. The lung is usually compressed and carnified.

Symptoms.—The onset is usually sudden and characterized by severe pain in the side, urgent dyspnœa, and signs of general distress, as indicated by slight lividity and a very rapid and feeble pulse. There may, however, be no urgent symptoms, particularly in cases of long-standing phthisis. On more than one occasion I have found, post mortem, a pneumothorax which was unsuspected during life. West states that even in healthy adults this latent pneumothorax may occasionally occur.

A remarkable recurrent variety has been described by S. West, Goodhart, and Furney. In Goodhart's case the pneumothorax developed first in one side and then in the other.

The *physical signs* are very distinctive. *Inspection* shows marked enlargement of the affected side with immobility. The heart impulse is usually much displaced. On *palpation* the fremitus is greatly diminished or more commonly abolished. On *percussion* the resonance may be tympanitic or even have an amphoric quality. This, however, is not always the case. It may be a flat tympany, resembling Skoda's resonance. In some instances it may be a full, hyperresonant note, like emphysema; while in others—and this is very deceptive—there is dulness. These extreme variations depend doubtless upon the degree of intrapleural tension. On several occasions I have known an error in diagnosis to result from ignorance of the fact that, in certain instances, the percussion note may be " muffled, toneless, almost dull " (Walshe). There is usually dulness at the base from effused fluid, which can readily be made to change the level by altering the position of the patient. Movable dulness can be obtained much more readily in pneumothorax than in a simple pleurisy. On *auscultation* the breath-sounds are suppressed. Sometimes there is only a distant feeble inspiratory murmur of marked amphoric quality. The contrast between the loud exaggerated breath-sounds on the normal side and the absence of the breath-sounds on the other is very suggestive. The rales have a peculiar metallic quality, and on coughing or deep inspiration there may be what Laennec termed the metallic tinkling. The voice, too, has a curious metallic echo. What is sometimes called the coin-sound, termed by Trousseau the *bruit d'airain*, is very characteristic. To obtain it the auscultator should place one ear on the back of the chest wall while the assistant taps one coin on another on the front of the chest. The metallic echoing sound which is produced in this way is one of the most constant and characteristic signs of pneumothorax. And, lastly, the Hippocratic succussion may be obtained when the auscultator's head is placed upon the chest while the patient's body is shaken. A splashing sound is produced, which may be audible at a distance. A patient may himself notice it in making abrupt changes in posture. Of other symptoms displacement of organs is most constant. As already mentioned, the heart may be drawn over to the opposite side, and the liver greatly displaced, so that its upper surface is below the level of the costal margin, a degree of dislocation never seen in simple effusion.

The *diagnosis* of pneumothorax rarely offers any difficulty, as the signs are very characteristic. In cases in which the percussion note is dull the condition may be mistaken for effusion. I made this mistake in a case of pulsating pleurisy, in which the pneumothorax followed heavy lifting, and it was not until several days later, after some of the fluid had been withdrawn, that a tympanitic note developed. Diaphragmatic hernia following a crush or other accident may closely simulate pneumothorax.

In cases of very large phthisical cavities with tympanitic percussion resonance and rales of an amphoric, metallic quality, the question of pneumothorax is sometimes raised. In those rare instances of total excavation of one lung the amphoric and metallic phenomena may be most intense, but the absence of dislocation of the organs, of the succussion splash, and of the coin-sound suffice to differentiate this condition. While this is true in the great majority of cases, I have recently heard the *bruit d'airain* over large cavities of the right upper lobe. The condition of pyo-pneumothorax subphrenicus may simulate closely true pneumothorax.

The *prognosis* in cases of pneumothorax depends largely upon the cause. S. West gives a mortality of 70 per cent. The tuberculous cases usually die within a few weeks. Of 39 cases, 29 died within a fortnight (West); 10 patients died on the first day, 2 within twenty and thirty minutes respectively of the attack. Pneumothorax developing in a healthy individual often ends in recovery. There are tuberculous cases in which the pneumothorax, if occurring early, seems to arrest the progress of the tuberculosis. This appeared to be the case in a man with chronic pneumothorax who was under my care in Philadelphia for between three and four years. It may be a chronic condition, as in the case just mentioned, and a fair measure of health may be enjoyed.

Treatment.—Practically these cases should be dealt with as ordinary pleurisy with effusion. Of course, when pneumothorax develops in advanced phthisis the indication is to relieve the pain and distress either by morphia or chloroform; but in cases which develop early the fluid should be withdrawn by aspiration, or, if purulent, permanent drainage should be obtained. Even when the condition has seemed to be most desperate I have known recovery to take place after thorough drainage of the sac. Portions of ribs may have to be excised, and during convalescence it is well for the patient to practise expansion of the lung in the manner already mentioned. There are cases of pneumothorax in phthisis in which the general condition is so good and the inconvenience so slight that to let well enough alone seems the best course. In such an occasional aspiration may be performed if the fluid increases. In some of the instances the mere tapping of the chest with a fine needle, so as to allow the escape of some of the air, seems to give relief by reducing the intrathoracic pressure. Good results are stated to have followed the method introduced by Potain, of replacing the air and fluid within the thorax by sterilized air.

V. AFFECTIONS OF THE MEDIASTINUM.

(1) **Simple Lymphadenitis.**—In all inflammatory affections of the bronchi and of the lungs the groups of lymph-glands in the mediastinum become swollen. In the bronchitis of measles, for example, and in simple broncho-pneumonia the bronchial glands are large and infiltrated, the tissue is engorged and œdematous, sometimes intensely hyperæmic. Much stress has been laid by some writers on this enlargement of the glands in the posterior mediastinum, and De Mussy held that it was an important factor in inducing paroxysms of whooping-cough. They may attain a size sufficient to induce dulness beneath the manubrium and in the upper part of the interscapular regions behind, though this is often difficult to determine. In reality the glands lie chiefly upon the spine, and unless those which are deep in the root of the lung are large enough to induce compression of the adjacent lung tissue, I doubt if the ordinary bronchial adenopathy ever can be determined by percussion in the upper interscapular region. I have never met with an instance in which the compression of either bronchus seemed to have resulted from the glands, however large. Tuberculous affection of these glands has already been considered.

(2) **Suppurative Lymphadenitis.**—Occasionally abscess in the bronchial or tracheal lymph-glands is found. It may follow the simple adenitis, but is most frequently associated with the presence of tubercle. The liquid portion may gradually become absorbed and the inspissated contents undergo calcification. Serious accidents occasionally occur, as perforation into the œsophagus or into a bronchus, or in rare instances, as in the case

reported by Sidney Phillips, perforation of the aorta, as well as a bronchus, which, it is remarkable to say, did not prove fatal rapidly, but caused repeated attacks of hæmoptysis during a period of sixteen months.

(3) **Tumors; Cancer and Sarcoma.**—In Hare's elaborate study of 520 cases of disease of the mediastinum * there were 134 cases of cancer, 98 cases of sarcoma, 21 cases of lymphoma, 7 cases of fibroma, 11 cases of dermoid cysts, 8 cases of hydatid cysts, and instances of lipoma, gumma, and enchondroma. From this we see that cancer is the most common form of growth. The tumor occurred in the anterior mediastinum alone in 48 of the cases of cancer and in 33 of the cases of sarcoma. There are three chief points of origin, the thymus, the lymph-glands, and the pleura and lung. Sarcoma is more frequently primary than cancer. Males are more frequently affected than females. The age of onset is most commonly between thirty and forty.

Symptoms.—The signs of mediastinal tumor are those of intrathoracic pressure. *Dyspnœa* is one of the earliest and most constant symptoms, and may be due either to pressure on the trachea or on the recurrent laryngeal nerves. It may indeed be cardiac, due to pressure upon the heart or its vessels. In a few cases it results from the pleural effusion which so frequently accompanies intrathoracic growths. Associated with the dyspnœa is a cough, often severe and paroxysmal in character, with the brazen quality of the so-called aneurismal cough when a recurrent nerve is involved. The voice may also be affected from a similar cause. Pressure on the vessels is common. The superior vena cava may be compressed and obliterated, and when the process goes on slowly the collateral circulation may be completely effected. Less commonly the inferior vena cava or one or other of the subclavian veins is compressed. The arteries are much less rarely obstructed. It is remarkable how little the aorta may be involved, though entirely surrounded by a sarcomatous or cancerous mass. There may be dysphagia, due to compression of the œsophagus. In rare instances there are pupillary changes, either dilatation or contraction, due to involvement of the sympathetic.

Physical Signs.—On inspection there may be orthopnœa and marked cyanosis of the upper part of the body. In such instances, if of long duration, there are signs of collateral circulation and the superficial mammary and epigastric veins are enlarged. In these cases of chronic obstruction the finger-tips may be clubbed. There may be bulging of the sternum or the tumor may erode the bone and form a prominent subcutaneous growth. The rapidly growing lymphoid tumors more commonly than others perforate the chest wall. In 4 of 13 cases of Hodgkin's disease, there was mediastinal growth, and in 3 instances the sternum was eroded and perforated. The perforation may be on one side of the breast-bone. The projecting tumor may pulsate; the heart may be dislocated and its impulse much out of place. Contraction of one side of the thorax has been noted in a few instances. On palpation the fremitus is absent wherever the tumor reaches the chest wall. If pulsating, it rarely has the forcible,

---

* Fothergillian Prize Essay of the Medical Society of London, Philadelphia, 1889.

heaving impulse of an aneurismal sac. On auscultation there is usually silence over the dull region. The heart-sounds are not transmitted and the respiratory murmur is feeble or inaudible, rarely bronchial. Vocal resonance is, as a rule, absent. Signs of pleural effusion occur in a great many instances of mediastinal growth, and in doubtful cases the aspirator needle should be used.

Tumors of the anterior mediastinum originate usually in the thymus; the sternum is pushed forward and often eroded. The growth may be felt in the suprasternal fossa; the cervical glands are usually involved. The pressure symptoms are chiefly upon the venous trunks. Dyspnœa is a prominent feature.

Intrathoracic tumors in the middle and posterior mediastinum originate most commonly in the lymph-glands. The symptoms are out of all proportion to the physical signs; there is urgent dyspnœa and cough, which is sometimes loud and ringing. The pressure symptoms are chiefly upon the gullet, the recurrent laryngeal, and sometimes upon the azygos vein.

In a third group, tumors originating in the pleura and the lung, the pressure symptoms are not so marked. Pleural exudate is very much more common; the patient becomes anæmic and emaciation is rapid. There may be secondary involvement of the lymph-glands in the neck. For a discussion of the symptomatology of these different groups, see Pepper and Stengel, Transactions of the Association of American Physicians, vol. x.

The *diagnosis* of mediastinal tumor from aneurism is sometimes extremely difficult. An interesting case reported and figured by Sokolosski, in Bd. 19 of the Deutsches Archiv für klinische Medicin, in which Oppolzer diagnosed aneurism and Skoda mediastinal tumor, illustrates how in some instances the most skilful of observers may be unable to agree. Scarcely a sign is found in aneurism which may not be duplicated in mediastinal tumor. This is not strange, since the symptoms in both are largely due to pressure. The time element is important. If a case has persisted for more than eighteen months the disease is probably aneurism. There are, however, exceptions to this. By far the most valuable sign of aneurism is the diastolic shock so often to be felt, and in a majority of cases to be heard, over the sac. This is rarely, if ever, present in mediastinal growths, even when they perforate the sternum and have communicated pulsation. Tracheal tugging is rarely present in tumor. Another point of importance is that a tumor, advancing from the mediastinum, eroding the sternum and appearing externally, if aneurismal, has forcible, heaving, and distinctly expansile pulsations. The radiating pain in the back and arms and neck is rather in favor of aneurism, as is also a beneficial influence on it of iodide of potassium.

The frequency of pleural effusion in connection with mediastinal tumor is to be constantly borne in mind. It may give curiously complex characters to the physical signs—characters which are profoundly modified after aspiration of the liquid.

(4) **Abscess of the Mediastinum.**—Hare collected 115 cases of mediastinal abscess, in 77 of which there were details sufficient to permit the

analysis. Of these cases the great majority occurred in males. Forty-four were instances of acute abscess. The anterior mediastinum is most commonly the seat of the suppuration. The cases are most frequently associated with trauma. Some have followed erysipelas or occurred in association with eruptive fevers. Many cases, particularly the chronic abscesses, are of tuberculous origin. Of *symptoms,* pain behind the sternum is the most common. It may be of a throbbing character, and in the acute cases is associated with fever, sometimes with chills and sweats. If the abscess is large there may be dyspnœa. The pus may burrow into the abdomen, perforate through an intercostal space, or it may erode the sternum. Instances are on record in which the abscess has discharged into the trachea or œsophagus. In many cases, particularly of chronic abscess, the pus becomes inspissated and produces no ill effect. The *physical signs* may be very indefinite. A pulsating and fluctuating tumor may appear at the border of the sternum or at the sternal notch. The absence of *bruit*, of the diastolic shock, and of the expansile pulsation usually enables a correct diagnosis to be made. When in doubt a fine hypodermic needle may be inserted.

(5) **Indurative Mediastino-Pericarditis.**—Harris has recently reviewed the subject. In one form there is adherent pericardium and great increase in the fibrous tissues of the mediastinum; in another there is adherent pericardium with union to surrounding parts, but very little mediastinitis; in a third the pericardium may be uninvolved. The disease is rare; of 22 cases 17 were in males; only 2 were above thirty years of age. The symptoms are essentially those of that form of adhesive pericardium which is associated with great hypertrophy and dilatation of the heart, and in which the patients present a picture of cyanosis, dyspnœa, anasarca, etc. The pulsus paradoxus, described by Kussmaul, is not distinctive. Occasionally there is also a proliferative peritonitis. Mediastinal friction is sometimes heard in patients with adhesive mediastino-pericarditis—dry, coarse, crackling rales heard along the sternum, particularly when the arms are raised.

(6) **Miscellaneous Affections.**—In Hare's monograph there were 7 instances of fibroma, 11 cases of dermoid cyst, 8 cases of hydatid cyst, and cases of lipoma and gumma.

(7) **Emphysema of the Mediastinum.**—Air in the cellular tissues of the mediastinum is met with in cases of trauma, and occasionally in fatal cases of diphtheria and in whooping-cough. It may extend to the subcutaneous tissues. Champneys has called attention to its frequency after tracheotomy, in which, he says, the conditions favoring the production are division of the deep fascia, obstruction in the air-passages, and inspiratory efforts. The deep fascia, he says, should not be raised from the trachea. It is often associated with pneumothorax. The condition seems by no means uncommon. Angel Money found it in 16 of 28 cases of tracheotomy, and in 2 of these pneumothorax also was present.

43

DISEASES OF THE CIRCULATORY SYSTEM.

I. DISEASES OF THE PERICARDIUM.

I. PERICARDITIS.

PERICARDITIS is the result of infective processes, primary or secondary, or arises by extension of inflammation from contiguous organs.

Etiology.—*Primary,* so-called idiopathic, inflammation of this membrane is rare; but cases are met with, most commonly in children, in which there is no evidence of rheumatism or of other conditions with which the disease is usually associated.

Pericarditis from injury usually comes under the care of the surgeon in connection with the primary wound. Interesting cases are those in which the traumatism is from within, due to the passage of some foreign body—such as a needle, a pin, or a bone—through the œsophagus into the pericardium.

As a *secondary* process pericarditis is met with in the following affections: (*a*) A majority of the cases occur in connection with rheumatism. The percentage given by different authors ranges from thirty to seventy. The articular trouble may be slight or, indeed, the disease may be associated with acute tonsillitis in rheumatic subjects. Cases are recorded in which the pericarditis has preceded the articular disease. (*b*) Septic processes rank next to rheumatism. In the acute necrosis of bone and puerperal fever it is not uncommon. (*c*) Tuberculosis, in which the disease may be primary or part of a general involvement of the serous sacs or associated with extensive pulmonary disease. (*d*) Eruptive fevers. In children, the disease is not infrequent after scarlatina. It is rarely met with in measles, small-pox, or typhoid fever. In other infective diseases, such as diphtheria and pneumonia, it is rare. Pericarditis sometimes complicates chorea; it was present in 19 of 73 autopsies which I collected; in only 8 of these was arthritis present. (*e*) Certain altered conditions of the system seem to render the pericardium more susceptible to infection. Of these gout takes the first place. In chronic Bright's disease pericarditis is by no means rare. The *pericardite brightique* of the French forms one of the most important groups of the disease in persons over fifty years of age, most frequently accompanying the chronic interstitial form of nephritis. Pericarditis has been met with also in scurvy and diabetes.

Pericarditis by extension of disease from contiguous organs. In pleuro-pneumonia it forms one of the most serious complications, and was present in 5 cases of 100 post mortems in this disease which I made at the Montreal General Hospital. It is most often met with in the pleuro-pneumonia of children and of alcoholics. The association with simple pleurisy is much less common. In ulcerative endocarditis, purulent myocarditis, and in aneurism of the aorta pericarditis is occasionally found. It may also result from extension of disease from the bronchial glands, the ribs, sternum, vertebræ, and even from the abdominal viscera. Of 100 consecutive cases at the Boston City Hospital analyzed by Sears, in 54 the exudate was dry, in 41 serous, in 4 hæmorrhagic, and in 5 purulent. Thirty-four cases showed signs of old valvular disease; rheumatism was a factor in 51; pneumonia in 18; and in 7 chronic nephritis. Of the 100 cases 43 died.

Pericarditis occurs at all ages. Cases are reported in the fœtus. In the new-born it may result from septic infection through the navel. Throughout childhood the incidence of rheumatism and scarlet fever makes it a frequent affection, whereas late in life it is most often associated with tuberculosis, Bright's disease, and gout. Males are somewhat more frequently attacked than females. Climatic and seasonal influences have been mentioned by some writers. The so-called epidemics of pericarditis have been outbreaks of pneumonia with this as a frequent complication.

Anatomically as well as clinically the disease may be considered under the following divisions:

1. Acute, plastic, or dry pericarditis.
2. Pericarditis with effusion—sero-fibrinous, hæmorrhagic, or purulent.
3. Chronic adhesive pericarditis (adherent pericardium).

Acute Plastic Pericarditis.—This, the most common form, occurs usually as a secondary process, and is distinguished by the small amount of fluid exudation, which does not, as in the next variety, give special characters to the disease. It is a benign form and never of itself proves fatal.

Anatomically it may be partial or general. In the mildest grades the serous membrane looks lustreless and roughened. This is due to the presence of a thin fibrinous sheeting, which can be lifted with the knife, showing the membrane beneath to be injected or in places ecchymotic. As the fibrinous sheeting increases in thickness the constant movement of the adjacent surfaces gives to it sometimes a ridge-like, at others a honey-combed appearance. With more abundant fibrinous exudation the membranes present an appearance resembling buttered surfaces which have been drawn apart. The fibrin is in long shreds, and the heart presents a curiously shaggy appearance—the so-called hairy heart of old writers—*cor villosum*.

In mild grades the subjacent muscle looks normal; but in the more prolonged and severe cases there is myocarditis, and for 2 or 3 mm. beneath the visceral layer the muscle presents a pale, turbid appearance. Many of these acute cases are tuberculous; covered by the layers of lymph the granulations are easily overlooked in a superficial examination.

Slight fluid exudation is invariably present, entangled in the meshes of fibrin, but there may be very thick fibrinous layers without much serous effusion.

Symptoms.—The majority of cases of simple plastic pericarditis, like those of simple endocarditis, present no symptoms, and unless sought for there are no objective signs indicating its existence. In the post-mortem room it is not uncommon to find it in cases in which its presence has been unsuspected during life.

Pain is a variable symptom, not usually intense, and in this form rarely excited by pressure. It is more marked in the early stage, and may be referred either to the præcordia or to the region of the xiphoid cartilage. Instances are recorded of pain of an aggravated and most distressing character resembling angina. Fever is usually present, but it is not always easy to say how much depends upon the primary febrile affection, and how much upon the pericarditis. It is as a rule not high, rarely exceeding 102.5°. In rheumatic cases hyperpyrexia has been observed.

Physical Signs.—*Inspection* is negative; *palpation* may reveal the presence of a distinct fremitus caused by the rubbing of the roughened pericardial surfaces. This is usually best marked over the right ventricle. It is not always to be felt, even when the friction sound on auscultation is loud and clear. *Auscultation:* The friction sound, due to the movement of the pericardial surfaces upon each other, is one of the most distinctive of physical signs. It is double, corresponding to the systole and diastole; but the synchronism with the heart-sounds is not accurate, and the to-and-fro murmur usually outlasts the time occupied by the first and second sound. In rare instances the friction is single; more frequently it appears to be triple in character—a sort of canter rhythm. The sounds have a peculiar rubbing, grating quality, characteristic when once recognized, and rarely simulated by endocardial murmurs. Sometimes instead of grating there is a creaking quality—the *bruit de cuir neuf*—the new-leather murmur of the French. The pericardial friction appears superficial, very close to the ear, and is usually intensified by pressure with the stethoscope. It is best heard over the right ventricle, the part of the heart which is most closely in contact with the front of the chest—that is, in the fourth and fifth interspaces and adjacent portions of the sternum. There are instances in which the friction is most marked at the base, over the aorta, and at the superior reflection of the pericardium. Occasionally it is best heard at the apex. It may be limited and heard over a very narrow area, or it may be transmitted up and down the sternum. There are, however, no definite lines of transmission as in the endocardial murmur. An important point is the variability of the sounds, both in position and quality; they may be heard at one visit and not at another. The maximum of intensity will be found to vary with position.

Diagnosis.—There is rarely any difficulty in determining the presence of a dry pericarditis, for the friction sounds are distinctive. The double murmur of aortic incompetency may simulate closely the to-and-fro pericardial rub. I recall one instance at least in which this mistake was made. The constant character of the aortic murmur, the direction of transmission, the phenomena in the arteries, and the associated conditions of the disease should be sufficient to prevent this error.

I have never known an instance in which pericarditis was mistaken for acute endocarditis, though writers refer to such, and give the differential diagnosis in the two affections. The only possible mistake could be made in those rare instances of single soft, systolic, pericardial friction.

Pleuro-pericardial friction is very common, and may be associated with endo-pericarditis, particularly in cases of pleuro-pneumonia. It is frequent, too, in phthisis. It is best heard over the left border of the heart, and is much affected by the respiratory movement. Holding the breath or taking a deep inspiration may annihilate it. The rhythm is not the simple to-and-fro diastolic and systolic, but the respiratory rhythm is superadded, usually intensifying the murmur during expiration and lessening it on inspiration. In phthisis there are instances in which, with the friction, a loud systolic click is heard, due to the compression of a thin layer of lung and the expulsion of a bubble of air from a small softening focus or from a bronchus.

And, lastly, it is not very uncommon, in the region of the apex beat, to hear a series of fine crepitant sounds, systolic in time, often very distinct, suggestive of pericardial adhesions, but heard too frequently for this cause.

Course and Termination.—Simple fibrinous pericarditis never kills, but it occurs so often in connection with serious affections that we have frequent opportunities to see all stages of its progress. In the majority of cases the inflammation subsides and the thin fibrinous laminæ gradually become converted into connective tissue, which unites the pericardial leaves firmly together. In other instances the inflammation progresses, with increase of the exudation, and the condition is changed from a " dry " to a " moist " pericarditis, or the pericarditis with effusion.

In a few instances—probably always tuberculous—the simple plastic pericarditis becomes chronic, and great thickening of both visceral and parietal layers is gradually induced.

Pericarditis with Effusion.—Though commonly a direct sequence of the dry or plastic pericarditis, of which it is sometimes called the second stage, this form presents special features and deserves separate consideration. It is found most frequently in association with acute rheumatism, tuberculosis, and septicæmia, and sets in usually with the symptoms above described, namely, præcordial pain, with slight fever or a distinct chill.

In children the disease may, like pleurisy, come on without local symptoms, and, after a week or two of failing health, slight fever, shortness of breath, and increasing pallor, the physician may find, to his astonishment, signs of most extensive pericardial effusion. These latent causes are often tuberculous. W. Ewart has called special attention to latent and ephemeral pericardial effusions, which he thinks are often of short duration and of moderate size, with an absence of the painful features of pericarditis. The effusion may be sero-fibrinous, hæmorrhagic, or purulent. The amount varies from 200 or 300 cc. to 2 litres. In the cases of sero-fibrinous exudation the pericardial membranes are covered with thick, creamy fibrin, which may be in ridges or honeycombed, or may present long, villous extensions. The parietal layer may be several millimetres in thickness and may form a firm, leathery membrane. The hæmorrhagic exudation is usually associated with tuberculous, or with cancerous pericarditis, or with the disease in the aged. The lymph is less abundant, but both surfaces are injected and often show numerous hæmorrhages. Thick, curdy masses of lymph are usually found in the dependent part of the sac. In the purulent effusion the fluid has a creamy consistency, particularly in tuberculosis. In many cases the effusion is really sero-purulent, a thin, turbid exudation containing flocculi of fibrin.

The pericardial layers are greatly thickened and covered with fibrin. When the fluid is pus, they present a grayish, rough, granular surface. Sometimes there are distinct erosions on the visceral membrane. The heart muscle in these cases becomes involved to a greater or less extent, and on section, the tissue, for a depth of from 2 to 3 mm., is pale and turbid, and shows evidence of fatty and granular change. Endocarditis coexists frequently, but rarely results from the extension of the inflammation through the wall of the heart.

Symptoms.—Even with copious effusion the onset and course may be so insidious that no suspicion of the true nature of the disease is aroused.

As in the simple pericarditis, pain may be present, either sharp and stabbing or as a sense of distress and discomfort in the cardiac region. It is more frequent with effusion than in the plastic form. Pressure at the lower end of the sternum usually aggravates it. Dyspnœa is a common and important symptom, one which, perhaps, more than any other, excites suspicion of grave disorder and leads to careful examination of heart and lungs. The patient is restless, lies upon the left side or, as the effusion increases, sits up in bed. Associated with the dyspnœa is in many cases a peculiarly dusky, anxious countenance. The pulse is rapid, small, sometimes regular, and may present the characters known as *pulsus paradoxus*, in which during each inspiration the pulse-beat becomes very weak or is lost. These symptoms are due, in great part, to the direct mechanical effect of the fluid within the pericardium which embarrasses the heart's action. Other pressure effects are distention of the veins of the neck, dysphagia, which may be a marked symptom, and irritative cough from compression of the trachea. Aphonia is not uncommon, owing to compression or irritation of the recurrent laryngeal as it winds round the aorta. Another important pressure effect is exercised upon the left lung. In massive effusion the pericardial sac occupies such a large portion of the antero-lateral region of the left side that the condition has frequently been mistaken for pleurisy. Even in moderate grades the left lung is somewhat compressed. This is an additional element in the production of the dyspnœa.

Great restlessness, insomnia, and in the later stages low delirium and coma are symptoms in the more severe cases. Delirium and marked cerebral symptoms are associated with the hyperpyrexia of rheumatic cases, but apart from the ordinary delirium there may be peculiar mental symptoms. The patient may become melancholic and show suicidal tendencies.

In other cases the condition resembles closely delirium tremens. Sibson, who has specially described this condition, states that the majority of such cases recover. Chorea may also occur, as was pointed out by Bright. Epilepsy is a rare complication which has occurred during paracentesis.

Physical Signs.—*Inspection.*—In children the præcordia bulges and with copious exudation the antero-lateral region of the left chest becomes enlarged. The intercostal spaces are prominent and there may be marked œdema of the wall. The epigastrium may be more prominent. Perforation externally through a space is very rare. Owing to the compression of the lung, the expansion of the left side is greatly diminished. The diaphragm and left lobe of the liver may be pushed down and may produce a distinct prominence in the epigastric region.

Palpation.—A gradual diminution and final obliteration of the cardiac shock is a striking feature in progressive effusion. The position of the apex beat is not constant. In large effusions it is usually not felt. In children as the fluid collects the pulsation may be best seen in the fourth space, but this may not be the apex itself. Ewart maintains that the position of the apex beat is unaltered, or even depressed. The pericardial friction may lessen with the effusion, though it often persists at the base when no longer palpable over the right ventricle, or may be felt in the erect and not in the recumbent posture. Fluctuation can rarely, if ever, be detected.

Percussion gives most important indications. The gradual distention of the pericardial sac pushes aside the margins of the lungs so that a large area comes in contact with the chest wall and gives a greatly increased percussion dulness. The form of this dulness is irregularly pear-shaped; the base or broad surface directed downward and the stem or apex directed upward toward the manubrium. A valuable sign, to which Rotch called attention, is the absence of resonance in the right fifth intercostal space. In the left infrascapular area there may be a patch of diminished resonance or even flatness (Ewart).

Auscultation.—The friction sound heard in the early stages may disappear when the effusion is copious, but often persists at the base or at the limited area of the apex. It may be audible in the erect and not in the recumbent posture. With the absorption of the fluid the friction returns. One of the most important signs is the gradual weakening of the heart-sounds, which with the increase in the effusion may become so muffled and indistinct as to be scarcely audible. The heart's action is usually increased and the rhythm disturbed. Occasionally a systolic endocardial murmur is heard. Early and persistent accentuation of the pulmonary second sound may be present (Warthin).

Important accessory signs in large effusion are due to pressure on the left lung. The antero-lateral margin of the lower lobe is pushed aside and in some instances compressed, so that percussion in the axillary region, in and just below the transverse nipple line, gives a modified percussion note, usually a flat tympany. Variations in the position of the patient may change materially this modified percussion area, over which on auscultation there is either feeble or tubular breathing.

Course.—Cases vary extremely in the rapidity with which the effusion takes place. In every instance, when a pericardial friction murmur has been detected, the practitioner should immediately outline with care—using the aniline pencil or nitrate of silver—the upper and lateral limits of cardiac dulness, since he will in this way have certain positive guides in determining the rate and grade of the effusion. In many instances the exudation is slight in amount, reaches a maximum within forty-eight hours, and then gradually subsides. In other instances the accumulation is more gradual and progressive, increasing for several weeks. To such cases the term chronic has been applied. The rapidity with which a sero-fibrinous effusion may be absorbed is surprising. The possibility of the absorption of a purulent exudate is shown by the cases in which the pericardium contains semi-solid grayish masses in all stages of calcification. With sero-fibrinous effusion, if moderate in amount, recovery is the rule, with inevitable union, however, of the pericardial layers. In some of the septic cases there is a rapid formation of pus and a fatal result may follow in three or four days. More commonly, when death occurs with large effusion, it is not until the second or third week and takes place by gradual asthenia.

Prognosis.—In the sero-fibrinous effusions the outlook is good, and a large majority of all the rheumatic cases recover. The purulent effusions are, of course, more dangerous; the septic cases are usually fatal, and recovery is rare in the slow, insidious tuberculous forms.

Diagnosis.—Probably no serious disease is so frequently overlooked by the practitioner. Post-mortem experience shows how often pericarditis is not recognized, or goes on to resolution and adhesion without attracting notice. In a case of rheumatism, watched from the outset, with the attention directed daily to the heart, it is one of the simplest of diseases to diagnose; but when one is called to a case for the first time and finds perhaps an increased area of præcordial dulness, it is often very hard to determine with certainty whether or not effusion is present.

The difficulty usually lies in distinguishing between dilatation of the heart and pericardial effusion. Although the differential signs are simple enough on paper, it is notoriously difficult in certain cases, particularly in stout persons, to say which of the conditions exists. The points which deserve attention are:

(a) The character of the impulse, which in dilatation, particularly in thin-chested people, is commonly visible and wavy.

(b) The shock of the cardiac sounds is more distinctly palpable in dilatation.

(c) The area of dulness in dilatation rarely has a triangular form; nor does it, except in cases of mitral stenosis, reach so high along the left sternal margin or so low in the fifth and sixth interspaces *without visible or palpable impulse.* An upper limit of dulness shifting with change of position speaks strongly for effusion.

(d) In dilatation the heart-sounds are clearer, often sharp, valvular, or fœtal in character; whereas in effusion the sounds are distant and muffled.

(e) Rarely in dilatation is the distention sufficient to compress the lung and produce the tympanitic note in the axillary region.

The number of excellent observers who have acknowledged that they have failed sometimes to discriminate between these two conditions, and who have indeed performed paracentesis *cordis* instead of paracentesis *pericardii*, is perhaps the best comment on the difficulties.

Massive (1½ to 2 litre) exudations have been confounded with a pleural effusion. On more than one occasion the pericardium has been tapped under the impression that the exudate was pleuritic. The flat tympany in the infrascapular region, the absence of well-defined movable dulness, and the feeble, muffled sounds are indicative points. If the case has been followed from day to day there is rarely much difficulty; but it is different when a case presents a large area of dulness in the antero-lateral region of the left chest, and there is no to-and-fro pericardial friction murmur. Many of the cases have been regarded as encapsulated pleural effusions.

The nature of the fluid cannot positively be determined without aspiration; but a fairly accurate opinion can be formed from the nature of the primary disease and the general condition of the patient. In rheumatic cases the exudation is usually sero-fibrinous; in septic and tuberculous cases it is often purulent from the outset; in senile, nephritic, and tuberculous cases the exudation is sometimes hæmorrhagic.

Treatment.—The patient should have absolute quiet, mentally and bodily, so as to reduce to a minimum the heart's action. Drugs given for this purpose, such as aconite or digitalis, are of doubtful utility. Local bloodletting by cupping or leeches is certainly advantageous in robust subjects, particularly in the cases of extension in pleuro-pneumonia. The ice-bag is of great value. It may be applied to the præcordia at first for an hour or more at a time, and then continuously. It reduces the frequency of the heart's action and seems to retard the progress of an effusion. Blisters are not indicated in the early stage.

When effusion is present, the following measures to promote absorption may be adopted: Blisters to the præcordia, a practice not so much in vogue now as formerly. It is surprising, however, in some instances, how quickly an effusion will subside on their application. If the patient's strength is good, a purge every other morning may be given. The diet should be light, dry, and nutritious. In cases in which the pulse is strong and the constitutional disturbance not great, iodide of potassium may be of service, and the action of the kidneys may be promoted by the infusion of digitalis and acetate of potash.

When the effusion is large, as soon as signs of serious impairment of the heart occur, as indicated by dyspnœa, small rapid pulse, dusky, anxious countenance, surgical measures should be resorted to, and paracentesis, or incision of the pericardium, at once be performed. With the sero-fibrinous exudate, such as commonly occurs after rheumatism, aspiration is sufficient; but when the exudate is purulent, the pericardium should be freely incised and freely drained. The puncture may be made in the fourth interspace, either at the left sternal margin or 2.5 cm. (an inch) from it. If made in the fifth interspace it is well to puncture an inch and a half from the left sternal margin. In large effusions the pericardium can also be readily reached without danger by thrusting the needle upward and backward close to the costal margin in the left costo-xiphoid angle. The results of paracentesis of the pericardium have so far not been satisfactory. With an earlier operation in many instances and a more radical one in others—a free incision and not aspiration when the fluid is purulent—the percentage of recoveries will be greatly increased. Of 35 cases of suppurative pericarditis treated by incision 15 recovered and 20 died (Roberts, Am. Jr. Med. Sciences, Dec., 1897).

Chronic Adhesive Pericarditis (*Adherent Pericardium*).—Two groups of cases may be recognized:

(*a*) Simple adhesion of the peri- and epicardial layers. This is a common sequence of pericarditis, and is frequently met with post mortem as an accidental lesion. It is not necessarily associated with disturbance in the function of the heart, and in a large proportion of the cases there is neither dilatation nor hypertrophy.

(*b*) Adherent pericardium with chronic mediastinitis and union of the outer layer of the pericardium to the pleura and to the chest walls. This constitutes one of the most serious forms of cardiac disease, particularly in early life, and may lead to an extreme grade of hypertrophy and dilatation of the heart. Even with partial adhesion between the epicardium and pericardium there may be enormous hypertrophy under the conditions just mentioned. The *symptoms* of adherent pericardium are uncertain and indefinite. In the second group the features are those of hypertrophy and dilatation of the heart, later cardiac insufficiency, and in a few instances signs of extension of the mediastinitis to the peritonæum, causing chronic proliferative peritonitis, with perihepatitis and perisplenitis.* Sudden death may occur after an unusual exertion or during parturition (Reynolds Wilson).

The following are important points in the diagnosis: *Inspection.*—A majority of the signs of value come under this heading. (*a*) The præcordia is prominent and there may be marked asymmetry, owing to the enormous enlargement of the heart. (*b*) The extent of the cardiac impulse is greatly increased, and may sometimes be seen from the third to the sixth interspaces, and in extreme cases from the right parasternal line to outside the left nipple. (*c*) The character of the cardiac impulse. It is undulatory, wavy, and in the apex region there is marked systolic retraction. (*d*) Diaphragm phenomena. J. W. Broadbent has called attention to a very valuable sign in adherent pericardium. When the heart is adherent over a large area of the diaphragm there is with each pulsation a systolic tug, which may be communicated through the diaphragm to the points of its attachment on the wall, causing a visible systolic tugging. This has long been recognized in the region of the seventh or eighth ribs in the left parasternal line, but Dr. Broadbent called attention to the fact that it was frequently best seen on the left side behind, between the eleventh and twelfth ribs. With each systole there may be here a distinct, visible retraction of the chest wall. This is a very valuable and quite common sign. Sir William Broadbent calls attention also to the fact that owing to the attachment of the

---

* For illustrative cases see Arch. of Pediatrics, 1896.

heart to the central tendon of the diaphragm this part does not descend with inspiration, during which act there is not the visible movement in the epigastrium. (*e*) Diastolic collapse of the cervical veins, the so-called Fried-reich's sign. This is not of much moment.

Palpation.—The apex beat is fixed, and turning the patient on the left side does not alter its position. This I have found, however, somewhat un-certain. On placing the hand over the heart there is felt a diastolic shock or rebound, which some have regarded as the most reliable of all signs of ad-herent pericardium.

Percussion.—The area of cardiac dulness is usually much increased. In a majority of instances there are adhesions between the pleura and the peri-cardium, and the limit of cardiac dulness above and to the left may be fixed and is uninfluenced by deep inspiration. This, too, is an uncertain sign, inasmuch as there may be close adhesions between the pleura and the pericardium and between the pleura and the chest wall, which at the same time allow a very considerable degree of mobility to the edge of the lung.

Auscultation.—The phenomena are variable and uncertain. In the cases in children with a history of rheumatism, endocarditis has usually been present. Even in the absence of chronic endocarditis, when the dila-tation reaches a certain grade there are murmurs of relative insufficiency, which, as in one case I have recorded, may be present not only at the mitral but also at the tricuspid and pulmonary orifices. Hale White has called attention to the fact that there may be a well-marked presystolic murmur in connection with adherent pericardium. This was present in one of my cases.

The pulsus paradoxus, in which during inspiration the pulse-wave is small and feeble, is sometimes present, but it is not a diagnostic sign of either simple pericardial adhesion or of the cicatricial mediastino-peri-carditis.

In children, chronic adhesive pericarditis and mediastinitis may be asso-ciated with proliferative peritonitis, perihepatitis, and perisplenitis, in which condition ascites may recur for months, or even for years.

II. OTHER AFFECTIONS OF THE PERICARDIUM.

(1) **Hydropericardium.**—Naturally there are in the pericardial sac a few cubic centimetres of clear, citron-colored fluid, which probably represents a post-mortem transudate. In certain conditions during life there may be a large secretion of serum forming what is known as dropsy of the peri-cardium. It occurs usually in connection with general dropsy, due to kid-ney or heart disease; more commonly the former. It rarely of itself proves fatal, though when the effusion is excessive it adds to the embarrassment of the heart and the lungs, particularly when the pleural cavities are the seat of similar exudation. There are rare instances in which effusion into the pericardium occurs after scarlet fever with few, if any, other dropsical symptoms. The physical signs are those already referred to in connection with pericarditis with effusion. It is frequently overlooked.

In rare cases the serum has a milky character—chylo-pericardium.

(2) **Hæmo-pericardium.**—This condition, by no means uncommon, is met with in aneurism of the first part of the aorta, of the cardiac wall, or of the coronary arteries, and in rupture and wounds of the heart. Death usually follows before there is time for the production of symptoms other than those of rapid heart-failure due to compression. Particularly is this the case in aneurism. In rupture of the heart the patient may live for many hours or even days with symptoms of progressive heart-failure, dyspnœa, and the physical signs of effusion.

As already mentioned, the inflammatory exudate of tubercle or cancer is often blood-stained. The same is true of the effusion in the pericarditis of Bright's disease and of old people.

(3) **Pneumo-pericardium.**—Gas is rarely found in the pericardial sac, and is due, as a rule, to perforation from without, as in the case of stab wounds, or is the result of perforation from the lungs, œsophagus, or stomach. Perforation from a tuberculous cavity is a not uncommon cause. In those cases, formerly so puzzling, in which the gas is present shortly after death (a few hours), the gas bacillus (*B. aërogenes capsulatus*) will be found. In a case at the Royal Victoria Hospital, in which the gas bacillus was isolated, the diagnosis was made during life (Nicholls). As a result of perforation, acute pericarditis is always excited, and the effusion rapidly becomes purulent. The physical signs are remarkable. When the effusion is copious the fluid and gas together give a movable area of percussion dulness with marked tympany in the region of the gas. On auscultation, remarkable splashing, churning, metallic phenomena are heard with friction and possibly feeble, distant heart-sounds. Death follows rapidly, even in thirty-six hours, as in a case (the only one which I have seen) of perforation of the pericardium in cancer of the stomach. Except as a result of injury, the condition is not one for which treatment is available. In a case of perforation from without with signs of effusion, to enlarge the wound by free incision would be justifiable.

II. DISEASES OF THE HEART.

I. ENDOCARDITIS.

Inflammation of the lining membrane of the heart is usually confined to the valves, so that the term is practically synonymous with valvular endocarditis. It occurs in two forms—*acute*, characterized by the presence of vegetations with loss of continuity or of substance in the valve tissues; *chronic*, a slow sclerotic change, resulting in thickening, puckering, and deformity.

ACUTE ENDOCARDITIS.

This occurs in rare instances as a primary, independent affection; but in the great majority of cases it is an accident in various infective processes, so that in reality the disease does not constitute an etiological entity.

For convenience of description we speak of a simple or benign, and a malignant or ulcerative endocarditis, between which, however, there is no essential anatomical difference, as all gradations can be traced, and they represent but different degrees of intensity of the same process.

Etiology.—*Simple endocarditis* does not constitute a disease of itself, but is invariably found with some other affection. The general experience of the profession has confirmed the original observation of Bouillaud as to the frequency of association of simple endocarditis with acute articular rheumatism. Possibly it is nothing in the disease itself, but simply an altered state of the fluid media—a reduction perhaps of the lethal influences which they normally exert—permitting the invasion of the blood by certain micro-organisms. Tonsillitis, which in some forms is regarded as a rheumatic affection, may be complicated with endocarditis. Of the specific diseases of childhood it is not uncommon in scarlet fever, while it is rare in measles and chicken-pox. In diphtheria simple endocarditis is rare. In small-pox it is not common. In typhoid fever I have met with it twice in 80 autopsies.

In pneumonia both simple and malignant endocarditis are common. In 100 autopsies in this disease made at the Montreal General Hospital there were 5 instances of the former. Acute endocarditis is by no means rare in phthisis. I have met with it in 12 cases in 216 post mortems.

In chorea simple warty vegetations are found on the valves in a large majority of all fatal cases, in 62 of 73 cases collected by me. There is no disease in which, post mortem, acute endocarditis has been so frequently found. And, lastly, simple endocarditis is met with in diseases associated with loss of flesh and progressive debility, as cancer, and such disorders as gout, diabetes, and Bright's disease.

A very common form is that which occurs on the sclerotic valves in old heart-disease—the so-called recurring endocarditis.

Malignant endocarditis is met with: (*a*) As a primary disease of the lining membrane of the heart or of its valves.

(*b*) As a secondary affection in acute rheumatism, pneumonia, and in various specific fevers; or as an associated condition in septic processes.

It is also known by the names of ulcerative, infectious, or diphtheritic endocarditis, but the term malignant seems most appropriate to characterize the essential clinical features of the disease.

The existence of a primary endocarditis has been doubted; but there are instances in which persons previously in good health, without any history of affections with which endocarditis is usually associated, have been attacked with symptoms resembling severe typhus or typhoid. In one case which I saw, death occurred on the sixth day and no lesions were found other than those of malignant endocarditis.

The simple endocarditis of rheumatism rarely develops into the malignant form. In only 24 of 209 cases the symptoms of severe endocarditis arose in the progress of acute or subacute rheumatism. In only 3 of my Montreal cases was there a history of rheumatism either before or during the attacks.

Malignant endocarditis is extremely rare in chorea. Of all acute diseases complicated with severe endocarditis pneumonia probably heads the list. This fact, which had been referred to by several of the older writers, was brought out in a striking manner by the figures on which my Gulstonian lectures were based. In 11 of the 23 Montreal cases the disease came on with lobar pneumonia, while it developed with this disease in 54 of the 209 cases analyzed—indeed, the endocarditis which occurs in pneumonia seems to be of an unusually malignant type, as in 16 cases of my 100 autopsies in this disease in which this lesion was present, 11 were of this form. This has been confirmed by Netter, Kanthack, and others. Meningitis was associated with endocarditis in 25 of the 209 cases, and in 15 there was also pneumonia.

The affection may complicate erysipelas, septicæmia (from whatever cause) and puerperal fever and gonorrhœa. Malignant endocarditis is very rare in tuberculosis, typhoid fever, and diphtheria.

It has been stated by many writers that endocarditis occurs in ague. With the unusual facilities for the study of this disease which I have had in the past nine years I have not yet met with an instance. Unquestionably, in the majority of these cases, the intermittent pyrexia, which has been regarded as characteristic of the ague, has depended upon the endocarditis. In dysentery cases have been described. In small-pox and scarlet fever, with which simple endocarditis is not infrequently complicated, the malignant form is extremely rare.

Morbid Anatomy of Simple and Malignant Endocarditis.—*Simple endocarditis* is characterized by the presence on the valves or on the lining membrane of the chambers of minute vegetations, ranging from 1 to 4 mm. in diameter, with an irregular and fissured surface, giving to them a warty or verrucose appearance. Often these little cauliflower-like excrescences are attached by very narrow pedicles. They are more common on the left side of the heart than the right, and occur on the mitral valves more often than on the aortic. The vegetations are usually above the line of closure of the valves. It is rare to see any swelling or macroscopic evidence of infiltration of the endocardium in the neighborhood of even the smallest of the granulations, and redness, indicative of distention of the vessels, is uncommon, even when they occur upon valves already the seat of sclerotic changes, in which capillary vessels extend to the edges. With time the vegetations may increase greatly in size, but in what may be called simple endocarditis the size rarely exceeds that mentioned above.

The earliest vegetations consist of elements derived from the blood, and are composed of blood platelets, leucocytes, and fibrin in varying proportions. At a later stage they appear as small outgrowths of connective tissue. The transition of one form into the other can often be followed. The process consists of a proliferation of the endothelial cells and the cells of the subendothelial layer which gradually invade the fresh vegetation, and ultimately entirely replace it. The blood-cells and fibrin undergo disintegration and gradually they are removed. The whole process has received the name of "organization." Even when the vegetation has been entirely converted into granulations or connective tissue it is often found at autopsy to be capped with a thin layer of fibrin and leucocytes.

Micro-organisms are generally, even if not invariably, found associated with the vegetations. They tend to be entangled in the granular and fibrillated fibrin or in the older ones to cap the apices.

In both man and animals there is a form of *chronic vegetative endocarditis* in which, without much or any loss of substance, the valves and chordæ tendineæ are covered with large, firm outgrowths. In several cases of this kind the clinical history has been characterized by a protracted fever of a marked remittent or even intermittent type.

Subsequent Changes.—(1) The vegetations may become organized and the valve restored to a normal state (?). (2) The process may extend, and a simple may become an ulcerative endocarditis. (3) The vegetations may be broken off and carried in the circulation to distant parts. (4) The vegetations become organized and disappear, but they initiate a nutritive change in the valve tissue which ultimately leads to sclerosis, thickening, and deformity. The danger in any case of simple endocarditis is not immediate, but remote, and consists in this perversion of the normal processes of nutrition which results in sclerosis of the valves.

A gradual transition from the simple to a more severe affection, to which the name *malignant* or *ulcerative endocarditis* has been given, may be traced. Practically every case of ulcerative endocarditis is attended by vegetations. In this form the loss of substance in the valve is more pronounced, the deposition—thrombus formation—from the blood is more extensive, and the micro-organisms are present in greater number and often show increased virulence. Ulcerative endocarditis is often found in connection with heart valves already the seat of chronic proliferative and sclerotic changes.

In malignant endocarditis there is distinct loss of substance in the heart valve. This loss may be superficial and limited to the endocardium, or, what is more common, it involves deeper structures, and not very infrequently leads to perforation of a valve, a septum, or even of the heart itself.

Upon microscopical examination the affected valve shows necrosis, with more or less loss of substance; the necrotic tissue is devoid of preserved nuclei and presents a coagulated appearance. Upon it a mixture of blood platelets, fibrin—granular or fibrillated—and leucocytes enclosing masses of micro-organisms are met with. The subjacent tissue often shows sclerotic thickening and always infiltration with exuded granulation tissue-cells.

Parts affected.—The following figures, taken from my Gulstonian lectures at the Royal College of Physicians, give an approximate estimate of the frequency with which in 209 cases different parts of the heart were affected in malignant endocarditis: Aortic and mitral valves together, in 41; aortic valves alone, in 53; mitral valves alone, in 77; tricuspid in 19; the pulmonary valves in 15; and the heart walls in 33. In 9 instances the right heart alone was involved, in most cases the auriculo-ventricular valves.

Mural endocarditis is seen most often at the upper part of the septum of the left ventricle. Next in order is the endocarditis of the left auricle on the postero-external wall. The vegetations may extend, as in a recent case in my wards, along the intima of the pulmonary artery into the hilum of the lung. The ulcerative changes may lead to perforation of a valve segment, erosion of the chordæ tendineæ, perforation of the septum, or even of the heart itself. A common result of the ulceration is the production of valvular aneurism. In three fourths of the cases the affected valves present old sclerotic changes. The process may extend to the aorta, producing, as in one of my cases, extensive endarteritis with multiple acute aneurisms.

Associated Lesions.—The associated pathological changes are partly those of the primary disease to which the endocarditis is secondary and partly those due to embolism. In the endocarditis of septic processes there is the local lesion—an acute necrosis, a suppurative wound, or puerperal disease. In many cases the lesions are those of pneumonia, rheumatism, or other febrile processes. The changes due to embolism constitute the most striking features, but it is remarkable that in some instances, even with endocarditis of a markedly ulcerative character, there may be no trace of embolic processes.

The infarcts may be few in number—only one or two, perhaps, in the spleen or kidney—or they may exist in hundreds throughout the various parts of the body. They may present the ordinary appearance of red or white infarcts of a suppurative character. They are most common in the spleen and kidneys, though they may be numerous in the brain, and in many cases are very abundant in the intestines. In right-sided endocarditis there may be infarcts in the lungs. In many of the cases there are innumerable miliary abscesses. Acute suppurative meningitis was met with in 5 of 23 of the Montreal cases, and in over 10 per cent of the 209 cases analyzed in the literature. Acute suppurative parotitis also may occur.

Bacteriology.—No distinction in the micro-organisms found in the two forms of endocarditis can be made. In both the pyogenic cocci—streptococci, staphylococci, pneumococci, and gonococci—are the most frequent bacteria met with. More rarely, especially in the simple vegetative endocarditis, the bacilli of tuberculosis, typhoid fever, and anthrax have been encountered. The bacillus coli communis has also been found, and Howard has described a case of malignant endocarditis due to an attenuated form of the diphtheria bacillus. Flexner * has analyzed 34 cases of acute endocarditis associated with chronic renal and cardiac disease, and found the micrococcus lanceolatus and the streptococcus pyogenes present each twelve times, the staphylococcus three times. Other bacteria encountered were bacillus pyocyaneus, coli, and influenzæ, and the gonococcus.

Symptoms.—Neither the clinical course nor the physical signs of *simple endocarditis* are in any respect characteristic. The great majority of the cases are latent and there is no indication whatever of cardiac mischief. Experience has taught us that endocarditis is frequently found post mortem in persons in whom it was not suspected during life. There are certain features, however, by which its presence is indicated with a degree of probability. The patient, as a rule, does not complain of any pain or cardiac distress. In a case of acute rheumatism, for example, the symptoms to excite suspicion would be increased rapidity of the heart's action, perhaps slight irregularity, and an increase in the fever without aggravation

---

* Journal of Experimental Medicine, 1896, i, p. 559.

of the joint trouble. Rows of tiny vegetations on the mitral or on the aortic segments seem a trifling matter to excite fever, and it is difficult in the endocarditis of febrile processes to say definitely in every instance that an increase in the fever depends upon the endocardial complication. But a study of the recurring endocarditis—which is of the warty variety, consisting of minute beads on old sclerotic valves—shows that this process may be associated, for days or weeks at a time, with slight fever ranging from 100° to 102½°. Palpitation may be a marked feature and is a symptom upon which certain authors lay great stress.

The *diagnosis* of the condition rests upon physical signs which are notoriously uncertain. The presence of a murmur at one or other of the cardiac areas in a case of fever is often regarded as indicative of the existence of endocarditis. This extremely common mistake has arisen from the fact that the *bruit de souffle* or bellows murmur is common to endocarditis and a number of other conditions which have nothing to do with it. At first there may be only a slight roughening of the first sound, which may gradually develop into a distinct murmur. Taken alone, it is, however, a very uncertain and fallacious sign.

It is difficult to give a satisfactory clinical picture of *malignant endocarditis* because the modes of onset are so varied and the symptoms so diverse. Arising in the course of some other disease, there may be simply an intensification of the fever or a change in its character. In a majority of the cases there are present certain general features, such as irregular pyrexia, sweating, delirium, and gradual failure of strength.

Embolic processes may give special characters, such as delirium, coma or paralysis from involvement of the brain or its membranes, pain in the side and local peritonitis from infarction of the spleen, bloody urine from implication of the kidneys, impaired vision from retinal hæmorrhage, and suppuration, and even gangrene, in various parts from the distribution of the emboli.

Two special types of the disease have been recognized—the septic or pyæmic and the typhoid. Other cases closely resemble true intermittent fever. In some the cardiac symptoms are most prominent, while in others again the main symptoms may be those of an acute affection of the cerebrospinal system.

The *septic type* is met with usually in connection with an external wound, the puerperal process, or an acute necrosis. There are rigors, sweats, irregular fevers, and all of the signs of septic infection. The heart symptoms may be completely masked by the general condition, and attention called to them only on the occurrence of embolism. In a most remarkable sub-group of this type the disease may simulate a quotidian or a tertian ague. The symptoms may develop in persons with chronic heart-disease without any external lesions. These cases may be much prolonged—for three or four months, or even longer, as in one of Bristowe's. The existence in some of these instances of a previous genuine malaria has been a very puzzling circumstance.

The *typhoid type* is by far the most common and is characterized by an irregular temperature, early prostration, delirium, somnolence, and coma,

44

relaxed bowels, sweating, which may be of a most drenching character, petechial and other rashes, and occasionally parotitis. The heart symptoms may be completely overlooked, and in some instances the most careful examination has failed to discover a murmur.

Under the *cardiac group*, as suggested by Bramwell, may be considered those cases in which patients with chronic valve disease are attacked with marked fever and evidence of recent endocarditis. Many such cases present symptoms of the pyæmic and typhoid character and may run a most acute course. In others the course is chronic, lasting for weeks or months. I have reported two cases of this chronic vegetative endocarditis, with intermittent fever, one of more than a year's duration. The autopsies showed extensive vegetative and ulcerative disease of the mitral valves.

There are cases in which it is often difficult to decide whether malignant endocarditis is present or not. Thus, a patient with aortic valve disease is under treatment for failing compensation and begins to have irregular fever with restlessness and cardiac distress; embolic phenomena may develop—sudden hemiplegia, pain in the region of the spleen, or bloody urine, or perhaps peripheral embolism. There may be a low delirium and the case may run a tolerably acute course; but in other instances the fever subsides and recovery occurs.

In what may be termed the *cerebral group* of cases the clinical picture may simulate a meningitis, either basilar or cerebro-spinal. There may be acute delirium or, as in three of the Montreal cases, the patient may be brought into the hospital unconscious. Heineman reports an instance, with autopsy, in which the clinical picture was that of an acute cerebro-spinal meningitis.

Certain special symptoms may be mentioned. The fever is not always of a remittent type, but may be high and continuous. Petechial rashes are very common and render the similarity very strong to certain cases of typhoid and cerebro-spinal fever. In one case the disease was thought to be hæmorrhagic small-pox. Erythematous rashes are not uncommon. The sweating may be most profuse, even exceeding that which occurs in phthisis and ague. Diarrhœa is not necessarily associated with embolic lesions in the intestines. Jaundice has been observed and cases are on record which were mistaken for acute yellow atrophy.

The heart symptoms may be entirely latent and are not found unless a careful search be made. Even on examination there may be no murmur present. Instances are recorded by careful observers, in which the examination of the heart has been negative. Cases with chronic valve disease usually present no difficulty in diagnosis.

The course of the disease is varied, depending largely upon the nature of the primary trouble. Except in the disease grafted upon chronic valvulitis the course is rarely extended beyond five or six weeks. As already mentioned, there are instances in which the disease is prolonged for months. The most rapidly fatal case on record is described by Eberth, the duration of which was scarcely two days.

Diagnosis.—In many cases the detection of the disease is very difficult; in others, with marked embolic symptoms, it is easy. From simple endocarditis it is readily distinguished, though confusion occasionally occurs in the transitional stage, when a simple is developing into a malignant form. The constitutional symptoms are of a graver type, the fever is higher, rigors are common, and septic and typhoid symptoms develop. Perhaps a majority of the cases not associated with puerperal processes or bone-disease are confounded with typhoid fever. A differential diagnosis may even be impossible, particularly when we consider that in typhoid fever infarctions and parotitis may occur. The diarrhœa and abdominal tenderness may also be present, which with the stupor and progressive asthenia make a picture not to be distinguished from this disease. Points which may guide us are: The more abrupt onset in endocarditis, the absence of any regularity of the pyrexia in the early stage of the disease, and the cardiac pain. Oppression and shortness of breath may be early symptoms in malignant endocarditis. Rigors, too, are not uncommon. There is a marked leucocytosis in infective endocarditis. Between pyæmia and malignant endocarditis there are practically no differential features, for the disease really constitutes an *arterial pyæmia* (Wilks). In the acute cases resembling malignant fevers, the diagnosis is usually made of typhus, typhoid, cerebro-spinal fever, or even of hæmorrhagic small-pox. The intermittent pyrexia, occurring for weeks or months, has led in some cases to the diagnosis of malaria, but this disease could now be positively excluded by the blood examination.

The cases usually terminate fatally. The instances of recovery are those more subacute forms, the so-called recurring endocarditis developing on old sclerotic valves in cases of chronic heart-disease.

Treatment.—We know no measures by which in rheumatism, chorea, or the eruptive fevers the onset of endocarditis can be prevented. As it is probable that many cases develop, particularly in children, in mild forms of these diseases, it is well to guard the patients against taking cold and insist upon rest and quiet, and to bear in mind that of all complications an acute endocarditis, though in its immediate effects harmless, is perhaps the most serious. This statement is enforced by the observations of Sibson that on a system of absolute rest the proportion of cases of rheumatism attacked by endocarditis was less than of those who were not so treated.

It is doubtful whether the salicylates in rheumatism have an influence in reducing the liability to endocarditis. When the endocarditis is present we know no remedies which will definitely influence the valvular lesions. If there is much vascular excitement aconite may be given and an ice-bag placed over the heart.

The salicylates are strongly advised by some writers and the sulphocarbolates have been recommended by Sansom. In the severer cases of malignant endocarditis the treatment is practically that of septicæmia.

CHRONIC ENDOCARDITIS.

This condition, which is a sclerosis of the valve, may be primary, but is oftener secondary to acute endocarditis, particularly the rheumatic form.

It is essentially a slow, insidious process which leads to deformity of the valve segment and is the foundation of chronic valvular disease.

Certain poisons appear capable of initiating the change, such as alcohol, syphilis, and gout, though we are at present ignorant of the way in which they act. A very important factor, particularly in the case of the aortic valves, is the strain of prolonged and heavy muscular exertion. In no other way can be explained the occurrence of so many cases of sclerosis of the aortic valves in young and middle-aged men whose occupations necessitate the overuse of the muscles.

Morbid Anatomy.—Vegetations in the form in which they occur in acute endocarditis are not present. In the early stage, which we have frequent opportunities of seeing, the edge of the valve is a little thickened and perhaps presents a few small nodular prominences, which in some cases may represent the healed vegetations of the acute process. In the aortic valves the tissue about the corpora Arantii is first affected, producing a slight thickening with an increase in the size of the nodules. The substance of the valve may lose its translucency, and the only change noticeable be a grayish opacity and a slight loss of its delicate tenuity. In the auriculo-ventricular valves these early changes are seen just within the margin and here it is not uncommon to find swellings of a grayish-red, somewhat infiltrated appearance, almost identical with the similar structures on the intima of the aorta in arterio-sclerosis. Even early there may be seen yellow or opaque-white subintimal fattily degenerated areas. As the sclerotic changes increase, the fibrous tissue contracts and produces thickening and deformity of the segment, the edges of which become round, curled, and incapable of that delicate apposition necessary for perfect closure. A sigmoid valve, for instance, may be narrowed one fourth or even one third across its face, the most extreme grade of insufficiency being induced without any special deformity and without any definite narrowing of the arterial orifice. In the auriculo-ventricular segments a simple process of thickening and curling of the edges of the valves, inducing a failure to close without forming any obstruction to the normal course of the blood-flow, is less common. Still, we meet with instances at the mitral orifice, particularly in children, in which the edges of the valves are curled and thickened, so that there is extreme insufficiency without any material narrowing of the orifice. More frequently, as the disease advances, the chordæ tendineæ become thickened, first at the valvular ends and then along their course. The edges of the valves at their angles are gradually drawn together and there is a definite narrowing of the orifice, leading in the aorta to more or less stenosis and in the left auriculo-ventricular orifice—the two sites most frequently involved—to constriction. Finally, in the sclerotic and necrotic tissues lime salts are deposited and may even reach the deeper structures of the fibrous rings, so that the entire valve becomes a dense calcareous mass with scarcely a remnant of normal tissue. The chordæ tendineæ may gradually become shortened, greatly thickened, and in extreme cases the papillary muscles are implanted directly upon the sclerotic and deformed valve. The apices of the papillary muscles usually show marked fibroid change.

In all stages of the process the vegetations of simple endocarditis may be present, and upon sclerotic valves we find the severer, ulcerative form of the disease.

Chronic *mural* endocarditis produces cicatricial-like patches of a grayish-white appearance which are sometimes seen on the muscular trabeculæ of the ventricle or in the auricles. It often occurs in association with myocarditis.

The frequency with which chronic endocarditis is met with may be gathered from the following figures: In the statistics, amounting to from 12,000 to 14,000 autopsies, reported from Dresden, Würzburg, and Prague the percentage ranged from four to nine. The relative frequency of involvement of the various valves is thus given in the collected statistics of Parrot: The mitral orifice was involved in 621, the aortic in 380, the tricuspid in 46, and the pulmonary in 11. This gives 57 instances in the right to 1,001 in the left heart.

The endocarditis of the fœtus is usually of the sclerotic form and involves the valves of the right more frequently than those of the left side.

II. CHRONIC VALVULAR DISEASE.

1. General Introduction.

The *incidence* of valvular lesions may be gathered from the following figures compiled by Gillespie from the records of the Royal Infirmary, Edinburgh: Of 2,368 cases with cardiac lesions, valvular disease occurred in 80.8 per cent; endocarditis and pericarditis in 5.3; myocardial lesions in 11.9 per cent; 66.2 per cent of the cases were in males.

Effects of Valve Lesions.—The general influence on the work of the heart may be briefly stated as follows: The sclerosis induces insufficiency or stenosis, which may exist separately or in combination. The narrowing retards in a measure the normal outflow and the insufficiency permits the blood current to take an abnormal course. In both instances the effect is dilatation of a chamber. The result in the former case is an increase in the difficulty which the chamber has in expelling its contents through the narrow orifice; in the other, the overfilling of a chamber by blood flowing into it from an improper source, as, for instance, in mitral insufficiency, when the left auricle receives blood both from the pulmonary veins and from the left ventricle.

The cardiac mechanism is fully prepared to meet ordinary grades of dilatation which constantly occur during sudden exertion. A man, for instance, at the end of a hundred-yard race has his right chambers greatly dilated and his reserve cardiac power worked to its full capacity. The slow progress of the sclerotic changes brings about a gradual, not an abrupt, insufficiency, and the moderate dilatation which follows is at first overcome by the exercise of the ordinary reserve strength of the heart muscle. Gradually a new factor is introduced. The reserve power which is capable of meeting sudden emergencies in such a remarkable manner is unable to cope long with a permanent and perhaps increasing dilatation. More work has to be done and, in accordance with definite physiological laws, more power is given by increase of the muscles. The heart hypertrophies and the effect of the valve lesion becomes, as we say, *compensated*. The equilibrium of the circulation is in this way maintained.

The nature of the process with which we have to deal is graphically illustrated in the accompanying diagrams, which we owe to Martius, of Rostock. The perpendicular lines in the figures represent the power of work of the heart. While the muscle in the healthy heart (Diagram I) has at its disposal the maximal force, $a\,c$, it carries on its work under ordinary circumstances (when the body is at rest) with the force $a\,b$. The force $b\,c$ is reserve force, by means of which the heart accommodates itself to greater exertion.

If now there be a gross valvular lesion, the force required to do the ordinary work of the heart (at rest) becomes very much increased (Diagram II). But in spite of this enormous call for force, insufficiency of the heart muscle does not necessarily result, for the working force required is still within the

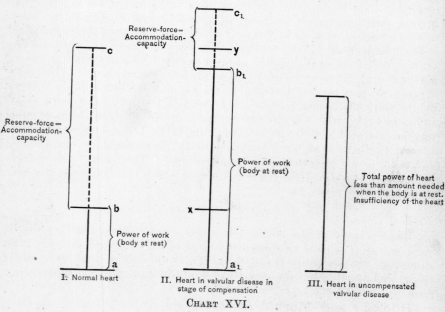

Reserve-force = Accommodation-capacity

Reserve-force = Accommodation-capacity

Power of work (body at rest)

Power of work (body at rest)

Total power of heart less than amount needed when the body is at rest. Insufficiency of the heart

I. Normal heart

II. Heart in valvular disease in stage of compensation

III. Heart in uncompensated valvular disease

CHART XVI.

limits of the maximal power of the heart, $a_1\,b_1$, being less than $a_1\,c_1$. The muscle accommodates itself to the new conditions by making its reserve force mobile (experiment of Rosenbach). If nothing further occurred, however, this condition could not be permanently maintained, for there would be left over for emergencies only the small reserve force, $b_1\,y$. Even when at rest the heart would be using continuously almost its entire maximal force. Any slight exertion requiring more extra force than that represented by the small value $b_1\,y$ (say the effort required on walking or on going upstairs) would bring the heart to the limit of its working power, and palpitation and dyspnœa would appear. Such a condition does not last long. The working power of the heart gradually increases. More and more exertion can be borne without causing dyspnœa, for *the heart hypertrophies*. Finally, a new, more or less permanent condition is attained, in that the hypertrophied heart possesses the maximal force, *a, c.* Owing to the increase in volume of the heart muscle, the total force of the heart is greater *absolutely* than that of the normal heart by the amount *y, c.* It is, however, *relatively* less efficient, for its reserve force is much less than that of the healthy heart. Its capacity for accommodating itself to unusual calls upon it is accordingly permanently diminished.

Turning now to the disturbances of compensation, it is to be distinctly borne in mind that any heart, normal or diseased, can become insufficient whenever a call upon it exceeds its maximal working capacity. The liability to such disturbance will depend, above all, upon the accommodation limits of the heart—the less the width of the latter, the easier will it be to go beyond the heart's efficiency. A comparison of Diagrams I and II will immediately make it clear that the heart in valvular disease will much earlier become insufficient than the heart of a healthy individual. If the heart muscle is compelled to do maximal or nearly maximal work for a long time, it becomes exhausted. It is obvious that the heart in valvular disease has on account of its small amount of reserve force to do maximal or nearly maximal work far more frequently than does the normal heart. The power of the heart may become decreased to the amount necessary simply to carry on the work of the heart when the body is at rest, or it may cease to be sufficient even for this. The reserve force gained through the compensatory process may be entirely lost (Diagram III). If the loss be only temporary, the exhausted heart muscle quickly recovering, the condition is spoken of as a " disturbance of compensation." The term " loss of compensation " is reserved for the condition in which the disturbance is continuous.

2. Aortic Incompetency.

Incompetency of the aortic valves arises either from inability of the valve segments to close an abnormally large orifice or more commonly from disease of the segments themselves. This best-defined and most easily recognized of valvular lesions was first carefully studied by Corrigan, whose name it sometimes bears.

Etiology and Morbid Anatomy.—It is more frequent in males than in females, affecting chiefly able-bodied, vigorous men at the middle period of life. The ratio which it bears to other valve diseases has been variously given from 30 to 50 per cent.

Among the important factors in producing this condition are: (*a*) Congenital malformation, particularly fusion of two segments—most commonly those behind which the coronary arteries are given off. It is probable that an aortic orifice may be competent with this bicuspid state of the valves, but a great danger is the liability of these malformed segments to sclerotic endocarditis. Of 17 cases which I have reported all presented sclerotic changes, and the majority of them had, during life, the clinical features of chronic heart-disease.

(*b*) Acute endocarditis. This does not produce aortic incompetency unless the process passes on to ulceration and destruction, under which circumstances it is often found, and may cause a rapidly fatal issue. Simple endocarditis associated with the specific fevers is not nearly so common on the aortic as on the mitral segments; so also with rheumatism, which plays a less important *rôle* here than in mitral valve disease.

(*c*) By far the most frequent cause of insufficiency is a slow, progressive sclerosis of the segments, resulting in a curling of the edges, which lessens the working surface of the valve. This may, of course, follow acute endocarditis, but it is so often met with in strong, able-bodied men among the working classes, without any history of rheumatism or special febrile diseases with which endocarditis is commonly associated, that other conditions must be sought for to explain its frequency. Of these, unquestionably strain is the most important—not a sudden, forcible strain, but a persistent increase of the normal tension to which the segments are subject during the diastole of the ventricle. Of circumstances increasing this tension, heavy and excessive use of the muscles is perhaps the most important. So often is this form of heart-disease found in persons devoted to athletics that it is sometimes called the "athlete's heart." Alcohol is a second important factor, and is stated to raise considerably the tension in the aortic system. A combination of these two causes is extremely common. A third element in inducing chronic sclerotic changes in these valves is syphilis. Cases are rarely seen in which other factors must not be taken into account, but the association is too frequent to be accidental. That syphilis is capable of inducing arterial sclerosis is, I think, acknowledged, although the way in which it does so is not yet clear. It is interesting to note with what frequency this form of valve disease occurs in soldiers. I was struck with this fact in the Philadelphia Hospital, to which so many veterans of the civil war are admitted. I was in the habit of enforcing upon my students the etiological lesson by a reference to Bacchus and Vulcan, at whose shrines a majority of the cases of aortic insufficiency have worshipped, and not a few at those of Mars and Venus.

The condition of the valves is such as has already been described in chronic endocarditis. It may be noted, however, how slight a grade of curling may produce serious incompetency. Associated with the valve disease is, in a majority of the cases, a more or less advanced arterio-sclerosis of the arch of the aorta, one serious effect of which may be a narrowing of the orifices of the coronary arteries. The sclerotic changes are often combined with atheroma, either in the fatty or calcareous stage. This may exist at the attached margin of the valves without inducing insufficiency. In other instances insufficiency may result from a calcified spike projecting from the aortic attachment into the body of the valve, and so preventing its proper closure. Some writers (Peter) have laid great stress upon the extension of the endarteritis to the valve, and would separate the instances of this kind from those of simple valvular endocarditis. I must say that I have not been able to recognize clinical differences between these two conditions, though anatomically we may separate the cases into two groups—the endocarditic and the arterio-sclerotic.

(*d*) And, lastly, insufficiency may be induced by rupture of a segment—a very rare event in healthy valves, but not uncommon in disease, either from excessive strain during heavy lifting or from the ordinary endarterial strain in a valve eroded and weakened by ulcerative endocarditis.

Relative insufficiency of the sigmoid valves, due to dilatation of the aortic ring, is a rare condition. It is said to occur in extensive arterial sclerosis of the ascending portion of the arch with great dilatation just above the valves. In such cases the valve segments are usually involved with the arterial coats. In aneurism just above the aortic ring, relative insufficiency of the valve may be present.

It would appear from the careful measurements of Beneke that the aortic orifice, which at birth is 20 mm., increases gradually with the growth of the heart until at one-and-twenty it is about 60 mm. At this it remains until the age of forty, beyond which date there is a gradual increase in the size up to the age of eighty, when it may reach from 68 to 70 mm. There is thus at the very period of life in which sclerosis of the valve is most common a physiological tendency toward the production of a state of relative insufficiency.

The insufficiency may be combined with various grades of narrowing, but the majority of the cases of aortic insufficiency present no signs of stenosis. On the other hand, cases of aortic stenosis almost without exception are associated with some grade, however slight, of regurgitation.

The direct effect of aortic insufficiency is the regurgitation of blood from the artery into the ventricle, causing an overdistention of the cavity and a reduction of the blood column; that is, a relative anæmia in the arterial tree. As an immediate effect of the double blood-flow into the left ventricle dilatation of the chamber occurs, and finally hypertrophy. In this way the valve defect is compensated and as with each ventricular systole a larger amount of blood is propelled into the arterial system, the regurgitation of a certain amount during diastole does not, for a time at least, seriously impair the nutrition of the peripheral parts. In this valve lesion dilatation and hypertrophy reach their most extreme limit. The heaviest hearts on record are described in connection with this affection. The so-called bovine heart, *cor bovinum,* may weigh 35 or 40 ounces, or even, as in a case of Dulles's, 48 ounces. The dilatation is usually extreme, and is in marked contrast to the condition of the chamber in cases of pure aortic stenosis. The papillary muscles may be greatly flattened. The mitral valves are usually not seriously affected, though the edges may present slight sclerosis, and there is often relative incompetency, owing to distention of the mitral ring. Dilatation and hypertrophy of the left auricle are common, and secondary enlargement of the right heart occurs in all cases of long standing. The myocardium usually presents changes, fibroid or fatty; more commonly the former in association with disease of the coronary arteries. The arch of the aorta may present extensive arterio-sclerosis and dilatation. In the endocarditic cases, particularly those following rheumatism, the intima is perfectly smooth, and the arch with its main branches not dilated. This condition may be found post mortem even when during life there have been the most characteristic signs of enlargement of the arch and of dilatation of the innominate and right carotid. I have even known the condition of aneurism to be diagnosed when post mortem no trace of dilatation or sclerosis was found, only an extreme grade of insufficiency with enormous dilatation and hypertrophy. The coronary arteries are usually involved in the sclerosis, and their orifices may be much narrowed. Although these vessels have been shown by Martin and Sedgwick to be filled during the ventricular systole, the circulation in them must be embarrassed in aortic incompetency. They must miss the effect of the blood-pressure in the sinuses of Valsalva during the elastic recoil of the arteries, which surely aids in keeping the coronary vessels full. The arteries of the body usually present more or less sclerosis consequent upon the strain which they undergo during the forcible ventricular systole.

Symptoms.—The condition is often discovered accidentally in persons who have not presented any features of cardiac disease.

Headache, dizziness, flashes of light, and a feeling of faintness on rising quickly are among the earliest symptoms. Palpitation and cardiac distress on slight exertion are common. Long before any signs of failing compensation pain may become a marked and troublesome feature. It is extremely variable in its manifestations. It may be of a dull, aching character confined to the præcordia. More frequently, however, it is sharp and radiating, and is transmitted up the neck and down the arms, particularly the left. Attacks of true angina pectoris are more frequent in this than in any other valvular disease. Anæmia is also common, much more so than in aortic stenosis or in mitral affections.

More serious symptoms, as compensation fails, are shortness of breath and œdema of the feet. The attacks of dyspnœa are liable to come on at night, and the patient has to sleep with the head high or even in a chair. Cyanosis is rare. It is most commonly due to complicating valve disease, or it is stated that it may result from bulging of the septum ventriculorum and encroachment upon the right ventricle. Of respiratory symptoms cough may develop, due to the congestion of the lungs or œdema. Hæmoptysis is less frequent than in mitral disease. I have reported a case in which it was profuse and believed to be due to tuberculosis of the lungs, inasmuch as the patient was admitted in a state of emaciation and profound exhaustion. General dropsy is not common, but œdema of the feet may occur early and is sometimes due to the anæmia, at others to the venous stasis, at times to both. Unless there is coexisting disease of the mitral valve, it is rare in aortic incompetency for the patient to die with general anasarca. Sudden death is frequent; more so in this than in other valvular diseases. As compensation fails the patient takes to bed and slight irregular fever, associated usually with a recurring endocarditis, is not uncommon toward the close. Embolic symptoms are not infrequent—pain in the splenic region with enlargement of the organ, hæmaturia, and in some cases paralysis. Distressing dreams and disturbed sleep are more common in this than in other forms of valvular disease.

Here may appropriately be mentioned the connection between mental symptoms and cardiac disease, as they are oftenest seen with this lesion. An admirable account of the relations between insanity and disease of the heart is to be found in Mickle's Gulstonian lectures for 1888. In general medical practice we seldom find marked mental symptoms, except toward the close of the disease, when there may be delirium, hallucinations, and morbid impulses. It is to be remembered that in many heart cases this terminal delirium is uræmic. The irritability and peevishness sometimes found in persons the subject of organic heart-disease cannot, I think, be associated with it in any special manner. We do meet insanity, breaking out in patients with aortic and mitral disease, in the stage of compensation, which appears to be related definitely to the cardiac lesion. It is important to bear this in mind, for cases occasionally display suicidal tendencies. I have twice had patients throw themselves from a window of the ward.

Physical Signs.—*Inspection* shows a wide and forcible area of cardiac impulse with the apex beat in the sixth or seventh interspace, and perhaps as far out as the anterior axillary line. In young subjects the præcordia may bulge. On palpation a thrill, diastolic in time, is occasionally felt, but is not common. The impulse is usually strong and heaving, unless in conditions of extreme dilatation, when it is wavy and indefinite. Occasionally two or three interspaces between the nipple line and sternum will be depressed with the systole as a result of atmospheric pressure. *Percussion* shows a greater increase in the area of heart dulness than is found in any other valvular lesion. It extends chiefly downward and to the left.

On *auscultation* there is heard a murmur during diastole in the second right interspace, which is propagated with intensity toward the ensiform cartilage, or down the left margin of the sternum toward the apex. In the majority of cases it is a soft, long-drawn *bruit*, and is of all cardiac murmurs the most trustworthy. It occurs during the time of, and is produced by, the reflux of blood from the aorta into the ventricle. In a large proportion of the cases there is also a systolic murmur heard at the aortic region, usually shorter, often rougher in quality, and which may be propagated upward into the neck. A common mistake is to regard this as indicating stenosis, whereas in the great majority of instances of aortic insufficiency there is no material narrowing, and the murmur is produced by roughening of the segments or of the intima of the arch. The second sound is usually obliterated, but when the valves are only slightly curled or if one cusp only is involved both the murmur and the valvular sound may be distinctly heard. At the apex murmurs are also heard, either transmitted from the aortic orifice or produced at the mitral. In the majority of cases with aortic incompetency of high grade, the mitral orifice is dilated, and there is relative insufficiency of the valves. It can frequently be determined that the systolic murmur at the apex differs in quality from that at the base. A second murmur at the apex, probably produced at the mitral orifice, is not uncommon. Attention was called to this by the late Austin Flint, and the murmur usually goes by his name. It has a distinctly rumbling quality, is limited in area, and is sometimes, though not always, exactly presystolic in time. The explanation of its occurrence, as given by Flint, is that in the extreme dilatation of the ventricle the mitral segments cannot during diastole be forced back against the wall, and therefore, remaining in the blood current, they produce a sort of relative narrowing, and in consequence a vibratory murmur not unlike in quality the presystolic murmur of mitral stenosis. Broadbent, on the other hand, suggests that the regurgitant current from the aorta impinging upon the anterior or aortic flap of the mitral may set it into vibration and thus produce the murmur. This apex diastolic murmur of aortic insufficiency occurs in a considerable proportion of all cases. It is variable, and may disappear as the dilatation of the ventricle diminishes. There is never the loud systolic shock which follows the murmur of mitral stenosis.

The examination of the arteries in aortic insufficiency is of great value. Visible pulsation is more commonly seen in the peripheral vessels in this than in any other condition. The carotids may be seen to throb forcibly, the temporals to dilate, and the brachials and radials to expand with each heart-beat. With the ophthalmoscope the retinal arteries are seen to pulsate. Not only is the pulsation evident, but the characteristic jerking quality is apparent. In the throat the throbbing carotids may lead to the diagnosis of aneurism. In many cases the pulsation can be seen in the suprasternal notch, and prominent, forcibly-throbbing vessels beneath the right sterno-mastoid muscle. The abdominal aorta may lift the epigastrium with each systole. To be mentioned with this is the capillary pulse, met very often in aortic insufficiency, and best seen in the finger-nails or by drawing a line upon the forehead, when the margin of hyperæmia on either side alternately blushes and pales. In extreme grades the face or the hand may blush visibly at each systole. It is met with also in profound anæmia, occasionally in neurasthenia, and in health in conditions of great relaxation of the peripheral arteries. Pulsation may also be present in the peripheral veins. On palpation the characteristic water-hammer or Corrigan pulse is felt. In the majority of instances the pulse wave strikes the finger forcibly with a quick jerking impulse, and immediately recedes or collapses. The characters of this are sometimes best appreciated by grasping the arm above the wrist and holding it up. Moreover, the pulse of aortic regurgitation is usually retarded or delayed—i. e., there is an appreciable interval between the beat of the heart and the pulsation in the radial artery, which varies according to the extent of the incompetence. On auscultation a double murmur may be heard in the carotids and subclavians when it is present at the aortic orifice. Occasionally in the carotid the second sound is distinctly audible when absent at the aortic cartilage. Indeed, according to Broadbent, it is at the carotid that we must listen for the second aortic sound, for when heard it indicates that the regurgitation is small in amount, and is consequently a very favorable prognostic element. In the femoral artery a double murmur also may be heard sometimes, as pointed out by Duroziez.

Aortic insufficiency may for years be fully compensated. Persons do not necessarily suffer any inconvenience, and the condition is often found accidentally. So long as the hypertrophy just equalizes the valvular defect there may be no symptoms and the individual may even take moderately heavy exercise without experiencing sensations of distress about the heart. The cases which last the longest are those in which the insufficiency follows endocarditis and is not a part of a general arterio-sclerosis. The age of the patient too, at the time the lesion is acquired, is a most important consideration, as in youth the heart is much more prone to take on compensatory changes. Coexistent lesions of the mitral valves tend early to disturb the compensation. It has scarcely been sufficiently recognized by the profession at large that pure aortic insufficiency is consistent with years of average health and with a tolerably active life. I know several physicians with aortic insufficiency who have been able to carry on for years large and somewhat onerous practices. One of them since the establishment of insufficiency has passed successfully through two attacks of acute rheumatism. In a large hospital practice, scarcely a month passes without the discovery of a case of aortic insufficiency in connection with some other affection.

With the onset of myocardial changes, with increasing degeneration of the arteries, particularly with a progressive sclerosis of the arch and involvement of the orifices of the coronary arteries, the compensation becomes disturbed. In advanced cases the changes about the aortic ring may be associated with alterations in the cardiac nerves and ganglia, and so introduce an important factor.

3. Aortic Stenosis.

Narrowing or stricture of the aortic orifice is not nearly so common as insufficiency. The two conditions, as already stated, may occur together, however, and probably in almost every case of stenosis there is some leakage.

Etiology and Morbid Anatomy.—In the milder grades there is adhesion between the segments, which are so stiffened that during systole they cannot be pressed back against the aortic wall. The process of cohesion between the segments may go on without great thickening, and produce a condition in which the orifice is guarded by a comparatively thin membrane, on the aortic face of which may be seen the primitive raphes separating the sinuses of Valsalva. In some instances this membrane is so thin and presents so few traces of atheromatous or sclerotic changes that the condition looks as if it had originated during fœtal life. More commonly the valve segments are thickened and rigid, and have a cartilaginous hardness. In advanced cases they may be represented by stiff, calcified masses obstructing the orifice, through which a circular or slit-like passage can be seen. The older the patient the more likely it is that the valves will be rigid and calcified.

We may speak of a relative stenosis of the aortic orifice when with normal valves and ring the aorta immediately beyond is greatly dilated. A stenosis due to involvement of the aortic ring in sclerotic and calcareous changes without lesion of the valves is referred to by some authors. I have never met with an instance of this kind. A subvalvular stenosis, the result of endocarditis in the mitro-sigmoidean sinus, usually occurs as the result of fœtal endocarditis. In comparison with aortic insufficiency, stenosis is a rare disease. It is usually met with at a more advanced period of life than insufficiency, and the most typical cases of it are found associated with extensive calcareous changes in the arterial system in old men.

When gradually produced and when there is not much insufficiency the dilatation of the left ventricle may be slight, though I think that in all cases it does occur. The walls of the ventricles become hypertrophied, and we see in this condition the most typical instances of what is called concentric hypertrophy, in which, without much, if any, enlargement of the cavity, the walls are greatly thickened, in contradistinction to the so-called eccentric hypertrophy, in which, with the increase in the thickness of the walls, the chamber itself is greatly dilated. There may be no changes in the other cardiac cavities if compensation is well maintained; but with its failure come dilatation, impeded auricular discharge, pulmonary congestion, and increased work for the right heart. The arterial changes are, as a rule, not so marked as in aortic insufficiency, for the walls have not to withstand the impulse of a greatly increased blood-wave with each systole. On the contrary, the amount of blood propelled through the narrow orifice may be smaller than normal, though when compensation is fully established the pulse-wave may be of medium volume.

Symptoms.—Physical Signs.—*Inspection* may fail to reveal any area of cardiac impulse. Particularly is this the case in old men with rigid chest walls and large emphysematous lungs. Under these circumstances there may be a high grade of hypertrophy without any visible impulse. Even when the apex beat is visible, it may be, as Traube pointed out, feeble and indefinite. In many cases the apex is seen displaced downward and outward, and the impulse looks strong and forcible.

Palpation reveals in many cases a thrill at the base of the heart of maximum force in the aortic region. With no other condition do we meet with thrills of greater intensity. The apex beat may not be palpable under the conditions above mentioned, or there may be a slow, heaving, forcible impulse.

Percussion never gives the same wide area of dulness as in aortic insufficiency. The extent of it depends largely on the state of the lungs, whether emphysematous or not.

Auscultation.—A systolic murmur of maximum intensity at the aortic cartilage, and propagated into the great vessels, is present in aortic stenosis, but is by no means pathognomonic. One of the last lessons learned by the student of physical diagnosis is to recognize the fact that this systolic murmur is only in comparatively rare cases produced by decided narrowing of the aortic orifice. Roughening of the valves, or the intima of the aorta, and hæmic states are much more frequent causes. In aortic stenosis the murmur often has a much harsher quality, is louder, and is more frequently musical than in the conditions just mentioned. When compensation fails and the ventricle is dilated and feeble, the murmur may be soft and distant. The second sound is rarely heard at the aortic cartilage, owing to the thickening and stiffness of the valve. A diastolic murmur is not uncommon, but in many cases it cannot be heard. Occasionally, as noted by W. H. Dickinson, there is a musical murmur of greatest intensity in the region of the apex, due probably to a slight regurgitation at high pressure through the mitral valves. The pulse in pure aortic stenosis is small, usually of good tension, well sustained, regular, and perhaps slower than normal.

The condition may be latent for an indefinite period, as long as the hypertrophy is maintained. Early symptoms are those due to defective blood-supply to the brain, dizziness, and fainting. Palpitation, pain about the heart, and anginal symptoms are not so marked as in insufficiency. With degeneration of the heart-muscle and dilatation relative insufficiency of the mitral valve is established, and the patient may present all the features of engorgement in the lesser and systemic circulations, with dyspnœa, cough, rusty expectoration, and the signs of anasarca in the lower part of the body. Many of the cases in old people, without presenting any dropsy, have symptoms pointing rather to general arterial disease. Cheyne-Stokes breathing is not uncommon with or without signs of uræmia.

Diagnosis.—With an extremely rough or musical murmur of maximum intensity at the aortic region and signs of hypertrophy of the left ventricle, a thrill, and especially a hard, slow pulse of moderate volume and fairly good tension, which in sphygmographic tracing gives a curve of slow rise, a broad well-sustained summit and slow decline, a diagnosis of aortic stenosis can be made with some degree of probability, particularly, if the subject is an old man. Mistakes are common, however, and a roughened or calcified valve segment, or, in some instances, a very roughened and prominent calcified plate in the aorta, and hypertrophy associated with renal disease, may produce similar symptoms.

Let me repeat that a murmur of maximum intensity at the aortic cartilage is of no importance in itself as a diagnostic sign of stenosis. Roughening of the valve, sclerosis of the intima of the arch, and anæmia are conditions more frequently associated with a systolic murmur in this region. Seldom is there difficulty in distinguishing the murmur due to anæmia, since it is rarely so intense and is not associated with thrill or with marked hypertrophy of the left ventricle. In aortic insufficiency a systolic murmur is usually present, but has neither the intensity nor the musical quality, nor is it accompanied with a thrill. With roughening and dilatation of the ascending aorta the murmur may be very harsh or musical; but the existence of a second sound, accentuated and ringing in quality, is usually sufficient to differentiate this condition.

4. Mitral Incompetency.

Etiology.—Insufficiency of the mitral valve results from: (a) Changes in the segments whereby they are contracted and shortened, usually combined with changes in the chordæ tendineæ, or with more or less narrowing of the orifice. (b) As a result of changes in the muscular walls of the ventricle, either dilatation, so that the valve segments fail to close an enlarged orifice, or changes in the muscular substance, so that the segments are imperfectly coapted during the systole—muscular incompetency. The common lesions producing insufficiency result from endocarditis, which causes a gradual thickening at the edges of the valves, contraction of the chordæ tendineæ, and union of the edges of the segments, so that in a majority of the instances there is not only insufficiency, but some grade of narrowing as well. Except in children, we rarely see the mitral leaflets curled and puckered without narrowing of the orifice. Calcareous plates at the base of the valve may prevent perfect closure of one of the segments. In long-standing cases the entire mitral structures are converted into a firm calcareous ring. From this valvular insufficiency the other condition of muscular incompetency must be carefully distinguished. It is met with in all conditions of extreme dilatation of the left ventricle, and also in weakening of the muscles in prolonged fevers and in anæmia.

Morbid Anatomy.—The effects of incompetency of the mitral segment upon the heart and circulation are as follows: (*a*) The imperfect closure allows a certain amount of blood to regurgitate from the ventricle into the auricle, so that at the end of auricular diastole this chamber contains not only the blood which it has received from the lungs, but also that which has regurgitated from the left ventricle. This necessitates dilatation, and, as increased work is thrown upon it in expelling the augmented contents, hypertrophy as well.

(*b*) With each systole of the left auricle a larger volume of blood is forced into the left ventricle, which also dilates and subsequently becomes hypertrophied.

(*c*) During the diastole of the left auricle, as blood is regurgitated into it from the left ventricle, the pulmonary veins are less readily emptied. In consequence the right ventricle expels its contents less freely, and in turn becomes dilated and hypertrophied.

(*d*) Finally, the right auricle also is involved, its chamber is enlarged, and its walls are increased in thickness.

(*e*) The effect upon the pulmonary vessels is to produce dilatation both of the arteries and veins—often in long-standing cases, atheromatous changes; the capillaries are distended, and ultimately the condition of brown induration is produced. Perfect compensation may be effected, chiefly through the hypertrophy of both ventricles, and the effect upon the peripheral circulation may not be manifested for years, as a normal volume of blood is discharged from the left heart at each systole. The time comes, however, when, owing either to increase in the grade of the incompetency or to failure of the compensation, the left ventricle is unable to send out its normal volume into the aorta. Then there is overfilling of the left auricle, engorgement in the lesser circulation, embarrassed action of the right heart, and congestion in the systemic veins. For years this somewhat congested condition may be limited to the lesser circulation, but finally the right auricle becomes dilated, the tricuspid valves incompetent, and the systemic veins are engorged. This gradually leads to the condition of cyanotic induration in the viscera and, when extreme, to dropsical effusion.

Muscular incompetency, due to impaired nutrition of the mitral and papillary muscles, is rarely followed by such perfect compensation. There may be in acute destruction of the aortic segments an acute dilatation of the left ventricle with relative incompetency of the mitral segments, great dilatation of the left auricle, and intense engorgement of the lungs, under which circumstances profuse hæmorrhage may result. In these cases there is little chance for the establishment of compensation. In cases of hypertrophy and dilatation of the heart, without valvular lesions, but associated with heavy work and alcohol, the insufficiency of the mitral valve may be extreme and lead to great pulmonary congestion, engorgement of the systemic veins, and a condition of cardiac dropsy, which cannot be distinguished by any feature from that of mitral incompetency due to lesion of the valve itself. In chronic Bright's disease the hypertrophy of the left ventricle may gradually fail, leading, in the later stages, to relative insufficiency of the mitral valve, and the production of a condition of pulmonary and systemic congestion, similar to that induced by the most extreme grade of lesion of the valve itself. Adherent pericardium, especially in children, may lead to like results.

Symptoms.—During the development of the lesion, unless the incompetency comes on acutely in consequence of rupture of the valve segment or of ulceration, the compensatory changes go hand in hand with the defect, and there are no subjective symptoms. So, also, in the stage of perfect compensation, there may be the most extreme grade of mitral insufficiency with enormous hypertrophy of the heart, yet the patient may not be aware of the existence of heart trouble, and may suffer no inconvenience except perhaps a little shortness of breath on exertion or on going upstairs. It is only when from any cause the compensation has not been perfectly effected, or, having been so, is broken abruptly or gradually, that the patients begin to be troubled. The symptoms may be divided into two groups:

(*a*) The minor manifestations while compensation is still good. Patients with extreme incompetency often have a congested appearance of the face, the lips and ears have a bluish tint, and the venules on the cheeks may be enlarged, which in many cases is very suggestive. In long-standing cases, particularly in children, the fingers may be clubbed, and there is shortness of breath on exertion. This is one of the most constant features in mitral insufficiency, and may exist for years, even when the compensation is perfect. Owing to the somewhat congested condition of the lungs these patients have a tendency to attacks of bronchitis or hæmoptysis. There may also be palpitation of the heart. As a rule, however, in well-balanced lesions in adults, this period of full compensation or latent stage is not associated with symptoms which call the attention to an affection of the heart, and with care the patient may reach old age in comparative comfort without being compelled to curtail seriously his pleasures or his work.

(*b*) Sooner or later comes a period of disturbed or broken compensation, in which the most intense symptoms are those of venous engorgement. There are palpitation, weak, irregular action of the heart, and signs of dilatation. Dyspnœa is an especial feature, and there may be cough. A distressing symptom is the cardiac "sleep-start," in which, just as the patient falls asleep, he wakes gasping and feeling as if the heart was stopping. There is usually a slight cyanosis, and even a jaundiced tint to the skin. The most marked symptoms, however, are those of venous stasis. The

45

overfilling of the pulmonary vessels accounts in part for the dyspnœa. There is cough, often with bloody or watery expectoration, and the alveolar epithelium containing brown pigment-grains is abundant. Dropsical effusion usually sets in, beginning in the feet and extending to the body and the serous sacs. The liver is enlarged, and there are signs of portal congestion, gastric irritation, and catarrh of the stomach and intestines. The urine is usually scanty and albuminous, and contains tube-casts and sometimes blood-corpuscles. With judicious treatment the compensation may be restored and all the serious symptoms may pass away. Patients usually have recurring attacks of this kind, and die of a general dropsy; or there is progressive dilatation of the heart, and death from asystole. Sudden death in these cases is rare.

Physical Signs.—*Inspection.*—In children the præcordia may bulge and there may be a large area of visible pulsation. The apex beat is to the left of the nipple, in some cases in the sixth interspace, in the anterior axillary line. There may be a wavy impulse in the cervical veins which are often full, particularly when the patient is recumbent.

Palpation.—A thrill is rare; when present it is felt at the apex, often in a limited area. The force of the impulse may depend largely upon the stage in which the case is examined. In full compensation it is forcible and heaving; when the compensation is disturbed, usually wavy and feeble.

Percussion.—The dulness is increased, particularly in a lateral direction. There is no disease of the valves which produces, in long-standing cases, a more extensive transverse area of heart dulness. It does not extend so much upward along the left margin of the sternum as beyond the right margin and to the left of the nipple line.

Auscultation.—At the apex there is a systolic murmur which wholly or partly obliterates the first sound. It is loudest here, and has a blowing, sometimes musical character, particularly toward the latter part. The murmur is transmitted to the axilla and may be heard at the back, in some instances over the entire chest. There are cases in which, as pointed out by Naunyn, the murmur is heard best along the left border of the sternum. Usually in diastole at the apex the loudly transmitted second sound may be heard. Occasionally there is also a soft, sometimes a rough or rumbling presystolic murmur. As a rule, in cases of extreme mitral insufficiency from valvular lesion with great hypertrophy of both ventricles, there is heard only a loud blowing murmur during systole. A murmur of mitral insufficiency may vary a great deal according to the position of the patient. It may be present in the recumbent and absent in the erect posture. In cases of dilatation, particularly when dropsy is present, there may be heard at the ensiform cartilage and in the lower sternal region a soft systolic murmur due to tricuspid regurgitation. An important sign on auscultation is the accentuated pulmonary second sound. This is heard to the left of the sternum in the second interspace, or over the third left costal cartilage.

The pulse in mitral insufficiency, during the period of full compensation, may be full and regular, often of low tension. Usually with the first onset of the symptoms the pulse becomes irregular, a feature which then dominates the case throughout. There may be no two beats of equal force or volume. Often after the disappearance of the symptoms of failure of compensation the irregularity of the pulse persists.

The three important physical signs then of mitral regurgitation are: (a) Systolic murmur of maximum intensity at the apex, which is propagated to the axilla and heard at the angle of the scapula; (b) accentuation of the pulmonary second sound; (c) evidence of enlargement of the heart, particularly the increase in the transverse diameter, due to hypertrophy of both right and left ventricles.

Diagnosis.—There is rarely any difficulty in the diagnosis of mitral insufficiency. The physical signs just referred to are quite characteristic and distinctive. Two points are to be borne in mind. First, a murmur, systolic in character, and of maximum intensity at the apex, and propagated even to the axilla, does not necessarily indicate incompetency of the mitral valve. There is heard in this region a large group of what are termed accidental murmurs, the precise nature of which is still doubtful. They are probably formed, however, in the ventricle, and are not associated with hypertrophy, or accentuation of pulmonary second sound.

Second, it is not always possible to say whether the insufficiency is due to lesion of the valve segment or to dilatation of the mitral ring and relative incompetency. Here neither the character of the murmur, the propagation, the accentuation of the pulmonary second sound, nor the hypertrophy assists in the differentiation. The history is sometimes of greater value in this matter than the physical examination. The cases most likely to lead to error are those of the so-called idiopathic dilatation and hypertrophy of the heart (in which the systolic murmur may be of the greatest intensity), and the instances of arterio-sclerosis with dilated heart. Balfour and others, however, maintain that organic disease of the mitral leaflets sufficient to produce incompetency is always accompanied with a certain degree of narrowing of the orifice, so that the only unequivocal proof of the actual disease of the mitral valve is the presence of a presystolic murmur.

5. MITRAL STENOSIS.

Etiology.—Narrowing of the mitral orifice is usually the result of valvular endocarditis occurring in the earlier years of life; very rarely it is congenital. It is very much more common in women than in men—in 63 of 80 cases noted by Duckworth, while in 4,791 autopsies at Guy's Hospital during ten years there were 196 cases, of which 107 were females and 89 males (Samways). This is not easy to explain, but there are at least two factors to be considered. Rheumatism prevails more in girls than in boys and, as is well known, endocarditis of the mitral valve is more common in rheumatism. Chorea, also, as suggested by Barlow, has an important influence, occurring more frequently in girls and being often associated with endocarditis. Of 140 cases of chorea which I examined at a period more than two years subsequent to the attack, 72 had signs of organic heart-disease, among which were 24 instances with the physical signs of mitral stenosis. Anæmia and chlorosis, which are prevalent in girls, have been regarded as possible factors. In a surprising number of cases no recognizable etiological factor can be discovered. This has been regarded by some writers as favoring the view that many cases are of congenital origin; but it is not improbable that with any of the febrile affections of childhood endocarditis may be associated. Whooping-cough, too, with its terrible strain on the heart-valves, may be accountable for certain cases. Congenital affections of the mitral valve are notoriously rare. While met with at all ages, stenosis is certainly more frequent in young persons.

Morbid Anatomy.—In a majority of instances with the stenosis there is some incompetency; indeed, Balfour maintains that we never find mitral stenosis without some degree of regurgitation. The narrowing results from thickening and contraction of the tissues of the ring, of the valve segments, and of the chordæ tendineæ. The condition varies a good deal according to the amount of atheromatous change. In many cases the curtains are so welded together and the whole valvular region so thickened that the orifice is reduced to a mere chink—Corrigan's button-hole contraction. In other cases the curtains are not much thickened, but narrowing has resulted from gradual adhesion at the edges, and thickening of the chordæ tendineæ, so that from the auricle it looks cone-like—the so-called funnel-shaped variety of stenosis. The instances in which the valve segments are very slightly deformed, but in which the orifice is considerably narrowed, are regarded by some as possibly of congenital origin. Occasionally the curtains are in great part free from disease, but the narrowing results from large calcareous masses, which project into them from the ring. The involvement of the chordæ tendineæ is usually extreme, and the papillary muscles may be inserted directly upon the valve. In moderate grades of constriction the orifice will admit the tip of the index-finger; in more extreme forms, the tip of the little finger; and occasionally one meets with a specimen in which the orifice seems almost obliterated, as in a case which came under my notice, which only admitted a medium-sized Bowman's probe.

The heart in mitral stenosis is not greatly enlarged, rarely weighing more than 14 or 15 ounces. Occasionally, in an elderly person, it may seem only slightly, if at all, enlarged, and again there are instances in which the weight may reach as much as 20 ounces. The left ventricle is usually small, and may look very small in comparison with the right ventricle, which forms the greater portion of the apex. In cases in which with the narrowing there is very considerable incompetency the left ventricle may be moderately dilated and hypertrophied.

These changes gradually induced are associated with secondary alterations of great importance in the heart. The left auricle discharges its blood with greater difficulty and in consequence dilates, and its walls reach three or four times their normal thickness. Although the auricle is by structure unfitted to compensate an extreme lesion, the probability is that for some time during the gradual production of stenosis, the increasing muscular power of the walls is sufficient to counterbalance the defect. Samways found in 36 cases of well-marked stenosis the auricle hypertrophied in 26, dilatation coexisting in 14. Eventually the tension is increased in the pulmonary circulation, owing to impeded outflow from the veins. To over-come this the right ventricle undergoes dilatation and hypertrophy, and upon this chamber falls the work of equalizing the circulation. Relative incompetency of the tricuspid and congestion of the systemic veins at last supervene.

It is not uncommon at the examination to find white thrombi in the appendix of the left auricle. Occasionally a large part of the auricle is occupied by an ante-mortem thrombus. Still more rarely the remarkable ball thrombus is found, in which a globular concretion, varying in size from a walnut to a small egg, lies free in the auricle, two examples of which have come under my observation.

Symptoms.—Physical Signs.—*Inspection.*—In children the lower sternum and the fifth and sixth left costal cartilages are often prominent, owing to hypertrophy of the right ventricle. The apex beat may be ill-defined. Usually, it is not dislocated far beyond the nipple line, and the chief impulse is over the lower sternum and adjacent costal cartilages. Often in thin-chested persons there is pulsation in the third and fourth left interspaces close to the sternum. When compensation fails, the præcordial impulse is much feebler, and in the veins of the neck there may be marked systolic regurgitation.

Palpation reveals in a majority of the cases a characteristic, well-defined fremitus or thrill, which is best felt, as a rule, in the fourth or fifth inter-space within the nipple line. It is of a rough, grating quality, often pecul-iarly limited in area, most marked during expiration, and can be felt to terminate in a sharp, sudden shock, synchronous with the impulse. This most characteristic of physical signs is pathognomonic of narrowing of the mitral orifice, and is perhaps the only instance in which the diagnosis of a valvular lesion can be made by palpation alone. The cardiac impulse is felt most forcibly in the lower sternum and in the fourth and fifth left in-terspaces. The impulse is felt very high in the third and fourth interspaces, or in rare cases even in the second, and it has been thought that in the latter interspace the impulse is due to pulsation of the auricle. It is always the impulse of the conus arteriosus of the right ventricle; even in the most extreme grades of mitral stenosis, there is never such tilting forward of the auricle or its appendix as would enable it to produce an impression on the chest wall.

Percussion gives an increase in the cardiac dulness to the right of the sternum and along the left margin; not usually a great increase beyond the nipple line, except in extreme cases, when the transverse dulness may reach from 5 cm. beyond the right margin of the sternum to 10 cm. beyond the nipple line.

Auscultation.—In the mitral area, usually to the inner side of the apex beat and often in a very limited region, is heard a rough, vibratory or purr-ing murmur, which terminates abruptly in the first sound. By combining palpation and auscultation the purring murmur is found to be synchro-nous with the thrill and the loud shock with the first sound. This is the presystolic murmur, about the time and mode of production of which so much discussion has occurred. I hold with those who regard it as occurring during the auricular systole. In whatever way produced, it remains one of the most distinctive and characteristic of murmurs and its presence is positively indicative of narrowing of the mitral orifice. The sole exception to this statement is the Flint murmur already referred to in aortic incompetency. Once, in a case of enormous enlargement of the spleen, with dropsy, in which the heart was greatly pushed up, I heard a presystolic murmur of rough quality, and the mitral valves were found post mortem to be normal. The presystolic murmur may occupy the entire period of the diastole, or the middle or only the latter half, corresponding to the auricular systole. The difference may sometimes be noted between the first and second portions of the murmur, when it occupies the entire time. Often there is a peculiar rumbling or echoing quality, which in some instances is very limited and may be heard only over a single bell-space of the stethoscope. A systolic murmur may be heard at the apex or along the left sternal border, often of extreme softness and audible only when the breath is held. Sometimes the systolic murmur is loud and distinct and is transmitted to the axilla. The second sound in the second left interspace is loudly accentuated, sometimes reduplicated. It may be transmitted far to the left and be heard with great clearness beyond the apex. In uncomplicated cases of mitral stenosis there are usually no murmurs audible at the aortic region, at which spot the second sound is less intense than at the pulmonary area. In the lower sternum and to the right a tricuspid murmur is sometimes heard in advanced cases. Other points to be noted are the following: The unusually sharp, clear first sound which follows the presystolic murmur, the cause of which is by no means easy to explain. It can scarcely be a valvular sound produced chiefly at the mitral orifice, since it may be heard with great intensity in cases in which the valves are rigid and calcified. It has been suggested by A. E. Sansom and others that it is a loud "snap" of the tricuspid valves caused by the powerful contraction of the greatly hypertrophied right ventricle. Broadbent's explanation is as follows: "Owing to the narrowing of the mitral orifice there is not time in the diastolic interval for a sufficient amount of blood to flow into the left ventricle to completely fill it. At the commencement of systole, therefore, the ventricular cavity is not fully distended with blood, so that the muscular walls at the first moment of their contraction meet with no resistance; then closing down rapidly, they are suddenly brought up and made tense as they encounter the contained blood. This sudden tension and abbreviated systole may thus account for the short first sound." The valvular sound may be audible at a distance, as one sits at the bedside of the patient (Graves).

These physical signs, it is to be borne in mind, are characteristic only of the stage in which compensation is maintained. Finally there comes a period in which, with rupture of compensation, the presystolic murmur disappears and there is heard in the apex region a sharp first sound, or sometimes a gallop rhythm. The marked systolic shock may be present after the disappearance of the thrill and the characteristic murmur. Under treatment, with gradual recovery of compensation, probably with increasing vigor of contraction of the right ventricle and left auricle, the presystolic murmur reappears. In cases seen at this stage of the disease the nature of the valve lesion may be entirely overlooked.

Stenosis of the mitral valve may for years be efficiently compensated by the hypertrophy of the right ventricle. Many persons with the characteristic physical signs of this lesion present no symptoms. They may for years perhaps be short of breath on going upstairs, but are able to pass through the ordinary duties of life without discomfort. The pulse is smaller in volume than normal, but may be perfectly regular. A special danger of this stage is the recurring endocarditis. Vegetations may be whipped off into the circulation and, blocking a cerebral vessel, may cause hemiplegia or aphasia, or both. This, unfortunately, is not an uncommon sequence in women. Patients with mitral stenosis may survive this accident for an indefinite period. A woman, above seventy years of age, died in one of my wards at the Philadelphia Hospital, who had been in the almshouse, hemiplegic, for more than thirty years. The heart presented an extreme grade of mitral stenosis which had probably existed at the time of the hemiplegic attack.

Pressure of the enlarged auricle on the left recurrent laryngeal nerve, causing paralysis of the vocal cord on the corresponding side, has been described by Ortner and by Herrick. I have met with two instances. It is a point to be borne in mind, as the diagnosis of aneurism of the arch of the aorta may be made.

Failure of compensation brings in its train the group of symptoms which have been discussed under mitral insufficiency. Briefly enumerated they are: Rapid and irregular action of the heart, shortness of breath, cough, signs of pulmonary engorgement, and very frequently hæmoptysis. Attacks of this kind may recur for years. Bronchitis or a febrile attack may cause shortness of breath or slight blueness. Inflammatory affections of the lungs or pleura seriously disturb the right heart, and these patients stand pneumonia very badly. Many, perhaps a majority of cases of mitral stenosis, do not have dropsy. The liver may be greatly enlarged, and in the late stages ascites is not uncommon, particularly in children. General anasarca is most frequently met with in those cases in which there is secondary narrowing of the tricuspid orifice (Broadbent).

6. Tricuspid Valve Disease.

(a) **Tricuspid Regurgitation.**—Occasionally this results from acute or chronic endocarditis with puckering; more commonly the condition is one of relative insufficiency, and is secondary to lesions of the valves on the left side, particularly of the mitral. It is met with also in all conditions of the lungs which cause obstruction to the circulation, such as cirrhosis and emphysema, particularly in combination with chronic bronchitis. The symptoms are those of obstruction in the lesser circulation with venous congestion in the systemic veins, such as has already been described in connection with mitral insufficiency. The signs of this condition are:

(1) Systolic regurgitation of the blood into the right auricle and the transmission of the pulse-wave into the veins of the neck. If the regurgi-

tation is slight or the contraction of the ventricle is feeble there may be no venous throbbing, but in other cases there is marked systolic pulsation in the cervical veins. That in the right jugular is more forcible than that in the left. It may be seen both in the internal and the external vein, particularly in the latter. Marked pulsation in these veins occurs only when the valves guarding them become incompetent. Slight oscillations are by no means uncommon, even when the valves are intact. The distention is sometimes enormous, particularly in the act of coughing, when the right jugular at the root of the neck may stand out, forming an extraordinary prominent ovoid mass. Occasionally the regurgitant pulse-wave may be widely transmitted and be seen in the subclavian and axillary veins, and even in the subcutaneous veins over the shoulder, or, as in a case recently under observation, in the superficial mammary veins.

Regurgitant pulsation through the tricuspid orifice may be transmitted to the inferior cava, and so to the hepatic veins, causing a systolic distention of the liver. This is best appreciated by bimanual palpation, placing one hand over the fifth and sixth costal cartilages and the other in the lateral region of the liver in the mid-axillary line. The rhythmical expansile pulsation may be readily distinguished, as a rule, from the systolic depression of the liver due to communicated pulsation from the left ventricle.

(2) The second important sign of tricuspid regurgitation is the occurrence of a systolic murmur of maximum intensity in the lower sternum. It is usually a soft, low murmur, often to be distinguished from a coexisting mitral murmur by differences in quality and pitch, and may be heard to the right as far as the axilla. Sometimes it is very limited in its distribution.

Together these two signs positively indicate tricuspid regurgitation. In addition, the percussion usually shows increase in the area of dulness to the right of the sternum, and the impulse in the lower sternal region is forcible. In the great majority of cases the symptoms are those of the associated lesions. In cirrhosis of the lung and in chronic emphysema the failure of compensation of the right ventricle with insufficiency of the tricuspid not infrequently leads either to acute asystole or to gradual failure with cardiac dropsy.

(b) **Tricuspid Stenosis.**—This interesting condition may be either congenital or acquired. The congenital cases are not uncommon, and are associated usually with other valvular defects which cause early death. The acquired form is not very infrequent. Bedford Fenwick collected 46 observations, of which 41 were in women. Leudet * has analyzed 117 cases. Of 101 of these in which the ages were mentioned, 80 were in women and 21 in men. A great majority of the cases were in adults, only 8 being between the ages of ten and twenty. Its rarity as an isolated condition may be gathered from the fact that of 114 autopsies, in 11 only was the lesion confined to this valve. In 21 the tricuspid, mitral, and aortic seg-

---

* Paris Thesis, 1888.

ments were involved, and in 78 the tricuspid and mitral. Practically the condition is almost always secondary to lesions of the left heart.

The physical signs are sometimes characteristic. For instance, a pre-systolic thrill has been noted by several observers. The percussion shows dulness to be increased, particularly to the right of the sternum. On auscultation a presystolic murmur has been determined in certain cases, and is heard best at the root of the ensiform cartilage, or a little to the right of it. Of general symptoms, cyanosis of the face and lips is very common, and in the late stages, when dropsy supervenes, it is apt to be intense. The lesion is interesting chiefly because it forms one of the most serious complications of mitral stenosis.

7. Pulmonary Valve Disease.

Murmurs in the region of the pulmonary valves are extremely common; lesions of the valves are exceedingly rare. Balfour has well called the pulmonic area the region of romance. A systolic murmur is heard here under many conditions—(1) very often in health, in thin-chested persons, particularly in children, during expiration and in the recumbent posture; (2) when the heart is acting rapidly, as in fever and after exertion; (3) it is a favorite situation of the cardio-respiratory murmur; (4) in anæmic states; and (5) as mentioned previously, the systolic murmur of mitral insufficiency may be transmitted along the left sternal margin. Actual lesions of the valves of the pulmonary artery are rare.

(a) *Stenosis* is almost invariably a congenital anomaly. It constitutes one of the most important of the congenital cardiac affections. The valve segments are usually united, leaving a small, narrow orifice. In the adult cases occasionally occur. In Case 608 of my post-mortem records there was extreme stenosis in a girl of eighteen, owing to great thickening and adhesion of the segments, and there were also numerous vegetations. The orifice was only 2 mm. in diameter. The congenital lesion is commonly associated with patency of the ductus Botalii and imperfection of the ventricular septum. There may also be tricuspid stenosis.

The physical signs are extremely uncertain. There may be a systolic murmur with a thrill heard best to the left of the sternum in the second intercostal space. This murmur may be very like a murmur of aortic stenosis, but is not transmitted into the vessels. Naturally the pulmonary second sound is weak or obliterated, or may be replaced by a diastolic murmur. Usually there is hypertrophy of the right heart.

(b) *Pulmonary Insufficiency.*—This rare affection is occasionally due to congenital malformation, particularly fusion of two of the segments. It is sometimes present, as Bramwell has shown, in cases of malignant endocarditis. Barie has collected 58 cases.

The physical signs are those of regurgitation into the right ventricle, but, as a rule, it is difficult to differentiate the murmur from that of aortic insufficiency, though the maximum intensity may be in the pulmonary area. The absence of the vascular features of aortic insufficiency is suggestive. Both Gibson and Graham Steell have called attention to the possibility of leakage through these valves in cases of great increase of pressure in the pulmonary artery, and to a soft diastolic murmur heard under these circumstances, which Steell calls " the murmur of high pressure in the pulmonary artery."

8. Combined Valvular Lesions.

These are extremely common. The mitral and aortic segments may be affected together; next in frequency comes the combination of mitral and tricuspid lesions; and then of aortic, mitral, and tricuspid. Aortic insufficiency or aortic stenosis is more frequently combined with mitral incompetency than aortic stenosis with mitral stenosis, or mitral stenosis with aortic insufficiency. In children the most common combination is aortic and mitral insufficiency. In adults, mitral insufficiency with thickening of the aortic valves and slight narrowing is perhaps the most common.

The diagnosis rests upon the character of the murmurs and the state of the chambers as regards hypertrophy and dilatation.

Prognosis in Valvular Disease.—The question is entirely one of efficient compensation. So long as this is maintained the patient may suffer no inconvenience, and even with the most serious forms of valve lesion the function of the heart may be little, if at all, disturbed.

Practitioners who are not adepts in auscultation and feel unable to estimate the value of the various heart murmurs should remember that the best judgment of the conditions may be gathered from inspection and palpation. With an apex beat in the normal situation and regular in rhythm the auscultatory phenomena may be practically disregarded.

As Sir Andrew Clark states, a murmur *per se* is of little or no moment in determining the prognosis in any given case. There is a large group of patients who present no other symptoms than a systolic murmur heard over the body of the heart, or over the apex, in whom the left ventricle is not hypertrophied, the heart rhythm is normal, and who may not have had rheumatism. Indeed, the condition is accidentally discovered, often during examination for life insurance. I know cases of this kind which have persisted unchanged for more than fifteen years. Among the conditions influencing prognosis are:

(*a*) *Age.*—Children under ten are bad subjects. Compensation is well effected, and they are free from many of the influences which disturb compensation in adults. The coronary arteries are healthy, and nutrition of the heart-muscle can be readily maintained. Yet, in spite of this, the outlook in cardiac lesions developing in very young children is usually bad. One reason is that the valve lesion itself is apt to be rapidly progressive, and the limit of cardiac reserve force is in such cases early reached. There seems to be proportionately a greater degree of hypertrophy and dilatation. Among other causes of the risks of this period are to be mentioned insufficient food in the poorer classes, the recurrence of rheumatic attacks, and the existence of pericardial adhesions. The outlook in a child who can be carefully supervised and prevented from damaging himself by overexertion is naturally better than in one who is constantly overtasking his muscles.

The valvular lesions which develop at, or subsequent to, the period of puberty are more likely to be permanently and efficiently compensated. Sudden death from heart-disease is very rare in children.

(b) *Sex.*—Women bear valve lesions, as a rule, better than men, owing partly to the fact that they live quieter lives, partly to the less common involvement of the coronary arteries, and to the greater frequency of mitral lesions. Pregnancy and parturition are disturbing factors, but are, I think, less serious than some writers would have us believe.

(c) *Valve affected.*—The relative prognosis of the different valve lesions is very difficult to estimate. Each case must, therefore, be judged on its own merits. Aortic insufficiency is unquestionably the most serious; yet for years it may be perfectly compensated. Favorable circumstances in any case are the moderate grade of hypertrophy and dilatation, the absence of all symptoms of cardiac distress, and the absence of extensive arterio-sclerosis and of angina. The prognosis rests in reality with the condition of the coronary arteries. Rheumatic lesions of the valves, inducing insufficiency, are less apt to be associated with endarteritis at the root of the aorta; and in such cases the coronary arteries may escape for years. I know a physician, now about forty-three years of age, who, when sixteen, had his first attack of rheumatism, which involved the aortic segments. He has had two subsequent attacks of rheumatism, but with care has been able to live a comfortable and fairly active life. On the other hand, when the aortic insufficiency is only a part of an extensive arterio-sclerosis at the root of the aorta, the coronary arteries are almost invariably involved, and the outlook in such cases is much more serious. Sudden death is not uncommon, either from acute dilatation during some exertion, or, more frequently, from blocking of one of the branches of the coronary arteries. The liability of this form to be associated with angina pectoris also adds to its severity. Aortic stenosis is a comparatively rare lesion, most commonly met with in middle-aged or elderly men, and is, as a rule, well compensated. In Broadbent's series of cases, in which autopsy showed definite aortic narrowing, forty years was the average age at death, and the oldest was but fifty-three.

In mitral lesions the outlook on the whole is much more favorable than in aortic insufficiency. Mitral insufficiency, when well compensated, carries with it a better prognosis than mitral stenosis. Practically it is the only valvular disease we meet with in patients over threescore years. It must be borne in mind that the cases which last the longest are those in which the valve orifice is more or less narrowed, as well as incompetent. There is, in reality, no valve lesion so poorly compensated and so rapidly fatal as that in which the mitral segments are gradually curled and puckered until they form a narrow strip around a wide mitral ring—a condition specially seen in children. There are many cases of mitral insufficiency in which the defect is thoroughly balanced for thirty or even forty years, without distress or inconvenience. Even with great hypertrophy and the apex beat almost in the mid-axillary line, there may be little or no distress, and the compensation may be most effective. Women may pass safely through repeated pregnancies, though here they are liable to accidents associated with the severe strain. I have had under my care for many years a patient who had her first attack of rheumatism at the age of fifteen, when she already had a well-marked mitral murmur. She first came under my observation, twenty-four years ago, with signs of hypertrophy of the left ventricle and a loud systolic murmur. She has had no cardiac disturbance whatever, though she has lived a very active life, has been unusually vigorous, has borne eleven children, and has passed through three subsequent attacks of rheumatism.

In mitral stenosis the prognosis is usually regarded as less favorable. My own experience has led me, however, to place this lesion almost on a level, particularly in women, with the mitral insufficiency. It is found very often in persons in perfect health, who have had neither palpitation nor signs of heart-failure, and who have lived laborious lives. The figures given, too, by Broadbent indicate that the date of death in mitral stenosis is comparatively advanced. Of 53 cases abstracted from the post-mortem records of St. Mary's Hospital, thirty-three was the age for males, and thirty-seven or thirty-eight for females. These women, too, pass through repeated pregnancies with safety. There are of course those too common accidents, the result of cerebral embolism, which are more likely to occur in this than in other forms.

Hard and fast lines cannot be drawn in the question of prognosis in valvular disease. Every case must be judged separately, and all the circumstances carefully balanced. There is no question which requires greater experience and more mature judgment, and even the most experienced are sometimes at fault.

The following brief summary of the conditions which justify a favorable prognosis embodies the large and varied clinical experience of Sir Andrew Clark: Good general health; just habits of living; no exceptional liability to rheumatic or catarrhal affections; origin of the valvular lesion independently of degeneration; existence of the valvular lesion without change for over three years; sound ventricles, of moderate frequency and general regularity of action; sound arteries, with a normal amount of blood and tension in the smaller vessels; free course of blood through the cervical veins; and, lastly, freedom from pulmonary, hepatic, and renal congestion.

Treatment of Valvular Lesions.—For this purpose the valvular lesion may be divided into the period of progressive development, with establishment and maintenance of hypertrophy, and the period of disturbed compensation.

(*a*) **Stage of Compensation.**—Medicinal treatment at this period is not necessary and is often hurtful. A very common error is to administer cardiac drugs, such as digitalis, on the discovery of a murmur or of hypertrophy. If the lesion has been found accidentally, it may be best not to tell the patient, but rather an intimate friend. Often it is necessary, however, to be perfectly frank in order that the patient may take certain preventive measures. He should lead a quiet, regulated, orderly life, free from excitement and worry, and the risk of sudden death makes it imperative that the patient suffering from aortic disease should be specially warned against overexertion and hurry. An ordinary wholesome diet in moderate quantities should be taken, tobacco should be interdicted, and stimulants not allowed. Exercise should be regulated entirely by the feelings of the patient. So long as no cardiac distress or palpitation follows, moderate exercise will prove very beneficial. The skin should be kept active by a daily bath. Hot baths should be avoided and the Turkish bath should be interdicted. In the case of full-blooded, somewhat corpulent individuals, an occasional saline purge should be taken. Patients with valvular lesions should not go into very high altitudes. The act of coition has serious risks, particularly in aortic insufficiency. Knowing that the causes which most surely and powerfully disturb the compensation are overexertion, mental worry, and malnutrition, the physician should give suitable instructions in each case. As it is always better to have the co-operation of an intelligent patient, he should, as a rule, be told of the condition, but in this matter the physician must be guided by circumstances, and there are cases in which reticence is the wiser policy.

(*b*) **Stage of Broken Compensation.**—The break may be immediate and final, as when sudden death results from acute dilatation or from blocking of a branch of the coronary artery, or it may be gradual. Among the first indications are shortness of breath on exertion or attacks of nocturnal dyspnœa. These are often associated with impaired nutrition, particularly with anæmia, and a course of iron or change of air may suffice to relieve the symptoms.

Irregularity of the action of the heart cannot always be termed an indication of failing compensation, particularly in instances of mitral disease. It has greater significance in aortic lesions. Serious failure of compensation is indicated by signs of dilatation of the heart, marked cyanosis, the gallop rhythm, or various forms of arrhythmia, with or without the existence of dropsy. Under these circumstances the following measures are to be carried out:

(1) *Rest.*—Disturbed compensation may be completely restored by rest of the body. Both in Montreal and in Philadelphia it was a favorite demonstration in practical therapeutics to show the benign influence of complete rest and quiet on the cardiac dilatation. In many cases with œdema of the ankles, moderate dilatation of the heart, and irregularity of the pulse, the rest in bed, a few doses of the compound tincture of cardamoms, and a saline purge suffice, within a week or ten days, to restore the compensation. One patient, in Ward 11 of the Montreal General Hospital, with aortic insufficiency recovered from four successive attacks of failing compensation with these measures alone.

(2) The relief of the embarrassed circulation.

(*a*) *By Venesection.*—In cases of dilatation, from whatever cause, whether in mitral or aortic lesions or distention of the right ventricle in emphysema, when signs of venous engorgement are marked and when there is orthopnœa with cyanosis, the abstraction of from 20 to 30 ounces of blood is indicated. This is the occasion in which timely venesection may save the patient's life. It is a condition in which I have had most satisfactory results from blood-letting. It is done much better early than late. I have on several occasions regretted its postponement, particularly in instances of acute dilatation and cyanosis in connection with emphysema.*

(b) *By Depletion through the Bowels.*—This is particularly valuable when dropsy is present. Of the various purges the salines are to be preferred, and may be given by Matthew Hay's method. Half an hour to an hour before breakfast from half an ounce to an ounce and a half of Epsom salts may be given in a concentrated form. This usually produces from three to five liquid evacuations. The compound jalap powder in half-drachm doses, or elaterium, may be employed for the same purpose. Even when the pulse is very feeble these hydragogue cathartics are well borne, and they deplete the portal system rapidly and efficiently.

(c) *The Use of Remedies which stimulate the Heart's Action.*—Of these, by far the most important is digitalis, which was introduced into practice by Withering. The indication for its use is dilatation; the contra-indication is a perfectly balanced compensatory hypertrophy, such as we see in all forms of valvular disease. Broken compensation, no matter what the valve lesion may be, is the signal for its use. It acts upon the heart, slowing and at the same time increasing the force of the contractions. It acts on the peripheral arteries, raising their tension, so that a steady and equable flow of blood is maintained in the capillaries, which, after all, is the prime aim and object of the circulation. The beneficial effects are best seen in cases of mitral disease with small, irregular pulse and cardiac dropsy. Its effects are not less striking in the dilatation of the left ventricle, in the failing compensation of aortic insufficiency or of arterio-sclerosis. On theoretical grounds it has been urged that its use is not so advantageous in aortic insufficiency, since it prolongs the diastole and leads to greater distention. This need not be considered, and digitalis is just as serviceable in this as in any other condition associated with progressive dilatation; larger doses are often required. It may be given as the tincture or the infusion. In cases of cardiac dropsy, from whatever cause, 15 minims of the tincture or half an ounce of the infusion may be given every three hours for two days, after which the dose may be reduced. Some prefer the tincture, others the infusion; it is a matter of indifference if the drug is good. The urine of a patient taking digitalis should be carefully estimated each day. As a rule, when its action is beneficial, there is within twenty-four hours an increase in the amount; often the flow is very great. Under its use the dyspnœa is relieved, the dropsy gradually disappears, the pulse becomes firmer, fuller in volume, and sometimes, if it has been very intermittent, regular.

Ill effects sometimes follow digitalis. There is no such thing as a cumulative action of the drug manifested by sudden symptoms. Toxic effects are seen in the production of nausea and vomiting. The pulse becomes irregular and small, and there may be two beats of the heart to one of the pulse, which, as pointed out by Broadbent, is found particularly in cases of mitral stenosis when they are under the influence of this drug.

---

* For illustrative cases from my wards see paper by H. A. Lafleur, Medical News, July, 1891.

The urine is reduced in amount. These symptoms subside on the withdrawal of the digitalis, and are rarely serious. There are patients who take digitalis uninterruptedly for years, and feel palpitation and distress if the drug is omitted. In mitral disease, even when it does good it does not always steady the pulse. There are many cases in which the irregularity is not affected by the digitalis. When the compensation has been re-established the drug may be omitted. When there is dyspnœa on exertion and cardiac distress, from 5 to 10 minims three times a day may be advantageously given for prolonged periods, but the effects should be carefully watched. In cardiac dropsy digitalis should be used at the outset with a free hand. Small doses should not be given, but from the first half-ounce doses of the infusion every three hours, or from 15 to 20 minims of the tincture. There are no substitutes for digitalis.

Of other remedies strophanthus alone is of service. Given in doses of from 5 to 8 minims of the tincture, it acts like digitalis. It certainly will sometimes steady the intermittent heart of mitral valve disease when digitalis fails to do so, but it is not to be compared with this drug when dropsy is present. Convallaria, citrate of caffeine, and *adonis vernalis* and *sparteine* are warmly recommended as substitutes for digitalis, but their inferiority is so manifest that their use is rarely indicated.

There are two valuable adjuncts in the treatment of valvular disease—iron and strychnia. When anæmia is a marked feature iron should be given in full doses. In some instances of failing compensation iron is the only medicine needed to restore the balance. Arsenic is occasionally an excellent substitute, and one or other of them should be administered in all instances of heart-trouble when pallor is present. Strychnia is a heart tonic of very great value. It may be given alone or in combination with the digitalis in 1 or 2 drop doses of the 1-per-cent solution. Alcoholic stimulants in moderation are occasionally useful, especially in tiding over a period of acute cardiac weakness.

Treatment of Special Symptoms. (*a*) *Dropsy.*—The increased arterial tension and activity of the capillary circulation under the influence of digitalis hastens the interstitial lymph flow and favors resorption of the fluid. The hydragogue cathartics, by rapidly depleting the blood, promote, too, the absorption of the fluid from the lymph spaces and the lymph sacs. These two measures usually suffice to rid the patient of the dropsy. In some cases, however, it cannot be relieved, and then Southey's tubes may be used or the legs punctured. If done with care, after a thorough washing of the parts, and if antiseptic precautions are taken, scarification is a very serviceable measure, and should be resorted to more frequently than it is. Canton flannel bandages may be applied on the œdematous legs.

(*b*) *Dyspnœa.*—The patients are usually unable to lie down. A comfortable bed-rest should therefore be provided—if possible, one with lateral projections, so that in sleeping the head can be supported as it falls over. The shortness of breath is associated with dilatation, chronic bronchitis, or hydrothorax. The chest should be carefully examined in all these cases, as hydrothorax of one side or of both is a common cause of shortness of breath. There are cases of mitral regurgitation with recurring hydrothorax as the sole dropsical symptom, which is relieved, week by week or month by month, by tapping. For the nocturnal dyspnœa, particularly when combined with restlessness, morphia is invaluable and may be given without hesitation. The value of the calming influence of opium in all conditions of cardiac insufficiency is not enough recognized. There are instances of cardiac dyspnœa unassociated with dropsy, particularly in mitral valve disease, in which nitroglycerin is of great service, if given in the 1-per-cent solution in increasing doses. It is especially serviceable in the cases in which the pulse tension is high.

(c) *Palpitation and Cardiac Distress.*—In instances of great hypertrophy and in the throbbing which is so distressing in some cases of aortic insufficiency, aconite is of service in doses of from 1 to 3 minims every two or three hours. An ice-bag over the heart or Leiter's coil is also of service in allaying the rapid action and the throbbing. For the pains, which are often so marked in aortic lesions, iodide of potassium in 10-grain doses, three times a day, or the nitroglycerin may be tried. Small blisters are sometimes advantageous. It must be remembered that an important cause of palpitation and cardiac distress is flatulent distention of the stomach or colon, against which suitable measures must be directed.

(d) *Gastric Symptoms.*—The cases of cardiac insufficiency which do badly and fail to respond to digitalis are most often those in which nausea and vomiting are prominent features. The liver is often greatly enlarged in these cases; there is more or less stasis in the hepatic vessels, and but little can be expected of drugs until the venous engorgement is relieved. If the vomiting persists, it is best to stop the food and give small bits of ice, small quantities of milk and lime water, and effervescing drinks, such as Apollinaris water and champagne. Creasote, hydrocyanic acid, and the oxalate of cerium are sometimes useful; but, as a rule, the condition is obstinate and always serious.

(e) *Cough and Hæmoptysis.*—The former is almost a necessary concomitant of cardiac insufficiency, owing to engorgement of the pulmonary vessels and more or less bronchitis. It is allayed by measures directed rather to the heart than to the lungs. Hæmoptysis in chronic valvular disease is sometimes a salutary symptom. An army surgeon, who was invalided during the late civil war on account of hæmoptysis, supposed to be due to tuberculosis, has since that time had, in association with mitral insufficiency and enlarged heart, many attacks of hæmoptysis. He assures me that his condition is invariably better after the attack. It is rarely fatal, except in some cases of acute dilatation, and seldom calls for special treatment.

(f) *Sleeplessness.*—One of the most distressing features of valvular lesions, even in the stage of compensation, is disturbed sleep. Patients may wake suddenly with throbbing of the heart, often in an attack of nightmare. Subsequently, when the compensation has failed, it is also a worrying symptom. The sleep is broken, restless, and frequently disturbed by frightful dreams. Sometimes a dose of the spirits of chloroform or of ether, with half a drachm of spirits of camphor, given in a little hot whisky, will give a quiet night. The compound spirits of ether, Hoffman's anodyne,

though very unpleasant to take, is frequently a great boon in the intermediate period when compensation has partially failed and the patients
suffer from restless and sleepless nights.   Paraldehyde and amylene hydrate
are sometimes serviceable.   Urethan, sulphonal, and chloralamide are rarely
efficacious, and it is best, after a few trials, particularly if the paraldehyde
does not answer, to resort to morphia.   It may be given in combination with
atropine.

(g) *Renal Symptoms.*—With ruptured compensation and lowering of
the tension in the aorta, the urinary secretion is greatly diminished, and
the amount may sink to 5 or 6 ounces in the day.   Digitalis, and strophanthus when efficient, usually increase the flow.   A brisk purge may be followed by augmented secretion.   The combination in pill form of digitalis,
squill, and the black oxide of mercury, will sometimes prove effective when
the infusion or tincture of digitalis alone has failed.   Calomel acts well in
some cases, given in 3-grain doses every six hours for three or four days.

The *diet* in chronic valve-diseases is often very difficult to regulate.
With the dilatation and venous engorgement come nausea and often a great
distaste for food.   The amount of liquid should be restricted, and milk,
beef-juice, or egg albumen given every three hours.   When the serious
symptoms have passed, eggs, scraped meat, fish, and fowl may be allowed.
Starchy foods, and all articles likely to cause flatulency, should be forbidden.   Stimulants are usually necessary, either whisky or brandy.

III. HYPERTROPHY AND DILATATION.

Hypertrophy is an enlargement of the heart due to an increased thickness, total or partial, in the muscular walls.   Dilatation is an increase in
size of one or more of the chambers, with or without thickening of the walls.
The conditions usually coexist, and could be more correctly described together under the term enlargement of the heart.   Simple hypertrophy, in
which the cavities remain of a normal size and the walls are increased,
occurs, but simple dilatation, in which the cavities are increased and the
walls remain of a normal diameter, probably does not, as it is always associated with thinning or with thickening of the coats.   Commonly we have
the forms of simple hypertrophy, hypertrophy with dilatation, and dilatation
with thinning of the coats.

Hypertrophy of the Heart.

There are two forms—the simple hypertrophy, in which the cavity or
cavities are of normal size; and hypertrophy with dilatation (eccentric
hypertrophy), in which the cavities are enlarged and the walls increased in
thickness.   The condition formerly spoken of as concentric hypertrophy,
in which there is diminution in the size of the cavity with thickening of
the walls, is, as a rule, a post-mortem change.

The enlargement may affect the entire organ, one side, or only one
chamber.   Naturally, as the left ventricle does the chief work in forcing

46

the blood through the systemic arteries, the change is most frequently found in it.

Etiology.—Hypertrophy of the heart follows the law governing muscles, that within certain limits, if the nutrition is kept up, increased work is followed by increased size—i. e., hypertrophy. Hypertrophy of the left ventricle alone, or with general enlargement of the heart, is brought about by—

Conditions affecting the heart itself: (1) Disease of the aortic valve; (2) mitral insufficiency; (3) pericardial adhesions; (4) sclerotic myocarditis; (5) disturbed innervation, with overaction, as in exophthalmic goitre, in long-continued nervous palpitation, and as a result of the action of certain articles, such as tea, alcohol, and tobacco. In all of these conditions the work of the heart is increased. In the case of the valve lesions the increase is due to the increased intraventricular pressure; in the case of the adherent pericardium and myocarditis, to direct interference with the symmetrical and orderly contraction of the chambers.

Conditions acting upon the blood-vessels: (1) General arterio-sclerosis, with or without renal disease; (2) all states of increased arterial tension induced by the contraction of the smaller arteries under the influence of certain toxic substances, which, as Bright suggested, "by affecting the minute capillary circulation, render greater action necessary to send the blood through the distant subdivisions of the vascular system"; (3) prolonged muscular exertion, which enormously increases the blood-pressure in the arteries; (4) narrowing of the aorta, as in the congenital stenosis.

Hypertrophy of the right ventricle is met with under the following conditions—

(1) Lesions of the mitral valve, either incompetence or stenosis, which act by increasing the resistance in the pulmonary vessels. (2) Pulmonary lesions, obliteration of any number of blood-vessels within the lungs, such as occurs in emphysema or cirrhosis, is followed by hypertrophy of the right ventricle. (3) Valvular lesions on the right side occasionally cause hypertrophy in the adult, not infrequently in the fœtus. (4) Chronic valvular disease of the left heart and pericardial adhesions are sooner or later associated with hypertrophy of the right ventricle.

In the auricles simple hypertrophy is never seen; it is always dilatation with hypertrophy. In the left auricle the condition develops in lesions at the mitral orifice, particularly stenosis. The right auricle hypertrophies when there is greatly increased blood-pressure in the lesser circulation, whether due to mitral stenosis or pulmonary lesions. Narrowing of the tricuspid orifice is a less frequent cause.

Morbid Anatomy.—The heart of an average-sized man weighs about 9 ounces (280 grammes); that of a woman, about 8 ounces (250 grammes). In case of general hypertrophy the heart may weigh from 16 to 20 ounces. Weights above 25 ounces are rare. So far as I know, the heaviest heart on record is one of 53 ounces, described by Beverly Robinson. Dulles has reported one weighing 48 ounces. The measurement of the thickness of the walls is, next to weighing, the best means of determining the hypertrophy. In extreme dilatation the walls, though actually thickened, may look thin. When *rigor mortis* is present, the cavity may be small and the walls may appear greatly thickened. The measurements should not be made until the heart has been soaked in water and thoroughly relaxed. In the left ventricle a thickness of ten lines, or from 20 to 25 mm., indicates hypertrophy. The right ventricle is thinner than the left, and has an average diameter of from 4 to 7 mm. In hypertrophy it may measure from 13 to 20 mm. The left auricle has a normal thickness of about 3 mm., which may be doubled in hypertrophy. The wall of the right auricle is thinner than that of the left, rarely exceeding 2 mm. in diameter. The appendices of the auricles often present marked increase in thickness and the musculi pectinati are greatly developed.

The shape of the heart is altered in hypertrophy; with great enlargement of the ventricles, the apex is broadened, and the conical shape is lost. In the enormous enlargement of aortic insufficiency this rotundity of the apex is very marked. When the right ventricle is chiefly affected it occupies the largest share of the apex. In mitral stenosis the contrast is very striking between the large, broad right ventricle, reaching to the apex, and the small left chamber.

The hypertrophied muscle has a deep red color, is firm, and is cut with increasing resistance. The right ventricle, as Rokitansky noted, may have a peculiar hard, leathery consistence. In simple hypertrophy of the left ventricle the papillary muscles and the columnæ carneæ may be enlarged, but the former are often much flattened in dilated hypertrophy. The muscular trabeculæ are more developed, as a rule, in the right ventricle than in the left.

The increase in size of the heart is probably due to a definite numerical increase, resulting from development of new fibres.

Symptoms.—Hypertrophy is a conservative process, secondary to some valvular or arterial lesion, and is not necessarily accompanied by symptoms. So admirable is the adjusting power of the heart that, for example, an advancing stenosis of aortic or mitral orifice may for years be perfectly equalized by a progressive hypertrophy, and the subject of the affection be happily unconscious of the existence of heart trouble. Hypertrophy is in almost all cases an unmixed good; the symptoms which arise are usually to be attributed to its failure, or, as we say, to disturbance of compensation.

Among the most common symptoms are unpleasant feelings about the heart—a sense of fulness and discomfort, rarely amounting to pain. This may be very noticeable when the patient is recumbent on the left side. Actual pain is rare, except in the irritable heart from tobacco or in neurasthenics. Palpitation may not occur, nor do patients always have sensations from the violent shocks of a greatly hypertrophied organ. There are instances in which very uneasy feelings arise from a moderately exaggerated pulsation. The general condition has much to do with this. In health we are not conscious of the heart's pulsations, but one of the first indications of exhaustion from excesses or overstudy is the consciousness of the heart's action, not necessarily with palpitation. Headaches, flushings of the face, noises in the ears, and flashes of light may be present.

Certain untoward effects of long-continued hypertrophy of the left ventricle must be mentioned, chief among which is the production of arterio-sclerosis. Particularly is this the case when the hypertrophy results from increased peripheral resistance. The heightened blood-pressure (expressed by the word strain) in the arteries gradually induces an endarteritis and a stiff, inelastic state of those vessels most exposed to it—viz., the aorta and its primary divisions. In overcoming the peripheral obstruction the hypertrophy "ruins the arteries as a sequential result" (Fothergill). Prolonged muscular exertion also acts injuriously in this way.

Another danger is rupture of the blood-vessels, particularly those of the brain. In general arterial degeneration associated with contracted kidneys and hypertrophied left heart apoplexy is common. Indeed, in the majority of cases of cerebral hæmorrhage there is sclerosis of the smaller vessels, often with the development of miliary aneurisms, and the rupture may be caused by the forcible action of the heart.

Physical Signs.—*Inspection* may show bulging of the præcordia, producing in children marked asymmetry of the chest. It may occur without pericardial adhesions, which Schroetter thinks are invariably associated with this condition. The intercostal spaces are widened, and the area of visible impulse is much increased. On *palpation* the impulse is forcible and heaving, and with each systole the hand or the ear applied over the heart may be visibly raised. A slow, heaving impulse is one of the best signs of simple hypertrophy. With large dilated hypertrophy the forcible impulse is often more sudden and abrupt. A second, weaker impulse can sometimes be felt, due perhaps to a rebound from the aortic valves (Gowers). The beat may be felt in the sixth, seventh, or eighth interspace from 1 to 3 inches outside the nipple. This downward dislocation of the apex is an important sign in hypertrophy of the left ventricle. In moderate grades, such as are seen in chronic Bright's disease, the impulse may be in the sixth interspace in the nipple line, or a little outside of it.

Percussion reveals increased dulness, which in the parasternal line may begin at the third rib or in the second interspace, and transversely may extend from half an inch to 2 inches beyond the nipple line and an equal distance beyond the middle line of the sternum. The dull area is more ovoid than in health. When carefully delimited the colossal hypertrophy of aortic valve disease may give an area of dulness from 7 to 8 inches in transverse extent. In moderate grades a transverse dulness of 4 inches is not uncommon.

On *auscultation* the sounds, when the valves are healthy, may present no special changes, but the first sound is often prolonged and dull. When there is dilatation as well, it may be very clear and sharp. Reduplication is common in the hypertrophy of renal disease. A peculiar clink—the *tintement métallique* of Bouillaud—may be heard just to the right of the apex beat. The second sound is clear and loud, sometimes ringing in character or reduplicated. With valvular lesions, the sounds, of course, are much altered, and are replaced or accompanied by murmurs.

In simple hypertrophy not dependent on valvular lesions, the pulse is usually regular, full, strong, and of high tension. It may be increased in rapidity, but is often normal. In eccentric hypertrophy the pulse is full, but softer, and usually more rapid. One of the earliest signs of failure and dilatation is irregularity and intermittence of the pulse.

Hypertrophy of the *right ventricle* in the adult very rarely follows valvular disease on the right side, but results from increased resistance in the pulmonary circulation, as in cirrhosis of the lung and emphysema, or in stenosis of the mitral orifice. With perfect compensation, which fully maintains the equilibrium of the circulation, there are no symptoms. Extra exertion, as the ascent of stairs or running, may cause shortness of breath, but in many ways hypertrophy of the right ventricle is the most enduring and salutary form in the whole cycle of cardiac affections. For long periods of years the effects of mitral stenosis may be counterbalanced, and only sudden death by accident or an acute disease reveal the existence of an unsuspected lesion. In the hypertrophy secondary to emphysema or cirrhosis of the lungs, there may be sensations of distress in the cardiac region, with cough and shortness of breath; but as long as the dilatation is moderate the symptoms are not marked. With great dilatation and tricuspid leakage come venous engorgement, œdema, and pulmonary troubles. The increased pressure in the lesser circulation leads to sclerosis of the pulmonary arteries and the constant engorgement of the capillaries leads ultimately to a deposition of pigment and increase in the fibrous elements in the lung—the brown induration. Extreme pulmonary congestion and apoplexy are more often associated with dilatation. Hæmoptysis may result from rupture of vessels during sudden exertion.

Physical Signs.—Bulging of the lower part of the sternum and left cartilages occurs. The apex beat is forced to the left, but is not so often displaced downward. The most marked impulse may be in the angle between the ensiform cartilage and the seventh rib or beneath the cartilages of the sixth and seventh ribs. The pulsation is rather diffuse, not punctate, particularly if there is much dilatation. In thin-walled chests there may be pulsation in the third and fourth right interspaces. The cardiac dulness is increased transversely and toward the right; it may extend an inch or more beyond the border of the sternum. On auscultation the first sound at the lower part of the sternum is louder and fuller than normal, but the differences are not very marked unless there is much dilatation, when the sound is clearer and sharper. Accentuation and reduplication of the second sound are heard in the pulmonary artery on account of the increased tension. The pulse at the wrist is usually small. Pulsation occurs in the jugulars when there is tricuspid incompetence.

Hypertrophy of the *auricles* always occurs with dilatation. It is more common in the left chamber, which hypertrophies in mitral stenosis and incompetency, and naturally assists in restoring the balance of the circulation. There are no distinctive physical signs, and we usually can infer its presence only by the existence of mitral stenosis and a presystolic murmur. Increased dulness may be determined to the left of the sternum, and there may be a presystolic wave in the second left interspace.

Hypertrophy and dilatation of the right auricle are met with (associated with a similar condition in the right ventricle and incompetency of the tricuspid) in emphysema, cirrhosis of the lung, chronic bronchitis, and mitral disease. In comparison with the left auricle the greater development and hypertrophy of the appendix and its musculi pectinati is very striking. The latter may be distributed over the anterior wall of the sinus to a greater extent than in health. There are increased dulness in the third and fourth interspaces, pulsation sometimes presystolic in rhythm, signs of venous engorgement, jugular pulsation, and other evidences of dilatation of the right heart.

Diagnosis.—Among conditions to be distinguished are:

(1) Neurotic palpitation, from whatever cause, even when very forcible, has not the heaving impulse of genuine hypertrophy. Enlargement of the organ may, however, follow prolonged overaction, as in the smoker's heart, the irritable heart of neurasthenics, and in exophthalmic goitre, but it is usually slight.

(2) The increased area of dulness may be due to a variety of causes, some of which may closely simulate hypertrophy, such as pericardial effusion, aneurism, mediastinal growths, or displacement of the heart from pressure, or the existence of malformation of the chest. With the exercise of ordinary care, however, the diagnosis can usually be made. There are two opposite conditions which frequently give trouble. With the left lung contracted from pleurisy, phthisis, or cirrhosis, a large surface of the heart is exposed; the pulsation may be extensive and forcible, and may at first sight suggest hypertrophy. In this condition there is dislocation upward and to the left. The existence of pulmonary or pleuritic disease and the fixation of the lung on deep inspiration will suffice to prevent mistakes. A less extensive exposure of the heart may occur without any disease in very narrow-chested persons with ill-developed lungs; here, though the area of dulness may be much increased, the normal position of the apex, the absence of forcible, heaving impulse, and of any obvious cause of hypertrophy will afford satisfactory criteria for a diagnosis. The reverse condition exists in some cases in which emphysema masks moderate cardiac hypertrophy. The area of dulness may be normal, or even diminished, and the pulse and character of the sounds will help in the diagnosis; but it is sometimes a difficult matter.

Prognosis.—The course of any case of cardiac hypertrophy may be divided into three stages:

(a) The period of development, which varies with the nature of the primary lesion. For example, in rupture of an aortic valve, during a sudden exertion, it may require months before the hypertrophy becomes fully developed; or, indeed, it may never do so, and death may follow from an uncompensated dilatation. On the other hand, in sclerotic affections of the valves, with stenosis or incompetency, the hypertrophy develops step by step with the lesion, and may continue to counterbalance the progressive and increasing impairment of the valve.

(b) The period of full compensation—the latent stage—during which the heart's vigor meets the requirements of the circulation. This period may last an indefinite time, and a patient may never be made aware by any symptoms that he has a valvular lesion.

(c) The period of broken compensation, which may come on suddenly during very severe exertion. Death may result from acute dilatation; but more commonly it takes place slowly and results from degeneration and weakening of the heart-muscle.

The breaking or rupture of cardiac compensation may be induced by many causes, among which the most important are: (1) Failure of the general nutrition. In many instances of heart-disease, exposure, poor food, and alcohol combine to bring about disturbance of a well-balanced heart lesion. Acute illnesses, particularly the fevers, may induce general debility and with it weakening of the heart-muscle. (2) Disturbance of the local nutrition of the heart, owing to gradual sclerosis of the coronary arteries, is a common cause. (3) Very severe muscular exertion, which may disturb a compensation, perfect for years, and induce death in a few days (Traube). (4) Mental emotions. Severe grief or fright may bring on failure of compensation.

The prognosis is largely, as already stated, a matter of maintained compensation. Once established, the hypertrophy rarely, if ever, disappears, inasmuch as the cause usually persists. Occasionally, perhaps, the hypertrophy associated with neurotic palpitation from tobacco, or other causes, or the hypertrophy following muscular overexertion, may disappear.

DILATATION OF THE HEART.

Two varieties are recognized, dilatation with thickening and dilatation with thinning. The former is the more common, and corresponds to the dilated or eccentric hypertrophy.

Etiology.—Two important causes combine to produce dilatation—increased pressure within the cavities and impaired resistance, due to weakening of the muscular wall—which may act singly, but are often combined. A weakened wall may yield to a normal distending force, or a normal wall may yield under a heightened blood-pressure.

(1) Heightened endocardiac pressure results either from an increased quantity of blood to be moved or an obstacle to be overcome, and is the more frequent cause. It does not necessarily bring about dilatation; simple hypertrophy may follow, as in the early period of aortic stenosis, and in the hypertrophy of the left ventricle in Bright's disease.

A majority of the important causes of increased endocardiac pressure have already been discussed under hypertrophy. One or two may be considered more in detail.

The size of the cardiac chambers varies in health. With slow action of the heart the dilatation is complete and fuller than it is with rapid action. Physiologically, the limits of dilatation are reached when the chamber does not empty itself during the systole. This may occur as an acute, transient condition in severe exertion—during, for example, the ascent of a mountain. There may be great dilatation of the right heart, as shown by the increased epigastric pulsation, and even increase in the cardiac dulness. The safety-valve action of the tricuspid valves may here come into play, relieving the lungs by permitting regurgitation into the auricle. With rest the condition is removed, but if it has been extreme, the heart may suffer a strain from which it may recover slowly, or, indeed, the individual may never be able again to undertake severe exertion. In the process of training, the getting wind, as it is called, is largely a gradual increase in the capability of the heart, particularly of the right chambers. A degree of exertion can be safely maintained in full training which would be quite impossible under other circumstances, because, by a gradual process of what we may call physical education, the heart has strengthened its reserve force—widened enormously its limits of physiological work. Endurance in prolonged contests is measured by the capabilities of the heart, and its essence consists in being able to meet the continuous tendency to overstep the limits of dilatation.

We have no positive knowledge of the nature of the changes in the heart which occur in this process, but it must be in the direction of increased muscular and nervous energy. The large heart of athletes may be due to the prolonged use of their muscles, but no man becomes a great runner or oarsman who has not naturally a capable if not a large heart. Master McGrath, the celebrated greyhound, and Eclipse, the race-horse, both famous for endurance rather than speed, had very large hearts.

Excessive dilatation during severe muscular effort results in heart-strain. A man, perhaps in poor condition, calls upon his heart for extra work during the ascent of a high mountain, and is at once seized with pain about the heart and a sense of distress in the epigastrium. He breathes rapidly for some time, is " puffed," as we say, but the symptoms pass off after a night's quiet. An attempt to repeat the exercise is followed by another attack, or, indeed, an attack of cardiac dyspnœa may come on while he is at rest. For months such a man may be unfitted for severe exertion, or he may be permanently incapacitated. In some way he has over-strained his heart and become " broken-winded." Exactly what has taken place in these hearts we cannot say, but their reserve force is lost, and with it the power of meeting the demands exacted in maintaining the circulation during severe exertion. The " heart-shock " of Latham includes cases of this nature—sudden cardiac breakdown during exertion, not due to rupture of a valve. It seems probable that sudden death in men during long-continued efforts, as in a race, is sometimes due to overdistention and paralysis of the heart.

Examples of dilatation occur in all forms of valve lesions. In aortic incompetency blood enters the left ventricle during diastole from the unguarded aorta and from the left auricle, and the quantity of blood at the termination of diastole subjects the walls to an extreme degree of pressure, under which they inevitably yield. In time they augment in thickness, and present the typical eccentric hypertrophy of this condition.

In mitral insufficiency blood which should have been driven into the aorta is forced into and dilates the auricle from which it came, and then in the diastole of the ventricle a large amount is returned from the auricle, and with increased force. In mitral stenosis the left auricle is the seat of greatly increased tension during diastole, and dilates as well as hypertrophies; the distention, too, may be enormous. Dilatation of the right ventricle is produced by a number of conditions, which were considered under hypertrophy. All circumstances, such as mitral stenosis, emphysema, etc., which permanently increase the tension of the blood in the pulmonary vessels, cause its dilatation.

(2) Impaired nutrition of the heart-walls may lead to a diminution of the resisting power so that dilatation readily occurs.

The loss of tone due to parenchymatous degeneration or myocarditis in fevers may lead to a fatal condition of acute dilatation. It is a recognized cause of death in scarlatinal dropsy (Goodhart), and may occur in rheumatic fever, typhus, typhoid, erysipelas, etc. The changes in the heart-muscle which accompany acute endocarditis or pericarditis may lead to dilatation, especially in the latter disease. In anæmia, leukæmia, and chlorosis the dilatation may be considerable. In sclerosis of the walls, the yielding is always where this process is most advanced, as at the left apex. Under any of these circumstances the walls may yield with normal blood-pressure.

Pericardial adhesions are a cause of dilatation, and we generally find in cases with extensive and firm union considerable hypertrophy and dilatation. There is usually here some impairment as well of the superficial layers of muscle.

Morbid Anatomy.—The condition usually exists with hypertrophy in two or more chambers. It is more common on the right than on the left side. The most extreme dilatation is in cases of aortic incompetency, in which all the cavities may be enormously distended. In mitral stenosis the left auricle is often trebled in capacity, and the right chambers also are very capacious. The auricles may contain from 18 to 20 ounces of blood. In chronic lesions of the lungs the right chambers are chiefly involved. In great distention of one ventricle the septum may bulge toward the other side. The auriculo-ventricular rings are often dilated, and there may be an increase in the circumference of $1\frac{1}{2}$ or even 2 inches. Thus, the tricuspid orifice, the circumference of which is about $4\frac{1}{2}$ inches, may freely admit a graduated heart-cone of above 6 inches; and the mitral orifice, which normally is about $3\frac{1}{2}$ inches, may admit the cone to $5\frac{1}{2}$ inches or even more. Great dilatation is always accompanied by relative incompetency of the valves, so that free regurgitation into the auricles is permitted. The orifices of the venæ cavæ and of the pulmonary veins may be greatly dilated.

The endocardium is often opaque, particularly that of the auricles. The muscle substance varies according to the presence or absence of degenerations. The microscope may show marked fatty or parenchymatous change, but in some instances no special alteration may be noticeable. There is much truth in Niemeyer's assertion " that it is not possible by means of the microscope to recognize all the alterations of the muscular fibrillæ which diminish the functional power of the heart." Of the changes in the ganglia of the heart we know very little. As centres of control they probably have more to do with cardiac atony and breakdown than we generally admit. Degeneration of them has been noted by Putjakin, Ott, and others.

Symptoms and Physical Signs.—Dilatation causes weakness of the cardiac walls, diminishes the vigor of their contractions, and is therefore the reverse of hypertrophy. So long as compensation is maintained the enlargement of a cavity may be considerable. The limit is reached when the hypertrophied walls in the systole can no longer expel all the contents, part of which remain, so that at each diastole the chamber is abnormally full. Thus, in aortic incompetency blood enters the left ventricle from the aorta as well as the auricle; dilatation ensues, and also hypertrophy as a direct effect of the increased pressure and increased amount of blood to be moved. But if from any cause the hypertrophy weakens and the ventricle during systole fails to empty itself completely, a still larger amount is in it at the end of each diastole, and the dilatation becomes greater. The amount remaining after systole prevents the blood from entering freely from the auricle. Incompetency of the auriculo-ventricular valves follows, with dilatation of the auricle and impeded blood-flow in the pulmonary veins. Dilatation and hypertrophy of the right heart may compensate for a time, but when this fails the venous system becomes engorged and dropsy may result. The consideration of the symptoms of chronic valvular lesions is largely that of dilatation and its effects. Acute dilatation, such as we see in fevers or in sudden failure of a hypertrophied heart, is accompanied by three chief symptoms—weak, usually rapid, impulse, dyspnœa, and signs of obstructed venous circulation. Cardiac pain may be present, but is often absent.

The *physical signs* of dilatation are those of a weak and enlarged organ. The impulse is diffuse, often undulatory, and is felt over a wide area, and an apex beat or a point of maximum intensity may not be found. When it does exist, it may be visible and yet cannot be felt—a valuable observation made by Walshe. An extensive area of impulse with a quick, weak maximum apex beat may be present. When the right heart is chiefly dilated the left may be pushed over so as to occupy a much less extensive area in front of the heart, and the true apex beat cannot be felt; but the chief impulse is just below, or to the right of, the xiphoid cartilage, and there is a wavy pulsation in the fourth, fifth, and sixth interspaces to the left of the sternum. In extreme dilatation of the right auricle a pulsation may sometimes be seen in the third right interspace close to the sternum, and with free tricuspid regurgitation this may be systolic in character. Whether the pulsation frequently seen in the second left interspace is ever due to a dilated left auricle has not been determined. I have sometimes thought it was presystolic in rhythm, though it may be distinctly systolic. Post mortem, it is rare in the most extreme distention to see the auricular appendix so far forward as to warrant the belief that it could beat against the second interspace. The area of dulness is increased, but an emphysematous lung or the fully distended organ in a state of brown induration may cover over the heart and greatly limit the extent. The directions of increase were considered in connection with hypertrophy.

The first sound is shorter, sharper, more valvular in character, and more like the second. As the dilatation becomes excessive it gets weaker. Reduplication is not common, but occasionally differences may be heard in the first sound over the right and left hearts. The sounds are frequently obscured by murmurs, which are produced by incompetency of the valves due to the great dilatation, or are associated with the chronic valve disease on which the condition depends. The aortic second sound is replaced by a murmur in aortic regurgitation. The pulmonary sound is accentuated in mitral regurgitation and pulmonary congestion, but with extreme dilatation it may be much weakened. The heart's action is irregular and intermittent, and the pulse is small, weak, and quick.

On auscultation both the sounds may be free from murmur. There is the condition known as embryocardia or fœtal heart-rhythm, in which the first and second sounds are very alike, and the long pause is shortened. In other instances there is the typical and characteristic gallop rhythm, rarely found apart from conditions of dilatation. With the various valvular lesions the corresponding murmurs may be heard. Murmurs, however, which have been present may disappear, as in the case of mitral stenosis. In other instances a loud systolic murmur may be heard at the apex, and when the case first comes under observation it may be impossible to say whether this is due to organic mitral lesion. The murmur may be confined to the apex region, or propagated well to the back. It is extremely common in the dilatation which follows the hypertrophy of the left ventricle in arterio-sclerosis. Under treatment, with the gradual disappearance of the dilatation, a murmur of this kind, even though most intense, may completely disappear, showing that it has been due to a relative insufficiency, not to a valvular lesion. All varieties of arrhythmia may occur in dilatation of the heart. The pulse, as a rule, is small, weak, quick, and often irregular.

Dilation and Hypertrophy due to Overexertion and Alcohol.—There is a group of cases of dilatation and hypertrophy dependent upon prolonged overexertion, which rarely comes under observation until compensation has failed, and which then may be very difficult to distinguish from the similar conditions produced by valvular disease. The patients are able-bodied men at the middle period of life, and complain first of palpitation or irregularity of the action of the heart and shortness of breath; subsequently the usual symptoms of cardiac insufficiency develop. On inquiring into the history of these patients none of the usual etiological factors causing valve-disease are present, but they have always been engaged in laborious occupations and have usually been in the habit of taking stimulants freely. This is the affection which has been specially studied by McLean, Clifford Allbutt, Seitz, and others, and in its earlier condition by Da Costa, in what he termed the irritable heart. It is met with very frequently in soldiers. These cases may return to hospital three or four times with cardiac insufficiency, sometimes with slight anasarca, hæmoptysis, and signs of pulmonary engorgement. The condition is by no means infrequent. Bollinger has called attention to the common occurrence of dilatation and hypertrophy in beer-drinkers, particularly in the workers in the German breweries, who drink 20 or more litres in the day. Strümpell, at his Erlangen clinic, told me that this condition was very common in the draymen and workers in the breweries of that town, very few of whom pass the forty-fifth year without indications of hypertrophy and dilatation of the heart. On post-mortem examination the valves may be quite healthy, the aorta smooth, and extensive arterio-sclerosis or renal disease absent. The heart weighs from 18 to 25 ounces; the chambers are dilated. The condition has been met with also in animals, and Houghton states that the heart of the celebrated greyhound Master McGrath weighed 9.57 ounces, just threefold in excess of the normal proportion of heart-weight to body-weight.

Idiopathic Dilatation.—And, lastly, there are other cases in which dilatation of the heart occurs without discoverable cause. In some instances there has been a history of sudden exercise or of mental emotion, but in other cases the condition seems to have come on spontaneously. In some it is acute and the patient has dyspnœa, slight cyanosis, cough, and great cardiac distress. Death may occur in a few days, or dropsy may supervene and the case may become chronic. Delafield has reported an interesting series of cases of this group.

Treatment.—The treatment of hypertrophy and dilatation has already been considered under the section on valvular lesions. I would only here emphasize the fact that with signs of dilatation, as indicated by gallop rhythm, urgent dyspnœa, and slight lividity, venesection is in many cases the only means by which the life of the patient may be saved, and from 25 to 30 ounces of blood should be abstracted without delay. Subsequently stimulants, such as ammonia and digitalis, may be administered, but they are accessories only to the bleeding in the critical condition of acute dilatation, which is so frequently met with in cardiac lesions.

IV. AFFECTIONS OF THE MYOCARDIUM.

1. Lesions due to Disease of the Coronary Arteries.—A knowledge of the changes produced in the myocardium by disease of the coronary vessels gives a key to the understanding of many problems in cardiac pathology. The terminal branches of the coronary vessels are end-arteries; that is, the communication between neighboring branches is through capillaries only. F. H. Pratt * has lately shown that the vessels of Thebesius, which open from the ventricles and auricles into a system of fine branches and thus communicate with the cardiac capillaries and coronary veins, may be capable of feeding the myocardium sufficiently to keep it alive even when the coronary arteries are occluded. The blocking of one of these vessels by a thrombus or an embolus leads usually to a condition which is known as—

(a) *Anæmic necrosis*, or white infarct. When this does not occur the reason may be sought in (1) the existence of abnormal anastomoses, which by their presence take the coronary system out of the group of end-arteries; or (2) the vicarious flow through the vessels of Thebesius and the coronary veins. The condition is most commonly seen in the left ventricle and in the septum, in the territory of distribution of the anterior coronary artery. The

---

* The American Journal of Physiology, vol. i, 1898.

affected area has a yellowish-white color, sometimes a turbid, parboiled aspect, at other times a grayish-red tint. It may be somewhat wedge-shaped, more often it is irregular in contour and projects above the surface. Microscopically the changes are very characteristic. The nuclei either disappear from the muscle fibres or they undergo fragmentation. Leucocytes wander in from the surrounding tissue, and these may suffer disintegration. At a later stage a new growth of fibrous tissue is found in the periphery of the infarct which ultimately may entirely replace the dead fibres. The fibres present a homogeneous, hyaline appearance. In some instances there is complete transformation, and even to the naked eye a firm white patch of hyaline degeneration may appear in the centre of the area. Sudden death not infrequently follows the blocking of one of the branches of the coronary artery and the production of this anæmic necrosis. *In medico-legal cases it is a point of primary importance to remember that this is one of the common causes of sudden death.* This condition should be carefully sought for, inasmuch as it may be the sole lesion, except a general, sometimes slight arterio-sclerosis. Rupture of the heart may be associated with anæmic necrosis.

(*b*) The second important effect of coronary-artery disease upon the myocardium is seen in the production of *fibrous myocarditis*. This may result from the gradual transformation of areas of anæmic necrosis. More commonly it is caused by the narrowing of a coronary branch in a process of obliterative endarteritis. Where the process is gradual evidences of granulation tissue are often wanting, and any distinction between the necrotic muscle fibres and the new scar tissue is difficult to establish. J. B. MacCallum has shown that the muscle fibres undergo a change the reverse of that of their normal development and lose their fibril bundles preliminary to their complete replacement by connective tissue. The sclerosis is most frequently seen at the apex of the left ventricle and in the septum, but it may occur in any portion. In the septum and walls there are often streaks and patches which are only seen in carefully made systematic sections. Hypertrophy of the heart is commonly associated with this degeneration. It is the invariable precursor of aneurism of the heart.

Complete obliteration of one coronary artery, if produced suddenly, is usually fatal. When induced slowly, either by arterio-sclerosis at the orifice of the artery at the root of the aorta or by an obliterating endarteritis in the course of the vessel, the circulation may be carried on through the other vessel. Sudden death is not uncommon, owing to thrombosis of a vessel which has become narrowed by sclerosis. In the most extreme grade one coronary artery may be entirely blocked, with the production of extensive fibroid disease, and a main branch of the other also may be occluded. A large, powerfully built imbecile, aged thirty-five, at the Elwyn Institution, Pennsylvania, who had for years enjoyed doing the heavy work about the place, died suddenly, without any preliminary symptoms. The heart, which is in my collection, weighed over 20 ounces; the anterior coronary artery was practically occluded by obliterating endarteritis, and of the posterior artery one main branch was blocked.

(*c*) *Septic Infarcts.*—In pyæmia the smaller branches of the coronary arteries may be blocked with emboli which give rise to infectious or septic infarcts in the myocardium in the form of abscesses, varying in size from a pea to a pin's head. These may not cause any disturbance, but when large they may perforate into the ventricle or into the pericardium, forming what has been called acute ulcer of the heart.

2. **Acute Interstitial Myocarditis.**—In some infectious diseases and in acute pericarditis the intermuscular connective tissue may be swollen and infiltrated with small round cells and leucocytes, the blood-vessels dilated, and the muscle fibres the seat of granular, fatty, and hyaline degeneration. Occasionally, in pyæmia the infiltration with pus-cells has been diffuse and confined chiefly to the interstitial tissue. Councilman has described this condition of the heart wall in gonorrhœa, and succeeded in demonstrating the gonococcus in the diseased areas. The commonest examples are found in diphtheria, typhoid fever, and acute endocarditis, as shown by the studies of Romberg. The foci may be the starting-points of patches of fibrous myocarditis.

3. **Fragmentation and Segmentation.**—This condition was described by Renaut and Landouzy in 1877, and has been carefully studied by different pathologists.* Two forms are met with: 1. Segmentation. The muscle fibres have separated at the cement line. 2. Fragmentation. The fracture has been across the fibre itself, and perhaps at the level of the nucleus. Longitudinal division is unusual. Although the condition doubtless arises in some instances during the death agony, as in cases of sudden death by violence, in others it would seem to have clinical and pathological significance. It is found associated with other lesions, fibrous myocarditis, infarction, and fatty degeneration. J. B. MacCallum distinguishes a simple from a degenerative fragmentation. The first takes place in the normal fibre, which, however, shows irregular extensions and contractions. The second succeeds degeneration in the fibre. Hearts the seat of marked fragmentation are lax, easily torn, the muscle fibres widely separated, and often pale and cloudy.

4. **Parenchymatous Degeneration.**—This is usually met with in fevers, or in connection with endocarditis or pericarditis, and in infections and intoxications generally. It is characterized by a pale, turbid state of the cardiac muscle, which is general, not localized. Turbidity and softness are the special features. It is the softened heart of Laennec and Louis. Stokes speaks of an instance in which " so great was the softening of the organ that when the heart was grasped by the great vessels and held with the apex pointing upward, it fell down over the hand, covering it like a cap of a large mushroom."

Histologically, there is a degeneration of the muscle fibres, which are infiltrated to a various extent with granules which resist the action of ether, but are dissolved in acetic acid. Sometimes this granular change in the fibres is extreme, and no trace of the striæ can be detected. It is probably the effect of a toxic agent, and is seen in its most exquisite form in the lumbar muscles in cases of toxic hæmoglobinuria in the horse. It is met

---

* Hektoen, American Journal of the Medical Sciences, 1897.

with in cases of typhoid, typhus, small-pox, and other infectious diseases, particularly when the course is protracted. There is no definite relation between it and the high temperature.

5. Fatty Heart.—Under this term are embraced fatty degeneration and fatty overgrowth.

(*a*) *Fatty degeneration* is a very common condition, and mild grades are met with in many diseases. It is found in the failing nutrition of old age, of wasting diseases, and of cachectic states; in prolonged infectious fevers, in which it may follow or accompany the parenchymatous change; associated with acute and chronic anæmias. Certain poisons, such as phosphorus, produce an intense fatty degeneration. Local causes: Pericarditis is usually associated with fatty or parenchymatous changes in the superficial layers of the myocardium. Disease of the coronary arteries is a common and important cause, and it is associated with fat embolism. Lastly, in the hypertrophied ventricular wall in chronic heart-disease fatty change is by no means infrequent. This degeneration may be limited to the heart or it may be more or less general in the solid viscera. The diaphragm may also be involved, even when the other muscles show no special changes. There appears to be a special proneness to fatty degeneration in the heart-muscle, which may perhaps be connected with its incessant activity. So great is its need of an abundant oxygen supply that it feels at once any deficiency, and is in consequence the first muscle to show nutritional changes.

Anatomically the condition may be local or general. The left ventricle is most frequently affected. If the process is advanced and general, the heart looks large and is flabby and relaxed. It has a light yellowish-brown tint, or, as it is called, a faded-leaf color. Its consistence is reduced and the substance tears easily. In the left ventricle the papillary columns and the muscle beneath the endocardium show a streaked or patchy appearance. Microscopically, the fibres are seen to be occupied by minute globules distributed in rows along the line of the primitive fibres (Welch). In advanced grades the fibres seem completely occupied by the minute globules.

(*b*) *Fatty Overgrowth.*—This is usually a simple excess of the normal subpericardial fat, to which the term *cor adiposum* was given by the older writers. In pronounced instances the fat infiltrates between the muscular substance and, separating the strands, may reach even to the endocardium. In corpulent persons there is always much pericardial fat. It forms part of the general obesity, and occasionally leads to dangerous or even fatal impairment of the contractile power of the heart. Of 122 cases analyzed by Forchheimer there were 88 males and 34 females. Over 80 per cent occurred between the fortieth and seventieth years.

The entire heart may be enveloped in a thick sheeting of fat through which not a trace of muscle substance can be seen. On section, the fat infiltrates the muscle, separating the fibres, and in extreme cases—particularly in the right ventricle—reaches the endocardium. In some places there may be even complete substitution of fat for the muscle substance. In rare instances the fat may be in the papillary muscles. The heart is usually much relaxed and the chambers are dilated. Microscopically the muscle-fibres may show, in addition to the atrophy, marked fatty degeneration.

6. Other Degenerations of the Myocardium. (*a*) *Brown Atrophy.*— This is a common change in the heart-muscle, particularly in chronic valvular lesions and in the senile heart. When advanced, the color of the muscles is a dark red-brown, and the consistence is usually increased. The fibres present an accumulation of yellow-brown pigment chiefly about the nuclei. The cement substance is often unusually distinct, but seems more fragile than in healthy muscle.

(*b*) Amyloid degeneration of the heart is occasionally seen. It occurs in the intermuscular connective tissue and in the blood-vessels, not in the fibres.

(*c*) The hyaline transformation of Zenker is sometimes met with in prolonged fevers. The affected fibres are swollen, homogeneous, translucent, and the striæ are very faint or entirely absent.

(*d*) Calcareous degeneration may occur in the myocardium, and the muscle fibres may be infiltrated and yet retain their appearance as figured and described by Coats in his Text-book of Pathology.

Symptoms of Myocardial Disease.—These are notoriously uncertain. A man with advanced fibroid myocarditis may drop dead suddenly, while doing heavy work, without having complained of cardiac distress. On the other hand, a patient may present enfeebled, irregular action and signs of dilatation; he may have shortness of breath, œdema, and the general symptoms believed to be characteristic of cases of fibroid and fatty heart, and the post mortem show little or no change in the myocardium.

Cardio-sclerosis or fibroid heart is in some cases characterized by a feeble, irregular, slow pulse, with dyspnœa on exertion and occasional attacks of angina. Irregularity is present in many, but not in all cases. The pulse may be very slow, even 30 or 40 per minute. Ultimately the cases come under observation with the symptoms of cardiac insufficiency. The arrhythmia, which may have been present, becomes aggravated and, according to Riegel, may not only precede, but also persist after the cardiac insufficiency has passed away.

Fatty degeneration of the heart presents the same difficulties. Extreme fatty changes, as in pernicious anæmia, may be consistent with a full, regular pulse and a regularly acting heart. In some of these cases the fat does not appear to interfere seriously with the function of the organ. The truth is, it may exist in an extreme grade without producing symptoms, so long as great dilatation of the chambers does not occur. The cardiac irregularity, the dyspnœa, palpitation, and small pulse are in reality not symptoms of the fatty degeneration, but of dilatation which has supervened. The fatty *arcus senilis* is of no moment in the diagnosis of fatty heart. The heart-sounds may be weak and the action irregular. When dilatation occurs, there is often the gallop rhythm, shortening of the long pause, and a systolic murmur at the apex. Shortness of breath on exertion is an early feature in many cases, and anginal attacks may occur. There is sometimes a tendency to syncope, and in both fibroid and fatty heart there are attacks in which the patient feels cold and depressed and the pulse sinks to 40 or 30, or even, as in one case which I saw, to 26. The patient may wake from sleep in the early morning with an attack of severe cardiac asthma. These "spells" may be associated with nausea and may alternate with others in which there are anginal symptoms. These are the cases, too, in which for weeks there may be mental symptoms. The patient has delusions and may even become maniacal. Toward the close, the type of breathing known as Cheyne-Stokes may occur. It was described in the following terms by John Cheyne, speaking of a case of fatty heart (Dublin Hospital Reports, vol. ii, p. 221, 1818): "For several days his breathing was irregular; it would entirely cease for a quarter of a minute, then it would become perceptible, though very low, then by degrees it became heaving and quick, and then it would gradually cease again: this revolution in the state of his breathing lasted about a minute, during which there were about thirty acts of respiration." It is seen much more frequently in arterio-sclerosis and uræmic states than in fatty heart.

Fatty overgrowth of the heart is a condition certain to exist in very obese persons. It produces no symptoms until the muscular fibre is so weakened that dilatation occurs. These patients may for years present a feeble but regular pulse; the heart-sounds are weak and muffled, and a murmur may be heard at the apex. Attacks of cardiac asthma are not uncommon, and the patient may suffer from bronchitis. Dizziness and pseudo-apoplectic seizures may occur. Sudden death may result from syncope or from rupture of the heart. The physical examination is often difficult because of the great increase in the fat, and it may be impossible to define the area of dulness.

For practical purposes we may group the cases of myocardial disease as follows:

(1) Those in which sudden death occurs with or without previous indications of heart-trouble. Sclerosis of the coronary arteries exists—in some instances with recent thrombus and white infarcts; in others, extensive fibroid disease; in others again, fatty degeneration. Many patients never complain of cardiac distress, but, as in the case of Chalmers, the celebrated Scottish divine, enjoy unusual vigor of mind and body.

(2) Cases in which there are cardiac arrhythmia, shortness of breath on exertion, attacks of cardiac asthma, sometimes anginal attacks, collapse symptoms with sweats and extremely slow pulse, and occasionally marked mental symptoms. These are the cases in which the condition may be strongly suspected and, in some instances, diagnosed. It is rarely possible to make a distinction between the fatty and fibroid heart.

(3) Cases in which there are cardiac insufficiency and symptoms of dilatation of the heart. Dropsy is often present, and with a loud murmur at the apex it may be difficult, unless the case has been seen from the outset, to determine whether or not a valvular lesion is present.

Prognosis.—The outlook in affections of the myocardium is extremely grave. Patients recover, however, in a surprising way from the most serious attacks, particularly those of the second group.

Treatment.—Many cases never come under treatment; the first are the final symptoms.

Cases with signs of well-marked cardiac insufficiency, as manifested by dyspnœa, weak, irregular, rapid heart, and œdema, may be treated on the

47

plan laid down for the treatment of broken compensation in valvular disease. Digitalis may be given even if fatty degeneration is suspected, and is often very beneficial.

Much more difficult is the management of those cases in which there is marked cardiac arrhythmia, with a feeble, irregular, very slow pulse, and syncope or angina. Dropsy is not, as a rule, present; the heart-sounds may be perfectly clear, and there are no signs of dilatation. Digitalis, under these circumstances, is not advisable, particularly when the pulse is infrequent. Complete rest in bed, a carefully regulated diet, and the use of the aromatic spirits of ammonia, sulphuric ether, and stimulants are indicated. For the restlessness and distressing feelings of anxiety morphia is invaluable. From an eightieth to a sixtieth of a grain of strychnia may be given three times a day. If, as is sometimes the case, the pulse is hard and firm, nitroglycerin may be cautiously administered, beginning with 1 minim of the 1-per-cent solution three times a day and increased gradually.

In certain cases of weak heart, particularly when it is due to fatty overgrowth, the plans recommended by Oertel and by Schott are advantageous. They are invaluable methods in those forms of heart-weakness due to intemperance in eating and drinking and defective bodily exercise. The Oertel plan consists of three parts: First, the reduction in the amount of liquid. This is an important factor in reducing the fat in these patients. It also slightly increases the density of the blood. Oertel allows daily about 36 ounces of liquid, which includes the amount taken with the solid food. Free perspiration is promoted by bathing (if advisable, the Turkish bath), or even by the use of pilocarpine.

The second important point in his treatment is the diet, which should consist largely of proteids.

Morning.—Cup of coffee or tea, with a little milk, about 6 ounces altogether. Bread, 3 ounces.

Noon.—Three to 4 ounces of soup, 7 to 8 ounces of roast beef, veal, game, or poultry, salad or a light vegetable, a little fish; 1 ounce of bread or farinaceous pudding; 3 to 6 ounces of fruit for dessert. No liquids at this meal, as a rule, but in hot weather 6 ounces of light wine may be taken.

Afternoon.—Six ounces of coffee or tea, with as much water. As an indulgence an ounce of bread.

Evening.—One or 2 soft-boiled eggs, an ounce of bread, perhaps a small slice of cheese, salad, and fruit; 6 to 8 ounces of wine with 4 or 5 ounces of water (Yeo).

The most important element of all is graduated exercise, not on the level, but up hills of various grades. The distance walked each day is marked off and is gradually lengthened. In this way the heart is systematically exercised and strengthened.

The Schott Treatment.—This consists in a combination of baths with exercises at Nauheim. The water has a temperature of from 82°–95° F., and is very richly charged with CO_2. The good effects of the bath are claimed by Schott to come from a cutaneous excitation, induced by the mineral and gaseous constituents of the bath, and a stimulation of the sensory nerves. There is no question that the bath, in suitable cases, will alter the position of the apex beat, and that it lessens the area of cardiac dulness; this means that it diminishes the dilatation of the heart. Artificial baths are used, consisting of forty gallons of water, with various strengths of sodium chloride and calcium chloride. The exercises, resistance gymnastics, consist in slow movements executed by the patient and resisted by the operator. Any one wishing to carry out in private the Schott treatment should consult the work of Besley Thorne. Camac's articles (J. H. H. Bulletin, vol. viii, and Jour. of the Am. Med. Assoc., 1897, ii) give a brief account of our experience with it.

ANEURISM OF THE HEART.

(a) **Aneurism of a valve** results from acute endocarditis, which produces softening or erosion and may lead either to perforation of the segment or to gradual dilatation of a limited area under the influence of the blood-pressure. The aneurisms are usually spheroidal and project from the ventricular face of a sigmoid valve. They are much less common on the mitral segments. They frequently rupture and produce extensive destruction and incompetency of the valves.

(b) **Aneurism of the walls** results from the weakening induced by chronic myocarditis, or occasionally it follows acute mural endocarditis, which more commonly, however, leads to perforation. It has followed a stab-wound, a gumma of the ventricle, and, according to some authors, pericardial adhesions. The left ventricle near the apex is usually the seat, this being the situation in which fibrous degeneration is most common. Fifty-nine of the 60 cases collected by Legg were situated here. In the early stages the anterior wall of the ventricle, near the septum, sometimes even the septum itself, is slightly dilated, the endocardium opaque, and the muscular tissue sclerotic. In a more advanced stage the dilatation is pronounced and layers of thrombi occupy the sac. Ultimately a large rounded tumor may project from the ventricle and may attain a size equal to that of the heart. Occasionally the aneurism is sacculated and communicates with the ventricle through a very small orifice. The sac may be double, as in the cases of Janeway and Sailer. In the museum of Guy's Hospital there is a specimen showing the wall of the ventricle covered with aneurismal bulgings. Rupture occurred in 7 of the 90 cases collected by Legg.

The *symptoms* produced by aneurism of the heart are indefinite. Occasionally there is marked bulging in the apex region and the tumor may perforate the chest wall. In mitral stenosis the right ventricle may bulge and produce a visible pulsating tumor below the left costal border, which I have known to be mistaken for cardiac aneurism. When the sac is large and produces pressure upon the heart itself, there may be a marked disproportion between the strong cardiac impulse and the feeble pulsation in the peripheral arteries.

RUPTURE OF THE HEART.

This rare event is usually associated with fatty infiltration or degeneration of the heart-muscles. In some instances, acute softening in consequence of embolism of a branch of the coronary artery, suppurative myocarditis, or a gummatous growth has been the cause. Of 100 cases collected by Quain, fatty degeneration was noted in 77. Two thirds of the patients were over sixty years of age.

The rent may occur in any of the chambers, but is found most frequently in the left ventricle on the anterior wall, not far from the septum. The accident usually takes place during exertion. There may be no preliminary symptoms, but without any warning the patient may fall and die in a few moments. Sudden death occurred in 71 per cent of Quain's cases. In other instances there may be in the cardiac region a sense of anguish and suffocation, and life may be prolonged for several hours. In a Montreal case, which I examined, the patient walked up a steep hill after the onset of the symptoms, and lived for thirteen hours. A case is on record in which the patient lived for eleven days.

New Growths and Parasites.

Tubercle and syphilis have already been considered. Primary cancer or sarcoma is extremely rare. Secondary tumors may be single or multiple, and are usually unattended with symptoms, even when the disease is most extensive. In one case I found in the wall of the right ventricle a mass which involved the anterior segment of the tricuspid valve and partly blocked the orifice. The surface was eroded and there were numerous cancerous emboli in the pulmonary artery. In another instance the heart was greatly enlarged, owing to the presence of innumerable masses of colloid cancer the size of cherries. The mediastinal sarcoma may penetrate the heart, though it is remarkable how extensive the disease of the mediastinal glands may be without involvement of the heart or vessels.

Cysts in the heart are rare. They are found in different parts, and are filled either with a brownish or a clear fluid. Blood-cysts occasionally occur.

The parasites have been discussed under the appropriate section, but it may be mentioned here that both the *cysticerus cellulosæ* and the echinococcus cysts occur occasionally in the heart.

Wounds and Foreign Bodies.

Wounds of the heart are usually fatal, although there are many instances in which recovery has taken place. Bullets have been found encysted inside the ventricle. A majority of the cases of gunshot wounds, however, are necessarily fatal. Puncture of the heart by a sharp-pointed body, such as a needle or a stiletto, does not always prove fatal. Peabody has reported a case in which a pin was found embedded in the left ventricle. Suicide has been attempted by passing a needle or pin into the heart. This is not, however, necessarily fatal. Moxon mentioned a case, at the Clinical Society of London, in which a medical student, while on a spree, passed a pin into his heart. The pericardium was opened, and the head of the pin was found outside of the right ventricle. It was grasped and an attempt made to remove it, but it was withdrawn into the heart and, it is said, caused the patient no further trouble. Hysterical girls sometimes swallow pins and needles, which, passing through the œsophagus and stomach, are found in various parts of the body. A remarkable case is reported by Allen J. Smith of a girl from whom several dozen needles and pins were removed, chiefly from subcutaneous abscesses. Several years later she developed symptoms of chronic heart-disease. At the post mortem needles were found in the tissues of the adherent pericardium, and between thirty and forty were embedded in the thickened pleural membranes of the left side.

Puncture of the heart has been recommended as a therapeutic procedure to stimulate it to action, as in chloroform narcosis, and experimental evidence has been brought forward by B. A. Watson in favor of the operation. He advises abstraction of blood in combination with the puncture—cardiocentesis. The proceeding is not without risk. Hæmorrhage may take place from the puncture, though it is not often extensive. Sloane has recently urged its use in all cases of asphyxia and in suffocation by drowning and from coal-gas. The successful case which he reports illustrates forcibly its stimulating action.

V. NEUROSES OF THE HEART.

PALPITATION.

In health we are unconscious of the action of the heart. In some people one of the first indications of debility or overwork is the consciousness of the cardiac pulsations, which may, however, be perfectly regular and orderly. This is not palpitation. The term is properly limited to irregular or forcible action of the heart perceptible to the individual.

Etiology.—The expression "perceptible to the individual" covers the essential element in palpitation of the heart. The most extreme disturbance of rhythm, a condition even of what is termed *delirium cordis*, may be unattended with subjective sensations of distress, and there may be no consciousness of disturbed action. On the other hand, there are cases in which complaint is made of the most distressing palpitation and sensations of throbbing, in which the physical examination reveals a regularly acting heart, the sensations being entirely subjective. We meet with this symptom in a large group of cases in which there is increased excitability of the nervous system. Palpitation may be a marked feature at the time of puberty, at the climacteric, and occasionally during menstruation. It is a very common symptom in hysteria and neurasthenia, particularly in the form of the latter which is associated with dyspepsia. Emotions, such as fright, are common causes of palpitation. It may occur as a sequence of the acute fevers. Females are more liable to the affection than males.

In a second group the palpitation results from the action upon the heart of certain substances, such as tobacco, coffee, tea, and alcohol. And, lastly, palpitation may be associated with organic disease of the heart, either of the myocardium or of the valves. As a rule, however, it is a purely nervous phenomenon—seldom associated with organic disease—in which the most violent action and the most extreme irregularity may exist without that subjective element of consciousness of the disturbance which constitutes the essential feature of palpitation.

The irritable heart described by Da Costa, which was so common among the young soldiers during the civil war, is a neurosis of this kind. The chief symptoms were palpitation with great frequency of the pulse on exertion, a variable amount of cardiac pain, and dyspnœa. The factors at work in producing this condition appeared to be the mental excitement, the unwonted muscular exertion associated with the drill, and diarrhœa. The condition is not infrequent in civil life among young men, and it leads in some cases to hypertrophy of the heart.

Symptoms.—In the mildest form, such as occurs during a dyspeptic attack, there is slight fluttering of the heart and a sense of what patients sometimes call "goneness." In more severe attacks the heart beats violently, its pulsations against the chest wall are visible, the rapidity of the action is much increased, the arteries throb forcibly, and there is a sense of great distress. In some instances the heart's action is not at all quickened. The most striking cases are in neurasthenic women, in whom the mere entrance of a person into the room may cause the most violent action of the heart and throbbing of the peripheral arteries. The pulse may be rapidly increased until it reaches 150 or 160. A diffuse flushing of the skin may appear at the same time. After such attacks, there may be the passage of a large quantity of pale urine. In many cases of palpitation, particularly in young men, the condition is at once relieved by exertion. A patient with extreme irregularity of the heart may, after walking quickly 100 yards or running upstairs, return with the pulse perfectly regular. This is not infrequently seen, too, in the irregular action of the heart in mitral valve disease.

The physical examination of the heart is usually negative. The sounds, the shock of which may be very palpable, are on auscultation clear, ringing, and metallic, but not associated with murmurs. The second sound at the base may be greatly accentuated. A murmur may sometimes be heard over the pulmonary artery or even at the apex in cases of rapid action in neurasthenia or in severe anæmia. The attacks may be transient, lasting only for a few minutes, or may persist for an hour or more. In some instances any attempt at exertion renews the attack.

The *prognosis* is usually good, though it may be extremely difficult to remove the conditions underlying the palpitation.

ARRHYTHMIA.

An intermission occurs when one or more beats of the heart are dropped. Irregularity is the condition when the beats are unequal in volume and force, or follow each other at unequal distances. Allorrhythmia is a term which is also used to express deviations from the normal heart rhythm.

The following varieties of arrhythmical action may be recognized:

(1) The paradoxical pulse of Kussmaul, in which the beats during in-

spiration are more frequent but less full than during expiration. This is found in weak heart, in chronic pericarditis, and when fibrous bands encircle the root of the aorta; but it may also occur normally from the influence of the respirations upon the heart. It is sometimes to be felt in sleeping children.

(2) Intermittence, in which there is simply an intermission or dropping of a cardiac beat. The term *deficience* is more correctly applied to those instances in which the absence of the heart-sound proves that the systole is really omitted. The systole may be so weak as not to produce a pulsation, and yet at the same time a feeble first sound may be heard.

(3) The alternate heart-beat, in which strong and weak contractions alternate regularly and which is expressed in the peripheral arteries by alternate full and feeble pulse-beats.

(4) The bigeminal and trigeminal pulsations occur when two or three beats follow each other in rapid succession, each group being separated from the following by a longer interval. This is not very uncommon in mitral disease and as an effect of digitalis. In the bigeminal pulse the first beat of the pair is usually the stronger. Indeed, in the condition known as heart bigeminism the second systole is so feeble that the pulse wave does not reach the peripheral arteries and the two systoles are represented by only a single pulse-beat at the wrist.

(5) Delirium cordis, in which these various factors are combined and the heart's action is wholly irregular.

(6) Fœtal heart rhythm—embryocardia—described by Stokes, is a very common condition in which the long pause is shortened and the characters of the sounds are "almost completely identical." The resemblance to the fœtal heart-beat is very striking. In the later stages of fevers and in extreme dilatation this form of heart rhythm is very frequently heard.

(7) Gallop rhythm, in which the sounds resemble the footfall of a horse at canter, usually results from the reduplication of the sounds in a rapidly acting heart. It is expressed by the words "rat-ta-tat." Sometimes it seems as if the first sound was split; more commonly it is the second. It is most frequently heard in the failing heart of interstitial nephritis and arterio-sclerosis. Its mode of origin has been much discussed, and it is doubtful whether a satisfactory explanation has yet been given. As Graham Steell states, its presence indicates muscle weakness. It is interesting among disturbances of rhythm as the only one which we can see and feel as well as hear.

The causes of these various disturbances of rhythm are thus classified by G. Baumgarten: *

(1) Those due to central—cerebral—causes, either organic disease, as in hæmorrhage, or concussion; more commonly psychical influences.

(2) Reflex influences, such as produce the cardiac irregularity in dyspepsia and diseases of the liver, lungs, and kidneys.

(3) Toxic influences. Tobacco, coffee, and tea are common causes of

---

* Transactions of the Association of American Physicians, vol. iii.

arrhythmia. Various drugs, such as digitalis, belladonna, and aconite, may also induce it.

(4) Changes in the heart itself. (*a*) In the cardiac ganglia. Fatty, pigmentary, and sclerotic changes have been described in cases of this sort and may have an important influence in producing disturbances in the rhythm; but as yet we do not know their exact significance. They may be present in cases which have not presented arrhythmia. (*b*) Mural changes are common in conditions of this kind. Simple dilatation, fatty degeneration, and sclerosis are most commonly present, the two latter usually associated with sclerosis of the coronary arteries.

The significance of arrhythmia is not always easy to determine. Simple irregular action of the heart may persist for years. The late Chancellor Ferrier, of McGill University, a man of unusual bodily and mental vigor, who died at the age of eighty-seven, had an extremely irregular pulse for almost fifty years of his life. One or two other instances have come under my notice of persons in good health, without arterial or cardiac disease, in whom the heart's action was persistently irregular. The bigeminal and trigeminal pulsations are found more frequently in mitral than in other conditions. The delirium cordis is met with in the dilatation associated with valvular lesions, particularly toward the latter stages. Fœtal heart rhythm is rarely found apart from dilatation.

Rapid Heart—Tachycardia.

The rapid action may be perfectly natural. There are individuals whose normal heart action is at 100 or even more per minute. It may be caused by the various conditions which induce palpitation; but the two are not necessarily associated. Emotional causes, violent exercise, and fevers all produce great increase in the rapidity of the heart's action. The extremely rapid action which follows fright may persist for days, or even weeks. Traube reports an instance in which, after violent exercise, the rapidity of the heart continued. Cases are not uncommon at the menopause.

There are cases again in which the condition can hardly be termed a neurosis, since it depends upon definite changes in the pneumogastrics or in the medulla. Cases have been reported in which tumor or clot in or about the medulla or pressure upon the vagi has been associated with heart hurry. Some of the cases of frequent action of the heart in women have been thought to be due to reflex irritation from ovarian or uterine disease.

Paroxysmal tachycardia is a remarkable affection, characterized by spells of heart hurry, during which the action is greatly increased, the pulse reaching 200 and over. The cases are not common. The condition has been thoroughly studied by Nothnagel. The attack may be quite short and persist only for an hour or so. A patient at the Philadelphia Infirmary for Nervous Diseases was attacked every week or two; the pulse would rise to 220 or 230, and there were such feelings of distress and uneasiness that the patient always had to lie down. There may be, however, no subjective disturbance, and in another case the patient was able to walk about during the paroxysm and had no dyspnœa. One of the most remarkable cases is reported by H. C. Wood. A physician in his eighty-seventh year had had attacks at intervals since his thirty-seventh year. The onset was abrupt and the pulse would rapidly rise to 200 a minute. For more than twenty years the taking of ice-water or strong coffee would arrest the attacks. Bouveret has analyzed a number of cases of this essential or idiopathic form; he finds that a permanent cure is rare, and that the patients suffer for ten or more years. Four instances terminated fatally from heart-failure. Martius looks upon it as a symptom of an acute dilatation of the heart, appearing paroxysmally. Wood suggests that these cardiac paroxysms are caused by discharging lesions affecting the centres of the accelerator nerves. François Franck has shown that the acceleration of the heart's action is due to the shortening of the diastole, and during the systole so little blood is expelled from the heart that the average amount in the minute is not increased. Moreover, the accelerators appear to have no trophic relation to the heart, and stimulation of them is not accompanied either by increased arterial pressure or by augmentation of the work done by the heart.

Slow Heart—Brachycardia (*Bradycardia*).

Slow action of the heart is sometimes normal and may be a family peculiarity. Napoleon is stated to have had a pulse of only 40 per minute.

In any case of slow pulse it is important first to make sure that the number of heart and arterial beats correspond. In many instances this is not the case, and with a radial pulse at 40 the cardiac pulsations may be 80, half the beats not reaching the wrist. The heart contractions, not the pulse wave, should be taken into account. A most exhaustive study of this condition has been made by Riegel, whose division is here followed:

(*a*) Physiological brachycardia. In the puerperal state the pulse may beat from 44 to 60 per minute, or may even be as low as 34. It is seen in premature labor as well as at term. The explanation of its occurrence at this period is not clear. Slowness of the pulse is associated with hunger. Brachycardia depending on individual peculiarity is extremely rare.

(*b*) Pathological brachycardia, which is met with under the following conditions: (1) In convalescence from acute fevers. This is extremely common, particularly after pneumonia, typhoid fever, acute rheumatism, and diphtheria. It is most frequently seen in young persons and in cases which have run a normal course. Traube's explanation that it is due to exhaustion is probably the correct one. (2) In diseases of the digestive system, such as chronic dyspepsia, ulcer or cancer of the stomach, and jaundice. The largest number of Riegel's cases were of this group. (3) In diseases of the respiratory system. Here it is by no means so common, but is seen not infrequently in emphysema. (4) In diseases of the circulatory system. Excluding all cases of irregularity of the heart, brachycardia is not common in diseases of the valves. It is most frequently seen in fatty and fibroid changes in the heart, but is not constant in them. (5) In diseases of the urinary organs. It occurs occasionally in nephritis and may be a feature of uræmia. (6) From the action of toxic agents. It occurs in uræmia, poisoning by lead, alcohol, and follows the use of tobacco, coffee, and digitalis. (7) In constitutional disorders, such as anæmia, chlorosis, and diabetes. (8) In diseases of the nervous system. Apoplexy, epilepsy, the cerebral tumors, affections of the medulla, and diseases and injuries of the cervical cord may be associated with very slow pulse. In general paresis, mania, and melancholia it is not infrequent. (9) It occurs occasionally in affections of the skin and sexual organs, and in sunstroke, or in prolonged exhaustion from any cause.

The Stokes-Adams Syndrome.—*Slow Pulse with Syncopal Attacks.*— Robert Adams and Stokes described a remarkable condition in which the pulse was permanently slow in association with attacks of syncope. The patients are usually advanced in years and show an extreme grade of arterio-sclerosis. The pulse-rate may be 30 or 20 to the minute, or, as in Prentice's case, as low as 12, or even 10 or 5. The cerebral symptoms are very remarkable, and Stokes suggested for them the name of false or pseudo-apoplexy. Attacks of vertigo, which may recur several times in the day, attacks of syncope, in which the patient is insensible for four or five minutes, or epileptiform attacks, as in Ogle's cases, are the most pronounced cerebral symptoms. Huchard regards the condition as the result of changes in the pneumogastric centres due to disease of the arteries of the medulla. (See Lecture IV in my monograph on Angina Pectoris and Allied States.)

Treatment of Palpitation and Arrhythmia.—An important element in many cases is to get the patient's mind quieted, and he can be assured that there is no actual danger. The mental element is oftentimes very strong. In palpitation, before using medicines, it is well to try the effect of hygienic measures. As a rule, moderate exercise may be taken with advantage. Regular hours should be kept, and at least ten hours out of the twenty-four should be spent in the recumbent posture. A tepid bath may be taken in the morning, or, if the patient is weakly and nervous, in the evening, followed by a thorough rubbing. Hot baths and the Turkish bath should be avoided. The dietetic management is most important. It is best to prohibit absolutely alcohol, tea, and coffee. The diet should be light and the patient should avoid taking large meals. Articles of food known to cause flatulency should not be used. If a smoker, the patient should give up tobacco. Sexual excitement is particularly pernicious, and the patient should be warned specially on this point. For the distressing attacks of palpitation which occur with neurasthenia, particularly in women, a rigid Weir Mitchell course is the most satisfactory. It is in these cases that we find the most distressing throbbing in the abdomen, which is apt to come on after meals, and is very much aggravated by flatulency. The cases of palpitation due to excesses or to errors in diet and dyspepsia are readily remedied by hygienic measures.

A course of iron is often useful. Strychnia is particularly valuable, and is perhaps best administered as the tincture of nux vomica in large doses. Very little good is obtained from the smaller quantities. It should be given freely, 20 minims three times a day.

If there is great rapidity of action, aconite may be tried or veratrum viride. There are cases associated with sleeplessness and restlessness which are greatly benefited by bromide of potassium. Digitalis is very rarely indicated, but in obstinate cases it may be tried with the nux vomica.

Cases of heart hurry are often extremely obstinate, as may be judged from the case of the physician reported by H. C. Wood, in whom the condition persisted in spite of all measures for fifty years. The bromides are sometimes useful; the general condition of neurasthenia should be treated, and during the paroxysm an ice-bag may be placed upon the heart, or Leiter's coil, through which ice-water may be passed. Electricity, in the form of galvanism, is sometimes serviceable, and for its mental effect the Franklinic current. For the condition of slow pulse but little can be done. A great majority of the cases are not dangerous.

Angina Pectoris.

Stenocardia, or the breast-pang, described by Heberden, is not an independent affection, but a symptom associated with a number of morbid conditions of the heart and vessels, more particularly with sclerosis of the root of the aorta and changes in the coronary arteries. True angina, which is a rare disease, is characterized by paroxysms of agonizing pain in the region of the heart, extending into the arms and neck. In violent attacks there is a sensation of impending death.

Etiology.—It is a disease of adult life and occurs almost exclusively in men. In Huchard's statistics of 237 cases only 42 were in women. In my series of 40 cases there was only one woman. It may occur through several generations, as in the Arnold family. Gout, diabetes, and syphilis are important factors. A number of cases of angina pectoris have followed influenza. Attacks are not infrequent in certain forms of heart-disease, particularly aortic insufficiency and adherent pericardium. It is much less common in disease of the mitral valve. Almost without exception the subjects of true angina have arterio-sclerosis, either general or localized, at the root of the aorta, with changes in the coronary arteries and in the myocardium.

Phenomena of the Attack.—The exciting cause is in a majority of all cases well defined. In only rare instances do the patients have attacks when quiet. They come on during exertion most frequently, as in walking up hill or something entailing sudden muscular effort; occasionally even the effort of dressing or of stooping to lace the shoes may bring on a paroxysm. Mental emotion is a second very potent cause. John Hunter appreciated this when he said that " his life was in the hands of any rascal who chose to annoy and tease him." In his case a fatal attack occurred during a fit of anger. A third, and in many instances the most important, factor is flatulent distention of the stomach. Another common exciting cause is cold; even the chill of getting out of bed in the morning or on bathing may bring on a paroxysm.

Usually during exertion or intense mental emotion the patient is seized with an agonizing pain in the region of the heart and a sense of constriction, as if the heart had been seized in a vice. The pains radiate up the neck and down the arm, and there may be numbness of the fingers or in the cardiac region. The face is usually pallid and may assume an ashy-gray tint, and not infrequently a profuse sweat breaks out over the surface. The paroxysm lasts from several seconds to a minute or two, during which, in severe attacks, the patient feels as if death were imminent. As pointed out by Latham, there are two elements in the paroxysm, the pain—*dolor pectoris*—and the indescribable feeling of anguish and sense of imminent dissolution—*angor animi*. There are great restlessness and anxiety, and the patient may drop dead at the height of the attack or faint and pass away in syncope. The condition of the heart during the attack is variable; the pulsations may be uniform and regular. The pulse tension, however, is usually increased, but it is surprising, even in cases of extreme severity, how slightly the character of the pulse may be altered. After the attack there may be eructations, or the passage of a large quantity of clear urine. The patient usually feels exhausted, and for a day or two may be badly shaken; in other instances in an hour or two the patient feels himself again. While dyspnœa is not a constant feature, the paroxysm is not infrequently associated with a form of asthma; there is wheezing in the bronchial tubes, which may come on very rapidly, and the patient gets short of breath. Many patients the subject of angina die suddenly without warning and not in a paroxysm. In other instances death follows in the first well-marked paroxysm, as in the case of Thomas Arnold. In a third group there are recurring attacks over long periods of years, as in John Hunter's case; while in a fourth group of cases there are rapidly recurring attacks for several days in succession, with progressive and increasing weakness of the heart.

With reference to the radiation of pain in angina, the studies of Mackenzie and of Head are of great interest. Head concludes that (1) in diseases of the heart, and more particularly in aortic disease, the pain is referred along the first, second, third, and fourth dorsal areas; (2) in angina pectoris the pain may be referred in addition along the fifth, sixth, and seventh, and even the eighth and ninth dorsal areas, and is always accompanied by pain in certain cervical areas.

Theories of Angina Pectoris.—(1) That it is a neuralgia of the cardiac nerves. In the true form the agonizing cramp-like character of the pain, the suddenness of the onset, and the associated features, are unlike any neuralgic affection. The pain, however, is undoubtedly in the cardiac plexus and radiates to adjacent nerves. It is interesting to note, in connection with the almost constant sclerosis of the coronary arteries in angina, that Thoma has found marked sclerosis of the temporal artery in migraine and Dana has met with local thickening of the arteries in some cases of neuralgia. (2) Heberden believes that it was a cramp of the heart-muscle itself. Cramp of certain muscular territories would better explain the attack. (3) That it is due to the extreme tension of the ventricular walls, in consequence of an acute dilatation associated, in the majority of cases, with affection of the coronary arteries. Traube, who supported this view, held that the agonizing pain resulted from the great stretching and tension of the nerves in the muscular substance. A modified form of this view is that there is a spasm of the coronary arteries with great increase of the intracardiac pressure.

(4) The theory of Allan Burns, revived by Potain and others, that the condition is one of transient ischæmia of the heart-muscle in consequence of disease, or spasm, of the coronary arteries. The condition known as intermittent claudication illustrates what may take place. In man (and in the horse), in consequence of thrombosis of the abdominal aorta or iliacs, transient paraplegia and spasm may follow exertion. The collateral circulation, ample when the limbs are at rest, is insufficient after the muscles are actively used, and a state of relative ischæmia is induced with loss of power, which disappears in a short time. This " intermittent claudication " theory has been applied to explain the angina paroxysm. A heart the coronary arteries of which are sclerotic or calcified, is in an analogous state, and any extra exertion is likely to be followed by a relative ischæmia and spasm. In Allan Burns's work on The Heart (1809) the theory is discussed at length, but he does not think that spasm is a necessary accompaniment of the ischæmia.

In fatal cases of angina the coronary arteries are almost invariably diseased either in their main divisions, or there is chronic endarteritis with great narrowing of the orifices at the root of the aorta. Experimentally, occlusion of the coronary arteries produces slowing of the heart's action, gradual dilatation, and death within a very few minutes. Cohnheim has shown that in the dog ligation of one of the large coronary branches produces within a minute a condition of arrhythmia, and within two minutes the heart ceases in diastole. These experiments, however, do not throw much light upon the etiology of angina pectoris. Extreme sclerosis of the coronary arteries is common, and a large majority of the cases present no symptoms of angina. Even in the cases of sudden death due to blocking of an artery, particularly the anterior branch of the coronary artery, there is usually no great pain either before or during the attack.

Diagnosis.—There are many grades of true angina. A man may have slight præcordial pain, a sense of distress and uneasiness, and radiation of the pains to the arm and neck. Such attacks following slight exertion, an indiscretion in diet, or a disturbing emotion, may alternate with attacks of much greater severity, or they may occur in connection with a pulse of increased tension and signs of general arterio-sclerosis. In the milder grades the diagnosis cannot rest upon the symptoms of the attack itself, since they may be simulated by the pseudo-angina; but the diagnosis should be based upon the examination of the heart and arteries and a careful consideration of the mode of onset and symptoms. The cases of pseudo-angina pectoris in women are, after all, the ones which call for the greatest care in the diagnosis, and attention to the points given in the table of Huchard will be of the greatest aid.

Pseudo-Angina Pectoris.—False angina may be divided into two main groups, the neurotic and the toxic. The former embraces the hysterical and neurasthenic cases, which are very common in women. Huchard has given an excellent differential table between the true and the spurious attacks.

TRUE ANGINA.	PSEUDO-ANGINA.
Most common between the ages of forty and fifty years.	At every age, even six years.
Most common in men. Attacks brought on by exertion.	Most common in women. Attacks spontaneous.
Attacks rarely periodical or nocturnal.	Often periodical and nocturnal.
Not associated with other symptoms.	Associated with nervous symptoms.
Vaso-motor form rare. Agonizing pain and sensation of compression by a vice.	Vaso-motor form common. Pain less severe; sensation of distention.
Pain of short duration. Attitude: silence, immobility.	Pain lasts one or two hours. Agitation and activity.
Lesions : sclerosis of coronary artery.	Neuralgia of nerves and cardioplexus.
Prognosis grave, often fatal.	Never fatal.
Arterial medication.	Antineuralgic medication.

A form which Nothnagel has described as *vaso-motor angina* is not infrequent. The symptoms set in with coldness and numbness in the extremities, followed by great præcordial pain and feelings of faintness. Some have recognized also a reflex variety.

Toxic Angina.—This embraces cases due to the abuse of tea, coffee, and tobacco. There are three groups of cases of so-called tobacco heart: First, the irritable heart of smokers, seen particularly in young lads, in which the symptoms are palpitation, irregularity, and rapid action; secondly, heart pain of a sharp, shooting character, which may be very severe; and, thirdly, attacks of such severity that they deserve the name of angina. Huchard remarks that they are usually of the vaso-motor type, accompanied with chilling of the extremities, feeble pulse, and a tendency to syncope. This author distinguishes between functional tobacco angina, due, he thinks, to spasmodic contraction of the coronary arteries, and an organic tobacco angina due to a nicotine arterio-sclerosis of these vessels.

Prognosis.—Cardiac pain without evidence of arterio-sclerosis or valve-disease is not of much moment. True angina is almost invariably associated with marked cardio-vascular lesions, in which the prognosis is always grave. With judicious treatment the attacks, however, may be long deferred, and a few instances recover completely. The prognosis is naturally more serious with aortic insufficiency and advanced arterio-sclerosis. Patients who have had well-marked attacks may live for many years, but much depends upon the care with which they regulate their daily life.

Treatment.—Patients subject to this affection should live a quiet life, avoiding particularly excitement and sudden muscular exertion. During the attack nitrite of amyl should be inhaled, as advised by Lauder Brunton. From 2 to 5 drops may be placed upon cotton-wool in a tumbler or upon the handkerchief. This is frequently of great service in the attack, relieving the agonizing pain and distress. Subjects of the disease should carry the *perles* of the nitrite of amyl with them, and use them on the first indication of an attack. In some instances the nitrite of amyl is quite powerless, though given freely. If within a minute or two relief is not obtained in this way, chloroform should at once be given. A few inhalations act promptly and give great relief. Should the pains continue, a hypodermic of morphia may be administered. In severe and repeated paroxysms a patient may display remarkable resistance to the action of this drug.

In the intervals, nitroglycerin may be given in full doses, as recommended by Murrell, or the nitrite of sodium (Matthew Hay). The nitroglycerin should be used for a long time and in increasing doses, beginning with 1 minim three times a day of the 1-per-cent solution, and increasing the dose 1 minim every five or six days until the patient complains of flushing or headache. The fluid extract of English hawthorn—crategus oxyacantha—has been strongly recommended by Jennings, Clements, and others.

Huchard recommends the iodides, believing that their prolonged use influences the arterio-sclerosis. Twenty grains three times a day may be given for several years, omitting the medicine for about ten days in each month. In some instances this treatment is certainly beneficial. Two men, both with arterio-sclerosis, ringing, accentuated aortic sound, and attacks of true angina, have under its use remained practically free from attacks—one case for nearly three, and the other for fully eight years. This treatment is, however, not always satisfactory, and I have had several cases in which the condition has not been at all relieved by it.

For the pseudo-angina, the treatment must be directed to the general nervous condition. Electricity is sometimes very beneficial, particularly the Franklinic form.

VI. CONGENITAL AFFECTIONS OF THE HEART.

These have only a limited clinical interest, as in a large proportion of the cases the anomaly is not compatible with life, and in others nothing can be done to remedy the defect or even to relieve the symptoms.

The congenital affections result from interruption of the normal course of development or from inflammatory processes—endocarditis; sometimes from a combination of both.

(a) Of *general anomalies* of development the following conditions may be mentioned: *Acardia*, absence of the heart, which has been met with in the monstrosity known by the same name; *double heart*, which has occasionally been found in extreme grades of fœtal deformity; *dextrocardia*, in which the heart is on the right side, either alone or as part of a general transposition of the viscera; *ectopia cordis*, a condition associated with fission of the chest wall and of the abdomen. The heart may be situated in the cervical, pectoral, or abdominal regions. Except in the abdominal variety the condition is very rarely compatible with extra-uterine life. Occasionally, as in a case reported by Holt, the child lives for some months, and the heart may be seen and felt beating beneath the skin in the epigastric region. This infant was five months old at the date of examination.

(*b*) **Anomalies of the Cardiac Septa.**—The septa of both auricles and ventricles may be defective, in which case the heart consists of but two chambers, the *cor biloculare* or reptilian heart. In the septum of the auricles there is a very common defect, owing to the fact that the membrane closing the foramen ovale has failed at one point to become attached to the ring, and leaves a valvular slit which may be large enough to admit the handle of a scalpel. Neither this nor the small cribriform perforations of the membrane are of any significance.

The foramen ovale may be patent without a trace of membrane closing it. In some instances this exists with other serious defects, such as stenosis of the pulmonary artery, or imperfection of the ventricular septum. In others the patent foramen ovale is the only anomaly, and in many instances it does not appear to have caused any embarrassment, as the condition has been found in persons who have died of various affections. The ventricular septum may be absent, the condition known as trilocular heart. Much more frequently there is a small defect in the upper portion of the septum, either in the situation of the membranous portion known as the "undefended space" or in the region situated just anterior to this. The anomaly is very frequently associated with narrowing of the pulmonary orifice or of the conus arteriosus of the right ventricle.

(*c*) **Anomalies and Lesions of the Valves.**—Numerical anomalies of the valves are not uncommon. The semilunar segments at the arterial orifices are not infrequently increased or diminished in number. Supernumerary segments are more frequent in the pulmonary artery than in the aorta. Four, or sometimes five, valves have been found. The segments may be of equal size, but, as a rule, the supernumerary valve is small.

Instead of three there may be only two semilunar valves, or, as it is termed, the *bicuspid condition*. In my experience, this is most frequent in the aortic valve. Of 21 instances only 2 occurred at the pulmonary orifice. Two of the valves have united, and from the ventricular face show either no trace of division or else a slight depression indicating where the union had occurred. From the aortic side there is usually to be seen some trace of division into two sinuses of Valsalva. There has been a discussion as to the origin of this condition, whether it is really an anomaly or whether it is not due to endocarditis, fœtal or post-natal. The combined segment is usually thickened, but the fact that this anomaly is met with in the fœtus without a trace of sclerosis or endocarditis shows that it may, in some cases at least, result from a developmental error.

Clinically this is a very important congenital defect, owing to the liability of the combined valve to sclerotic changes. Except two fœtal specimens all of my cases showed thickening and deformity, and in 15 of those which I have reported death resulted directly or indirectly from the lesion.

The little fenestrations at the margins of the sigmoid valves have no significance; they occur in a considerable proportion of all bodies.

Anomalies of the auriculo-ventricular valves are not often met with.

Fœtal endocarditis may occur either at the arterial or auriculo-ventricular orifices. It is nearly always of the chronic or sclerotic variety. Very rarely indeed is it of the warty or verrucose form. There are little nodular bodies, sometimes six or eight in number, on the mitral and tricuspid segments—the nodules of Albini—which represent the remains of fœtal structures, and must not be mistaken for endocardial outgrowths. The little rounded, bead-like hæmorrhages of a deep purple color, which are very common on the heart valves of children, are also not to be mistaken for the products of endocarditis. In fœtal endocarditis the segments are usually thickened at the edges, shrunken, and smooth. In the mitral and tricuspid valves the cusps are found united and the chordæ tendineæ are thickened and shortened. In the semilunar valves all trace of the segments has disappeared, leaving a stiff membranous diaphragm perforated by an oval or rounded orifice. It is sometimes very difficult to say whether this condition has resulted from fœtal endocarditis or whether it is an error in development. In very many instances the processes are combined; an anomalous valve becomes the seat of chronic sclerotic changes, and, according to Rauchfuss, endocarditis is more common on the right side of the heart only because the valves are here most often the seat of developmental errors.

Lesions at the Pulmonary Orifice.—*Stenosis* of this orifice is one of the commonest and most important of congenital heart affections. A slow endocarditis causes gradual union of the segments and narrowing of the orifice to such a degree that it only admits the smallest-sized probe. In some of the cases the smooth membranous condition of the combined segments is such that it would appear to be the result of faulty development. In some instances vegetations develop. The condition is compatible with life for many years, and in a considerable proportion of the cases of heart-disease above the tenth year this lesion is present. With it there may be defect of the ventricular septum. Pulmonary tuberculosis is a very common cause of death. Obliteration or *atresia* of the pulmonary orifice is less frequent but a more serious condition than stenosis. It is associated with defect of the ventricular septum or patency of the foramen ovale and persistence of the ductus arteriosus with hypertrophy of the right heart. *Stenosis of the conus arteriosus* of the right ventricle exists in a considerable proportion of the cases of obstruction at the pulmonary orifice. At the outset a developmental error, it may be combined with sclerotic changes. The ventricular septum is imperfect, the foramen ovale is usually open, and the ductus arteriosus patent. These three lesions at the pulmonary orifice constitute the most important group of all congenital cardiac affections. Of 181 instances of various congenital anomalies collected by Peacock 119 cases came under this category, and, according to this author, in 86 per cent of the patients living beyond the twelfth year the lesion is at this orifice.

Congenital lesions of the aortic orifice are not very frequent. Rauchfuss has collected 24 cases of stenosis and atresia; stenosis of the left conus arteriosus may also occur, a condition which is not incompatible with pro-

48

longed life. Ten of the 16 cases tabulated by Dilg were over thirty years of age.

Transposition of the large arterial trunks is a not uncommon anomaly. There may be neither hypertrophy, cyanosis, nor heart murmur.

Symptoms of Congenital Heart-disease.—Cyanosis occurs in over 90 per cent of the cases, and forms so distinctive a feature that the terms " blue disease " and " morbus cæruleus " are practically synonyms for congenital heart-disease. The lividity in a majority of cases appears early, within the first week of life, and may be general or confined to the lips, nose, and ears, and to the fingers and toes. In some instances there is in addition a general dusky suffusion, and in the most extreme grades the skin is almost purple. It may vary a good deal and may only be intense on exertion. The external temperature is low. Dyspnœa on exertion and cough are common symptoms. A great increase in the number of the red corpuscles has been noted by Gibson and by Vaquez. In a case of Gibson's there were above eight millions of red blood-corpuscles to the cubic millimetre. The children rarely thrive, and often display a lethargy of both mind and body. The fingers and toes are clubbed to a degree rarely met with in any other affection. The cause of the cyanosis has been much discussed. Morgagni referred it to the general congestion of the venous system due to obstruction, and this view was supported in a paper, one of the ablest that has been written on the subject, by Moreton Stillé. Morrison's recent analysis of 75 cases of congenital heart-disease shows that closure of the pulmonary orifice and patency of the foramen ovale and the ventricular septum are the lesions most frequently associated with cyanosis, and he concludes that the deficient aëration of the blood owing to diminished lung function is the most important factor. Another view, advocated by William Hunter, was that the discoloration was due to the admixture in the heart of venous and arterial blood; but lesions may exist which permit of very free mixture without producing cyanosis. The question of the cause of cyanosis really cannot be considered as settled. Variot has recently made the suggestion that the cause is not entirely cardiac, but is associated with disturbance throughout the whole circulatory system, and particularly a vaso-motor paresis and malaëration of the red blood-corpuscles.

Diagnosis.—In the case of children, cyanosis, with or without enlargement of the heart, and the existence of a murmur are sufficient, as a rule, to determine the presence of a congenital heart-lesion. The cyanosis gives us no clew to the precise nature of the trouble, as it is a symptom common to many lesions and it may be absent in certain conditions. The murmur is usually systolic in character. It is, however, not always present, and there are instances on record of complicated congenital lesions in which the examination showed normal heart-sounds. In two or three instances fœtal endocarditis has been diagnosed *in gravida* by the presence of a rough systolic murmur, and the condition has been corroborated subsequent to the birth of the child. Hypertrophy is present in a majority of the cases of congenital defect. The fatal event may be caused by abscess of the brain. It is impossible in a work of this sort to enter upon elaborate details in differential diagnosis between the various congenital heart-lesions. I here abstract the conclusions of Hochsinger:

" (1) In childhood, loud, rough, musical heart-murmurs, with normal or only slight increase in the heart-dulness, occur only in congenital heart-disease. The acquired endocardial defects with loud heart-murmurs in young children are almost always associated with great increase in the heart-dulness. In the transposition of the large arterial trunks there may be no cyanosis, no heart-murmur, and an absence of hypertrophy.

" (2) In young children heart-murmurs with great increase in the cardiac dulness and feeble apex beat suggest congenital changes. The increased dulness is chiefly of the right heart, whereas the left is only slightly altered. On the other hand, in the acquired endocarditis in children, the left heart is chiefly affected and the apex beat is visible; the dilatation of the right heart comes late and does not materially change the increased strength of the apex beat.

" (3) The entire absence of murmurs at the apex, with their evident presence in the region of the auricles and over the pulmonary orifice, is always an important element in differential diagnosis, and points rather to septum defect or pulmonary stenosis than to endocarditis.

" (4) An abnormally weak second pulmonic sound associated with a distinct systolic murmur is a symptom which in early childhood is only to be explained by the assumption of a congenital pulmonary stenosis, and possesses therefore an importance from a point of differential diagnosis which is not to be underestimated.

" (5) Absence of a palpable thrill, despite loud murmurs which are heard over the whole præcordial region, is rare except with congenital defects in the septum, and it speaks therefore against an acquired cardiac affection.

" (6) Loud, especially vibratory, systolic murmurs, with the point of maximum intensity over the upper third of the sternum, associated with a lack of marked symptoms of hypertrophy of the left ventricle, are very important for the diagnosis of a persistence of the ductus Botalli, and cannot be explained by the assumption of an endocarditis of the aortic valve."

Treatment.—The child should be warmly clad and guarded from all circumstances liable to excite bronchitis. In the attacks of urgent dyspnœa with lividity blood should be freely let. Saline cathartics are also useful. Digitalis must be used with care; it is sometimes beneficial in the later stages. When the compensation fails, the indications for treatment are those of valvular disease in adults.

III. DISEASES OF THE ARTERIES.

I. DEGENERATIONS.

Fatty degeneration of the intima is extremely common, and is seen in the form of yellowish-white spots in the aorta and larger vessels. *Calcification* of the arterial wall follows fatty degeneration and sclerosis, and is associated with atheromatous changes. It occurs in the intima and the media. In the latter it produces what is sometimes known as annular calcification, which occurs particularly in the middle coat of medium-sized vessels and may convert them into firm tubes.

Hyaline degeneration may attack either the larger or the smaller vessels. In the former the intima is converted into a smooth, homogeneous substance; this is commonly an initial stage of arterio-sclerosis; here it is a transformation of the endothelial lining. Of the smaller arteries and capillaries hyaline metamorphosis is oftenest seen in the glomeruli of the kidneys. It is not to be confounded with the amyloid change which is prone to occur in the same situation. The condition is variously regarded as due to coagulation of an albuminous fluid and hyaline metamorphosis of leucocytes or of fibrin. This substance reacts like the last with Weigert's fibrin stain.

II. ARTERIO-SCLEROSIS (*Arterio-capillary Fibrosis*).

The conception of arterio-sclerosis as an independent affection—a general disease of the vascular system—is due to Gull and Sutton.

Definition.—A condition of thickening, diffuse or circumscribed, beginning in the intima, consequent upon primary changes in the media and adventitia, but which later involves the other coats. The process leads, in the larger arteries, to what is known as atheroma and to endarteritis deformans.

Etiology.—(1) As an involution process arterio-sclerosis is an accompaniment of old age, and is the expression of the natural wear and tear to which the tubes are subjected. Longevity is a vascular question, which has been well expressed in the axiom that "a man is only as old as his arteries." To a majority of men death comes primarily or secondarily through this portal. The onset of what may be called physiological arterio-sclerosis depends, in the first place, upon the quality of arterial tissue (vital rubber) which the individual has inherited, and secondly upon the amount of wear and tear to which he has subjected it. That the former plays the most important *rôle* is shown in the cases in which arterio-sclerosis sets in early in life in individuals in whom none of the recognized etiological factors can be found. Thus, for instance, a man of twenty-eight or twenty-nine may have the arteries of a man of sixty, and a man of forty may present vessels as much degenerated as they should be at eighty. Entire families sometimes show this tendency to early arterio-sclerosis—a tendency which cannot be explained in any other way than that in the make-up of the machine bad material was used for the tubing.

More commonly the arterio-sclerosis results from the bad use of good vessels, and among the circumstances which tend to produce this condition are the following:

(2) *Chronic Intoxications.*—Alcohol, lead, gout, and syphilis play an important *rôle* in the causation of arterio-sclerosis, although the precise mode of their action is not yet very clear. They may act, as Traube suggests, by increasing the peripheral resistance in the smaller vessels and in this way raising the blood tension, or possibly, as Bright taught, they alter the quality of the blood and render more difficult its passage through the capillaries.

The poison of syphilis and of gout may act directly on the arteries, producing degenerative changes in the media and adventitia.

(3) *Overeating.*—Many authors attribute an important part of the etiology of arterio-sclerosis to the overfilling of the blood-vessels which occurs when unnecessarily large quantities of food and drink are taken. Particularly is this the case in stout persons who take very little exercise.

(4) *Overwork of the muscles,* which acts by increasing the peripheral resistance and by raising the blood-pressure.

(5) *Renal Disease.*—The relation between the arterial and kidney lesions has been much discussed, some regarding the arterial degeneration as secondary, others as primary. There are certainly two groups of cases, one in which the arterio-sclerosis is the first change, and the other in which it appears to be secondary to a primary affection of the kidneys. The former occurs, I believe, with much greater frequency than has been supposed.

Morbid Anatomy.—Thoma divides the cases into *primary* arterio-sclerosis, in which there are local changes in the arteries leading to dilatation and a compensatory increase of the connective tissue of the intima; *secondary* arterio-sclerosis, due to changes in the arteries which follow increased resistance to the blood-flow in the peripheral vessels. This increased tension leads to dilatation and to slowing of the blood-stream and a secondary compensatory development of the intima.

In a study of 41 autopsies upon arterio-sclerotic cases from my wards, Councilman follows the useful division into nodular, senile, and diffuse forms.

(a) *Nodular Form.*—In the circumscribed or nodular variety the macroscopic changes are very characteristic. The aorta presents, in the early stages, from the ring to bifurcation, numerous flat projections, yellowish or yellowish-white in color, hemispherical in outline, and situated particularly about the orifices of the branches. In the early stage these patches are scattered and do not involve the entire intima. In more advanced grades the patches undergo atheromatous changes. The material constituting the button undergoes softening and breaks up into granular material, consisting of molecular *débris*—the so-called atheromatous abscess.

In the circumscribed or nodular arterio-sclerosis the primary alteration consists in a degeneration or a local infiltration in the media and adventitia, chiefly about the vasa vasorum. The affection is really a mesarteritis and a periarteritis. These changes lead to the weakening of the wall in the affected area, at which spot the proliferative changes commence in the intima, particularly in the subendothelial structures, with gradual thickening and the formation of an atheromatous button or a patch of nodular arterio-sclerosis. The researches of Thoma have shown that this is really a compensatory process, and that before its degeneration the nodular button, which post mortem projects beyond the lumen, during life fills up and obliterates what would otherwise be a depression of the wall in consequence of the weakening of the media. A similar process goes on in the smaller vessels, and in any one of the smaller branches it can be readily seen on section that each patch of endarteritis corresponds to a defect in the media and often to changes in the adventitia. The condition is one which may lead to rapid dilatation or to the production of an aneurism, particularly in the early stage, before the weakened spot is thickened and strengthened by the intimal changes.

(b) *Senile Arterio-sclerosis.*—The larger arteries are dilated and tortuous, the walls thin but stiff, and often converted into rigid tubes. The subendothelial tissue undergoes degeneration and in spots breaks down, forming the so-called atheromatous abscess, the contents of which consist of a molecular *débris.* They may open into the lumen, when they are known as atheromatous ulcers. The greater portion of the intima may be occupied by rough calcareous plates, with here and there fissures and losses of substance, upon which not infrequently white thrombi are deposited. Microscopically there is extreme degeneration of the coats, particularly of the media. Senile atrophy of the liver and kidneys usually accompanies these changes. Senile changes are common in other organs. The heart may be small and is not necessarily hypertrophied. In 7 of 14 cases of Councilman's series there was no enlargement. Brown atrophy is common.

(c) *Diffuse Arterio-sclerosis.*—The process is widespread throughout the aorta and its branches, in the former usually, but not necessarily, associated with the nodular form. The subjects of this variety are usually middle-aged men, but it may occur early. Of the 27 in Councilman's series belonging to this group the majority were between the ages of forty and fifty-five. The youngest was a negro of twenty-three and the oldest a man of sixty. The affection is very prevalent among negroes; less than 50 per cent were in whites, whereas the ratio of colored to white patients in the wards is one to seven. The affection is met with in strongly built, muscular men and, as Councilman remarks, they rarely present on the autopsy table signs of general anasarca or, if œdema exists, it has come on during the last few days of life. The aorta and its branches are more or less dilated, the branches sometimes more than the trunk. The intima may be smooth and show very slight changes to the naked eye; more commonly there are scattered elevated areas of an opaque white color, some of which may have undergone atheromatous changes as in the senile form.

Microscopically in the several forms the *media* shows necrotic and hyaline changes, involving in the larger arteries both muscular and elastic elements, and the *intima* presents a great increase in the subendothelial connective tissue, which is particularly marked opposite areas of advanced degeneration in the media. The small arteries—those in the kidneys, for example—show " a thickening of the wall, due to the formation of a homogeneous hyaline tissue within the muscular coat. This tissue contains but few cells, is faintly striated, and stains a light brown in the osmic acid used in the hardening solution. In many of the smallest vessels nothing can be seen of the elastic lamina, in others only fragments can be made out, in others it is preserved. . . . The muscular fibres of the media show marked atrophic changes. Fatty degeneration of the cells can be made out both in fresh sections and after hardening in Flemming's solution. The nuclei are thin and atrophic and vacuoles are sometimes seen in them. In some arteries the muscle-fibres have almost disappeared and the media is changed into a homogeneous tissue, similar to that in the thickened intima " (Councilman). The degeneration of the media is most marked in the smaller arteries. The capillaries are thickened, particularly those of the glomeruli of the kidneys, which are often obliterated and involved in extensive hyaline degeneration.

It is in this group of cases that the heart shows the most important changes. The average weight in the cases referred to was over 450 grammes, and there were two cases in which without valvular disease the weight was over 800 grammes. Fibrous myocarditis is often present, particularly when the coronary arteries are involved. The semilunar valves are sometimes opaque and sclerotic, and may be incompetent. The kidneys may show extensive sclerosis, but in many cases the changes are so slight that macroscopically they might be overlooked. They may be increased in size. The capsule is usually adherent, the surface a little rough, and very often presents atrophic areas at a lower level, of a deep-red color. Increased consistence is always present.

Sclerosis of the pulmonary artery is met with in all conditions which for a long time increase the tension in the lesser circulation, particularly in mitral valve disease and in emphysema. Sometimes the sclerosis reaches a high grade and is accompanied with aneurismal dilatation of the primary and secondary branches, more rarely with insufficiency of the pulmonary valve. In a remarkable case of a young man of twenty-four, reported by Romberg from Curschmann's clinic, the pulmonary arteries were involved in most extensive arterio-sclerosis; the main branches were dilated, and the smaller branches were the seat of the most extreme sclerotic changes. On the other hand, the aorta and its branches were normal. The heart was greatly hypertrophied, and the clinical symptoms were those of a congenital heart affection. In many cases of arterio-sclerosis the condition is not confined to the arteries, but extends not only to the capillaries but also to the veins, and may properly be termed an *angio-sclerosis*.

Sclerosis of the veins—*phlebo-sclerosis*—is not at all an uncommon accompaniment of arterio-sclerosis, and is a condition to which of late a good deal of attention has been paid. It is seen in conditions of heightened blood-pressure, as in the portal system in cirrhosis of the liver and in the pulmonary veins in mitral stenosis. The affected vessels are usually dilated, and the intima shows, as in the arteries, a compensatory thickening, which is particularly marked in those regions in which the media is thinned. The new-formed tissue in the endophlebitis may undergo hyaline degeneration, and is sometimes extensively calcified. In a case of fibroid obliteration of the portal vein of long standing, I found the intima of the greatly dilated gastric, splenic, and mesenteric veins extensively calcified. Without existing arterio-sclerosis the peripheral veins may be sclerotic, usually in conditions of debility, but occasionally in young persons.

Symptoms.—*Increased Tension.*—The pressure with which the blood flows in the arteries depends upon the degree of peripheral resistance and the force of the ventricular contraction. A high-tension pulse may exist with very little arterio-sclerosis; but, as a rule, when the condition has been persistent, the sclerosis and high tension are found together. The pulse wave is slow in its ascent, enduring, subsides slowly, and in the intervals between the beats the vessel remains full and firm. It may be very difficult to obliterate the pulse, and the firmest pressure on the radial or the temporal artery may not be sufficient to annihilate the pulse wave beyond the point of pressure. This is not always a sign of high tension. The anastomotic or recurrent pulse may be felt even when the tension is low, as in the early stage of typhoid fever. Pressure on the ulnar artery at once obliterates it.* The sphygmographic tracing shows a sloping, short up-stroke, no percussion wave, and a slow, gradual descent, in which the dicrotic wave is very slightly marked. It may be difficult to estimate how much of the hardness and firmness is due to the tension of the blood within the vessel, and how much to the thickening of the wall. But if, for example, when the radial is compressed with the index-finger the artery can be felt beyond the point of compression, its walls are sclerosed.

Hypertrophy of the Heart.—In consequence of the peripheral resistance and increased work the left ventricle increases in size, and some of the purest examples of simple hypertrophy occur in this condition. The chamber may be little, if at all, dilated. The apex beat is dislocated in advanced cases an inch or more beyond the nipple line. The impulse is heaving and forcible. The aortic second sound is clear, ringing, and accentuated.

The combination of increased arterial tension, a palpable thickening of the arteries, hypertrophy of the left ventricle, and accentuation of the aortic second sound are signs pathognomonic of arterio-sclerosis. From this period of establishment the course of the disease may be very varied. For years the patient may have good health, and be in a condition analogous to that of a person with a well-compensated valvular lesion. There may be no renal symptoms, or there may be the passage of a larger amount of urine than normal, with transient albuminuria, and now and then hyaline tube-casts. The subsequent history is extraordinarily diverse, depending upon the vascular territory in which the sclerosis is most advanced, or upon the accidents which are so liable to happen, and the symptoms may be cardiac, cerebral, renal, etc.

(1) *Cardiac.*—The involvement of the coronary arteries may lead to the various symptoms already referred to under that section—thrombosis

---

* The student is referred to Ewart On the Pulse, and to his larger Heart Studies.

with sudden death, fibroid degeneration of the heart, aneurism of the heart, rupture, and angina pectoris. Angina pectoris is not uncommon, and in the true variety is almost always associated with arterio-sclerosis. A second important group of cardiac symptoms results from the dilatation which ultimately may follow the hypertrophy. The patient then presents all the symptoms of cardiac insufficiency—dyspnœa, scanty urine, and very often serous effusions. If the case has come under observation for the first time the clinical picture is that of chronic valvular disease, and the existence of a loud blowing murmur at the apex may throw the practitioner off his guard. Many cases terminate in this way.

(2) The *cerebral* symptoms of arterio-sclerosis are varied and important, and embrace those of many degenerative processes, acute and chronic (which follow sclerosis of the smaller branches), and cerebral hæmorrhage.

Transient hemiplegia, monoplegia, or aphasia may occur in advanced arterio-sclerosis. Recovery may be perfect. It is difficult to say upon what these attacks depend. Spasm of the arteries has been suggested, but the condition of the smallest arteries is not very favorable to this view. Peabody has recently called attention to these cases, which are more common than is indicated in the literature. Vertigo occurs frequently, and may be either simple, or is associated with slow pulse and syncopal or epileptiform attacks (Grasset, Church).

(3) *Renal* symptoms supervene in a large number of the cases. A sclerosis, patchy or diffuse, is present in a majority of the cases at the time of autopsy, and the condition is practically that of contracted kidney. It is seen in a typical manner in the senile form, and not infrequently develops early in life as a direct sequence of the diffuse variety. It is often difficult to decide clinically (and the question is one upon which good observers might not agree in a given case) whether the arterial or the renal disease has been primary.

(4) Among other events in arterio-sclerosis may be mentioned gangrene of the extremities, due either directly to endarteritis or to the dislodgment of thrombi. Respiratory symptoms are not uncommon, particularly bronchitis and the symptoms associated with emphysema.

Treatment.—In the late stages the conditions must be treated as they arise in connection with the various viscera. In the early stages, before any local symptoms are manifest, the patient should be enjoined to live a quiet, well-regulated life, avoiding excesses in food and drink. It is usually best to explain frankly the condition of affairs, and so gain his intelligent co-operation. Special attention should be paid to the state of the bowels and urine, and the secretion of the skin should be kept active by daily baths. Alcohol in all forms should be prohibited, and the food should be restricted to plain, wholesome articles. The use of mineral waters or a residence every year at one of the mineral springs is usually serviceable. If there has been a syphilitic history an occasional course of iodide of potassium is indicated, and whenever the pulse tension is high nitroglycerin may be used.

In cases which come under observation for the first time with dyspnœa, slight lividity, and signs of cardiac insufficiency, venesection is indicated.

In some instances, with very high tension, striking relief is afforded by the abstraction of 20 ounces of blood.

III. ANEURISM.

The following forms of aneurism are usually recognized:

(a) The *true,* in which the sac is formed of one or more of the arterial coats. This may be fusiform, cylindrical, or cirsoid (in which the dilatation is in an artery and its branches), or it may be circumscribed or sacculated. Aneurisms are usually fusiform, resulting from uniform dilatation of the vessel, or saccular.

(b) The *false* aneurism, in which there is rupture of all the coats, and the blood is free (or circumscribed) in the tissues.

(c) The *dissecting* aneurism, which results from injury or laceration of the internal coat. The blood dissects betwen the layers; hence the name, dissecting aneurism. This occurs usually in the aorta, persisting for years.

(d) *Arterio-venous* aneurism results when a communication is established between an artery and a vein. A sac may intervene, in which case we have what is called a varicose aneurism; but in many cases the communication is direct and the chief change is in the vein, which is dilated, tortuous, and pulsating, the condition being termed an aneurismal varix.

Etiology and Pathology.—Aneurisms arise: (a) By the gradual diffuse distention of the arterial coats, which have been weakened by arterio-sclerosis, particularly in its early stages, before compensatory endarteritis develops. The arch of the aorta is often dilated in this way so as to form an irregular aneurism.

(b) In consequence of circumscribed loss of resisting power in the media and adventitia, and often from a laceration of the media. This is the most common cause of sacculated aneurism. The laceration is frequently found in the ascending portion of the arch and occurs early in the process of arterio-sclerosis, before the compensatory thickening has taken place. Occasionally one meets with remarkable specimens illustrating the important part played by this process. The intima may also be torn. In a case of Daland's there was just above the aortic valves an old transverse tear of the intima, extending almost the entire circumference of the vessel. Sclerosis of the media and adventitia had taken place and the process was evidently of some standing. An inch or more above it was a fresh transverse rent which had produced a dissecting aneurism. These arterio-sclerotic aneurisms, as they are called, are found also in the smaller vessels.

(c) *Embolic Aneurism.*—When an embolus has lodged in a vessel and permanently plugged it, aneurismal dilatation may follow on the proximal side. The embolus itself may, if a calcified fragment from a valve, lacerate the wall, or if infected may produce inflammation and softening.

(d) *Mycotic Aneurism.*—The importance of this form has been specially considered by Eppinger in his exhaustive monograph. The occurrence of multiple aneurisms in malignant endocarditis has been observed by several writers. Probably the first case in which the mycotic nature was recognized was one which occurred at the Montreal General Hospital and is reported in full in my lectures on malignant endocarditis. In addition to the ulceration of the valves there were four aneurisms of the arch, of which one was large and saccular, and three were not bigger than cherries. An extensive growth of micrococci was present.

A form of parasitic aneurism which occurs with great frequency in the mesenteric arteries of the horse is due to the development of the *strongylus armatus*.

Thoma has described a "traction" aneurism of the concavity of the arch at the point of insertion of the remnant of the ductus Botalli (Virchow's Archiv, Bd. 122).

And, lastly, there are cases in which without any definite cause there is a tendency to the development of aneurisms in various parts of the body. A remarkable instance of it in our profession was afforded by the brilliant Thomas King Chambers, who first had an aneurism in the left popliteal artery, eleven years subsequently an aneurism in the right leg which was cured by pressure, and finally aneurism of both carotid arteries.

Incidence of Aneurism.—At St. Bartholomew's Hospital during thirty years there were 631 cases of aneurism. In 468 the disease affected the aorta, in 80 the popliteal, in 21 the femoral, in 14 the subclavian, in 8 the carotid, in 6 the external iliac artery (Oswald A. Browne).

ANEURISM OF THE THORACIC AORTA.

The causes which favor the development of arterio-sclerosis prevail in aortic aneurism, particularly alcohol, syphilis, and overwork. The greatest danger probably is in strong muscular men with commencing degenerative processes in the arteries (a consequence of syphilis or alcohol or a result of hereditary weakness of the arterial tissues), who during a sudden muscular exertion are liable to lacerate the media, the intima not yet being strengthened by compensatory thickening over a spot of mesarteritis. Aneurisms of the thoracic aorta vary greatly in size and shape. A majority of them are saccular. They may be small and situated just above the aortic ring. Others form large tumors which project externally and occupy a large portion of the upper thorax. Small sacs from the descending portion of the arch may compress the trachea or the bronchi. In the thoracic portion the sac may erode the vertebræ or grow into the pleural cavity and compress the lung. In some instances it grows through the ribs and appears in the back.

Symptoms.—The chief influence of an aneurism is manifested in what are known as pressure effects. In the absence of these the aneurisms attain a large size without producing symptoms or seriously interfering with the circulation. Indeed, a useful clinical subdivision as given by Bramwell is into three groups—aneurisms which are entirely latent and give no physical signs; aneurisms which present signs of intrathoracic pressure, although it is difficult or impossible to determine the nature of the lesion producing the pressure; and, lastly, aneurisms which produce distinct tumors with well-marked pressure symptoms and external signs. Broadbent makes another useful division into aneurism of symptoms and aneurism of physical signs. It is perhaps best to consider aneurisms of the aorta according to the situation of the tumor.

(*a*) *Aneurisms of the Ascending Portion of the Arch.*—When just above the sinuses of Valsalva they are often small and latent. The first symptom may be rupture, which usually takes place into the pericardium and causes instant death. Above the sinuses, along the convex border of the ascending part, aneurism frequently develops, and may grow to a large size, either passing out into the right pleura or forward, pointing at the second or third interspace, eroding the ribs and sternum, and producing large external tumors. In this situation the sac is liable, indeed, to compress the superior vena cava, causing engorgement of the vessels of the head and arm, sometimes compressing only the subclavian vein, and causing enlargement and œdema of the right arm. Perforation may take place into the superior vena cava, of which accident Pepper and Griffith have collected 29 cases. In rare instances, when the aneurism springs from the concave side of the vessels, the tumor may appear to the left of the sternum. Large aneurisms in this situation may cause much dislocation of the heart, pushing it down and to the left, and sometimes compressing the inferior vena cava, and causing swelling of the feet and ascites. The right recurrent laryngeal nerve is often pressed upon by these tumors. The innominate artery is rarely involved. Death commonly follows from rupture into the pericardium, the pleura, or into the superior cava; less commonly from rupture externally, sometimes from syncope.

(*b*) *Aneurisms of the Transverse Arch.*—The direction of their growth is most commonly backward, but they may grow forward, erode the sternum, and produce large tumors. The tumor presents in the middle line and to the right of the sternum much more often than to the left, which occurred in only 4 of 35 aneurisms in this situation (O. A. Browne). Even when small and producing no external tumor they may cause marked pressure signs in their growth backward toward the spine, involving the trachea and the œsophagus, and giving rise to cough, which is often of a paroxysmal character, and dysphagia. The left recurrent laryngeal is often involved in its course round the arch. A small aneurism from the lower or posterior wall of the arch may compress a bronchus, inducing bronchorrhœa, gradual bronchiectasy, and suppuration in the lung—a process which by no means infrequently causes death in aneurism, and a condition which at the Montreal General Hospital we were in the habit of terming aneurismal phthisis. Occasionally enormous aneurisms develop in this situation, and grow into both pleuræ, extending between the manubrium and the vertebræ; they may persist for years. The sac may be evident at the sternal notch. The innominate artery, less commonly the left carotid and subclavian, may be involved in the sac, and the radial or carotid pulse may be absent or retarded. Pressure on the sympathetic may at first cause dilatation and subsequently contraction of the pupil. Sometimes the thoracic duct is compressed.

The ascending and transverse portions of the arch are not infrequently involved together, usually without the branches; the tumor grows upward, or upward and to the right.

(*c*) *Aneurisms of the Descending Portion of the Arch.*—The sac projects to the left and backward, and often erodes the vertebræ from the third to the sixth dorsal, causing great pain and sometimes compression of the spinal cord. Dysphagia is common. Pressure on the bronchi may induce bronchiectasy, with retention of secretions, and fever. A tumor may appear externally in the region of the scapula, and here attain an enormous size. Death not infrequently occurs from rupture into the pleura.

(*d*) *Aneurisms of the Descending Thoracic Aorta.*—The larger number occur close to the diaphragm, the sac lying upon or to the left of the bodies of the lower dorsal vertebræ, which are often eroded. The sac may reach a large size and form a very large tumor in the back.

Diagnosis and Physical Signs.—*Inspection.*—A good light is essential; cases are often overlooked owing to a hasty inspection. In many instances it is negative. On either side of the sternum there may be abnormal pulsation, due to dislocation of the heart, to deformity of the thorax, or to retraction of the lung. The aneurismal pulsation is usually above the level of the third rib and most commonly to the right of the sternum, either in the first or second interspace. It may be only a diffuse heaving impulse without any external tumor. Often the impulse is noticed only when the chest is looked at obliquely in a favorable light. When the innominate is involved the throbbing may pass into the neck or be apparent at the sternal notch. Posteriorly, when pulsation occurs, it is most commonly found to the left of the spine. An external tumor is present in many cases, projecting either through the upper part of the sternum or to the right, sometimes involving the sternum and costal cartilages on both sides, forming a swelling the size of a cocoa-nut or even larger. The skin is thin, often blood-stained, or it may have ruptured, exposing the laminæ of the sac. The apex beat may be much dislocated, particularly when the sac is large. It is more commonly a dislocation from pressure than from enlargement of the heart itself.

Palpation.—The area and degree of pulsation are best determined by palpation. When the aneurism is deep-seated and not apparent externally, the bimanual method should be used, one hand upon the spine and the other on the sternum. When the sac has perforated the chest wall the impulse is, as a rule, forcible, slow, heaving, and expansile. The resistance may be very great if there are thick laminæ beneath the skin; more rarely the sac is soft and fluctuating. The hand upon the sac, or on the region in which it is in contact with the chest wall, feels in many cases a diastolic shock, often of great intensity, which forms one of the valuable physical signs of aneurism. A systolic thrill is sometimes present, not so often in saccular aneurisms as in the dilatation of the arch. The pulsation may sometimes be felt in the suprasternal notch.

Percussion.—The small and deep-seated aneurisms are in this respect negative. In the larger tumors, as soon as the sac reaches the chest wall, there is produced an area of abnormal dulness, the position of which depends upon the part of the aorta affected. Aneurisms of the ascending arch grow forward and to the right, producing dulness on one side of the manubrium; those from the transverse arch produce dulness in the middle line, extending toward the left of the sternum, while aneurisms of the descending portion most commonly produce dulness in the left interscapular and scapular regions. The percussion note is flat and gives a feeling of increased resistance.

Auscultation.—Adventitious sounds are not always to be heard. Even in a large sac there may be no murmur. Much depends upon the thickness of the laminæ of fibrin. An important sign, particularly if heard over a dull region, is a ringing, accentuated second sound, a phenomenon rarely missed in large aneurisms of the aortic arch. A systolic murmur may be present; sometimes a double murmur, in which case the diastolic *bruit* is usually due to associated aortic insufficiency. The systolic murmur alone is of little moment in the diagnosis of an aneurismal sac. With the single stethoscope the shock of the impulse with the first sound is sometimes very marked.

Among other physical signs of importance are slowing of the pulse in the arteries beyond the aneurism, or in those involved in the sac. There may, for instance, be a marked difference between the right and left radial, both in volume and time. A physical sign of large thoracic aneurism, which I have not seen referred to, is obliteration of the pulse in the abdominal aorta and its branches. My attention was called to this in a patient who was stated to have aortic insufficiency. There was a well-marked diastolic murmur, but in the femorals and in the aorta I was surprised to find no trace of pulsation, and not the slightest throbbing in the abdominal aorta or in the peripheral arteries of the leg. The circulation was, however, unimpaired in them and there was no dilatation of the veins. Attracted by this, I then made a careful examination of the patient's back, when the circumstance was discovered, which neither the patient himself nor any of his physicians had noticed, that he had a very large area of pulsation in the left scapular region. The sac probably was large enough to act as a reservoir annihilating the ventricular systole, and converting the intermittent into a continuous stream.

The *tracheal tugging*, a valuable sign in deep-seated aneurisms, was described by Surgeon-Major Oliver, and was specially studied by my colleagues Ross and MacDonnell * at the Montreal General Hospital. Oliver gives the following directions: " Place the patient in the erect position, and direct him to close his mouth and elevate his chin to almost the full extent; then grasp the cricoid cartilage between the finger and thumb, and use steady and gentle upward pressure on it, when, if dilatation or aneurism exists, the pulsation of the aorta will be distinctly felt transmitted through the trachea to the hand." On several occasions I have known this to be a sign of great value in the diagnosis of deep-seated aneurisms. I have never felt it in tumors, or in the extreme dynamic dilatation of aortic insufficiency. It may be visible in the thyroid cartilage.

Occasionally a systolic murmur may be heard in the trachea, as pointed

---

* London Lancet, 1891.

out by David Drummond, or even at the patient's mouth, when opened. This is either the sound conveyed from the sac, or is produced by the air as it is driven out of the wind-pipe during the systole.

An important but variable feature in thoracic aneurism is *pain,* which is particularly marked in deep-seated tumors. It is usually paroxysmal, sharp, and lancinating, often very severe when the tumor is eroding the vertebræ, or perforating the chest wall. In the latter case, after perforation the pain may cease. Anginal attacks are not uncommon, particularly in aneurisms at the root of the aorta. Frequently the pain radiates down the left arm or up the neck, sometimes along the upper intercostal nerves. *Cough* results either from the direct pressure on the wind-pipe, or is associated with bronchitis. The expectoration in these instances is abundant, thin, and watery; subsequently it becomes thick and turbid. Paroxysmal cough of a peculiar brazen, ringing character is a characteristic symptom in some cases, particularly when there is pressure on the recurrent laryngeal nerves, or the cough may have a peculiar wheezy quality—the " goose cough."

Dyspnœa, which is common in cases of aneurism of the transverse portion, is not necessarily associated with pressure on the recurrent laryngeal nerves, but may be due directly to compression of the trachea or the left bronchus. It may occur with marked stridor. Loss of voice and hoarseness are consequences of pressure on the recurrent laryngeal, usually the left, inducing either a spasm in the muscles of the left vocal cord or paralysis.

Paralysis of an abductor on one side may be present without any symptoms. It is more particularly, as Semon states, when the paralytic contractures supervene that the attention is called to laryngeal symptoms.

Hæmorrhage in thoracic aneurism may come from (*a*) the soft granulations in the trachea at the point of compression, in which case the sputa are blood-tinged, but large quantities of blood are not lost; (*b*) from rupture of the sac into the trachea or bronchi; (*c*) from perforation into the lung or erosion of the lung tissue. The bleeding may be profuse, rapidly proving fatal, and is a common cause of death. It may persist for weeks or months, in which case it is simply hæmorrhagic weeping through the sac, which is exposed in the trachea. In some instances, even after a very profuse hæmorrhage, the patient recovers and may live for years. A man with well-marked thoracic aneurism, whom I showed to my class at the University of Pennsylvania and who had had several brisk hæmorrhages, died four years after, having in the meantime enjoyed average health. Death from hæmorrhage is relatively more common in aneurism of the third portion of the arch and of the descending aorta.

Difficulty of swallowing is a comparatively rare symptom, and may be due either to spasm or to direct compression. The sound should never be passed in these cases, as the œsophagus may be almost eroded and a perforation may be made.

Heart Symptoms.—Pain has been referred to; it is often anginal in character, and is most common when the root of the aorta is involved. The heart is hypertrophied in less than one half the cases. The aortic valves are sometimes incompetent, either from disease of the segments or from stretching of the aortic ring.

Among other signs and symptoms, venous compression, which has already been mentioned, may involve one subclavian or the superior vena cava. A curious phenomenon in intrathoracic aneurism is the clubbing of the fingers and incurving of the nails of one hand, of which two examples have been under my care, in both without any special distention or signs of venous engorgement. Tumors of the arch may involve the pulmonary artery, producing compression, or in some instances adhesion of the pulmonary segments and insufficiency of the valve; or the sac may rupture into the artery, an accident which happened in two of my cases, producing instantaneous death.

Pressure on the sympathetic is particularly liable to occur in growths from the ascending portion of the arch. Either the upper dorsal or the lower cervical ganglion is involved. The symptoms are variable. If the nerve is simply irritated, there is stimulation of the vaso-dilator fibres and dilatation of the pupil. With this may be associated pallor of the same side of the face. On the other hand, destruction of the cilio-spinal branches causes paralysis of the dilator fibres, in consequence of which the iris contracts, the vessels on the side of the head dilate, causing congestion, and in some instances unilateral sweating. It is much more common to see the pupillary symptoms alone than in combination either with pallor, redness, or sweating.

The clinical picture of aneurism of the aorta is extremely varied. Many cases present characteristic symptoms and no physical signs, while others have well-marked physical signs and no symptoms. As Broadbent remarks, the aneurism of *physical signs* springs from the ascending portion of the aorta; the aneurism of *symptoms* grows from the transverse arch.

Aneurism of the aorta may be confounded with: (*a*) The violent throbbing impulse of the arch in aortic insufficiency. I have already referred to a case of this kind in which the diagnosis of aneurism was made by several good observers.

(*b*) *Simple Dynamic Pulsation.*—No instance of this, which is common in the abdominal aorta, has ever come under my notice. One which came under the care of William Murray and Bramwell presented, without any pain or pressure symptoms, pulsation and dulness over the aorta. The condition gradually disappeared and was thought to be neurotic.

(*c*) Dislocation of the heart in curvature of the spine may cause great displacement of the aorta, so that it has been known to pulsate forcibly to the right of the sternum.

(*d*) *Solid Tumors.*—When the tumor projects externally and pulsates the difficulty may be considerable. In tumor the heaving, *expansile* pulsation is absent, and there is not that sense of force and power which is so striking in the throbbing of a perforating aneurism. There is not to be felt as in aortic aneurism the shock of the heart-sounds, particularly the diastolic shock. Auscultatory sounds are less definite, as large aneurisms may occur without murmur; and, on the other hand, murmurs may be heard over tumors. The greatest difficulty is in the deep-seated thoracic tumors, and here the diagnosis may be impossible. I have already referred to the case which was regarded by Skoda as aneurism and by Oppolzer as tumor. The physical signs may be indefinite. The ringing aortic second sound is of great importance and is rarely, if ever, heard over tumor. Tracheal tugging is here a valuable sign. Pressure phenomena are less common in tumor, whereas pain is more frequent. The general appearance of the patient in aneurism is much better than in tumor, in which there may be cachexia and enlargement of the glands in the axilla or in the neck. Healthy, strong males who have worked hard and have had syphilis are the most common subjects of aneurism. Occasionally cancer of the œsophagus may simulate aneurism, producing pressure on the left bronchus, and in one instance at the Philadelphia Hospital, with a husky, brazen cough, the symptoms were very suggestive.

(e) *Pulsating Pleurisy.*—In cases of *empyema necessitatis,* if the projecting tumor is in the neighborhood of the heart and pulsates, the condition may readily be mistaken for aneurism. The absence of the heaving, firm distention and of the diastolic shock would, together with the history and the existence of pleural effusion, determine the nature of the case. If necessary, puncture may be made with a fine hypodermic needle. In a majority of the cases of pulsating pleurisy the throbbing is diffuse and widespread, moving the whole side.

Prognosis.—The outlook in thoracic aneurism is always grave. Life may be prolonged for some years, but the patients are in constant jeopardy. Spontaneous cure is not very infrequent in the small sacculated tumors of the ascending and thoracic portions. The cavity becomes filled with laminæ of firm fibrin, which become more and more dense and hard, the sac shrinks considerably, and finally lime salts are deposited in the old fibrin. The laminæ of fibrin may be on a level with the lumen of the vessel, causing complete obliteration of the sac. The cases which rupture externally, as a rule run a rapid course, although to this there are exceptions; the sac may contract, become firm and hard, and the patient may live for five, or even, as in a case mentioned by Balfour, for ten years. The cases which have lasted longest in my experience have been those in which a saccular aneurism has projected from the ascending arch. One patient in Montreal had been known to have aneurism for eleven years. The aneurism may be enormous, occupying a large area of the chest, and yet life be prolonged for many years, as in the case mentioned as under the care of Skoda and Oppolzer. One of the most remarkable instances is the case of dissecting aneurism reported by Graham. The patient was invalided after the Crimean War with aneurism of the aorta, and for years was under the observation of J. H. Richardson, of Toronto, under whose care he died in 1885. The autopsy showed a healed aneurism of the arch, with a dissecting aneurism extending the whole length of the aorta, which formed a double tube.

Treatment.—In a large proportion of the cases this can only be palliative. Still in every instance measures should be taken which are known to promote clotting and consolidation within the sac. In any large series of cured aneurisms a considerable majority of the patients have not been

49

known to be subjects of the disease, but the obliterated sac has been found accidentally at the post mortem.

The most satisfactory plan in early cases, when it can be carried out thoroughly, is that advised by the late Mr. Tufnell, of Dublin, the essentials of which are rest and a restricted diet. Rest is essential and should, as far as possible, be absolute. The reduction of the daily number of heart-beats, when a patient is recumbent and makes no exertion whatever, amounts to many thousands, and is one of the principal advantages of this plan. Mental quiet should also be enjoined. The diet advised by Tufnell is extremely rigid—for breakfast, 2 ounces of bread and butter and 2 ounces of milk; for dinner, 2 or 3 ounces of meat and 3 or 4 ounces of milk or claret; for supper, 2 ounces of bread and 2 ounces of milk. This low diet diminishes the blood-volume and is thought also to render the blood more fibrinous. It reduces greatly the blood-pressure within the sac, in this manner favoring coagulation. This treatment should be pursued for several months, but, except in persons of a good deal of mental stamina, it is impossible to carry it out for more than a few weeks at a time. It is a form of treatment adapted only for the saccular form of aneurism, and in cases of large sacs communicating with the aorta by a comparatively small orifice the chances of consolidation are fairly good. Unquestionably rest and the restriction of the liquids are the important parts of the treatment, and a greater variety and quantity of food may be allowed with advantage. If this plan cannot be thoroughly carried out, the patient should at any rate be advised to live a very quiet life, moving about with deliberation and avoiding all sudden mental or bodily excitement. The bowels should be kept regular, and constipation and straining should be carefully avoided. Of medicines, iodide of potassium, as advised by Balfour, is of great value. It may be given in doses of from 10 to 15 or 20 grains three times a day. Larger doses are not necessary. The mode of action is not well understood. It may act by increasing the secretions and so inspissating the blood, by lowering the blood-pressure, or, as Balfour thinks, by causing thickening and contraction of the sac. The most striking effect of the iodide in my experience has been the relief of the pain. The evidence is not conclusive that the syphilitic cases are more benefited by it than the non-syphilitic. All these measures have little value unless the sac is of a suitable form and size. The large tumors with wide mouths communicating with the ascending portion of the aorta may be treated on the most approved plans for months without the slightest influence other than reduction in the intensity of the throbbing. A patient with a tumor projecting into the right pleura remained on the most rigid Tufnell treatment for more than one hundred days, during which time he also took iodide of potassium faithfully. The pulsations were greatly reduced and the area of dulness diminished, and we congratulated ourselves that the sac was probably consolidating. Sudden death followed rupture into the pleura, and the sac contained only fluid blood, not a shred of fibrin. In cases in which the tumor is large, or in which there seems to be very little prospect of consolidation, it is perhaps better to advise a man to go on quietly with his occupation, avoiding excitement and worry. Our profession has offered many examples of good work, thoroughly and conscientiously carried out, by men with aneurism of the aorta, who wisely, I think, preferred, as did the late Hilton Fagge, to die in harness.

Surgical Measures.—In a few cases consolidation may be promoted in the sac by the introduction of a foreign body, such as wire, horse-hair, or by the combination of wiring and electrolysis. Moore, in 1864, first wired a sac, putting in 28 feet of fine wire. Death occurred on the fifth day. Corradi proposed the combined method of wiring with electrolysis, which was first used by Burresi in 1879. His patient lived for three and a half months. Horse-hair, watch-spring wire, catgut, and Florence silk have been used. Hunner has collected for me the statistics of Moore's method (wiring), of which there were 13 cases, 8 of thoracic aneurism, all fatal; 5 aneurisms of the abdominal aorta, 2 of which were successful. Of 10 cases treated by wiring and electrolysis (Corradi's method), all were thoracic; of these, the cases of Kerr, Rosenstirn, D. D. Stewart, and Hershey, all American cases, were successful. The most favorable cases are those in which the aneurism is sacculated, but this is a point not easily determined, and often from a sac particularly favorable for wiring there may be secondary projections of great thinness. In a case of abdominal aneurism recently operated upon by Halsted all the conditions were very favorable, and the man seemed doing very well when sudden death occurred on the third day from rupture of a small projection of the sac through the diaphragm into the pleura.

Other Symptoms requiring Treatment.—Pressure on veins causing engorgement, particularly of the head and arms, is sometimes promptly relieved by free venesection, and at any time during the course of a thoracic aneurism, if attacks of dyspnœa with lividity supervene, bleeding may be resorted to with great benefit. It has the advantage also of promptly checking the pain, for which symptom, as already mentioned, the iodide of potassium often gives relief. In the final stages morphia is, as a rule, necessary. Dyspnœa, if associated with cyanosis, is best relieved by bleeding. Chloroform inhalations may be necessary. The question sometimes comes up with reference to tracheotomy in these cases of urgent dyspnœa. If it can be shown by laryngoscopic examination that it is due to bilateral abductor paralysis the trachea may be opened, but this is extremely rare, and in nearly every instance the urgent dyspnœa is caused by pressure about the bifurcation. When the sac appears etxernally and grows large, an ice-cap may be applied upon it, or a belladonna plaster to allay the pain. In some instances an elastic support may be used with advantage, and I saw a physician with an enormous external aneurism in the right mammary region who for many months had obtained great relief by the elastic support, passing over the shoulder and under the arm of the opposite side.

Digitalis, ergot, aconite, and veratrum viride are rarely, if ever, of service in thoracic aneurism.

ANEURISM OF THE ABDOMINAL AORTA.

The sac is most common just below the diaphragm in the neighborhood of the cœliac axis. This variety is rare in comparison with thoracic aneurism. Of the 468 cases of aortic aneurism at St. Bartholomew's Hospital, 23 involved the abdominal aorta. The tumor may be fusiform or sacculated, and it is sometimes multiple. Projecting backward, it erodes the vertebræ and may cause numbness and tingling in the legs and finally paraplegia, or it may pass into the thorax and burst into the pleura. More commonly the sac is on the anterior wall and projects forward as a definite tumor, which may be either in the middle line or a little to the left. The tumor may project in the epigastric region (which is most common), in the left hypochondrium, in the left flank, or in the lumbar region. When high up beneath the pillar of the diaphragm it may attain considerable size without being very apparent on palpation.

The symptoms are chiefly pain, very often of a cardialgic nature, passing round to the sides or localized in the back, and gastric symptoms, particularly vomiting. Retardation of the pulse in the femoral is a very common symptom.

Diagnosis and Physical Signs.—Inspection may show marked pulsation in the epigastric region, sometimes a definite tumor. A thrill is not uncommon. The pulsation is forcible, expansile, and sometimes double when the sac is large and in contact with the pericardium. On palpation a *definite tumor can be felt*. If large, there is some degree of dulness on percussion which usually merges with that of the left lobe of the liver. On auscultation, a systolic murmur is, as a rule, audible, and is sometimes best heard at the back. A diastolic murmur is occasionally present, usually very soft in quality. One of the commonest of clinical errors is to mistake a throbbing aorta for an aneurism. It is to be remembered that no pulsation, however forcible, or the presence of a thrill or a systolic murmur justifies the diagnosis of abdominal aneurism unless there is a *definite tumor which can be grasped and which has an expansile pulsation*. Attention to this rule will save many errors. The throbbing aorta —the "preternatural pulsation in the epigastrium," as Allan Burns calls it—is met with in all neurasthenic conditions, particularly in women. In anæmia, particularly in some instances of traumatic anæmia, the throbbing may be very great. In the case of a large, stout man with severe hæmorrhages from a duodenal ulcer the throbbing of the abdominal aorta not only shook violently the whole abdomen, but communicated a pulsation to the bed, the shock of which was distinctly perceptible to any one sitting upon it. Very frequently a tumor of the pylorus, of the pancreas, or of the left lobe of the liver is lifted with each impulse of the aorta and may be confounded with aneurism. The absence of the forcible expansile impulse and the examination in the knee-elbow position, in which the tumor, as a rule, falls forward, and the pulsation is not then communicated, suffice for differentiation. The tumor of abdominal aneurism, though usually fixed, may be very freely movable.

The outlook in abdominal aneurism is bad. A few cases heal spontaneously. Death may result from (*a*) complete obliteration of the lumen by clots; (*b*) compression paraplegia; (*c*) rupture (which is almost the rule) either into the pleura, retroperitoneal tissues, peritonæum or the intestines, very commonly the duodenum; (*d*) by embolism of the superior mesenteric artery, producing infarction of the intestines.

The *treatment* is such as already advised in thoracic aneurism. When the aneurism is low down pressure has been successfully applied in a case by Murray, of Newcastle. It must be kept up for many hours under chloroform. The plan is not without risk, as patients have died from bruising and injury of the sac.

Aneurism of the Branches of the Abdominal Aorta.

The *cœliac axis* is itself not infrequently involved in aneurism of the first portion of the abdominal aorta. Of its branches, the *splenic artery* is occasionally the seat of aneurism. This rarely causes a tumor large enough to be felt; sometimes, however, the tumor is of large size. I have reported a case in a man, aged thirty, who had an illness of several months' duration, severe epigastric pain and vomiting, which led his physicians in New York to diagnose gastric ulcer. There was a deep-seated tumor in the left hypochondriac region, the dulness of which merged with that of the spleen. There was no pulsation, but it was thought on one occasion that a *bruit* was heard. The chief symptoms while under observation were vomiting, severe epigastric pain, occasional hæmatemesis, and finally severe hæmorrhage from the bowels. An aneurism of the splenic artery the size of a cocoa-nut was situated between the stomach above and the transverse colon below, and extended to the left as far as the level of the navel. The sac contained densely laminated fibrin. It had perforated the colon. I have twice seen small aneurisms on the splenic artery. Of 39 instances of aneurism on the branches of the abdominal aorta collected by Lebert, 10 were of the splenic artery.

Aneurism of the *hepatic artery* is very rare, and there are only 10 or 12 cases on record. The symptoms are extremely indefinite; the condition could rarely be diagnosed. In the case reported by Ross and myself, a man aged twenty-one had the symptoms of pyæmia. The liver was greatly enlarged, weighed nearly 5,000 grammes, and presented innumerable small abscesses. An oval aneurism, half the size of a small lemon, involved the right and part of the left branches. In J. B. S. Jackson's * case the aneurism perforated the hepatic duct.

A few cases of aneurism of the *superior mesenteric artery* are on record. The diagnosis is scarcely possible. Plugging of the branches or of the main stem may cause the symptoms of infarction of the bowels which have already been considered.

Small aneurisms of the *renal artery* are not very uncommon. Large tumors are rare. The sac may rupture and give rise to extensive retroperitoneal hæmorrhage.

---

* Medical Magazine, 1834, iii.

Arterio-venous Aneurism.

In this form there is abnormal communication between an artery and a vein. When a tumor lies between the two it is known as varicose aneurism; when there is a direct communication without tumor the vein is chiefly distended and the condition is known as aneurismal varix.

An aneurism of the ascending portion of the arch may open directly into the vena cava. Twenty-nine cases of this lesion have been analyzed by Pepper and Griffith. Cyanosis, œdema, and great distention of the veins of the upper part of the body are the most frequent symptoms, and develop, as a rule, with suddenness. Of the physical signs a thrill is present in some cases. A continuous murmur with systolic intensification is of great diagnostic value. In a recent case, after the existence for some time of pressure symptoms, intense cyanosis developed with engorgement of the veins of the head and arms. Over the aortic region there was a loud continuous murmur with systolic intensification.

A majority of the cases of arterio-venous aneurism and of aneurismal varix result from the accidental opening of an artery and vein as in venesection, and are met with at the bend of the elbow or sometimes in the temporal region. The condition may persist for years without causing any trouble. Pulsation, a loud thrill, and a continuous humming murmur are usually present.

Congenital Aneurism.

In consequence of failure of proper development of the elastic coat in many places in the arterial system, multiple aneurisms may develop. In the well-known case described by Kussmaul and Maier, upon many of the medium-sized arteries there were nodular prominences, which consisted of thickening of the intima and infiltration of the adventitia and of the media, with a nuclear growth which in places looked quite sarcomatous. They called it a case of *periarteritis nodosa*, and Eppinger holds that it belongs to the category which he makes of congenital aneurism. As many as 63 aneurismal tumors have been found in one case. In the smaller branches, such as the coronary and the mesenteric arteries or in the pulmonary arteries, there may be numerous elongated or saccular aneurisms varying in size from a cherry to a hazel-nut. These are true aneurismal dilatations, and, according to Eppinger's careful study, the wall consists of the intima and the adventitia, the elastic lamina having disappeared. The condition has been met with in children. Some of the cases, however, have been in adults; but the term as applied by Eppinger expresses, and probably correctly, the deep-seated fundamental error in development which must be at the basis of this condition. A favorite situation is in the coronary arteries; a case has been reported by Gee in a boy of seven.

SECTION VIII.

DISEASES OF THE BLOOD AND DUCTLESS GLANDS.

I. ANÆMIA.

ANÆMIA may be defined as a reduction in the amount of the blood as a whole or of its corpuscles, or of certain of its more important constituents, such as albumin and hæmoglobin. The condition may be general or local. The former alone we are here considering. It is interesting to note, however, that the pallor, particularly of the face, which is one of the most striking symptoms of anæmia, is just as characteristic of local anæmia due to fright or to nausea. There are persons persistently pale without actual anæmia in whom the condition may be due to inherited peculiarities.

Our knowledge is not yet sufficiently advanced to classify satisfactorily the various forms of anæmia. The following provisional grouping may be made: (1) Secondary or symptomatic anæmia; (2) primary, essential, or cytogenic anæmia.

SECONDARY ANÆMIA.

Under this division comes a large proportion of all cases. The following are the most important groups, based on the etiology:

(1) *Anæmia from hæmorrhage*, either traumatic or spontaneous. The loss of blood may be rapid, as in lesions of large vessels, in injury or in rupture of aneurisms, in cases of ulcer of the stomach or duodenum, or in post-partum hæmorrhage. If the loss is excessive, death results from lowering of the arterial pressure. In sudden profuse hæmorrhage the loss of 3 or 4 pounds of blood may prove fatal. In the rupture of an aneurism into the pleura the loss of blood may amount to $7\frac{1}{2}$ pounds, the largest quantity I have known to be shed into one cavity. In a case of hæmatemesis the patient lost over 10 pounds by measurement in one week and yet recovered from the immediate effects. Even after very severe hæmorrhage the number of red blood-corpuscles is not reduced so greatly as in forms of idiopathic anæmia. Thus in one case just mentioned, at the termination of the week of bleeding there were nearly 1,390,000 red blood-corpuscles to the cubic millimetre. The process of regeneration goes on with great rapidity, and in some "bleeders" a week or ten days suffice

to re-establish the normal amount. The watery and saline constituents of the blood are readily restored by absorption from the gastro-intestinal tract. The albuminous elements also are quickly renewed, but it may take weeks or months for the corpuscles to reach the normal standard. The

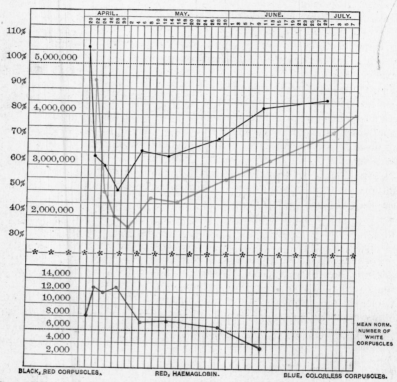

BLACK, RED CORPUSCLES.   RED, HAEMAGLOBIN.   BLUE, COLORLESS CORPUSCLES.

CHART XVII.—Illustrates the rapidity with which anæmia is produced in purpura hæmorrhagica and the gradual recovery.*

hæmoglobin is restored more slowly than the corpuscles. The accompanying chart illustrates the rapid fall and gradual restitution in a case of severe purpura hæmorrhagica.

The microscopical characters of the blood after severe hæmorrhage may not be greatly changed. The red corpuscles show, usually, rather more marked differences in size than normally, while the average size may be a trifle reduced; there may be a moderate poikilocytosis. The corpuscles are paler than normally. Nucleated red corpuscles appear, almost always, soon after the hæmorrhage; they are, however, not numerous. These are small bodies of about the same size as a normal red corpuscle with a small,

---

* On September 27th the patient returned from the country, where she had spent the summer. The blood-count was then: Red corpuscles, 5,350,000; white corpuscles, 5,500; hæmoglobin, 94 per cent.

round, deeply staining nucleus. Free nuclei may be found. The color-less corpuscles are, at first, increased in number. There is a moderate leucocytosis, the differential count showing an increase in the multinuclear neutrophiles with a diminution in the small mononuclear elements. During recovery the leucocytosis diminishes.

The reduction in hæmoglobin is always proportionately greater than that in the corpuscles.

In some instances a rapidly fatal anæmia may follow a single severe hæmorrhage, or repeated small hæmorrhages as in purpura. Here the appearances of the red corpuscles are much the same, except in the total absence of nucleated red corpuscles.

The leucocytes in these cases are usually reduced in number; the poly-nuclear elements are present in a relatively diminished proportion, while the small mononuclear forms are numerous. The autopsy, in these cases, reveals usually a total absence of any regenerative activity on the part of the bone-marrow.

(2) Anæmia is frequently produced by long-continued drain on the albuminous materials of the blood, as in chronic suppuration and Bright's disease. Prolonged lactation acts in the same way. Rapidly growing tumors may cause a profound anæmia, as in gastric cancer. The charac-ters of the blood here may be much the same as in the acute cases. Usu-ally, though, the poikilocytosis is much more marked; in severe cases it may be excessive. The presence, however, of the very large corpuscles, such as one sees in pernicious anæmia, is not noted, the average size ap-pearing to be rather smaller than normal.

Nucleated red corpuscles are usually scanty. In long-continued chronic secondary anæmias occasional larger nucleated red corpuscles may be seen, bodies with larger palely staining nuclei; in some of these cells karyo-kinetic figures occur. Nucleated red corpuscles with fragmentary nuclei may also be seen.

The leucocytes may be increased in number, though in some severe chronic cases there may be a diminution.

(3) *Anæmia from Inanition.*—This may be brought about by defective food supply, or by conditions which interfere with the proper reception and preparation of the food, as in cancer of the œsophagus and chronic dyspepsia. The reduction of the blood mass may be extreme, but the plasma suffers proportionately more than the corpuscles, which, even in the wasting of cancer of the œsophagus, may not be reduced more than one half or three fourths. In some instances the reduction in the plasma may be so great that the corpuscles show an apparent increase.

(4) *Toxic anæmia*, induced by the action of certain poisons on the blood, such as lead, mercury, and arsenic, among inorganic substances, and the virus of syphilis and malaria among organic poisons. They act either by directly destroying the red blood-corpuscles, as in malaria, or by increasing the rate of ordinary consumption. The anæmia of pyrexia may in part be due to a toxic action, but is also caused in part by the dis-turbance of digestion and interference with the function of the blood-making organs.

PRIMARY OR ESSENTIAL ANÆMIA.

1. Chlorosis.

Definition.—An anæmia of unknown cause, occurring in young girls, characterized by a marked relative diminution of the hæmoglobin.

Etiology.—It is a disease of girls, more often of blondes than of brunettes. It is doubtful if males are ever affected. I have never seen true chlorosis in a boy. The age of onset is between the fourteenth and seventeenth years; under the age of twelve cases are rare. Recurrences, which are common, may extend into the third decade. Of the essential cause of the disease we know nothing. There exists a lowered energy in the blood-making organs, associated in some obscure way with the evolution of the sexual apparatus in women. Hereditary influences, particularly chlorosis and tuberculosis, play a part in some cases. Sometimes, as Virchow pointed out, the condition exists with a defective development (hypoplasia) of the circulatory and generative organs.

The disease is most common among the ill-fed, overworked girls of large towns, who are confined all day in close, badly lighted rooms, or have to do much stair-climbing. Cases are frequent, however, under the most favorable conditions of life. Lack of proper exercise and of fresh air, and the use of improper food are important factors. Emotional and nervous disturbances may be prominent—so prominent that certain writers have regarded the disease as a neurosis. De Sauvages speaks of a *chlorose par amour*. Newly arrived Irish girls were very prone to the disease in Montreal. The " corset and chlorosis " expresses O. Rosenbach's opinion. Menstrual disturbances are not uncommon, but are probably a sequence, not a cause, of chlorosis. Sir Andrew Clark believed that constipation plays an important *rôle*, and that the condition is in reality a *copræmia* due to the absorption of poisons—leucomaines and ptomaines—from the large bowel, a view which always appeared to me baseless, considering the great frequency of the condition in women.

Symptoms.—(*a*) **General.**—The symptoms of chlorosis are those of anæmia. The subcutaneous fat is well retained or even increased in amount. The complexion is peculiar; neither the blanched aspect of hæmorrhage nor the muddy pallor of grave anæmia, but a curious yellow-green tinge, which has given to the disease its name, and its popular designation, the green sickness. Occasionally the skin shows areas of pigmentation, particularly about the joints. In cases of moderate grade the color may be deceptive, as the cheeks have a reddish tint, particularly on exertion (chlorosis rubra). The subjects complain of breathlessness and palpitation, and there may be a tendency to fainting—symptoms which often lead to the suspicion of heart or lung disease. Puffiness of the face and swelling of the ankles may suggest nephritis. The disposition often changes, and the girl becomes low-spirited and irritable. The eyes have a peculiar brilliancy and the sclerotics are of a bluish color.

(*b*) **Special Features.**—*Blood.*—The drop as expressed looks pale. Johann Duncan, in 1867, first called attention to the fact that the essential feature was not a great reduction in the number of the corpuscles, but a quantitative change in the hæmoglobin. The corpuscles themselves look pale. In 63 consecutive cases examined at my clinic by Thayer, the average number per cubic millimetre of the red blood-corpuscles was 4,096,544, or over 80 per cent, whereas the percentage of hæmoglobin for the total number was 42.3 per cent. The accompanying chart illustrates well these striking differences. There may, however, be well-marked actual anæmia. The lowest blood-count in the series of cases referred to above was 1,932,000. There may be all the physical characteristics and symptoms of a profound anæmia with the number of the blood-corpuscles nearly at the normal

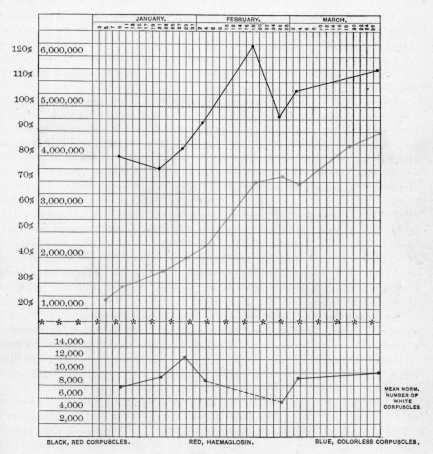

CHART XVIII.—Chlorosis.

standard. Thus in one instance the globular richness was over 85 per cent, with the hæmoglobin about 35. No other form of anæmia presents this feature, at least with the same constancy and in the same degree. The importance of the reduction in the hæmoglobin depends upon the fact that it is the iron-containing elements of the blood with which in respiration the oxygen enters into combination. This marked diminution in the iron has also been determined by chemical analysis of the blood. The microscopical characteristics of the blood are as follows: In severe cases the corpuscles may be extremely irregular in size and shape—poikilocytosis, which may occasionally be as marked as in some cases of pernicious anæmia. The large forms of red blood-cells are not as common, and the average size is stated to be below normal. The color of the corpuscles is noticeably pale and the deficiency may be seen either in individual corpuscles or in the blood mixture prepared for counting. Nucleated red corpuscles (normoblasts) are not very uncommon, and may vary greatly in numbers in the same case at different periods. The leucocytes may show a slight increase; the average in the 63 cases above referred to was 8,467 per cubic millimetre.

(c) **Gastro-intestinal Symptoms.**—The appetite is capricious, and patients often have a longing for unusual articles, particularly acids. In some instances they eat all sorts of indigestible things, such as chalk or even earth. Superacidity of the gastric juice is commonly associated with chlorosis. In 19 out of 21 cases in Riegel's clinic this condition was found to exist. In the other two instances the acidity was normal or a trifle increased. Distress after eating and even cardialgic attacks may be associated with it. Constipation is a common symptom, and, as already mentioned, has been regarded as an important element in causing the disease. A majority of chlorotic girls who wear corsets have gastroptosis, and on inflation the stomach will be found vertically placed; sometimes the organ is very much dilated. The motor power is usually well retained. Enteroptosis with palpable right kidney is not uncommon.

(d) **Circulatory Symptoms.**—Palpitation of the heart occurs on exertion, and may be the most distressing symptom of which the patient complains. Percussion may show slight increase in the transverse dulness. A systolic murmur is heard at the apex or at the base; more commonly at the latter, but in extreme cases at both. A diastolic murmur is rarely heard. The systolic murmur is usually loudest in the second left intercostal space, where there is sometimes a distinct pulsation. The exact mode of production is still in dispute. Balfour holds that it is produced at the mitral orifice by relative insufficiency of the valves in the dilated condition of the ventricle. On the right side of the neck over the jugular vein a continuous murmur is heard, the *bruit de diable*, or humming-top murmur.

The pulse is usually full and soft. Pulsation in the peripheral veins is sometimes seen. There is a tendency to thrombosis in the veins; most commonly in the femoral, but in other instances in the longitudinal sinus; or the thrombosis may be multiple. Except in the sinuses, the condition is rarely serious. Tuckwell has reported an instance in which there was embolism of the right axillary artery with the loss of a thumb and part of the fingers. Brayton Ball has recently called attention to the importance of this feature of chlorosis.

As in all forms of essential anæmia, fever is not uncommon. Especial attention has of late been directed to this by French writers. Chlorotic patients suffer frequently from headache and neuralgia, which may be paroxysmal. The hands and feet are often cold. Dermatographia is common. Hysterical manifestations are not infrequent. Menstrual disturbances are very common—amenorrhœa or dysmenorrhœa. With the improvement in the blood condition this function is usually restored.

Diagnosis.—The green sickness, as it is sometimes called, is in many instances recognized at a glance. The well-nourished condition of the girl, the peculiar complexion, which is most marked in brunettes, and the white or bluish sclerotics are very characteristic. A special danger exists in mistaking the apparent anæmia of the early stage of pulmonary tuberculosis for chlorosis. Mistakes of this sort may often be avoided by the very simple test furnished by allowing a drop of blood to fall on a white towel or a piece of blotting paper—a deficiency in hæmoglobin is readily appreciated. The palpitation of the heart and shortness of breath frequently suggest heart-disease, and the œdema of the feet and general pallor cause the cases to be mistaken for Bright's disease. In the great majority of cases the characters of the blood readily separate chlorosis from other forms of anæmia.

2. Idiopathic or Progressive Pernicious Anæmia.

The disease was first clearly described by Addison, who called it idiopathic anæmia. Channing and Gusserow described the cases occurring post partum, but to Biermer we owe a revival of interest in the subject.

Etiology.—The existence of a separate disease worthy of the term progressive pernicious anæmia has been doubted, but there are unquestionably cases in which, as Addison says, there exist none of the usual causes or concomitants of anæmia. Clinically there are several different groups which present the characters of a progressive and pernicious anæmia and are etiologically different. Thus, a fatal anæmia may be due to the presence of parasites, or may follow hæmorrhage, or be associated with chronic atrophy of the stomach; but when we have excluded all these causes there remains a group which, in the words of Addison, is characterized by a " general anæmia occurring without any discoverable cause whatever, cases in which there had been no previous loss of blood, no exhausting diarrhœa, no chlorosis, no purpura, no renal, splenic, miasmatic, glandular, strumous, or malignant disease."

Idiopathic anæmia is widely distributed. It is of frequent occurrence in the Swiss cantons, and it is not uncommon in this country. It affects middle-aged persons, but instances in children have been described. Griffith mentions about 10 cases occurring under twelve years of age. The youngest patient I have seen was a girl of twenty. Males are more frequently affected than females. Of my 27 cases, 10 were females and 17 were males. Of 110 cases collected by Coupland, 56 were in men and 54 in women. Sinkler and Eshner give 3 cases in one family, the father and two girls; the father had symptoms of posterior sclerosis.

With the following conditions may be associated a profound anæmia not to be distinguished clinically from Addison's idiopathic form:

(*a*) *Pregnancy and Parturition.*—The symptoms may develop during pregnancy, as in 19 of 29 cases of this group in Eichhorst's table. More commonly, in my experience, the condition has been post partum; thus, of my 27 cases, 5 followed delivery.

(*b*) *Atrophy of the Stomach.*—This condition, early recognized by Flint and Fenwick, may certainly cause a progressive pernicious anæmia. By modern methods it may now be possible to exclude this extreme gastric atrophy.

(*c*) *Parasites.*—The most severe form may be due to the presence of parasites, and the accounts of cases depending upon the anchylostoma and the bothriocephalus describe a progressive and often pernicious anæmia.

After the exclusion of these forms there remains a large proportion, numbering 18 cases in my series, which correspond to Addison's description. The etiology of these cases is still dark. The researches of Quincke and his student Peters showed that there was an enormous increase in the iron in the liver, and they suggested that the affection was probably due to increased hæmolysis. This has been strongly supported by the extensive observations of Hunter, who has also shown that the urine excreted is darker in color and contains pathological urobilin. The lemon tint of the skin or the actual jaundice is attributed, on this view, to an overproduction. To explain the hæmolysis, it has been thought that in the condition of faulty gastro-intestinal digestion, which is so commonly associated with these cases, poisonous materials are developed, which when absorbed cause destruction of the corpuscles. Certainly the evidence for hæmolysis is very strong, but we are still far away from a full knowledge of the conditions under which it is produced.

Stockman suggests that repeated small capillary hæmorrhages—chiefly internal—play an important *rôle* in the causation of the disease, which also explains, he holds, the existence of a great excess of iron in the liver.

On the other hand, F. P. Henry, Stephen Mackenzie, Rindflcisch, and other authorities incline to the belief that the essence of the disease is in defective hæmogenesis, in consequence of which the red blood-corpuscles are abnormally vulnerable. A point noted by Copeman, that the hæmoglobin crystallizes from the blood-corpuscles with great readiness, can scarcely be regarded as favoring the view of imperfect hæmogenesis, since this is a feature specially characteristic of the blood of the young.

Morbid Anatomy.—The body is rarely emaciated. A lemon tint of the skin is present in a majority of the cases. The muscles often are intensely red in color, like horse-flesh, while the fat is light yellow. Hæmorrhages are common on the skin and serous surfaces. The heart is usually large, flabby, and empty. In one instance I obtained only 2 drachms of blood from the right heart, and between 3 and 4 from the left. The muscle substance of the heart is intensely fatty, and of a pale, light-yellow color. In no affection do we see more extreme fatty degeneration. The lungs show no special changes. The stomach in many instances is normal, but in some cases of fatal anæmia the mucosa has been extensively atrophied. In the case described by Henry and myself the mucous membrane had a smooth, cuticular appearance, and there was complete atrophy of the secreting tubules. The liver may be enlarged and fatty. In most of my autopsies it was normal in size, but usually fatty. The iron is in excess, a striking contrast to the condition in cases of secondary anæmia. It is deposited in the outer and middle zones of the lobules, and in two specimens, which I examined, seemed to have such a distribution that the bile capillaries were distinctly outlined. This, Hunter states, is a special and characteristic lesion, possibly peculiar to pernicious anæmia. A. J. Scott examined for me the livers in 45 consecutive autopsies without finding (except in pernicious anæmia) this special distribution of pigment.

The spleen shows no important changes. In one of Palmer Howard's cases the organ weighed only 1 ounce and 5 drachms. The iron pigment is usually in excess. The lymph-glands may be of a deep red color. The amount of iron pigment is increased in the kidneys, chiefly in the convoluted tubules. The bone marrow, as pointed out by H. C. Wood, is usually red, lymphoid in character, showing great numbers of nucleated red corpuscles, especially the larger forms called by Ehrlich gigantoblasts. Changes in the ganglion cells of the sympathetic have been reported on several occasions. Lichtheim has found sclerosis in the posterior columns of the cord. Burr described a series of cases. The subject is referred to again under diseases of the spinal cord (University Med. Magazine, 1895).

Symptoms.—The patient may have been in previous good health, but in many cases there is a history of gastro-intestinal disturbance, mental shock, or worry. The description given by Addison presents the chief features of the disease in a masterly way. " It makes its approach in so slow and insidious a manner that the patient can hardly fix a date to the earliest feeling of that languor which is shortly to become so extreme. The countenance gets pale, the whites of the eyes become pearly, the general frame flabby rather than wasted, the pulse perhaps large, but remarkably soft and compressible, and occasionally with a slight jerk, especially under the slightest excitement. There is an increasing indisposition to exertion, with an uncomfortable feeling of faintness or breathlessness in attempting it; the heart is readily made to palpitate; the whole surface of the body presents a blanched, smooth, and waxy appearance; the lips, gums, and tongue seem bloodless, the flabbiness of the solids increases, the appetite fails, extreme languor and faintness supervene, breathlessness and palpitations are produced by the most trifling exertion or emotion; some slight œdema is probably perceived about the ankles; the debility becomes extreme—the patient can no longer rise from bed; the mind occasionally wanders; he falls into a prostrate and half-torpid state, and at length expires; nevertheless, to the very last, and after a sickness of several months' duration, the bulkiness of the general frame and the amount of obesity often present a most striking contrast to the failure and exhaustion observable in every other respect."

The Blood.—The corpuscles may fall to one fifth or less of the normal number. They may sink to 500,000 per cubic millimetre, and in a case of Quincke's the number was reduced to 143,000 per cubic millimetre. The hæmoglobin is relatively increased, so that the individual globular richness is plus, a condition exactly the opposite to that which occurs in chlorosis and the secondary anæmia, in which the corpuscular richness in coloring matter is minus. The relative increase in the hæmoglobin is probably associated with the average increase in the size of the red blood-corpuscles. The accompanying chart illustrates these points. Microscopically the red blood-corpuscles present a great variation in size, and there can be seen large giant forms, megalocytes, which are often ovoid in form,

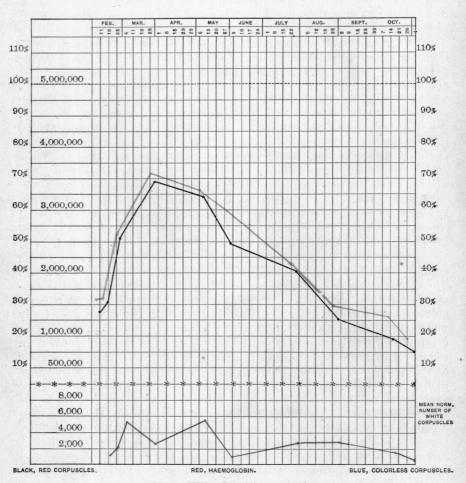

CHART XIX.—Pernicious anæmia.

measuring 8, 11, or even 15 μ in diameter—a circumstance which Henry regards as indicating a reversion to a lower type. Laache thinks these pathognomonic, and they certainly form a constant feature. There are also small round cells, microcytes, from 2 to 6 μ in diameter, and of a deep red color. The corpuscles show a remarkable irregularity in form; they are elongated and rodlike or pyriform; one end of a corpuscle may retain its shape while the other is narrow and extended. To this condition of irregularity Quincke gave the name poikilocytosis.

Nucleated red blood-corpuscles are almost always present, as pointed out by Ehrlich. Besides the ordinary form, which is of the same size as the common corpuscle and which has a small, deeply stained nucleus (normoblasts), there are very large forms with palely staining nuclei (gigantoblasts), which resemble somewhat the larger megalocytes. Ehrlich regards the presence of these as almost distinctive of progressive pernicious anæmia. Though these large forms are most characteristic, occasionally forms closely similar to them may be found in the graver secondary anæmias—e. g., bothriocephalus anæmia, anchylostomiasis—and in leukæmia. Karyokinetic figures may be seen in these bodies. Red corpuscles with fragmenting nuclei are common in pernicious anæmia. The leucocytes are generally normal or diminished in number; and in the graver cases a marked relative increase in the small mononuclear forms, with a diminution in the polynuclear leucocytes, is often noted. The blood-plates are either absent or very scanty.

The cardio-vascular symptoms are important and are noted in the description given above. Hæmic murmurs are constantly present. The larger arteries pulsate visibly and the throbbing in them may be distressing to the patient. The pulse is full and frequently suggests the water-hammer beat of aortic insufficiency. The capillary pulse is frequently to be seen. The superficial veins are often prominent, and in 2 cases I have seen well-marked pulsation in them. Hæmorrhages may occur, either in the skin or from the mucous surfaces. Retinal hæmorrhages are common. There are rarely symptoms in the respiratory organs.

Gastro-intestinal symptoms, such as dyspepsia, nausea, and vomiting, may be present throughout the disease. Diarrhœa is not infrequent. The urine is usually of a low specific gravity and sometimes pale, but in other instances it is of a deep sherry color, shown by Hunter and Mott to be due to great excess of urobilin. Fever is a variable symptom. For weeks at a time the temperature may be normal, and then irregular pyrexia may develop. Nervous symptoms may occur, numbness and tingling, and occasionally symptoms resembling those of tabes. Lepine reports a case of extensive paralysis.

Diagnosis.—From chlorosis the disease is readily distinguished. I have not seen a case in which the two diseases could have been confounded. Several points in the blood examination are of especial importance, namely, the relative increase in the hæmoglobin and the presence of megalocytes and of the large forms of nucleated red blood-corpuscles, the gigantoblasts of Ehrlich. Poikilocytosis may occur in any severe anæmia. The separation of the different clinical forms above referred to can usually be made. The profound secondary anæmia of cancer of the stomach may sometimes be puzzling, but the skin is rarely, if ever, lemon-tinted, and the blood has the characteristics of a secondary, not a primary, anæmia.

Prognosis.—In the true Addisonian cases the outlook is bad, though of late years on the arsenic treatment the proportion of recovery has increased. My personal experience of progressive pernicious anæmia to January, 1895, was as follows: Of 27 cases, 4 were then under observation, 2 of these having recovered with arsenic. Of the remaining 23, 4 of the 5 post-partum cases recovered, and when I left Montreal 3 of these cases had remained in good health for several years. Of the remaining 18 cases 2 were lost sight of; 1 had improved very much. The remaining 16 were dead. Six of these fatal cases recovered from the first attack; one had an interval of nearly three years, and another nearly two years, before the return. One patient in hospital in 1890 recovered completely, and died in, 1896 of cancer of the stomach. In Pye-Smith's article in the Guy's Hospital Reports, he mentions 20 cases of recovery. Hale White, in a recent article, states that one of these cases, treated with arsenic in 1880, remained alive and well January, 1891. One of my patients made an apparently complete recovery and resumed active business and political duties. So characteristic are recurrences in this affection that Stephen Mackenzie, in his lectures, considered them under a separate heading of relapsing pernicious anæmia. The examination of the blood may give us some help. The presence of numerous normoblasts appears in some instances to be indicative of an active regeneration in the marrow. Cases in which a majority of the nucleated red corpuscles are gigantoblasts are generally more malignant. A marked relative increase in the small mononuclear leucocytes appears to be also an unfavorable sign.

Treatment of Anæmia.—*Secondary Anæmia.*—The traumatic cases do best, and with plenty of good food and fresh air the blood is readily restored. The extraordinary rapidity with which the normal percentage of red blood-corpuscles is reached without any medication whatever is an important lesson. The cause of the hæmorrhage should be sought and the necessary indications met. The large group depending on the drain on the albuminous materials of the blood, as in Bright's disease, suppuration, and fever, is difficult to treat successfully, and so long as the cause keeps up it is impossible to restore the normal blood condition. The anæmia of inanition requires plenty of nourishing food. When dependent on organic changes in the gastro-intestinal mucosa not much can be expected from either food or medicine. In the toxic cases due to mercury and lead, the poison must be eliminated and a nutritious diet given with full doses of iron. In a great majority of these cases there is deficient blood formation, and the indications are briefly three: plenty of food, an open-air life, and iron. As a rule it makes but little difference what form of the drug is administered.

The treatment of *chlorosis* affords one of the most brilliant instances— of which we have but three or four—of the specific action of a remedy. Apart from the action of quinine in malarial fever, and of mercury and iodide of potassium in syphilis, there is no other drug the beneficial effects of which we can trace with the accuracy of a scientific experiment. It is a minor matter *how* the iron cures chlorosis. In a week we give to a case as much iron as is contained in the entire blood, as even in the worst case of chlorosis there is rarely more than a deficit of 2 grammes of this metal. Iron is present in the fæces of chlorotic patients before they are placed upon any treatment, so that the disease does not result from any deficiency of available iron in the food. Bunge believes that it is the sulphur which interferes with the digestion and assimilation of this natural iron. The sulphides are produced in the process of fermentation and decomposition in the fæces, and interfere with the assimilation of the normal iron contained in the food. By the administration of an inorganic preparation of iron, with which these sulphides unite, the natural organic combinations in the food are spared. In studying a number of charts of chlorosis, it is seen that there is an increase in the red blood-corpuscles under the influence of the iron, and in some instances the globular richness rises above normal. The increase in the hæmoglobin is slower and the maximum percentage may not be reached for a long time. I have for years in the treatment of chlorosis used with the greatest success Blaud's pills, made and given according to the formula in Niemeyer's text-book, in which each pill contains 2 grains of the sulphate of iron. During the first week one pill is given three times a day; in the second week, two pills; in the third week, three pills, three times a day. This dose should be continued for four or five weeks at least before reduction. An important feature in the treatment of chlorosis is to persist in the use of the iron for at least three months, and, if necessary, subsequently to resume it in smaller doses, as recurrences are so common. The diet should consist of good, easily digested food. Special care should be directed to the bowels, and if constipation is present a saline purge should be given each morning. Such stress does Sir Andrew Clark lay on the importance of constipation in chlorosis, that he states that if limited to the choice of one drug in the treatment of the disease he would choose a purgative. The good influence of alkaline waters in association with the treatment by iron has been noted by von Jaksch. In many instances the dyspeptic symptoms may be relieved by alkalies and a treatment directed toward a moderate superacidity. Dilute hydrochloric acid, manganese, phosphorus, and oxygen have been recommended.

Treatment of Pernicious Anæmia.—Since the introduction by Byrom Bramwell of arsenic in this affection a large number of cases have been temporarily, a few permanently, cured by it. It should be given as Fowler's solution in increasing doses. It is usually well borne, and patients, as a rule, take up to 20 minims three times a day without any disturbance. I usually begin with 3 minims and increase to 5 at the end of the first week, to 10 at the end of the second week, to 15 at the end of the third week, and, if necessary, go up to 20 or 25. In a case in which the recovery persisted for nearly three years the dose was gradually increased to 30 minims. These patients seem to stand the arsenic extremely well. It is sometimes better borne as arsenious acid in pill form. Vomiting and diarrhœa are rare; occasionally puffiness of the face is produced, and in some cases pigmentation of the skin.

Rest in bed and a light but nutritious diet (giving the food in small amounts and at fixed intervals) are the first indications. I always prefer to begin the treatment of a case of pernicious anæmia, whatever the grade may be, with rest in bed as one of the essential elements. The beneficial effect of massage has been shown by J. K. Mitchell. I have abandoned the use of rectal injections of dried blood. Iron rarely acts well in this form, but in a case in which the arsenic disagrees it may be tried. Bone marrow has been recommended. It is best given as a glycerin extract. I have not seen any benefit follow its administration. Inhalations of oxygen may be tried.

II. LEUKÆMIA.

Definition.—An affection characterized by persistent increase in the white blood-corpuscles, associated with changes, either alone or together, in the spleen, lymphatic glands, or bone marrow.

The disease was described almost simultaneously by Virchow and by Bennett, who gave to it the name leucocythæmia. It is ordinarily seen in two main types, though combinations and variations may occur:

(1) Spleno-medullary leukæmia, in which the changes are especially localized in the spleen and the bone marrow, while the blood shows a great increase in elements which are derived especially from the latter tissue, a condition which Müller has termed "myelæmia." Ehrlich prefers to call this type of the disease "myelogenous leukæmia," believing the part played by the spleen in the process to be purely passive.

(2) Lymphatic leukæmia, in which the changes are chiefly localized in the lymphatic apparatus, the blood showing an especial increase in those elements derived from the lymph-glands.

Etiology.—We know nothing of the conditions under which the disease develops. It is not uncommon on this continent. Of 26 cases of which I have notes, to January, 1895, 11 occurred in Montreal, 2 in Philadelphia, and 13 in hospital and private work in Baltimore. It does not seem more frequent in the southern parts of the country.

The disease is most common in the middle period of life. The youngest of my patients was a child of eight months, and cases are on record of the disease as early as the eighth or tenth week. It may occur as late as the seventieth year. Males are more prone to the affection than females. Of my cases, 17 were in males and 9 in females. Birch-Hirschfeld states that of 200 cases collected from the literature, 135 were males and 65 females.

A tendency to hæmorrhage has been noted in many cases, and some of the patients have suffered repeatedly from nose-bleeding. In women the disease is most common at the climacteric. There are instances in which it has developed during pregnancy. The case described by J. Chalmers Cameron, of Montreal, is in this respect remarkable, as the patient passed through three pregnancies, bearing on each occasion non-leukæmic children. The case is interesting, too, as showing the hereditary character of the affection, as the grandmother and mother, as well as a brother, suffered from symptoms strongly suggestive of leukæmia. One of the patient's children had leukæmia before the mother showed any signs, and a second died of the disease. At the last report this patient had gradually recovered from the third confinement, and the red blood-corpuscles had risen to 4,000,000 per cubic millimetre, and the ratio of white to red was 1 to 200. Sänger has reported a case in which a healthy mother bore a leukæmic child.

Malaria is believed by some to be an etiological factor. Of 150 cases analyzed by Gowers, there was a history of malaria in 30; in my series there was a history in at least 9. Syphilis appears in some cases to have been closely associated with leukæmia. The disease has followed injury or a blow.

The lower animals are subject to the affection, and cases have been described in horses, dogs, oxen, cats, swine, and mice.

Morbid Anatomy.—The wasting may be extreme, and dropsy is sometimes present. There is in many cases a remarkable condition of polyæmia; the heart and veins are distended with large blood-clots. In Case XI of my series the weight of blood in the heart chambers alone was 620 grammes. There may be remarkable distention of the portal, cerebral, pulmonary, and subcutaneous veins. The blood is usually clotted, and the enormous increase in the leucocytes gives a pus-like appearance to the coagula, so that it has happened more than once, as in Virchow's memorable case, that on opening the right auricle the observer at first thought he had cut into an abscess. The coagula have a peculiar greenish color, somewhat like the fat of a turtle. The alkalinity of the blood is diminished. The fibrin is increased. The character of the corpuscles will be described under the symptoms. Charcot's octohedral crystals may separate from the blood after death. The specific gravity of the blood is somewhat lowered. There may be pericardial ecchymoses.

In the spleno-medullary form the spleen is greatly enlarged. Strong adhesions may unite it to the abdominal wall, the diaphragm, or the stomach. The capsule may be thickened. The vessels at the hilus are enlarged; the weight may range from 2 to 18 pounds. The organ is in a condition of chronic hyperplasia. It cuts with resistance, has a uniformly reddish-brown color, and the Malpighian bodies are invisible. Grayish-white, circumscribed, lymphoid tumors may occur throughout the organ, contrasting strongly with the reddish-brown matrix. In the early stage the swollen spleen pulp is softer, and it is stated that rupture has occurred from the intense hyperæmia.

In association with these changes in the spleen, the bone marrow is involved, the lieno-medullary form of the Germans. The essential change, indeed, in the disease appears to be the extraordinary hyperplasia of the red marrow, and the appearance of an hyperplastic cellular tissue in regions where in the adults the marrow is fatty. Instead of a fatty tissue, the medulla of the long bones may resemble the consistent matter which forms the core of an abscess, or it may be dark brown in color. In Ponfick's case there were hæmorrhagic infarctions. There may be much expansion of the shell of bone, and localized swellings which are tender and may even yield to firm pressure. Histologically, there are found in the medulla large numbers of nucleated red corpuscles in all stages of development, numerous cells with eosinophilic granules, both small polynuclear forms and large almost giant mononuclear elements. There are also many large cells with single large nuclei and neutrophilic granules—the cellules medullaires of Cornil—the *myelocytes* which are found in the blood. Great numbers of polynuclear leucocytes are also present, as well as a certain number of small mononuclear elements.

In the lymphatic forms of the disease there is a general lymphatic enlargement, which is usually associated with a certain amount of enlargement of the spleen. In only one of my cases was the splenic enlargement notable. In the cases of lymphatic leukæmia the cervical, axillary, mesenteric, and inguinal groups may be much enlarged, but the glands are usually soft, isolated, and movable. They may vary considerably in size during the course of the disease. The tonsils and the lymph follicles of the tongue, pharynx, and mouth may be enlarged. Numerous mitoses may be found in the small cells of the lymphatic tissue.

In some instances there are leukæmic enlargements in the solitary and agminated glands of Peyer. In a case of Willcocks' there were growths on the surface of the stomach and gastro-splenic omentum. The thymus is rarely involved, though it has been enlarged in some of the cases of acute lymphatic leukæmia. The bone marrow in these cases may be replaced by a lymphoid tissue. Nucleated red corpuscles and the normal granular marrow elements may be greatly reduced in number.

The liver may be enlarged, and in a case described by Welch it weighed over 13 pounds. The enlargement is usually due to a diffuse leukæmic infiltration. The columns of liver cells are widely separated by leucocytes, which are partly within and partly outside the lobular capillaries. There may be definite leukæmic growths.

There are rarely changes of importance in the lungs. The kidneys are often enlarged and pale, the capillaries may be distended with leucocytes, and leukæmic tumors may occur. The skin may be involved, as in a case described by Kaposi.

Leukæmic tumors in the organs are not common. They were present in only 1 of the 12 autopsies in my series. In 159 cases collected by Gowers there were only 13 instances of leukæmic nodules in the liver and 10 in the kidneys. These new growths probably develop from leucocytes which leave the capillaries. Bizzozero has shown that the cells which compose them are in active fission.

Symptoms.—The onset is insidious, and, as a rule, the patient seeks advice for progressive enlargement of the abdomen and shortness of breath, or for the enlarged glands or the pallor, palpitation, and other symptoms of anæmia. Bleeding at the nose is common. Gastro-intestinal symptoms may precede the onset. Occasionally the first symptoms are of a very serious nature. In one of the cases of my series the boy played lacrosse two days before the onset of the final hæmatemesis; and in another case a girl, who had, it was supposed, only a slight chlorosis, died of fatal hæmorrhage from the stomach before any suspicion had been aroused as to the true condition.

Anæmia is not a necessary accompaniment of all stages of the disease; the subjects may look very healthy and well.

As has been stated, the disease is most commonly seen in two main types, though combinations may occur.

(1) Spleno-medullary Leukæmia.

This is much the commonest type of the disease. The gradual increase in the volume of the spleen is the most prominent symptom in a majority of the cases. Pain and tenderness are common, though the progressive enlargement may be painless. A creaking fremitus may be felt on palpation. The enlarged organ extends downward to the right, and may be felt just at the costal edge, or when large it may extend as far over as the navel. In many cases it occupies fully one half of the abdomen, reaching to the pubes below and extending beyond the middle line. As a rule, the edge, in some the notch or notches, can be felt distinctly. Its size varies greatly from time to time. It may be perceptibly larger after meals. A hæmorrhage or free diarrhœa may reduce the size. The pressure of the enlarged organ may cause distress after eating; in one case it caused fatal obstruction of the bowels. A murmur may sometimes be heard over the spleen, and Gerhardt has described a pulsation in it.

The pulse is usually rapid, soft, compressible, but often full in volume. There are rarely any cardiac symptoms. The apex beat may be lifted an interspace by the enlarged spleen. Toward the close, as a consequence of the feeble circulation, œdema may occur in the feet or there may be general anasarca. Hæmorrhage is a common symptom and may be either late or early. There may be most extensive purpura. Epistaxis is the most frequent form. Hæmoptysis and hæmaturia are rare. Bleeding from the gums may be present. Hæmatemesis proved fatal in two of my cases, and in a third a large cerebral hæmorrhage rapidly killed. The leukæmic retinitis is a part of the hæmorrhagic manifestations.

Local gangrene may develop, with signs of intense infection and high fever. There are very few pulmonary symptoms. The shortness of breath is due, as a rule, to the anæmia. Toward the end there may be œdema of the lungs, or pneumonia may carry off the patient. The gastro-intestinal symptoms are rarely absent. Nausea and vomiting are early features in some cases. Diarrhœa may be very troublesome, even fatal. Intestinal hæmorrhage is not common. There may be a dysenteric process in the colon. Jaundice rarely occurs, though in one case of my series there were recurrent attacks. Ascites may be a prominent symptom, probably due to the presence of the splenic tumor. A leukæmic peritonitis also may be present, due to new growths in the membranes.

The nervous system is not often involved. Headache, dizziness, and fainting spells are due to anæmia. The patients are usually tranquil and resigned. Sudden coma may follow cerebral hæmorrhage.

The special senses are often affected. There is a peculiar retinitis, due chiefly to the extravasation of blood, but there may be aggregations of leucocytes, forming small leukæmic growths. Optic neuritis is rare. Deafness has frequently been observed; it may appear early and possibly is due to hæmorrhage.

The urine presents no constant changes. The uric acid excreted is always in excess, and possibly, as Salkowski suggests, stands in direct relation to the splenic tumor, or to the abundant leucocytes.

Priapism is a curious symptom which has been present in a large num-

50

ber of cases. It may, as in one of Edes' cases, be the first symptom. Peabody reports a case in which it persisted for six weeks. The cause is not known.

Slight fever is present in a majority of cases. Periods of pyrexia may alternate with prolonged intervals of freedom. The temperature may range from 102° to 103°.

Blood.—In all forms of the disease the diagnosis must be made by the examination of the blood, as it alone offers distinctive features.

The most striking change in the more common form, the lienomyelogenic, is the increase in the colorless corpuscles. The average normal number of white per cubic millimetre is estimated at about 6,000–7,000; thus the proportion of white to red is 1 to 500–1,000. In leukæmia the proportion may be 1 to 10, or 1 to 5, or may even reach 1 to 1. There are instances on record in which the number of leucocytes has exceeded that of the red corpuscles.

The character of the cells in splenic myelogenous leukæmia is as follows: The small mononuclear forms are little if at all increased; relatively they are greatly diminished. The eosinophiles are present in normal or increased relative proportion, so that there is a great total increase, and their presence is a striking feature in the stained blood-slide. The polynuclear neutrophiles may be in normal proportion; more frequently they are relatively diminished, and in the later stages they may form but a small proportion of the colorless elements. Marked differences in size between individual polynuclear leucocytes may be noted; the same is true of the eosinophiles. The most characteristic features of the blood in this form of leukæmia is the presence of cells which do not occur in normal blood. They appear to be derived from the marrow, and are called by Ehrlich *myelocytes.* They are considerably larger than the large mononuclear leucocytes, and are similar to them in appearance, but differ from them in the fact that the protoplasm is filled with the fine neutrophilic granules. Müller has recently found many large mononuclear elements with karyokinetic figures in leukæmic blood and in the marrow. These probably correspond to the myelocytes of Ehrlich as well as to the " cellules médullaires " of Cornil. Polynuclear cells with coarse basophilic granules, " Mastzellen," are always present in this form of leukæmia in considerable numbers. The granules do not stain in Ehrlich's triacid mixture, and the cells may be recognized as polynuclear non-granular elements. These cells, which form only about 0.28 per cent of the leucocytes of normal blood, may be even more numerous than the eosinophiles.

Nucleated red blood-corpuscles are present in considerable numbers. These are usually " normoblasts," but cells with larger paler nuclei, some showing evidences of mitosis, may be seen. Red cells with fragmented nuclei are common, while true gigantoblasts may be found. There is, as a rule, only a moderate reduction in the number of red blood-corpuscles; the number is rarely under 2,000,000 per cubic millimetre. The hæmoglobin is usually reduced in a somewhat greater proportion. The accompanying blood chart is from a case of leukæmia with an enormously enlarged spleen. Among other points about leukæmic blood may be men-

tioned the feebleness of the amœboid movement, as noted by Cafavy, which
may be accounted for by the large number of mononuclear elements present,
the polynuclear alone possessing this power. The blood-plates exist in variable numbers; they may be remarkably abundant. The fibrin network
between the corpuscles is usually thick and dense. In blood-slides which

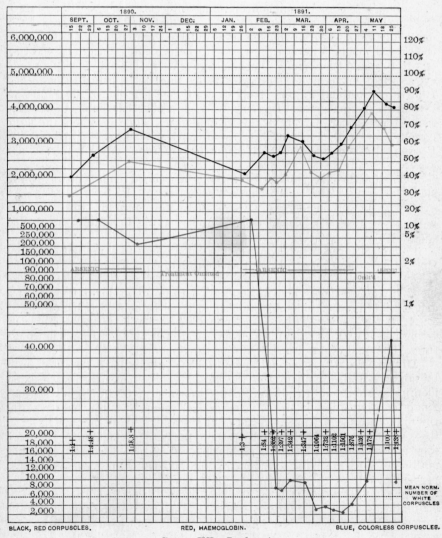

CHART XX.—Leukæmia.

are kept for a short time, Charcot's octohedral crystals separate, and in the
blood of leukæmia the hæmoglobin shows a remarkable tendency to crys-
tallize.

2. Lymphatic Leukæmia.

This form of leukæmia is rare. As mentioned, in but 4 of my series of 26 cases were the glands enlarged. The superficial groups are usually most involved, and even when affected it is rare to see such large bunches as in Hodgkin's disease. External lymph tumors are rare. Lymphatic leukæmia is often more rapid and fatal in its course, though chronic cases may occur. It is more common in young subjects.

The histological characters of the *blood* in lymphatic leukæmia differ materially from those in the spleno-medullary form. The increase in the colorless elements is never so great as in the preceding form; a proportion of 1 to 10 would be extreme. This increase takes place solely in the lymphocytes, all other forms of leucocytes being present in greatly diminished relative proportion. In one of my cases over 98 per cent of all the leucocytes were lymphocytes. In some cases, as Cabot has pointed out, this increase takes place largely in the smaller forms, while in others the large lymphocytes—cells nearly as large as polynuclear leucocytes—predominate. Eosinophiles and nucleated red corpuscles are rare. Myelocytes are not present.

The pure myelogenous cases without associated enlargement of the spleen are rare. The most extreme hyperplasia of the bone marrow may exist without any tenderness. Occasionally the sternum, ribs, and flat bones show great irregularity and deformity, owing to definite tumor-like expansions.

Combined forms of leukæmia may occur, though they are not common. One such instance occurred at the Johns Hopkins Hospital. Here the spleen, marrow, and lymphatic glands all showed marked changes. The blood in this instance showed, besides a large proportion of lymphocytes and myelocytes, a considerable number of large mononuclear leucocytes.

Acute Leukæmia.—This is usually of the lymphatic type, and occurs in young persons. Fussell and Taylor have collected 56 cases from the literature. The fatal event occurs in two or three months.

Diagnosis.—The recognition of leukæmia can be determined only by microscopical examination of the blood. The clinical features may be identical with those of ordinary splenic anæmia, or of Hodgkin's disease. An interesting question arises whether real increase in the leucocytes is the only criterion of the existence of the disease. Thus, for instance, in the case whose chart is given on page 807, the patient came under observation in September, 1890, with 2,000,000 red blood-corpuscles per cubic millimetre, 30 per cent of hæmoglobin, and 500,000 white blood-corpuscles per cubic millimetre—a proportion of 1 to 4. As shown by the chart, throughout September, October, November, and December, this ratio was maintained. Early in January, under treatment with arsenic, the white corpuscles began to decrease, and gradually, as shown in the chart, the normal ratio was reached. At this time could it be said that the case was one of leukæmia without increase in the number of leucocytes? The blood examination by Ehrlich's method, as made by Thayer, showed that nucleated red corpuscles in large numbers as well as the characteristic myelocytes, elements which are but rarely found in normal blood, were still present in numbers sufficient, at any rate, to suggest, if the patient had come under observation for the first time, that leukæmia might occur. By Ehrlich's method of blood examination a condition of leucocytosis can readily be distinguished from that of leukæmia, for in all ordinary leucocytoses the increase takes place solely in the polynuclear neutrophilic cells.

The remarkable "green cancer" or chloroma is, according to Dock, "a lymphomatous process similar in its classical features to leukæmia and pseudo-leukæmia."

Prognosis.—Recovery occasionally occurs. A great majority of the cases prove fatal within two or three years. Unfavorable signs are a tendency to hæmorrhage, persistent diarrhœa, early dropsy, and high fever. Remarkable variations are displayed in the course, and a transient improvement may take place for weeks or even months. The pure lymphatic form seems to be of particular malignancy, some cases proving fatal in from six to eight weeks; but there are exceptions, and I have recently seen a case in which the diagnosis was made ten years ago by W. H. Draper. The patient has had enlarged glands ever since, and, though not anæmic, the leucocytes were 242,000 per cubic millimetre, above 90 per cent of them being lymphocytes.

Treatment.—Fresh air, good diet, and abstention from mental worry and care, are the important general indications. The *indicatio morbi* cannot be met. There are certain remedies which have an influence upon the disease. Of these, arsenic, given in large doses, is the best. I have repeatedly seen improvement under its use. On the other hand, there are curious remissions in the disease which render therapeutical deductions very fallacious. I have seen such marked improvement without special treatment that the patient, from a bed-ridden, wretched condition, recovered strength enough to enable him to attend to light duties.

Quinine may be given in cases with a malarial history. Iron may be of value in some cases, as may also inhalations of oxygen.

Excision of the leukæmic spleen has been performed 24 times, with 1 recovery—the case of Franzolini. Fussell gives the statistics of 105 cases of splenectomy with 48 deaths. Of the cases of simple hypertrophy, 28 in number, 9 recovered. Of 16 cases of floating spleen, 15 recovered.

III. HODGKIN'S DISEASE.

Definition.—An affection characterized by progressive hyperplasia of the lymph-glands, with anæmia, and occasionally the development of secondary lymphoid growths in the liver, spleen, and other organs. The disease has also the names *pseudo-leukæmia, general lymphadenoma*, and *adénie.*

Hodgkin, the well-known morbid anatomist of Guy's Hospital, first described cases in detail, and by the labors of Wilks, Virchow, Billroth, and Cohnheim the disease attained definite recognition.

Etiology.—A majority of the cases are in young persons. In Gowers' table of 100 cases, 30 were under twenty years, 34 between twenty and forty, and 36 above forty. Three fourths of the cases are in males. In a few instances heredity has been adduced as a possible cause, and antecedent disease, such as syphilis; but these are doubtful factors. More important is local irritation, upon which Trousseau lays special stress, and gives instances in which chronic irritation of the skin, chronic nasal catarrh, or the irritation of a decayed tooth gave rise to local gland swellings, which preceded a general development of the disease. In a large majority of the cases the disease comes on insidiously, without any recognizable cause.

Morbid Anatomy.—*The Lymph-glands.*—In a few cases the enlarged glands are hard and firm, but in a majority the growth is soft and elastic. In the early stage the individual glands are isolated, not larger than almonds or walnuts, and readily separated and movable. In more advanced stages the glands fuse together, and a group, as in the neck, may form a large tumor, the size of an orange or even of a cocoa-nut. About such masses the capsular tissues are hard and dense, forming a firm investment. A growth may perforate the capsule and invade contiguous parts, such as the muscles, skin, or the solid organs. On section, the tumor has a grayish-white appearance; it is smooth, and of variable consistence, either firm and dry or soft and juicy. Suppuration is most frequently seen when the growth reaches the skin. In the deep glands the formation of pus is rare. Caseation is not common; occasionally there are areas of necrosis very like it. The superficial glands are most often attacked, particularly the cervical groups, and they may be traced as continuous chains along the trachea and the carotids, uniting the axillary and mediastinal glands.

The axillary group is involved next in order of frequency, and the masses may pass beneath the pectorals and beneath the scapulæ. The inguinal glands occasionally form very large masses. Of the internal groups, those of the thorax are most often affected, either the chain in the posterior mediastinum or the bronchial group, or those of the anterior mediastinum. The trachea and the aorta with its branches may be completely surrounded by the growths, and be but little compressed. From the anterior mediastinum the masses may perforate the sternum and appear as an external tumor.

Of the abdominal groups, the retroperitoneal is most frequently involved and may form a continuous chain from the diaphragm to the inguinal canals, and extend into the pelvis. The glands may compress the ureters, involve the sacral or lumbar nerves, or impinge upon the iliac veins. Occasionally they adhere to the uterus and broad ligament so as to simulate fibroids. I saw, some years ago, one of the most distinguished gynæcologists of Germany perform laparotomy in a case of this kind, in which the diagnosis of myomatous tumors of the uterus had been made. Occasionally the mesenteric or hepatic lymph-glands may form large abdominal tumors.

Histologically the chief change is an increase in the cells, with or without thickening of the reticulum. In the early stage there is simple hyperplasia and the relations of the lymph paths are maintained, but when the glands are greatly enlarged the normal arrangement is disturbed. The reticulum varies extremely; in the softer growths it is expanded and can scarcely be found; in the harder structures the network of fibres is very distinct, and there is probably an increased development of the adenoid tissue.

Spleen.—In 75 per cent of the cases collected by Gowers this organ was hypertrophied, and in 56 of these it presented lymphoid growths. The enlargement is rarely great, and does not approximate to that of the large leukæmic spleen. The lymphoid tumors form grayish-white bodies ranging in size from a pea to a walnut, and may resemble lymph-glands in appearance and consistence. Histologically, they consist of lymph corpuscles in a fibrous reticulum.

The marrow of the long bones may be converted into a rich lymphoid tissue; in a few instances the pyoid form, such as is more common in leukæmia, has been found. The tonsils may be involved and the follicles at the root of the tongue. Occasionally secondary growths are seen in the intestines.

The liver is often enlarged and may present scattered lymphoid tumors. The kidneys are occasionally involved and are the seat of growths similar to those in the spleen and liver. The lungs are occasionally directly attacked from the bronchial glands at the root, and secondary nodules may be found throughout their substance. Pleural effusions are not uncommon. Involvement of the nervous system is rare, but paraplegia may be induced by invasion of the spinal canal. The skin may be the seat of adenoid growths, as in a case reported by Greenfield.

Symptoms.—Enlargement of the glands of the neck, axilla, or groins is usually the first symptom noticed. In a few cases the anæmia and constitutional symptoms attract attention before the glandular involvement is evident. When the trouble begins in the deeper groups, pressure effects may be first noticed; thus, paroxysmal dyspnœa with pain in the chest may result from enlargement of the bronchial glands before any physical signs can be detected. Œdema of the feet and shooting pains in the nerves were the first symptoms in one case which I dissected for Ross, and in another case at the Montreal General Hospital there was paraplegia from pressure on the cord. Such instances, however, are exceptional, and in the majority of cases the swelling of the superficial glands is the earliest symptom. Epistaxis has occasionally been noted, but not so frequently as in leukæmia. With progressive enlargement of the glands the patient becomes anæmic.

Usually, the cervical group is first affected, and it may be impossible to decide whether the enlargement is syphilitic, tuberculous, or lymphadenomatous. One side is first affected as a rule, and it may be months or even, as in one of my cases, three years before the affection extends to other groups. Ultimately huge tumors may develop, which obliterate the neck and extend upon the shoulders and over the clavicles and sternum. The trachea is surrounded, great dyspnœa is produced, and not infrequently tracheotomy is necessary. In the later stages, the skin becomes involved and ulcerates. The axillary group may form large tumors, which compress the brachial or axillary veins and cause swelling of the arms. The inguinal glands may form large or even pendulous tumors.

In the thoracic glands, as mentioned, the various groups may be involved and produce pressure upon the veins or upon the trachea. In a case recently under observation the superior cava was completely obliterated and a very extensive collateral circulation was established by means of the mammary and epigastric veins. The skin over the sternum was a mass of fluctuating veins, some of which contained phleboliths. In the abdomen the mesenteric glands may be enlarged, or more commonly the retroperitoneal group. When the patient is thin there may be no difficulty in detecting these, but in stout persons the diagnosis may be impossible. In connection with the affections of the abdominal glands there may be bronzing of the skin, which was well marked in Case IV of my series. A remarkable feature is the variations in the rate of growth and in the size of the glands. They may reduce rapidly and almost disappear from a region, and before death the number of those visible may diminish very much. The spleen may be enlarged and readily palpable. The thyroid also may be involved, and in a few instances the thymus has been affected. Though present in a majority of the cases, there may be enormous enlargement of the lymph-glands without marked anæmia. In one of my cases the blood-corpuscles did not sink below 4,000,000 per cubic millimetre, and in only one instance have I counted the blood below 2,000,000. The red blood-corpuscles rarely show extreme poikilocytosis. The white corpuscles may be moderately increased and the lymphocytes abundant, though usually there is little that is characteristic in the blood. Occasionally the leucocytes are greatly increased and the characters of the blood become those of a lymphatic leukæmia. Nucleated red blood-corpuscles may be present, but not in such numbers as in leukæmia.

Of cardiac symptoms, palpitation is common. Hæmic murmurs are often heard over the heart. Shortness of breath may be due to the anæmia, to pressure upon the trachea, or, in some instances, to pleuritic effusion associated with mediastinal growths. Fever is observed in nearly all cases; even in the early stages there is slight elevation. It may be of an irregular hectic type, or continuous, with evening exacerbation. Very remarkable are the cases with ague-like paroxysms, which may persist for weeks or months. They were present in Case I of my series. Pel, of Amsterdam, has given a thorough description of these attacks, and Ebstein has described a case under the remarkable title of Chronic Recurrent Fever, a New Infectious Disease. In his case during nine months the attacks were present for periods of from twelve to fourteen days and alternated with an apyrexia of ten or eleven days.

The digestive symptoms are usually not marked. It is not uncommon to find albumin in the urine. Headache, giddiness, and noises in the ear may be associated with the anæmia. Delirium and coma may ensue. Deafness may be produced by growth of the adenoid tissue in the pharynx close to the Eustachian tubes. Inequality of the pupils may be present, owing to pressure of the glands on the cervical sympathetic. The skin may show definite secondary lymphatic tumors, bronzing may occur, and occasionally a most intense and troublesome prurigo.

Diagnosis.—A tuberculous adenitis may at first be very difficult to differentiate. The chief points of distinction are as follows: Tuberculous adenitis is more common in the young and involves the submaxillary group of glands more frequently than those of the anterior and posterior cervical triangles, which are usually affected first in Hodgkin's disease. The enlargement may last for years in a group without extending. The bunches are often, when small, welded together and, most important of all, tend to suppurate—a feature rarely seen in true lymphadenoma, except when it has attained very large size. Strict limitation to one side of the neck or to the axilla is suggestive of tuberculous disease rather than lymphadenoma.

There is an acute tuberculous adenitis, which may involve the lymphglands of the neck, producing enormous enlargement. A man, aged twenty-four, was admitted to the General Hospital, Montreal, with great swelling of the cervical glands on both sides, tonsillitis, and sloughing pharyngitis, with irregular fever and diarrhœa. The case was at first regarded as one of Hodgkin's disease. The occurrence of rigors and intermittent pyrexia is in favor of lymphadenoma. There are cases in which it may for a time be impossible to make a diagnosis. When the glands are only moderately enlarged on one side of the neck or axilla, they should be removed, and the diagnosis can then be thoroughly established.

Prognosis.—Recovery is very rare. The course of the disease is extremely variable. Early and rapid growth in the mediastinal groups may produce pressure effects and cause death before the development is extreme. In some cases the enlargements spread rapidly and group after group becomes involved in a few months. These acute case may run a course in three or four months. Chronic cases may last for three or four years. Periods of quiescence are not uncommon. The tumors may not only cease to grow, but gradually diminish and even disappear, without special treatment. Usually a cachexia develops, the anæmia progresses, and there are dropsical symptoms. The mode of death is usually by asthenia; less commonly by pressure from a tumor; and occasionally in coma.

Treatment.—When small and localized the glands should be removed. Local applications are of doubtful benefit. I have never seen special improvement follow the persistent use of iodine or the various ointments.

Arsenic has a positive value in the disease. It should be given in increasing doses, and stopped when unpleasant effects are manifested. The results have in many instances been striking. Due allowance must be made for the fluctuations in the size of the growths which occur spontaneously. Ill effects from the administration of Fowler's solution, even for months at a time, are rare, but I have had a case in which neuritis followed the use of ℥ iv ℨ j ℳxviij within a period of less than three months. Recoveries have been reported under this treatment. Personally, no instance of recovery has come under my notice in the cases of which I have notes. Phosphorus is recommended by Gowers and Broadbent, and should be used if the arsenic is not well borne. Quinine, iron, and cod-liver oil are useful as tonics. Every possible means must be taken to support the patient's strength.

IV. PURPURA.

Strictly speaking, purpura is a symptom, not a disease; but under this term are conveniently arranged a number of affections characterized by extravasations of the blood into the skin. In the present state of our knowledge a satisfactory classification cannot be made. Excluding symptomatic purpura, W. Koch groups all forms, including hæmophilia, under the designation *hæmorrhagic diathesis*, believing that intermediate forms link the mild purpura simplex and the most intense purpura hæmorrhagica; while F. A. Hoffmann considers them all (except hæmophilia) under the heading *morbus maculosus*. The purpuric spots vary from 1 to 3 or 4 mm. in diameter. When small and pin-point-like they are called petechiæ; when large, they are known as ecchymoses. At first bright red in color, they become darker, and gradually fade to brownish stains. They do not disappear on pressure.

In all cases of purpura the coagulation time of the blood should be estimated (Wright); the coagulometer is a useful clinical instrument for the purpose. Normal blood clots in the tubes in from three to five minutes. In some forms of purpura the coagulation time is retarded to ten or fifteen minutes, and in hæmophilia it has been delayed to fifty minutes.

The following is a provisional grouping of the cases:

Symptomatic Purpura.—(*a*) **Infectious.**—In pyæmia, septicæmia, and malignant endocarditis (particularly in the last affection), ecchymoses may be very abundant. In typhus fever the rash is always purpuric. Measles, scarlet fever, and more particularly small-pox, have each a variety characterized by an extensive purpuric rash.

(*b*) **Toxic.**—The virus of snakes produces with great rapidity extravasation of blood—a condition which has been very carefully studied by Weir Mitchell. Certain medicines, particularly copaiba, quinine, belladonna, mercury, ergot, and the iodides occasionally, are followed by a petechial rash. Purpura may follow the use of comparatively small doses of iodide of potassium. It is not a very common occurrence, considering the great frequency with which the drug is employed. A fatal event may be caused by a small amount, as in a case reported by Stephen Mackenzie of a child which died after a dose of $2\frac{1}{2}$ grains. An erythema may precede the hæmorrhage. It is not always a simple purpura, but may be an acute febrile eruption of great intensity. In September, 1894, a man aged forty-eight was admitted under my care with arterio-sclerosis and dropsy. The latter yielded rapidly to digitalis and diuretin. When convalescent he was ordered iodide of potassium in 10-grain doses three times a day, and took in fourteen days 420 grains. He had high fever, coryza, swelling of the throat, and the most extensive purpura over the whole body. Under this division, too, comes the purpura so often associated with jaundice.

(*c*) **Cachectic.**—Under this heading are best described the instances of purpura which develop in the constitutional disturbance of cancer, tuberculosis, Hodgkin's disease, Bright's disease, scurvy, and in the debility of old age. In these cases the spots are usually confined to the extremities.

They may be very abundant on the lower limbs and about the wrists and hands. This constitutes, probably, the commonest variety of the disease, and many examples of it can be seen in the wards of any large hospital.

(*d*) **Neurotic.**—One variety is met with in cases of organic disease. It is the so-called myelopathic purpura, which is seen occasionally in loco-motor ataxia, particularly following attacks of the lightning pains and, as a rule, involving the area of the skin in which the pains have been most intense. Cases have been met with also in acute myelitis and in transverse myelitis, and occasionally in severe neuralgia. Another form is the re-markable hysterical condition in which stigmata, or bleeding points, appear upon the skin.

(*e*) **Mechanical.**—This variety is most frequently seen in venous stasis of any form, as in the paroxysms of whooping-cough and in epilepsy.

Arthritic.—This form is characterized by involvement of the joints. It is usually known, therefore, as rheumatic, though in reality the evidence upon which this view is based is not conclusive. Of 200 cases of purpura analyzed by Stephen Mackenzie, 61 had a history of rheumatism. For the present it seems more satisfactory to use the designation arthritic. Three groups of cases may be recognized:

(*a*) A mild form, often known as **Purpura simplex,** seen most com-monly in children, in whom, with or without articular pain, a crop of purpuric spots appears upon the legs, less commonly upon the trunk and arms. As pointed out by Graves, this form is not infrequently associated with diarrhœa. The disease is seldom severe. There may be loss of ap-petite, and slight anæmia. Fever is not, as a rule, present, and the pa-tients get well in a week or ten days. These cases are usually regarded as rheumatic, and are certainly associated, in some instances, with un-doubted rheumatic manifestations; yet in a majority of the patients which I have seen the arthritis was slighter than in the ordinary rheumatism of children, and no other manifestations were present.

(*b*) **Purpura (Peliosis) rheumatica** (*Schönlein's Disease*).—This remark-able affection is characterized by multiple arthritis, and an eruption which varies greatly in character, sometimes *purpuric*, more commonly associated with *urticaria* or with *erythema exudativum*. The disease is most common in males between the ages of twenty and thirty. It not infre-quently sets in with sore throat, a fever from 101° to 103°, and articular pains. The rash, which makes its appearance first on the legs or about the affected joints, may be a simple purpura or may show ordinary urticarial wheals. In other instances there are nodular infiltrations, not to be distin-guished from erythema nodosum. The combination of wheals and purpura, the *purpura urticans*, is very distinctive. Much more rarely vesication is met with, the so-called *pemphigoid purpura*. The amount of œdema is vari-able; occasionally it is excessive. In one case, which I saw in Montreal with Molson, the chin and lower lip were enormously swollen, tense, glazed, and deeply ecchymotic. The eyelids were swollen and purpuric, while scattered over the cheeks and about the joints were numerous spots of purpura urticans. These are the cases which have been described as *febrile* *purpuric œdema.* The temperature range, in mild cases, is not high, but may reach 102° or 103°.

The urine is sometimes reduced in amount and may be albuminous. The joint affections are usually slight, though associated with much pain, particularly as the rash comes out. Relapses may occur and the disease may return at the same time for several years in succession.

The diagnosis of Schönlein's disease offers no difficulty. The association of multiple arthritis with purpura and urticaria is very characteristic. In a case which I saw with Musser there was endo-pericarditis, and the question at first arose whether the patient had malignant endocarditis with extensive cutaneous infarcts.

Schönlein's peliosis is thought by most writers to be of rheumatic origin, and certainly many of the cases have the characters of ordinary rheumatic fever, *plus* purpura. By many, however, it is regarded as a special affection, of which the arthritis is a manifestation analogous to that which occurs in hæmophilia and in scurvy. The frequency with which sore throat precedes the attack, and the occasional occurrence of endocarditis or pericarditis, are certainly very suggestive of true rheumatism.

The cases usually do well, and a fatal event is extremely rare. The throat symptoms may persist and give trouble. In two instances I have seen necrosis and sloughing of a portion of the uvula.

(*c*) **Henoch's Purpura.**—This variety, seen chiefly in children, is characterized by (1) relapses or recurrences, often extending over several years; (2) cutaneous lesions, which are those of erythema multiforme rather than of simple purpura; (3) gastro-intestinal crises—pain, vomiting, and diarrhœa; (4) joint pains or swelling, often trifling; (5) hæmorrhages from the mucous membranes. When from the kidney, an intense hæmorrhagic nephritis may supervene, which proved fatal, with the symptoms of acute Bright's disease, in one of my cases, and became chronic in a case under D. W. Prentiss. Any one or two of the above symptoms may be absent; the intestinal crises with enlargement of the spleen may be present and recur for months before the true nature of the trouble becomes manifest. This form has an interesting connection with the angio-neurotic œdema, which is also characterized by severe gastro-intestinal crises. The prognosis is, as a rule, good; 3 of the 11 cases which I have reported died.*

Purpura Hæmorrhagica.—Under this heading may be considered the cases of very severe purpura with hæmorrhages from the mucous membranes. The affection, known as the *morbus maculosus* of Werlhof, is most commonly met with in young and delicate individuals, particularly in girls; but cases are described in which the disease has attacked adults in full vigor. After a few days of weakness and debility, purpuric spots appear on the skin and rapidly increase in numbers and size. Bleeding from the mucous surfaces sets in, and the epistaxis, hæmaturia, and hæmoptysis may cause profound anæmia. Chart XXI illustrates the rapidity with which anæmia is produced and the gradual recovery. Death may take place from loss of blood, or from hæmorrhage into the brain. Slight

---

* Am. Jour. of the Med. Sciences, December, 1895.

fever usually accompanies the disease. In favorable cases the affection terminates in from ten days to two weeks. There are instances of purpura hæmorrhagica of great malignancy, which may prove fatal within twenty-four hours—*purpura fulminans*. This form is most commonly met with in children, and is characterized by cutaneous hæmorrhages, which develop with great rapidity. Death may occur before any bleeding takes place from the mucous membranes.

In the *diagnosis* of purpura hæmorrhagica it is important to exclude scurvy, which may be done by the consideration of the previous health,

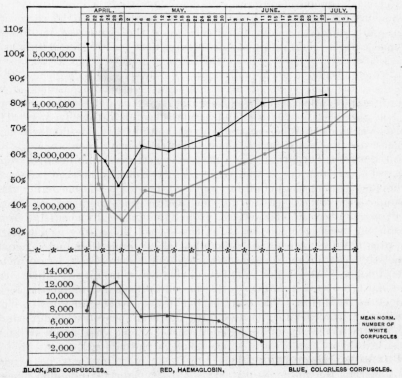

CHART XXI.—Illustrates the rapidity with which anæmia is produced in purpura hæmorrhagica and the gradual recovery.

the circumstances under which the disease develops, and by the absence of swelling of the gums. The malignant forms of the fevers, particularly small-pox and measles, are distinguished by the prodromes and the higher temperature.

Treatment.—In symptomatic purpura attention should be paid to the conditions under which it develops, and measures should be employed to increase the strength and to restore a normal blood condition. Tonics, good food, and fresh air meet these indications. In the simple purpura of children, or that associated with slight articular trouble, arsenic in full doses should be given. No good is obtained from the small doses, but the Fowler's solution should be pushed freely until physiological effects are obtained. In peliosis rheumatica the sodium salicylates may be given, but with discretion. I confess not to have seen any special control of the hæmorrhages by this remedy.

Aromatic sulphuric acid, ergot, turpentine, acetate of lead, or tannic and gallic acids, may be used, and in some instances they seem to check the bleeding. Oil of turpentine is perhaps the best remedy, in 10 or 15 minims doses three or four times a day. Wright, of Netley, advises the use of calcium chloride in 20-grain doses four times a day (for three or four days) to increase the coagulability of the blood. In bleeding from the mouth, gums, and nose, the inhalation of the carbon dioxide is sometimes useful. The rinsing of the mouth with gelatin has been recommended.

HÆMORRHAGIC DISEASES OF THE NEW-BORN.

1. Syphilis Hæmorrhagica Neonatorum.—The child may be born healthy, or there may be signs of hæmorrhage at birth. Then in a few days there are extensive cutaneous extravasations and bleeding from the mucous surfaces and from the navel. The child may become deeply jaundiced. The post mortem shows numerous extravasations in the internal organs and extensive syphilitic changes in the liver and other organs.

2. Epidemic Hæmoglobinuria (*Winckel's Disease*).—Hæmoglobinuria in the new-born, which occasionally develops in epidemic form in lying-in institutions, is a very fatal affection, which sets in usually about the fourth day of life. The child becomes jaundiced, and there are marked gastro-intestinal symptoms, with fever, jaundice, rapid respiration, and sometimes cyanosis. The urine contains albumin and blood-coloring matter—methæmoglobin. The disease has to be distinguished from the simple icterus neonatorum, with which there may sometimes be blood or blood-coloring matter in the urine. The post mortem shows an absence of any septic condition of the umbilical vessels, but the spleen is swollen, and there are punctiform hæmorrhages in different parts. Some cases have shown in a marked degree acute fatty degeneration of the internal organs—the so-called Buhl's disease.

3. Morbus Maculosus Neonatorum.—Apart from the common visceral hæmorrhages, the result of injuries at birth, bleeding from one or more of the surfaces is a not uncommon event in the new-born, particularly in hospital practice. Forty-five cases occurred in 6,700 deliveries (C. W. Townsend). The bleeding may be from the navel alone, but more commonly it is general. Of Townsend's 50 cases, in 20 the blood came from the bowels (*melæna neonatorum*), in 14 from the stomach, in 14 from the mouth, in 12 from the nose, in 18 from the navel, in 3 from the navel alone. The bleeding begins within the first week, but in rare instances is delayed to the second or third. Thirty-one of the cases died and 19 recovered. The disease is usually of brief duration, death occurring in from one to seven days. The temperature is often elevated. The nature of the disease is unknown. As a rule, nothing abnormal is found post mortem. The general and not local nature of the affection, its self-limited character, the presence of fever, and the greater prevalence of the disease in hospitals, suggest an infectious origin (Townsend). The bleeding may be associated with intense hæmatogenous jaundice. Not every case of bleeding from the stomach or bowels belongs in this category. Ulcers of the œsophagus, stomach, and duodenum have been found in the new-born dead of *melæna neonatorum*. The child may draw the blood from the breast and subsequently vomit it. In the treatment the external warmth must be maintained, and in feeble infants the *couveuse* may be used. Camphor is recommended and ergotin hypodermically.

V. HÆMOPHILIA.

Definition.—An hereditary, constitutional fault, characterized by a tendency to uncontrollable bleeding, either spontaneous or from slight wounds, sometimes associated with a form of arthritis. The coagulation time of the blood is usually much retarded.

Early in the century several physicians of this country called attention to the occurrence of profuse hæmorrhage from slight causes. The fact that fatal hæmorrhage might occur from slight, trifling wounds had been known for centuries. The recognition of the family nature of the disease is due to the writings of Buel, Otto, Hay, Coates, and others in this country. The disease has been elaborately treated in the monographs of Legg and Grandidier.

Etiology.—In a majority of cases the disposition is hereditary. The fault may be acquired, however, but nothing is known of the conditions under which the disease may thus arise in healthy stock.

The hereditary transmission in this disease is remarkable. In the Appleton-Swain family, of Reading, Mass., there have been cases for nearly two centuries; and F. F. Brown, of that town, tells me that instances have already occurred in the seventh generation. The usual mode of transmission is through the mother, who is not herself a bleeder, but the daughter of one. Atavism through the female alone is almost the rule, and the daughters of a bleeder, though healthy and free from any tendency, are almost certain to transmit the disposition to the male offspring. The affection is much more common in males than in females, the proportion being estimated at 11 to 1, or even 13 to 1. The tendency usually appears within the first two years of life. It is rare for manifestations to be delayed until the tenth or twelfth year. Families in all conditions of life are affected. The bleeder families are usually large. The members are healthy-looking, and have fine, soft skins.

Morbid Anatomy.—No special peculiarities have been described. In some instances changes have been found in the smaller vessels; but in others careful studies have been negative. An unusual thinness of the vessels has been noted. Hæmorrhages have been found in and about the capsules of the joints, and in a few instances inflammation of the synovial surfaces. The nature of the disease is undetermined, and we do not yet know whether it depends upon a peculiar frailty of the blood-vessels or some peculiarity in the constitution of the blood, which prevents the normal thrombus formation in a wound.

Symptoms.—Usually hæmophilia is not noted in the child until a trifling cut is followed by serious or uncontrollable hæmorrhage, or spontaneous bleeding occurs and presents insuperable difficulties in its arrest. The symptoms may be grouped under three divisions: external bleedings, spontaneous and traumatic; interstitial bleedings, petechiæ and ecchymoses; and the joint affections. The external bleedings may be spontaneous, but more commonly they follow cuts and wounds. In 334 cases (Grandidier) the chief bleedings were epistaxis, 169; from the mouth, 43; stomach, 15; bowels, 36; urethra, 16; lungs, 17; and in a few instances bleeding from the skin of the head, the tongue, finger-tips, tear-papilla, eyelids, external ear, vulva, navel, and scrotum.

Traumatic bleeding may result from blows, cuts, scratches, etc., and the blood may be diffused into the tissues or discharged externally. Trivial operations have proved fatal, such as the extraction of teeth, circumcision, or venesection. It is possible that there may be local defects which make bleeding from certain parts of the body more dangerous. D. Hayes Agnew mentioned to me the case of a bleeder who had always bled from cuts and bruises above the neck, never from those below. The bleeding is a capillary oozing. It may last for hours, or even many days. Epistaxis may prove fatal in twenty-four hours. In the slow bleeding from the mucous surfaces large blood tumors may form and project from the nose or mouth, forming remarkable-looking structures, and showing that the blood has the power of coagulation. The interstitial hæmorrhages may be spontaneous, or may result from injury. Petechiæ or large extravasations—hæmatomata—may occur, the latter usually following blows.

The joint affections of hæmophilia are remarkable. There may simply be pain, or attacks which come on suddenly with fever, and closely resemble acute rheumatism. The larger joints are usually affected. Arthritis may usher in an attack of hæmorrhage.

So far as the blood examination goes the only changes of special moment which have been noted are the absence or scanty number of blood plates and the retardation of the coagulation time, which may be even fifty-four seconds.

Diagnosis.—In the diagnosis of the condition the family tendency is important. A single uncontrollable hæmorrhage in child or adult is not to be ranked as hæmophilia; but it is only when a person shows a marked tendency to multiply hæmorrhages, spontaneous or traumatic, which tendency is not transitory but persists, and particularly if there have been joint affections, that we may consider the condition hæmophilia. Such conditions as epistaxis, recurring for years—if no other hæmorrhage occurs—or recurring hæmaturia from one kidney, which has been spoken of as unilateral renal hæmophilia, have no association with the true disease. Peliosis rheumatica is an affection which touches hæmophilia very closely, particularly in the relation of the joint swellings. It may also show itself in several members of a family. The diagnosis from the various forms of purpura is usually easy.

Prognosis.—The patients rarely die in the first bleeding. The younger the individual the worse is the outlook, though it is rarely fatal in the first year. Grandidier states that of 152 boy subjects, 81 died before the termination of the seventh year. The longer the bleeder survives the greater the chance of his outliving the tendency; but it may persist to old age, as shown in the case of Oliver Appleton, the first reported American bleeder, who died at an advanced age of hæmorrhage from a bed-sore and from the urethra. The prognosis is graver in a boy than in a girl. In the latter menstruation is sometimes early and excessive, but fortunately, in the female members of hæmophilic families, neither this function nor the act of parturition brings with it special dangers.

Treatment.—Members of a bleeder's family, particularly the boys, should be guarded from injury, and operations of all sorts should be avoided. The daughters should not marry, as it is through them that the tendency is propagated.

When an injury or wound has occurred, absolute rest and compression should first be tried, and if these fail the styptics may be used. In epistaxis ice, tannic and gallic acid may be tried before resorting to plugging. Internally ergot seems to have done good in several cases. Legg advises the perchloride of iron in half-drachm doses every two hours with a purge of sulphate of soda. For the epistaxis of the disease the inhalation of carbon dioxide through the nostrils, as recommended by A. E. Wright, may be tried. He also recommends a solution of fibrin ferment and chloride of calcium as a styptic. Biendwald has reported a case of a child in which the application of fresh blood to the wound checked the bleeding after all other means had failed. Gelatin in 5-per-cent solution is warmly recommended. Venesection has been tried in several cases. Transfusion has been employed, but without success. During convalescence, iron and arsenic should be freely used.

VI. SCURVY (*Scorbutus*).

Definition.—A constitutional disease characterized by great debility, with anæmia, a spongy condition of the gums, and a tendency to hæmorrhages.

Etiology.—The disease has been known from the earliest times, and has prevailed particularly in armies in the field and among sailors on long voyages.

From the early part of this century, owing largely to the efforts of Lind and to a knowledge of the conditions upon which the disease depends, scurvy has gradually disappeared from the naval service. In the mercantile marine, cases still occasionally occur, owing to the lack of proper and suitable food.

The disease develops whenever individuals have subsisted for prolonged periods upon a diet in which fresh vegetables or their substitutes are lacking. An insufficient diet appears to be an essential element in the disease, and all observers are now unanimous that it is the absence of those ingredients in the food which are supplied by fresh vegetables. What these constituents are has not yet been definitely determined. Garrod holds that the defect is in the absence of the potassic salts. Others believe that the essential factor is the absence of the organic salts present in fruits and vegetables. Ralfe, who has made a very careful study of the subject, believes that the absence from the food of the malates, citrates, and lactates reduces the alkalinity of the blood, which depends upon the carbonate directly derived from these salts. This diminished alkalinity, gradually produced in the scurvy patients, is, he believes, identical with the effect which can be artificially produced in animals by feeding them with an excess of acid salts; the nutrition is impaired, there are ecchymoses, and profound alterations in the characters of the blood. The acidity of the urine is greatly reduced and the alkaline phosphates are diminished in amount. One of the most interesting of recent facts relating to scurvy has been the great frequency of it in children, in connection, as a rule, with improper diet. It will be referred to more fully in a subsection.

In opposition to this chemical view it has been urged that the disease really depends upon a specific (as yet unknown) micro-organism.

In the United States scurvy has become a very rare disease. To the hospitals in the seaport towns sailors are now and then admitted with it. In large almshouses outbreaks occasionally occur. A very great increase of foreign population of a low grade has in certain districts made the disease not at all uncommon. In the mining districts of Pennsylvania the Hungarian, Bohemian, and Italian settlers are not infrequently attacked. McGrew has recently reported 42 cases in Chicago, limited entirely to Poles. He ascertained that in a large proportion of the cases the diet was composed of bread, strong coffee, and meat. Occasionally one meets with scurvy among quite well-to-do people. One of the most characteristic cases I have ever seen was in a woman with chronic dyspepsia, who had lived for many months chiefly on tea and bread. Some years ago scurvy was not infrequent in the large lumbering camps in the Ottawa Valley. Judging from the Report of the American Pædiatric Society, we must infer that infantile scurvy is on the increase in this country.

In parts of Russia scurvy is endemic, at certain seasons reaching epidemic proportions; and the leading authorities upon the disorder, now in that country, are almost unanimous, according to Hoffmann,* in regarding it as infectious.

Other factors play an important part in the disease, particularly physical and moral influences—overcrowding, dwelling in cold, damp quarters, and prolonged fatigue under depressing influences, as during the retreat of an army. Among prisoners, mental depression plays an important rôle. It is stated that epidemics of the disease have broken out in the French convict-ships en route to New Caledonia even when the diet was amply

---

* Lehrbuch der Constitutionskrankheiten, F. A. Hoffmann (1893), a work to which the student is referred for the best exposition of this group of disorders.

sufficient. Nostalgia is sometimes an important element. It is an interesting fact that prolonged starvation in itself does not necessarily cause scurvy. Not one of the professional fasters of late years has displayed any scorbutic symptom. The disease attacks all ages, but the old are more susceptible to it. Sex has no special influence, but during the siege of Paris it was noted that the males attacked were greatly in excess of the females.

Morbid Anatomy.—The anatomical changes are marked, though by no means specific, and are chiefly those associated with hæmorrhage. The blood is dark and fluid. The microscopical alterations are those of a severe anæmia, without leucocytosis. The bacteriological examination has not yielded anything very positive. Practically there are no changes in the blood, either anatomical or chemical, which can be regarded as peculiar to the disease. The skin shows the ecchymoses evident during life. There are hæmorrhages into the muscles, and occasionally about or even into the joints. Hæmorrhages occur in the internal organs, particularly on the serous membranes and in the kidneys and bladder. The gums are swollen and sometimes ulcerated, so that in advanced cases the teeth are loose and have even fallen out. Ulcers are occasionally met with in the ileum and colon. Hæmorrhages into the mucous membranes are extremely common. The spleen is enlarged and soft. Parenchymatous changes are constant in the liver, kidneys, and heart.

Symptoms.—The disease is insidious in its onset. Early symptoms are loss in weight, progressively developing weakness, and pallor. Very soon the gums are noticed to be swollen and spongy, to bleed easily, and in extreme cases to present a fungous appearance. These changes, regarded as characteristic, are sometimes absent. The teeth may become loose and even fall out. Actual necrosis of the jaw is not common. The breath is excessively foul. The tongue is swollen, but may be red and not much furred. The salivary glands are occasionally enlarged. Hæmorrhages beneath the mucous membranes of the mouth are common. The skin becomes dry and rough, and ecchymoses soon appear, first on the legs and then on the arms and trunk, and particularly into and about the hair-follicles. They are petechial, but may become larger, and when subcutaneous may cause distinct swellings. In severe cases, particularly in the legs, there may be effusion between the periosteum and the bone, forming irregular nodes, which, in the case of a sailor from a whaling vessel who came under my observation, had broken down and formed foul-looking sores. The slightest bruise or injury causes hæmorrhages into the injured part. Œdema about the ankles is common. The " scurvy sclerosis," seen oftenest in the legs, is a remarkable infiltration of the subcutaneous tissues and muscles, forming a brawny induration, the skin over which may be blood-stained. Hæmorrhages from the mucous membranes are less constant symptoms; epistaxis is, however, frequent. Hæmoptysis and hæmatemesis are uncommon. Hæmaturia and bleeding from the bowels may be present in very severe cases.

Palpitation of the heart and feebleness and irregularity of the impulse are prominent symptoms. A hæmic murmur can usually be heard at the base. Hæmorrhagic infarction of the lungs and spleen has been described. Respiratory symptoms are not common. The appetite is impaired, and owing to the soreness of the gums the patient is unable to chew the food. Constipation is more frequent than diarrhœa. Pain, tenderness, or swelling in the joints were present in 13 of McGrew's 42 cases. The urine is often albuminous. The changes in its composition are not constant; the specific gravity is high; the color is deeper; and the phosphates are increased. The statements with reference to the inorganic constituents are contradictory. Some say the phosphates and potash are deficient; others that they are increased.

There are mental depression, indifference, in some cases headache, and in the later stages delirium. Cases of convulsions, of hemiplegia, and of meningeal hæmorrhage have been described. Remarkable ocular symptoms are occasionally met with, such as night-blindness or day-blindness.

In advanced cases necrosis of the bones may occur, and in young persons even separation of the epiphyses. There are instances in which the cartilages have separated from the sternum. The callus of a recently repaired fracture has been known to undergo destruction. Fever is not present, except in the later stages, or when secondary inflammations in the internal organs appear. The temperature may, indeed, be sometimes below normal. Acute arthritis is an occasional complication.

Diagnosis.—No difficulty is met in the recognition of scurvy when a number of persons are affected together. In isolated cases, however, the disease is distinguished with difficulty from certain forms of purpura. The association with manifest insufficiency in diet, and the rapid amelioration with suitable food, are points by which the diagnosis can be readily settled.

Prognosis.—The outlook is good, unless the disease is far advanced and the conditions persist which lead to its development. The mortality now is rarely great. Death results from gradual heart-failure, occasionally from sudden syncope. Meningeal hæmorrhage, extravasation into the serous cavities, entero-colitis, and other intercurrent affections may prove fatal.

Prophylaxis.—The regulations of the Board of Trade require that a sufficient supply of antiscorbutic articles of diet be taken on each ship; so that now, except as the result of accident, the occurrence of scurvy is rare in sailors.

Treatment.—The juice of two or three lemons daily and a varied diet, with plenty of fresh vegetables, suffice to cure all cases of scurvy, unless far advanced. When the stomach is much disordered, small quantities of scraped meat and milk should be given at short intervals, and the lemon-juice in gradually increasing quantities. A bitter tonic, or a steel and bark mixture, may be given. As the patient gains in strength, the diet may be more liberal, and he may eat freely of potatoes, cabbage, water-cresses, and lettuce. The stomatitis is the symptom which causes the greatest distress. The permanganate of potash or dilute carbolic acid forms the best mouth-wash. Pencilling the swollen gums with a tolerably strong solution of nitrate of silver is very useful. The solution is better than the solid stick, as it reaches to the crevices between the granulations. The constipation which is so common is best treated with large enemata. For other conditions, such as hæmorrhages and ulcerations, suitable measures must be employed.

INFANTILE SCURVY (*Barlow's Disease*).

As in adults, scurvy may occur in children in consequence of imperfect food supply.

W. B. Cheadle and Gee, in London, have described in very young children a cachexia associated with hæmorrhage. Cheadle regarded the cases as scurvy ingrafted on a rickety stock. Gee called his cases periosteal cachexia. Cases had previously been regarded as acute rickets.

A few years later Barlow made an exhaustive study of the condition with careful anatomical observations. The affection is now recognized as infantile scurvy, and in Germany is called Barlow's Disease. The American Pædiatric Society has collected (1898) in this country 379 cases. Of these, the hygienic surroundings were good in 303. A majority of the patients were under twelve months. The proprietary foods, particularly malted milk and condensed milk, seem to be the most important factors in producing the disease. There are instances in which it has developed in breast-fed infants, and in others fed on the carefully prepared milk of the Walker-Gordon laboratories.

The following is a general clinical summary, taken from Barlow's Bradshaw Lecture, 1894:

" So long as it is left alone the child is tolerably quiet; the lower limbs are kept drawn up and still; but when placed in its bath or otherwise moved there is continuous crying, and it soon becomes clear that the pain is connected with the lower limbs. At this period the upper limbs may be touched with impunity, but any attempt to move the legs or thighs gives rise to screams. Next, some obscure swelling may be detected, first on one lower limb, then on the other, though it is not absolutely symmetrical. . . . The swelling is ill-defined, but is suggestive of thickening round the shafts of the bones, beginning above the epiphyseal junctions. Gradually the bulk of the limbs affected becomes visibly increased. . . . The position of the limbs becomes somewhat different from what it was at the outset. Instead of being flexed they lie everted and immobile, in a state of pseudo-paralysis. . . . About this time, if not before, great weakness of the back becomes manifest. A little swelling of one or both scapulæ may appear, and the upper limbs may show changes. These are rarely so considerable as the alterations in the lower limbs. There may be swelling above the wrists, extending for a short distance up the forearm, and some swelling in the neighborhood of the epiphyses of the humerus. There is symmetry of lesions, but it is not absolute; and the limb affection is generally consecutive, though the involvement of one limb follows very close upon another. The joints are free. In severe cases another symptom may not be found—namely, crepitus in the regions adjacent to the junctions of the shafts with the epiphyses. The upper and lower extremities of the femur, and the upper extremity of the tibia, are the common

51

sites of such fractures; but the upper end of the humerus may also be so affected. . . . A very startling appearance may be observed at this period in the front of the chest. The sternum, with the adjacent costal cartilages and a small portion of the contiguous ribs, seems to have sunk bodily back, *en bloc*, as though it had been subjected to some violence which had fractured several ribs in the front and driven them back. Occasionally thickenings of varying extent may be found on the exterior of the vault of the skull, or even on some of the bones of the face. . . . Here also must be mentioned a remarkable eye phenomenon. There develops a rather sudden proptosis of one eyeball, with puffiness and very slight staining of the upper lid. Within a day or two the other eye presents similar appearances, though they may be of less severity. The ocular conjunctiva may show a little ecchymosis, or may be quite free. With respect to the constitutional symptoms accompanying the above series of events the most important feature is the profound anæmia which is developed. . . . The anæmia is proportional to the amount of limb involvement. As the case proceeds, there is a certain earthy-colored or sallow tint, which is noteworthy in severe cases, and when once this is established bruise-like ecchymoses may appear, and more rarely small purpuræ. Emaciation is not a marked feature, but asthenia is extreme and suggestive of muscular failure. The temperature is very erratic; it is often raised for a day or two, when successive limbs are involved, especially during the tense stage, but is rarely above 101° or 102°. At other times it may be normal or subnormal." If the teeth have appeared the gums may be spongy.

The condition must always be looked for in young children with difficulty in moving the lower limbs, or in whom paralysis is suspected. What is known sometimes as Parrot's disease, or syphilitic pseudo-paralysis, may be confounded with it. In it the loss of motion is more or less sudden in the upper or lower limbs, or in both, due to a solution of continuity and separation of the cartilage at the end of the diaphysis. There are usually crepitation and much pain on movement.

The essential lesion is a subperiosteal blood extravasation, which causes the thickening and tenderness in the shafts of the bones. In some instances there is hæmorrhage in the intramuscular tissue.

The prophylaxis is most important. The various proprietary forms of condensed milk and preserved foods for infants should not be used. The fresh cow's milk should be substituted, and a teaspoonful of meat-juice or gravy may be given with a little mashed potato. Orange-juice or lemon-juice should be given three or four times a day. Recovery is usually prompt and satisfactory.

VII. STATUS LYMPHATICUS. LYMPHATISM.

Much attention has been paid lately to a somewhat rare condition met with chiefly in children and young persons, in which the lymphatic glands and lymph tissues throughout the body, the spleen, the thymus, and the lymphoid bone marrow are in a state of hyperplasia. These features have been found associated with rickets and with hypoplasia of the heart and aorta. The special interest lies in the fact that these pathological conditions have been met with frequently in cases of sudden death. Paltauf and others of the Vienna school, who have written extensively on the subject, believe that individuals with this hyperplasia have lowered powers of resistance, and are particularly liable to paralysis of the heart. The condition has not received much attention in England and in this country. An excellent account of it, by James Ewing, appeared in the New York Medical Journal of July 10, 1897.

Anatomical Condition.—(*a*) *Lymph-glands.*—The pharyngeal, thoracic, and abdominal groups are most frequently affected. The cervical, axillary, and inguinal are less commonly involved, but these glands may show slight enlargement. The lymphatic structures of the alimentary tract, the tissues of the tonsils, the adenoid structures in the upper pharynx, and the solitary and agminated follicles of the small and large intestines are usually much enlarged. The hyperplasia of the intestinal lymphatic structures may be the most remarkable, the individual glands standing out like peas.

(*b*) *Spleen.*—Enlargement of this organ is usually moderate in degree. The Malpighian bodies may show very prominently, and when anæmic may look like large tubercles. The organ is usually soft and hyperæmic.

(*c*) The *thymus* is enlarged, and may measure as much as 10 cm. in length. It looks swollen and soft, and on section may exude a milky white fluid.

(*d*) The *bone marrow* has been found in a state of hyperplasia, and the yellow marrow of the long bones in young adults, and even in persons between the ages of twenty and thirty, has been found replaced by red marrow. Among other associated conditions of this *constitutio lymphatica*, as it has been called, are hypoplasia of the heart and aorta and enlargement of the thyroid gland. In a large number of the cases in children rickets is coincident.

The *diagnosis* of the lymphatic constitution is not always easy. Enlargement of the superficial glands, with hypertrophy of the tonsils, signs of slight swelling of the thyroid, dulness over the sternum, with signs of enlargement of the mesenteric glands, are among the most important features. Signs of hypoplasia of the vascular system are still more uncertain, though Quincke believes that in such instances the left ventricle is dilated and the peripheral arteries may be much smaller than normal. The subjects are usually ill-developed and infantile in conformation.

Sudden Death in the status lymphaticus.—What has directed the attention of writers more particularly to this condition is the frequency with which it has been found in cases of unexpected death from very trifling and inadequate causes. A good deal of attention was directed to the subject by the death of the son of Professor Langhans, of Berlin, immediately after the preventive inoculation with the antitoxine of diphtheria. In another child death occurred under similar circumstances. The condition has also been met with in a number of cases of sudden death under anæsthetics, and I know of one instance during anæsthesia for adenoid growths. Cases of sudden death of persons in the water, who have fallen in and, though immediately recovered, were dead, or who have died suddenly while bathing, are referred by Paltauf to this condition. And, lastly, there is the large group of cases of sudden death in children without recognizable cause, in whom post mortem the thymus has been found enlarged— the so-called "Thymus Tod" (see under Thymus Gland). It has also been suggested that certain of the sudden deaths during convalescence from the infectious fevers are to be referred to this status lymphaticus. Escherich thinks that certain measures usually harmless, such as hydrotherapy, may have an untoward effect in children in this condition of lymphatism, and adds that tetany and laryngismus may be associated with it.

The whole question is one which deserves the most careful study. The anatomical features appear fairly well defined. The clinical features are by no means so clear, nor is it at all certain in what way sudden death is caused in these cases. The students of the question have, however, in the past few years brought forward evidence enough to show that the subjects of this lymphatic constitution have a diminished vital resistance, and are especially prone to fatal collapse under ordinarily very inadequate exciting causes.

VIII. DISEASES OF THE SUPRARENAL BODIES.

1. ADDISON'S DISEASE.

Definition.—A constitutional affection characterized by asthenia, depressed circulation, irritability of the stomach, and pigmentation of the skin. Tuberculosis of the adrenals is the common anatomical change. Recent observations indicate that the symptoms are due to loss of function of the suprarenal bodies.

The recognition of the disease is due to Addison, of Guy's Hospital, whose monograph on The Constitutional and Local Effects of Disease of the Suprarenal Capsules was published in 1855.

Etiology.—Males are more frequently attacked than females. In Greenhow's analysis of 183 cases 119 were males and 64 females. A majority of the cases occur between the twentieth and the fortieth year. A congenital case has been described in which the skin had a yellow-gray tint. The child lived for eight weeks, and post mortem the adrenals were found to be large and cystic. Injury such as a blow upon the abdomen or back, and caries of the spine, have in many cases preceded the attack. The disease is rare in America. The number of deaths during the census year 1890 was 99—59 males and 40 females. Twelve cases have come under my personal observation, 9 in men. One case was in a negro.

Morbid Anatomy and Pathology.—There is rarely emaciation or anæmia. Rolleston * thus summarizes the condition of the suprarenal bodies in Addison's disease:

---

* Gulstonian Lectures, Royal College of Physicians, British Medical Journal, 1895, i, to which the student is referred for an exhaustive consideration of the entire question.

" 1. The fibro-caseous lesion due to tuberculosis—far the commonest condition found. 2. Simple atrophy. 3. Chronic interstitial inflammation leading to atrophy. 4. Malignant disease invading the capsules, including Addison's case of malignant nodule compressing the suprarenal vein. 5. Blood extravasated into the suprarenal bodies. 6. No lesion of the suprarenal bodies themselves, but pressure or inflammation involving the semilunar ganglia.

" The first is the only common cause of Addison's disease. The others, with the exception of simple atrophy, may be considered as very rare."

Among other anatomical features the condition of the abdominal sympathetic has been specially studied. The nerve-cells of the semilunar ganglia have been described as degenerated and deeply pigmented, and the nerves sclerotic. The ganglia are not uncommonly entangled in the cicatricial tissue about the adrenals. The spleen has occasionally been found enlarged; the thymus may have persisted and be larger than normal.

It is difficult to explain satisfactorily all the symptoms of this remarkable disease. The two chief theories which have been advanced are briefly as follows: (a) That the disease depended upon the loss of function of the adrenals. This was the view of Addison. The balance of experimental evidence is in favor of the view that the adrenals are functional glands, which furnish an internal secretion essential to the normal metabolism. Schäfer and Oliver have shown that the human adrenals contain a very powerful extract, which is not to be obtained in cases of Addison's disease; they have also studied the toxic effects on animals of the extracts of the glands. In the cases in which the adrenals have been found involved without the symptoms of Addison's disease, accessory glands may have been present; while in the rare cases in which the symptoms of the disease have been present with healthy adrenals the semilunar ganglia and adjacent tissues have been involved in dense adhesions, which may have interfered readily with the vessels or lymphatics of the glands. On this view Addison's disease is due to an inadequate supply of the adrenal secretion, just as myxœdema is caused by loss of function of the thyroid gland. " Whether the deficiency in this internal secretion leads to a toxic condition of the blood or to a general atony and apathy is a question which must remain open " (Rolleston). (b) That it is an affection of the abdominal sympathetic system, induced most commonly by disease of the adrenals, but also by other chronic disorders which involve the solar plexus and its ganglia. According to this view, it is an affection of the nervous system, and the pigmentation has its origin in changes induced through the trophic nerves. The pronounced debility is the outcome of disturbed tissue metabolism, and the circulatory, respiratory, and digestive symptoms are due to implication of the pneumogastric. The changes found in the abdominal sympathetic are held to support this view, and its advocates urge the occurrence of pigmentation of the skin in tuberculosis of the peritonæum, cancer of the pancreas, or aneurism of the abdominal aorta. Bramwell thinks that the symptoms may be in part due to irritation of the sympathetic and in part to renal inadequacy.

Symptoms.—In the words of Addison, the characteristic symptoms are " anæmia, general languor or debility, remarkable feebleness of the heart's action, irritability of the stomach, and a peculiar change of color in the skin."

The onset is, as a rule, insidious. The feelings of weakness, as a rule, precede the pigmentation. In other instances the gastro-intestinal symptoms, the weakness, and the pigmentation come on together. There are a few cases in the literature in which the whole process has been acute, following a shock or some special depression. There are three important symptoms of the disease:

(1) *Pigmentation of the Skin.*—This, as a rule, first attracts the attention of the patient's friends. The grade of coloration ranges from a light yellow to a deep brown, or even black. In typical cases it is diffuse, but always deeper on the exposed parts and in the regions where the normal pigmentation is more intense, as the areolæ of the nipples and about the genitals; also wherever the skin is compressed or irritated, as by the waistband. At first it may be confined to the face and hands. Occasionally it is absent. Patches showing atrophy of pigment, leucoderma, may occur. The pigmentation is found on the mucous membranes of the mouth, conjunctivæ, and vagina. A patchy pigmentation of the serous membranes has often been found. Over the diffusely pigmented skin there may be little mole-like spots of deeper pigmentation. The pigmentation of the skin alone, unless the mucous membranes are also involved, is rarely sufficient in itself to make the diagnosis clear.

(2) *Gastro-intestinal Symptoms.*—The disease may set in with attacks of nausea and vomiting, spontaneous in character. Toward the close there may be pain with retraction of the abdomen, and even features suggestive of peritonitis (Ebstein). An intense anorexia may be present. The gastric symptoms are variable throughout the course; occasionally they are absent. Attacks of diarrhœa are frequent and come on without obvious cause.

(3) *Asthenia.*—This is perhaps the most characteristic feature of the disease. It may be manifested early as a feeling of inability to carry on the ordinary occupation, and the patient complains constantly of feeling tired. The weakness is specially marked in the muscular and cardio-vascular systems. There may be an extreme degree of muscular prostration in an individual apparently well nourished and whose muscles feel firm and hard. The cardio-vascular asthenia is manifest in a feeble, irregular action of the heart, which may come on in paroxysms, in attacks of vertigo, or of syncope, in one of which the disease may prove fatal. Headache is a frequent symptom; convulsions occasionally occur. McMunn has described an increase in the urinary pigments, and a pigment has been isolated of very much the same character as the melanin of the skin.

Anæmia was a symptom specially referred to by Addison, but it has been present in a marked degree in only one of my cases. I saw an instance, in Philadelphia, with J. C. Wilson, in which the diagnosis at first was not at all clear between Addison's disease and pernicious anæmia.

The mode of termination is either by syncope, which may occur even early in the disease, by gradual progressive asthenia, or by the development of tuberculous lesions. In two cases I have known a noisy delirium with urgent dyspnœa to precede the fatal event.

Diagnosis.—Pigmentation of the skin is not confined to Addison's disease. The following are the conditions which may give rise to an increase in the pigment:

(1) Abdominal growths—tubercle, cancer, or lymphoma. In tuberculosis of the peritonæum pigmentation is not uncommon.

(2) Pregnancy, in which the discoloration is usually limited to the face, the so-called *masque des femmes ençeintes*. Uterine disease is a common cause of a patchy melasma.

(3) Hepatic disease, which may induce definite pigmentation, as in the diabetic cirrhosis. More commonly in overworked persons of constipated habit and with sluggish livers there is a patchy staining about the face and forehead.

(4) The vagabond's discoloration, caused by the irritation of lice and dirt, which may reach a very high grade, and has sometimes been mistaken for Addison's disease.

(5) In rare instances there is deep discoloration of the skin in melanotic cancer, so deep and general that it has been confounded with *melasma suprarenale*.

(6) In certain cases of exophthalmic goitre abnormal pigmentation occurs, as noted by Drummond and others.

(7) In a few rare instances the pigmentation common in scleroderma may be general and deep.

(8) In the face there may be an extraordinary degree of pigmentation due to innumerable small black comedones. If not seen in a very good light, the face may suggest argyria. Pigmentation of an advanced grade may occur in chronic ulcer of the stomach and in dilatation of the organ.

(9) Argyria could scarcely be mistaken, and yet I was consulted this year by a woman in whom the diagnosis of Addison's disease had been made by several good observers, but the character of the pigmentation, the length of time it had lasted, and her freedom from all symptoms pointed undoubtedly to argyria, though, so far as she or her physician knew, she had never taken nitrate of silver medicinally.

In any case of unusual pigmentation these various conditions must be sought for; the diagnosis of Addison's disease is scarcely justifiable without the asthenia. In many instances it is difficult early in the disease to arrive at a definite conclusion. The occurrence of fainting fits, of nausea, and gastric irritability are important indications. As the lesion of the capsules is almost always tuberculous, in doubtful cases the tuberculin test may be used. In a recent case, a robust, healthy-looking man with symptoms of Addison's disease, the characteristic reaction was obtained.

Prognosis.—The disease is usually fatal. The cases in which the bronzing is slight or does not occur run a more rapid course. There are occasionally acute cases which, with great weakness, vomiting, and diarrhœa, prove fatal in a few weeks. In a few cases the disease is much prolonged, even to six or ten years. In rare instances recovery has taken place, and periods of improvement, lasting many months, may occur.

Treatment.—The causal indications cannot be met. When there is profound asthenia the patient should be confined to bed, as fatal syncope may at any time occur. In three of my cases death was sudden. When anæmia is present iron may be given in full doses. Arsenic and strychnia are useful tonics. For the diarrhœa large doses of bismuth should be given; for the irritability of the stomach, creasote, hydrocyanic acid, ice, and champagne. The diet should be light and nutritious. Many patients thrive best on a strict milk diet.

Treatment by Suprarenal Extract.—Following the researches of Schäfer and Oliver, the latter used the gland in the treatment of the disease. Kinnicutt has collected 48 cases treated with adrenal preparations. Of these, 6 were reported as cured and 22 as improved. I have used it in 4 cases, of which one has been already reported. The patient was greatly benefited, gained 19 pounds, the symptoms of asthenia disappeared, and he was alive two years subsequently, but was still pigmented. The 3 other cases were not benefited in the slightest degree. The gland may be given raw or partially cooked or in a glycerin extract. Tabloids of the dried extract are used, one grain of which corresponds to fifteen of the gland. Three of the tabloids may be given daily. Operation has been suggested, but has not been carried out on any undoubted case.

2. OTHER DISEASES OF THE SUPRARENAL CAPSULES.

Hæmorrhage into the gland is not uncommon, particularly in new-born children (Spencer). *Tuberculosis* may occur without the symptoms of Addison's disease. Among 157 cases of tuberculous disease in various parts of the body, caseous tuberculous foci were found in 20 in the suprarenals without signs of Addison's disease (Rolleston).

Tumors of the Suprarenals.—*Adenomata* are common, particularly the small yellowish nodules. *Fibromata* and *fatty* tumors occur, but are rare.

Of *malignant growths* secondary tumors are not uncommon. In 63 cases of secondary carcinoma, in 7 the suprarenal bodies were the seat of growths (Rolleston). Of the primary growths, both sarcoma and carcinoma may occur. Affleck and Leith have collected 20 cases of primary sarcoma. Ramsay informs me that we have had 3 cases of primary tumor of the suprarenals at the Johns Hopkins Hospital—2 in females and 1 in a male. Two were sarcomata and 1 a carcinoma. The diagnosis in all was malignant tumor of the kidney. The cases were operated upon, 1 with complete recovery.

IX. DISEASES OF THE SPLEEN.*

Apart from the acute swelling in fever, the chronic enlargement of the organ in paludism, leukæmia, cirrhosis of the liver, and heart-disease, we

---

* For a good discussion of the general pathology of the spleen, see Rolleston in Allbutt's System of Medicine.

see very few instances of disease of the spleen. These affections have been fully described, but there remain several conditions to which brief reference may be made.

1. MOVABLE SPLEEN.

Movable or wandering spleen is seen most frequently in women the subjects of enteroptosis. It is occasionally met with without signs of displacement of other organs. It may be found accidentally in individuals who present no symptoms whatever. In other cases there are dragging, uneasy feelings in the back and side. All grades are met with, from a spleen that can be felt completely below the margin of the ribs to a condition in which the tumor is felt as low as the pelvis; indeed, the organ has been found in an inguinal hernia! In the large majority of all cases the spleen is enlarged. Sometimes it appears that the enlargement has caused relaxation of the ligaments; in other instances the relaxation seems congenital, as movable spleens have been found in different members of the same family. Possibly traumatism may account for some of the cases. Apart from the dragging, uneasy sensations and the worry in nervous patients, wandering spleen causes very few serious symptoms. Torsion of the pedicle may produce a very alarming and serious condition, leading to great swelling of the organ, high fever, or even to necrosis. A young woman was admitted to my colleague Kelly's ward with a tumor supposed to be ovarian, but which proved to be a wandering, moderately enlarged spleen. She was transferred to the medical ward, where she developed suddenly very great pain in the abdomen, a large swelling in the left flank, and much tenderness. Halsted operated and found an enormously enlarged spleen in a condition of necrosis, adherent to the adjacent parts and to the abdominal wall. He laid it open freely, and large necrotic masses of spleen tissue discharged for some time. She made a good recovery.

The *diagnosis* of a wandering spleen is usually easy unless the organ becomes fixed and is deformed by adhesions and perisplenitis. The shape of the organ and the sharp margin with the notches are the points to be specially noted.

The *treatment* of the condition is important. Occasionally the organ may be kept in position by a properly adapted belt and a pad under the left costal margin. Removal of the displaced organ has been advised and carried out in many cases, and nowadays it is not a very serious operation. It is, however, as a rule unnecessary. In 2 cases of enlarged spleen under my care, with great mobility, causing much discomfort and uneasiness, Halsted completely relieved the condition by replacing the spleen, packing it in position with gauze, and allowing firm adhesions to take place. Both these patients were seen more than eighteen months after the operation and the organ had remained in position.

2. RUPTURE OF THE SPLEEN.

This is of interest medically in connection with the spontaneous rupture in cases of acute enlargement during typhoid fever or malaria. The condition seems very rare in this country. We have had instances of rupture of a malarial spleen following a blow, but neither in this disease nor in typhoid have we had an instance of spontaneous rupture. In India and in Mauritius rupture of the spleen is stated to be very common. Fatal hæmorrhage may follow puncture of a swollen spleen with a hypodermic needle. Occasionally the rupture results from the breaking of an infarct or of an abscess. The symptoms are those of hæmorrhage into the peritonæum, and the condition demands immediate laparotomy.

3. Infarct and Abscess of the Spleen.

Emboli in the splenic arteries causing infarcts may be either infective or simple. They are seen most frequently in ulcerative endocarditis and in septic conditions. Infarcts may also follow the formation of thrombi in the branches of the splenic artery in cases of fever. They are not very infrequent in typhoid. In a few instances the infarcts have followed thrombosis in the splenic veins. They are chiefly of pathological interest. The infarct of the spleen may be suspected in cases of septicæmia or pyæmia when there is pain in the splenic region, tenderness on pressure, and slight swelling of the organ; on several occasions I have heard a well-marked peritoneal friction rub. Occasionally in the infective infarcts large abscesses are formed, and in rare instances the whole organ may be converted into a sac of pus.

Tumors of the spleen, *hydatid* and other *cysts* of the organ, and *gummata* are rare conditions of anatomical interest, for an account of which the reader is referred to Rolleston's article and to the section on the spleen, by G. R. Lockwood, in Loomis and Thompson's System of Medicine.

4. Splenic Anæmia.

This condition, usually regarded as the splenic form of Hodgkin's disease, as such was well described, in 1871, by H. C. Wood. Strümpell, Banti, and others, however, think it should be separated and regarded as a special form. It is a disease characterized by great enlargement of the organ, profound anæmia, without leucocytosis and without the coexistence of malaria, rickets, or other states in which enlargement of the spleen is secondary; hence it is often spoken of as *primitive spleno-megaly*. While true primitive cases are rare, in this region, at least, an anæmia associated with enlargement of the spleen is not very uncommon, particularly as a result of the effects of prolonged residence in malarial regions. As I write a patient from South Carolina is in the wards with an enlarged spleen and great pallor. The anæmia is of a distinctly chlorotic type, as his blood-count is nearly 4,000,000, but the hæmoglobin is only 40 per cent. He has no leucocytosis. He has not had chills and fever for fifteen years, but has been living in a malarial region. There are cases, too, in which the enlarged spleen persists for many years with no anæmia, good color, and a fair muscular vigor. I remember a soldier invalided from India, admitted to the Montreal General Hospital with an enormous spleen and slight anæmia. He died shortly after admission of a profuse hæmorrhage from the stomach. A patient from Jamaica, referred to me a few years ago by Henderson, of Kingston, without any malarial history, had an enormous spleen, had had several attacks of profound anæmia, but at the time of observation had a blood-count nearly normal. I see many more cases of primitive spleno-megaly without than with anæmia.

S. West, in Allbutt's System, gives the following as the main features of splenic anæmia: " The disease may be divided into three stages: In the initial stage the symptoms are those of extreme anæmia, with great loss of muscular power and some wasting of muscle, though usually without emaciation. As in this stage the disease presents no specific features, it can rarely be recognized. The second stage is characterized by progressive enlargement of the spleen and by attacks of severe pain in the splenic region; the anæmia is more profound, the loss of strength is extreme, and the patients are liable to repeated attacks of bleeding, especially from the nose; the temperature is now usually raised and of hectic character, reaching 102° or more in the evening. It is in this second stage that the disease is first recognized.

" In the last stage the condition is one of progressive asthenia, which ends in death; there is in it nothing especially characteristic."

The blood condition is one simply of profound anæmia without increase in the leucocytes and not always with marked poikilocytosis. The tendency to hæmorrhage is marked, both from the mucous surfaces and in the skin.

Anatomically, the only special changes that have been noted have been a peculiar atrophy of the Malpighian corpuscles in some cases.

The treatment of the condition is that of other forms of profound anæmia.

X. DISEASES OF THE THYROID GLAND.

1. Goitre.

Definition.—Hypertrophy of the thyroid gland, occurring sporadically or endemically.

In this country sporadic cases are common. The endemic centres referred to in Barton's monograph (1810) and in Hirsch's Geographical Pathology no longer exist. The disease is very prevalent about the eastern end of Lake Ontario, and in parts of Michigan (Dock). Endemically it is found particularly in the mountainous regions of Switzerland and in parts of Italy. No satisfactory explanation has been given of the existence of the disease in this form.

Anatomically the following varieties may be distinguished: (a) Parenchymatous, in which the enlargement is general and the follicles, usually newly formed, contain a gelatinous colloid material. (b) Vascular, in which the enlargement is chiefly due to dilatation of the blood-vessels without the new formation of glandular tissue. (c) Cystic goitre, in which the enlarged gland is occupied by large cysts, the walls of which often undergo calcification.

Symptoms.—The enlargement may be uniform throughout the entire gland, or affect only one lobe, or the isthmus alone. When small, a goitre causes no inconvenience. In its growth it may compress the trachea, causing dyspnœa, or may pass beneath the sternum and compress the veins. These, however, are exceptional circumstances, and in a large proportion of all cases no serious symptoms are noted. The affection usually comes under the care of the surgeon. Sudden death occasionally occurs in large bronchoceles. In some instances it may be difficult to determine the cause, and it has been thought to be associated with pressure on the vagi. I have reported an instance in which it resulted from hæmorrhage into the gland and into the adjacent tissues. The blood passed into the cellular tissues of the neck and under the sternum, covering the aorta and pericardium. In regions in which goitre prevails the drinking-water should be boiled. Change of locality is sometimes followed by cure. The medicinal treatment is very unsatisfactory. Iodine and various counterirritants externally, iodide of potash, ergot, and many other drugs are recommended by writers. The thyroid extract has been used with success by Bruns in 9 of 12 cases.

2. Tumors of the Thyroid.

These are very varied. (*a*) Adenomata, either simple or malignant. The latter may form extensive metastases. A case is reported by Hayward in which growths resembling thyroid tissue occurred in the lungs and various bones of the body. (*b*) Cancer, of which several forms have been described. (*c*) Sarcoma. All of these have a surgical rather than a medical interest.

It may be mentioned that the aberrant or accessory thyroid gland may form large tumors in the mediastinum or in the pleura. Cases have been reported by F. A. Packard and myself, and an instance is on record in which an enormous cystic accessory thyroid occupied the entire right pleura.

Lingual goitre occasionally develops at the base of the tongue, and is an enlarged accessory thyroid in that situation. It may lead to difficult deglutition and interference with articulation.

Thyroid abscess is rare. In Havel's monograph on Strumitis (1892) cases are given after nearly every one of the specific diseases, and he reports 18 cases from Kocher's clinic, nearly all secondary or metastatic.

3. Exophthalmic Goitre (*Parry's Disease*).

Definition.—A disease characterized by exophthalmos, enlargement of the thyroid, and functional disturbance of the vascular system. It is very possibly caused by disturbed function of the thyroid gland (hyperthyroidism).

Historical Note.—In the posthumous writings of Caleb Hillier Parry (1825) is a description of 8 cases of Enlargement of the Thyroid Gland in Connection with Enlargement or Palpitation of the Heart. In the first case, seen in 1786, he also describes the exophthalmos: "The eyes were protruded from their sockets, and the countenance exhibited an appearance of agitation and distress, especially in any muscular movement." The Italians claim that Flajani described the disease in 1800. I have not been able to see his original account, but Moebius states that it is meagre and inaccurate, and bears no comparison with that of Parry. If the name of any physician is to be associated with the disease, undoubtedly it should be that of the distinguished old Bath physician. Graves described the disease in 1835 and Basedow in 1840.

Etiology.—The disease is more frequent in women than in men. Of 200 cases tabulated by Eshner, there were 161 females. The age of onset is usually from the twentieth to the thirtieth year. It is sometimes seen in several members of the same family. Worry, fright, and depressing emotions precede the development of the disease in a number of cases.

The disease is regarded by some as a pure neurosis, in favor of which is urged the onset after a profound emotion, the absence of lesions, and the cure which has followed in a few cases after operations upon the nose. Others believe that it is caused by a central lesion in the medulla oblongata. In support of this there is a certain amount of experimental evidence, and in a few autopsies changes have been found in the medulla. Of late years the view has been urged, particularly by Moebius and by Greenfield, that exophthalmic goitre is primarily a disease of the thyroid gland (*hyperthyrea*), in antithesis to myxœdema (*athyrea*). The clinical contrast between these two diseases is most suggestive—the increased excitability of the nervous system, the flushed, moist skin, the vascular erythism in the one; the dull apathy, the low temperature, slow pulse, and dry skin of the other. The changes in the gland in exophthalmic goitre are, as shown by Greenfield, those of an organ in active evolution—viz., increased proliferation, with the production of newly formed tubular spaces and absorption of the colloid material which is replaced by a more mucinous fluid (Bradshaw Lecture, 1893). The thyroid extract given in excess produces symptoms not unlike those of Parry's disease—tachycardia, tremor, headache, sweating, and prostration. Beclère has recently reported a case in which exophthalmos developed after an overdose. Use of the thyroid extract usually aggravates the symptoms of exophthalmic goitre. The most successful line of treatment has been that directed to diminish the bulk of the goitre. These are some of the considerations which favor the view that the symptoms are due to disturbed function of the thyroid gland, probably to a hypersecretion of certain materials, which induce a sort of chronic intoxication. Myxœdema may develop in the late stages, and there are transient œdema and in a few cases scleroderma, which indicate that the nutrition of the skin is involved. Persistence of the thymus is almost the rule (Hector Mackenzie), but its significance is unknown.

Symptoms.—Acute and chronic forms may be recognized. In the acute form the disease may develop with great rapidity. In a patient of J. H. Lloyd's, of Philadelphia, a woman, aged thirty-nine, who had been considered perfectly healthy, but whose friends had noticed that for some time her eyes looked rather large, was suddenly seized with intense vomiting and diarrhœa, rapid action of the heart, and great throbbing of the arteries. The eyes were prominent and staring and the thyroid gland was found much enlarged and soft. The gastro-intestinal symptoms continued, the pulse became more rapid, the vomiting was incessant, and the patient died on the third day of the illness. Only the abdominal and thoracic organs could be examined and no changes were found. Two rapidly fatal cases occurred at the Philadelphia Hospital, one of which, under F. P. Henry's care, had marked cerebral symptoms. The acute cases are not always associated with delirium. In a case reported by Sutcliff death occurred within three months from the onset of the symptoms, owing to repeated and uncontrollable vomiting. More frequently the onset is gradual and the disease is chronic. There are four characteristic symptoms of the disease—exophthalmos, tachycardia, enlargement of the thyroid, and tremor.

Tachycardia.—Rapid heart action is only one of a series of remarkable vascular phenomena in the disease. The pulse-rate at first may be not more than 95 or 100, but when the disease is established it may be from 140 to 160, or even higher. Irregularity is not common, except toward the close. In a well-developed case the visible area of cardiac pulsation is much increased, the action is heaving and forcible, and the shock of the heart-sounds is well felt. The large arteries at the root of the neck throb forcibly. There is visible pulsation in the peripheral arteries. The capillary pulse is readily seen, and there are few diseases in which one may see at times with greater distinctness the venous pulse in the veins of the hand. The throbbing pulsation of the arteries may be felt even in the finger tips. On auscultation murmurs are usually heard over the heart, a loud apex systolic and loud bruits at the base and over the manubrium. The sounds of the heart may be very intense. In rare instances they may be heard at some distance from the patient; according to Graves, as far as four feet.

Exophthalmos, which may be unilateral, usually follows the vascular disturbance. It is readily recognized by the protrusion of the balls, and partly by the fact that the lids do not completely cover the sclerotics, so that a rim of white is seen above and below the cornea. The protrusion may become very great and the eye may even be dislocated from the socket, or both eyes may be destroyed by panophthalmitis, a condition present in one of Basedow's cases. The vision is normal. Graefe noted that when the eyeball is moved downward the upper lid does not follow it as in health. This is known as Graefe's sign. It seems to be rare; it was not present in any one of 17 cases examined at my clinic (Oppenheimer). The palpebral aperture is wider than in health, owing to spasm or retraction of the upper lid (Stellwag's sign). The patient winks less frequently than in health. Moebius has called attention to the lack of convergence of the two eyes. Changes in the pupils and in the optic nerves are rare. Pulsation of the retinal arteries is common.

Enlargement of the thyroid commonly develops with the exophthalmos. It may be general or in only one lobe, and is rarely so large as in ordinary goitre. The vessels are usually much dilated, and the whole gland may be seen to pulsate. A thrill may be felt on palpation and on auscultation a loud systolic murmur, or more commonly a *bruit de diable*. A double murmur is common and is pathognomonic (Guttmann).

Tremor is the fourth cardinal symptom, and was really first described by Basedow. It is involuntary, fine, about eight to the second. It is of great importance in the diagnosis of the early cases.

Among other symptoms which may develop are anæmia, emaciation, and slight fever. Attacks of vomiting and diarrhœa may occur. The latter may be very severe and distressing, recurring at intervals. The greatest complaint is of the forcible throbbing in the arteries, often accompanied with unpleasant flushes of heat and profuse perspirations. Skin symptoms are not infrequent—pigmentation, which may be intense and simulate Addison's disease, patches of leucoderma, or atrophy of pigment, and urticaria. Patches of solid œdema have been seen. Occasionally myxœdema has been present. In the very acute case above referred to urticaria was a prominent symptom. Occasionally pruritus is an early and most distressing symptom. I have seen one case in which it persisted and became almost unbearable. Irritability of temper, change in disposition, and great mental depression have been described. An important complication is acute mania, in which the patient may die in a few days. Weakness of the muscles is not uncommon, particularly a feeling of "giving way" of the legs. If the patient holds the head down and is asked to look up without raising the head, the forehead remains smooth and is not wrinkled, as in a normal individual (Joffroy). A feature of interest noted by Charcot is the great diminution in the electrical resistance, which may be due to the saturation of the skin with moisture owing to the vaso-motor dilatation (Hirt). Bryson has noted the fact that the chest expansion may be greatly diminished. The emaciation may be extreme. Glycosuria and albuminuria are not infrequent complications. True diabetes may also develop.

The course of the disease is usually chronic, lasting several years. After persisting for six months or a year the symptoms may disappear. There are remarkable instances in which the symptoms have come on with great intensity, following fright, and have disappeared again in a few days. A certain proportion of the cases get well, but when the disease is well developed recovery is rare.

Treatment.—Medicinal measures are notoriously uncertain. The combination of digitalis and iron may be tried, and, when there is anæmia, often does good. I have never seen any advantage from the use of aconite or veratrum viride. The tincture of strophanthus will sometimes reduce the rapidity of the heart's action. Ergot is warmly recommended by some writers. Belladonna gives relief occasionally, and should be administered until the dryness of the throat is obtained. I have seen one case of apparent cure under its use. No measures are so successful as rest in bed with an ice-bag or Leiter's tube applied occasionally over the heart, or, what is sometimes more agreeable, over the lower part of the neck and manubrium sterni. I have known the pulse to be reduced in this way from 140 to 90. Electricity has been much lauded and instances of cure have been reported. In many cases temporary improvement certainly follows the use of the galvanic current. Erb states that the anode should be placed over the cervical spine and the cathode upon the peripheral nerves. The use of the thyroid extract has not been successful. The thymus extract has not proved satisfactory. The treatment of the disease by small doses of opium has been successful in some cases (Musser). Operative measures seem to offer the greatest relief. Removal of one lobe of the gland, tying the arteries of the gland, and exothyroplexia have all been tried. The patients, as a rule, stand the anæsthetic badly; death on the table is more frequent than the published records indicate. Recently good results have been reported from the division of the cords of the cervical sympathetic.

4. MYXŒDEMA (*Athyrea*).

Definition.—A constitutional affection, due to the loss of function of the thyroid gland. The disease, which was described by Sir William Gull as a cretinoid change, and later by Ord, is characterized clinically by a myxœdematous condition of the subcutaneous tissues and mental failure, and anatomically by atrophy of the thyroid gland.

Clinical Forms.—Three groups of cases may be recognized—cretinism, myxœdema proper, and operative myxœdema.

CRETINISM.

This remarkable impairment of nutrition follows absence or loss of function of the thyroid gland, either congenital or appearing at any time before puberty. There is remarkable retardation of development, retention of the infantile state, and an extraordinary disproportion between the different parts of the body. Two forms of cretinism are recognized, the *sporadic* and the *endemic*. In the sporadic form the gland may be congenitally absent, it may be atrophied after one of the specific fevers, or the condition may develop with goitre. Since we have learned to recognize the disease it is surprising how many cases have been reported. I was able to collect 60 cases in this country to May 1, 1897.*

The condition is rarely recognized before the infant is six or seven months old. Then it is noticed that the child does not grow so rapidly and is not bright mentally. The tongue looks large and hangs out of the mouth. The hair may be thin and the skin very dry. Usually by the end of the first year and during the second year the signs of cretinism become very marked. The face is large, looks bloated, the eyelids are puffy and swollen; the alæ nasi are thick, the nose looks depressed and flat. Dentition is delayed, and the teeth which appear decay early. The abdomen is swollen, the legs are thick and short, and the hands and feet are undeveloped and pudgy. The face is pale and sometimes has a waxy, sallow tint. The fontanelles remain open; there is much muscular weakness, and the child cannot support itself. In the supraclavicular regions there are large pads of fat. The child does not develop mentally; there are various grades of idiocy and imbecility.

---

* Sporadic cretinism in America, Transactions of the Congress of American Physicians and Surgeons, vol. iv.

A very interesting form is that in which, after the child has thriven and developed until its fourth or fifth year, or even later, the symptoms begin after a fever, in consequence of an atrophy of the gland. Parker suggests for this variety the name juvenile myxœdema.

Endemic cretinism develops under local conditions, as yet unknown, in association with goitre. It is met with chiefly in Switzerland and parts of Italy and France. The common opinion is that it too is associated with loss of function of the thyroid.

The *diagnosis* of cretinism is very easy after one has seen a case or good illustrations. Infants a year or so old sometimes become flabby, lose their vivacity, or show a protuberant abdomen and lax skin with slight cretinoid appearance. These milder forms, as they have been termed, are probably due to transient functional disturbance in the gland. There is rarely any difficulty in recognizing the different other types of idiocy. The condition known as *fœtal rickets, achondroplasia,* or the *chondrodystrophia fœtalis,* is more likely to be mistaken for cretinism. The children which survive birth grow up as a remarkable form of dwarfs, characterized by shortness of the limbs (micromelia) and enormous enlargement of the articulations, due to hyperplasia of the cartilaginous ends of the bones. *Infantilism*— the condition characterized by a preservation in the adult of the exterior form of infancy with the non-appearance of the secondary sexual characters—could scarcely be mistaken for cretinism.

Myxœdema of Adults (*Gull's Disease*).

In this, women are very much more frequently affected than men—in a ratio of 6 to 1. The disease may affect several members of a family, and it may be transmitted through the mother. In some instances there has been first the appearance of exophthalmic goitre. Though occurring most commonly in women, it seems to have no special relation to the catamenia or to pregnancy; the symptoms of myxœdema may disappear during pregnancy or may develop post partum. Myxœdema and exophthalmic goitre may occur in sisters. It is not so common in this country as in England. The symptoms of this form, as given by Ord,* are marked increase in the general bulk of the body, a firm, inelastic swelling of the skin, which does not pit on pressure; dryness and roughness, which tend, with the swelling, to obliterate in the face the lines of expression; imperfect nutrition of the hair; local tumefaction of the skin and subcutaneous tissues, particularly in the supraclavicular region. The physiognomy is altered in a remarkable way: the features are coarse and broad, the lips thick, the nostrils broad and thick, and the mouth is enlarged. Over the cheeks, sometimes the nose, there is a reddish patch. There is a striking slowness of thought and of movement. The memory becomes defective, the patients grow irritable and suspicious, and there may be headache. In some instances there are delusions and hallucinations, leading to a final condition of dementia. The gait is heavy and slow. The temperature may be below

---

* Report on Myxœdema, Clinical Society's Transactions, 1888.

normal. The functions of the heart, lungs, and abdominal organs are normal. Hæmorrhage sometimes occurs. Albuminuria is sometimes present, more rarely glycosuria. Death is usually due to some intercurrent disease, most frequently tuberculosis (Greenfield). The thyroid gland is diminished in size and may become completely atrophied and converted into a fibrous mass. The subcutaneous fat is abundant, and in one or two instances a great increase in the mucin has been found.

The course of the disease is slow but progressive, and extends over ten or fifteen years. A condition of acute and temporary myxœdema may develop in connection with enlargement of the thyroid in young persons. Myxœdema may follow exophthalmic goitre. In other instances the symptoms of the two diseases have been combined. I have reported a case in which a young man became bloated and increased in weight enormously during three months, then developed tachycardia with tremor and active delirium, and died within six months of the onset of the symptoms.

OPERATIVE MYXŒDEMA; CACHEXIA STRUMIPRIVA.

Horsley, in a series of interesting experiments, showed that complete removal of the thyroid in monkeys was followed by the production of a condition similar to that of myxœdema and often associated with spasms or tetanoid contractures, and followed by apathy and coma. When the monkeys were kept warm myxœdema was averted, and, instead of an acute myxœdema, the animals developed a condition which closely resembled cretinism. An identical condition may follow extirpation of the thyroid in man. Kocher, of Bern, found that after complete extirpation a cachectic condition followed in many cases, the symptoms of which are practically identical with those of myxœdema. The disease follows only a certain number of total and a much smaller proportion of partial removals of the thyroid gland. Of 408 cases, in 69 the operative myxœdema developed. It has been thought that if a small fragment of the thyroid remains, or if there are accessory glands, which in animals are very common, these symptoms do not develop. It is possible that in men, in the cases of complete removal, the accessory fragments subserve the function of the gland. Operative myxœdema is very rare in America; I have been able to find only 2 cases in this country. McGraw's case, referred to in previous editions of this work, has since been cured with the thyroid extract.

The *diagnosis* of myxœdema is easy, as a rule. The general aspect of the patient—the subcutaneous swelling and the pallor—suggests Bright's disease, which may be strengthened by the discovery of tube-casts and of albumin in the urine; but the solid character of the swelling, the exceeding dryness of the skin, the yellowish-white color, the low temperature, the loss of hair, and the dull, listless mental state should suffice to differentiate the two conditions. In dubious cases not too much stress should be laid upon the supraclavicular swellings. There may be marked fibrofatty enlargements in this situation in healthy persons, the supraclavicular pseudo-lipomata of Verneuil.

Treatment.—The patients suffer in cold and improve greatly in warm weather. They should therefore be kept at an even temperature, and should, if possible, move to a warm climate during the winter months. Repeated warm baths with shampooing are useful. Our art has made no more brilliant advance than in the cure of these disorders due to disturbed function of the thyroid gland. That we can to-day rescue children otherwise doomed to helpless idiocy—that we can restore to life the hopeless victims of myxœdema—is a triumph of experimental medicine for which we are indebted very largely to Victor Horsley and to his pupil Murray. Transplantation of the gland was first tried; then Murray used an extract subcutaneously. Hector Mackenzie in London and Howitz in Copenhagen introduced the method of feeding. We now know that the gland, taken either fresh, or as the watery or glycerin extract, or dried and powdered, is equally efficacious in a majority of all the cases of myxœdema in infants or adults. Many preparations are now on the market, but it makes little difference how the gland is administered. The dried powdered gland and the glycerin extract are most convenient. It is well to begin with the powdered gland, 1 grain three times a day, of the Parke-Davis preparation, or one of the Burroughs and Welcome tablets. The dose may be increased gradually until the patient takes 10 or 15 grains in the day. In many cases there are no unpleasant symptoms; in others there are irritation of the skin, restlessness, rapid pulse, and delirium; in rare instances tonic spasms, the condition to which the term *thyroidism* is applied. The results, as a rule, are most astounding—unparalleled by anything in the whole range of curative measures. Within six weeks a poor, feeble-minded, toad-like caricature of humanity may be restored to mental and bodily health. Loss of weight is one of the first and most striking effects; one of my patients lost over 30 pounds within six weeks. The skin becomes moist, the urine is increased, the perspiration returns, the temperature rises, the pulse-rate quickens and the mental torpor lessens. Ill effects are rare. Two or three cases with old heart lesions have died during or after the treatment; in one instance a temporary condition of Graves' disease was induced.

The treatment, as Murray suggests, must be carried out in two stages—one, early, in which full doses are given until the cure is effected; the other, the permanent use of small doses sufficient to preserve the normal metabolism. The literature of thyroid therapy and a list of all the cases of myxœdema and cretinism treated to December 31, 1894, are given by Heinsheimer.*

XI. DISEASES OF THE THYMUS GLAND.

The functions of this gland are unknown. It is a suggestive fact that Baumann found in it minute quantities of a compound containing iodine. It has been thought that its internal secretion has an influence in combating infective agents. The weight of the organ is about 14 grammes at birth, about 20 at the ninth month, and 25 to 30 at the second year.

---

* Die Schilddrüsenbehandlung, München, 1895.

The organ, after reaching its largest size about the end of the second year, gradually wastes, until at the time of puberty it is a mere fatty remnant, in which, however, there are " traces of its original structure in the form of small masses of thymus corpuscles, and even of concentric corpuscles " (Quain). A complete consideration of the affections of this gland is to be found in Friedleben's remarkable monograph, Die Physiologie der Thymusdrüse, 1858. The following are the most important conditions:

I. **Persistence of the organ** after the fifteenth year, met with occasionally, but under circumstances so varied that a satisfactory explanation cannot be offered. It is said that the existence of the gland may be determined by the presence of an area of dulness along the left sternal border from the second to the fourth ribs.

II. **Hypertrophy of the Thymus.**—The size of the gland varies widely, so that it is difficult to define exactly the limits between persistence and enlargement. The condition is of interest from three standpoints: (a) The supposed occurrence of *thymic asthma*, due to pressure from the enlarged gland. A number of observers have attributed the symptoms of laryngismus stridulus to pressure exerted by the enlarged thymus. Many German writers consider thymic asthma identical with the laryngismus stridulus of English authors, who, as a rule, have laid no stress whatever on the association. There can be, I think, no question that the ordinary laryngismus seen in rickety children is a convulsive affection and is not the result of compression. But a very greatly enlarged thymus may seriously hamper the structures within the thorax. Jacobi, in his monograph on the gland (Transactions of the Association of American Physicians, vol. iii), states that in an infant of eight months the distance between the manubrium sterni and the vertebral column is 2.2 cm., a space which he thinks might be completely filled by an enlarged and congested thymus. Siegel's case also points to the possibility of this compression. A boy aged two years and a half had had for two weeks cough and bronchial rales with dyspnœa, which was more or less constant with nocturnal exacerbations. Laryngismus stridulus was diagnosed. Tracheotomy was performed shortly after admission without relief, but when subsequently the anterior mediastinum was opened from above by extending the incision from the tracheotomy wound, a piece of the thymus as large as a hazel-nut appeared with each inspiration. The gland was drawn up with forceps and fastened by three stitches to the fascia over the sternum. The child rested quietly after the operation, had no dyspnœa, and made a complete recovery (Berl. klin. Woch., 1896, No. 40). From a child aged two months (dyspnœic from the eighth day) Koenig removed a portion of the thymus, leaving the substernal part. These are cases that go far to disprove Friedleben's dictum—*es giebt kein asthma thymicum.*

(b) *Thymus Enlargement and Sudden Death.*—In considering the question of the so-called lymphatic constitution, with which an enlarged thymus is usually associated, we have spoken of the occurrence of sudden death. Two groups of cases are met with in the literature: First, such instances as those described by Grawitz, Jacobi, and others, in which young infants have been either found dead in bed or have been attacked suddenly with dyspnœa, have become cyanotic and died in a few minutes. In such cases the thymus has been found greatly enlarged, and death has been thought to be directly due either to pressure on the air-passages, pressure on the pneumogastric (causing spasm of the glottis), or pressure on the great vessels. To the second group belong the cases in adults which have been described of late by Nordmann, Paltauf, Ohlmacher, and others, in which the sudden death has occurred under such conditions as anæsthesia or while bathing. In a number of these cases not only has the thymus been found enlarged, but the spleen and lymphatic tissues generally. The question is one of considerable medico-legal interest, and has been spoken of under Lymphatism.

Rolleston reports a case of sudden death after signs of cardiac failure lasting for only twenty minutes, in which there was hyperplasia of a persistent thymus. The gland with the trachea weighed 11 ounces.

(c) *Thymus Gland and Exophthalmic Goitre.*—That there is some association between these conditions is urged on two grounds: First, the persistence of the gland in Graves' disease. W. W. Ord and Hector Mackenzie state that it has been found enlarged in all the cases recently examined at St. Thomas's Hospital. Hektoen concludes from a very thorough study of the question that the coexistence is more than accidental. Secondly, the good results which are stated to follow the feeding of the thymus gland in Graves' disease are held to bear out the idea that the enlargement during life is compensatory. The general conclusion, however, reached by Hector Mackenzie and by Kinnicutt is that the thymus feeding has at best only slight influence upon Graves' disease.

It is interesting to note in connection with the question of enlarged thymus and sudden death that two of Hale White's cases of exophthalmic goitre died suddenly, and autopsy showed no reasonable cause of death.

Among other conditions with which enlarged thymus has been associated may be mentioned epilepsy (Ohlmacher).

III. Other Morbid Conditions of the Thymus.—*Hæmorrhages* are not uncommon, and are found particularly in children who have died of asphyxia.

Tumors of the gland, particularly sarcoma and lympho-sarcoma, have been frequently described. Many mediastinal tumors originate in the remnants of the thymus. Dermoid tumors and cysts have also been met with. Tuberculosis of the gland, chiefly in the form of miliary nodules, is well described in Jacobi's monograph. There is a well-authenticated case in which it was primary. Focal necroses in diphtheria have also been described by Jacobi.

Abscess of the Thymus.—Dubois, in 1850, noted the occurrence of foci of suppuration in the gland in subjects of congenital syphilis. Throughout it round or fissure-like cavities are seen filled with a purulent fluid. Chiari states that some of these supposed abscesses are areas of post-mortem softening, or cysts lined with flattened epithelium containing detritus of thymus cells. In one case Jacobi found a small gumma.

SECTION IX.

DISEASES OF THE KIDNEYS.

I. MALFORMATIONS.

Newman classifies the malformations of the kidney as follows: A. Displacements without mobility—(1) congenital displacement without deformity; (2) congenital displacement with deformity; (3) acquired displacements. B. Malformations of the kidney. I. Variations in number—(a) supernumerary kidney; (b) single kidney, congenital absence of one kidney, atrophy of one kidney; (c) absence of both kidneys. II. Variations in form and size—(a) general variations in form, lobulation, etc.; (b) hypertrophy of one kidney; (c) fusion of two kidneys—horseshoe kidney, sigmoid kidney, disk-shaped kidney. C. Variations in pelvis, ureters, and blood-vessels.

The fused kidneys may form a large mass, which is often displaced, being either in an iliac fossa or in the middle line of the abdomen, or even in the pelvis. Under these circumstances it may be mistaken for a new growth. In Polk's case the organ was removed under the belief that it was a floating kidney.* The patient lived eleven days, had complete anuria, and it was found post mortem that a single unsymmetrical kidney, as this form is called, had been removed.

II. MOVABLE KIDNEY.

(Floating Kidney; Palpable Kidney; Ren mobilis; Nephroptosis).

The kidney is held in position by its fatty capsule, by the peritonæum which passes in front of it, and by the blood-vessels. Normally the kidney is firmly fixed, but under certain circumstances one or another organ, more rarely both, becomes movable. In very rare cases the kidney is surrounded, to a greater or less extent, by the peritonæum, and is anchored at the hilus by a mesonephron. Some would limit the term floating kidney to this condition.

Movable kidney is almost always acquired. It is more common in

---

* New York Medical Journal, 1883.

women. Of the 667 cases collected in the literature by Kuttner, 584 were in women and only 83 in men. It is more common on the right than on the left side. Of 727 cases analyzed by this author, it occurred on the right in 553 cases, on the left in 81, and on both sides in 93. The greater frequency of the condition in women may be attributed to compression of the lower thoracic zone by tight lacing, and, more important still, to the relaxation of the abdominal walls which follows repeated pregnancies. This does not account for all the cases, as movable kidney is by no means uncommon in nulliparæ. Drummond believes that in a majority of the cases there is a congenitally relaxed condition of the peritoneal attachments. The condition has been met with in infants. Wasting of the fat about the kidney may be a cause in some instances. Trauma and the lifting of heavy weights are occasionally factors in its production. The kidney is sometimes dragged down by tumors. The greater frequency on the right side is probably associated with the position of the kidney just beneath the liver, and the depression to which the organ is subjected with each descent of the diaphragm in inspiration.

And, lastly, movable kidney is met with in many cases which present that combination of neurasthenia with gastro-intestinal disturbance which has been described by Glénard as *enteroptosis* (see p. 541).

To determine the presence of a movable kidney the patient should be placed in the dorsal position, with the head moderately low and the abdominal walls relaxed. The left hand is placed in the lumbar region behind the eleventh and twelfth ribs; the right hand in the hypochondriac region, in the nipple line, just under the edge of the liver. Bimanual palpation may detect the presence of a firm, rounded body just below the edge of the ribs. If nothing can be felt, the patient should be asked to draw a deep breath, when, if the organ is palpable, it is touched by the fingers of the right hand. Various grades of mobility may be recognized. It may be possible barely to feel the lower edge on deep palpation—*palpable kidney*— or the organ may be so far displaced that on drawing the deepest breath the fingers of the right hand may be, in a thin person, slipped above the upper end of the organ, which can be readily held down, but cannot be pushed below the level of the navel—*movable kidney*. In a third group of cases the organ is freely movable, and may even be felt just above Poupart's ligament, or may be in the middle line of the abdomen, or can even be pushed over beyond this point. To this the term *floating kidney* is appropriate.

The movable kidney is not painful on pressure, except when it is grasped very firmly, when there is a dull pain, or sometimes a sickening sensation. Examination of the patient from behind may show a distinct flattening in the lumbar region on the side in which the kidney is mobile.

Symptoms.—In a large majority of cases there are no symptoms, and if detected accidentally it is well not to let the patient know of its presence. Far too much stress has been laid upon the condition of late years. In other instances there is pain in the lumbar region or a sense of dragging and discomfort, or there may be intercostal neuralgia. In a large group the symptoms are those of neurasthenia with dyspeptic disturbance. In women the hysterical symptoms may be marked, and in men various grades of hypochondriasis. The gastric disturbance is usually a form of nervous dyspepsia. Dilatation of the stomach has been observed, owing, as suggested by Bartels, to pressure of the dislocated kidney upon the duodenum. This view has been supported by Oser, Landau, and Ewald. On the other hand, Litten holds that the dilatation of the stomach is the cause of the mobility of the kidney, and he found in 40 cases of depression and dilatation of the stomach 22 instances of dislocation of the kidney on the right side. My own experience coincides with that of Drummond, who has very exceptionally found the two conditions to coexist. The association, however, with a *depressed* stomach is certainly not uncommon in women. Constipation is not infrequent. Some writers have described pressure upon the gall-ducts, with jaundice, but it is not very likely to occur. Fæcal accumulation and even obstruction may be associated with the displaced organ.

Dietl's Crises.—In floating kidney there are attacks characterized by severe abdominal pain, chills, nausea, vomiting, fever, and collapse. Scarcely any mention is made of such symptoms, which were first described by Dietl in 1864, and a more widespread knowledge of their occurrence in connection with this condition is desirable. My attention was called to them in 1880 by Palmer Howard in the case of a stout lady, who suffered repeatedly with the most severe attacks of abdominal pain and vomiting, which constantly required morphia. A tumor was discovered a little to the right of the navel, and the diagnosis of probable neoplasm was concurred in by Flint (Sr.) and Gaillard Thomas. The patient lost weight rapidly, became emaciated, and in the spring of 1881 again went to New York, where she saw Van Buren, who diagnosed a floating kidney and said that these paroxysms were associated with it in a gouty person. He cut off all stimulants, reassured the lady that she had no cancer, and from that time she rapidly recovered, and the attacks have been few and far between. In this patient any overindulgence in eating or in drinking is still liable to be followed by a very severe attack. These attacks may also be mistaken for renal colic, and the operation of nephrotomy has been performed.

In other instances the attacks of pain may be thought to be due to intestinal disease or to recurring appendicitis. The cause of these paroxysmal attacks is not quite clear. Dietl thought they were due to strangulation of the kidney or to twists or kinks in the renal vessels due to the extreme mobility. During the attacks the urine is sometimes high-colored and contains an excess of uric acid or of the oxalates. It is stated, too, that blood or pus may be present. The kidney may be tender, swollen, and less freely movable.

Intermittent hydronephrosis is sometimes associated with movable kidney. Three cases are reported in my Lectures on Abdominal Tumors. In two the condition has been completely relieved by a well-adapted pad and belt; in the third, attacks recur at long intervals.

The *diagnosis* is rarely doubtful, as the shape of the organ is usually distinctive and the mobility marked. Tumors of the gall-bladder, ovarian growths, and tumors of the bowels may in rare instances be confounded with it.

Treatment.—The kidney has been extirpated in many instances, but the operation is not without risk, and there have been several fatal cases. Stitching of the kidney—nephrorrhaphy—as recommended by Hahn, is the most suitable procedure, and statistics published by Keen show that relief is afforded in many cases by the procedure. It does not, however, always succeed.

In many instances the greatest relief is experienced from a bandage and pad. It should be applied in the morning, with the patient in the recumbent posture, and she should be taught how to push up the kidney. An air pad may be used if the organ is sensitive. In other cases a broad bandage well padded in the lower abdominal zone pushes up the intestines and makes them act as a support. In the attacks of severe colic morphia is required. When dependent, as seems sometimes the case, upon an excess of uric acid or the oxalates, the diet must be carefully regulated.

For an exhaustive consideration of all aspects of the subject, see Fischer, in Nos. 1–5 of the Centralblatt f. d. Grenzgebiete der Medicin und Chirurgie, 1898.

III. CIRCULATORY DISTURBANCES.

Normally the secretion of urine is accomplished by the maintenance of a certain blood-pressure within the glomeruli and by the activity of the renal epithelium. Bowman's views on this question have been generally accepted, and the watery elements are held to be filtered from the glomeruli; the amount depending on the rapidity and the pressure of the blood current; the quality, whether normal or abnormal, depending upon the condition of the capillary and glomerular epithelium; while the greater portion of the solid ingredients are excreted by the epithelium of the convoluted tubules. The integrity of the epithelium covering the capillary tufts within Bowman's capsule is essential to the production of a normal urine. If under any circumstances their nutrition fails, as when, for example, the rapidity of the blood current is lowered, so that they are deprived of the necessary amount of oxygen, the material which filters through is no longer normal (i. e., water), but contains serum albumin. Cohnheim has shown that the renal epithelium is extremely sensitive to circulatory changes, and that compression of the renal artery for only a few minutes causes serious disturbance.

The circulation of the kidney is remarkably influenced by reflex stimuli coming from the skin. Exposure to cold causes heightened blood-pressure within the kidneys and increased secretion of urine. Bradford has shown that after excision of portions of the kidney, to as much as one third of the total weight, there is a remarkable increase in the flow of urine.

Congestion of the Kidneys.—(1) *Active Congestion ; Hyperæmia.*—Acute congestion of the kidney is met with in the early stage of nephritis, whether due to cold or to the action of poisons and severe irritants. Turpentine, cubebs, cantharides, and copaiba are all stated to cause extreme hyperæmia of the organ. The most typical congestion of the kidney which we see post mortem is that in the early stage of acute Bright's disease, when the organ may be large, soft, of a dark color, and on section blood drips from it freely.

It has been held that in all the acute fevers the kidneys are congested, and that this explained the scanty, high-colored, and often albuminous urine. On the other hand, by Roy's oncometer, Walter Mendelson has shown that the kidney in acute fever is in a state of extreme anæmia, small, pale, and bloodless; and that this anæmia, increasing with the pyrexia and interfering with the nutrition of the glomerular epithelium, accounts for the scanty, dark-colored urine of fever and for the presence of albumin. In the prolonged fevers, however, it is probable that relaxation of the arteries again takes place. Certainly it is rare to find post mortem such a condition of the kidney as is described by Mendelson. On the contrary, the kidney of fever is commonly swollen, the blood-vessels are congested, and the cortex frequently shows traces of cloudy swelling. However, the circulatory disturbances in acute fevers are probably less important than the irritative effects of either the specific agents of the disease or the products produced in their growth or in the altered metabolism of the tissues. The urine is diminished in amount, and may contain albumin and tube-casts.

(2) *Passive Congestion; Mechanical Hyperæmia.*—This is found in cases of chronic disease of the heart or lung, with impeded circulation, and as a result of pressure upon the renal veins by tumors, the pregnant uterus, or ascitic fluid. In the cardiac kidney, as it is called, the cyanotic induration associated with chronic heart-disease, the organs are enlarged and firm, the capsule strips off, as a rule, readily, the cortex is of a deep red color, and the pyramids of a purple red. The section is coarse-looking, the substance is very firm, and resists cutting and tearing. The interstitial tissue is increased, and there is a small-celled infiltration between the tubules. Here and there the Malpighian tufts have become sclerosed. The blood-vessels are usually thickened, and there may be more or less granular, fatty, or hyaline changes in the epithelium of the tubules. The condition is indeed a diffuse nephritis. The urine is usually reduced, is of high specific gravity, and contains more or less albumin. Hyaline tube-casts and blood-corpuscles are not uncommon. In uncomplicated cases of the cyanotic induration uræmia is rare. On the other hand, in the cardiac cases with extensive arterio-sclerosis, the kidneys are more involved and the renal function is likely to be disturbed.

IV. ANOMALIES OF THE URINARY SECRETION.

1. Anuria.

Total suppression of urine occurs under the following conditions:

(1) As an event in the intense congestion of acute nephritis. For a time no urine may be formed; more often the amount is greatly reduced.

(2) More commonly complete anuria is seen in subjects of renal stone, fragments of which block both ureters. Sir William Roberts calls the con-

dition "latent uræmia." There may be very little discomfort, and the symptoms are very unlike those of ordinary uræmia. Convulsions occurred in only 5 of 41 cases (Herter); headache in only 6; vomiting in only 12. Consciousness is retained; the pupils are usually contracted; the temperature may be low; there are twitchings and perhaps occasional vomiting. Of 41 cases in the literature, 35 occurred in males. Of 36 cases in which there was absolute anuria, in 11 the condition lasted more than four days, in 18 cases from seven to fourteen days, and in 7 cases longer than fourteen days (Herter).

(3) Cases occur occasionally in which the suppression is prerenal. The following are among the more important conditions with which this form of anuria may be associated (Hensley): Fevers and inflammations; acute poisoning by phosphorus, lead, and turpentine; in the collapse after severe injuries or after operations, or, indeed, after the passing of a catheter; in the collapse stage of cholera and yellow fever; and, lastly, there is an hysterical anuria, of which Charcot reports a case in which the suppression lasted for eleven days. Bailey reports the case of a young girl, aged eleven, inmate of an orphan asylum, who passed no urine from October 10th to December 12th (when 8 ounces were withdrawn), and again from this date to March 1st! The question of hysterical deception was considered in the case.

A patient may live for from ten days to two weeks with complete suppression. In Polk's case, in which the only kidney was removed, the patient lived eleven days. It is remarkable that in many instances there are no toxic features. Adams reports a case of recovery after nineteen days of suppression.

In the obstructive cases surgical interference should be resorted to. In the non-obstructive cases, particularly when due to extreme congestion of the kidney, cupping over the loins, hot applications, free purging, and sweating with pilocarpine and hot air are indicated. When the secretion is once started diuretin often acts well. Large hot irrigations, with normal salt solution, with Kemp's double-current rectal tubes, should be tried, as they are stated to stimulate the activity of the kidneys in a remarkable way.

2. HÆMATURIA.

The following division may be made of the causes of hæmaturia:

(1) *General Diseases.*—The malignant forms of the acute specific fevers. Occasionally in leukæmia hæmaturia occurs.

(2) *Renal Causes.*—Acute congestion and inflammation, as in Bright's disease, or the effect of toxic agents, such as turpentine, carbolic acid, and cantharides. When the carbolic spray was in use many surgeons suffered from hæmaturia in consequence of this poison. Renal infarction, as in ulcerative endocarditis. New growths, in which the bleeding is usually profuse. In tuberculosis at the onset, when the papillæ are involved, there may be bleeding. Stone in the kidney is a frequent cause. Parasites: The *Filaria sanguinis hominis* and the *Bilharzia* cause a form of hæmaturia met with in the tropics. The echinococcus is rarely associated with hæmorrhage.

. (3) *Affections of the Urinary Passages.*—Stone in the ureter, tumor or ulceration of the bladder, the presence of a calculus, parasites, and, very rarely, ruptured veins in the bladder. Bleeding from the urethra occasionally occurs in gonorrhœa and as a result of the lodgment of a calculus.

(4) *Traumatism.*—Injuries may produce bleeding from any part of the urinary passages. By a fall or blow on the back the kidney may be ruptured, and this may be followed by very free bleeding; less commonly the blood comes from injury of the bladder or of the prostate. Blood from the urethra is frequently due to injury by the passage of a catheter, or sometimes to falls or blows.

And, lastly, there is a very interesting group, carefully studied of late years, particularly by Klemperer and M. L. Harris, in which no known lesions have been found. It is probably in this group of cases that Gull's "renal epistaxis" occurs. Harris has recently collected 18 of these cases from the literature. The first-named author thinks it is a form of angioneurotic hæmaturia. An interesting point is that in the 18 cases collected by Harris nephrotomy was done; of these, 9 cases were completely relieved.

Of special interest is the malarial hæmaturia which prevails in certain districts and has already been considered in the section on paludism.

The *diagnosis* of hæmaturia is usually easy. The color of the urine varies from a light smoky to a bright red, or it may have a dark porter color. Examined with the microscope, the blood-corpuscles are readily recognized, either plainly visible and retaining their color, in which case they are usually crenated, or simply as shadows. In ammoniacal urine or urines of low specific gravity the hæmoglobin is rapidly dissolved from the corpuscles, but in normal urine they remain for many hours unchanged.

For other tests the student is referred to the works on Clinical Diagnosis, by Simon and by von Jaksch.

It is important to distinguish between blood coming from the bladder and from the kidneys, though this is not always easy. From the bladder the blood may be found only with the last portions of urine, or only at the termination of micturition. In hæmorrhage from the kidneys the blood and urine are intimately mixed. Clots are more commonly found in the blood from the kidneys, and may form moulds of the pelvis or of the ureter. When the seat of the bleeding is in the bladder, on washing out this organ, the water is more or less blood-tinged; but if the source of the bleeding is higher, the water comes away clear. In many instances it is difficult to settle the question by the examination of the urine alone, and the symptoms and the physical signs must also be taken into account. Cystoscopic examination of the bladder and catheterization of the ureters may aid in the diagnosis in obscure cases.

3. HÆMOGLOBINURIA.

This condition is characterized by the presence of blood-pigment in the urine. The blood-cells are either absent or in insignificant numbers.

The coloring matter is not hæmatin, as indicated by the old name, *hæmatinuria*, nor in reality always hæmoglobin, but it is most frequently methæmoglobin. The urine has a red or brownish-red, sometimes quite black color, and usually deposits a very heavy brownish sediment. When the hæmoglobin occurs only in small quantities, it may give a lake or smoky color to the urine. Microscopical examination shows the presence of granular pigment, sometimes fragments of blood-disks, epithelium, and very often darkly pigmented urates. The urine is also albuminous. The number of red blood-corpuscles bears no proportion whatever to the intensity of the color of the urine. Examined spectroscopically, there are either the two absorption bands of oxyhæmoglobin, which is rare, or, more commonly, there are the three absorption bands of methæmoglobin, of which the one in the red near C is characteristic. Two clinical groups may be distinguished.

(1) **Toxic Hæmoglobinuria.**—This is caused by poisons which produce rapid dissolution of the blood-corpuscles, such as chlorate of potash in large doses, pyrogallic acid, carbolic acid, arseniuretted hydrogen, carbon monoxide, naphthol, and muscarine; also the poisons of scarlet fever, yellow fever, typhoid fever, malaria, and syphilis. According to Bastianelli, hæmoglobinuria due to the administration of quinine never occurs excepting in patients who are suffering or who have recently suffered from malarial fever. It has also followed severe burns. Exposure to excessive cold and violent muscular exertion are stated to produce hæmoglobinuria. A most remarkable toxic form occurs in horses, coming on with great suddenness and associated with paresis of the hind legs. Death may occur in a few hours or a few days. The animals are attacked only after being stalled for some days and then taken out and driven, particularly in cold weather. The form of hæmoglobinuria from cold and exertion is extremely rare. No instance of it, even in association with frost-bites, came under my observation in Canada. Blood transfused from one mammal into another causes dissolution of the corpuscles with the production of hæmoglobinuria; and, lastly, there is the *epidemic hæmoglobinuria* of the new-born, associated with jaundice, cyanosis, and nervous symptoms.

(2) **Paroxysmal Hæmoglobinuria.**—This rare disease is characterized by the occasional passage of bloody urine, in which the coloring matter only is present. It is more frequent in males than in females, and occurs chiefly in adults. It seems specially associated with cold and exertion, and has often been brought on, in a susceptible person, by the use of a cold foot-bath. Paroxysmal hæmoglobinuria has been found, too, in persons subject to the various forms of Raynaud's disease. Many regard the relation between these two affections as extremely close; some hold that they are manifestations of one and the same disorder. Druitt, the author of the well-known Surgical Vade-mecum, has given a graphic description of his sufferings, which lasted for many years, and were accompanied with local asphyxia and local syncope. The connection, however, is not very common. In only one of the cases of Raynaud's disease which I have seen was paroxysmal hæmoglobinuria present, and in it epileptic attacks occurred at the same time. The relation of the disease to malaria is not so close as has been

thought by many writers. Bastianelli asserts that it is practically proved that malarial hæmoglobinuria occurs only in infections with the æstivo-autumnal parasite. It rarely, if ever, occurs in the first attack, usually appearing with the first relapse or after repeated relapses. No doubt it has been frequently confounded with a malarial hæmaturia.

The attacks may come on suddenly after exposure to cold or as a result of mental or bodily exhaustion. They may be preceded by chills and pyrexia. In other instances the temperature is subnormal. There may be vomiting and diarrhœa. Pain in the lumbar region is not uncommon. The hæmoglobinuria rarely persists for more than a day or two—sometimes, indeed, not for a day. There are instances in which, even in the course of a single day, there have been two or three paroxysms, and in the intervals clear urine has been passed. Jaundice has been present in a number of cases. According to Ralfe, paroxysmal hæmoglobinuria may alternate with general symptoms of the same character, but associated only with the passage of albumin and an increased quantity of urea in the urine. In such cases he supposes that the toxic agent, whatever its nature, has destroyed only a limited number of the corpuscles, the coloring matter of which is readily dealt with by the spleen and liver, while the globulin is excreted in the urine. The cases are rarely if ever fatal.

The essential pathology of the disease is unknown, and it is difficult to form a theory which will meet all the facts—particularly the relation with Raynaud's disease, which is rightly regarded as a vaso-motor disorder. Increased hæmolysis and solution of the hæmoglobin in the blood-serum (hæmoglobinæmia) precedes, in each instance, the appearance of the coloring matter in the urine. A full discussion of the subject is to be found in F. Chvostek's monograph.

Treatment.—In all forms of hæmaturia rest is essential. In that produced by renal calculi the recumbent posture may suffice to check the bleeding. Full doses of acetate of lead and opium should be tried, then ergot, gallic and tannic acid, and the dilute sulphuric acid. The oil of turpentine, which is sometimes recommended, is a risky remedy in hæmaturia. Extr. hamamelis virgin. and extr. hydrastis canad. are also recommended. Cold may be applied to the loins or dry cups in the lumbar region.

The treatment of hæmoglobinuria is unsatisfactory. Amyl nitrite will sometimes cut short or prevent an attack (Chvostek). During the paroxysm the patient should be kept warm and given hot drinks. Quinine is recommended in large doses, on the supposition—as yet unwarranted—that the disease is specially connected with malaria. If there is a syphilitic history, iodide of potassium in full doses may be tried. In a warm climate the attacks are much less frequent.

4. ALBUMINURIA.

The presence of albumin in the urine, formerly regarded as indicative of Bright's disease, is now recognized as occurring under many circumstances without the existence of serious organic change in the kidney. Two groups of cases may be recognized—those in which the kidneys show no coarse lesions, and those in which there are evident anatomical changes.

Albuminuria without Coarse Renal Lesions.—(*a*) *Functional, so-called Physiological Albuminuria.*—In a normal condition of the kidney only the water and the salts are allowed to pass from the blood. When albuminous substances transude there is probably disturbance in the nutrition of the epithelium of the capillaries of the tuft, or of the cells surrounding the glomerulus. This statement is still, however, in dispute, and Senator, Grainger Stewart, and others hold that there is a physiological albuminuria which may follow muscular work, the ingestion of food rich in albumin, violent emotions, cold bathing, and dyspepsia. The differences of opinion on this point are striking, and observers of equal thoroughness and relia-bility have arrived at directly opposite conclusions. The presence of albu-min in the urine, in any form and under any circumstance, may be regarded as indicative of change in the renal or glomerular epithelium, a change, however, which may be transient, slight, and unimportant, depending upon variations in the circulation or upon the irritating effects of substances taken with the food or temporarily present, as in febrile states.

Albuminuria of adolescence and cyclic albuminuria, in which the albu-min is present only at certain times during the day, are interesting forms. A majority of the cases occur in young persons—boys more commonly than girls—and the condition is often discovered accidentally. The urine, as a rule, contains only a very small quantity of albumin, but in some instances large quantities are present. The most striking feature is the variability. It may be absent in the morning and only present after exertion, or it may be greatly increased after taking food, particularly proteids. The quan-tity of urine may be but little, if at all, increased, the specific gravity is usually normal, and the color may be high. Occasionally hyaline casts may be found, and in some instances there has been transient glycosuria. As a rule, the pulse is not of high tension and the second aortic sound is not accentuated.

Various forms of this affection have been recognized by writers, such as neurotic, dietetic, cyclic, intermittent, and paroxysmal—names which indicate the characters of the different varieties. A large proportion of the cases get well after the condition has persisted for a variable period. This in itself is an evidence that the changes, whatever their nature, were transient and slight. In these instances the albumin exists in small quan-tity, tube-casts are rarely present, and the arterial tension is not increased. In a second group the albumin is more persistent, the amount is larger, though it may vary from day to day, and the pulse tension is increased. In such instances the persistent albuminuria probably indicates actual organic change in the kidney.

(*b*) *Febrile Albuminuria.*—Pyrexia, by whatever cause produced, may cause slight albuminuria. The presence of the albumin is due to slight changes in the glomeruli induced by the fever, such as cloudy swelling, which cannot be regarded as an organic lesion. It is extremely common, occurring in pneumonia, diphtheria, typhoid fever, malaria, and even in the fever of acute tonsillitis. The amount of albumin is slight, and it usually disappears from the urine with the cessation of the fever. Hyaline and even epithelial casts accompany the condition.

(c) *Hæmic Changes.*—Purpura, scurvy, chronic poisoning by lead or mercury, syphilis, leukæmia, and profound anæmia may be associated with slight albuminuria. Abnormal ingredients in the blood, such as bile-pigment and sugar, may cause the passage of small amounts of albumin.

The transient albuminuria of pregnancy may belong to this hæmic group, although in a majority of such cases there are changes in the renal tissue. Albumin may be found sometimes after the inhalation of ether or chloroform.

(d) Albuminuria occurs in certain affections of the *nervous system.* This so-called neurotic albuminuria is seen after an epileptic seizure and in apoplexy, tetanus, exophthalmic goitre, and injuries of the head.

Albuminuria with Definite Lesions of the Urinary Organs.—(a) Congestion of the kidney, either active, such as follows exposure to cold and is associated with the early stages of nephritis, or passive, due to obstructed outflow in disease of the heart or lungs, or to pressure on the renal veins by the pregnant uterus or tumors.

(b) Organic disease of the kidneys—acute and chronic Bright's disease, amyloid and fatty degeneration, suppurative nephritis, and tumors.

(c) Affections of the pelvis, ureters, and bladder, when associated with the formation of pus.

Tests for Albumin.—Both morning and evening urine should be examined, and in doubtful cases at least three specimens. If turbid, the urine should be filtered, though turbidity from the urates is of no moment, since it disappears at once on the application of heat.

Heat and Nitric-acid Test.—The urine is boiled in a test-tube over a spirit-lamp, and a drop of nitric acid is then added. If a cloudiness occurs on boiling, it may be due to phosphates, which are dissolved on the addition of an acid. Persistence of the cloudiness indicates albumin.

Heller's Test.—A small quantity of fuming nitric acid is poured into the test-tube, and with a pipette the urine is allowed to flow gently down the side upon the acid. At the line of junction of the two fluids, if albumin is present, a white ring is formed. This contact method is trustworthy, and, for the routine clinical work, is probably the most satisfactory. A diffused haze, due to mucin (nucleo-albumin), is sometimes seen just above the white ring of albumin; and in very concentrated urines, or after the taking of balsamic remedies, a slight cloudiness may be due to urates or uric acid, which clears on heating or warming. A colored ring at the junction of the acid and the urine is due to the oxidation of the coloring matters in the urine.

Ferrocyanide-of-potassium and Acetic-acid Test.—Fill an ordinary test-tube half full of urine, and add 5 or 6 cc. of potassium-ferrocyanide solution (1 in 20). Thoroughly mix the urine and reagent and add 10 to 15 drops of acetic acid. If albumin be present, a cloudiness varying in degree according to the amount of albumin will be produced. This is a very reliable test, as it precipitates all forms of albumin, acid and alkaline, but does not precipitate mucin, peptones, phosphates, urates, vegetable alkaloids, or the pine acids.

Sir William Roberts strongly recommends the *magnesium-nitric test*. One volume of strong nitric acid is mixed with five volumes of the saturated solution of sulphate of magnesium. This is used in the same way as the nitric acid in Heller's test.

Picric acid, introduced by George Johnson, is a delicate and useful test for albumin. A saturated solution is used and employed as in the contact method. It has been urged against this test that it throws down the mucin, peptones, and certain vegetable alkaloids, but these are dissolved by heat.

For minute traces of albumin the trichloracetic acid may be used, or Millard's fluid, which is extremely delicate and consists of glacial carbolic acid (95 per cent), 2 drachms; pure acetic acid, 7 drachms; liquor potassæ, 2 ounces 6 drachms.

A quantitative estimate of the albumin can be made by means of Esbach's tube, but the rough method of heating and boiling a certain quantity of acidulated urine in a test-tube and allowing it to stand, is often employed. The depth of deposit can then be compared with the whole amount of urine, and the proportion is expressed as a mere trace, almost solid—one fourth, one half, and so on. This, of course, does not give an accurate indication of the proportion of albumin in the total quantity of urine. For the more elaborate methods the reader is referred to the works on urinalysis.

The above tests refer entirely to serum albumin. Other albuminous substances occur, such as albumose, serum globulin, peptones, and hemialbumose or propepton. They are not of much clinical importance.

Albumosuria.—Traces of *peptones* (albumoses) are found in the urine in many febrile diseases and in chronic suppuration. Albumosuria has but little clinical significance except in one connection. In 1848 Bence-Jones described a case of osteo-malacia in which he found a modified form of albumin in the urine. Of late years renewed interest has been taken in the subject by the discovery of the association of albumose with multiple myelomata of the bones. As Kahler called special attention to it, the Italians have given the condition his name. Fitz reported an instance at the last meeting (1898) of the Association of American Physicians, the only one recognized, so far as I know, in this country. In Bradshaw's case the patient passed at intervals for a year a turbid, milky urine, which deposited a copious white sediment. On adding nitric acid to a urine containing albumose a white precipitate is formed, which is dissolved when the specimen is boiled, but reappears on cooling.

Globulin rarely occurs in the urine alone, but generally in association with serum-albumin. The latter is usually present in greater quantity, but in severe organic renal disease and in diabetes Maguire has found that the proportion of globulin to albumin is often 2.5 to 1. Senator states that more globulin is present in lardaceous kidney than in other forms of nephritis. The clinical significance of globulin is the same as that of serum-albumin.

53

Prognosis.—This depends, of course, entirely upon the cause. Febrile albuminuria is transient, and in a majority of the cases depending upon hæmic causes the condition disappears and leaves the kidneys intact. An occasional trace of albumin in a man over forty, with or without a few hyaline casts, and with increased tension and thick vessel walls, usually indicates changes in the kidneys. The persistence of a slight amount of albumin in young men without increased arterial tension is less serious, as even after continuing for years it may disappear. I have already spoken of the outlook in the so-called cyclic albuminuria.

Practically in all cases the presence of albumin indicates a change of some sort in the glomeruli, the nature, extent, and gravity of which it is difficult to estimate; so that other considerations, such as the presence of tube-casts, the existence of increased tension, the general condition of the patient, and the influence of digestion upon the albumin, must be carefully considered.

The physician is daily consulted as to the relation of albuminuria and life assurance. As his function is to protect the interests of the company, he should reject all cases in which albumin occurs in the urine. It is even doubtful if an exception should be made in young persons with transient albuminuria. Naturally, companies lay great stress upon the presence or absence of albumin, but in the most serious and fatal malady with which they have to deal—chronic interstitial nephritis—the albumin is often absent or transient, even when the disease is well developed. After the fortieth year, from a standpoint of life insurance, the state of the arteries is far more important than the condition of the urine.

With reference to the significance of albuminuria in adults, I quite agree with the following conclusions of F. C. Shattuck:

(1) Renal albuminuria, as proved by the presence of both albumin and casts, is much more common in adults, quite apart from Bright's disease or any obvious source of renal irritation, than is generally supposed.

(2) The frequency increases steadily and progressively with advancing age.

(3) This increase with age suggests the explanation that the albuminuria is often an indication of senile degeneration.

(4) Though it cannot be regarded as yet as absolutely proved, it is highly probable that faint traces of albumin and hyaline and finely granular casts of small diameter are often, especially in those past fifty years of age, of little or no practical importance.

5. Pyuria (*Pus in the Urine*).

Causes.—(1) *Pyelitis and Pyelonephritis.*—In large abscesses of the kidney, pyonephrosis, the pus may be intermittent, and for days or even weeks the urine is free. In calculous and tuberculous pyelitis the pyuria is usually continuous, though varying in intensity. In these cases, as a rule, the pus is mixed with the urine, which is acid in reaction. In the early stages of pyelitis the transitional epithelium may be abundant, but is not in any way distinctive. In the pyelitis and pyelonephritis following cystitis the urine is usually alkaline, and contains more mucus; micturition is usually more frequent, and the history points to a previous bladder affection.

(2) *Cystitis.*—The urine is alkaline, often fetid, the pus ropy, and the amount of urine greatly increased. The ropy, thick mucus usually comes with the last portions of the urine. Triple phosphate crystals may be present in the freshly passed urine.

(3) *Urethritis,* particularly gonorrhœa. The pus appears first, is in small quantities, and there are signs of local inflammation.

(4) In *leucorrhœa* the quantity of pus is usually small, and large flakes of vaginal epithelium are numerous. In doubtful cases, when leucorrhœa is present, the urine should be withdraw through a catheter.

(5) *Rupture of Abscesses into the Urinary Passages.*—In such cases as pelvic or perityphlitic abscess there have been previous symptoms of pus formation. A large amount is passed within a short time, then the discharge stops abruptly or rapidly diminishes within a few days.

Pus gives to the urine a white or yellowish-white appearance. On settling there is a heavy grayish sediment, and the supernatant fluid is usually turbid. The sediment is often tenacious and ropy. The reaction is generally alkaline, and the odor may be ammoniacal even when passed. Examination with the microscope reveals the presence of a large number of pus-corpuscles, which are usually, when the pus comes from the bladder, well formed; the protoplasm is granular, and often shows many translucent processes.

The only sediment likely to be confounded with pus is that of the phosphates; but it is whiter and less dense, and is distinguished immediately by microscopical examination.

With the pus there is always more or less epithelium from the bladder and pelves of the kidneys, but since in these situations the forms of cells are practically identical, they afford no information as to the locality from which the pus has come.

The treatment of pus in the urine is considered under the conditions in which it occurs.

6. Chyluria—Non-parasitic.

This is a rare affection, occurring in temperate regions and unassociated with the *Filaria Bancrofti.* The urine is of an opaque white color; it resembles milk closely, is occasionally mixed with blood (hæmatochyluria), and sometimes coagulates into a firm, jelly-like mass. In other instances there is at the bottom of the vessel a loose clot which may be distinctly blood-tinged. Under the microscope the turbidity seems to be caused by numerous minute granules—more rarely oil droplets similar to those of milk. In Montreal I made the dissection of a case of thirteen years' duration and could find no trace of parasites.

7. Lithuria (*Lithœmia; Lithic-acid Diathesis*).

The general relations of uric acid have already been considered in speaking of gout.

Occurrence in the Urine.—The uric acid occurs in combination chiefly with ammonium and sodium, forming the acid urates. In smaller quantities are the potassium, calcium, and lithium salts. The uric acid may be separated from its bases and crystallizes in rhombs or prisms, which are usually of a deep red color, owing to the staining of the urinary pigments. The sediment formed is granular and the groups of crystals look like grains of Cayenne pepper. It is very important not to mistake a deposit of uric acid for an excess. The deposition of numerous grains in the urine within a few hours after passing is more likely to be due to conditions which diminish the solvent power than to increase in the quantity. Of the conditions which cause precipitation of the uric acid Roberts gives the following: "(1) High acidity; (2) poverty in mineral salts; (3) low pigmentation; and (4) high percentage of uric acid." The grade of acidity is probably the most important element.

In health the weight of uric acid excreted bears a fairly constant ratio to the weight of urea eliminated. According to von Noorden, the average ratio is 1 to 50, while the average ratio of the nitrogen of uric acid to the total nitrogen eliminated in the urine is 1 to 70. In several of the cases of gout in my wards Futcher found that in the intervals between the acute arthritic attacks the uric acid was reduced to a much greater extent than the urea, so that the ratio of the former to the latter often varied between 1 to 300 up to (in one case) 1 to 1,500, a return to about the normal proportions occurring during the acute attacks.

More common is the precipitation of amorphous urates, forming the so-called brick-dust or lateritious deposit, which has a pinkish color, due to the presence of urinary pigment. It is composed chiefly of the acid sodium urates. It occurs particularly in very acid urine of a high specific gravity. As the urates are more soluble in warm solutions, they frequently deposit as the urine cools. Here, too, the deposition does not necessarily, indeed usually does not, mean an excessive excretion, but the existence of conditions favoring the deposit.

Lithæmia.—In addition to what has already been said under *gout*, we may consider here the hypothetical condition known as lithæmia, or the uric-acid diathesis. Murchison introduced the term to designate certain symptoms due, as he supposed, to functional disturbance of the liver. Not only have his views been widely adopted, but, as is so often the case when we give the rein to theoretical conceptions of disease, the so-called manifestations of this state have so multiplied that some authors attribute to this cause a considerable proportion of the ailments affecting the various systems of the body. Thus one writer enumerates not fewer than thirty-nine separate morbid conditions associated with lithæmia! From our lack of knowledge of the mode of formation and elimination of uric acid it is very evident that the physiology of the subject must be widely extended before we are in a position to draw safe conclusions. Thus it is by no means sure that, as Murchison supposed, the essential defect is in a functional disorder of the liver, disturbing the metabolism of the albuminous ingredients, nor is it at all certain that the only offending substance is uric acid. In the present imperfect state of knowledge it is impossible with any clearness to define the pathology of the so-called uric-acid diathesis. We may say that certain symptoms arise in connection with defective food or tissue metabolism, more particularly of the nitrogenous elements. Deficient oxidation is probably the most essential factor in the process, with the result of the formation of less readily soluble and less readily eliminated products of retrograde metamorphosis. This faulty metabolism if long continued may lead to gout, with uratic deposits in the joints, acute inflammations, and arterial and renal disease. In a large group of cases the disturbed metabolism produces high tension in the arteries (probably as a direct sequence of interference with the capillary circulation) and ultimately degenerations in various tissues, particularly the scleroses.

Overeating and overdrinking, when combined with deficient muscular exercise, lie at the basis of this nutritional disturbance. The symptoms which are believed to characterize the uric-acid diathesis have already been briefly treated of under the section on irregular gout, and the question of diet and exercise has also been there considered.

8. Oxaluria.

Oxalic acid occurs in the urine, in combination with lime, forming an oxalate which is held in solution by the acid phosphate of soda. About .01 to .02 gramme is excreted in the day. It never forms a heavy deposit, but the crystals—usually octahedral, rarely dumb-bell-shaped—collect in the mucus-cloud and on the sides of the vessel. The amount varies extremely with the diet, and it is increased largely when such fruits and vegetables as tomatoes and rhubarb are taken. It is also a product of incomplete oxidation of the organic substances in the body, and in conditions of increased metabolism the amount in the urine becomes larger. It is stated also to result from the acid fermentation of the mucus in the urinary passages, and the crystals are usually abundant in spermatorrhœa.

When in excess and present for any considerable time, the condition is known as oxaluria, the chief interest of which is in the fact that the crystals may be deposited before the urine is voided, and form a calculus. It is held by many that there is a special diathesis associated with this state and manifested clinically by dyspepsia, particularly the nervous form, irritability, depression of spirits, lassitude, and sometimes marked hypochondriasis. There may be in addition neuralgic pains and the general symptoms of neurasthenia. The local and general symptoms are probably dependent upon some disturbance of metabolism of which the oxaluria is one of the manifestations. It is a feature also in many gouty persons, and in the condition called lithæmia.

9. Cystinuria.

Stadthogen claims that normal urine does not contain cystin, though Baumann and Goldmann succeeded in separating it in very small quantities from healthy urine as a benzoyl compound. It is associated with elimination of diamines both in the fæces and urine. It is very rarely met with, and its chief interest is owing to the fact that it may form a calculus. Its presence in the urine has been determined in many members of the same family, and the condition appears sometimes to be hereditary. As it contains sulphur, it is thought to be formed from the taurin of the bile.

10. PHOSPHATURIA.

The phosphoric acid is excreted from the body in combination with potassium, sodium, calcium, and magnesium, forming two classes, the alkaline phosphates of sodium and potassium and the earthy phosphates of lime and magnesia. The amount of phosphoric acid (P_2O_5) excreted in the twenty-four hours varies, according to Hammarsten, between 1 and 5 grammes, with an average of 2.5 grammes. It is derived mainly from the phosphoric acid taken in the food, but also in part as a decomposition product from nuclein, protagon, and lecithin. Of the alkaline phosphates, those in combination with sodium are the most abundant. The alkaline phosphates of the urine are more abundant than the earthy phosphates.

Of the *earthy phosphates,* those of lime are abundant, of magnesium scanty. In urine which has undergone the ammoniacal fermentation, either inside or outside the body, there is in addition the ammonio-magnesium or triple phosphate, which occurs in triangular prisms or in feathery or stellate crystals; hence the term given to this form of stellar phosphates. The earthy phosphates occur as a sediment in the urine when the alkalinity is due to a fixed alkali, or under certain circumstances the deposit may take place within the bladder, and then the phosphates are passed at the end of micturition as a whitish fluid, which is popularly confounded with spermatorrhœa. The calcium phosphate may be precipitated by heat and produce a cloudiness which may be mistaken for albumin, but is at once dissolved upon making the urine acid. This condition is very frequent in persons suffering from dyspepsia or from debility of any kind. The phosphates may be in great excess, rising in the twenty-four hours to from 7 to 9 grammes (Tessier), whereas the normal amount is not more than 2.5 grammes. And, lastly, the phosphates may be deposited in urine which has undergone decomposition, in which the carbonate of ammonia from the urea combines with the magnesium phosphates, forming the triple salt. This is seen in cystitis, and is due to the introduction of a bacterial ferment.

The clinical significance of an excess of phosphates, to which the term phosphaturia is applied, has been much discussed. It must be remembered that a deposit does not necessarily mean an excess, to determine which a careful analysis of the twenty-four hours' secretion should be made. It has long been thought that there is a relation between the activity of the nerve-tissues and the output of phosphoric acid; but the question cannot yet be considered settled. The amount is increased in wasting diseases, such as phthisis, acute yellow atrophy of the liver, leukæmia, and severe anæmia, whereas it is diminished in acute diseases and during pregnancy.

In a condition termed by Tessier, Ralfe, and others, phosphatic diabetes there are polyuria, thirst, emaciation, and a great increase in the excretion of phosphates, which may be as much as from 7 to 9 grammes in the day. The urine is usually acid and free from sugar; the patients are nervous; in some instances sugar has been present in the urine, and in others it subsequently makes its appearance.

11. INDICANURIA.

The substance in the urine which has received this name is the indoxyl-sulphate of potassium, in which form it appears in the urine and is colorless. When concentrated acids or strong oxidizing agents are added to the urine, this substance is decomposed and the indigo set free. It is present only in small quantities in healthy urine. It is derived from the indol, a product formed in the intestine by the decomposition of the albumin under the influence of bacteria. When absorbed, this is oxidized in the tissues to indoxyl, which combines with the potassium sulphate, forming the above-named substance.

The quantity of indican is diminished on a milk (and a Kefir) diet. It is increased in all wasting diseases, as carcinoma, and whenever any large quantities of albuminous substances are undergoing rapid decomposition, as in the severer forms of peritonitis and empyema. It is not usually increased in constipation, but is met with in ileus, particularly in obstruction of the small intestine. Indican has occasionally been found in calculi. Though, as a rule, the urine is colorless when passed, there are instances in which the decomposition has taken place within the body, and a blue color has been noticed immediately after the urine was voided. Sometimes, too, in alkaline urine on exposure there is a bluish film on the surface.

To test for indican, place 4 or 5 cc. of nitric or hydrochloric acid in a test-tube; boil, and add an equal quantity of urine. A bluish ring develops at the point of contact. Add 1 or 2 cc. of chloroform and shake the test-tube; on separation the chloroform has a violet or bluish color due to the presence of indican.

12. MELANURIA.

In melanotic cancer the urine, either at the time of voiding or after exposure to the air, may present a dark color. This pigment is known as melanin, and it may occur in solution or in the form of small granules. The urine may be voided clear, and subsequently, on exposure to the air or on the addition of oxidizing substances, becomes dark. In these cases it contains a chromogen called melanogen, which turns dark by oxidation. Von Jaksch has found that "in urine containing melanin or its precursor, melanogen, Prussian blue is formed by adding a nitroprusside, aqueous potash, and an acid. This reaction, however, does not seem to depend on the presence of melanin, as it is not given by that substance when separated from the urine, but apparently by some other at present unknown substance, which is present in traces in normal urine and is increased in cases of melanuria, and also in those conditions where excess of indigo occurs in the urine" (Halliburton).

13. Pneumaturia.

Gas may be passed with the urine—

1. After mechanical introduction of air in vesical irrigation or cysto-scopic examination in the knee-elbow position.

2. As a result of the introduction of gas-forming organisms in catheter-ization or other operation. Glycosuria has been present in a majority of the cases. The yeast fungus, the colon bacillus, and the bacillus aërogenes capsulatus have been found.

3. In cases of vesico-enteric fistula.

In gas production within the bladder the symptoms are those of a mild cystitis, with the passage of gas at the end of micturition, sometimes with a loud sound. The diagnosis is readily made by causing the patient to urinate in a bath or by plunging the end of the catheter under water.

14. Other Substances.

Fat in the urine, or *lipuria*, occurs, according to Halliburton, first, with-out disease of the kidneys, as in excess of fat in the food, after the admin-istration of cod-liver oil, in fat embolism occurring after fractures, in the fatty degeneration in phosphorus poisoning, in prolonged suppuration, as in phthisis and pyæmia, in the lipæmia of diabetes mellitus; secondly, with disease of the kidneys, as in the fatty stage of chronic Bright's disease, in which fat casts are sometimes present, and, according to Ebstein, in pyo-nephrosis; and, thirdly, in the affection known as chyluria. The urine is usually turbid, but there may be fat drops as well, and fatty crystals have been found.

Lipaciduria is a term applied by von Jaksch to the condition in which there are volatile fatty acids in the urine, such as acetic, butyric, formic, and propionic acid.

Acetonuria.—Von Jaksch distinguishes the following forms of patho-logical acetonuria: The febrile, the diabetic, the acetonuria with certain forms of cancer, the form associated with inanition, acetonuria in psychoses, and the acetonuria which results from auto-intoxication. It is doubtful, however, whether the symptoms in these are really due to the acetone. It may be the substances from which this is formed, particularly the diacetic acid or the β-oxy-butyric acid. The odor of the acetone may be marked in the breath and evident in the urine. The tests have been given in the section on diabetes.

Diacetic acid is probably never present in the urine in health. With a solution of ferric chloride it gives a Burgundy-red color. A similar re-action is given by acetic, formic, and oxy-butyric acids; it may be present in the urine of patients who are taking antipyrin, thallin, and the sali-cylates. Hammarsten states that if the reaction be due to the presence of diacetic acid, it will not be obtained in carrying out the test with a second specimen of urine which has been boiled and allowed to cool. The ethereal extract of the acidulated urine gives the reaction if diacetic acid be present, whereas the other substances which may be mistaken for diacetic acid are insoluble in ether.

β-oxy-butyric acid is believed by Stadelmann, Külz, and Minkowski to be the cause of diabetic coma. It is a product of the decomposition of the tissue albumins, and from it diacetic acid is readily formed by oxidation. Its tests have already been given.

Alcaptonuria.—Aromatic compounds occur after the administration of carbolic acid or gallic acid, and the urine on exposure to air becomes dark. In carboluria the substance causing the black color is known as hydro-chinon. Many years ago Boedeker met with cases in which the urine became dark, owing to the presence of an aromatic compound which he called alcapton. The urine is clear on passing, and then darkens on exposure to the air, or on the addition of liquor potassæ. Baumann isolated a substance from the urine of a case of alcaptonuria, to which he gave the name of homogentisinic acid. Later observers have isolated this substance in other cases. Kirk believed the reaction in his case was due to uroleucinic acid. In several instances more than one member of a family has shown this urinary change. The substance is apparently without clinical significance except in so far as it is capable of reducing the Fehling solution, and may be mistaken for sugar. Alcapton urine may be distinguished from diabetic urine from the fact that it does not ferment nor reduce alkaline bismuth solutions, and because it is optically inactive (see Alcaptonuria, by T. B. Futcher, New York Med. Jour., 1897, ii).

Choluria and glycosuria have already been considered under jaundice and diabetes.

Hæmatoporphyrin occasionally occurs in the urine. It was first recognized by Hoppe-Seyler. Nencki and Sieler determined its exact formula, and the former demonstrated that the only chemical difference between hæmatin and hæmatoporphyrin is that the latter is simply hæmatin free from iron. It has been found in the urine in pulmonary tuberculosis, pleurisy with effusion, acute rheumatism, lead poisoning, and intestinal hæmorrhages. This pigment has been found very frequently after the administration of sulphonal, and sometimes imparts a very dark color to the urine.

V. URÆMIA.

Definition.—A toxæmia developing in the course of nephritis or in conditions associated with anuria. The nature of the poison or poisons is as yet unknown, whether they are the retained normal products or the products of an abnormal metabolism.

Theories of Uræmia.—The view most widely held is that uræmia is due to the accumulation in the blood of excrementitious material—body poisons—which should be thrown off by the kidneys. "If, however, from any cause, these organs make default, or if there be any prolonged obstruction to the outflow of urine, accumulation of some or of all the poisons takes place, and the characteristic symptoms are manifested, but the accumulation may be very slow and the earlier symptoms, corresponding to the comparatively small dose of poison, may be very slight; yet they are in kind, though not in degree, as indicative of uræmia as are the more alarming, which appear toward the end, and to which alone the name uræmia is often given" (Carter). Herter and others have shown that the toxicity of the blood-serum in uræmic states is increased. The part played by urea itself, by the salts, and by the nitrogenous extractives has not been determined.

Another view is that uræmia depends on the products of an abnormal metabolism. Brown-Séquard suggested that the kidney has an internal secretion, and it is urged that the symptoms of uræmia are due to its disturbance. Bradford's experiments show that the kidneys do influence profoundly the metabolism of the tissues of the body, particularly of the muscles. If more than one third of the total kidney weight be removed, there is an extraordinary increase in the production of urea and of the nitrogenous bodies of the creatin class. He favors this view, but acknowledges that we are still ignorant of the nature of the poison. From a careful study of the question, Hughes and Carter concluded that the poison was an albuminous product quite different from anything in normal urine. In Bradford's Gulstonian Lectures (1898) will be found a full discussion of the question.

Traube believed that the symptoms of uræmia, particularly the coma and convulsions, were due to localized œdema of the brain.

Symptoms.—Clinically, we may recognize latent, acute, and chronic forms of uræmia. The latent form has been considered under the section on anuria. Acute uræmia may develop in any form of nephritis. It is more common in the post-febrile varieties. Bradford thinks that it is specially associated with a form of contracted white kidney in young subjects. Chronic forms of uræmia are more frequent in the arterio-sclerotic and granular kidney. For convenience the symptoms of uræmia may be described under cerebral, dyspnœic, and gastro-intestinal manifestations.

Among the *cerebral* symptoms of uræmia may be described:

(*a*) *Mania.*—This may come on abruptly in an individual who has shown no previous indications of mental trouble, and who may not be known to have Bright's disease. In a remarkable case of this kind which came under my observation the patient became suddenly maniacal and died in six days. More commonly the delirium is less violent, but the patient is noisy, talkative, restless, and sleepless.

(*b*) *Delusional Insanity (Folie Brightique).*—Cases are by no means uncommon, and excellent clinical reports have been issued on the subject from several of the asylums of this country, particularly by Bremer, Christian, and Alice Bennett. Delusions of persecution are common. One of my cases committed suicide by jumping out of a window. The condition is of interest medico-legally because of its bearing on testamentary capacity. Profound melancholia may also supervene.

(*c*) *Convulsions.*—These may come on unexpectedly or be preceded by pain in the head and restlessness. The attacks may be general and identical with those of ordinary epilepsy, though the initial cry may not be present. The fits may recur rapidly, and in the interval the patient is usually unconscious. Sometimes the temperature is elevated, but more frequently it is depressed, and may sink rapidly after the attack. Local or Jacksonian epilepsy may occur in most characteristic form in uræmia.

A remarkable sequence of the convulsions is blindness—*uræmic amaurosis* —which may persist for several days. This, however, may occur apart from the convulsions. It usually passes off in a day or two. There are, as a rule, no ophthalmoscopic changes. Sometimes uræmic deafness supervenes, and is probably also a cerebral manifestation. It may also occur in connection with persistent headache, nausea, and other gastric symptoms.

(*d*) *Coma.*—Unconsciousness invariably accompanies the general convulsions, but a coma may develop gradually without any convulsive seizures. Frequently it is preceded by headache, and the patient gradually becomes dull and apathetic. In these cases there may have been no previous indications of renal disease, and unless the urine is examined the nature of the case may be overlooked. Twitchings of the muscles occur, particularly in the face and hands, but there are many cases of coma in which the muscles are not involved. In some of these cases a condition of torpor persists for weeks or even months. The tongue is usually furred and the breath very foul and heavy.

(*e*) *Local Palsies.*—In the course of chronic Bright's disease hemiplegia or monoplegia may come on spontaneously or follow a convulsion, and post mortem no gross lesions of the brain be found, but only a localized or diffused œdema. These cases, which are not very uncommon, may simulate almost every form of organic paralysis of cerebral origin.

(*f*) Of other cerebral symptoms, headache is important. It is most often occipital and extends to the neck. It may be an early feature and associated with giddiness. Other nervous symptoms of uræmia are intense itching of the skin, numbness and tingling in the fingers, and cramps in the muscles of the calves, particularly at night. An erythema may be present.

Uræmic dyspnœa is classified by Palmer Howard as follows: (1) Continuous dyspnœa; (2) paroxysmal dyspnœa; (3) both types alternating; and (4) Cheyne-Stokes breathing. The attacks of dyspnœa are most commonly nocturnal; the patient may sit up, gasp for breath, and evince as much distress as in true asthma. Occasionally the breathing is noisy and stridulous. The Cheyne-Stokes type may persist for weeks, and is not necessarily associated with coma. I have seen it in a man who travelled over a hundred miles to consult a physician. In another instance a patient, up and about, could only when at meals feed himself in the apnœa period. Though usually of serious omen and occurring with coma and other symptoms, recovery may follow even after persistence for weeks or even months.

The *gastro-intestinal* manifestations of uræmia often set in with abruptness. Uncontrollable vomiting may come on and its cause be quite unrecognizable. A young married woman was admitted to my wards in the Montreal General Hospital with persistent vomiting of four or five days' duration. The urine was slightly albuminous, but she had none of the usual signs of uræmia, and the case was not regarded as one of Bright's disease. The vomiting persisted and caused death. The post mortem showed extensive sclerosis of both kidneys. The attacks may be preceded by nausea and may be associated with diarrhœa. In some instances the diarrhœa may come on without the vomiting; sometimes it is profuse and associated with an intense catarrhal or even diphtheritic inflammation of the colon.

A special uræmic *stomatitis* has been described (Barie) in which the mucosa of the lips, gums, and tongue is swollen and erythematous. The saliva may be increased, and there is difficulty in swallowing and in mastication. The tongue is usually very foul and the breath heavy and fetid. A cutaneous erythema may be present in uræmia.

Fever is not uncommon in uræmic states, and may occur with the acute nephritis, with the complications, and as a manifestation of the uræmia itself (Stengel).

Very many patients with chronic uræmia succumb to what I have called terminal infections—acute peritonitis, pericarditis, pleurisy, meningitis, or endocarditis.

Diagnosis.—Herter calls attention to the value of the clinical determination of the urea in the blood (for which purpose only a few cubic centimetres are required) as an index of the degree of renal inadequacy. So far as the urine is concerned, the volume and specific gravity indicate the total solids, and the determination of the urea itself in the urine gives no indication of the quantity in the blood. Uræmia may be confounded with:

(*a*) Cerebral lesions, such as hæmorrhage, meningitis, or even tumor. In apoplexy, which is so commonly associated with kidney disease and stiff arteries, the sudden loss of consciousness, particularly if with convulsions, may simulate a uræmic attack; but the mode of onset, the existence of complete hemiplegia, with conjugate deviation of the eyes, suggest hæmorrhage. As already noted, there are cases of uræmic hemiplegia or monoplegia which cannot be separated from those of organic lesion and which post mortem show no trace of coarse disease of the brain. I know of an instance in which a consultation was held upon the propriety of operation in a case of hemiplegia believed to be due to subdural hæmorrhage which post mortem was shown to be uræmic. Indeed, in some of these cases it is quite impossible to distinguish between the two conditions. So, too, cases of meningitis, in a condition of deep coma, with perhaps slight fever, furred tongue, and without localizing symptoms, may readily be confounded with uræmia.

(*b*) With certain infectious diseases. Uræmia may persist for weeks or months and the patient lies in a condition of torpor or even unconsciousness, with a heavily coated, perhaps dry, tongue, muscular twitchings, a rapid feeble pulse, with slight fever. This state not unnaturally suggests the existence of one of the infectious diseases. Cases of the kind are not uncommon, and I have known them to be mistaken for typhoid fever and for miliary tuberculosis.

(*c*) Uræmic coma may be confounded with poisoning by alcohol or opium. In opium poisoning the pupils are contracted; in alcoholism they are more commonly dilated. In uræmia they are not constant; they may be either widely dilated or of medium size. The examination of the eyeground should be made to determine the presence or absence of albuminuric retinitis. The urine should be drawn off and examined. The odor of the breath sometimes gives an important hint.

The condition of the heart and arteries should also be taken into account. Sudden uræmic coma is more common in the chronic interstitial nephritis. The character of the delirium in alcoholism is sometimes important, and the coma is not so deep as in uræmia or opium poisoning. It may for a time be impossible to determine whether the condition is due to uræmia, profound alcoholism, or hæmorrhage into the pons Varolii.

And lastly, in connection with sudden coma, it is to be remembered that insensibility may occur after prolonged muscular exertion, as after running a ten-mile race. In some instances unconsciousness has come on rapidly with stertorous breathing and dilated pupils. Cases have occurred under conditions in which sun-stroke could be excluded; and Poore, who reports a case in the Lancet (1894), considers that the condition is due to the too rapid accumulation of waste products in the blood, and to hyperpyrexia from suspension of sweating.

The treatment will be considered under Chronic Bright's Disease.

VI. ACUTE BRIGHT'S DISEASE.

Definition.—Acute diffuse nephritis, due to the action of cold or of toxic agents upon the kidneys.

In all instances changes exist in the epithelial, vascular, and intertubular tissues, which vary in intensity in different forms; hence writers have described a tubular, a glomerular, and an acute interstitial nephritis. Delafield recognizes *acute exudative* and *acute productive* forms, the latter characterized by proliferation of the connective-tissue stroma and of the cells of the Malpighian tufts.

Etiology.—The following are the principal causes of acute nephritis:

(1) Cold. Exposure to cold and wet is one of the most common causes. It is particularly prone to follow exposure after a drinking-bout.

(2) The poisons of the specific fevers, particularly scarlet fever, less commonly typhoid fever, measles, diphtheria, small-pox, chicken-pox, malaria, cholera, yellow fever, meningitis, and, very rarely, dysentery. As already mentioned, acute nephritis may be associated with syphilis. In acute tuberculosis nephritis is not uncommon. It may also occur in septicæmia. The frequency of acute nephritis in malaria has been emphasized by Thayer in a recent analysis of the cases at the Johns Hopkins Hospital. Among 1,832 cases there were 26 of nephritis.

(3) Toxic agents, such as turpentine, cantharides, chlorate of potash, and carbolic acid may cause an acute congestion which sometimes terminates in nephritis. Alcohol probably never excites an acute nephritis.

(4) Pregnancy, in which the condition is thought by some to result from compression of the renal veins, although this is not yet finally settled. The condition may in reality be due to toxic products as yet undetermined.

(5) Acute nephritis occurs occasionally in connection with extensive lesions of the skin, as in burns or in chronic skin-diseases.

Morbid Anatomy.—The kidneys may present to the naked eye in mild cases no evident alterations. When seen early in more severe forms the organs are congested, swollen, dark, and on section may drip blood. In other instances the surface is pale and mottled, the capsule strips off readily, and the cortex is swollen, turbid, and of a grayish-red color, while the pyramids have an intense beefy-red tint. The glomeruli in some instances stand out plainly, being deeply swollen and congested; in other instances they are pale.

The histology may be thus summarized: (a) Glomerular changes. In a majority of the cases of nephritis due to toxic agents, which reach the kidney through the blood-vessels, the tufts suffer first, and there is either an acute intracapillary glomerulitis, in which the capillaries become filled with cells and thrombi, or involvement of the epithelium of the tuft and of Bowman's capsule, the cavity of which contains leucocytes and red blood-corpuscles. Hyaline degeneration of the contents and of the walls of the capillaries of the tuft is an extremely common event. These processes are perhaps best marked in scarlatinal nephritis. There may be proliferation about Bowman's capsule. These changes interfere with the circulation in the tufts and seriously influence the nutrition of the tubular structures beyond them.

(b) The alterations in the tubular epithelium consist in cloudy swelling, fatty change, and hyaline degeneration. In the convoluted tubules, the accumulation of altered cells with leucocytes and blood-corpuscles causes the enlargement and swelling of the organ. The epithelial cells lose their striation, the nuclei are obscured, and hyaline droplets often accumulate in them.

(c) Interstitial changes. In the milder forms a simple inflammatory exudate—serum mixed with leucocytes and red blood-corpuscles—exists between the tubules. In severer cases areas of small-celled infiltration occur about the capsules and between the convoluted tubes. These changes may be widespread and uniform throughout the organs or more intense in certain regions.

Councilman has described an *acute interstitial nephritis* occurring chiefly in children after fevers, characterized by the presence of cells similar to those described by Unna as plasma cells. He thinks that these cells are formed in other organs, chiefly the spleen and bone marrow, and are carried to the kidneys in the blood current.

Symptoms.—The onset is usually sudden, and when the nephritis follows cold, dropsy may be noticed within twenty-four hours. After fevers the onset is less abrupt, but the patient gradually becomes pale and a puffiness of the face or swelling of the ankles is first noticed. In children there may at the outset be convulsions. Chilliness or rigors initiate the attack in a limited number of cases. Pain in the back, nausea, and vomiting may be present. The fever is variable. Many cases in adults have no rise in temperature. In young children with nephritis from cold or scarlet fever the temperature may, for a few days, range from 101° to 103°.

The most characteristic symptoms are the urinary changes. There may at first be suppression; more commonly the urine is scanty, highly colored, and contains blood, albumin, and tube-casts. The quantity is reduced and only 4 or 5 ounces may be passed in the twenty-four hours; the specific gravity is high—1.025, or even more; the color varies from a smoky to a deep porter color, but is seldom bright red. On standing there is a heavy deposit; microscopically there are blood-corpuscles, epithelium from the urinary passages, and hyaline, blood, and epithelial tube-casts. The albumin is abundant, forming a curdy, thick precipitate. The total excretion of urea is reduced, though the percentage is high.

Anæmia is an early and marked symptom. In cases of extensive dropsy, effusion may take place into the pleuræ and peritonæum. There are cases of scarlatinal nephritis in which the dropsy of the extremities is trivial and effusion into the pleuræ extensive. The lungs may become œdematous. In rare cases there is œdema of the glottis. Epistaxis may occur or cutaneous ecchymoses may develop in the course of the disease.

The pulse may be hard, the tension increased, and the second sound in the aortic area accentuated. Occasionally dilatation of the heart comes on rapidly and may cause sudden death (Goodhart). The skin is dry and it may be difficult to induce sweating.

Uræmic symptoms develop in a limited number of cases. They may occur at the onset with suppression, more commonly later in the disease. Ocular changes are not so common in acute as in chronic Bright's disease, but hæmorrhagic retinitis may occur and occasionally papillitis.

The course of acute Bright's disease varies considerably. The description just given is of the form which most commonly follows cold or scarlet fever. In many of the febrile cases dropsy is not a prominent symptom, and the diagnosis rests rather with the examination of the urine. Moreover, the condition may be transient and less serious. In other cases, as in the acute nephritis of typhoid fever, there may be hæmaturia and pronounced signs of interference with the renal function. The most intense acute nephritis may exist without anasarca.

In scarlatinal nephritis, in which the glomeruli are most seriously affected, suppression of the urine may be an early symptom, the dropsy is apt to be extreme, and uræmic manifestations are common. Acute Bright's disease in children, however, may set in very insidiously and be associated with transient or slight œdema, and the symptoms may point rather to affection of the digestive system or to brain-disease.

Diagnosis.—It is very important to bear in mind that the most serious involvement of the kidneys may be manifested only by slight œdema of the feet or puffiness of the eyelids, without impairment of the general health. The first indication of trouble may be a uræmic convulsion. This is particularly the case in the acute nephritis of pregnancy, and it is a good rule for the practitioner, when engaged to attend a case, invariably to ask that during the seventh and eighth months the urine should occasionally be sent for examination.

In nephritis from cold and in scarlet fever the symptoms are usually marked and the diagnosis is rarely in doubt. As already mentioned, every case in which albumin is present must not be called acute Bright's disease, not even if tube-casts be present. Thus the common febrile albuminuria, although it represents the first link in the chain of events leading to acute Bright's disease, should not be placed in the same category.

There are occasional cases of acute Bright's disease with anasarca, in which albumin is either absent or present only as a trace. This is a rare condition. Tube-casts are usually found, and the absence of albumin is rarely permanent. The urine may be reduced in amount.

The character of the casts is of use in the diagnosis of the form of Bright's disease, but scarcely of such extreme value as has been stated. Thus, the hyaline and granular casts are common to all varieties. The blood and epithelial casts, particularly those made up of leucocytes, are most common in the acute cases.

Prognosis.—The outlook varies somewhat with the cause of the disease. Recoveries in the form following exposure to cold are much more frequent than after scarlatinal nephritis. In young children the mortality is high, amounting to at least one third of the cases. Serious symptoms are low arterial tension, the occurrence of uræmia, and effusion into the serous sacs. The persistence of the dropsy after the first month, intense pallor, and a large amount of albumin indicate the possibility of the disease becoming chronic. For some months after the disappearance of the dropsy there may be traces of albumin and a few tube-casts.

In a week or ten days, in a case of scarlatinal nephritis, if the progress is favorable, the dropsy diminishes, the urine increases, the albumin lessens, and by the end of a month the dropsy has disappeared and the urine is nearly free. In very young children the course may be rapid, and I have known the urine to be free from albumin in the fourth week. Other cases are more insidious, and though the dropsy may disappear, the albumin persists in the urine, the anæmia is marked, and the condition becomes chronic, or, after several recurrences of the dropsy, improves and complete recovery takes place.

Treatment.—The patient should be in bed and there remain until all traces of the disease have disappeared. As sweating plays such an important part in the treatment, it is well, if possible, to accustom the patient to blankets. He should also be clad in thin Canton flannel.

The diet should consist of milk or butter-milk, gruels made of arrowroot or oat-meal, barley water, and, if necessary, beef tea and chicken broth. It is better, if possible, to confine the patient to a strictly milk diet. As convalescence is established, bread and butter, lettuce, water-cress, grapes, oranges, and other fruits may be given. The return to a meat diet should be gradual.

The patient should drink freely of alkaline mineral waters, ordinary water, or lemonade. The fluids keep the kidneys flushed and wash out the débris from the tubes. A useful drink is a drachm of cream of tartar in a pint of boiling water, to which may be added the juice of half a lemon and a little sugar. Taken when cold, this is a pleasant and satisfactory diluent drink.

No remedies, so far as known, control directly the changes which are going on in the kidneys. The indications are: (1) To give the excretory function of the kidney rest by utilizing the skin and the bowels, in the hope that the natural processes may be sufficient to effect a cure; (2) to meet the symptoms as they arise.

In a case of scarlet fever it may occasionally be possible to avert an attack, the premonitory symptoms of which are marked increase in the arterial tension and the presence of blood coloring matter in the urine (Mahomed). An active saline cathartic may completely relieve this condition.

At the onset, when there is pain in the back or hæmaturia, the Paquelin cautery or the dry or wet cups give relief. The last should not be used in children. Warm poultices are often grateful. In cases which set in with suppression of urine, these measures should be adopted, and in addition the hot bath with subsequent pack, copious diluents, and a free purge. The dropsy is best treated by hydrotherapy—either the hot bath, the wet pack, or the hot-air bath. In children the wet pack is usually satisfactory. It is applied by wringing a blanket out of hot water, wrapping the child in it, covering this with a dry blanket, and then with a rubber cloth. In this the child may remain for an hour. It may be repeated daily. In the case of adults, the hot-air bath or the vapor bath may be conveniently given by allowing the vapor or air to pass from a funnel beneath the bed-clothes, which are raised on a low cradle. More efficient, as a rule, is a hot bath of from fifteen or twenty minutes, after which the patient is wrapped in blankets. The sweating produced by these measures is usually profuse, rarely exhausting, and in a majority of cases the dropsy can in this way be relieved. There are some cases, however, in which the skin does not respond to the baths, and if the symptoms are serious, particularly if uræmia supervenes, jaborandi or its active principle, pilocarpine, may be used. The latter may be given hypodermically, in doses of from a sixth to an eighth of a grain in adults, and from a twentieth to a twelfth of a grain in children from two to ten years.

The bowels should be kept open by a morning saline purge; in children the fluid magnesia is readily taken; in adults the sulphate of magnesia may be given by Hay's method, in concentrated form, in the morning, before anything is taken into the stomach. In Bright's disease it not infrequently causes vomiting. The compound powder of jalap, in half-drachm doses, or, if necessary, elaterium may be used. If the dropsy is not extreme, the urine not very concentrated, and uræmic symptoms are not present, the bowels should be kept loose without active purgation. If these measures fail to reduce the dropsy and it has become extreme, the skin may be punctured with a lancet or drained by a small silver canula (Southey's tube), which is inserted beneath it. A fine aspirator needle may be used, and the fluid allowed to drain through a piece of long, narrow rubber tubing into a vessel beneath the bed. If the dyspnœa is marked, owing to pressure of fluid in the pleuræ, aspiration should be performed. In rare instances the ascites is extreme and may require paracentesis, or a Southey's tube may be inserted and the fluid gradually withdrawn. If uræmic convulsions occur, the intensity of the paroxysms may be limited by the use of chloroform; to an adult a pilocarpine injection should be at once given, and from a robust, strong man 20 ounces of blood may be withdrawn. In children the loins may be dry cupped, the wet pack used, and a brisk purgative given. Bromide of potassium and chloral sometimes prove useful.

54

Vomiting may be relieved by ice and by restricting the amount of food. Drop doses of creasote, iodine, and carbolic acid may be given. The dilute hydrocyanic acid with bismuth is often effectual.

The question of the use of diuretics in acute Bright's disease is not yet settled. The best diuretic, after all, is water, which may be taken freely with the citrate of potash or the benzoate of soda, salts which are held to favor the conversion of the urates into less irritating and more easily excreted compounds. Digitalis and strophanthus are useful diuretics, and may be employed without risk when the arterial tension is low and the cardiac impulse is not forcible. I have never seen any injurious effects from their employment after the early symptoms had lessened in intensity.

For the persistent albuminuria, I agree with Roberts and Rosenstein that we have no remedy of the slightest value. Nothing indicates more clearly our helplessness in controlling kidney metabolism than inability to meet this common symptom. Astringents, alkalies, nitroglycerin, and mercury have been recommended.

For the anæmia always associated with acute Bright's disease iron should be employed. It should not be given until the acute symptoms have subsided. In the adult it may be used in the form of the perchloride in increasing doses, as convalescence proceeds. In children, the syrup of the iodide of iron or the syrup of the phosphate of iron are better preparations. Tyson has recently urged caution in the too free use of iron in kidney disease. The dilatation of the heart is best treated with digitalis, strophanthus, and strychnia.

In the convalescence from acute Bright's disease, care should be taken to guard the patient against cold. The diet should still consist chiefly of milk and a return to mixed food should be gradual. A change of air is often beneficial, particularly a residence in a warm, equable climate.

VII. CHRONIC BRIGHT'S DISEASE.

Here, too, in all forms we deal with a diffuse process, involving epithelial, interstitial, and glomerular tissues. Clinically two groups are recognized—(a) the chronic parenchymatous nephritis, which follows the acute attack or comes on insidiously, is characterized by marked dropsy, and post mortem by the *large white kidney.* In the later stages of this process the kidney may be smaller—a condition known as the *small white kidney;* (b) chronic interstitial nephritis, in which dropsy is not common and the cardiovascular changes are pronounced. Delafield recognizes a chronic diffuse nephritis with exudation and a chronic productive diffuse nephritis without exudation, the latter corresponding to the contracted kidney of authors.

The amyloid kidney is usually spoken of as a variety of Bright's disease, but in reality it is a degeneration which may accompany any form of nephritis.

Chronic Parenchymatous Nephritis

(Chronic Desquamative and Chronic Tubal Nephritis; Chronic Diffuse Nephritis with Exudation).

Etiology.—In many cases the disease follows the acute nephritis of cold, scarlet fever, or pregnancy. More frequently than is usually stated the disease has an insidious onset and occurs independently of any acute attack. The fevers may play an important *rôle* in certain of these cases. Rosenstein, Bartels, and, in this country, I. E. Atkinson and Thayer have laid special stress upon malaria as a cause. Beer and alcohol are believed to lead to this form of nephritis. In chronic suppuration, syphilis, and tuberculosis the diffuse parenchymatous nephritis is not uncommon, and is usually associated with amyloid disease. Males are rather more subject to the affection than females. It is met with most commonly in young adults, and is by no means infrequent in children as a sequence of scarlatinal nephritis.

Morbid Anatomy.—Several varieties of this form have been recognized. The most common is the *large white kidney* of Wilks, in which the organ is enlarged, the capsule is thin, and the surface white with the stellate veins injected. On section the cortex is swollen and yellowish white in color, and often presents opaque areas. The pyramids may be deeply congested. On microscopical examination it is seen that the epithelium is granular and fatty, and the tubules of the cortex are distended, and contain tube-casts. Hyaline changes are also present in the epithelial cells. The glomeruli are large, the capsules thickened, the capillaries show hyaline changes, and the epithelium of the tuft and of the capsule is extensively altered. The interstitial tissue is everywhere increased, though not to an extreme degree.

The second variety of this form results from the gradual increase in the connective tissue and the subsequent shrinkage, forming what is called the *small white kidney* or the pale granular kidney. It is doubtful whether this is always preceded by the large white kidney. Some observers hold that it may be a primary independent form. The capsule is thickened and the surface is rough and granular. On section the resistance is greatly increased, the cortex is reduced and presents numerous opaque white or whitish-yellow foci, consisting of accumulations of fatty epithelium in the convoluted tubules. This combination of contracted kidney with the areas of marked fatty degeneration has given the name of small granular, fatty kidney to this form. The interstitial changes are marked, many of the glomeruli are destroyed, the degeneration of epithelium in the convoluted tubules is widespread, and the arteries are greatly thickened.

Belonging to this chronic tubal nephritis is a variety known as the *chronic hæmorrhagic nephritis*, in which the organs are enlarged, yellowish white in color, and in the cortex are many brownish-red areas, due to hæmorrhage into and about the tubes. In other respects the changes are identical with those in the large white kidney.

Of changes in the other organs the most marked are thickening of the blood-vessels and hypertrophy of the left heart.

Symptoms.—Following an acute nephritis, the disease may present, in a modified way, the symptoms of that affection. In many cases it sets in insidiously, and after an attack of dyspepsia or a period of failing health and loss of strength the patient becomes pale, and puffiness of the eyelids or swollen feet are noticed in the morning.

The symptoms are as follows: The urine is, as a rule, diminished in quantity, often scanty. It has a dirty-yellow, sometimes smoky, color, and is turbid from the presence of urates. On standing, a heavy sediment falls, in which are found numerous tube-casts of various forms and sizes, hyaline, both large and small, epithelial, granular, and fatty casts. Leucocytes are abundant; red blood-corpuscles are frequently met with, and epithelium from the kidneys and pelves. The albumin is abundant and may amount to one half or one third of the urine boiled. It is more abundant in the urine passed during the day. The specific gravity may be high in the early stages—from 1.020 to 1.025—though in the later stages it is lower. The urea is always reduced in quantity.

Dropsy is a marked and obstinate symptom of this form of Bright's disease. The face is pale and puffy, and in the morning the eyelids are œdematous. The anasarca is general, and there may be involvement of the serous sacs. In these chronic cases associated with large white kidney there is often a distinctive appearance in the face; the complexion is pasty, the pallor marked, and the eyelids are œdematous. The dropsy is peculiarly obstinate. Uræmic symptoms are common, though convulsions are perhaps less frequent than in the interstitial nephritis.

The tension of the pulse is usually increased; the vessels ultimately become stiff and the heart hypertrophied, though there are instances of this form of nephritis in which the heart is not enlarged. The aortic second sound is accentuated. Retinal changes though less frequent than in the chronic interstitial nephritis, occur in a considerable number of cases.

Gastro-intestinal symptoms are common. Vomiting is frequently a distressing and serious symptom, and diarrhœa may be profuse. Ulceration of the colon may occur and prove fatal.

It is sometimes impossible to determine, even by the most careful examination of the urine or by analysis of the symptoms, whether the condition of the kidney is that of the large white or of the small white form. In cases, however, which have lasted for several years, with the progressive increase in the renal connective tissue and the cardio-vascular changes, the clinical picture may approach, in certain respects, that of the contracted kidney. The urine is increased, with low specific gravity. It is often turbid, may contain traces of blood, the tube-casts are numerous and of every variety of form and size, and the albumin is abundant. Dropsy is usually present, though not so extensive as in the early stages.

The *prognosis* is extremely grave. In a case which has persisted for more than a year recovery rarely takes place. Death is caused either by great effusion with œdema of the lungs, by uræmia, or by secondary inflammation of the serous membranes. Occasionally in children, even when the disease has persisted for two years, the symptoms disappear and recovery takes place.

Treatment.—Essentially the same treatment should be carried out as in acute Bright's disease. Milk or butter-milk should constitute the chief article of food. The dropsy should be treated by hydrotherapy. Iron preparations should be given when there is marked anæmia. It is to be remembered that the pallor of the face may not be a good index of the blood condition. Tyson thinks that the profession has been much too free in the use of iron in these cases. The acetate of potash, digitalis, and diuretin are useful in increasing the flow of urine. Basham's mixture given in plenty of water will be found beneficial.

CHRONIC INTERSTITIAL NEPHRITIS

(Contracted Kidney; Granular Kidney; Cirrhosis of the Kidney; Gouty Kidney; Renal Sclerosis).

Sclerosis of the kidney is met with (*a*) as a sequence of the large white kidney, forming the so-called pale granular or secondary contracted kidney; (*b*) as an independent primary affection; (*c*) as a sequence of arterio-sclerosis.

Etiology.—The primary form is chronic from the outset, and is a slow, creeping degeneration of the kidney substance—in many respects only an anticipation of the gradual changes which take place in the organ in extreme old age. In many cases no satisfactory cause can be assigned. In others there are hereditary influences, as in the remarkable family studied by Dickinson, in which a pronounced tendency to chronic Bright's disease occurred in four generations. Families in which the arteries tend to degenerate early are more prone to interstitial nephritis. Syphilis is held by some to be a cause. Alcohol probably plays an important part, particularly in conjunction with other factors. Among the better classes in this country chronic Bright's disease is very common, and is, I believe, caused more frequently by overeating than by excesses in alcohol. Some believe excessive use of meat is injurious, since it increases the materials out of which uric acid is formed. By many a functional disorder of the liver, leading to lithæmia, is regarded as the most efficient factor. It is quite possible that in persons who habitually eat and drink too much the work thrown upon this organ is excessive, and the elaboration of certain materials is so defective that in their excretion from the general circulation they irritate the kidneys.

Actual gout, which in England is a common cause of interstitial nephritis, is not an important factor here. On the other hand, the nutritional disorder known as lithæmia is very common, either with or without dyspepsia. Lead, as is well known, may produce renal sclerosis, but it is a minor factor in comparison with other causes. It is doubtful if climate has any influence. Purdy regards the cold, moist regions of the Northeastern States as specially favorable to the disease.

Other factors which may account for the prevalence of chronic Bright's disease in the better classes in this country may be the intense worry and strain of business, combined, as they often are, with habits of hurried and excessive eating and a lack of proper exercise. Males are more commonly attacked than females. Under twenty-five years of age it is a rare disease; between twenty-five and forty a few well-marked cases occur; between forty and sixty it is common.

Morbid Anatomy.—The kidneys are usually small, and together may weigh no more than an ounce and a half. The capsule is thick and adherent; the surface of the organ irregular and covered with small nodules, which have given to it the name of granular kidney. In stripping off the capsule, portions of the kidney substance are removed. Small cysts are frequently seen on the surface. The color is usually reddish, often a very dark red. On section the substance is tough and resists cutting; the cortex is thin and may measure no more than a couple of millimetres. The pyramids are less wasted. The small arteries are greatly thickened and stand out prominently. The fat about the pelvis is greatly increased.

Microscopically there is seen a marked increase in the connective tissue and degeneration and atrophy of the secreting structures, glomerular and tubal, the former predominating and giving the main characters to the lesion. The following are the most important changes:

(*a*) An increase in the fibrous elements, widely distributed throughout the organ, but more advanced in the cortex, particularly in the tissue between the medullary rays. In the pyramids the distribution of new growth is less patchy and more diffuse. In the early stages of the process there is a small-celled infiltration between the tubes and around the glomeruli, and finally this becomes fibrillated and is seen encircling the tubules and Bowman's capsules, around the latter often forming concentric layers.

(*b*) The changes in the glomeruli are striking, and in advanced cases a very considerable number of them have undergone complete atrophy and are represented as densely encapsulated hyaline structures. The atrophy is partly due to changes in the capillary walls and multiplication of cells between the loops, partly to extensive hyaline degeneration, and in part, no doubt, to the alterations in the afferent vessels. The normal glomeruli usually show some thickening of the capsule and increase in the cells of the tufts.

(*c*) The tubules show changes in the epithelium, which vary a good deal in different localities. Where the connective-tissue growth is most advanced they are greatly atrophied and the epithelium may be represented by small cubical cells. In other instances the epithelium has entirely disappeared. On the other hand, in the regions represented by the projecting granules the tubules are usually dilated, and the epithelium shows hyaline, fatty, and granular changes. Very many of them contain dark masses of epithelial *débris* and tube-casts. In the interstitial tissue and in the tubules there may be pigmentary changes due to hæmorrhage. The dilatation of the tubules may reach an extreme grade, forming definite cysts.

(*d*) The arteries show an advanced sclerosis. The intima is greatly thickened and there are changes in the adventitia and in the media, consisting in increase in the thickness due to proliferation of the connective tissue, in the latter coat at the expense of the muscular elements.

The view most generally entertained at present is that the essential lesion is in the secreting tissues of the tubules and the glomeruli, and that the connective-tissue overgrowth is secondary to this. Greenfield holds that the primary change is in most instances in the glomeruli, to which both the degeneration in the epithelium of the convoluted tubules and the increase in the intertubular connective tissue are secondary.

Associated with contracted kidney are general arterio-sclerosis and hypertrophy of the heart. The changes in the arteries have already been described in the section on arterio-sclerosis. The hypertrophy of the heart is constant, and the enlargement may reach an extreme grade. Variations depend, no doubt, in part upon the extent of the diffuse arterial degeneration, but there are instances in which the term *cor bovinum* may be applied to the enlarged organ. In such cases the hypertrophy is not confined to the left ventricle, but involves the entire heart. The explanation of this hypertrophy has been much discussed. It was at first held to be due to the increased work thrown upon the organ in driving the impure blood through the capillary system. Basing his opinion upon the supposed muscular increase in the smaller arteries, Johnson regarded the hypertrophy as an effort to overcome a sort of stop-cock action of these vessels, which, under the influence of the irritating ingredient in the blood, contracted and increased greatly the peripheral resistance. Traube believed that the obliteration of a large number of capillary territories in the kidney materially raised the arterial pressure, and in this way led to the hypertrophy of the heart; an additional factor, he thought, was the diminished excretion of water, which also heightened the pressure within the blood-vessels.

With our present knowledge the most satisfactory explanation is that given by Cohnheim, which is thus clearly and succinctly put by Fagge: " He gives reasons for thinking that the activity of the circulation through the kidneys at any moment—in other words, the state of the smaller renal arteries as regards contraction or dilatation—depends not (as in the case of the tissues generally) upon the need of those organs for blood, but solely upon the amount of material for the urinary secretion that the circulatory fluid happens then to contain. This suggestion has bearings . . . upon the development of hypertrophy in one kidney when the other has been entirely destroyed. But another consequence deducible from it is that when parts of both kidneys have undergone atrophy, the blood-flow to the parts that remain must, *cæteris paribus*, be as great as it would have been to the whole of the organs if they had been intact. But in order that such a quantity of blood should pass through the restricted capillary area now open to it, an excessive pressure must obviously be necessary. This can be brought to bear only by the exertion of more than the normal degree of force on the part of the left ventricle, combined with the maintenance of a corresponding resistance in all other districts of the arterial system. And so one can account at once for the high arterial pressure and for the cardio-vascular changes that are secondary to it."

Symptoms.—Perhaps a majority of the cases are latent, and are not recognized until the occurrence of one of the serious or fatal complications. Even an advanced grade of contracted kidney may be compatible with great mental and bodily activity. There may have been no symptoms whatever to suggest to the patient the existence of a serious malady. In other cases the general health is disturbed. The patient complains of lassitude, is sleepless, has to get up at night to micturate; the digestion is disordered, the tongue is furred; there are complaints of headache, failing vision, and breathlessness on exertion.

So complex and varied is the clinical picture of chronic Bright's disease that it will be best to consider the symptoms under the various systems.

Urinary System.—The amount of urine is usually increased, and from 2 to 4 litres may be passed. Frequently the patient has to get up two or three times during the night to empty the bladder, and there is increased thirst. It is for these symptoms occasionally that relief is sought. It is to be remembered, however, that frequent micturition at night may be associated with irritability of the prostate and, in certain cases, with super-acidity of the urine. The secretion is clear, the mucous cloud is well marked, but there is no definite sediment. The color is a light yellow, and the specific gravity ranges from 1.005 to 1.012. Persistent low specific gravity is one of the most constant and important features of the disease. Traces of albumin are found, but may be absent at times, particularly in the early morning urine. It is often simply a slight cloudiness, and may be apparent only with the more delicate tests. The sediment is scanty, and in it a few hyaline or granular casts are found. The quantity of the solid constituents of the urine is, as a rule, diminished, though in some instances the urea may be excreted in full amount. In attacks of dyspepsia or bronchitis, or in the later stages when the heart fails, the quantity of albumin may be greatly increased and the urine diminished. Occasionally blood occurs in the urine, and there may even be hæmaturia (S. West). Slight leakage, represented by the constant presence of a few red cells, may be present early in the disease and persist for years. In other instances there may be, particularly after exercise, flecks of blood in a pale, smoky urine.

Circulatory System.—The pulse is hard, the tension increased, and the vessel wall, as a rule, thickened. As already mentioned, a distinction must be made between increased tension and thickening of the arterial wall. The tension may be plus in a normal vessel, but in chronic Bright's disease it is more common to have increased tension in a stiff artery.

A pulse of increased tension has the following characters: It is hard and incompressible, requiring a good deal of force to overcome it; it is persistent, and in the intervals between the beats the vessel feels full and can be rolled beneath the finger. These characters may be present in a vessel the walls of which are little, if at all, increased in thickness. To estimate the latter the pulse wave should be obliterated in the radial, and the vessel wall felt beyond it. In a perfectly normal vessel the arterial coats, under these circumstances, cannot be differentiated from the surrounding tissue; whereas, if thickened, the vessel can be rolled beneath the finger. Persistent high tension is one of the earliest and most important symptoms of interstitial nephritis. The cardiac features are equally important, though often less obvious. Hypertrophy of the left ventricle occurs to overcome the resistance offered in the arteries. The enlargement of the heart ultimately becomes more general. The apex is displaced downward and to the left; the impulse is forcible and may be heaving. In elderly persons with emphysema, the displacement of the apex may not be evident. The first sound at the apex may be duplicated; more commonly the second sound at the aortic cartilage is accentuated, a very characteristic sign of increased tension. The sound in extreme cases may have a bell-like quality. In many cases a systolic murmur develops at the apex, probably as a result of relative insufficiency. It may be loud and transmitted to the axilla. Finally the hypertrophy fails, the heart becomes dilated, gallop rhythm is present, and the general condition is that of a chronic heart-lesion.

Respiratory System.—Sudden œdema of the glottis may occur. Effusion into the pleuræ or sudden œdema of the lungs may prove fatal. Acute pleurisy and pneumonia are not uncommon. Bronchitis is a frequent accompaniment, particularly in the winter. Sudden attacks of oppressed breathing, particularly at night, are not infrequent. This is often a uræmic symptom, but is sometimes cardiac. The patient may sit up in bed and gasp for breath, as in true asthma. Cheyne-Stokes breathing may be present, most commonly toward the close, but the patient may be walking about and even attending to his occupation.

Digestive System.—Dyspepsia and loss of appetite are common. Severe and uncontrollable vomiting may be the first symptom. This is usually regarded as a manifestation of uræmia, but it may be present without any other indications, and I have known it to prove fatal without any suspicion that chronic Bright's disease was present. Severe and even fatal diarrhœa may develop. The tongue may be coated and the breath heavy and urinous.

Nervous System.—Various cerebral manifestations have already been mentioned under uræmia. Headache, sometimes of the migraine type, may be an early and persistent feature of chronic Bright's disease. Cerebral apoplexy is closely related to interstitial nephritis. The hæmorrhage may take place into the meninges or the cerebrum. It is usually associated with marked changes in the vessels. Neuralgias, in various regions, are not uncommon.

Special Senses.—Troubles in vision may be the first symptom of the disease. It is remarkable in how many cases of interstitial nephritis the condition is diagnosed first by the ophthalmic surgeon. The flame-shaped retinal hæmorrhages are the most common. Less frequent is diffuse retinitis or papillitis. Sudden blindness may supervene without retinal changes— uræmic amaurosis. Diplopia is a rare event. I have seen but one case. Knies says that it is frequent. Auditory troubles are by no means infrequent in chronic Bright's disease. Ringing in the ears, with dizziness, is not uncommon. Various forms of deafness may occur.

Skin.—Œdema is not common in interstitial nephritis. Slight puffiness of the ankles may be present, but in a majority of the cases dropsy does not supervene. When extensive, it is almost always the result of gradual failure of the hypertrophied heart. The skin is often dry and pale, and sweats are not common. In some instances the sweat may deposit a white frost of urea on the surface of the skin. Eczema is a common accompaniment of chronic interstitial nephritis. Tingling of the fingers or numbness and pallor—the dead fingers—are not, as some suppose, in any way peculiar to Bright's disease. Intolerable itching of the skin may be present, and cramps in the muscles are by no means rare.

Hæmorrhages are not infrequent; thus, epistaxis may occur and prove serious. Purpura may develop. Broncho-pulmonary hæmorrhages are said, by some French writers, to be common, but no instance of it has come under my observation. Ascites is rare except in association with cirrhosis of the liver.

Diagnosis.—The autopsy often discloses the true nature of the disease, one of the many intercurrent affections of which may have proved fatal. The early stages of interstitial nephritis are not recognizable. In a patient with increased pulse tension (particularly if the vessel wall is sclerotic), with the apex beat of the heart dislocated to the left, the second aortic sound ringing and accentuated, the urine abundant and of low specific gravity, with a trace of albumin and an occasional hyaline or granular cast, the diagnosis of interstitial nephritis may be safely made. Of all the indications, that offered by the pulse is the most important. Persistent high tension with thickening of the arterial wall in a man under fifty means that serious mischief has already taken place, that cardio-vascular changes are certainly, and renal most probably, present. It is important in the diagnosis of this condition not to rest content with a single examination of the urine. Both the evening and the morning secretion should be studied. The sediment should be collected in a conical glass, and in looking for tube-casts a large surface should be examined with a tolerably low power and little light. The arterio-sclerotic kidney may exist for a long time without the occurrence of albumin, or the albumin may be in very small quantities. In many cases it is impossible to differentiate the primary interstitial nephritis from an arterio-sclerotic kidney, nor clinically is it of any special value so to do. In persons under forty, with very high tension, great thickening of the superficial arteries, and marked hypertrophy of the heart, the renal are more likely to be secondary to the arterial changes.

Prognosis.—Chronic Bright's disease is an incurable affection, and the anatomical conditions on which it depends are quite as much beyond the reach of medicines as wrinkled skin or gray hair. Interstitial nephritis, however, is compatible with the enjoyment of life for many years, and it is now universally recognized that increased tension, thickening of the arterial walls, and polyuria with a small quantity of albumin, neither doom a man to death within a short time nor necessarily interfere with the pursuits of an active life so long as proper care be taken. I know patients who have had high tension and a little albumin in the urine with hyaline casts for ten, twelve, and, in one instance, fifteen years. Serious indications are the development of uræmic symptoms, dilatation of the heart, the onset of serous effusions, the development of Cheyne-Stokes breathing, persistent vomiting, and diarrhœa.

Treatment.—Patients without local indications or in whom the condition has been accidentally discovered should so regulate their lives as to throw the least possible strain upon heart, arteries, and kidneys. A quiet life without mental worry, with gentle but not excessive exercise, and residence in an equable climate, should be recommended. In addition they should be told to keep the bowels regular, the skin active by a daily tepid bath with friction, and the urinary secretion free by drinking daily a definite amount of either distilled water or some pleasant mineral water. Alcohol should be strictly prohibited. Tea and coffee are allowable.

The diet should be light and nourishing, and the patient should be warned not to eat excessively, and not to take meat more than once a day. Care in food and drink is probably the most important element in the treatment of these early cases.

A patient in good circumstances may be urged to go away during the winter months, or, if necessary, to move altogether to a warm equable climate, like that of Southern California. There is no doubt of the value in these cases of removal from the changeable, irregular weather which prevails in the temperate regions from November until April.

At this period medicines are not required unless for certain special symptoms. Patients derive much benefit from an annual visit to certain mineral springs, such as Poland, Bedford, Saratoga, in this country, and Vichy and others in Europe. Mineral waters have no curative influence upon chronic Bright's disease; they simply help the interstitial circulation and keep the drains flushed. In this early stage, when the patient's condition is good, the tension not high, and the quantity of albumin small, medicines are not indicated, since no remedies are known to have the slightest influence upon the progress of the disease. Sooner or later symptoms arise which demand treatment. Of these the following are the most important:

(a) *Greatly Increased Arterial Tension.*—It is to be remembered that a certain increase of tension is not only necessary but unavoidable in chronic Bright's disease, and probably the most serious danger is too great lowering of the blood tension. The happy medium must be sought between such heightened tension as throws a serious strain upon the heart and risks rupture of the vessels and the low tension which, under these circumstances, is specially liable to be associated with serous effusions. In cases with persistent high tension the diet should be light, an occasional saline purge should be given, and sweating promoted by means of hot air or the hot bath. If these measures do not suffice, nitroglycerin may be tried, beginning with 1 minim of the 1-per-cent solution three times a day, and gradually increasing the dose if necessary. Patients vary so much in susceptibility to this drug that in each case it must be tested, the limit of dosage being that at which the patient experiences the physiological effect. As much as 10 minims of the 1-per-cent solution may be given three times a day. In many case I have given it in much larger doses for weeks at a time. I have never seen any ill effects from it. If the dose is excessive the patients complain at once of flushing or headache. Its use may be kept up for six or seven weeks, then stopped for a week and resumed. Its value is seen not only in the reduction of the tension, but also in the striking manner in which it relieves the headache, dizziness, and dyspnœa.

(b) More or less *anæmia* is present in advanced cases, and is best met by the use of iron. Weir Mitchell, who has had a unique experience in certain forms of chronic Bright's disease, gives the tincture of the perchloride of iron in large doses—from half a drachm to a drachm three times a day. He thinks that it not only benefits the anæmia, but that it also is an important means of reducing the arterial tension.

(c) Many patients with Bright's disease present themselves for treatment with signs of cardiac dilatation; there is a gallop rhythm or the heart sounds have a fœtal character, the breath is short, the urine scanty and highly albuminous, and there are signs of local dropsy. In these cases the treatment must be directed to the heart. A morning dose of salts or calomel may be given, and digitalis in 10-minim doses, three or four times a day. Strychnia may be used with benefit in this condition. In some instances other cardiac tonics may be necessary, but as a rule the digitalis acts promptly and well.

(d) *Uræmic Symptoms.*—Even before marked manifestations are present there may be extreme restlessness, mental wandering, a heavy, foul breath, and a coated tongue. Headache is not often complained of, though intense frontal headache may be an early symptom of uræmia. In this condition, too, the patient may complain of palpitation, feelings of numbness, and sometimes nocturnal cramps. For these symptoms the saline purgatives should be ordered, and hot baths, so as to induce copious sweating. Grandin states that irrigation of the bowel with water at a temperature from 120° to 150° is most useful. Nitroglycerin also may be freely used to reduce the tension. For the uræmic convulsions, if severe, inhalations of chloroform may be used. If the patient is robust and full-blooded, from 12 to 20 ounces of blood should be removed. The patient should be freely sweated, and if the convulsions tend to recur chloral may be given, either by the mouth or per rectum, or, better still, morphia. Uræmic coma must be treated by active purgation, and sweating should be promoted by the use of pilocarpine or the hot bath. For the restlessness and delirium morphia is indispensable. Since its recommendation in uræmic states some years ago, by Stephen MacKenzie, I have used this remedy extensively and can speak of its great value in these cases. I have never seen ill effects or any tendency to coma follow. It is of special value in the dyspnœa and Cheyne-Stokes breathing of advanced arterio-sclerosis with chronic uræmia.

VIII. AMYLOID DISEASE.

Amyloid (lardaceous or waxy) degeneration of the kidneys is simply an event in the process of chronic Bright's disease, most commonly in the chronic parenchymatous nephritis following fevers, or of cachectic states. It has no claim to be regarded as one of the varieties of Bright's disease. The affection of the kidneys is generally a part of a widespread amyloid degeneration occurring in prolonged suppuration, as in disease of the bone, in syphilis, tuberculosis, and occasionally leukæmia, lead poisoning, and gout. It varies curiously in frequency in different localities.

Anatomically the amyloid kidney is large and pale, the surface smooth, and the venæ stellatæ well marked. On section the cortex is large and may show a peculiar glistening, infiltrated appearance, and the glomeruli are very distinct. The pyramids, in striking contrast to the cortex, are of a deep red color. A section soaked in dilute tincture of iodine shows spots of a walnut or mahogany brown color. The Malpighian tufts and the straight vessels may be most affected. In lardaceous disease of the kidneys the organs are not always enlarged. They may be normal in size or small, pale, and granular. The amyloid change is first seen in the Malpighian tufts, and then involves the afferent and efferent vessels and the straight vessels. It may be confined entirely to them. In later stages of the disease the tubules are affected, chiefly the membrane, rarely, if ever, the cells themselves. In addition, the kidneys always show signs of diffuse nephritis. The Bowman's capsules are thickened, there may be glomerulitis, and the tubal epithelium is swollen, granular, and fatty.

Symptoms.—The renal features alone may not indicate the presence of this degeneration. Usually the associated condition gives a hint of the nature of the process. The urine, as a rule, shows important changes; the quantity is increased, and it is pale, clear, and of low specific gravity. The albumin is usually abundant, but it may be scanty, and in rare instances absent. Possibly the variations in the situation of the amyloid changes may account for this, since albumin is less likely to be present when the change is confined to the vasa recta. In addition to ordinary albumin globulin may be present. The tube-casts are variable, usually hyaline, often fatty or finely granular. Occasionally the amyloid reaction can be detected in the hyaline casts. Dropsy is present in many instances, particularly when there is much anæmia or profound cachexia. It is not, however, an invariable symptom, and there are cases in which it does not develop. Diarrhœa is a common accompaniment.

Increased arterial tension and cardiac hypertrophy are not usually present, except in those cases in which amyloid degeneration occurs in the secondary contracted kidney; under which circumstances there may be uræmia and retinal changes, which, as a rule, are not met with in other forms.

Diagnosis.—By the condition of the urine alone it is not possible to recognize amyloid changes in the kidney. Usually, however, there is no difficulty, since the Bright's disease comes on in association with syphilis, prolonged suppuration, disease of the bone, or tuberculosis, and there is evidence of enlargement of the liver and spleen. A suspicious circumstance is the existence of polyuria with a large amount of albumin in the urine, or when, in these constitutional affections, a large quantity of clear, pale urine is passed, even without the presence of albumin.

The prognosis depends rather on the condition with which the nephritis is associated. As a rule it is grave.

The treatment of the condition is that of chronic Bright's disease.

IX. PYELITIS

(*Consecutive Nephritis; Pyelonephritis; Pyonephrosis*).

Definition.—Inflammation of the pelvis of the kidney and the conditions which result from it.

Etiology.—Pyelitis is induced by many causes, among which the following are the most important: (*a*) The irritation of calculi—a very frequent cause. (*b*) Tubercle. (*c*) The infectious pyelitis which develops in fevers, in which an acute inflammation of the pelvis of the kidney may occur, sometimes hæmorrhagic in character, more frequently diphtheritic. (*d*) The presence of decomposing urine, following pressure upon the ureter by tumors or bladder-disease. By far the most frequent form of pyelitis is that which is consecutive to cystitis, from whatever cause. In these cases the inflammation may not be confined to the pelvis, but pass to the kidney, inducing pyelonephritis. (*e*) Occasional causes are cancer, hydatids, the ova of certain parasites, and, according to some, the irritation of the saccharine urine of diabetes, and the irritation of turpentine or cubebs. (*f*) A primary pyelitis or pyelonephritis has been described as coming on after cold or overexertion, but such cases are extremely rare. The condition is met with in children (Holt), and in one case which I saw with Holmes, of Chatham, the pus and the chills, after recurring at intervals for many months, disappeared after circumcising the boy, who had a very narrow prepuce. (*g*) Following attacks of Dietl's crises in movable kidney pyelitis may be present.

Morbid Anatomy.—In the early stages of pyelitis the mucous membrane is turbid, somewhat swollen, and may show ecchymoses or a grayish pseudo-membrane. The urine in the pelvis is cloudy, and, on examination, numbers of epithelial cells are seen.

In the calculous pyelitis there may be only slight turbidity of the membrane, which has been called by some catarrhal pyelitis. More commonly the mucosa is roughened, grayish in color, and thick. Under these circumstances there is almost always more or less dilatation of the calyces and flattening of the papillæ. Following this condition there may be (*a*) extension of the suppurative process to the kidney itself, forming a pyelonephritis; (*b*) a gradual dilatation of the calyces with atrophy of the kidney substance, and finally the production of the condition of pyonephrosis, in which the entire organ is represented by a sac of pus with or without a thin shell of renal tissue. (*c*) After the kidney structure has been destroyed by suppuration, if the obstruction at the orifice of the pelvis persists, the fluid portions may be absorbed and the pus become inspissated, so that the organ is represented by a series of sacculi containing grayish, putty-like masses, which may become impregnated with lime salts.

Tuberculous pyelitis, as already described, usually starts upon the apices of the pyramids, and may at first be limited in extent. Ultimately the condition produced may be similar to that of calculous pyelitis. Pyonephrosis is quite as frequent a sequence, while the final transformation of the pus into a putty-like material impregnated with salts, forming the so-called scrofulous kidney, is even commoner.

The pyelitis consecutive to cystitis is usually bilateral, and the kidney is apt to be involved, forming the so-called *surgical kidney*—acute suppurative nephritis. There are lines of suppuration extending along the pyramids, or small abscesses in the cortex, often just beneath the capsule; or there may be wedge-shaped abscesses. The pus organisms either pass up the tubules or, as Steven has shown, through the lymphatics.

Symptoms.—The forms associated with the fevers rarely cause any symptoms, even when the process is extensive. In mild grades there is pain in the back or there may be tenderness on deep pressure on the affected side. The urine is turbid, contains a few mucous and pus cells, and occasionally blood-corpuscles. The urine is acid, and there may be a trace of albumin.

Before the condition of pyuria is established there may be attacks of pain on the affected side (not amounting to the severe agony of renal colic), rigors, high fever, and sweats. Under these circumstances the urine, which may have been clear, becomes turbid or smoky from the presence of blood, and may contain large numbers of mucus cells and transitional epithelium. These cases are not common, but I have twice had opportunity of studying such attacks for a prolonged period. In one patient the occurrence of the rigor and fever could sometimes be predicted from the change in the condition of the urine. Such cases occur, I believe, in association with calculi in the pelvis.

The statement is not infrequently made that the epithelium in the urine in pyelitis is distinctive and characteristic. This is erroneous, as may be readily demonstrated by comparing scrapings of the mucosa of the renal pelvis and of the bladder. In both the epithelium belongs to what is called the transitional variety, and in both regions the same conical, fusiform and irregular cells with long tails are found.

When the pyelitis, whether calculous or tuberculous, has become chronic and discharges, the symptoms are:

(1) *Pyuria.*—The pus is in variable amount, and may be intermittent. Thus, as is often the case when only one kidney is involved, the ureter may be temporarily blocked, and normal urine is passed for a time; then there is a sudden outflow of the pent-up pus and the urine becomes purulent. Coincident with this retention, a tumor mass may be felt on the side affected. The pus has the ordinary characters, but the transitional epithelium is not so abundant at this stage and comes from the bladder or from the pelvis of the healthy side. Occasionally in rapidly advancing pyelonephritis, portions of the kidney tissue, particularly of the apices of the pyramids, may slough away and appear in the urine; or, as in a remarkable specimen shown to me by Tyson, solid cheesy moulds of the calyces are passed. Casts from the kidney tubules are sometimes present. The reaction of the urine is at first acid, and may remain so even when the pus is passed in large quantities. If it remains any time in the bladder or if cystitis exists it becomes ammoniacal. Micturition may be very frequent and irritability of the bladder may be present.

(2) Intermittent fever associated with rigors is usually present in cases of suppurative pyelitis. The chills may recur at regular intervals, and the cases are often mistaken for malaria. Owen-Rees called attention to the frequent occurrence of these rigors, which form a characteristic feature of both calculous and tuberculous pyelitis. Ultimately the fever assumes a hectic type and the rigors may cease.

(3) The general condition of the patient usually indicates prolonged suppuration. There is more or less wasting with anæmia and a progressive failure of health. Secondary abscesses may develop and the clinical picture becomes that of pyæmia. In some instances, particularly of tuberculous pyelitis, the clinical course may resemble that of typhoid fever. There are instances of pyuria recurring, at intervals, for many years without impairment of the bodily vigor.

(4) Physical examination in chronic pyelitis usually reveals tenderness on the affected side or a definite swelling, which may vary much in size and ultimately attain large dimensions if the kidney becomes enormously distended, as in pyonephrosis.

(5) Occasionally nervous symptoms, which may be associated with dyspnœa, supervene, or the termination may be by coma, not unlike that of diabetes. These have been attributed to the absorption of the decomposing materials in the urine, whence the so-called ammoniæmia. A form of paraplegia has been described in connection with some cases of abscess of the kidney, but whether due to a myelitis or to a peripheral neuritis has not yet been determined.

In suppurative nephritis or surgical kidney following cystitis, the patient complains of pain in the back, the fever becomes high, irregular, and associated with chills, and in acute cases a typhoid state develops in which death occurs.

Diagnosis.—Between the tuberculous and the calculous forms of pyelitis it may be difficult or impossible to distinguish, except by the detection of tubercle bacilli in the pus. The examination for bacilli should be made systematically in all suspicious cases. The tuberculin test may be used with advantage. From perinephric abscess pyonephrosis is distinguished by the more definite character of the tumor, the absence of œdematous swelling in the lumbar region, and, most important of all, the history of the case. The urine, too, in perinephric abscess may be free from pus. There are cases, however, in which it is difficult indeed to make a satisfactory diagnosis. A patient, whom I saw with Fussell, had had cystitis through her pregnancy, subsequently pus in the urine for several months, and then a large fluctuating abscess developed in the right lumbar region. It did not seem possible, either before or during the operation, to determine whether the case was a simple pyonephrosis or whether there had been a perinephric abscess caused by the pyelitis.

Suppurative pyelitis and cystitis are frequently confounded. I have known instances of the former in which perineal section was performed on the supposition of the existence of an intractable cystitis. The two conditions may, of course, coexist and prove puzzling, but the history, the acid character of the pus in many instances, the less frequent occurrence of ammoniacal decomposition, the local signs in one lumbar region, and the absence of pain in the bladder should be sufficient to differentiate the affections. In women, by catheterization of the ureters, it may be definitely determined whether the pus comes from the kidneys or from the bladder. The cystoscope may be used for this purpose.

Prognosis.—Cases coming on during the fevers usually recover. Tuberculous pyelitis may terminate favorably by inspissation of the pus and conversion into a putty-like substance with deposition of lime salts. When pyonephrosis develops the dangers are increased. Perforation may occur, the patient may be worn out by the hectic fever, or amyloid disease may develop.

Treatment.—In mild cases fluids should be taken freely, particularly the alkaline mineral waters, to which the citrate of potash may be added.

The treatment of the calculous form will be considered later. Practically there are no remedies which have much influence upon the pyuria. Astringents in no way control the discharge, nor have I seen the slightest benefit from buchu, copaiba, sandal-wood oil, or uva ursi. Tonics should be given, a nourishing diet, and milk and butter-milk may be taken freely. When the tumor has formed or even before it is perceptible, if the symptoms are serious and severe, the kidney should be explored, and, if necessary, nephrotomy should be performed.

X. HYDRONEPHROSIS.

Definition.—Dilatation of the pelvis and calyces of the kidney with atrophy of its substance, caused by the accumulation of non-purulent fluids, the result of obstruction.

Etiology.—The condition may be congenital, owing to some abnormality in the ureter or urethra. The tumor produced may be large enough to retard labor. Sometimes it is associated with other malformations. There is a condition of moderate dilatation, apparently congenital, which is not connected with any obstruction in the ducts. A case of the kind was shown at the Philadelphia Pathological Society by Daland.

In some instances there has been contraction or twisting of the ureter, or it has been inserted into the kidney at an acute angle or at a high level. In adult life the condition may be due to lodgment of a calculus, or to a cicatricial stricture following ulcer.

New growths, such as tubercle or cancer, occasionally induce hydronephrosis; more commonly, pressure upon the ureter from without, particularly tumors of the ovaries and uterus. Occasionally cicatricial bands compress the ureter. Obstruction within the bladder may result from cancer, from hypertrophy of the prostate with cystitis, and in the urethra from stricture. It is stated that slight grades of hydronephrosis have been found in patients with excessive polyuria.

In whatever way produced, when the ureter is blocked the secretion accumulates in the pelvis and infundibula. Sometimes acute inflammation follows, but more commonly the slow, gradual pressure causes atrophy of

55

the papillæ with gradual distention and wasting of the organ. In acquired cases from pressure, even when dilatation is extreme, there may usually be seen a thin layer of renal structure. In the most extreme stages the kidney is represented by a large cyst, which may perhaps show on its inner surface imperfect septa. The fluid is thin and yellowish in color, and contains traces of urinary salts, urea, uric acid, and sometimes albumin. The secretion may be turbid from admixture with small quantities of pus.

Total occlusion does not always lead to a hydronephrosis, but may be followed by atrophy of the kidney. It appears that when the obstruction is intermittent or not complete the greatest dilatation is apt to follow. The sac may be enormous, and cause an abdominal tumor of the largest size. The condition has even been mistaken for ascites. Enlargement of the other kidney may compensate for the defect. Hypertrophy of the left side of the heart usually follows.

Symptoms.—When small, it may not be noticed. The congenital cases when bilateral usually prove fatal within a few days; when unilateral, the tumor may not be noticed for some time. It increases progressively and has all the characters of a tumor in the renal region. In adult life many of the cases, due to pressure by tumors, as in cancer of the uterus and enlargement of the prostate, etc., give rise to no symptoms.

There are remarkable instances of *intermittent* hydronephrosis in which the tumor suddenly disappears with the discharge of a large quantity of clear fluid. The sac gradually refills, and the process may be repeated for years. In these cases the obstruction is unilateral; a cicatricial stricture exists, or a valve is present in the ureter, or the ureter enters the upper part of the pelvis. Many of the cases are in women and associated with movable kidney.

The examination of the abdomen shows, in unilateral hydronephrosis, a tumor occupying the renal region. When of moderate size it is readily recognized, but when large it may be confounded with ovarian or other tumors. In young children it may be mistaken for sarcoma of the kidney or of the retroperitoneal glands, the common cause of abdominal tumor in early life. Aspiration alone would enable us to differentiate between hydronephrosis and tumor. The large hydronephrotic sac is frequently mistaken for ovarian tumor. The latter is, as a rule, more mobile, and rarely fills the deeper portion of the lumbar region so thoroughly. The ascending colon can often be detected passing over the renal tumor, and examination per vaginam, particularly under ether, will give important indications as to the condition of the ovaries. In doubtful cases the sac should be aspirated. The fluid of the renal cyst is clear, or turbid from the presence of cell elements, rarely colloid in character; the specific gravity is low; albumin and traces of urea and uric acid are usually present; and the epithelial elements in it may be similar to those found in the pelvis of the kidney. In old sacs, however, the fluid may not be characteristic, since the urinary salts disappear, but in one case of several years' duration oxalate of lime and urea were found.

Perhaps the greatest difficulty is offered by the condition of hydronephrosis in a movable kidney. Here, the history of sudden disappearance of the tumor with the passage of a large quantity of clear fluid would be a point of great importance in the diagnosis. In those rare instances of an enormous sac filling the entire abdomen, and sometimes mistaken for ascites, the character of the fluid might be the only point of difference. The tumor of pyonephrosis may be practically the same in physical characteristics. Fever is usually present, and pus is often found in the urine. In these cases, when in doubt, exploratory puncture should be made.

The outlook in hydronephrosis depends much upon the cause. When single, the condition may never produce serious trouble, and the intermittent cases may persist for years and finally disappear. Occasionally the cyst ruptures into the peritonæum, more rarely through the diaphragm into the lung. A remarkable case of this kind was under the care of my colleague, Halsted. A man, aged twenty-one, had, from his second year, attacks of abdominal pain in which a swelling would appear between the hip and costal margin and subside with the passage of a large amount of urine. In January, 1888, the sac discharged through the right lung.* Reaccumulations occurred on several occasions, and on June 9, 1891, the sac was opened and drained. He remains well, though there is still a sinus through which a clear, probably urinous, fluid is discharged.

The sac may discharge spontaneously through the ureter and the fluid never reaccumulate. In bilateral hydronephrosis there is a danger that uræmia may supervene. There are instances, too, in which blocking of the ureter on the sound side by calculus has been followed by uræmia. And, lastly, the sac may suppurate, and the condition change to one of pyonephrosis.

Treatment.—Cases of intermittent hydronephrosis which do not cause serious symptoms should be let alone. It is stated that, in sacs of moderate size, the obstruction has been overcome by shampooing. If practised, it should be done with great care. When the sac reaches a large size aspiration may be performed and repeated if necessary. Puncture should be made in the flank, midway between the ilium and the last rib. If the fluid reaccumulates and the sac becomes large, it may be incised and drained, or, as a last resort, the kidney may be removed. In women a carefully adapted pad and bandage will sometimes prevent the recurrence of an intermittent hydronephrosis.†

XI. NEPHROLITHIASIS (*Renal Calculus*).

Definition.—The formation in the kidney or in its pelvis of concretions, by the deposition of certain of the solid constituents of the urine.

Etiology and Pathology.—In the kidney substance itself the separation of the urinary salts produces a condition to which, unfortunately, the term infarct has been applied. Three varieties may be recognized: (1) The uric-acid infarct, usually met with at the apices of the pyramids in

---

* Sowers, New York Medical Record, 1888.

† See illustrative cases in my Lectures on Abdominal Tumors, 1894.

new-born children and during the first weeks of life. It is readily recognized as a yellowish linear streak in the pyramids and is of no significance; (2) the urate of soda infarct, sometimes associated with urate of ammonia, which forms whitish lines at the apices of the pyramids and is met with chiefly, but not always, in gouty persons; and (3) the lime infarcts, forming very opaque white lines in the pyramids, usually in old people.

In the pelvis and calyces concretions of the following forms occur: (*a*) Small gritty particles, *renal sand*, ranging in size from the individual grains of the uric-acid sediment to bodies 1 or 2 mm. in diameter. These may be passed in the urine for long periods without producing any symptoms, since they are too fine to be arrested in their downward passage.

(*b*) Larger concretions, ranging in size from a small pea to a bean, and either solitary or multiple in the calyces and pelvis. It is the smaller of these calculi which, in their passage, produce the attacks of renal colic. They may be rounded and smooth, or present numerous irregular projections.

(*c*) The dendritic form of calculus. The orifice of the ureter may be blocked by a Y-shaped stone. The pelvis itself may be occupied by the concretion, which forms a more or less distinct mould. These are the remarkable *coral calculi*, which form in the pelvis complete moulds of infundibula and calyces, the latter even presenting cup-like depressions corresponding to the apices of the papillæ. Some of these casts in stone of the renal pelvis are as beautifully moulded as Hyrtl's corrosion preparations.

Chemically the varieties of calculi are: (1) Uric acid, by far the most important, which may form the renal sand, the small solitary, or the large dendritic stones. They are very hard, the surface is smooth, and the color reddish. The larger stones are usually stratified and very dense. Usually the uric acid and the urates are mixed, but in children stones composed of urates alone may occur.

(2) Oxalate of lime, which forms mulberry-shaped calculi, studded with points and spines. They are often very dark in color, intensely hard, and are a mixture of oxalate of lime and uric acid.

(3) Phosphatic calculi are composed of the phosphate of lime and the ammonio-magnesium phosphate, sometimes mixed with a small amount of carbonate of lime. They are not common, since the phosphatic salts are oftener deposited about the uric acid or the oxalate of lime stones.

(4) Rare forms of calculi are made up of cystine, xanthine, carbonate of lime, indigo, and urostealith.

The mode of formation of calculi has been much discussed. They may be produced by an excess of a sparingly soluble abnormal ingredient, such as cystine or xanthine; more frequently by the presence of uric acid in a very acid urine which favors its deposition. Sir William Roberts thus briefly states the conditions which lead to the formation of the uric-acid concretions: high acidity, poverty in salines, low pigmentation, and high percentage of uric acid. The presence of albumin and mucus may determine, as Ord suggests, the deposition of the uric acid and thus form the starting point of a stone. Ova of parasites, blood-clots, casts, and shreds of epithelium may form the nuclei of stones. The question of bacterial infection has to be considered, as in the case of gall-stones.

Renal calculi are most common in the early and later periods of life. They are moderately frequent in this country, but there do not appear to be special districts, corresponding to the "stone counties" in England. Men are more often affected than women. Sedentary occupations seem to predispose to stone.

The effects of the calculi are varied. It is by no means uncommon to find a dozen or more stones of various sizes in the calyces without any destruction of the mucous membrane or dilatation of the pelvis. A turbid urine fills the pelvis in which there are numerous cells from the epithelial lining. There are cases of this sort in which, apparently, the stones may go on forming and are passed for years without seriously impairing the health and without inconvenience, except the attacks of renal colic. Still more remarkable are the cases of coral-like calculi, which may occupy the entire pelvis and calyces without causing pyelitis, but which gradually lead to more or less induration of the kidney. The most serious effects are when the stone excites a suppurative pyelitis and pyonephrosis.

Symptoms.—Patients may pass gravel for years without having an attack of renal colic, and a stone may never lodge in the ureter. In other instances, the formation of calculi goes on year by year and the patient has recurring attacks such as have been so graphically described by Montaigne. in his own case. A patient may pass an enormous number of calculi. Some years ago I was consulted by a commercial traveller, an extremely vigorous man, who for many years had had repeated attacks of renal colic, and had passed several hundred calculi of various sizes. His collection filled an ounce bottle. A patient may pass a single calculus, and never be troubled again. The large coral calculi may excite no symptoms. In a remarkable specimen of the kind, presented to the McGill Medical Museum by J. A. Macdonald, the patient, a middle-aged woman, died suddenly with uræmic symptoms. There was no pyelitis, but the kidneys were sclerotic.

Renal colic ensues when a stone enters the ureter. An attack may set in abruptly without apparent cause, or may follow a strain in lifting. It is characterized by agonizing pain, which starts in the flank of the affected side, passes down the ureter, and is felt in the testicle and along the inner side of the thigh. The pain may also radiate through the abdomen and chest, and be very intense in the back. In severe attacks there are nausea and vomiting and the patient is collapsed. The perspiration breaks out upon the face and the pulse is feeble and quick. A chill may precede the outbreak, and the temperature may rise as high as 103°. No one has more graphically described an attack of "the stone" than Montaigne,* who was a sufferer for many years: "Thou art seen to sweat with pain, to look pale and red, to tremble, to vomit well-nigh to blood, to suffer strange contortions and convulsions, by starts to let tears drop from thine eyes, to urine thick, black, and frightful water, or to have it suppressed by some sharp and craggy stone, that cruelly pricks and tears thee." The

---

* Essays, Book III, 13.

symptoms persist for a variable period. In short attacks they do not last longer than an hour; in other instances they continue for a day or more, with temporary relief. Micturition is frequent, occasionally painful, and the urine, as a rule, is bloody. There are instances in which a large amount of clear urine is passed, probably from the other kidney. In rare cases the secretion of urine is completely suppressed, even when the kidney on the opposite side is normal, and death may occur from uræmia. This most frequently happens when the second kidney is extensively diseased, or when only a single kidney exists. A number of cases of this kind have been recorded. The condition has been termed, by Sir William Roberts, obstructive suppression. It is met with also when cancer compresses both ureters or involves their orifices in the bladder. The patient may not appear to be seriously ill at first, and uræmic symptoms may not develop for a week, when twitching of the muscles, great restlessness, and sometimes drowsiness supervene, but, strange to say, neither convulsions nor coma. Death takes place usually within twelve days from the onset of the obstruction.

After the attack of colic has passed there is more or less aching on the affected side, and the patient can usually tell from which kidney the stone has come. Examination during the attack is usually negative. Very rarely the kidney becomes palpable. Tenderness on the affected side is common. In very thin persons it may be possible, on examination of the abdomen, to feel the stone in the ureter; or the patient may complain of a grating sensation.

When the calculi remain in the kidney they may produce very definite and characteristic symptoms, of which the following are the most important:

(1) *Pain*, usually in the back, which is often no more than a dull soreness, but which may be severe and come on in paroxysms. It is usually on the side affected, but may be referred to the opposite kidney, and there are instances in which the pain has been confined to the sound side. Pains of a similar nature may occur in movable kidneys, and there arc several instances on record in which surgeons have incised the kidney for stone and found none. In an instance in which pain was present for a couple of years the exploration revealed only a contracted kidney.

(2) *Hæmaturia.*—Although this occurs most frequently when the stone becomes engaged in the ureter, it may also come on when the stones are in the pelvis. The bleeding is seldom profuse, as in cancer, but in some instances may persist for a long time. It is aggravated by exertion and lessened by rest. Frequently it only gives to the urine a smoky hue. The urine may be free for days, and then a sudden exertion or a prolonged ride may cause smokiness, or blood may be passed in considerable quantities.

(3) *Pyelitis.*—(a) There may be attacks of severe pain in the back, not amounting to actual colic, which are initiated by a heavy chill followed by fever, in which the temperature may reach 104° or 105°, followed by profuse sweating. The urine, which has been clear, may become turbid and smoky and contain blood and abundant epithelium from the pelvis. Attacks of this description may recur at intervals for months or even

years, and are generally mistaken for malaria, unless special attention is paid to the urine and to the existence of the pain in the back. This renal intermittent fever, due to the presence of calculi, is analogous to the hepatic intermittent fever, due to gall-stones, and in both it is important to remember that the most intense paroxysms may occur without any evidence of suppuration.

(b) More frequently the symptoms of purulent pyelitis, which have already been described, are present; pain in the renal region, recurring chills, and pus in the urine, with or without indications of pyonephrosis.

(4) *Pyuria.*—There are instances of stone in the kidney in which pus occurs continuously or intermittently in the urine for many years. On many occasions between 1875 and 1884 I examined the urine of a physician who had passed calculi when a student in 1845, and has had pus in the urine at intervals to 1891. In spite of the prolonged suppuration he has had remarkable mental and bodily vigor.

Patients with stone in the kidney are often robust, high livers, and gouty. Attacks of dyspepsia are not uncommon, or they may have severe headaches.

Diagnosis.—Renal may be mistaken for intestinal colic, particularly if the distention of the bowels is marked, or for biliary colic. The situation and direction of the pain, the retraction and tenderness of the testicle, the occurrence of hæmaturia, and the altered character of the urine are distinctive features. Attention may again be called to the fact that attacks simulating renal colic are associated with movable kidney, or even, it has been supposed, without mobility of the kidney, with the accumulation of the oxalates or uric acid in the pelvis of the kidney. The diagnosis between a stone in the kidney and stone in the bladder is not always easy, though in the latter the pain is particularly about the neck of the bladder, and not limited to one side. Important points are the reaction of the urine, which in stone in the bladder is almost invariably alkaline, and the abundance of mucus with the pus. It is stated that certain differences occur in the symptoms produced by different sorts of calculi. The large uric-acid calculi less frequently produce severe symptoms. On the other hand, as the oxalate of lime is a rougher calculus, it is apt to produce more pain (often of a radiating character) than the lithic-acid form, and to cause hæmorrhage. In both these forms the urine is acid. The phosphatic calculi are stated to produce the most intense pain, and the urine is commonly alkaline. In a few cases the Roentgen rays have been of use in determining the presence of a stone.

Treatment.—In the attacks of renal colic great relief is experienced by the hot bath, which is sometimes sufficient to relax the spasm. When the pain is very intense morphia should be given hypodermically, and inhalations of chloroform may be necessary until the effects of the anodyne are manifest. Local applications are sometimes grateful—hot poultices, or cloths wrung out of hot water. The patient may drink freely of hot lemonade, soda water, or barley water. Occasionally change in posture will give great relief, and inversion of the patient is said to be followed by immediate cessation of the pain.

In the intervals the patient should, as far as possible, live a quiet life, avoiding sudden exertion of all sorts. The essential feature in the treatment is to keep the urine abundant and, in a majority of the cases, alkaline. The patient should drink daily a large but definite quantity of mineral waters * or distilled water, which is just as satisfactory. The citrate or bicarbonate of potash may be added. The aching pains in the back are often greatly relieved by this treatment. Many patients find benefit from a stay at Saratoga, Bedford, Poland, or other mineral springs in this country, or at Vichy or Ems in Europe.

The diet should be carefully regulated, and similar to that indicated in the early stages of gout. Sir William Roberts recommends what is known as the solvent treatment for uric-acid calculi. The citrate of potash is given in large doses, half a drachm to a drachm, every three hours in a tumblerful of water. This should be kept up for several months. I have had no success with this treatment, nor, when one considers the character of the uric-acid stones usually met with in the kidney, does it seem likely that any solvent action could be exercised upon them by changes in the urine. This treatment should be abandoned if the urine becomes ammoniacal.

The value of piperazine as a solvent of uric-acid gravel or of uric-acid stones has been much discussed of late. While outside the body a watery solution of the drug has this power in a marked degree, the amount excreted in the urine as given in the ordinary doses of 15 grains daily seems to have very little influence. Several observers have shown that the percentage of piperazine excreted in the urine, when taken in doses of from 1 to 2 grammes, has, when tested outside of the body, little or no influence as a solvent (Fawcett, Gordon).

XII. TUMORS OF THE KIDNEY.

These are benign and malignant. Of the benign tumors, the most common are the small nodular *fibromata* which occur frequently in the pyramids, the *aberrant adrenals*, which Grawitz has described, and occasionally *lipoma, angioma,* or *lymphadenoma*. The *adenomata* may be congenital. In one of my cases the kidneys were greatly enlarged, contained small cysts, and numerous adenomatous structures throughout both organs.

Malignant growths—*cancer* or *sarcoma*—may be either primary or secondary. The sarcomata are the most common, either alveolar sarcoma or the remarkable form containing striped muscular fibres—rhabdo-myoma. They are very common tumors in children. G. Walker (Annals of Surgery, 1897) has analyzed the literature of the subject to date. Carcinoma is less frequent, and is of the encephaloid variety.

The tumors attain a very large size. In one of my cases the left kidney weighed 12 pounds and almost filled the abdomen. In children they may

---

* Some of these, if we judge by the laudatory reports, are as potent as the waters of Corsena, declared by Montaigne to be "powerful enough to break stones."

reach an enormous size. Morris states that in a boy at the Middlesex Hospital the tumor weighed 31 pounds. They grow rapidly, are often soft, and hæmorrhage frequently takes place into them. In the sarcomata, invasion of the pelvis or of the renal vein is common. The rhabdo-myomas rarely form very large tumors, and death occurs shortly after birth. In one of my cases the child lived to the age of three years and a half. The tumor grew into the renal vein and inferior cava. A detached fragment passed as an embolus into the pulmonary artery, and a portion of it blocked the tricuspid orifice.

Symptoms.—The following are the most important: (1) Hæmaturia. This may be the first indication. The blood is fluid or clotted, and there may be very characteristic moulds of the pelvis of the kidney and of the ureter. It would no doubt be possible for such to form in the hæmaturia from calculus, but I have never met with a case of blood-casts of the pelvis and of the ureter, either alone or together, except in cancer. It is rare indeed that cancer elements can be recognized in the urine.

(2) Pain is an uncertain symptom. In several of the largest tumors which have come under my observation there has been no discomfort from beginning to close. When present, it is of a dragging, dull character, situated in the flank and radiating down the thigh. The passage of the clots may cause great pain. In a recent case the growth was at first upward, and the symptoms for some months were those of pleurisy.

(3) Progressive emaciation. The loss of flesh is usually marked and advances rapidly. There may, however, be a very large tumor without emaciation.

Physical Signs.—In almost all instances tumor is present. When small and on the right side, it may be very movable; in some instances, occupying a position in the iliac fossa, it has been mistaken for ovarian tumor. The large growths fill the flank and gradually extend toward the middle line, occupying the right or left half of the abdomen. Inspection may show two or three hemispherical projections corresponding to distended sections of the organ. In children the abdomen may reach an enormous size and the veins are prominent and distended. On bimanual palpation the tumor is felt to occupy the lumbar region and can usually be lifted slightly from its bed; in some cases it is very movable, even when large; in others it is fixed, firm, and solid. The respiratory movements have but slight influence upon it. Rapidly growing renal tumors are soft, and on palpation may give a sense of fluctuation. A point of considerable importance is the fact that the colon crosses the tumor, and can usually be detected without difficulty.

Diagnosis.—In children very large abdominal tumors are either renal or retroperitoneal. The retroperitoneal sarcoma (Lobstein's cancer) is more central, but may attain as large a size. If the case is seen only toward the end, a differential diagnosis may be impossible; but as a rule the sarcoma is less movable. It is to be remembered that these tumors may invade the kidney. On the left side an enlarged spleen is readily distinguished, as the edge is very distinct and the notch or notches well marked; it descends during respiration, and the colon lies behind, not in front of it. On the

56

right side growths of the liver are occasionally confounded with renal tumors; but such instances are rare, and there can usually be detected a zone of resonance between the upper margin of the renal tumor and the ribs. Late in the disease, however, this is not possible, for the renal tumor is in close union with the liver.

A malignant growth in a movable kidney may be very deceptive and may simulate cancer of the ovary or myoma of the uterus. The great mobility upward of the renal growth and the negative result of examination of the pelvic viscera are the reliable points.

Medicinal treatment is of no avail. When the growth is small and the patient in good condition removal of the organ may be undertaken, but the percentage of cases of recovery is very small, only 5.4 per cent (G. Walker).

XIII. CYSTIC DISEASE OF THE KIDNEY.

The following varieties of cysts are met with:

(1) The small cysts, already described in connection with the chronic nephritis, which result from dilatation of obstructed tubules or of Bowman's capsules. There are cases very difficult to classify, in which the kidneys are greatly enlarged, and very cystic in middle-aged or elderly persons, and yet not so large as in the congenital form.

(2) Solitary cysts, ranging in size from a marble to an orange, or even larger, are occasionally found in kidneys which present no other changes. In exceptional cases, they may form tumors of considerable size. Newman operated on one which contained 25 ounces of blood. They, too, in all probability, result from obstruction.

(3) The congenital cystic kidneys. In this remarkable condition the kidneys are represented by a conglomeration of cysts, varying in size from a pea to a marble. The organs are greatly enlarged, and together may weigh 6 or more pounds. In the fœtus they may attain a size sufficient to impede labor. Little or no renal tissue may be noticeable, although in microscopical sections it is seen that a considerable amount remains in the interspaces. The cysts contain a clear or turbid fluid, sometimes reddish brown or even blackish in color, and may be of a colloidal consistence. Albumin, blood crystals, cholesterin, with triple phosphates and fat drops are found in the contents. Urea and uric acid are rarely present. The cysts are lined by a flattened epithelium. It is not yet accurately known how these cysts originate. That it is a defect in development rather than a pathological change is suggested by the fact that in the embryo it is often associated with other anomalies, particularly imperforate anus. Both Shattock and Bland Sutton, who have studied the question carefully, believe that the anomaly of development is in the failure of complete differentiation of the Wolffian bodies, which are, as it were, mixed with the kidneys and give rise to the cysts. Though the condition is congenital, yet from the history of certain cases it is evident that the organs must increase enormously in size. In a patient of Dr. Alfred King's, of Portland, Me., a man aged fifty-four, the abdomen presented nothing abnormal on careful

examination three years before his death, but three months prior to this date there were large bilateral tumors in the renal regions, which were readily diagnosed as cystic kidneys. The organs weighed 4 pounds each.

In a large majority of the cases death occurs, either *in utero* or shortly after birth; but instances are met with at all ages up to fifty or sixty, and I see no reason to suppose that these are not instances of persistence of the congenital form.

In the adult the tumors may be felt in the lumbar region as large rounded masses.

The *symptoms* are those of chronic interstitial nephritis. Many of the cases have presented no indications whatever until a sudden attack of uræmia; others have died of heart-failure. A rare termination, as in a case at the University Hospital, Philadelphia, is the rupture of one of the cysts and the production of a perinephritic abscess. The cardio-vascular changes induced are similar to those of interstitial nephritis. The left ventricle is hypertrophied and the arterial tension is greatly increased. The condition is compatible with excellent health. Hæmaturia may occur. The dangers are those associated with chronic Bright's disease. It is important to remember that the conglomerate cystic kidney is almost invariably bilateral. One kidney may be somewhat larger and more cystic than the other.

The diagnosis can sometimes be made. Great enlargement of both organs, with hypertrophy of the left heart and increased arterial tension, would suggest the condition.

Operative interference is not justifiable. I know of an instance in which one kidney was removed and the patient died within twenty-four hours.

(4) Occasionally the kidneys and liver present numerous small cysts scattered through the substance. The spleen and the thyroid also may be involved, and there may be congenital malformation of the heart. The cysts in the kidney are small, and neither so numerous nor so thickly set as in the conglomerate form, though in these cases the condition is probably the result of some congenital defect. There are cases, however, in which the kidneys are very large. It is more common in the lower animals than in man. I have seen several instances of it in the hog; in one case the liver weighed 40 pounds, and was converted into a mass of simple cysts. The kidneys were less involved. Charles Kennedy * states that he has found references to 12 cases of combined cystic disease of the liver and kidneys.

The echinococcus cysts have been described under the section on parasites. Paranephric cysts (external to the capsule) are rare; they may reach a large size.

---

* Laboratory Reports of the Royal College of Physicians, Edinburgh, vol. iii.

XIV. PERINEPHRIC ABSCESS.

Suppuration in the connective tissue about the kidney may follow (1) blows and injuries; (2) the extension of inflammation from the pelvis of the kidney, the kidney itself, or the ureters; (3) perforation of the bowel, most commonly the appendix, in some instances the colon; (4) extension of suppuration from the spine, as in caries, or from the pleura, as in empyema; (5) as a sequel of the fevers, particularly in children.

Post mortem the kidney is surrounded by pus, particularly at the posterior part, though the pus may lie altogether in front, between the kidney and the peritonæum. Usually the abscess cavity is extensive. The pus is often offensive and may have a distinctly fæcal odor from contact with the large bowel. It may burrow in various directions and burst into the pleura and be discharged through the lungs. A more frequent direction is down the psoas muscle, when it appears in the groin, or it may pass along the iliacus fascia and appear at Poupart's ligament. It may perforate the bowel or rupture into the peritonæum; sometimes it penetrates the bladder or vagina.

Post mortem we occasionally find a condition of chronic perinephritis in which the fatty capsule of the kidney is extremely firm, with numerous bands of fibrous tissue, and is stripped off from the proper capsule with the greatest difficulty. Such a condition probably produces no symptoms.

Symptoms.—There may be intense pain, aggravated by pressure, in the lumbar region. In other instances, the onset is insidious, without pain in the renal region; on examination signs of deep-seated suppuration may be detected. On the affected side there is usually pain, which may be referred to the neighborhood of the hip-joint or to the joint itself, or radiate down the thigh and be associated with retraction of the testis. The patient lies with the thigh flexed, so as to relax the psoas muscle, and in walking throws, as far as possible, the weight on the opposite leg. The patient keeps the spine immobile, assumes a stooping posture in walking, and has great difficulty in voluntarily adducting the thigh (Gibney).

There may be pus in the urine if the disease has extended from the pelvis or the kidney, but in other forms the urine is clear. When pus has formed there are usually chills with irregular fever and sweats. On examination, deep-seated induration is felt between the last rib and the crest of the ilium. Bimanual palpation may reveal a distinct tumor mass. Œdema or puffiness of the skin is frequently present.

The *diagnosis* is usually easy; when doubt exists the aspirator needle should be used. We cannot always differentiate the primary forms from those due to perforation of the kidney or of the bowel. This, however, makes but little difference, for the treatment is identical. It is usually possible by the history and examination to exclude diseases of the vertebra. In children hip-joint disease may be suspected, but the pain is higher, and there is no fulness or tenderness over the hip-joint itself.

The *treatment* is clear—early, free, and permanent drainage.

SECTION X.

DISEASES OF THE NERVOUS SYSTEM.

I. GENERAL INTRODUCTION.

In diseases of the nervous system it is of the greatest importance to know accurately the position of the morbid process, and here, even more than in the other departments of medicine, a thorough knowledge of anatomy and physiology is essential. For full details the student is referred to the text-books on the subject, as it is not possible to do more than touch on the subject in this place.

Recent studies have modified our conceptions of the fundamental structure of the nervous system. At present we think of it as a combination of an immense number of units, called *neurones,* all having an essentially similar structure. Each neurone is composed of a cell body, the protoplasmic processes or dendrites, and the axis-cylinder process or axone. The nutrition of the neurone depends in large part upon the condition of the cell body, and this in turn in all probability upon the activity of the nucleus. If the cell is injured in any manner the processes degenerate, or if the processes are separated from the cell they degenerate. Whether or not the neurones are organically connected with one another is still in dispute. The weight of evidence is in favor of complete anatomical and relative physiological independence. The terminals of the axone of one neurone are related to the dendrites and cell bodies of other neurones by contact (Ramón y Cajal) or by concrescence (Held). It is generally admitted, however, that occasional coarse anastomoses exist between neighboring dendrites (according to Dogiel), especially in the retina. The studies of Apáthy speak in favor of a general interconnection by means of neurofibrils and protoplasmic bridges. In general, it may be stated that the dendrites or protoplasmic processes conduct impulses toward the cell body (cellulipetal conduction), and the axis-cylinder process conducts them away from the cell (cellulifugal conduction). The axis-cylinder process after leaving the cell gives off at varying intervals lateral branches called collaterals, which run at right angles to the process. The collaterals and finally the axis-cylinder process itself at their terminations split up into many fine fibres, forming the endbrushes. These, known as arborizations, surround the body of one or more of the many other cells, or interlace with their protoplasmic processes. The cell bodies of the neurones are collected more or less closely together in the gray matter of the brain and spinal cord and in the ganglia of the peripheral nerves. Their processes, especially the axis-cylinder processes, run for the most part in the white tracts of the brain and spinal cord and in the peripheral nerves. In this way the different parts of the central nervous system are brought into relation with each other and with the rest of the body. In many cases the connections are extremely complicated and have only just begun to be unravelled, but, fortunately for the clinician, the nervous mechanism upon which motion depends is the best understood and is the simplest.

A voluntary motor impulse starting from the brain cortex must pass through at least two neurones before it can reach the muscles, and we therefore speak of the motor tract as being composed of two segments—an upper and a lower. The neurones of the lower segment have the cell bodies and their protoplasmic processes in the different levels of the ventral horns of the spinal cord and in the motor nuclei of the cerebral nerves. The axis-cylinder processes of the lower motor neurones leave the spinal cord in the ventral roots and run in the peripheral nerves, to be distributed to all the muscles of the body, where they end in arborizations in the motor end plates. These neurones are direct—that is, their cell bodies, their processes, and the muscles in which they end are all on the same side of the body.*

The neurones of the upper motor segment have their cell bodies and protoplasmic processes in the cortex of the brain about the fissure of Rolando. Their axis-cylinder processes run in the white matter of the brain through the internal capsule and the cerebral peduncles into the pons, medulla, and cord, ending in arborizations around the protoplasmic processes and cell bodies of the lower motor neurones. The upper segment is, in the main, a crossed tract—that is to say, the neurones which compose it have their protoplasmic processes and cell bodies on one side of the body, whereas their axis-cylinder processes cross the middle line, to end about cell bodies of the lower motor neurones on the opposite side of the body. A certain number of the axones of the pyramidal tract, however, run to the lower motor neurones of the same side.

Motor impulses starting in the left side of the brain cause contractions of muscles on the right side of the body, and those from the right side of the brain in muscles of the left side of the body. Leaving out of consideration the exceptions which have been mentioned, it may be stated as a general rule that the motor path is crossed, and that the crossing takes place in the upper segment (Figs. 1 and 2). Every muscular movement, even the simplest, requires the activity of many neurones. In the production of each movement special neurones are brought into play in a definite combination, and whenever these neurones act in this combination that specific movement is the result. In other words, all the movements of the

---

* The root fibres of the nervus trochlearis and a portion of the root fibres of the nervus oculomotorius are well-known exceptions to this rule.

body are represented in the central nervous system by combinations of neurones—that is, they are localized. Muscular movements are localized in every part of the motor path, and in cases of disease of the nervous system a study of the motor defect often enables one to fix upon the site of the process, and it would be hard to overestimate the importance of a thorough knowledge of such localization.

The axis-cylinder processes of the lower motor neurones run in the peripheral nerves. Each nerve contains processes which are supplied to definite muscles, and we have in this way a peripheral localization. (See sections on Diseases of the Cerebral and Spinal Nerves.)

The axis-cylinder processes which run in the peripheral nerves leave the central nervous system from its ventral aspect. The ventral roots of the spinal cord are from above down, collected into small groups, which, after joining with the dorsal roots of the same level of the cord, leave the spinal canal between the vertebræ as the spinal nerves. That part of the cord from which the roots forming a single spinal nerve arise is called a segment, and corresponds to the nerve which arises from it and not to the vertebra to which it may be opposite. The axis-cylinder processes which go to make up any one peripheral nerve do not necessarily arise from the same segment of the spinal cord; in fact, most peripheral nerves contain processes from several often quite widely separated segments, and so it happens that the movements are represented in the spinal cord in a different manner—that is, there is spinal localization, or, better, lower level localization, since it also includes the motor nuclei of the cerebral nerves.

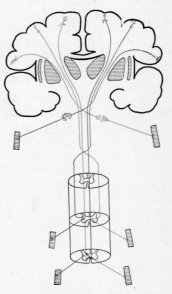

Fig. 1.—Diagram of motor path, showing the crossing of the path, which takes place in the upper segment. (Van Gehuchten, colored.)

Our knowledge of the localization of the muscular movements in the gray matter of the lower motor segment is far from complete, but enough is known to aid materially in determining the site of a spinal lesion. A number of tables have been prepared by different observers to represent our present knowledge of this subject. They differ from each other in minor details, but agree in the main. The following is the table prepared by Starr, in which the names of the muscles are given whose movements are represented in each of the spinal segments. Movements, not muscles, are localized in the central nervous system, a point carefully to be borne in mind by the student.

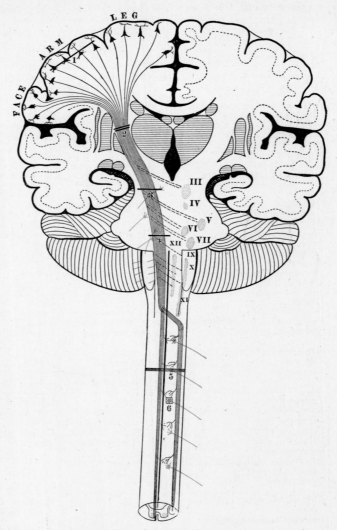

FIG. 2.—Diagram of motor path from right brain. The upper segment is black, the lower red. The nuclei of the motor cerebral nerves are shown on the left side: on the right side the cerebral nerves of that side are indicated. A lesion at 1 would cause upper segment paralysis in the arm of the opposite side—cerebral monoplegia; at 2, upper segment paralysis of the whole opposite side of the body—hemiplegia; at 3, upper segment paralysis of the opposite face, arm, and leg, and lower segment paralysis of the eye muscles on the same side—crossed paralysis; at 4, upper segment paralysis of opposite arm and leg, and lower segment paralysis of the face and the external rectus on the same side—crossed paralysis: at 5, upper segment paralysis of all muscles below lesion, and lower segment paralysis of muscles represented at level of lesion—spinal paraplegia; at 6, lower segment paralysis of muscles localized at seat of lesion—anterior poliomyelitis. (Van Gehuchten, modified.)

Localization of the Functions of the Segments of the Spinal Cord.

Segment.	Muscles.	Reflex.	Sensation.
II and III C.	Sterno-mastoid. Trapezius. Scaleni and neck. Diaphragm.	Hypochondrium (?). Sudden inspiration produced by sudden pressure beneath the lower border of ribs.	Back of head to vertex. Neck.
IV C.	Diaphragm. Deltoid. Biceps. Coraco-brachialis. Supinator longus. Rhomboid. Supra- and infra-spinatus.	Pupil. 4th to 7th cervical. Dilatation of the pupil produced by irritation of neck.	Neck. Upper shoulder. Outer arm.
V C.	Deltoid. Biceps. Coraco-brachialis. Brachialis anticus. Supinator longus. Supinator brevis. Rhomboid. Teres minor. Pectoralis (clavicular part). Serratus magnus.	Scapular. 5th cervical to 1st thoracic. Irritation of skin over the scapula produces contraction of the scapular muscles. Supinator longus. Tapping its tendon in wrist produces flexion of forearm.	Back of shoulder and arm. Outer side of arm and forearm, front and back.
VI C.	Biceps. Brachialis anticus. Pectoralis (clavicular part). Serratus magnus. Triceps. Extensors of wrist and fingers. Pronators.	Triceps. 5th to 6th cervical. Tapping elbow tendon produces extension of forearm. Posterior wrist. 6th to 8th cervical. Tapping tendons causes extension of hand.	Outer side of forearm, front and back. Outer half of hand.
VII C.	Triceps (long head). Extensors of wrist and fingers. Pronators of wrist. Flexors of wrist. Subscapular. Pectoralis (costal part). Latissimus dorsi. Teres major.	Anterior wrist. 7th to 8th cervical. Tapping anterior tendons causes flexion of wrist. Palmar. 7th cervical to 1st thoracic. Stroking palm causes closure of fingers.	Inner side and back of arm and forearm. Radial half of the hand.
VIII C.	Flexors of wrist and fingers. Intrinsic muscles of hand.		Forearm and hand, inner half.
I T.	Extensors of thumb. Intrinsic hand muscles. Thenar and hypothenar eminences.		Forearm, inner half. Ulnar distribution to hand.
II to XII T.	Muscles of back and abdomen. Erectores spinæ.	Epigastric. 4th to 7th thoracic. Tickling mammary regions causes retraction of epigastrium. Abdominal. 7th to 11th thoracic. Stroking side of abdomen causes retraction of belly.	Skin of chest and abdomen in bands running around and downward, corresponding to spinal nerves. Upper gluteal region.

Segment.	Muscles.	Reflex.	Sensation.
I L.	Ilio-psoas. Sartorius. Muscles of abdomen.	Cremasteric. 1st to 3d lumbar. Stroking inner thigh causes retraction of scrotum.	Skin over groin and front of scrotum.
II L.	Ilio-psoas. Sartorius. Flexors of knee (Remak). Quadriceps femoris.	Patellar tendon. Tapping tendon causes extension of leg.	Outer side of thigh.
III L.	Quadriceps femoris. Inner rotators of thigh. Abductors of thigh.		Front and inner side of thigh.
IV L.	Abductors of thigh. Adductors of thigh. Flexors of knee (Ferrier). Tibialis anticus.	Gluteal. 4th to 5th lumbar. Stroking buttock causes dimpling in fold of buttock.	Inner side of thigh and leg to ankle. Inner side of foot.
V L.	Outward rotators of thigh. Flexors of knee (Ferrier). Flexors of ankle. Extensors of toes.		Back of thigh, back of leg, and outer part of foot.
I to II S.	Flexors of ankle. Long flexor of toes. Peronæi. Intrinsic muscles of foot.	Plantar. Tickling sole of foot causes flexion of toes and retraction of leg.	Back of thigh. Leg and foot, outer side.
III to V S.	Perineal muscles.	Foot reflex. Achilles tendon. Overextension of foot causes rapid flexion; ankle-clonus. Bladder and rectal centres.	Skin over sacrum. Anus. Perinæum. Genitals.

The above table refers only to localization in the spinal cord. The manner in which movements are represented in the pons and medulla is about as follows. This table is constructed from above downward in reference to the motor nuclei of the cranial nerves:

Nuclei.

III. Sphincter. Ciliary muscles.
Levator palpebræ superioris. Rectus internus (in convergence).
Rectus superior. Rectus inferior.
Obliquus inferior.
IV. Obliquus superior.
(Upper facial group.)

V. (Associated movement of levator palpebræ.)
Muscles of lower jaw.

VI. Rectus externus. Rectus inter. of opposite side in lateral movements.

VII.—Facial muscles.

XII. (Lower facial group).
Muscles of tongue.

IX. Muscles of pharynx.
X. Muscles of œsophagus.
XI. Muscles of larynx.

Cerebral Motor Localization.—The cell bodies of the upper motor neurones are found in the brain cortex about the fissure of Rolando, and it is in this region that we find the movements of the body again represented.

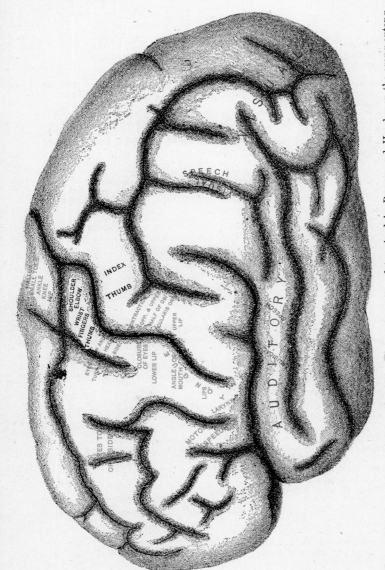

Fig. 3.—Diagram of cerebral localization. The motor areas determined by Beevor and Horsley on the orang-outang have been transferred approximately to Schäfer's drawing (Quain's Anatomy) somewhat simplified. The areas of the representation of the cutaneous sensations are too little known to be included, and those of auditory and visual sensations are merely indicated, but their boundaries are not accurately defined.

The clinical studies of Hughlings Jackson, and the experiments of Hitzig and Fritsch, and of Ferrier, laid the foundation for the great mass of most excellent work which has been done upon this subject. We owe much to Victor Horsley and his associates for their careful work in this direction, and the following description is based largely upon their writings, and especially upon the paper of Beevor and Horsley, in which they give the results of their experimental work on the orang-outang. Clinical observation and electrical stimulation of the brain cortex during operations on human beings have confirmed the results of experiments upon animals.

The motor area comprises the anterior central convolution, and to a less extent the posterior central convolution, the hinder part of the three frontal convolutions and the paracentral lobule. In the orang-outang and man not every part of this region is excitable by electrical stimulation. The movements are quite sharply localized, and there are inexcitable areas between the areas of representation of the larger divisions of the body. The diagram (Fig. 3) shows the centres as given by Beevor and Horsley. Certain landmarks are important. The genu of the fissure of Rolando, which when present in man is found at a point about midway or even higher between the upper margin of the hemisphere and the fissure of Sylvius, marks the boundary between the area of representation of the arm from that of the face. The level of the superior frontal sulcus indicates the division of the leg from the arm area. From above down the areas of representation occur in this order: leg, arm, face. Those of the leg and arm occupy the upper half of the convolution, and that for the face is spread out over the lower half. The diagram indicates the localization of the movements of the different parts of the extremities.

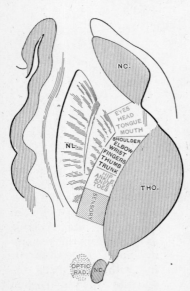

FIG. 4.—Diagram of motor and sensory representation in the internal capsule. NL., Lenticular nucleus. NC., Caudate nucleus. THO., Optic thalamus. The motor paths are red and black, the sensory are blue.

The centres for the trunk are, according to Schäfer, situated in the marginal gyrus just within the longitudinal fissure in the paracentral lobule. In man the motor speech centre is localized in the posterior part of the left inferior frontal convolution.

The axis-cylinder processes of the upper motor neurones after leaving the gray matter of the motor cortex pass into the white matter of the brain and form part of the corona radiata. They converge and pass between the basal ganglia in the internal capsule. Here the motor axis-cylinders are collected into a compact bundle—the pyramidal tract—occupying the knee and anterior two thirds of the posterior limb of the internal capsule. The order in which the movements of the opposite side of the body are represented here is given in Fig. 4.

After passing through the internal capsule the fibres of the pyramidal tract leave the hemisphere by the crus, in which they occupy about the middle three fifths (Fig. 5). The movements of the tongue and lips are represented nearest the middle line.

As soon as the tract enters the crus, some of its axis-cylinder processes leave it and cross the middle line to end in arborizations about the ganglion cells in the nucleus of the third nerve on the opposite side; and in this way, as the pyramidal tract passes down, it gives off at different levels fibres which end in the nuclei of all the motor cerebral nerves on the opposite side of the body. Some fibres, however, go to the nuclei of the same side

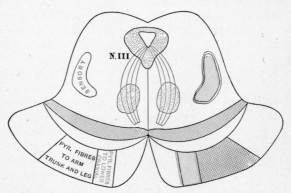

Fig. 5.—Diagram of motor and sensory paths in Crura.

(Hoche). From the crus, the pyramidal tract runs through the pons and forms in the medulla oblongata the pyramid, which gives its name to the tract. At the lower part of the medulla, after the fibres going to the cerebral nerves have crossed the middle line, a large proportion of the remaining fibres cross, decussating with those from the opposite pyramid, and pass into the opposite side of the spinal cord, forming the crossed pyramidal tract of the lateral column (fasciculus cerebrospinalis lateralis) (Fig. 6, 1). The smaller number of fibres which do not at this time cross, descend in the ventral column of the same side, forming the direct pyramidal tract, or Türck's column (fasciculus cerebrospinalis ventralis) (Fig. 6, 2).

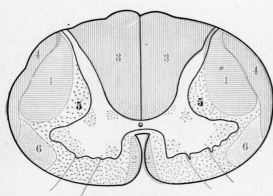

Fig. 6.—Diagram of cross-section of spinal cord, showing motor, red, and sensory, blue paths. 1, Lateral pyramidal tract. 2, Ventral pyramidal tract. 3, Dorsal columns. 4, Direct cerebellar tract. 5, Ventro-lateral ground bundles. 6, Ventro-lateral ascending tract of Gowers. (Van Gehuchten, colored.)

At every level of the spinal cord axis-cylinder processes leave the crossed pyramidal tract to enter the ventral horns and end about the cell bodies of the lower motor neurones. The tract diminishes in size from above downward. The fibres of the direct

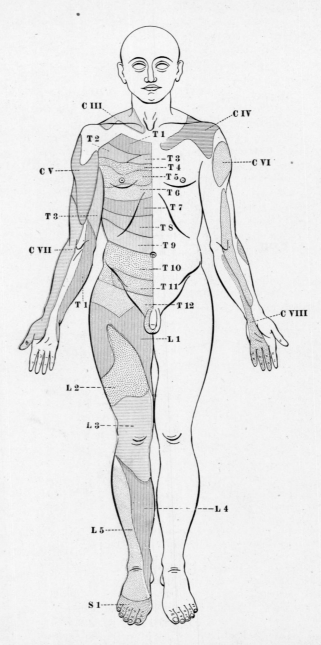

FIG. 7.—Diagram of skin areas corresponding to the different spinal segments.
(Combined from Head's diagrams.)

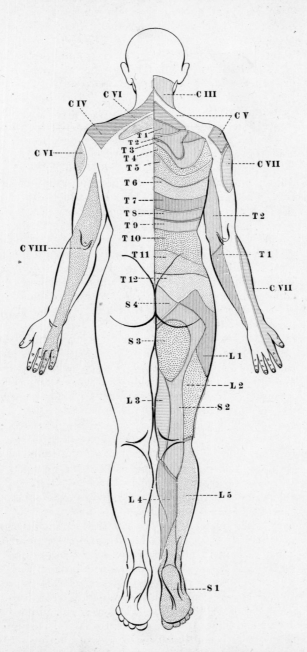

FIG. 8.—Diagram of skin areas corresponding to the different spinal segments. (Combined from Head's diagrams.)

pyramidal tract cross at different levels in the ventral white commissure, and also, it is believed, end about cells in the ventral horns on the opposite side of the cord. This tract usually ends about the middle of the thoracic region of the cord.

The path for sensory conduction is more complicated than the motor path, and in its simplest form is composed of at least three sets of neurones, one above the other. The cell bodies of the lowest neurones are in the ganglia, on the dorsal roots of the spinal nerves, and the ganglia of the sensory cerebral nerves. These ganglion cells have a special form, having apparently but a single process, which, soon after leaving the cell, divides in a T-shaped manner, one portion running into the central nervous system and the other to the periphery of the body. Embryological and comparative anatomical studies have made it probable that the peripheral sensory fibre, the process which conducts toward the cell, represents the protoplasmic processes, while that which conducts away from the cell is the axis-cylinder process. In the peripheral sensory nerves we have, then, the dendrites of the lower sensory neurones. These start in the periphery of the body from their various specialized end organs. The axis-cylinder processes leave the ganglia and enter the spinal cord by the dorsal roots of the spinal nerves. After entering the cord each axis-cylinder process divides into an ascending and a descending branch, which run in the dorsal fasciculi. The descending branch runs but a short distance, and ends in the gray matter of the same side of the cord. It gives off a number of collaterals, which also end in the gray matter. The ascending branch may end in the gray matter soon after entering, or it may run in the dorsal fasciculi as far as the medulla, and end in the nuclei of these. In any case it does not cross the middle line. The lower sensory neurone is direct.

The cells about which the axis-cylinder processes and their collaterals of the lower sensory neurone end are of various kinds. They are known as sensory neurones of the second order. In the first place, some of them end about the cell bodies of the lower motor neurones, forming the path for reflexes. They also end about cells whose axis-cylinder processes cross the middle line and run to the opposite side of the brain. In the spinal cord these cells are found in the different parts of the gray matter, and their axis-cylinder processes run in the opposite ventro-lateral ascending tract of Gowers (Fig. 6, 6) and in the ground bundles (fasciculus lateralis proprius and fasciculus ventralis proprius).

In the medulla the nuclei of the dorsal fasciculi (nucleus fasciculi gracilis (Golli) and nucleus fasciculi cuneati (Burdachi)) contain for the most part cells of this character. Their axis-cylinder processes, after crossing, run toward the brain in the medial lemniscus or bundle of the fillet; certain of the longitudinal bundles in the formatio reticularis also represent sensory paths from the spinal cord and medulla toward higher centres. The fibres of the medial lemniscus or fillet do not, however, run directly to the cerebral cortex. They end about cells in the ventro-lateral portion of the optic thalamus, and the tract is continued on by way of another set of neurones, which send processes to end in the cortex of the central convolutions and the parietal lobe. This is the most direct path of sensory conduction, but by no means the only one. The peripheral sensory neurones may also end about cells in the cord whose axones run but a short distance toward the brain before ending again in the gray matter, and the path, if path it can be called, is made up of a series of these superimposed neurones. The gray matter of the cord itself is also believed to offer paths of sensory conduction. All these paths reach the tegmentum and optic thalamus, and from thence are distributed to the cortex along with the other sensory paths. There may also be paths of sensory conduction through the cerebellum by way of the direct cerebellar tract and Gowers' bundle. From this short summary it is evident that the possible paths of sensory conduction are many, and that our knowledge of them is as yet very indefinite; for this reason disturbances in sensation do not give us as much help in making a local diagnosis as do those of motion. Certain facts are important to keep in mind. The different peripheral nerves contain sensory fibres from definite areas of the skin, and upon this depends the peripheral sensory representation. (See section on Diseases of the Spinal Nerves.)

The sensory areas of the skin are represented in the spinal cord in an entirely different manner from the peripheral representation, just as is the case in regard to motion. The surface of the body has been mapped out into areas which are meant to correspond to the different dorsal roots or spinal segments. In Starr's table the third column indicates his belief. His more recent division of the sensory areas on the limbs is pictured in the American Journal of the Medical Sciences, June, 1895. Figs. 7 and 8 embody the result of Head's work. They are also the areas in which the referred pain and cutaneous tenderness in visceral diseases make their appearance. The cutaneous sensory impressions are in man conducted toward the brain, probably on the opposite side of the cord—that is, the path crosses to the opposite side soon after entering the cord. Muscular sense, on the other hand, is conducted on the same side of the cord in the fasciculi of Goll, to cross above by means of the axones of sensory neurones of the second order in the medulla.

The localization of sensory impressions in the cortex of the brain is not definitely determined, but in a general way it corresponds to the motor representation. Sensation seems, however, to be more widely represented than motion, and to occupy most of the parietal lobe as well as the central convolutions.

The paths for the conduction of the stimuli which underlie the special senses are given in the section upon the cerebral nerves, and it is only necessary here to refer to what is known of the cortical representation of these senses.

Visual impressions are localized in the occipital lobes. The primary visual centre is on the mesial surface in the cuneus, especially about the calcarine fissure, and here are represented the opposite half-visual fields. Some authors believe that there is another higher centre on the outer surface of the occipital lobe, in which the vision of the opposite eye is chiefly represented. However this may be, most authors hold that the angular gyrus of the left hemisphere is a part of the brain in which are stored the memories of the meaning of letters, words, figures, and indeed of all seen

57

objects. This is designated in the visual speech centre on the diagram (Fig. 3). Flechsig and Monokow do not admit this.

Auditory impressions are localized for the most part in the first temporal convolution and the transverse temporal gyri, and it is in this region in the left hemisphere that the memories of the meanings of heard words and sounds are stored. Musical memories are localized somewhat in front of those for words (Fig. 3). The cortical centres for smell include a part of the base of the frontal lobe, the uncus, and perhaps the gyrus hippocampi. The centres for taste are supposed to be situated near those for smell, but we possess as yet no definite information about them.

Topical Diagnosis.—The successful diagnosis of the position of a lesion in the nervous system depends upon a careful and exhaustive examination into all the symptoms that are present, and then endeavoring with the help of anatomy and physiology to determine the place, a disturbance at which might produce these symptoms.

The abnormalities of motion are usually the most important localizing symptoms, both on account of the ease with which they can be demonstrated, and also because of the comparative accuracy of our knowledge of the motor path.

Lesions in any part of the motor path cause disturbances of motion. If destructive, the function of the part is abolished, and as the result there is *paralysis*. If, on the other hand, the lesion is an irritative one, the structures are thrown into abnormal activity, which produces *abnormal muscular contraction*. The character of the paralysis or of the abnormal muscular contraction varies with lesions of the upper and lower motor segment, the variations depending, first, upon the anatomical position of the two segments; and, secondly, upon the symptoms which are the result of secondary degeneration in each of the segments.

(*a*) **Lesions of the Lower or Spino-muscular Segment.**—*Destructive Lesions.*—It has been stated above that the nutrition of all parts of a neurone depends upon their connection with its healthy cell body; and if the cell body be injured, its processes undergo degeneration, or if a portion of a process be separated from the cell body, that part degenerates along its whole length. This so-called secondary degeneration plays a very important *rôle* in the symptomatology.

In the lower motor segment the degeneration not only affects the axis-cylinder processes which run in the peripheral nerves, but also the muscle fibres in which the axis-cylinder processes end. The degeneration of the nerves and muscles is made evident, first, by the muscles becoming smaller and flabby, and, secondly, by change in their reaction to electrical stimulation. The degenerated nerve gives no response to either the galvanic or the faradic current, and the muscle does not respond to faradic stimulation, but reacts in a characteristic manner to the galvanic current. The contraction, instead of being sharp, quick, lightning-like, as in that of a normal muscle, is slow and lazy, and is often produced by a weaker current, and the anode-closing contraction may be greater than the cathode-closing contraction. This is the reaction of degeneration, but it is not always present in the classical form. The essential feature is the slow, lazy contraction of the muscle to the galvanic current, and when this is present the muscle is degenerated.

The myotatic irritability, or muscle reflex, and the muscle tonus depend upon the integrity of the reflex arc, of which the lower motor segment is the efferent limb, and in a paralysis due to lesion of this segment the muscle reflexes (tendon reflexes) are abolished and there is a diminished muscular tension.

Lower segment paralyses have for their characteristics degenerative atrophy with the reaction of degeneration in the affected muscles, loss of their reflex excitability, and a diminished muscular tension. These are the general characteristics, but the anatomical relations of this segment also give certain peculiarities in the distribution of the paralyses which help to distinguish them from those which follow lesions of the upper segment, and which also aid in determining the site of the lesion in the lower segment itself. The cell bodies of this segment are distributed in groups, from the level of the peduncles of the brain throughout the whole extent of the spinal cord to its termination opposite the second lumbar vertebra, and their axis-cylinder processes run in the peripheral nerves to every muscle in the body; so that the component parts are more or less widely separated from each other, and a local lesion causes paralysis of only a few muscles or groups of muscles, and not of a whole section of the body, as is the case where lesions affect the upper segment. The muscles which are paralyzed indicate whether the disease is in the peripheral nerves or spinal cord; for, as we have seen above, the muscles are represented differently in the peripheral nerves and in the spinal cord. Sensory symptoms, which may accompany the paralysis, are often of great assistance in making a local diagnosis. Thus, in a paralysis with the characteristics of a lesion of the lower motor segment, if the paralyzed muscles are all supplied by one nerve, and the anæsthetic area of the skin is supplied by that nerve, it is evident that the lesion must be in the nerve itself. On the other hand, if the muscles paralyzed are not supplied by a single nerve, but are represented close together in the spinal cord, and the anæsthetic area corresponds to that section of the cord (see table), it is equally clear that the lesion must be in the cord itself or in its nerve roots.

Irritative Lesions of the Lower Motor Segment.—Lesions of this segment cause comparatively few symptoms of irritation, and our knowledge on the point is neither extensive nor accurate. The fibrillary contractions which are so common in muscles undergoing degeneration are probably due to stimulation of the cell bodies in their slow degeneration, as in progressive muscular atrophy, or to irritation of the axis-cylinder processes in the peripheral nerves, as in neuritis. Lesions which affect the motor roots as they leave the central nervous system may cause spasmodic contractions in the muscles supplied by them. Certain convulsive paroxysms, of which laryngismus stridulus is a type, and to which the spasms of tetany also belong, are believed to be due to abnormal activity in the lower motor centres. These are the "lowest level fits" of Hughlings Jackson. Certain poisons, as strychnia and that of tetanus, act particularly upon these centres.

The principle diseases in which the lower motor segment may be involved are: all diseases involving the peripheral nerves, cerebral and spinal meningitis, injuries, hæmorrhages and tumors of the medulla and cord or their membranes, lesions of the gray matter of the segment, anterior poliomyelitis, progressive muscular atrophy, bulbar paralysis, ophthalmoplegia, syringo-myelia, etc.

(b) **Lesions of the Upper Motor Segment.**—*Destructive lesions* cause, as in the lower motor segment, paralysis, and here again the secondary degeneration which follows the lesion gives to the paralysis its distinctive characteristics. In this case the paralysis is accompanied by a spastic condition, shown in an exaggeration of muscle reflex and an increase in the tension of the muscle. It is not accurately known how the degeneration of the pyramidal fibres causes this excess of the muscle reflex. The usual explanation is, that under normal circumstances the upper motor centres are constantly exerting a restraining influence upon the activity of the lower centres, and that when the influence ceases to act, on account of disease of the pyramidal fibres, the latter take on increased activity, which is made manifest by an exaggeration of the muscle reflex.

We have seen that the neurones composing each segment of the motor path are to be considered as nutritional units, and therefore the secondary degeneration in the upper segment stops at the beginning of the lower. For this reason the muscles paralyzed from lesions in the upper segment do not undergo degenerative atrophy, nor do they show any marked change in their electrical reactions.

The separate parts of the upper motor segment lie much more closely together than do those of the lower segment, and therefore a small lesion may cause paralysis in many muscles. This is more particularly true in the internal capsule, where all the axis-cylinder processes of this segment are collected into a compact bundle—the pyramidal tract. A lesion in this region usually causes paralysis of all the muscles on the opposite side of the body—that is, hemiplegia. The pyramidal tract continues in a compact bundle, giving off fibres to the motor nuclei at different levels; a lesion anywhere in its course is followed by paralysis of all the muscles whose nuclei are situated below the lesion. When the disease is above the decussation, the paralysis is on the opposite side of the body; when below, the paralyzed muscles are on the same side as the lesion. Above the internal capsule the path is somewhat more separated, and in the cortex the centres for the movements of the different sections of the body are comparatively far apart, and a sharply localized lesion in this region may cause a more limited paralysis, affecting a limb or a segment of a limb—the cerebral monoplegias; but even here the paralysis is not confined to an individual muscle or group of muscles, as is commonly the case in lower segment paralysis (see Fig. 2 and explanation).

To sum up, the paralyses due to lesions of the upper motor segment are widespread, often hemiplegic; the paralyzed muscles are spastic (the tendon reflexes exaggerated), they do not undergo degenerative atrophy, and they do not present the degenerative reaction to electrical stimulation.

There is an exception to the above statement—that is, in the paralyses which follow a complete transverse lesion of the spinal cord. Here the limbs are of course completely paralyzed, but instead of being spastic they are flaccid and the deep reflexes are absent. There is, however, no marked atrophy in the muscles, and they react normally to electricity. There is no satisfactory explanation of why the reflexes should be abolished under these conditions.

Irritative Lesions of the Upper Motor Segment.—Our knowledge of such lesions is confined for the most part to those acting on the motor cortex. The abnormal muscular contractions resulting from lesions so situated have as their type the localized convulsive seizures classed under Jacksonian or cortical epilepsy, which are characterized by the convulsion beginning in a single muscle or group of muscles and involving other muscles in a definite order, depending upon the position of their representation in the cortex. For instance, such a convulsion, beginning in the muscles of the face, next involves those of the arm and hand, and then the leg. The convulsion is usually accompanied by sensory phenomena and followed by a weakness of the muscles involved.

A majority of lesions of the motor cortex are both destructive and irritative—i. e., they destroy the nerve cells of a certain centre, and either in their growth or by their presence throw into abnormal activity those of the surrounding centres.

The upper motor segment is involved in nearly all the diseases of the brain and spinal cord, especially in injuries, tumors, abscesses, and hæmorrhages; transverse lesions of the cord; syringomyelia, progressive muscular atrophy, bulbar paralysis, etc. One lesion often involves both the upper and the lower motor segments, and we have paralysis in the different parts of the body, with the characteristics of each. Such a combination enables us in many cases to make an accurate local diagnosis.

Lesions in the optic path and in the different speech centres also give localizing symptoms, which should be always looked for.

(c) Lesions of the Sensory Path.—Here again the lesion may be either irritative or destructive. *Irritative lesions* cause abnormal subjective sensory impressions—paræsthesia, formication, a sense of cold or constriction, and pain of every grade of intensity. The character of the sensory symptoms gives very little indication as to the position of the irritating process. Intense pain is, as a rule, a symptom of a lesion in the peripheral sensory neurones, but it may be caused by a disease of the sensory path within the central nervous system.

The exact distribution of symptoms gives us more accurate data, for if they are confined to the distribution of a peripheral nerve or of a spinal segment the indication is plain. If one side of the body is more or less completely affected, we must think of a lesion somewhere within the brain, etc.

Destructive Lesions.—A complete destruction of the sensory paths from any part of the body would of course deprive that part of sensation in all its qualities. This occurs most frequently from injury to the peripheral sensory neurones within the peripheral nerves, and the area of anæsthesia depends upon the nerve injured. Complete transverse lesion of the cord causes complete anæsthesia below the injury.

Unilateral lesions of the cord, medulla, dorsal part of the pons, tegmentum, thalamus, internal capsule, and cortex cause disturbances of sensation on the opposite side of the body; here again the extent of the defect more than its character helps us to determine the position of the lesion. Hemianæsthesia involving the face as well as the rest of the body can only occur above the place where the sensory paths from the fifth nerve have crossed the middle line on their way to the cortex. This is in the upper part of the pons. From this point to where they leave the internal capsule the sensory paths are in fairly close relation, and are at times involved in a very small lesion. Above the internal capsule the paths diverge quickly, and for this reason only an extensive lesion can involve them all, and in lesions of this part we are more apt to have the sensory disturbances confined to one or the other segments of the body. Unilateral lesions of the pons, medulla, and cord usually cause sensory disturbances on the same side of the body, as well as those on the opposite side. These are due to the involvement of the sensory paths as they enter the central nervous system at or a little below the site of the lesion and before the axones of the sensory neurones of the second order have crossed the middle line. The area of disturbed sensation is limited to the distribution of one or more spinal segments and often indicates accurately the position and extent of the diseased process. As a rule, destructive lesions of the central nervous system do not involve all the paths of sensory conduction, and the loss of sensation is not complete. It is often astonishing how very slight the sensory disturbances are which result from an extensive lesion of the nervous system. Sensation may be diminished in all of its qualities, or, what is more common, certain qualities may be affected while others are normal. These cases of dissociation of sensation, or so-called elective sensory paralysis, have been much studied of late. Thus the sense of pain and temperature may be lost while that of touch remains normal, as is often the case in diseases of the spinal cord, or there may be simply a loss of the muscular sense and of the stereognostic sense (the complex sensory impression which enables one to recognize an object placed in the hand), as occurs frequently from lesions of the cortex. Occasionally pain sensation persists with loss of tactile and thermic sensations. Almost every other combination has been described. It is the distribution more than the character of the sensory defect that is of importance, and often the distribution gives but uncertain indication of the position of the lesion. The combination of the sensory defect with different forms of paralysis gives the most certain diagnostic signs. The student is referred to the sections on the individual parts of the nervous system for a more detailed consideration of the subject.

II. SYSTEM DISEASES.

I. INTRODUCTION.

There are certain diseases of the nervous system which are confined, if not absolutely, still in great part, to definite tracts (combinations of neurones) which subserve like functions. These tracts are called *systems*, and a disease which is confined to one of them is a *system disease*. If more than one system is involved, the process is called a combined system disease. Just what diseases should be classed under these names has given rise to much discussion but to very little agreement. We cannot speak positively; our knowledge is as yet not sufficiently accurate, either in regard to the exact limits of the systems themselves, or to the nature and extent of the morbid process in the several diseases. In the classification which has been adopted in this edition the endeavor has been to make the arrangement as simple as possible, and, while it is based upon what is believed to be the best founded views of the systems and their diseases, there has been no attempt to carry the classification to its logical conclusion, nor have the limits of the theory been always respected.

In general it may be said that the nervous system is composed of two great systems of neurones, the afferent or sensory system and the efferent or motor system, and the connections between them. (See General Introduction.)

Locomotor ataxia is a disease confined to the afferent system, and progressive muscular atrophy is one of the efferent system. Representing typical system diseases as we now understand them, they have been taken as the basis of the classification. Several theories have been advanced to explain why a disease should be limited to a definite system of neurones. One view is based upon the idea that in certain individuals one or the other of these systems has an innate tendency to undergo degeneration; another assumes that neurones with a similar function have a similar chemical construction (which differs from that of neurones with a different function), and this is taken to explain why a poison circulating in the blood should show a selective action for a single functional system of neurones.

In the afferent tract locomotor ataxia stands alone as a system disease. In the efferent tract progressive (central) muscular atrophy is the chief representative, as in it the whole motor path is more or less involved. Theoretically, primary lateral sclerosis is a disease confined to the upper segment of the efferent tract, while anterior poliomyelitis involves the lower segment of the tract.

In connection with progressive (central) muscular atrophy, the other forms of muscular atrophy are considered as a matter of convenience. In other instances, too, diseases are arranged in positions to which they might not be entitled, had a rigid classification of system diseases been maintained.

II. DISEASES OF THE AFFERENT OR SENSORY SYSTEM.

Locomotor Ataxia

(Tabes Dorsalis ; Posterior Spinal Sclerosis).

Definition.—An affection characterized clinically by incoördination, sensory and trophic disturbances, and involvement of the special senses, particularly the eyes. Anatomically there are found degeneration of the posterior roots and of the dorsal columns of the cord; sometimes the spinal ganglia and peripheral nerves are affected. Foci of degeneration in the basal ganglia and degenerative changes in the cortex cerebri have been described.

Etiology.—It is a widespread disease, more frequent in cities than in the country. The relative proportion may be judged from the fact that of 8,642 cases in the neurological dispensary of the Johns Hopkins Hospital there were 89 cases of locomotor ataxia (H. M. Thomas). Males are attacked more frequently than females, the proportion being at least 10 to 1. Mitchell has called attention to the fact that it is a rare disease in the negro. It is a disease of adult life, a majority of the cases occurring between the thirtieth and fortieth years. Occasionally cases are seen in young men. The form of ataxia which occurs in children is a different disease. Of special causes syphilis is the most important. According to the figures of Erb, Fournier, and Gowers, in from 50 to 75 per cent of all cases there is a history of this disease. Erb's recent figures are most striking; of 300 cases of tabes in private practice 89 per cent had had syphilis. Moebius goes so far as to say, " The longer I reflect upon it, the more firmly I believe that tabes never originates without syphilis."

Excessive fatigue, overexertion, injury, exposure to cold and wet, and sexual excesses are all assigned as causes. There are instances in which the disease has closely followed severe exposure. James Stewart has noted that the Ottawa lumbermen, who live a very hard life in the camps during the winter months, are frequently the subjects of locomotor ataxia. Trauma has been noted in a few cases. Alcoholic excess does not seem to predispose to the disease. Among patients in the better classes of life I do not remember one in which there had been a previous history of prolonged drunkenness. There are now a good many cases on record of the existence of the disease in both husband and wife.

Morbid Anatomy and Pathology.—Our conception of tabes dorsalis has undergone radical alteration, and the studies of Leyden, Redlich, Marie, and others have shown that it can no longer be regarded as a primary sclerosis of the dorsal columns. These, it will be remembered, are made up, in great part, of the axis-cylinder processes of the spinal ganglia, and they, with their branches, represent in the cord the paths of sensory conduction. The peripheral sensory nerves represent the protoplasmic processes of the spinal ganglia, which important structures are the trophic centres both for the sensory nerves as well as for the axis-cylinder processes which make up the dorsal columns of the cord. Marie calls attention also to the possibility of the existence of peripheral or terminal ganglion cells, which are found in different organs—cells from which certain of the sensory fibres are derived which go to form the dorsal nerve-roots. According to the general laws of nerve physiology, already mentioned, lesions of the nerve ganglia would be followed by degeneration of the dorsal root-fibres and of their continuation in the cord, and this is practically what the recent theory of tabes involves. The changes in the dorsal columns are merely a sequence, and not the primary disease. The fibres of the dorsal root are divided into three sets:

(1) The short fibres, which pass almost directly into the dorsal cornu after entering the cord.

(2) Fibres of moderate length, which run upward in the cord; some of them enter the dorsal horn at its middle part, while others pass into Clarke's column. The fibres of this group run in the fasciculus cuneatus of Burdach.

(3) A group of long fibres, which are derived chiefly from the roots of the cauda equina, and which pass the whole length of the cord to enter certain nuclei in the medulla. They form the fasciculus gracilis of Goll.

The initial cord lesion in tabes is found in the dorsal root-zone and in the zone or tract of Lissauer, a narrow portion situated between the margin of the cord and the apex of the posterior horn. In the fasciculus of Burdach the sclerosis is in almost direct proportion to the duration of the disease, slight at first and centrally placed, and becoming widespread as the disease advances. The fasciculus of Goll is affected slightly in the early stages, but in the advanced stage there is extensive sclerosis. Marie correlates the sclerosis of these different parts with the different groups of nerve-fibres of the dorsal root, the dorsal root-zone and the zone of Lissauer degenerating from the involvement of the short fibres; the sclerosis of the fasciculi of Burdach and the disappearance of the network of the nerve-fibres in the column of Clarke being due to the degeneration of the second group, the fibres of moderate length; while the sclerosis of the fasciculi of Goll is caused by the degeneration of the third group, namely, the long fibres. He suggests also that groups of fibres in the different dorsal roots are not simultaneously affected, and the lesions may be in an advanced stage in one region and but slight in the other. " *The lesions of the spinal cord in tabes occur by segments*, each dorsal root bringing into the dorsal column a fresh contingent of degenerated fibres."

According to this interesting hypothesis the lesions of the ganglia of the dorsal roots are responsible, in part at least, for the peripheral neuritis, since in degeneration of the spinal ganglia and consequent loss of trophic influence there would necessarily be degeneration in the peripheral nerve-trunks. Possibly, too, Marie suggests, the degeneration of the *peripheral* ganglion cells may have a good deal to do with the neuritis of tabes.

Obersteiner and Redlich, while agreeing that the degeneration of the dorsal columns of the cord is dependent upon a disease in the dorsal roots, believe, at least for most cases, that the change in the latter is secondary to a chronic inflammation of the pia mater, which, by making pressure on the

58

dorsal root-fibres just where they are poor in myeline, causes them to degenerate.

The spinal ganglia have been found diseased in certain cases, but in other cases no change whatever could be detected, even by the aid of the most delicate technique, and Marie acknowledges that there is very little anatomical proof for his theory that it is these structures that are primarily affected in tabes.

Trepinski has divided the dorsal fasciculi into different systems according to the time of the development of their myeline, and has endeavored to show that the sclerosis in tabes follows these systems.

Symptoms.—These are best considered under three stages—the incipient stage, the ataxic stage, and the paralytic stage.

The Incipient Stage.—This is sometimes called the preataxic stage. The manner in which tabes makes its onset differs very widely in the different cases, and mistakes in diagnosis are often made early in the disease. The following are the most characteristic initial symptoms:

Pains, usually of a sharp stabbing character; hence the term lightning pains. They last for only a second or two and are most common in the legs. They may be associated with a hot burning feeling. Occasionally herpes may develop at the site of the pain. They may occur at irregular intervals, and are more prone to follow excesses or to come on when health is impaired. The gastric crises and other crises may occur in the disease. Paræsthesia may also be among the first symptoms. Numbness of the feet, tingling, etc., and at times a sense of constriction about the body.

Ocular Symptoms.—(*a*) Optic atrophy. This occurs in about 10 per cent of the cases, and is often an early and even the first symptom. There is a gradual loss of vision, which in a large majority of cases leads to total blindness. (*b*) Ptosis, which may be double or single. (*c*) Paralysis of the external muscles of the eye. This may be of a single muscle or occasionally of all of the muscles of the eye. The paralysis is often transient, the patient merely complaining that he saw double for a certain period. (*d*) Argyll Robertson pupil, in which there is loss of the iris reflex to light but contraction during accommodation. The pupils are very small—spinal myosis.

Bladder Symptoms.—The first warning of the disease which the patient has may be a certain difficulty in emptying the bladder. Incontinence of urine occurs only at a later stage of the disease. Decrease in sexual desire and power may also be an early symptom.

Trophic Disturbances.—These usually occur later in the disease, but at times they are very early symptoms and it is not very infrequent to have one's attention called to the trouble by the presence of a perforating ulcer or of a characteristic Charcot's joint.

Loss of the Knee-jerk.—This early and most important symptom may occur years before the development of ataxia. Even alone it is of great moment, since it is very rare to meet with individuals in whom the knee-jerk is normally absent. The combination of loss of the knee-kick with one or more of the symptoms mentioned above, especially with the lightning pains and ptosis or Argyll Robertson pupil, is practically diagnostic. The knee-jerk is not lost suddenly, but gradually decreases, often disappearing in one leg before the other.

These are the most common symptoms of the initial stage of tabes and may persist for years without the development of incoördination. The patient may look well and feel well, and be troubled only by occasional attacks of lightning pains or of one of the other subjective symptoms. Moebius goes so far as to state that the typical Argyll Robertson pupil means either tabes or general paralysis, and that paralysis of the external muscles of the eye developing in adults are of almost equal importance, especially if they develop painlessly.

The time between the syphilitic infection and the occurrence of the first symptoms of locomotor ataxia varies within wide limits. About one half the cases occur between the sixth and fifteenth year, but many begin even later than this.

The disease may never progress beyond this stage, and when optic atrophy develops early and leads to blindness, ataxia rarely, if ever, supervenes. There is a sort of antagonism between the ocular symptoms and the progress of the ataxia. Charcot laid considerable stress upon this, and both Dejerine and Spiller have since emphasized the point.

Ataxic Stage.—*Motor Symptoms.*—The ataxia is believed to be due to a disturbance or loss of the afferent impulses from the muscles, and a disturbance of the muscle sense itself can usually be demonstrated. It develops gradually. One of the first indications to the patient is inability to get about readily in the dark or to maintain his equilibrium when washing his face with the eyes shut. When the patient stands with the feet together and the eyes closed, he sways and has difficulty in maintaining his position, and he may be quite unable to stand on one leg. This is known as Romberg's symptom. He does not start off promptly at the word of command. On turning quickly he is apt to fall. He descends stairs with more difficulty than he ascends them. Gradually the characteristic ataxic gait develops. The patient, as a rule, walks with a stick, the eyes are directed to the ground, the body is thrown forward, and the legs are wide apart. In walking, the leg is thrown out violently, the foot is raised too high and is brought down in a stamping manner with the heel first, or the whole sole comes in contact with the ground. Ultimately the patient may be unable to walk without the assistance of two canes. This gait is very characteristic, and unlike that seen in any other disease. The incoördination is not only in walking, but in the performance of other movements. If the patient is asked, when in the recumbent posture, to touch the knee with one foot, the irregularity in the movement is very evident. Incoördination of the arms is less common, but usually develops in some grade. It may in rare instances exist before the incoördination of the legs. It may be tested by asking the patient to close his eyes and to touch the tip of the nose or the tip of the ear with the finger, or with the arms thrust out to bring the tips of the fingers together. The incoördination may early be noticed by a difficulty which the patient experiences in buttoning his collar or in performing one of the ordinary routine acts of dressing.

One of the most striking features of the disease is that with marked incoördination there is no loss of muscular power. The grip of the hands may be strong and firm, the power of the legs, tested by trying to flex them, may be unimpaired, and their nutrition, except toward the close, may be unaffected.

There is a remarkable muscular relaxation which enables the joints to be placed in positions of hyperextension and hyperflexion. It gives sometimes a marked backward curve to the legs. Fränkel, who calls the condition hypotonia, says it may be an early symptom.

Sensory Symptoms.—The lightning pains may persist. They vary greatly in different cases. Some patients are rendered miserable by the frequent occurrence of the attacks; others escape altogther. In addition, common symptoms are tingling, pins and needles, particularly in the feet, and areas of hyperæsthesia or of anæsthesia. The patient may complain of a change in the sensation in the soles of the feet, as if cotton was interposed between the floor and the skin. Sensory disturbances occur less frequently in the hands. Objective sensory disturbances can usually be demonstrated, and indeed almost every variety of sensory disturbance has been described. They have been carefully studied in this country by Knapp and by Patrick, and in Europe by many observers. Bands about the chest of a moderate grade of anæsthesia are not uncommon; they are apt to follow the distribution of spinal segments. The most marked disturbances are usually found on the legs. Retardation of the sense of pain is common, and a pin-prick on the foot is first felt as a simple tactile impression, and the sense of pain is not perceived for a second or two or may be delayed for as much as ten seconds. The pain felt may persist. A curious phenomenon is the loss of the power of localizing the pain. For instance, if the patient is pricked on one limb he may say that he feels it on the other (allocheiria), or a pin-prick on the foot may be felt on both feet. The muscular sense which is usually affected early, becomes much impaired and the patient no longer recognizes the position in which his limbs are placed. This may be present in the pre-ataxic stage.

Reflexes.—As mentioned, the loss of the knee-jerk is one of the earliest symptoms of the disease. Occasionally a case is found in which it is retained. The skin reflexes may at first be increased, but later are usually involved with the deep reflexes.

Special Senses.—The eye symptoms noted above may be present, but, as mentioned, ataxia is rare with atrophy of the optic nerve.

Deafness may develop, due to lesion of the auditory nerve. There may also be attacks of vertigo. Olfactory symptoms are rare.

Visceral Symptoms.—Among the most remarkable sensory disturbances are the tabetic crises, severe paroxysms of pain referred to various viscera; thus laryngeal, gastric, nephric, rectal, urethral, and clitoral crises have been described. The most common are the gastric and laryngeal. In the former there are intense pains in the stomach, vomiting, and a secretion of hyperacid gastric juice. The attack may last for several days or even longer. There may be severe pain without any vomiting. The attacks are of variable intensity and usually require morphia. Paroxysms of rectal pain and tenesmus are described. They have not been common in my experience. Laryngeal crises also are rare. There may be true spasm with dyspnœa and noisy inspiration. In one instance at least the patient has died in the attack.

The sphincters are frequently involved. Early in the disease there may be a retardation or hesitancy in making water. Later there is retention, and cystitis may occur. Unless great care is taken the inflammation may extend to the kidneys. Constipation is extremely common. Late in the disease the sphincter ani is weakened. The sexual power is usually lost in the ataxic stage.

Trophic Changes.—Skin rashes may develop in the course of the lightning pains, such as herpes, œdema, or local sweating. Alteration in the nails may occur. A perforating ulcer may develop on the foot, usually beneath the great toe. A perforating buccal ulcer has also been described. Onychia may prove very troublesome.

The arthropathies or joint lesions affect chiefly the knees. They are unquestionably associated with the disease itself, and are not necessarily a result of trauma. The condition, known as Charcot's joint, is anatomically similar to that of chronic arthritis deformans. The effusion may be rapid and there may be great disintegration and destruction of the cartilages and bones, leading to dislocation and deformity. Suppuration may occur. Spontaneous fractures may occur. Among other trophic disturbances may be mentioned atrophy of the muscles, which is usually a late manifestation, but may be localized and associated with neuritis. In any very large collection of cases many instances of atrophy are found, due either to involvement of the ventral horns or to peripheral neuritis.

Cerebral Symptoms.—Hemiplegia may develop at any stage of the disease, more commonly when it is well advanced. It may be due to hæmorrhagic softening in consequence of disease of the vessels or to progressive cortical changes. Hemianæsthesia is sometimes present. Very rarely the hemiplegia is due to coarse syphilitic disease.

Dementia paralytica frequently exists with tabes, and it may be extremely difficult to determine which has been the primary affection; indeed, some authors believe that these two diseases are simply different localizations of the same morbid process. In a majority of the cases the symptoms of locomotor ataxia have preceded those of general paresis. In other instances melancholia, dementia, or paranoia develop.

(*c*) **Paralytic Stage.**—After persisting for an indefinite number of years the patient gradually loses the power of walking and becomes bedridden or paralyzed. In this condition he is very likely to be carried off by some intercurrent affection, such as pyelo-nephritis, pneumonia, or tuberculosis.

The Course of the Disease.—A patient may remain in the pre-ataxic stage for an indefinite period; and the loss of knee-jerk and the gray atrophy of the optic nerves may be the sole indication of the true nature of the disease. In such cases incoördination rarely develops. In a majority of cases the progress is slow, and after six or eight years, sometimes less, the ataxia is well developed. The symptoms may vary a good deal; thus the pains, which may have been excessive at first, often lessen. The disease may remain stationary for years; then exacerbations occur and it makes rapid progress. Occasionally the process seems to be arrested. There are instances of what may be called acute ataxia, in which, within a year or even less, the incoördination is marked, and the paralytic stage may develop within a few months. The disease itself rarely causes death, and after becoming bedridden the patient may live for fifteen or twenty years.

Diagnosis.—In the initial stage the combination of lightning pains and the absence of knee-jerk is distinctive. The association of progressive atrophy of the optic nerves with loss of knee-jerk is also characteristic. The early ocular palsies are of the greatest importance. A squint, ptosis, or the Argyll Robertson pupil may be the first symptom, and may exist with the loss only of the knee-jerk. Loss of the knee-jerk alone, however, does occasionally occur in healthy individuals. A history of preceding syphilis lends added weight to the symptoms, and its presence or absence may be of the utmost importance in determining the diagnosis. If the possibility of syphilitic infection can be excluded, a circumstance but too rarely met with, only the most unequivocal combination of symptoms can justify the diagnosis of locomotor ataxia.

The diseases most likely to be confounded with locomotor ataxia are: (1) *Peripheral Neuritis.*—The steppage gait of arsenical, alcoholic, or diabetic paralysis is quite unlike that of locomotor ataxia. In these forms there is a paralysis of the feet and the leg is lifted high in order that the toes may clear the floor. The use of the word tabes in this connection should no longer be continued. In the rare cases in which the muscle sense nerves are particularly affected and in which there is true ataxia, the absence of the lightning pains and eye symptoms and the history will suffice in the majority of cases to make the diagnosis clear. In diphtheritic paralysis the early loss of the knee-jerk and the associated eye symptoms may suggest tabes, but the history, the existence of paralysis of the throat, and the absence of pains render a diagnosis easy.

(2) *Ataxic Paraplegia.*—Marked incoördination with spastic paralysis is characteristic of the condition which Gowers has termed ataxic paraplegia. In a majority of the cases this affection is distinguished also by the absence of pains and of eye symptoms.

(3) *Cerebral Disease.*—In diseases of the brain involving the afferent tracts ataxia is at times a prominent symptom. It is usually unilateral or limited to one limb; this, with the history and the associated symptoms, excludes tabes.

(4) *Cerebellar Disease.*—The cerebellar incoördination has only a superficial resemblance to that of locomotor ataxia, and is more a disturbance of equilibrium than a true ataxia; the knee-jerk is usually present, there are no lightning pains, no sensory disturbances; while, on the other hand, there are headache, optic neuritis, and vomiting.

(5) Some *acute affections* involving the dorsal columns of the cord may be followed by incoördination and resemble tabes very closely. In a case under my care, the gait was characteristic and Romberg's symptom was present. The knee-jerk, however, was retained and there were no ocular symptoms. The condition had developed within three or four months, and

there was a well-marked history of syphilis.   Under large doses of iodide of potassium the ataxia and other symptoms completely disappeared.

(6) *General Paresis.*—In some cases this offers a serious difficulty.   In the first place, in general paresis, tabetic symptoms often develop; on the other hand, there are cases of locomotor ataxia in which, toward the end, there are symptoms of general paresis.   Cases of unusually acute ataxia with mental symptoms belong, as a rule, to the former disease.   The question will be considered under general paresis.

(7) Visceral crises and neuralgic symptoms may lead to error, and in middle-aged men with severe, recurring attacks of gastralgia it is always well to bear in mind the possibility of tabes, and to make a careful examination of the eyes and of the knee-jerk.

Prognosis.—Complete recovery cannot be expected, but arrest of the process is not uncommon and a marked amelioration of the symptoms is frequent.   Optic-nerve atrophy, one of the most serious events in the disease, has this hopeful aspect—that incoördination rarely follows and the progress may be arrested.   The optic atrophy itself is occasionally checked. On the whole, the prognosis in tabes is bad.   The experience of such men as Weir Mitchell, Charcot, and Gowers is distinctly opposed to the belief that locomotor ataxia is ever completely cured.*   No such instance has come under my personal observation.

Treatment.—To arrest the progress and to relieve, if possible, the symptoms are the objects which the practitioner should have in view.   A quiet, well-regulated method of life is essential.   It is not well, as a rule, for a patient to give up his occupation so long as he is able to keep about and perform ordinary work.   I know tabetics who have for years conducted large businesses, and there have been several notable instances in our profession of men who have risen to distinction in spite of the existence of this disease.   Excesses of all sorts, more particularly *in baccho et venere*, should be carefully avoided.   A man in the pre-ataxic stage should not marry.

Care should be taken in the diet, particularly if gastric crises have occurred.   To secure arrest of the disease many remedies have been employed.   Although syphilis plays such an important *rôle* in the etiology, it is universally acknowledged that neither mercury nor the iodide of potassium have as a rule the slightest influence over the tabetic lesions.   To this there is but one exception—when the syphilis is comparatively recent; when the symptoms develop within two years of the primary infection, there is then a possibility of arrest by mercury and iodide of potassium. However, they do not always relieve.   In two cases of very rapidly progressing tabes following syphilis this medication was of no avail.   Of remedies which may be tried and are believed by some writers to retard the progress, the following are recommended: Arsenic in full doses, nitrate of silver in quarter-grain doses, Calabar bean, ergot, and the preparations of gold.

The treatment by suspension introduced a few years ago has already been practically abandoned.   Good effects certainly have followed in a few

---

* For a study of reputed cures, see L. C. Gray, N. Y. Medical Journal, November, 1889.

cases, but it was unreasonable from the outset, either on therapeutic or scientific grounds, to hope that by such a measure permanent changes could be induced in the pathological condition. The benefits were due in great part to suggestion and to psychical effects. In any case it must be used with caution.

For the pains, complete rest in bed, as advised by Weir Mitchell, and counter-irritation to the spine (either blisters or the thermo-cautery) may be employed. The severe spells which come on particularly after excesses of any kind are often promptly relieved by a hot bath or by a Turkish bath. A prolonged course of nitrate of silver seems in some cases to allay the pains and lessen the liability to the attacks. I have never seen ill effects from its use in spinal sclerosis. Antipyrin and antifebrin may be employed, and occasionally do good, but their analgesic powers in this disease have been greatly overrated. Cannabis indica is sometimes useful. In the severe paroxysms of pain hypodermics of morphia or of cocaine must be used. The use of morphia should be postponed as long as possible. Electricity is of very little benefit. For the severe attacks of gastralgia, morphia is also required. The laryngeal crises are rarely dangerous. An application of cocaine may be made during the spasm, or a few whiffs of chloroform may be given, or nitrite of amyl. In all cases of tabes with increased arterial tension the prolonged use of nitroglycerin, given in increasing doses until the physiological effect is produced, is of great service in allaying the neuralgic pains and diminishing the frequency of the crises. Its use must be guarded when there is aortic insufficiency. The special indication is increased tension. The bladder symptoms demand constant care. When the organ cannot be perfectly emptied the catheter should be used, and the patient may be taught its use and how to keep it thoroughly sterilized.

Fränkel's method of re-education often helps the patient to regain to a considerable extent the control of the voluntary movements which he has lost. By this method the patient is first taught, by repeated systematic efforts, to perform simple movements; from this he goes to more and more complex movements. The treatment should be directed and supervised by a trained teacher, as the result depends upon the skill of the teacher quite as much as upon the perseverance of the patient.

III. DISEASES OF THE EFFERENT OR MOTOR TRACT.

A. OF THE WHOLE TRACT.

1. Progressive (Central) Muscular Atrophy

(Poliomyelitis Anterior Chronica; Amyotrophic Lateral Sclerosis; Progressive Bulbar Paralysis).

Definition.—A disease characterized by a chronic degeneration of the motor tract. The whole tract is usually involved, but at times the degeneration is limited to the lower segments. Associated with it is a progressive atrophy of the muscles, combined with more or less spastic rigidity.

Three affections, as a rule described apart, belong together in this category: (*a*) Progressive muscular atrophy of spinal origin; (*b*) amyotrophic lateral sclerosis; and (*c*) progressive bulbar paralysis. A slow atrophic change in the motor neurones is the anatomical basis, and the disease is one of the whole motor path, involving, in many cases, the cortical, bulbar, and spinal centres. There may be simple muscular atrophy with little or no spasm, or progressive wasting with marked spasm and great increase in the reflexes. In others, there are added symptoms of involvement of the motor nuclei in the medulla—a glosso-labio-laryngeal paralysis; while in others, again, with atrophy (especially of the arms), a spastic condition of the legs and bulbar phenomena, tremors develop and signs of cortical lesion. These various stages may be traced in the same case.

For convenience, bulbar paralysis will be considered separately, and I shall here take up together *progressive muscular atrophy* and *amyotrophic lateral sclerosis.*

The disease is known as the Aran-Duchenne type of progressive muscular atrophy and as Cruveilhier's palsy, after the French physicians who early described it. Levy and Lockhart Clarke first demonstrated that the cells of the ventral horns of the spinal cord were diseased. Charcot separated two types —one with simple wasting of the muscles, due, he believed, to degeneration confined to the ventral horns (and to this he restricted the name progressive muscular atrophy—type, Aran-Duchenne); the other, in which there was spastic paralysis of the muscles followed by atrophy. As the anatomical basis for this he assumed a primary degeneration of the pyramidal tracts and a secondary atrophy of the ventral horns. To this he gave the name of amyotrophic lateral sclerosis. There is but little evidence, however, to show that any such sharp distinction can be made between these two diseases, and Leyden and Gowers regard them as identical.

Etiology.—The cause of the disease is unknown. It is more frequent in males than in females. It affects adults, developing after the thirtieth year, though occasionally younger persons are attacked. A large majority of all cases of progressive muscular atrophy under twenty-five years of age belong to the dystrophies. Cold, wet, exposure, fright, and mental worries are mentioned as possible causes. Erb has lately called attention to certain cases following injury. Hereditary influences are present in certain cases. The rare form which occurs in infancy usually affects several members of the same family. Hereditary and family influences, however, play but a small part in the etiology of this disease, and in this it is in contrast to progressive neural muscular atrophy and the dystrophies. Yet, in the Farr family, which I recorded some years ago, in which thirteen members were affected in two generations, with the exception of two, the cases occurred or proved fatal above the age of forty, and the late onset speaks rather for a central affection. The spastic form may develop late in life— after seventy—as a senile change.

Morbid Anatomy.—The essential anatomical change is a slow degeneration of the motor path, involving particularly the lower motor neurones. The upper neurones are also involved, either first, simultaneously, or at a later period. Associated with the degeneration in the cells of the ventral horns there is a degenerative atrophy of the muscles. The following are the important anatomical changes: (*a*) The gray matter of the cord shows the most marked alteration. The large ganglion cells of the ventral horns are atrophied, or, in places, have entirely disappeared, the neuroglia is increased, and the medullated fibres are much decreased. The fibres of the ventral nerve-roots passing through the white matter are wasted. (*b*) The ventral roots outside of the cord are also atrophied. (*c*) The muscles which are affected show degenerative atrophy, and the inter-muscular branches of the motor nerve are degenerated. (*d*) The degeneration of the gray matter is rarely confined to the cord, but extends to the medulla, where the nuclei of the motor cerebral nerves are found extensively wasted. (*e*) In a majority of all the cases there is sclerosis in the ventro-lateral white tracts, the lateral pyramidal tracts particularly are diseased, but the degeneration is not confined to these tracts, and extends into the ventro-lateral ground bundles. The direct cerebellar and the ventro-lateral ascending tracts are spared. The degeneration in the pyramidal tracts extends toward the brain to different levels, and in several cases has been traced to the motor cortex, the cells of which have been found degenerated. In the medulla the medial longitudinal fasciculus has been found diseased. (*f*) In those cases in which no sclerosis has been found in the pyramidal tracts there has been a sclerosis of the ventro-lateral ground bundle (short tracts).

Symptoms.—Irregular pains may precede the onset of the wasting, and cases may be treated for chronic rheumatism. The hands are usually first affected, and there is difficulty in performing delicate manipulations. The muscles of the ball of the thumb waste early, then the interossei and lumbricales, leaving marked depressions between the metacarpal bones. Ultimately the contraction of the flexor and extensor muscles and the extreme atrophy of the thumb muscles, the interossei, and lumbricales produces the claw-hand—*main en griffe* of Duchenne. The flexors or the forearm are usually involved before the extensors. In the shoulder-girdle the deltoid is first affected; it may waste even before the other muscles of the upper extremity. The trunk muscles are gradually attacked; the upper part of the trapezius long remains unaffected. Owing to the feebleness of the muscles which support it, the head tends to fall forward. The platysma myoides is unaffected and often hypertrophies. The arms and the trunk muscles may be much atrophied before the legs are attacked. The face muscles are attacked late. Ultimately the intercostal and abdominal muscles may be involved, the wasting proceeds to an extreme grade, and the patient may be actually " skin and bone," and, as " living skeletons," the cases are not uncommon in " museums " and " side-shows." Deformities and contractures result, and lordosis is almost always present. A curious twitching of the muscles (fibrillation) is a common symptom, and may occur in muscles which are not yet attacked. It is a most important symptom, but is not, as was formerly supposed, a characteristic feature of the disease. The irritability of the muscles is increased. Sensation is unimpaired, but the patient may complain of numbness and coldness of the affected limbs. The galvanic and faradic irritability of the muscles progressively diminishes and may become extinct, the galvanic persisting for the longer time. In cases of rapid wasting and paralysis there may be the reaction of degeneration. The excitability of the nerve-trunks may persist after the muscles have ceased to respond. The loss of power is usually proportionate to the wasting.

The foregoing description applies to the group of cases in which the atrophy and paralysis are flaccid—*atonic*, as Gowers calls it. In other cases, those which Charcot describes as amyotrophic lateral sclerosis, spastic paralysis precedes the wasting. This *tonic* atrophy first involves the arms and then the legs. The reflexes are greatly increased. It is one of the rare conditions in which a jaw clonus may be obtained. The most typical condition of spastic paraplegia may be produced. On starting to walk, the patient seems glued to the ground and makes ineffectual attempts to lift the toes; then four or five short, quick steps are taken on the toes with the body thrown forward; and finally he starts off, sometimes with great rapidity. Some of the patients can walk up and down stairs better than on the level. The wasting is never so extreme as in the atonic form, and the loss of power may be out of proportion to it. The sphincters are unaffected. Sexual power may be lost early. Cases are met with which correspond accurately to the clinical picture given by Charcot of amyotrophic lateral sclerosis. These are not very common, and it is much more usual to have a combination of the two types. A flaccid atrophic paralysis with increased reflexes is often met with. These differences depend upon the relative extent of the involvement of the upper and lower motor segments and the time of the involvement of each.

As the degeneration extends upward an important change takes place from the development of bulbar symptoms, which may, however, precede the spinal manifestations. The lips, tongue, face, pharynx, and larynx may be involved. The lips may be affected and articulation impaired for years before serious symptoms occur. In the final stage there may be tremor, the memory fails, and a condition of dementia may develop.

Gowers gives the following useful classification of the varieties of this affection: (1) Atonic atrophy, becoming extreme; (2) muscular weakness with spasm, but without wasting or with only slight wasting; and (3) atonic atrophy, rarely extreme in degree, with exaggeration of the reflexes. These conditions may "coexist in every degree and combination—between universal atonic atrophy on the one hand and universal spastic paralysis without wasting on the other."

Diagnosis.—Progressive (central) muscular atrophy begins, as a rule, in adult life, without hereditary or family influences (the early infantile form being an exception), and usually affects first the muscles of the thumb, and gradually involves the interossei and lumbricales. Fibrillary contractions are common, electrical changes occur, and the deep reflexes are usually increased. These characteristics are usually sufficient to distinguish it from the other forms of muscular wasting.

In syringo-myelia the symptoms may be very similar to those in the spastic form of muscular atrophy. The sensory disturbances in the former disease make, as a rule, the diagnosis clear, but when these are absent or but little developed it may be very difficult or even impossible to distinguish the diseases.

Treatment.—The disease is incurable. I have never seen the slightest benefit from drugs or electricity. The downward progress is slow but certain, though in a few cases a temporary arrest may take place. With a history of syphilis, mercury and iodide of potassium may be tried, and Gowers recommends courses of arsenic and the hypodermic injection of strychnine. Probably the most useful means is systematic massage, particularly in the spastic cases.

Bulbar Paralysis (Glosso-labio-laryngeal Paralysis).

When the disease affects the motor nuclei of the medulla first or early, it is called bulbar paralysis, but it has practically no independent existence, as the spinal cord is sooner or later involved.

Symptoms.—The disease usually begins with slight defect in the speech, and the patient has difficulty in pronouncing the dentals and linguals. The paralysis starts in the tongue, and the superior lingual muscle gradually becomes atrophied, and finally the mucous membrane is thrown into transverse folds. In the process of wasting the fibrillary tremors are seen. Owing to the loss of power in the tongue, the food is with difficulty pushed back into the pharynx. The saliva also may be increased, and is apt to accumulate in the mouth. When the lips become involved the patient can neither whistle nor pronounce the labial consonants. The mouth looks large, the lips are prominent, and there is constant drooling. The food is masticated with difficulty. Swallowing becomes difficult, owing partly to the regurgitation into the nostrils, partly to the involvement of the pharyngeal muscles. The muscles of the vocal cords waste and the voice becomes feeble, but the laryngeal paralysis is rarely so extreme as that of the lips and tongue.

The course of the disease is slow but progressive. Death often results from an aspiration pneumonia, sometimes from choking, more rarely from involvement of the respiratory centres. The mind usually remains clear. The patient may become emotional. In a majority of the cases the disease is only part of a progressive atrophy, either simple or associated with a spastic condition. In the latter stage of amyotrophic lateral sclerosis the bulbar lesions may paralyze the lips long before the pharynx or larynx becomes affected.

The *diagnosis* of the disease is readily made, either in the acute or chronic form. The involvement of the lips and tongue is usually well marked, while that of the palate may be long deferred. A condition has been described, however, which may closely simulate bulbar paralysis. This is the so-called *pseudo-bulbar* form or bulbar palsy of cerebral origin. Bilateral disease of the motor cortex in the lower part of the ascending frontal convolution, or about the knee of the internal capsule, may cause paralysis of the lips and tongue and pharynx, which closely simulates a lesion of the medulla. Sometimes the symptoms appear on one side, but in many instances they develop suddenly on both sides. A bilateral lesion has usually been found, but in several instances the disease was unilateral.

The so-called *acute bulbar paralysis* may be due to (*a*) hæmorrhagic or embolic softening in the pons and medulla; (*b*) acute inflammatory softening, analogous to polio-myelitis, occurring occasionally as a post-febrile affection. It usually comes on very suddenly, hence the term apoplectiform. The symptoms in this form may correspond closely to those of an advanced case of chronic bulbar paralysis. The sudden onset and the associated symptoms make the diagnosis easy. In these acute cases there may be loss of power in one arm, or hemiplegia, sometimes alternate hemiplegia, with paralysis on one side of the face and loss of power on the other side of the body.

2. Progressive Neural Muscular Atrophy.

This form, known also as the peroneal type, or by the names of the men who have described it most accurately of late—namely, Charcot, Marie, and Tooth—occurs either as a hereditary or as a family affection. It usually begins in early childhood, affecting first the muscles of the feet and the peroneal group; as a result of the weakening of these muscles, club-foot, either pes equinus or pes equino-varus occurs. In rare instances the disease may begin in the hands, but the upper limbs, as a rule, are not affected for some years after the legs are attacked, and the trouble then begins in the small muscles of the hands. Sensory disturbances are frequently present and form important diagnostic features. Fibrillary contractions and twitchings also occur. The electrical reactions are altered; there is either a loss or a very great decrease of the excitability, which can be demonstrated not only in the atrophic muscles, but also in muscles and nerves which are apparently normal.

This form of muscular atrophy seems to stand between the central form and the muscular dystrophies. Occurring in families and beginning in early life, it resembles the latter, but it is more like the former in that fibrillary contractions and muscular twitchings are common, that the small muscles of the hand are apt to be involved, and that electrical changes are present. In the prominence of sensory symptoms it differs from both. In cases of acquired double club-foot this disease should be suspected.

3. The Muscular Dystrophies

(*Dystrophia muscularis progressiva*, Erb).

Definition.—Muscular wasting, with or without an initial hypertrophy, beginning in various groups of muscles, usually progressive in character, and dependent on primary changes in the muscles themselves. A marked hereditary disposition is met with in the disease.

Etiology.—No etiological factors of any moment are known other than heredity. The influence may show itself by true heredity—the disease occurring in two or more generations—or several members of the same generation may be affected, showing a family tendency. Many members of the same family may be attacked through several generations. Males, as a rule, are more frequently affected than females. The diseas is usually transmitted through the mother, though she may not herself be affected. As many as 20 or 30 cases have been described in five generations. In Erb's cases 44 per cent showed no heredity. The disease usually sets in before puberty, but may be as late as the twentieth or twenty-fifth year, or in some instances even later.

Symptoms.—The first symptom noticed is, as a rule, clumsiness in the movements of the child, and on examination certain muscles or groups of muscles seem to be enlarged, particularly those of the calves. The extensors of the leg, the glutei, the lumbar muscles, the deltoid, triceps and infraspinatus, are the next most frequently involved, and may stand out with great prominence. The muscles of the neck, face, and forearm rarely suffer. Sometimes only a portion of a muscle is involved. With this hypertrophy of some muscles there is wasting of others, particularly the lower portion of the pectorals and the latissimus dorsi. The attitude when standing is very characteristic. The legs are far apart, the shoulders thrown back, the spine is greatly curved, and the abdomen protrudes. The gait is waddling and awkward. In getting up from the floor the position assumed, so well known now through Gowers' figures, is pathognomonic. The patient first turns over in the all-fours position and raises the trunk with his arms; the hands are then moved along the ground until the knees are reached; then with one hand upon a knee he lifts himself up, grasps the other knee, and gradually pushes himself into the erect posture, as it has been expressed, by climbing up his legs. The striking contrast between the feebleness of the child and the powerful-looking pseudo-hypertrophic muscles is very characteristic. The enlarged muscles may, however, be relatively very strong.

The course of the disease is slow, but progressive. Wasting proceeds and finally all traces of the enlarged condition of the muscles disappear. At this late period distortions and contractions are common.

The muscles of the shoulder-girdle are nearly always affected early in the disease, causing a symptom upon which Erb lays great stress. With the hands under the arms, when one endeavors to lift the patient, the shoulders are raised to the level of the ears, and one gets the impression as though the child were slipping through. These "loose shoulders" are very characteristic. The abnormal mobility of the shoulder-blades gives them a winged appearance, and makes the arms seem much longer than usual when they are stretched out.

The patients complain of no sensory symptoms. The atrophic muscles do not show the reaction of degeneration except in extremely rare instances.

Clinical Forms.—A number of different types have been described, depending upon the age at the onset, the muscles first affected, the occurrence of hypertrophy, the prominence of heredity, etc. But Erb has shown that there is no sharp division between these different forms, and classes them all under the name of *dystrophia muscularis progressiva*. For convenience of description he subdivides the disease into two large groups:

I. Those cases which occur in childhood.

II. The cases occurring in youth and adult life.

The first division is subdivided into (1) the hypertrophic and (2) the atrophic form.

Under the hypertrophic form, which is the pseudo-hypertrophic muscular paralysis of authors, he thinks it is useful to distinguish between the cases in which (a) the enlarged muscles have undergone lipomatosis—i. e., pseudo-hypertrophy—from those (b) in which there is a real hypertrophy.

The atrophic form also includes two subclasses: (a) Those cases in which the muscles of the face are involved early; this corresponds to the infantile form of Duchenne—the Landouzy-Dejerine type. (b) Those cases in which the face is not involved.

I. *Dystrophia muscularis progressiva infantum.*
   1. Hypertrophic form.
     (a) With pseudo-hypertrophy.
     (b) With real hypertrophy.
   2. Atrophic form.
     (a) With primary involvement of the face (infantile form of Duchenne).
     (b) Without involvement of the face.

II. *Dystrophia muscularis progressiva juvenum vel adultorum* (Erb's juvenile form).

Morbid Anatomy.—According to Erb, the disease consists in a change in the muscles themselves. At first the muscle-fibres hypertrophy, and become round; the nuclei increase, and the muscle-fibres may become fissured. At the same time there is a slight increase in the connective tissue. Sooner or later the muscle-fibres begin to atrophy, and the nuclei become greatly increased. Vacuoles and fissures appear, and the fibres finally become completely atrophic, the connective tissue becoming markedly increased. Fat may be deposited in the connective tissue to such an extent as to cause hypertrophic lipomatosis—pseudo-hypertrophy. The different stages of these changes may be found in a single muscle at the same time.

The nervous system has very generally been found to be without demonstrable lesions, but in certain cases changes in the cells of the ventral horn have been described.

Diagnosis.—The muscular dystrophies can usually be readily distinguished from the other forms of muscular atrophy.

(a) In the cerebral atrophy loss of power usually precedes the atrophy, which is either of a monoplegic or hemiplegic type.

(b) From progressive (central) muscular atrophy the distinctions are clearly marked. This form begins in the small muscles of the hand, a situation rarely if ever, affected by the dystrophies, which involve first those of the calves, the trunk, the face, or the shoulder-girdle. In the central atrophy the reaction of degeneration is present and fibrillary twitchings occur in both the atrophied and non-atrophied muscles. In many cases, in addition to the wasting in the arms, there is a spastic condition in the legs and increase in the reflexes. The central atrophies come on late in life; the dystrophies develop, as a rule, early. In the progressive muscular dystrophies heredity plays an important *rôle*, which in the central form is quite subsidiary.   In the rare cases of early infantile spinal muscular atrophy occurring in families the symptoms are so characteristic of a central disease that the diagnosis presents no difficulty.

(*c*) In the neuritic muscular atrophies, whether due to lead or to trauma, the general characters and the mode of onset are distinctive.   In the cases of multiple neuritis seen for the first time at a period when the wasting is marked there is often difficulty, but the absence of family history and the distribution are important features.   Moreover, the paralysis is out of proportion to the atrophy.   Sensory symptoms may be present, and in the cases in which the legs are chiefly involved there is usually the *steppage* gait so characteristic of peripheral neuritis.

(*d*) Progressive neural muscular atrophy.   Here heredity is also a factor, and the disease usually begins in early life, but the distribution of atrophy and paralysis, which in this affection is at first confined to the periphery of the extremities, helps to distinguish it from the dystrophies; while the occurrence of sensory symptoms, fibrillary contractions, and the marked decrease in the electrical excitability usually make the distinction clear.

The outlook in the primary muscular dystrophies is bad.   The wasting progresses uniformly, uninfluenced by treatment.   Erb holds that by electricity and massage the progress is occasionally arrested.   The general health should be carefully looked after, moderate exercise allowed, frictions with oil applied to the muscles, and when the patient becomes bedfast, as is inevitable sooner or later, care should be taken to prevent contractures in awkward positions.

The three forms of progressive muscular wasting—progressive (central) muscular atrophy, progressive neural muscular atrophy, and the muscular dystrophies—have been considered as distinct diseases, but certain recent writings make it probable that the distinction may not be so sharp as we believe.   Certain cases occur which seem not to belong to any one of the forms but to stand between them.   The changes in the muscles which were thought to be characteristic of the dystrophies have been found in the other forms.   The central form occurs as a family disease in infancy, and the nervous system has been found diseased in the dystrophies.

The whole question is in a chaotic state, and it is at present better to keep to the old divisions.   Even if it should turn out to be true, as Strümpell suggests, that all the forms depend upon a congenital tendency of the motor system to degenerate, they represent well-defined clinical types, into which the cases can, as a rule, be grouped without difficulty, while corresponding to each there is a fairly well-determined anatomical basis.

B. SYSTEM DISEASES OF THE UPPER MOTOR SEGMENT.

The question of an uncomplicated primary degeneration of the upper motor neurones has not been decided.   Cases with a clinical picture corresponding to this lesion are not uncommon, and they may persist for a long time without change.   Unfortunately the cases which have come to autopsy have shown various conditions.   In only two or three has the disease been so nearly confined to the pyramidal tract that they can be used as an argument for the independence of this condition. The cases of Minkowski, Dreschfeld, and Strümpell are not absolutely conclusive, as they are not quite pure, although they go far to prove that a degeneration in the pyramidal tract may be uncomplicated, at least for a long time. The same may be said for the group of cases described by Bernhardt and Strümpell under the name hereditary spastic spinal paralysis, in which the extensive systemic degeneration of the pyramidal tracts is combined with slight degeneration in other tracts of the cord.

1. Spastic Paralysis of Adults

(Tabes dorsalis spasmodique ; Primary Lateral Sclerosis).

Definition.—A gradual loss of power with spasm of the muscles of the body, the lower extremities being first and most affected, unaccompanied by muscular atrophy, sensory disturbance, or other symptoms. The pathological anatomy is undetermined, but a systemic degeneration of the pyramidal tracts is assumed.

Symptoms.—The general *symptoms* of spastic paraplegia in adults are very distinctive. The patient complains of feeling tired, of stiffness in the legs, and perhaps of pains of a dull aching character in the back or in the calves. There may be no definite loss of power, even when the spastic condition is well established. In other instances there is definite weakness. The stiffness is felt most in the morning. In a well-developed case the gait is most characteristic. The legs are moved stiffly and with hesitation, the toes drag and catch against the ground, and, in extreme cases, when the ball of the foot rests upon the ground a distinct clonus develops. The legs are kept close together, the knees touch, and in certain cases the adductor spasm may cause cross-legged progression. On examination, the legs may at first appear tolerably supple, perhaps flexed and extended readily. In other cases the rigidity is marked, particularly when the limbs are extended. The spasm of the adductors of the thigh may be so extreme that the legs are separated with the greatest difficulty. In cases of this extreme rigidity the patient usually loses the power of walking. The nutrition is well maintained, the muscles may be hypertrophied. The reflexes are greatly increased. The slightest touch upon the patellar tendon produces an active knee-jerk. The rectus clonus and the ankle clonus are easily obtained. In some instances the slightest touch may throw the legs into violent clonic spasm, the condition to which Brown-Séquard gave the name of spinal epilepsy. The superficial reflexes are also increased. The arms may be unaffected for years, but occasionally they become weak and stiff at the same time as the legs. This was the case in a colored boy who was in my wards for several years. He presented a degree of general spastic rigidity that I have never seen equalled. The disease had begun after puberty, developed gradually, and remained quite stationary for more than a year before he left the wards. There were no other symptoms.

The course of the disease is progressively downward. Years may elapse before the patient is bedridden. Involvement of the sphincters, as a rule,

59

is late; occasionally, however, it is early. The sensory symptoms rarely progress, and the patients may retain their general nutrition and enjoy excellent health. Ocular symptoms are rare.

The *diagnosis*, so far as the clinical picture is concerned, is readily made, but it is often very difficult to determine accurately the nature of the underlying pathological condition. A history of syphilis is present in many of the cases. Cases which have run a fairly typical clinical course upon coming to autopsy have been found to have been due to very different conditions—transverse myelitis, multiple sclerosis, cerebral tumor, etc. General paralysis of the insane may begin with symptoms of spastic paraplegia, and Westphal believed that it was only in relation to this disease that a primary sclerosis of the pyramidal tracts ever occurred. In any case the diagnosis of primary systemic degeneration of the pyramidal tract is, to say the least, doubtful.

2. Spastic Paralysis of Infants—Spastic Diplegia—Birth Palsies

(Paraplegia cerebralis spastica (Heine); Little's Disease).

In this condition there is a paralysis with spasm of all extremities, dating from or shortly succeeding birth, more rarely following the fevers or an attack of convulsions. The legs are usually more involved than the arms; there is no wasting, no disturbance of sensation. The reflexes are increased. The mental condition is usually much disturbed. The patients are often imbeciles or idiots, helpless in mind and body. Ataxic and athetoid movements of the most exaggerated kind may occur.

While a limited number only of cases of infantile hemiplegia are congenital, on the other hand, in spastic diplegia and paraplegia a large proportion of the cases results from injury at birth. The arms may be so slightly affected as to make it difficult to determine whether it is a case of diplegia or paraplegia. The disease usually dates from birth, and a majority of the children are born in first labors or are forceps cases, and are at birth asphyxiated blue babies. Ross suggests that in feet presentations there may be laceration or tearing of the cerebro-spinal membranes. Premature birth is also given as a cause.

Morbid Anatomy.—The birth palsies which ultimately induce the spastic diplegias or paraplegias are most frequently the result of meningeal hæmorrhage. The importance of this condition has been shown by the studies of Litzmann and Sarah J. McNutt. The bleeding may come from the veins, or, as in one case which I saw with Hirst, from the longitudinal sinus. The hæmorrhage has in many cases been thickest over the motor areas, and it seems probable that the sclerosis found in these cases may result from compression by the blood-clot. In other instances the condition may be due to a fœtal meningo-encephalitis. In 16 autopsies collected in the literature, in which the patients died at ages varying from two to thirty, the anatomical condition was either a diffuse atrophy, which was most common, or porencephalus. From the fact that certain of the cases are born prematurely, before the pyramidal tracts are developed, it has been assumed by some that a non-development of these tracts is the cause of the disease. This hypothonia has been urged by Marie, who limits the name spastic paraplegia to that group of the infantile cases in which there is no evidence of involvement of the brain—intellectual disturbances, epilepsy, etc., and it is in these cases that he believes the pyramidal tract has remained undeveloped.

Symptoms.—At first nothing abnormal may be noticed about the child. In some instances there have been early and frequent convulsions; then at the age when the child should begin to walk it is noticed that the limbs are not used readily, and on examination a stiffness of the legs and arms is found. Even at the age of two the child may not be able to sit up, and often the head is not well supported by the neck muscles. The rigidity, as a rule, is more marked in the legs, and there is adductor spasm. When supported on the feet, the child either rests on its toes and the inner surface of the feet, with the knees close together, or the legs may be crossed. The stiffness of the upper limbs varies. It may be scarcely noticeable or the rigidity may be as marked as in the legs. When the spastic condition affects the arms as well as the legs, we speak of the condition as diplegia; when the legs alone are involved, as paraplegia. There seems to be no sufficient reason for considering them separately. Constant irregular movements of the arms are not uncommon. The child has great difficulty in grasping an object. The spasm and weakness may be more evident on one side than the other. The mental condition is, as a rule, defective and convulsive seizures are common.

Associated with the spastic paralysis are two allied conditions of considerable interest, characterized by spasm and disordered movements. A child with spastic diplegia may present, in an unusual degree, irregular movements of the muscles. In attempting to grasp an object the fingers may be thrown out in a stiff, spasmodic, irregular manner, or there may be constant irregular movements of the shoulders, arms, and hands, with slight incoördination of the head. Cases of this description have been described as *chorea spastica,* and they may be difficult to separate from multiple sclerosis and from Friedreich's ataxia.

A still more remarkable condition is that of *bilateral athetosis,* in which there is a combination of spasm more or less marked with the most extraordinary bizarre movements of the muscles. The condition, as a rule, dates from infancy. The patient may not be able to walk. The head is turned from side to side; there are continual irregular movements of the face muscles, and the mouth is drawn and greatly distorted. The extremities are more or less rigid, particularly in extension. On the slightest attempt to move, often spontaneously, there are extraordinary movements of the arms and legs, particularly of the arms, somewhat like though much more exaggerated than athetosis. The patients are often unable to help themselves on account of these movements. The reflexes are increased. The mental condition is variable. The patient may be idiotic, but in 3 of the 6 cases which I have seen the patients were intelligent. Massalongo, who has carefully studied this condition, describes 3 cases in one family. I have collected 53 cases from the literature, 33 of which occurred in males and 20 in females.

3. Hereditary Spastic Paraplegia

(Hereditary Spastic Spinal Paralysis; Family form of Spastic Spinal Paralysis).

Much interest has been aroused in this type, cases of which have been described by Gee, Strümpell, Bernhardt, Latimer, Newmark, Erb, Tooth, Sachs, and others. Apparently we have to distinguish in this form two groups of cases. In one the disease develops in infancy or childhood, and the cases have all the characters of a *paraplegia spastica cerebralis*. In these cases, however, the symptoms pointing to disease of the brain, mental disturbances, epilepsy, etc., may be entirely wanting, and it was in relation to them that Erb made the suggestion that possibly too much stress had been laid upon the cerebral disease. He thought that a systemic degeneration of the lower part of the pyramidal tract accounted for the symptoms. The cases of amaurotic family idiocy described by Sachs, Peterson, Hirsch, and others do not belong here, although in them there is also a sclerosis of the pyramidal tract.

In the other group of cases, described by Bernhardt and Strümpell, the disease develops later, usually between twenty and thirty. The progress is very slow, extending over many years. At first there is no paralysis, only a spastic condition of the legs. The arms are affected later. Toward the end there may be a true paralysis, sensation may be affected, and the bladder may be slightly involved. In a fatal case of Strümpell's there was an extensive degeneration of the pyramidal tract and slight disease of the columns of Goll and of the direct cerebellar tract.

Amaurotic Family Idiocy.—A remarkable form of infantile paralysis has been described by Sachs, Peterson, and Hirsch. The symptoms as summarized by Sachs are: 1. Psychic disturbances that appear in early life (first or second year) and progress to total idiocy. 2. Paresis, and ultimately complete paralysis of the extremities, which may be either flaccid or spastic. 3. Increased, decreased, or normal tendon reflexes. 4. Partial, followed by total, blindness (macular changes, with subsequent atrophy of the optic nerve). 5. Marasmus and death, usually before the second year. 6. Distinct familial type. Occasional symptoms are nystagmus, strabismus, hyperacusis, or impairment of hearing. The pathological changes are primitive type of the cerebral convolutions, macrogyria, degenerative changes in the large pyramidal cells, absence of the tangential fibres, and decrease of the fibres of the white matter. The blood-vessels are normal. There is also degeneration of the pyramidal columns of the cord. Of 27 cases collected by Sachs, 17 occurred in six families; all in Jews.

4. Erb's Syphilitic Spinal Paralysis.

Erb has described a symptom group under the term syphilitic spinal paralysis, to which much attention has been given. The points upon which he lays stress are a very gradual onset with a development finally of the features of a spastic paresis; the tendon reflexes are greatly increased, but the muscular rigidity is slight in comparison with the exaggerated deep reflexes. There is rarely much pain, and the sensory disturbances are trivial, but there may be paræsthesia and the girdle sensation. The bladder and rectum are usually involved, and there is sexual failure or impotence. And, lastly, improvement is not infrequent. A majority of instances of spastic paralysis of adults not the result of slow compression of the cord are associated with syphilis and belong to this group.

Erb thought the lesion to be a special form of transverse myelitis, but perhaps it should be classed with the system diseases, under the name toxic spastic spinal paralysis.

5. Secondary Spastic Paralysis.

Following any lesion of the pyramidal tract we may have spastic paralysis; thus, in a transverse lesion of the cord, whether the result of slow compression (as in caries), chronic myelitis, the pressure of tumor, chronic meningo-myelitis, or multiple sclerosis, degeneration takes place in the pyramidal tracts, below the point of disease. The legs soon become stiff and rigid, and the reflexes increase. Bastian has shown that in compression paraplegia if the transverse lesion is complete, the limbs may be flaccid, without increase in the reflexes—*paraplégie flasque* of the French. The condition of the patient in these secondary forms varies very much. In chronic myelitis or in multiple sclerosis he may be able to walk about, but with a characteristic spastic gait. In the compression myelitis, in fracture, or in caries, there may be complete loss of power with rigidity.

It may be difficult or even impossible to distinguish these cases from those of primary spastic paralysis. Reliance is to be placed upon the associated symptoms; when these are absent no definite diagnosis as to the cause of the spastic paralysis can be given.

6. Hysterical Spastic Paraplegia.

There is no spinal-cord disease which may be so accurately mimicked as spastic paraplegia. In the hysterical form there is wasting, the sensory symptoms are not marked, the loss of power is not complete, and there is not that extensor spasm so characteristic of organic disease. The reflexes are, as a rule, increased. The knee-jerk is present, and there may be a well-developed ankle clonus. Gowers calls attention to the fact that it is usually a spurious clonus, " due to a half-voluntary contraction in the calf muscles." A true clonus does occur, however, and there may be the greatest difficulty in determining whether or not the case is one of hysterical paraplegia. The hysterical contracture will be considered later.

C. SYSTEM DISEASES OF THE LOWER MOTOR SEGMENT.

1. Chronic Anterior Polio-myelitis

(*Progressive Muscular Atrophy—Aran-Duchenne*).

This disease has been considered as one of the types making up the progressive (central) muscular atrophies. In certain rare cases the process is confined to the lower motor segments. They, however, differ so little clinically from many of the cases in which the pyramidal tracts are involved that it seems better to make no sharp distinction between them. The same may be said of chronic bulbar paralysis.

2. Ophthalmoplegia.

This disease is at times due to a chronic degeneration of the nuclei of the motor nerves of the eyeballs, and so is a system disease of the lower motor segment. It is treated of in connection with the other ocular palsies for the sake of simplicity and because all ophthalmoplegias are not due to nuclear disease.

3. Acute Anterior Polio-myelitis

(Atrophic Spinal Paralysis; Infantile Paralysis).

This disease was formerly believed to be due to an acute inflammation of the cells of the ventral horns, depending upon a selective action of the poison for these cells, and would on this theory have properly been classed as a system disease of the lower motor neurones. Later observations indicate that the distribution of the inflammation depends upon the blood supply, and possibly that a thrombotic or an embolic process may act as the exciting cause of the inflammation. Just why this process should always act through the arteries supplying the ventral horns has not been explained. In any case the disease appears to be a focal inflammation, and not a system disease in the sense that the term is used in this work.

Clinically, the symptoms are confined to the motor system, and for this reason it is considered here and not with the focal lesions of the spinal cord, where our present views of its pathology would place it.

Definition.—An affection occurring most commonly within the first three years of life, characterized by fever, loss of power in certain muscles, and rapid atrophy.

Etiology.—The cause of the disease is unknown. It has been attributed to cold, to the irritation from dentition, or to overexertion. Since the days of Mephibosheth, parents have been inclined to attribute this form of paralysis to the carelessness of nurses in letting the children fall, but very rarely is the disease induced by traumatism, and in perhaps a majority of the cases the child is attacked while in full health. As Sinkler has pointed out, the cases are more common in the warm months. Boys are more liable to be affected than girls. Several instances of the occurrence of numerous cases together in epidemic form have been described. Medin reports from Stockholm an epidemic in which from the 9th of August to the 23d of September 29 cases came under observation. In two instances two children in the same family were attacked within a few days.

The most remarkable epidemic is that which occurred in the vicinity of Rutland, Vt., and which has been recorded by Caverly (New York Medical Record, 1894, ii). One hundred and nineteen cases occurred during the summer of 1894; 85 were under six years of age; 18 died.

Although most frequent in children, it develops occasionally in young adults, or even in middle-aged persons.

Morbid Anatomy.—The disease is oftenest seen in either the cervical or lumbar enlargements. In very early cases, such as those described by David Drummond and Charlewood Turner, the lesion has been that of an acute hæmorrhagic myelitis with degeneration and rapid destruction of the large ganglion cells. The condition may be strictly confined to the ventral cornua; in some instances there is slight meningeal involvement. The investigations of Goldscheider, Siemerling, and others have demonstrated the arterial origin of the disease, which is localized in the parts supplied by the ventral median branch of the ventral spinal artery. Occasionally the changes are found in the region of distribution of the ventral radicular arteries. Marie thinks that the initial process is embolism or thrombosis of the arteries of the ventral horns, the result of an acute infection. In cases in which the examination is not made for some months or years the changes are very characteristic. The ventral cornu in the affected region is greatly atrophied and the large motor cells are either entirely absent or only a few remain. The affected half of the cord may be considerably smaller than the other. The ventro-lateral column may show slight sclerotic changes, chiefly in the pyramidal tract. The corresponding ventral nerve roots are atrophied, and the muscles are wasted and gradually undergo a fatty and sclerotic change.

Symptoms.—In a majority of the cases, after slight indisposition and feverishness, the child is noticed to have lost the use of one limb. Convulsions at the outset are rare, not constant as in the acute cerebral palsies of children. Fever is usually present, the temperature rising to 101°, sometimes to 103°. Pain is often complained of in the early stages. This may be localized in the back or between the shoulders; any pressure on the paralyzed limbs may be painful, causing the patient to cry out when he is moved in bed. The paralysis is abrupt in its onset and, as a rule, is not progressive, but reaches its maximum in a very short time, even within twenty-four hours. It is rarely generalized. The suddenness of onset is remarkable and suggests a primary affection of the blood-vessels, a view which the hæmorrhagic character of the early lesion supports. The distribution of the paralysis is very variable. Its irregularity and lack of symmetry is quite characteristic of the disease. One or both arms may be affected, one arm and one leg, or both legs; or it may be a crossed paralysis, the right leg and the left arm. In the upper extremities the paralysis is rarely complete and groups of muscles may be affected. As Remak has pointed out, there is an upper-arm and a lower-arm type of palsy. The deltoid, the biceps, brachialis anticus, and supinator longus may be affected in the former, and in the latter the extensors or flexors of the fingers and wrists. This distribution is due to the fact that muscles acting functionally together are represented near each other in the spinal cord.

In the legs the tibialis anticus and extensor groups of muscles are more affected than the hamstrings and glutei. The muscles of the face are very rarely, the sphincters hardly ever involved. While the rule is for the paralysis to be abrupt and sudden, there are cases in which it comes on slowly and takes from three to five days for its development. At first the affected limb looks natural, and as children between two and three are usually fat, very little change may be noticed for some time; but the atrophy proceeds rapidly, and the limb becomes flaccid and feels soft and flabby. Usually as early as the end of the first week the reaction of degeneration is present. The nerves are found to have lost their irritability. The muscles do not react to the induced current, but to the constant current they respond by a sluggish contraction, usually to a weaker current than is normal. The paralysis remains stationary for a time, and then there is gradual improvement. Complete recovery is rare, and, when the anatomical condition is considered, is scarcely to be expected. The large motor cells of the cornua, when thoroughly disintegrated, cannot be restored. In too many cases the improvement is only slight and permanent paralysis remains in certain groups. Sensation is unaffected; the skin reflexes are absent, and the deep reflexes in the affected muscles are usually lost.

When the paralysis persists the wasting is extreme, the growth of the bones of the affected limb is arrested, or at any rate retarded, and the joints may be very relaxed; as, for instance, when the deltoid is affected, the head of the humerus is no longer kept in contact with the glenoid cavity. In the later stages very serious deformities are produced by the contracture of the muscles.

Diagnosis.—The condition is only too evident in the majority of cases. There is a flaccid, flabby paralysis of one or more limbs which has set in abruptly. The rapid wasting, the lax state of the muscles, the electrical reactions, and the absence of reflexes distinguish it from the cerebral palsies. In multiple neuritis, a rare disease in childhood, the paralysis is bilaterally symmetrical, affects the muscles at the periphery of the limbs, and is combined with sensory symptoms. The pseudo-paresis of rickets is a condition to be carefully distinguished. In this the loss of power is in the legs, rapid atrophy is not present, certain movements are possible but painful. The general hyperæsthesia of the skin, the characteristic changes in the bones, and the diffuse sweats are present. Disease of the hip or knee may produce a pseudo-paralysis which can with care be readily distinguished.

Prognosis.—The outlook in any case for complete recovery is bad. The natural course of the disease must be borne in mind; the sudden onset, the rapid but not progressive loss of power, a stationary period, then marked improvement in certain muscle groups, and finally in many cases contractures and deformities. There is no other disease in which the physician is so often subject to unjust criticism, and the friends should be told at the outset that in the severe and extensive paralysis complete recovery should not be expected. The best to be hoped for is a gradual restoration of power in certain muscle groups. In estimating the probable grade of permanent paralysis, the electrical examination is of great value.

Treatment.—The treatment of acute infantile paralysis has a bright and a dark side. In a case of any extent complete recovery cannot be expected; on the other hand, it is remarkable how much improvement may finally take place in a limb which is at first completely flaccid and helpless. The following treatment may be pursued: If seen in the febrile stage, a brisk laxative and a fever mixture may be given. The child should be in bed and the affected limb or limbs wrapped in cotton. As in the great majority of cases the damage is already done when the physician is called and the disease makes no further progress, the application of blisters and other forms of counter-irritation to the back is irrational and only cruel to the child.

The general nutrition should be carefully maintained by feeding the child well, and taking it out of doors every day. As soon as the child can bear friction the affected part should be carefully rubbed; at first once a day, subsequently morning and evening. Any intelligent mother can be taught systematically to rub, knead, and pinch the muscles, using either the bare hand or, better still, sweet oil or cod-liver oil. This is worth all the other measures advised in the disease, and should be systematically practised for months, or even, if necessary, a year or more. Electricity has a much more limited use, and cannot be compared with massage in maintaining the nutrition of the muscles. The faradic current should be applied to those muscles which respond. The essence of the treatment is in maintaining the nutrition of the muscles, so that in the gradual improvement which takes place in parts, at least, of the affected segments of the cord the motor impulses may have to deal with well-nourished, not atrophied muscle fibres.

Of medicines, in the early stage ergot and belladonna have been warmly recommended, but it is unlikely that they have the slightest influence. Later in the disease strychnia may be used with advantage in one or two minim doses of the liquor strychniæ, which, if it has no other effect, is a useful tonic.

The most distressing cases are those which come under the notice of the physician six, eight, or twelve months after the onset of the paralysis, when one leg or one arm or both legs are flaccid and have little or no motion. Can nothing be done? A careful electrical test should be made to ascertain which muscles respond. This may not be apparent at first, and several applications may be necessary before any contractility is noticed. With a few lessons an intelligent mother can be taught to use the electricity as well as to apply the massage. If in a case in which the paralysis has lasted for six or eight months no observable improvement takes place in the next six months with thorough and systematic treatment, little or no hope can be entertained of further change.

In the later stage care should be taken to prevent the deformities resulting from the contractions. Great benefit results from a carefully applied apparatus. The tendon transplantation introduced by Goldthwaite seems to be a distinct advantage in many cases. Eulenberg has recently reported a case (1898) in which the pes equinus was marked; he was able to afford notable relief by tendon implantation. Half of the tendo-Achilles and a part of the tendon of the soleus were implanted upon the tendons of the peroneus longus et brevis, the remaining half of the tendo-Achilles being divided. The transference of the functions from the flexors to the pronators was satisfactorily accomplished, and the results were surprisingly beneficial.

4. Acute and Subacute Polio-myelitis in Adults.

An acute polio-myelitis in adults, the exact counterpart of the disease in children, is recognized. A majority, however, of the cases described under this heading have been multiple neuritis; but the suddenness of onset, the rapid wasting, and the marked reaction of degeneration are thought by some to be distinguishing features. Multiple neuritis may, however, set in with rapidity; there may be great wasting and the reaction of degeneration is sometimes present. The time element alone may determine the true nature. Recovery in a case of extensive multiple paralysis from polio-myelitis will certainly be with loss of power in certain groups of muscles; whereas, in multiple neuritis the recovery, while slow, may be perfect.

The subacute form, the *paralysie générale spinale antérieure subaiguë* of Duchenne, is in all probability a peripheral palsy. The paralysis usually begins in the legs with atrophy of the muscles, then the arms are involved, but not the face. Sensation is, as a rule, not involved.

5. Acute Ascending (Landry's) Paralysis.

Definition.—An advancing paralysis, beginning in the legs, rapidly extending to the trunk and arms, and finally, in many cases, involving the muscles of respiration. It presents a remarkable similarity in its symptoms to certain cases of polyneuritis, with which it is now grouped by many writers.

Etiology and Pathology.—This disease occurs most commonly in males between the twentieth and thirtieth years. It has sometimes followed the specific fevers. An elaborate study of 93 cases collected from the literature has been made by James Ross, who concludes that in etiology, symptoms, course, and termination it conforms to a peripheral neuritis. Neuwerk and Barth have reached a similar conclusion. In their case an interstitial neuritis was found in the nerve roots, but the peripheral nerves were normal. Spiller found in a rapidly fatal case destructive changes in the peripheral nerves and corresponding alterations in the cell bodies of the ventral horns. He suggests that the toxic agent acts on the lower motor neurones as a whole, and that possibly the reason why no lesions were found in some of the cases is that the more delicate histological methods were not used. We may regard the disease, then, as an acute poisoning of the lower motor neurones.

Symptoms.—Weakness of the legs, gradually progressing, often with tolerable rapidity, is the first symptom. In some cases within a few hours the paralysis of the legs becomes complete. The muscles of the trunk are next affected, and within a few days, or even less in more acute cases, the arms are also involved. The neck muscles are next attacked, and finally the muscles of respiration, deglutition, and articulation. The reflexes are lost, but the muscles neither waste nor show electrical changes. The sensory symptoms are variable; in some cases tingling, numbness, and hyperæsthesia have been present. In the more characteristic cases sensation is intact and the sphincters are uninvolved. Enlargement of the spleen has been noticed in several cases. The course of the disease is variable. It may prove fatal in less than two days. Other cases persist for a week or for two weeks. In some instances recovery has occurred, but in a large proportion of the cases the disease is fatal.

The *diagnosis* is difficult, particularly from certain forms of multiple neuritis, and if we include in Landry's paralysis the cases in which sensation is involved, distinction between the two affections is impossible. We apparently have to recognize the existence of a rapidly advancing motor paralysis without involvement of the sphincters, without wasting or electrical changes in the muscles, without trophic lesions, and without fever—features sufficient to distinguish it from either the acute central myelitis or the polio-myelitis anterior. It is doubtful, however, whether these characters always suffice to enable us to differentiate the cases of multiple neuritis.

6. ASTHENIC (BULBAR) PARALYSIS

(Myasthenia gravis pseudo-paralytica ; Erb-Goldflam's Symptom-complex).

During the last few years much attention has been given to this remarkable affection, of which a number of cases have been reported. The chief characteristics are the rapidity with which the muscles become exhausted, the great variability of the symptoms from day to day, the occurrence of remissions and relapses, the sudden attacks of paralysis of respiration and deglutition, and the absence of muscular atrophy, the reaction of degeneration and sensory symptoms. The onset is usually acute or subacute, chiefly in young persons. The external eye muscles, the muscles of mastication, the facial muscles, the muscles of deglutition, and certain spinal muscles may be quickly involved. Any repeated efforts with the affected muscles causes them to become completely exhausted and paralyzed for the time being. They recover their power after a rest. In certain cases there is a true paresis, which persists. After repeated stimulation by electricity the muscles may become exhausted and cease to respond (myasthenic reaction, Golly). The affection may prove fatal, and as no well-defined anatomical lesions have been discovered, a dynamic change in the lower motor neurones has been assumed to explain the condition.

IV. COMBINED SYSTEM DISEASES.

When the disease is not confined within the limits of either the afferent or efferent systems, but affects both, it is known as a *combined system disease*. Some authors contend that the diseases usually classed under this head are not really system diseases, but are diffuse processes. This is the view taken by Leyden and Goldscheider, who limit the term system disease to locomotor ataxia and progressive muscular atrophy.

In certain cases of locomotor ataxia which have run a fairly typical course there may be found after death, besides the anatomical picture corresponding to this disease, a moderate degeneration of the pyramidal tracts and of the ventral horns. In progressive muscular atrophy, on the other hand, there may be degeneration in the dorsal column. During life these secondary involvements of other systems, as they may be termed, may or may not be accompanied by demonstrable symptoms, and when such do occur they make their appearance late in the disease.

There is another group of cases in which from the very first the symptoms point to an involvement of both the afferent and efferent systems, and it is to these that the term primary combined system disease is usually limited.

1. Ataxic Paraplegia.

This name is applied by Gowers to a disease characterized clinically by a combination of ataxia and spastic paraplegia, and anatomically by involvement of the dorsal and lateral columns.

The disease is most common in middle-aged males. Exposure to cold and traumatism have been occasional antecedents. In striking contrast to ordinary tabes a history of syphilis is rarely to be obtained.

The anatomical features are a sclerosis of the dorsal columns, which is not more marked in the lumbar region and not specially localized in the root zone of the cuneate fasciculi. The involvement of the lateral columns is diffuse, not always limited to the pyramidal tracts, and there may be an annular sclerosis. Marie believes that in many cases the distribution of the sclerosis is due to the arterial supply and not to a true systemic degeneration, the vessels involved being branches of the dorsal spinal artery.

The *symptoms* are well defined. The patient complains of a tired feeling in the legs, not often of actual pain. The sensory symptoms of true tabes are absent. An unsteadiness in the gait gradually develops with progressive weakness. The reflexes are increased from the outset, and there may be well-developed ankle clonus. Rigidity of the legs slowly comes on, but it is rarely so marked as in the uncomplicated cases of lateral sclerosis. From the start incoördination is a well-characterized feature, and the difficulty of walking in the dark or swaying when the eyes are closed may, as in true tabes, be the first symptom to attract attention. In walking the patient uses a stick, keeps the eyes fixed on the ground, the legs far apart, but the stamping gait, with elevation and sudden descent of the feet, is not often seen. The incoördination may extend to the arms. Sensory symptoms are rare, but Gowers calls attention to a dull, aching pain in the sacral region. The sphincters usually become involved. Eye symptoms are rare. Late in the disease mental symptoms may develop, similar to those of general paresis.

In well-marked cases the *diagnosis* is easy. The combination of marked incoördination with retention of the reflexes and more or less spasm are characteristic features. The absence of ocular and sensory symptoms is an important point.

2. Primary Combined Sclerosis (Putnam).

In addition to the ataxic paraplegia just mentioned, here may be considered certain cases which are characterized anatomically by a relatively chronic sclerosis of the dorsal columns, of the lateral columns, chiefly the pyramidal tract, and also of the cerebellar tract. With these are usually associated more acute changes in adjoining areas, either diffuse or systemic, some grade of degeneration in the gray matter, and involvement of the nerve roots. This form has been studied by J. J. Putnam and Dana. The cases are usually in women—7 out of 19 collected by Dana; the ages, from forty-five to sixty-four. The disease runs a rather rapid course. Neuropathic inheritance is present in some instances. Putnam thinks that possibly both lead and arsenic play a part in the etiology.

The *symptoms* are both sensory and motor. The onset is usually with numbness in the extremities, progressive loss of strength, and emaciation. Paraplegia gradually develops, before which there have been, as a rule, spastic symptoms with exaggerated knee-jerk. The arms are affected less than the legs. Mental symptoms suggestive of dementia paralytica may develop toward the close.

The *diagnosis* of this mixed sclerosis rests upon the combination of sensory and motor symptoms with the presence of exaggerated reflexes. As stated, the sensory features consist chiefly of paræsthesia, and there may be difficulty in distinguishing the condition from multiple neuritis. The frequency of the disease in more or less enfeebled or anæmic women past middle life is also an important feature.

3. Hereditary Ataxia (*Friedreich's Ataxia*).

In 1861 Friedreich reported 6 cases of a form of hereditary ataxia, and the affection has usually gone by his name. Unfortunately, *paramyoclonus multiplex* is also called Friedreich's disease; so it is best, if his name is used in connection with this affection, to term it Friedreich's ataxia. It is a very different disease in many respects from ordinary tabes. It may or may not be hereditary. It is really a family disease, several brothers and sisters being, as a rule, affected. The 143 cases analyzed by Griffith occurred in 71 unrelated families. In his series inheritance of the disease itself occurred in only 33 cases. Various influences in the parents have been noted; alcoholism in only 7 cases. Syphilis has rarely been present. Of the 143 cases, 86 were males and 57 females. The disease sets in early in life, and in Griffith's series 15 occurred before the age of two years, 39 before the sixth year, 45 between the sixth and tenth years, 20 between the eleventh and fifteenth years, 18 between the sixteenth and twentieth years, and 5 between the twentieth and twenty-fifth years.

The *morbid anatomy* shows an extensive sclerosis of the dorsal and lateral columns of the spinal cord. The periphery, and the cerebellar tracts are usually involved. The observations of Dejerine and Letulle are of special interest, since they seem to indicate that the change in this disease is a neurogliar (ectodermal) sclerosis, differing entirely from the ordinary spinal sclerosis. According to this view, Friedreich's disease is a gliosis of the dorsal columns due to developmental errors; but the question is still unsettled.

Symptoms.—The ataxia differs somewhat from the ordinary form. The incoördination begins in the legs, but the gait is peculiar. It is swaying, irregular, and more like that of a drunken man. There is not the characteristic stamping gait of the true tabes. Romberg's symptom may or may not be present. The ataxia of the arms occurs early and is very marked; the movements are almost choreiform, irregular, and somewhat swaying. In making any voluntary movement the action is overdone, the prehension is claw-like, and the fingers may be spread or overextended just before grasping an object. The hand frequently moves about an object for a moment and then suddenly pounces upon it. There are irregular, swaying movements, some of which are choreiform, of the head and shoulders. There is present in many cases what is known as static ataxia, that is to say, ataxia of quiet action. It occurs when the body is held erect or when a limb is extended—irregular, oscillating movements of the head and body or of the extended limb.

Sensory symptoms are not usually present. The deep reflexes are lost early in the disease, and, next to the ataxia, this is the most constant and important symptom (Strümpell). The skin reflexes are usually normal, and the pupillary reflex to light is practically never affected.

Nystagmus is a characteristic symptom. Atrophy of the optic nerve rarely occurs. A striking feature is early deformity of the feet. There is talipes equinus, and the patient walks on the outer edge of the feet. The big toe is flexed dorsally on the first phalanx. Lateral curvature of the spine is very common.

Trophic lesions are rare. As the disease advances paralysis comes on and may ultimately be complete. Some of the patients never walk.

Disturbance of speech is common. It is usually slow and scanning; the expression is often dull; the mental power is, as a rule, maintained, but late in the disease becomes impaired.

The *diagnosis* of the disease is not difficult when several members of a family are affected. The onset in childhood, the curious form of incoördination, the loss of knee-kicks, the early talipes equinus, the position of the great toe, the scoliosis, the nystagmus, and scanning speech make up an unmistakable picture. The disease is often confounded with chorea, with the ordinary form of which it has nothing in common. With hereditary chorea it has certain similarities, but usually this disease does not set in until after the thirtieth year.

The affection lasts for many years and is incurable. Care should be taken to prevent contractures.

Cerebellar Type.—There is a form of hereditary ataxia, described by Marie as *cerebellar heredo-ataxia*, which starts later in life, after the age of twenty, with disability in the legs, but the gait is less ataxic than "groggy." The knee-jerks are retained, and a spastic condition of the legs ultimately develops. There is no scoliosis, nor does club-foot develop. Sanger Brown's cases, 25 in one family, and J. H. Neff's, 13, appear to belong to this type. The cerebellum has been found atrophied in 2 cases.

4. PROGRESSIVE INTERSTITIAL HYPERTROPHIC NEURITIS OF INFANTS.

Under this imposing title Dejerine and Sottas described a rare and interesting affection. It is a family disease, and begins in early life. The symptoms are those typical of locomotor ataxia, to which is added progressive muscular atrophy, with involvement of the face and a hypertrophy and hardening of the peripheral nerves. As the name indicates, it is an interstitial hypertrophic neuritis with secondary involvement of the dorsal columns of the cord. This disease has been associated with progressive neural muscular atrophy, but Dejerine has shown that it is quite distinct.

5. TOXIC COMBINED SCLEROSIS.

Certain poisons cause changes in the lateral and dorsal columns of the cord that resemble those of the combined system diseases. They have been demonstrated in pellagra and in ergotism, and have already been described. In pernicious anæmia and many chronic wasting disease these scleroses occur, and are believed to be due to the action of poisons produced within the system.

II₁. DIFFUSE DISEASES OF THE NERVOUS SYSTEM.

I. AFFECTIONS OF THE MENINGES.

DISEASES OF THE DURA MATER (*Pachymeningitis*).

Pachymeningitis Externa.—*Cerebral.*—Hæmorrhage often occurs as a result of fracture. Inflammation of the external layer of the dura is rare. Caries of the bone, either extension from middle-ear disease or due to syphilis, is the principal cause. In the syphilitic cases there may be a great thickening of the inner table and a large collection of pus between the dura and the bone.

Occasionally the pus is infiltrated between the two layers of the dura mater or may extend through and cause a dura-arachnitis.

The symptoms of external pachymeningitis are indefinite. In the syphilitic cases there may be a small sinus communicating with the exterior. Compression symptoms may occur with or without paralysis.

Spinal.—An acute form may occur in syphilitic affections of the bones, in tumors, and in aneurism. The symptoms are those of a compression of the cord. A chronic form is much more common, and is a constant accompaniment of tuberculous caries of the spine. The internal surface of the dura may be smooth, while the external is rough and covered with caseous masses. The entire dura may be surrounded or the process may be confined to the ventral surface.

Pachymeningitis Interna.—This occurs in three forms: (1) Pseudo-membranous, (2) purulent, and (3) hæmorrhagic. The first two are unimportant. Pseudo-membranous inflammation of the lining membrane of the dura is not usually recognized, but a most characteristic example of it came under my observation as a secondary process in pneumonia. Purulent pachymeningitis may follow an injury, but is more commonly the result of extension from inflammation of the pia. It is remarkable how rarely pus is found between the dura and arachnoid membranes.

HÆMORRHAGIC PACHYMENINGITIS (*Hæmatoma of the Dura Mater*).

Cerebral Form.—This remarkable condition, first described by Virchow, is very rare in general medical practice. During ten years no instance of it came under my observation at the Montreal General Hospital. On the other hand, in the post-mortem room of the Philadelphia Hospital, which received material from a large almshouse and asylum, the cases were not uncommon, and within three months I saw four characteristic examples, three of which came from the medical wards. The frequency of the condition in asylum work may be gathered from the fact that in 1,185 post mortems at the Government Hospital for the Insane, Washington, to June 30, 1897, there were 197 cases with " a true neo-membrane of internal pachymeningitis " (Blackburn). Of these cases, 45 were chronic dementia, 37 were general paresis, 30 senile dementia, 28 chronic mania, 28 chronic melancholia, 22 chronic epileptic insanity, 6 acute mania, and 1 case imbecility. Forty-two of the cases were in persons over seventy years of age.

It has also been found in profound anæmia and other diseases of the blood and of the blood-vessels, and is said to have followed certain of the acute fevers. Herter has called attention to the not infrequent occurrence of the lesion in badly nourished, cachectic children.

The morbid anatomy is interesting. Virchow's view that the delicate vascular membrane precedes the hæmorrhage is undoubtedly correct. Practically we see one of three conditions in these cases: (*a*) Subdural vascular membranes, often of extreme delicacy, formed by the penetration of blood-vessels and granulation tissue into an inflammatory exudate (so-called " organization " of an inflammatory exudate); (*b*) simple subdural hæmorrhage; (*c*) a combination of the two, vascular membrane and blood-clot. Certainly the vascular membrane may exist without a trace of hæmorrhage —simply a fibrous sheet of varying thickness, permeated with large vessels, which may form beautiful arborescent tufts. On the other hand, there are instances in which the subdural hæmorrhage is found alone, but it is possible that in some of these at least the hæmorrhage may have destroyed all trace of the vascular membrane. In some cases a series of laminated clots are found, forming a layer from 3 to 5 mm. in thickness. Cysts may occur within this membrane. The source of the hæmorrhage is probably the dural vessels. Huguenin and others hold that the bleeding comes from the vessels of the pia mater, but certainly in the early stage of the condition there is no evidence of this; on the other hand, the highly vascular subdural membrane may be seen covered with the thinnest possible sheeting of clot, which has evidently come from the dura. The subdural hæmorrhage is usually associated with atrophy of the convolutions, and it is held that this is one reason why it is so common in the insane, especially in dementia paralytica and dementia senilis; but there must be some other factor than atrophy, or we should meet with it in phthisis and various cachectic conditions in which the cerebral wasting is as common and almost as marked as in cases of insanity.

The symptoms are indefinite, or there may be none at all, especially when the hæmorrhages are small or have occurred very gradually, and the diagnosis cannot be made with certainty. Headache has been a prominent symptom in some cases, and when the condition exists on one side there may be hemiplegia. The most helpful symptoms for diagnosis, indicating that the hæmorrhage in an apoplectic attack is meningeal, are (1) those referable to increased intracerebral pressure (slowing and irregularity of the pulse, vomiting, coma, contracted pupils reacting to light slowly or not at all) and (2) paresis and paralysis, gradually increasing in extent, accompanied by symptoms which point to a *cortical* origin. Extensive bilateral disease may, however, exist without any symptoms whatever.

Spinal Form.—The spinal *pachymeningitis interna*, described by Charcot and Joffroy, involves chiefly the cervical region (*P. cervicalis hypertrophica*). The interspace between the cord and the dura is occupied by a firm, concentrically arranged, fibrinous growth, which is seen to have developed within, not outside of, the dura mater. It is a condition anatomically identical with the hæmorrhagic pachymeningitis interna of the brain. The cord is usually compressed; the central canal may be dilated—hydromyelus—and there are secondary degenerations. The nerve roots are involved in the growth and are damaged and compressed. The extent is variable. It may be limited to one segment, but more commonly involves a considerable portion of the cervical enlargement. The disease is chronic, and in some cases presents a characteristic group of symptoms. There are intense neuralgic pains in the course of the nerves whose roots are involved. They are chiefly in the arms and in the cervical region, and vary greatly in intensity. There may be hyperæsthesia with numbness and tingling; atrophic changes may develop, and there may be areas of anæsthesia. Gradually motor disturbances appear; the arms become weak and the muscles atrophied, particularly in certain groups, as the flexors of the hand. The extensors, on the other hand, remain intact, so that the condition of claw-hand is gradually produced. The grade of the atrophy depends much upon the extent of involvement of the cervical nerve roots, and in many cases the atrophy of the muscles of the shoulders and arms becomes extreme. The condition is one of cervical paraplegia, with contractures, flexion of the wrist, and typical *main en griffe*. Usually before the arms are greatly atrophied there are the symptoms of what the French writers term the second stage—namely, involvement of the lower extremities and the gradual production of a spastic paraplegia, which may develop several months after the onset of the disease, and is due to secondary changes in the cord.

The disease runs a chronic course, lasting, perhaps, two or more years.

60

In a few instances, in which symptoms pointed definitely to this condition, recovery has taken place. The disease is to be distinguished from amyotrophic lateral sclerosis, syringomyelia, and tumors. From the first it is separated by the marked severity of the initial pains in the neck and arms; from the second by the absence of the sensory changes characteristic of syringomyelia. From certain tumors it is very difficult to distinguish; in fact, the fibrinous layers form a tumor around the cord.

The condition known as *hæmatoma* of the dura mater may occur at any part of the cord, or, in its slow, progressive form—pachymeningitis hæmorrhagica interna—may be limited to the cervical region and produce the symptoms just mentioned. It is sometimes extensive, and may coexist with a similar condition of the cerebral dura. Cysts may occur filled with hæmorrhagic contents.

DISEASES OF THE PIA MATER (*Acute Cerebro-spinal Leptomeningitis*).

Etiology.—Under cerebro-spinal fever and tuberculosis the two most important forms of meningitis have been described. Other conditions with which meningitis is associated are: (1) *The acute fevers*, more particularly pneumonia, erysipelas, and septicæmia; less frequently small-pox, typhoid fever, scarlet fever, measles, etc. (2) *Injury or disease of the bones of the skull*. In this group by far the most frequent cause is necrosis of the petrous portion of the temporal bone in chronic otitis. (3) *Extension from disease of the nose*. Meningitis has followed perforation of the skull in sounding the frontal sinuses, suppurative disease of these sinuses, and necroses of the cribriform plate. As mentioned under cerebro-spinal fever, the infection is thought to be possible through the nose. (4) As a *terminal infection* in chronic nephritis, arterio-sclerosis, heart-disease, gout, and the wasting diseases of children. Bacteriologically, we may recognize four great groups of meningitides—the form due to the meningococcus (diplococus intracellularis), the pneumococcus meningitis, the form due to the tubercle bacillus, and the streptococcus meningitis. The gonococcus, the typhoid bacillus, the colon bacillus, and staphylococci also cause meningitis, but a great majority of all the cases are due to the four first-mentioned micro-organisms. I have already spoken of the pneumococcus meningitis, which not only occurs in connection with pneumonia, but as an independent infection. A majority of all the cases of so-called sporadic meningitis are probably caused by it.

The streptococcus meningitis is the usual form in the cases due to trauma, to otitis media, and in septic processes. In ulcerative endocarditis it is not uncommon; it occurred in 25 of 209 collected cases.

The terminal meningitides are caused by the streptococci, sometimes by staphylococci.

Morbid Anatomy.—The basal or cortical meninges may be chiefly attacked. The degree of involvement of the spinal meninges varies. In the form associated with pneumonia and ulcerative endocarditis the disease is bilateral and usually limited to the cortex. In extension from disease of the ear it is often unilateral and may be accompanied with abscess or with thrombosis of the sinuses. In the non-tuberculous form in children, in the meningitis of chronic Bright's disease, and in cachectic conditions the base is usually involved. In the cases secondary to pneumonia the effusion beneath the arachnoid may be very thick and purulent, completely hiding the convolutions. The ventricles also may be involved, though in these simple forms they rarely present the distention and softening which is so frequent in the tuberculous meningitis. For a more detailed description the student is referred to the sections on cerebro-spinal fever and tuberculous meningitis.

Symptoms.—The clinical features of meningitis have already been described at length in the diseases just referred to, and I shall here give a general summary. I have already, on several occasions, called attention to the fact that cortical meningitis is not to be recognized by any symptoms or set of symptoms from a condition which may be produced by the poison of many of the specific fevers. In the cases of so-called cerebral pneumonia, unless the base is involved and the nerves affected, the disease is unrecognizable, since identical symptoms may be produced by intense engorgement of the meninges. In typhoid fever, in which meningitis is very rare, the twitchings, spasms, and retractions of the neck are almost invariably associated with cerebro-spinal congestion, not with meningitis. Actual meningitis does, however, occur in typhoid fever, and, as Ohlmacher's cases show, the typhoid bacilli may be present in the exudate.

A knowledge of the etiology gives a very important clew. Thus, in middle-ear disease the development of high fever, delirium, vomiting, convulsions, and retraction of the head and neck would be extremely suggestive of meningitis or abscess. Headache, which may be severe and continuous, is the most common symptom. While the patient remains conscious this is usually the chief complaint, and even when semicomatose he may continue to groan and to place his hand on his head. In the fevers, particularly in pneumonia, there may be no complaint of headache. Delirium is frequently early, and is most marked when the fever is high. Convulsions are less common in simple than in tuberculous meningitis. They were not present in a single instance in the cases which I have seen in pneumonia, ulcerative endocarditis, or septicæmia. In the simple meningitis of children they may occur. Epileptiform attacks which come and go are highly characteristic of direct irritation of the cortex. Rigidity and spasm or twitchings of the muscles are more common. Stiffness and retraction of the muscles of the neck are important symptoms; but they are by no means constant, and are most frequent when the inflammation is extensive on the meninges of the cervical cord. There may be trismus, gritting of the teeth, or spastic contraction of the abdominal muscles. Vomiting is a common symptom in the early stages, particularly in basilar meningitis. Constipation is usually present. In the late stages the urine and fæces may be passed involuntarily. Optic neuritis is rare in the meningitis of the cortex, but is not uncommon when the base is involved. Leube lays stress on the hyperæsthesia of the skin and muscles, especially of the muscles of the neck and calves.

Important symptoms are due to lesions of the nerves at the base. Strabismus or ptosis may occur. The facial nerve may be involved, producing slight paralysis, or there may be damage to the fifth nerve, producing anæsthesia and, if the Gasserian ganglion is affected, trophic changes in the cornea. The pupils are at first contracted, subsequently dilated, and perhaps unequal. The reflexes in the extremities are often accentuated at the beginning of the disease; later they are diminished or entirely abolished. Herpes is common, particularly in the epidemic form.

Fever is present, moderate in grade, rarely rising above 103°. In the non-tuberculous leptomeningitis of debilitated children and in Bright's disease there may be little or no fever. The pulse may be increased in frequency at first, though this is unusual. One of the striking features of the disease is the slowness of the pulse in relation to the temperature, even in the early stages. Subsequently it may be irregular and still slower. The very rapid emaciation which often occurs is doubtless to be referred to a disturbance of the cerebral influence upon metabolism. The spinal meninges are so often affected simultaneously that lumbar puncture is exceedingly valuable for diagnosis. Not only does this frequently prove indisputably the existence of an acute meningitis, but the bacteriological examination may decide as to the etiological factor, and thus yield a more rational basis for treatment.

Treatment.—There are no remedies which in any way control the course of acute meningitis. An ice-bag should be applied to the head and, if the subject is young and full-blooded, general or local depletion may be practised. Absolute rest and quiet should be enjoined. When disease of the ear is present, a surgeon should be early called in consultation, and if there are symptoms of meningo-encephalitis which can in any way be localized trephining should be practised. An occasional saline purge will do more to relieve the congestion than blisters and local depletion. I have no belief whatever in the efficacy of counter-irritation to the back of the neck, and to apply a blister to a patient suffering with agonizing headache in meningitis is needlessly to add to the suffering. If counter-irritation is deemed essential, the thermo-cautery, lightly applied, is more satisfactory. Large doses of the perchloride of iron, iodide of potassium, and mercury are recommended by some authors.

The application of an ice-cap, attention to the bowels and stomach, and keeping the fever within moderate limits by sponging, are the necessary measures in a disease recognized as almost invariably fatal, and in which the cases of recovery are extremely doubtful. Quincke's lumbar puncture (see page 107) has been used as a therapeutic measure with success by Fürbringer; 60 cc. of cloudy fluid were removed, in which tubercle bacilli were found. The headache and other cerebral symptoms disappeared, and the patient, a man of twenty, recovered. Wallis Ord and Waterhouse report a case of recovery, in a child of five years, after trephining and drainage.

POSTERIOR MENINGITIS OF INFANTS (*Non-tuberculous Leptomeningitis Infantum*).

This form has been specially studied by Gee and Barlow, and has been called occlusive meningitis. Gee called it *cervical opisthotonos* of infants, from the most prominent feature of the disease. A careful study has been made of 11 cases by J. W. Carr. In all cases there was well-marked distention of the lateral and third ventricles, generally of the fourth also, with " effusion of lymph, thickening of the pia-arachnoid, and matting of the parts over the posterior and central area of the base of the brain from the lower end of the medulla to the optic commissure." The disease is most common in infants under one year. In only 3 cases a few flakes of lymph were found, and neither the choroid plexuses nor the ependema showed naked-eye appearances of inflammation. Head retraction appeared early and was persistent throughout, being absent in only one case. It is usually much more marked than in tuberculous meningitis. At a comparatively early stage, even weeks before death, the infants pass into stupor or complete coma. This form is sometimes met with in older children.

Chronic Leptomeningitis.—This is rarely seen apart from syphilis or tuberculosis, in which the meningitis is associated with the growth of the granulomata in the meninges and about the vessels. The symptoms in such cases are extremely variable, depending entirely upon the situation of the growth. They may closely resemble those of tumor and be associated with localized convulsions. The epidemic meningitis may run a very chronic course. The leptomeningitis infantum may be chronic. In the cases reported by Gee and Barlow the duration in some instances extended even to a year and a half. Quincke's *meningitis serosa* is considered with hydrocephalus.

II. SCLEROSES OF THE BRAIN.

General Remarks.—The connective tissue of the central nervous system is of two kinds—one, the neuroglia, special and peculiar, derived from the ectoderm, with distinct morphological and chemical characters; the other, in the meninges and accompanying the blood-vessels, derived from the mesoderm, identical with the ordinary collagenous fibrous tissue of the body. Both play important parts in indurative processes in the brain and cord. A convenient division of the cerebro-spinal scleroses is into degenerative, inflammatory, and developmental forms.

The *degenerative scleroses* comprise the largest and most important subdivision, in which provisionally the following groups may be made: (*a*) The common secondary degeneration which follows when nerve-fibres are cut off from their trophic centres (the severance of portions of neurones from the main portions containing the nuclei); (*b*) toxic forms, among which may be placed the scleroses from lead and ergot, and, most important of all, the sclerosis of the dorsal columns, due in such a large proportion of cases to the virus of syphilis. Other unknown toxic agents may possibly induce degeneration of the nerve-fibres in certain tracts. The systemic paths in the cord differ apparently in their susceptibility and the dorsal columns appear most prone to undergo this change; (c) the sclerosis associated with change in the smaller arteries and capillaries, which is met with as a senile process in the convolutions. In all probability some of the forms of insular sclerosis are due to primary alterations in the blood-vessels; but it is not yet settled whether the lesion in these cases is a primary degeneration of the nerve cells and fibres to which the sclerosis is secondary, or whether the essential factor is an alteration in nutrition caused by lesions of the capillaries and smaller arteries.

The *inflammatory scleroses* embrace a less important and less extensive group, comprising secondary forms which develop in consequence of irritative inflammation about tumors, foreign bodies, hæmorrhages, and abscess. Histologically these are chiefly mesodermic (vascular) scleroses, which arise from the connective tissue about the blood-vessels. Possibly a similar change may follow the primary, acute encephalitis, which Strümpell holds is the initial lesion in the cortical sclerosis which is so commonly found post mortem in infantile hemiplegia.

The *developmental scleroses* are believed to be of a purely neurogliar character, and embrace the new growth about the central canal in syringomyelia and, according to recent French writers, the sclerosis of the dorsal columns in Friedreich's ataxia. It is stated that histologically this form is different from the ordinary variety. It may be, too, that the diffuse cortical sclerosis met with as a congenital condition without thickening of the meninges belongs to this type. It is not improbable that many forms of scleroses are of a mixed character, in which both the ectodermic glia and mesodermic connective tissue are involved.

Anatomically we meet with the following varieties:

(1) **Miliary sclerosis** is a term which has been applied to several different conditions. Gowers mentions a case in which there were grayish-red spots at the junction of the white and gray matters, and in which the neuroglia was increased. There is also a condition in which, on the surface of the convolutions, there are small nodular projections, varying from a half to five or more millimetres in diameter. Single nodules of this sort are not uncommon; sometimes they are abundant. So far as is known no symptoms are produced by them.

(2) **Diffuse sclerosis,** which may involve an entire hemisphere, or a single lobe, in which case the term *sclérose lobaire* has been applied to it by the French. It is not an important condition in general medical practice, but occurs most frequently in idiots and imbeciles. In extensive cortical sclerosis of one hemisphere the ventricle is usually dilated.* The symptoms of this condition depend upon the region affected. There may be a considerable extent of sclerosis without symptoms or without much mental impairment. In a majority of cases there is hemiplegia or diplegia with imbecility or idiocy.

---

* In my monograph on Cerebral Palsies of Children I have given a description of the distribution of the sclerosis in ten specimens in the museum at the Elwyn Institution.

(3) **Tuberous Sclerosis.**—In this remarkable form, which is also known as hypertrophic sclerosis, there are on the convolutions areas, projecting beyond the surfaces, of an opaque white color and exceedingly firm. The sclerosis may not disturb the symmetry of the convolution, but simply cause a great enlargement, increase in the density, and a change in the color.

These three forms are not of much practical interest except in asylum and institution work. The last variety forms a well-characterized disease of considerable importance, namely:

(4) INSULAR SCLEROSIS (*Sclérose en plaques*).

Definition.—A chronic affection of the brain and cord, characterized by localized areas in which the nerve elements are more or less replaced by connective tissue. This may occur in the brain or cord alone, more commonly in both.

Etiology.—This is obscure. Kahler, Marie, and others assign great importance to the infectious diseases, particularly scarlet fever. It is found most commonly in young persons, and cases are not uncommon in children, in whom Pritchard states that more than 50 cases have been reported. Sachs has recently reviewed the whole subject (Jour. of Nerv. and Mental Diseases, 1898).

Morbid Anatomy.—The sclerotic areas are widely distributed through the brain and cord, and cases limited to either part alone are almost unknown. The grayish-red areas are scattered indifferently through the white and gray matter (E. W. Taylor). The patches are most abundant in the neighborhood of the ventricles, and in the pons, cerebellum, basal ganglia, and the medulla. The cord may be only slightly involved or there may be irregular areas in different regions. The cervical region is most often the seat of nodules. The nerve-roots and the branches of the cauda equina are often attacked. Histologically in the sclerosed patches there is very marked proliferation of the neuroglia, the fibres of which are denser and firmer. The gradual growth destroys the medulla of the nerves, but the axis cylinders persist in a remarkable way. There is as a consequence relatively little secondary degeneration of nerve tracts.

Symptoms.—The onset is slow and the disease is chronic. Feebleness of the legs with irregular pains and stiffness are among the early symptoms. Indeed, the clinical picture may be that of spastic paraplegia with great increase in the reflexes. The following are the most important features:

(*a*) *Volitional Tremor or So-called Intention Tremor.*—There is no paralysis of the arms, but on attempting to pick up an object there is trembling or rapid oscillation. A patient may be unable to lift even a glass of water to the mouth. The tremor may be marked in the legs and in the head, which shakes as he walks. When the patient is recumbent the muscles may be perfectly quiet. On attempting to raise the head from the pillow, trembling at once comes on. (*b*) *Scanning Speech.*—The words are pronounced slowly and separately, or the individual syllables may be accentuated. This staccato or syllabic utterance is a common feature. (*c*) *Nys-*

tagmus, a rapid oscillatory movement of both eyes, constitutes an important symptom.

Sensation is unaffected in a majority of the cases. Optic atrophy sometimes occurs, but not so frequently as in tabes. The sphincters, as a rule, are unaffected until the last stages. Mental debility is not uncommon. Remarkable remissions occur in the course of the disease, in which for a time all the symptoms may improve. Vertigo is common, and there may be sudden attacks of coma, such as occur in general paresis.

The symptoms, on the whole, are extraordinarily variable, corresponding to the very irregular distribution of the nodules.

The *diagnosis* in well-marked cases is easy. Volitional tremor, scanning speech, and nystagmus form a characteristic symptom-group. With this there is usually more or less spastic weakness of the legs. Paralysis agitans, certain cases of general paresis, and occasionally hysteria may simulate the disease very closely. If the case is not seen until near the end the diagnosis may be impossible. Buzzard holds that of all organic diseases of the nervous system disseminated sclerosis in its early stages is that which is most commonly mistaken for hysteria. The points to be relied upon in the differentiation are, in order of importance, the nystagmus, the bladder disturbances, and the volitional tremor. The tremor in hysteria is not volitional.

Much more puzzling, however, are the instances of *pseudo-sclérose en plaques,* which have been described by Westphal. French writers regard them as instances of hysterical tremor. In children the condition may with difficulty be separated from Friedreich's ataxia.

The *prognosis* is unfavorable. Ultimately, the patient, if not carried off by some intercurrent affection, becomes bedridden.

Treatment.—No known treatment has any influence on the progress of sclerosis of the brain. Neither the iodides nor mercury have the slightest effect, but a prolonged course of nitrate of silver may be tried, and arsenic is recommended.

III. CHRONIC DIFFUSE MENINGO-ENCEPHALITIS

(Dementia Paralytica; General Paresis).

Definition.—A chronic, progressive meningo-encephalitis associated with psychical and motor disturbances, finally leading to dementia and paralysis.

Etiology.—Males are affected much more frequently than females. It occurs chiefly between the ages of thirty and fifty-five. Heredity is a factor in only a few instances. An overwhelming majority of the cases are in married people. Statistics show that it is more common in the lower classes of society, but in this country in general medical practice the disease is certainly more common in the well-to-do classes. An important predisposing cause is "a life absorbed in ambitious projects with all its strongest mental efforts, its long-sustained anxieties, deferred hopes, and straining expectation" (Mickle). The habits of life so frequently seen in active business men in our large cities, and well expressed by the phrase "burning the candle at both ends," strongly predispose to the disease. The important individual factor is syphilis, which is an antecedent in from 70 to 90 per cent of all cases. To this disease dementia paralytica and tabes dorsalis are so closely related that Fournier describes them under the heading *Les Affections Parasyphilitiques*. His recent work, with this title, is full of interesting details gleaned from an enormous experience. He suggests that these two disorders may be not merely diverse expressions of one and the same morbid entity, but that they possibly may be one and the same disease.

Morbid Anatomy.—The essential histological changes in the cerebral cortex are thus summarized by Bevan Lewis: (1) A stage of inflammatory change in the tunica adventitia of the arteries with excessive nuclear proliferation, profound changes in the vascular channels, and trophic changes induced in the tissues around.

(2) A stage of extraordinary development of the lymph-connective system of the brain, with a parallel degeneration and disappearance of nerve elements and the axis cylinders of which they are denuded.

(3) A stage of general fibrillation with shrinking and extreme atrophy of the parts involved.

The macroscopical changes are: Increase in the cerebro-spinal fluid, œdema of the pia, and thickening and opacity of the meninges, which are adherent in places and tear the cortex on removal. The dura is sometimes thickened, and pachymeningitis hæmorrhagica interna may be present.

The convolutions are atrophied, usually in a marked degree, and in consequence the brain looks small. This is particularly noticeable in the frontal and parietal regions. Flechsig suggests, from his own experience and that of Tuczek, that the different types met with are dependent upon the localization of the malady in given cases, predominantly in the anterior or in the posterior "association centre." On section the brain cuts with firmness. In extreme cases the gray matter may be obscurely outlined. The grade of sclerosis varies much in different cases. The white matter may be firmer in consistence, but it does not show such important changes. The ventricles are dilated and the ependyma is extremely granular. In addition, there are frequently areas of softening or hæmorrhage associated with chronic arterio-sclerosis.

The degenerative changes are not limited to the cortex, but also invade subcortical regions and the spinal cord. In the spinal cord changes are almost constantly found, usually sclerosis of the dorsal fasciculi, either alone or, more commonly, with involvement of the lateral.

Symptoms.—(a) *Prodromal Stage.*—This is of variable duration, and is characterized by a general mental state which finds expression in symptoms trivial in themselves but important in connection with others. Irritability, inattention to business amounting sometimes to indifference or apathy, and sometimes a *change in character* marked by acts, which may astonish the friends and relatives, may be the first indications. There may be unaccountable fatigue after moderate physical or mental exertion. Instead of apathy or indifference there may be an extraordinary degree of physical and mental restlessness. The patient is continually planning and scheming, or may launch into extravagances and speculation of the wildest character. A common feature at this period is the display of an un-bounded egoism. He boasts of his personal attainments, his property, his position in life, or of his wife and children. Following these features are important indications of moral perversion, manifested in offences against decency or the law, many of which acts have about them a suspicious effrontery. Forgetfulness is common, and may be shown in inattention to business details and in the minor courtesies of life. At this period there may be no motor phenomena. The onset of the disease is usually insidi-ous, although cases are reported in which epileptiform or apoplectiform seizures were the first symptoms. Among the early motor features are tremor of the tongue and lips in speaking, slowness of speech and hesi-tancy, inequality of the pupils, and the Argyll Robertson pupil.

(b) *Second Stage.*—This is characterized in brief by mental exaltation or excitement and a progress in the motor symptoms. "The intensity of the excitement is often extreme, acute maniacal states are frequent; in-cessant restlessness, obstinate sleeplessness, noisy, boisterous excitement, and blind, uncalculating violence especially characterize such states" (Lewis). It is at this stage that the delusion of grandeur becomes marked and the patient believes himself to be possessed of countless millions or to have reached the most exalted sphere possible in profession or occupation. This expansive delirium, as it is called, is, however, not characteristic, as was formerly supposed, of paralytic dementia. Besides, it does not always oc-cur, but in its stead there may be marked melancholia or hypochondriasis, or, in other instances, alternate attacks of delirium and depression.

The facies has a peculiar stolidity, and in speaking there is marked tremulousness of the lips and facial muscles. The tongue is also tremu-lous, and may be protruded with difficulty. The speech is slow, inter-rupted, and blurred. Writing becomes difficult on account of unsteadi-ness of the hand. Letters, syllables, and words may be omitted. The sub-ject matter of the patient's letters gives valuable indications of the mental condition. In many instances the pupils are unequal, irregular, sluggish, sometimes large. Important symptoms in this stage are apoplectiform seizures and paralysis. There may be slight syncopal attacks in which the patient turns pale and may fall. Some of these are *petit mal.* In the true apoplectiform seizure the patient falls suddenly, becomes unconscious, the limbs are relaxed, the face is flushed, the breathing stertorous, the tem-perature increased, and death may occur. The epileptic seizures are more common than the apoplectiform and may occur in the disease. A definite aura is not uncommon. The attack usually begins on one side and may not spread. There may be twitchings either in the facial or brachial muscles. Typical Jacksonian epilepsy may occur. In a case which died recently under my care, these seizures were among the early symptoms and the dis-ease was regarded as cerebral syphilis. Paralysis, either monoplegic or hemiplegic, may follow these epileptic seizures, or may come on with great suddenness and be transient. In this stage the gait becomes impaired, the patient trips readily, has difficulty in going up or down stairs, and the walk may be spastic or occasionally tabetic. This paresis may be progressive. The knee-jerk is usually increased. Bladder or rectal symptoms gradually develop. The patient becomes helpless, bedridden, and completely demented, and unless care is taken may suffer from bedsores. Death occurs from exhaustion or from some intercurrent affection. The absence of pain reaction on pressure upon the ulnar nerve behind the elbow (Biernacki's symptom) is apparently not of any special value. The spinal-cord features of dementia paralytica may come on with or precede the mental troubles; in 80 per cent of the cases they follow them. There are cases in which one is in doubt for a time whether the symptoms indicate tabes or dementia paralytica, and it is well to bear in mind that every feature of pre-ataxic tabes may exist in the early stage of general paresis.

Diagnosis.—The recognition of the disease in the earliest stage is extremely difficult, as it is often impossible to decide that the slight alteration in conduct is anything more than one of the moods or phases to which most men are at times subject. The following description by Folsom is an admirable presentation of the diagnostic characters of the early stage of the disease: " It should arouse suspicion if, for instance, a strong, healthy man, in or near the prime of life, distinctly not of the ' nervous,' neurotic, or neurasthenic type, shows some loss of interest in his affairs or impaired faculty of attending to them; if he becomes varyingly absent-minded, heedless, indifferent, negligent, apathetic, inconsiderate, and, although able to follow his routine duties, his ability to take up new work is, no matter how little, diminished; if he can less well command mental attention and concentration, conception, perception, reflection, judgment; if there is an unwonted lack of initiative, and if exertion causes unwonted mental and physical fatigue; if the emotions are intensified and easily change, or are excited readily from trifling causes; if the sexual instinct is not reasonably controlled; if the finer feelings are even slightly blunted; if the person in question regards with a placid apathy his own acts of indifference and irritability and their consequences, and especially if at times he sees himself in his true light and suddenly fails again to do so; if any symptoms of cerebral vaso-motor disturbances are noticed, however vague or variable."

There are cases of cerebral syphilis which closely simulate dementia paralytica. The mode of onset is important, particularly since paralytic symptoms are usually early in syphilis. The affection of the speech and tongue is not present. Epileptic seizures are more common and more liable to be cortical or Jacksonian in character. The expansive delirium is rare. While symptoms of general paresis are not common in connection with the development of gummata or definite gummatous meningitis, there are, on the other hand, instances of paresis which follow syphilitic infection so closely that an etiological connection between the two must be acknowledged. Post mortem in such cases there may be nothing more than a general arterio-sclerosis and diffuse meningo-encephalitis, which may present nothing distinctive, but the lesions, nevertheless, may be caused by the syphilitic virus. There are certain forms of lead encephalopathy which resemble general paresis, and, considering the association of plumbism with arterio-sclerosis, it is not unlikely that the anatomical substratum of the disease may result from this poison.   Tumor may sometimes simulate progressive paresis, but in the former the signs of general increase of the intracranial pressure (pain in the head, choked disks, slowing of the pulse-rate, projectile vomiting) are usually present.

Prognosis.—The disease rarely ends in recovery.   As a rule the progress is slowly downward and the case terminates in a few years, although it is occasionally prolonged ten or fifteen years.

Treatment.—The only hope of permanent relief is in the cases following syphilis, which should be placed upon large doses of iodide of potassium.   Careful nursing and the orderly life of an asylum are the only measures necessary in a great majority of the cases.   For sleeplessness and the epileptic seizures bromides may be used.   Prolonged remissions, which are not uncommon, are often erroneously attributed to the action of remedies.   Active treatment in the early stage by wet-packs, cold to the head, and systematic massage have been followed by temporary improvement.

IV. DIFFUSE AND FOCAL DISEASES OF THE SPINAL CORD.

I. TOPICAL DIAGNOSIS.

We have seen that a lesion involving a definite part of the gray matter of the lower motor segment is accompanied by loss of the power to perform certain definite movements.   A disease, such as anterior polio-myelitis, which is confined to the gray matter, gives as its only symptom a characteristic lower-segment paralysis.   The muscles paralyzed reveal the seat of the lesion.   In many instances a transverse section of the spinal cord is involved to a greater or less extent; if complete, there is lower-segment paralysis at the level of the lesion.   If the muscles so paralyzed are the same on the two sides of the body, the lesion is strictly transverse, for, obviously, if the cord is involved higher on one side than on the other the paralyzed muscles will vary accordingly.   Besides the paralysis due to involvement of the lower segment, the muscles whose centres are below the lesion may also be paralyzed by the involvement of the upper segment in the pyramidal tract, and present all the characteristics of such a paralysis. The degree of the paralysis depends upon the intensity of the lesion of the pyramidal tract, and varies from a slight weakness in the flexion of the ankle to an absolute paralysis of all the muscles below the lesion.   The sphincter muscles of the bladder and rectum are also often paralyzed.

Sensory symptoms are usually less prominent, but when the spinal cord is much diseased there is a dulling of sensation all over the body below the lesion.   The upper border of disturbed sensation often indicates the level of the disease, especially when this is in the thoracic region, where the corresponding motor paralysis is not easy to demonstrate.   It is to be noted that the anæsthesia does not reach quite to the level of the lesion; thus if the fifth thoracic segment be involved, the anæsthesia will include the area supplied by the sixth segment, but not that supplied by the fifth. This is due to the overlapping of the areas. There is often a narrow zone of hyperæsthesia above the anæsthetic region.

When the transverse lesion is complete and the lower part of the cord is cut off from all influence from above, there is complete sensory and motor -paralysis, and the deep reflexes instead of being exaggerated are lost.

The different reflexes are dependent upon different levels of the cord (see Starr's table, p. 905), and their absence or presence may be important localizing symptoms.

Unilateral Lesions.—The motor symptoms which follow lesions confined to one half of the cross-section of the spinal cord follow the same rules as those given for transverse lesions, except that they are confined to one side of the body—that is, they are on the same side as the lesion.

The sensory symptoms are peculiar. On the side corresponding to the disease—the paralyzed side—there is anæsthesia corresponding to the segment of the cord involved; above this there is a narrow zone of hyperæsthesia, but below this there is no diminution in the senses of touch, pain, or temperature; indeed, there is often hyperæsthesia. The muscular sense, however, is impaired. On the side opposite to the lesion there may be complete loss of the sense of touch, pain, and temperature, or it may only involve one or two of these, pain and temperature usually being associated.

The following table, slightly modified from Gowers, illustrates the distribution of these symptoms in a complete hemi-lesion of the cord:

Cord.

	Lesion.	
Zone of cutaneous hyperæsthesia. Zone of cutaneous anæsthesia. Lower segment paralysis with atrophy.		
Upper segment paralysis. Hyperæsthesia of skin. Muscular sense impaired. Reflex action first lessened and then increased. Temperature raised.		Muscular power normal. Loss of sensibility of skin. Muscular sense normal. Reflex action normal. Temperature same as that above lesion.

It is only in exceptional cases that all these features are met with, for they vary with its extent and intensity.

This combination of symptoms was first recognized by Brown-Séquard, after whom it has been named. It may follow tumors, stab-wounds, fracture and caries of the spine, and it is not infrequently associated with syringomyelia and hæmorrhages into the cord.

The explanation of the disturbance in sensation is not satisfactory, and cannot be until our knowledge of the paths of sensory conduction is more accurate. These cases have convinced most clinicians that in man the paths for touch, pain, and temperature cross in the middle line soon after entering the spinal cord, and proceed toward the brain in the opposite side, while that for muscular sense remains in the dorsal columns of the same side. We have seen that anatomy lends some support to this view, and this is the explanation that is usually given. The experiments on animals have thrown some doubt on this view, especially those of Mott on monkeys, which seem to indicate that the sensory paths for the most part remain on the same side of the cord.

II. AFFECTIONS OF THE BLOOD-VESSELS.

1. CONGESTION.

Apart from actual myelitis, we rarely see post mortem evidences of congestion of the spinal cord, and when we do, it is usually limited either to the gray matter or to a definite portion of the organ. There is necessarily, from the posture of the body post mortem, a greater degree of vascularity in the dorsal portion of the cord. The white matter is rarely found congested, even when inflamed; in fact, it is remarkable how uniformly pale this portion of the cord is. The gray matter often has a reddish-pink tint, but rarely a deep reddish hue, except when myelitis is present. If we know little anatomically of conditions of congestion of the cord, we know less clinically, for there are no features in any way characteristic of it.

2. ANÆMIA.

So, too, with this state. There may be extreme grades of anæmia of the cord without symptoms. In chlorosis and pernicious anæmia there are rarely symptoms pointing to the cord, and there is no reason to suppose that such sensations as heaviness in the limbs and tingling are especially associated with anæmia.

There are, however, some very interesting facts with reference to the profound anæmia of the cord which follows ligature of the aorta. In experiments made in Welch's laboratory by Herter, it was found that within a few moments after the application of the ligature to the aorta paraplegia came on. Paralysis of the sphincters developed, but less rapidly. This condition is of interest in connection with the occasional rapid development of a paraplegia after profuse hæmorrhage, usually from the stomach or uterus. It may come on at once or at the end of a week or ten days, and is probably due to an anatomical change in the nerve elements similar to that produced in Herter's experiments. The degeneration of the dorsal columns of the cord in pernicious anæmia has already been described.

3. EMBOLISM AND THROMBOSIS.

Blocking of the spinal arteries by emboli rarely occurs. It may be produced experimentally, and Money found that it was associated with choreiform movements. Thrombosis of the smaller vessels in connection with endarteritis plays an important part in many of the acute and chronic changes in the cord.

4. Endarteritis.

It is remarkable how frequently in persons over fifty the arteries of the spinal cord are found sclerotic. The following forms may be met with: (1) A nodular peri-arteritis or endarteritis associated with syphilis and sometimes with gummata of the meninges; (2) an arteritis obliterans, with great thickening of the intima and narrowing of the lumen of the vessels, involving chiefly the medium and larger-sized arteries. Miliary aneurisms or aneurisms of the larger vessels are rarely found in the spinal cord. In the classical work of Leyden but a single instance of the latter is mentioned.

5. Hæmorrhage into the Spinal Membranes; Hæmatorrhachis.

In meningeal apoplexy, as it is called, the blood may be between the dura mater and the spinal canal—extra-meningeal hæmorrhage—or within the dura mater—intra-meningeal hæmorrhage.

(a) *Extra-meningeal hæmorrhage* occurs usually as a result of trauma. The exudation may be extensive without compression of the cord. The blood comes from the large plexuses of veins which may surround the dura. The rupture of an aneurism into the spinal canal may produce extensive and rapidly fatal hæmorrhage.

(b) *Intra-meningeal hæmorrhage* is rather more common, but is rarely extensive from causes acting directly on the spinal meninges themselves. Scattered hæmorrhages are not unfrequent in the acute infectious fevers, and I have twice, in malignant small-pox, seen much effusion. Bleeding occurs also in death from convulsive disorders, such as epilepsy, tetanus, and strychnia poisoning. The most extensive hæmorrhages occur in cases in which the blood comes from rupture of an aneurism at the base of the brain, either of the basilar or vertebral artery. In several cases of this kind I have found a large amount of blood in the spinal meninges. In ventricular apoplexy the blood may pass from the fourth ventricle into the spinal meninges. There is a specimen in the medical museum of McGill College of the most extensive intraventricular hæmorrhage, in which the blood passed into the fourth ventricle, and descended beneath the spinal arachnoid for a considerable distance. On the other hand, hæmorrhage into the spinal meninges may possibly ascend into the brain.

The *symptoms* in moderate grades may be slight and indefinite. In the non-traumatic cases the hæmorrhage may either come on suddenly or after a day or two of uneasy sensations along the spine. As a rule, the onset is abrupt, with sharp pain in the back and symptoms of irritation in the course of the nerves. There may be muscular spasms, or paralysis may come on suddenly, either in the legs alone or both in the legs and arms. In some instances the paralysis develops more slowly and is not complete. There is no loss of consciousness, and there are no signs of cerebral disturbance. The clinical picture naturally varies with the site of the hæmorrhage. If in the lumbar region, the legs alone are involved, the reflexes may be abolished, and the action of the bladder and rectum is impaired. If in the thoracic region, there is more or less complete paraplegia, the reflexes are usually retained, and there are signs of disturbance in the thoracic nerves, such as girdle sensations, pains, and sometimes eruption of herpes. In the cervical region the arms as well as the legs may be involved; there may be difficulty in breathing, stiffness of the muscles of the neck, and occasionally pupillary symptoms.

The prognosis depends much upon the cause of the hæmorrhage. Recovery may take place in the traumatic cases, and in those associated with the infectious diseases.

6. Hæmorrhage into the Spinal Cord (*Hæmatomyelia*).

It is more common in males than in females, and at the middle period of life. The cases have followed either cold and exposure or overexertion, and, most frequently of all, traumatism. It is most frequent in the lower cervical region, the most common site for dislocation and fracture of the spine. It occurs also in tetanus and convulsions. Hæmorrhage into the cord may follow injuries of the spinal column, gun-shot wounds, etc., even when the cord itself has not been touched (H. Cushing). Hæmorrhage may be associated with tumors, with syringo-myelia, or with myelitis; it is often difficult to determine whether the case is one of primary hæmorrhage with myelitis, or myelitis with a secondary hæmorrhage.

The *anatomical condition* is very varied. The cord may be enlarged at the site of the hæmorrhage, and occasionally the white substance may be lacerated and blood may escape beneath the meninges. The extravasation is chiefly in the gray matter, and may be limited or focal, or very diffuse, extending a considerable distance in the cord. In a case which occurred at the Montreal General Hospital under Wilkins the hæmorrhage occupied a position opposite the region of the fifth and sixth cervical nerves and on transverse section the cord was occupied by a dark-red clot measuring 12 by 5 mm., around which the white substance formed a thin, ragged wall. The clot could be traced upward as far as the second cervical, and downward as far as the fourth thoracic segment.

The sudden onset of the *symptoms* is the most characteristic feature in hæmatomyelia. The loss of power necessarily varies with the locality affected. If in the cervical region, both arms and legs may be involved; but if in the thoracic or lumbar, there is only paraplegia. There is usually loss of sensation, and at first loss of reflexes. Myelitis frequently develops and becomes extensive, with fever and trophic changes. The condition may rapidly prove fatal; in other instances there is gradual recovery, often with partial paralysis.

The diagnosis may be made in some instances, particularly those in which the onset is sudden after injury, but there is great difficulty in differentiating hæmorrhagic myelitis from certain cases of hæmorrhage into the spinal meninges.

7. CAISSON DISEASE (*Diver's Paralysis; Compressed Air Disease*).

This remarkable affection, found in divers and in workers in caissons, is characterized by a paraplegia, more rarely a general palsy, which supervenes on returning from the compressed atmosphere to the surface.

The disease has been carefully studied by the French writers, by Leyden and Schultze in Germany, and in this country particularly by A. H. Smith. It has been made the subject of a special monograph by Snell. The pressure must be more than that of three atmospheres. The symptoms are especially apt to come on if the change from the high to the ordinary atmospheric pressure is quickly made. They may supervene immediately on leaving the caisson, or they may be delayed for several hours. In the mildest form there are simply pains about the knees and in the legs, often of great severity, and occurring in paroxysms. Abdominal pain and vomiting are not uncommon. The legs may be tender to the touch, and the patient may walk with a stiff gait. Dizziness and headache may accompany these neuralgic symptoms, or may occur alone. More commonly in the severe form there is paralysis both of motion and sensation, usually a paraplegia, but it may be general, involving the trunk and arms. Monoplegia and hemiplegia are rare. In the most extreme instances the attacks resemble apoplexy; the patient rapidly becomes comatose and death occurs in a few hours. In the case of paraplegia the outlook is usually good, and the paralysis may pass off in a day, or may continue for several weeks or even for months.

The explanation of this condition is by no means satisfactory. Several careful autopsies have been made. In Leyden's case death occurred on the fifteenth day, and in the thoracic portion of the cord there were numerous foci of hæmorrhages and signs of an acute myelitis. In Schultze's case death occurred in two and a half months, and a disseminated myelitis was found in the thoracic region. In both cases there were fissures, and appearances as if tissue had been lacerated. In a case examined on the third day (Ziegler's Beiträge, 1892) this condition of fissuring and laceration was found. It has been suggested that the symptoms are due to the liberation in the spinal cord of bubbles of nitrogen which have been absorbed by the blood under the high pressure, and the condition found at the autopsies just referred to is held to favor this view.

A large majority of the cases recover. The severe neuralgic pains often require morphia. Inhalations of oxygen and the use of compressed air have been advised. When paraplegia develops the treatment is similar to that of other forms. In all caisson work care should be exercised that the time in passing through the lock from the high to the ordinary pressure be sufficiently prolonged. Snell lays less stress on this than on the proper ventilation of the caisson.

III. COMPRESSION OF THE SPINAL CORD

(*Compression Myelitis*).

Definition.—Interruption of the functions of the cord by slow compression.

Etiology.—Caries of the spine, new growths, aneurism, and parasites are the important causes of slow compression. Caries, or Pott's disease, as it is usually called, after the surgeon who first described it, is in the great majority of instances a tuberculous affection. In a few cases it is due to syphilis and occasionally to extension of disease from the pharynx. It is most common in early life, but may occur after middle age. It follows trauma in a few cases. Compression occasionally results from aneurism of the thoracic aorta or the abdominal aorta, in the neighborhood of the cœliac axis.

Malignant growths frequently cause a compression paraplegia. A retroperitoneal sarcoma or the lymphadenomatous growths of Hodgkin's disease may invade the vertebræ. More commonly, however, the involvement is secondary to scirrhus of the breast.

Of parasites, the echinococcus and the cysticercus occasionally occur in the spinal canal. For a masterly consideration of the whole question, particularly from a surgical standpoint, Kocher's monograph is all-important (Mitt. a. d. Grenzgebiet. der Chir. u. d. Med., 1896, Bd. i).

Symptoms.—These may be considered as they affect the bones, the nerves, and the cord.

(1) **Vertebral.**—In malignant diseases and in aneurism, erosion of the bodies may take place without producing any deformity of the spine. Fatal hæmorrhage may follow erosion of the vertebral artery. In caries, on the other hand, it is the rule to find more or less deformity, amounting often to angular curvature. The compression is largely due to the thickening of the dura and the presence of caseous and inflammatory products between this membrane and the bone. The compression is rarely produced directly by the bone. Pain is a constant and, in the case of aneurism and tumor, an agonizing feature. In caries, the spinal processes of the affected vertebræ are tender on pressure, and pain follows jarring movements or twisting of the spine. There may be extensive tuberculous disease without much deformity, particularly in the cervical region.

(2) **Nerve-root Symptoms.**—These result from compression of the nerve roots as they pass out between the vertebræ. A cervico-brachial neuralgia may be an early symptom. It is remarkable how frequently, even in extensive caries, they escape and the patient does not complain of radiating pains in the distribution of the nerves from the affected segment. Pains are more common in cancer of the spine secondary to that of the breast, and in such cases may be agonizing. There may be acutely painful areas— the *anæsthesia dolorosa*, in regions of the skin which are anæsthetic to tactile and painful impressions. Trophic disturbances may occur, particularly herpes. In the cervical or lumbar regions pressure on the ventral roots may give rise to wasting of the muscles supplied by the affected nerves.

(3) Cord Symptoms.—(*a*) *Cervical Region.*—Not infrequently the caries is high up between the axis and the atlas or between the latter and the occipital bone. In such instances a retropharyngeal abscess may be present, giving rise to difficulty in swallowing. There may be spasm of the cervical muscles, the head may be fixed, and movements may either be impossible or cause great pain. In a case of this kind in the Montreal General Hospital movement was liable to be followed by transient, instantaneous paralysis of all four extremities, owing to compression of the cord. In one of these attacks the patient died.

In the lower cervical region there may be signs of interference with the cilio-spinal centre and dilatation of the pupils. Occasionally there is flushing of the face and ear of one side or unilateral sweating. Deformity is not so common, but healing may take place with the production of a callus of enormous breadth, with complete rigidity of the neck.

(*b*) *Thoracic Region.*—The deformity is here more marked and pressure symptoms are more common. The time of onset of the paralysis varies very much. It may be an early symptom, even before the curvature is manifest. More commonly it is late, occurring many months after the curvature has developed. The paraplegia is slow in its development; the patient at first feels weak in the legs or has disturbance of sensation, numbness, tingling, pins and needles. The girdle sensation may be marked, or severe pains in the course of the intercostal nerves. Motion is, as a rule, more quickly lost than sensation. Bastian's symptom—abolition of the reflexes—is rarely met with in compression from caries. Finally, there is complete interruption with the production of paraplegia, usually of the spastic type, with exaggeration of the reflexes. This may persist for months, or even for more than a year, and recovery still be possible.

(*c*) *Lumbar Region.*—In the lower dorsal and lumbar regions the symptoms are practically the same, but the sphincter centres are involved and the reflexes are not exaggerated.

Diagnosis.—Caries is by far the most frequent cause of slow compression of the cord, and when there are external signs the recognition is easy. There are cases in which the exudation in the spinal canal between the dura and the bone leads to compression before there are any signs of caries, and if the root symptoms are absent it may be extremely difficult to arrive at a diagnosis. Janeway has called attention to persistent lumbago as a symptom of importance in masked Pott's disease, particularly after injury. Brown-Séquard's paralysis is more common in tumor and in injuries than in caries. Pressure on the nerve roots, too, is less frequent in caries than in malignant disease. The cervical form of pachymeningitis also produces a pressure paralysis, the symptoms of which have already been detailed. Pressure from secondary carcinoma is naturally suggested when spinal symptoms follow within a few years after an operation for cancer of the breast. In paraplegia following tumor of the vertebra secondary to cancer of the breast, and in the erosion of the spine by retroperitoneal growths, the suffering is most intense. The condition has been well termed *paraplegia dolorosa*. I have seen 2 cases in which the breast tumor had not been recognized.

Treatment.—In compression by aneurism or tumor the condition is hopeless. In the former the pains are often not very severe, but in the latter morphia is always necessary. On the other hand, compression by caries is often successfully relieved even after the paralysis has persisted for a long period. When caries is recognized early, rest and support to the spine by the various methods now used by surgeons may do much to prevent the onset of paraplegia. When paralysis has developed, rest with extension gives the best hope of recovery. It is to be remembered that restoration may occur after compression of the cord has lasted for many months, or even more than a year. Cases have been cured by rest alone; the extradural and inflammatory products are absorbed and the caries heals. The most brilliant results in these cases have been obtained by suspension, a method introduced by J. K. Mitchell in 1826, and pursued with remarkable success by his son, Weir Mitchell. During my association with the Infirmary for Nervous Diseases I had numerous opportunities of witnessing the really remarkable effects of persistent suspension, even in apparently desperate and protracted cases. Mitchell's conclusions are that suspension should be employed early in Pott's disease; that used with care it enables us slowly to lessen the curve; that in these cases there must be, in some form, a replacement of the crumpled tissues; that unless there is great loss of power the use of the spine-car or chair of J. K. Mitchell enables suspension, especially in children, to be combined with some exercise; that no case of Pott's disease should be considered desperate without its trial; that suspension has succeeded after failures of other accepted methods; that the pull probably acts more or less directly on the cord itself, and that the gain is not explicable merely by obvious effects on the angular bone curve; that the methods of extension to be used in carious cases may be very varied, provided only we get active extension; that the plan and the length of time of extension must be made to conform to the needs, endurance, and sensation of the individual case. It may be months before there are any signs of improvement. In protracted cases, after suspension has been tried for months, laminectomy may be considered, and has in some instances been successful.

The general treatment of caries is that of tuberculosis—fresh air, good food, cod-liver oil, and arsenic. Counter-irritation in these instances is of doubtful value.

LESIONS OF THE CAUDA EQUINA AND CONUS MEDULLARIS.

The spinal cord extends only to the second lumbar vertebra. Injury, tumors, and caries at or below this level involve not the cord itself, but the bundle of nerves known as the cauda equina and the terminal portion of the cord, the conus medullaris. Much attention has been given to lesions of this part. The whole subject is admirably discussed in Thorburn's work. Fractures and dislocations are common in the lumbo-sacral region, tumors not infrequently involve the filaments of the cauda equina, and some of the nerves may be entangled in the cicatrix of a spina bifida.

In a fracture or dislocation of the first lumbar vertebra the conus medullaris may be compressed with the last sacral nerves given off from it. In a case reported by Kirchhoff there was laceration of the conus with complete paralysis of the bladder and rectum, a case which is held to favor the view that the ano-vesical centre in man is situated in this region of the cord. There are several instances on record in which injury of the cauda equina has produced paralysis of the bladder and rectum alone, sometimes with a slight patch of anæsthesia in the neighborhood of the coccyx or the perinæum. More commonly branches of the sacral or lumbar nerve roots are involved, producing an irregularly distributed motor and sensory paralysis in the legs. When the lumbar nerve roots from the second to the fifth are compressed, there is paralysis of the muscles of the legs, with the exception of the flexors of the ankles, the peronæi, the long flexors of the toes, and the intrinsic muscles of the feet, and loss of sensation in the front, inner and outer part of the thighs, the inner side of the legs, and the inner side of the foot. The sacral roots may alone be involved. Thus in a case which I have reported the patient fell from a bridge and had paralysis of the legs and of the bladder and rectum. When seen sixteen years after the injury, there was slight weakness, with wasting of the left leg; there was complete loss of the function in the ano-vesical and genital centres, and anæsthesia in a strip at the back part of the thigh (in the distribution of the small sciatic), and of the perinæum, scrotum, and penis. The urethra was also insensitive.

Starr's table and Head's figures, given in the general introduction, will be found useful in determining the nerve fibres and segments involved in these cases of injury of the cauda equina.

IV. TUMORS OF THE SPINAL CORD AND ITS MEMBRANES.

New growths may develop in the cord or in its membranes, or may extend into them from the spine. The first two alone will be considered. Occasionally lipoma and parasites occur in the extradural space. Within the dura fibromata, sarcomata, and syphilitic and tuberculous growths are most common. In the cord itself, and attached to the pia mater, the tuberculous, syphilitic, and gliomatous growths are most frequent. Of 50 cases of tumor of the spinal cord and its envelopes, analyzed by Mills and Lloyd, only 3 were parasitic. Of these, 26 were some form of neoplasm, of which sarcomata were most common, 5 were gummatous, and 4 tuberculous. Herter has recently reported 3 cases of solitary tubercle in the cord, and has analyzed others from the literature. Of 24 cases in which the age was given, 15 occurred between the ages of fifteen and thirty-five, and 5 before the fifth year. The tumor is most common in the dorsal and lumbar regions, and is usually met with in connection with tuberculous lesions elsewhere.

The anatomical effects of tumor are very varied. Slow compression is usually produced by growths external to the cord, and it is remarkable what a high grade of compression the cord will bear without serious interference with its functions. In cases of prolonged interruption ascending and descending degenerations occur. Tumors developing within the cord may lead to syringo-myelia. And, lastly, tumors not infrequently excite intense myelitis.

Symptoms.—These will naturally vary a good deal with the segment involved and with the degree of pressure and the extent of implication of the nerve roots.

Within the cord the symptoms are those of a gradually progressing paraplegia, which may at first have the picture of a Brown-Séquard paralysis. Atrophy follows the involvement of the ventral cornua, and vaso-motor disturbances may be marked. The reflexes are lost at the level of the lesion, but if this be in the thoracic cord, the reflexes are retained in the legs. The symptoms are apt to be complicated with those of acute or sub-acute myelitis, which may completely alter the clinical picture. Tumors of the spinal membranes are characterized by the early onset and persist-ence of the root symptoms, which consist of radiating pains, the girdle sen-sation, and hyperæsthesia, or anæsthesia in various portions of the trunk. There may even be severe pain in the anæsthetic areas. Irritation of the motor roots may cause spasm of the muscles supplied, or wasting with paralysis. The paraplegia supervenes some time after the occurrence of the root symptoms. In the thoracic region the level of the growth is usu-ally accurately defined by the level of the pain and the condition of the reflexes.

The diagnosis of tumor within the cord is sometimes easy, the charac-teristic features being the constancy and severity of the root symptoms at the level of the growth and the progressive paralysis. Caries may cause identical symptoms, but the radiating pains are rarely so severe. Cervical meningitis simulates tumor very closely, and in reality produces identical effects, but the very slow progress and the bilateral character from the outset may be sufficient to distinguish it.

In chronic transverse myelitis the symptoms may, according to Gowers, simulate tumor very closely and present radiating pains, a sense of con-striction, and progressive paralysis.

The nature of the tumor can rarely be indicated with precision. With a marked syphilitic history gumma may naturally be suspected, and with coexisting tuberculous disease a solitary tubercle.

Treatment.—If the possibility of syphilitic infection is present the iodide of potassium should be given in large and increasing doses. For the severe pains counter-irritation is sometimes beneficial, particularly the thermo-cautery; morphia is, however, often necessary.

In a few instances tumors of the cord or of the membranes are amena-ble to surgical treatment. The removal by Horsley of a growth from the spinal membranes was one of the most brilliant of recent operations.

Abscess of the cord is a rare lesion, of which only 3 or 4 cases have been described, all metastatic. It may occur without meningitis.

V. SYRINGOMYELIA.

Definition.—A gliomatous new formation about the central canal of the spinal cord, with cavity formation.

Etiology and Morbid Anatomy.—Syringomyelia must be distinguished from dilatation of the central canal—hydromyelus—slight grades of which are not very uncommon either as a congenital condition or as a result of the pressure of tumors. The cavity of syringomyelia has a variable extent in the cord, sometimes running the entire length, but in many cases involving only the cervical and thoracic regions or a more limited area. It is usually in the dorsal portion of the cord and may extend only into one dorsal cornu. The transverse section may be oval or circular or narrow and fissure-like. It varies at different levels. The condition is now regarded as a *gliosis*, a development of embryonal neurogliar tissue in which hæmorrhage or degeneration takes place with the formation of cavities.

Of 190 cases, 133 were in men, 57 in women (Schlesinger). A large majority of the cases begin before the thirtieth year. The disease has been met with in three members of the same family.

Symptoms.—The clinical features are extremely complex. In the classical form there are irregular pains, chiefly in the cervical region; muscular atrophy develops, which may be confined to the arms, or sometimes extends to the legs. The reflexes are increased and a spastic condition develops in the legs. Ultimately the clinical picture may be that of an amyotrophic lateral sclerosis. The tactile sensation is usually intact and the muscular sense is retained, but painful and thermic sensations are not recognized, or there may be in rare instances complete anæsthesia of the skin and of the mucous membranes (Dejerine). This combination of loss of painful and thermic sensations with paralysis of an amyotrophic type is regarded as pathognomonic of the disease. The special senses are usually intact and the sphincters uninvolved. Trophic troubles are not uncommon. Owing to the loss of the pain and heat sensations, the patients are apt to injure themselves. Scoliosis also may be present in these cases. The loss of painful and thermic impressions is due to the fact that these pass to the brain in the peri-ependymal gray matter, particularly that portion in the dorsal roots, which is almost constantly involved in syringomyelia. The tactile sensation is retained because the postero-lateral column is uninvolved.

Schlesinger, in his recent monograph (1895), recognizes the following types: (1) With the classical features above described, which may begin in the cervical or lumbar regions: (2) a motor type, with the picture of an amyotrophic or a spastic paralysis—the sensation may be undisturbed for years; (3) with predominant sensory features, simulating hysterical hemiplegia, or with general pain and temperature anæsthesia; (4) with pronounced trophic disturbances—to this type belong the cases described as Morvan's disease, an affection characterized by neuralgic pains, cutaneous anæsthesia, and painless, destructive whitlows; and (5) the tabetic type, either a combination of the symptoms of tabes in the lower, and of syringomyelia in the upper extremities, or a pure tabetic symptom-complex, due to invasion by the gliosis of the dorsal columns (Oppenheim). Arthropathies occur in about 10 per cent of the cases.

In typical cases the *diagnosis* is easy. The combination of an amyotrophic paralysis, the picture of progressive muscular atrophy of the Aran-Duchenne type, with retention of tactile and loss of thermic and painful sensation, is probably pathognomonic of the disease. Of affections with which it may be confounded, anæsthetic leprosy is the most important, since the anæsthesia and the wasting may closely simulate it; but, as a rule, in leprosy trophic changes are more or less marked. There is often loss of phalanges and there is no characteristic dissociation of sensory impressions.

VI. ACUTE MYELITIS.

Etiology.—Acute myelitis results from many causes, and may affect the cord in a limited or extended portion—the gray matter chiefly, or the gray and white matter together. It is met with: (*a*) As an independent affection following exposure to cold, or exertion, and leading to rapid loss of power with the symptoms of an acute ascending paralysis. (*b*) As a sequel of the infectious diseases, such as small-pox, typhus, and measles. (*c*) As a result of traumatism, either fracture of the spine or very severe muscular effort. Concussion without fracture may produce it, but this is rare. Acute myelitis, for instance, scarcely ever follows railway accidents. (*d*) In diseases of the bones of the spine, either caries or cancer. This is a more common cause of localized acute transverse myelitis than of the diffuse affection. (*e*) In disease of the cord itself, such as tumors and syphilis; in the latter, either in association with gummata, in which case it is usually a late manifestation; or it may follow within a year or eighteen months of the primary affection.

Morbid Anatomy.—In localized acute myelitis affecting white and gray matter, as met with after accident or an acute compression, the cord is swollen, the pia injected, the consistence greatly reduced, and on incising the membrane an almost diffluent fluid may escape. In less intense grades, on section at the affected area, the distinction between the gray and white matter is lost, or is extremely indistinct. The tissue may be injected, or, as is often the case, hæmorrhagic. It is particularly in these forms, due to extension of disease from without or to acute compression, that we find definite involvement of the white matter. In other instances the gray matter is chiefly affected. There may be localized areas throughout the cord in which the gray matter is reduced in consistence and hæmorrhagic, the so-called red softening. There may be definite cavity formations in these foci. In some cases of disseminated or focal myelitis the meninges also are involved and there is a myelomeningitis. And, lastly, there are instances in which, throughout a long section of the cord, sometimes through the lumbar and the greater part of the thoracic, or in the thoracic and cervical regions, there is a diffuse myelitis of the gray substance.

Histologically the nerve fibres are much swollen and irregularly distorted, the axis cylinders are beaded, the myelin droplets are abundant, and the laminated bodies known as corpora amylacea may be seen. The granular fatty cells are also numerous and there may be leucocytes and red blood-corpuscles. Changes in the blood-vessels are striking; the smaller veins are distended and may show varicosities. The perivascular lymph spaces contain numerous leucocytes, and the smaller arteries themselves are frequently the seat of hyaline thrombi. The ganglion cells are swollen and irregular in outline, the protoplasm is extremely granular and vacuolated, and the nuclei, though usually invisible, may show signs of division, and the processes of the cells are not seen.

In cases which persist for some time we have an opportunity of seeing the later stages of acute myelitis. The acute, inflammatory, hyperæmic or red softening is succeeded by stages in which the affected area becomes more yellow from gradual alteration of the blood-pigment, and finally white in color from the advancing fatty degeneration. In cases of compression myelitis, a sclerosis may gradually be produced with the anatomical picture of a chronic diffuse myelitis.

Symptoms.—(*a*) *Acute Central Myelitis.*—It is this form which comes on spontaneously after cold, or in connection with syphilis or one of the infectious diseases, or is seen in a typical manner in the extension from injuries or from tumor. The onset, though scarcely so abrupt as in hæmorrhage, may be sudden; a person may be attacked on the street and have difficulty in getting home. In some instances, the onset is preceded by pains in the legs or back, or a girdle sensation is present. It may be marked by chills, occasionally by convulsions; fever is usually present from the beginning—at first slight, but subsequently it may become high.

The *motor* functions are rapidly lost, sometimes as quickly as in Landry's ascending paralysis. The paraplegia may be complete, and, if the myelitis extends to the cervical region, there may be impairment of motion, and ultimately complete loss of power of the upper extremities as well. The sensation is lost, but there may at first be hyperæsthesia. The reflexes in the initial stage are increased, but in acute central myelitis, unless limited in extent to the thoracic and cervical regions, the reflexes are usually abolished. The rectum and bladder are paralyzed. Trophic disturbances are marked; the muscles waste rapidly; the skin is often congested, and there may be localized sweating. The temperature of the affected limbs may be lowered. Acute bed-sores may develop over the sacrum or on the heels, and sometimes a multiple arthritis is present. In these acute cases the general symptoms become greatly aggravated, the pulse is rapid, the tongue becomes dry; there is delirium, the fever increases, and may reach 107° or 108°.

The course of the disease is variable. In very acute cases death follows in from five to ten days. The cases following the infectious diseases, particularly the fevers and sometimes syphilis, may run a milder course.

The *diagnosis* of this variety of acute myelitis is rarely difficult. In common with the acute ascending paralysis of Landry, and with certain cases of multiple neuritis, it presents a rapid and progressive motor paralysis. From the former it is distinguished by the more marked involvement of sensation, the trophic disturbances, the paralysis of bladder and rectum, the rapid wasting, the electrical changes, and the fever. From acute cases of multiple neuritis it may be more difficult to distinguish, as the sensory features in these cases may be marked, though there is rarely, if ever, in multiple neuritis complete anæsthesia; the wasting, moreover, is more rapid in myelitis. The bladder and rectum are rarely involved—though in exceptional cases they may be—and, most important of all, the trophic changes, the development of bullæ, bed-sores, etc., are not seen in multiple neuritis.

(b) *Acute Transverse Myelitis.*—The symptoms naturally differ with the situation of the lesion.

(1) Acute transverse myelitis in the *thoracic region*, the most common situation, produces a very characteristic picture. The symptoms of onset are variable. There may be initial pains or numbness and tingling in the legs. The paralysis may set in quickly and become complete within a few days; but more commonly it is preceded for a day or two by sensations of pain, heaviness, and dragging in the legs. The paralysis of the lower limbs is usually complete, and if at the level, say, of the sixth thoracic vertebra, the abdominal muscles are involved. Sensation may be partially or completely lost. At the onset there may be numbness, tingling, or even hyperæsthesia in the legs. At the level of the lesion there is often a zone of hyperæsthesia, which is discovered by passing a test-tube containing hot water along the spine, when the sensation of warmth changes to one of actual pain. A girdle sensation may occur early, and when the lesion is in this situation it is usually felt between the ensiform and umbilical regions. The reflex functions are variable. There may at first be abolition of the reflexes; subsequently, the reflexes, which pass through the segments lower than the one affected, may be exaggerated and the limbs may take on a condition of spastic rigidity. It does not always happen, however, that the reflexes are increased in a total transverse lesion of the cord. They may be entirely lost, as first pointed out by Bastian. That this is not due to the preliminary shock is shown by the fact that the abolition of the reflexes may continue for four or more months. The trophic changes are not marked. The muscles become extremely flabby, but not wasted in an extreme degree; subsequently rigidity develops. If the gray matter of the lumbar cord is involved, the flaccidity persists and the wasting may be considerable. The reaction of regeneration is not present. The temperature of the paralyzed limbs is variable. It may at first rise, then fall and become subnormal. Lesions of the skin are not uncommon, and bed-sores are apt to form. There is at first retention of urine and subsequent incontinence. If the lumbar centres are involved, there are from the outset vesical symptoms. The urine is alkaline in reaction and may rapidly become ammoniacal. The bowels are constipated and there is usually incontinence of the fæces. Some writers attribute the cystitis associated with transverse myelitis to disturbed trophic influence.

The course of complete transverse myelitis depends a good deal upon its cause. Death may result from extension. Segments of the cord may be completely and permanently destroyed, in which case there is persistent paraplegia. The pyramidal fibres below the lesion undergo the secondary degeneration, and there is an ascending degeneration of the dorsal median columns. If the lower segments of the cord are involved the legs may remain flaccid. In some instances a transverse myelitis of the thoracic region involves the ventral horns above and below the lesion, producing flaccidity of the muscles, with wasting, fibrillar contractions, and the reaction of degeneration. More commonly, however, in the cases which last many months there is more or less rigidity of the muscles with spasm or persistent contraction of the flexors of the knee.

(2) *Transverse Myelitis of the Cervical Region.*—If the lesion is at the level of the sixth or seventh cervical nerves, there is paralysis of the upper extremities, more or less complete, sometimes sparing the muscles of the shoulder. Gradually there is loss of sensation. The paralysis is usually complete below the point of lesion, but there are rare instances in which the arms only are affected, the so-called cervical paraplegia. In addition to the symptoms already mentioned there are several which are more characteristic of transverse myelitis in the cervical region, such as the occurrence of vomiting, hiccough, and slow pulse, which may sink to 20 or 30, pupillary changes—myosis—sometimes attacks of dysphagia, dyspnœa, or syncope.

Treatment of Acute Myelitis.—In the rapidly developing form due either to a diffuse inflammation in the gray matter or to transverse myelitis, the important measures are: Scrupulous cleanliness, care and watchfulness in guarding against bed-sores, the avoidance of cystitis, either by systematic catheterization or, if there is incontinence, by a carefully adjusted bed urinal, or the use of antiseptic cotton-wool repeatedly changed. In an acute onset in a healthy subject the spine may be cupped. Counter-irritation is of doubtful advantage. Chapman's ice-bag is sometimes useful. No drugs have the slightest influence upon an acute myelitis, and even in subjects with well-marked syphilis neither mercury nor iodide of potassium is curative. Tonic remedies, such as quinine, arsenic, and strychnia, may be used in the later stages. When the muscles have wasted, massage is beneficial in maintaining their nutrition. Electricity should not be used in the early stages of myelitis. It is of no value in the transverse myelitis in the thoracic region with retention of the nutrition in the muscles of the leg.

V. DIFFUSE AND FOCAL DISEASES OF THE BRAIN.

I. TOPICAL DIAGNOSIS.

Only certain regions of the brain give localizing symptoms. These are the cortical motor centres, the speech centres, the centres for the special senses, and the tracts which connect these cortical areas with each other and with other parts of the nervous system.

The following is a brief summary of the effects of lesions from the cortex to the spinal cord:

1. The Cerebral Cortex.—(*a*) Destructive lesions of the motor cortex (central gyri, lobulus paracentralis, posterior portions of the three frontal gyri, especially of the inferior) cause *spastic paralysis* in the muscles of the opposite side of the body. The paralysis is at first flaccid, but contractures subsequently develop. The extent of the paralysis depends upon that of the lesion. It is apt to be limited to the muscles of the face or of an extremity, giving rise to the cerebral monoplegias (Fig. 11, 1). One group of muscles may be much more affected than others, especially in lesions of the highly differentiated area for the upper extremity. It is uncommon to find all the muscle groups of an extremity equally involved in cortical monoplegia. Very rarely through small bilaterally symmetrical lesions monoplegia of the tongue may result without paralysis of the face. A lesion may involve centres lying close together or overlapping one another, thus producing associated monoplegias—e. g., paralysis of the face and arm, or of the arm and leg, but not of the face and leg without involvement of the arm. Very rarely the whole motor cortex is involved, causing paralysis of the opposite side—cortical hemiplegia. Usually in such instances there is marked recovery, so that only a monoplegia persists.

The motor area corresponds also, at least in large part, to the region of the cortex in which the impulses concerned in general bodily sensation (cutaneous sensibility, muscle sense, visceral sensations) first arrive (the somæsthetic area). Combined with the muscular weakness there is usually some disturbance of sensations, particularly of those of the muscular sense. The stereognostic sense is very often affected. In brachial monoplegia, for example, a coin or a knife when placed in the hand of the paralyzed limb, the patient's eyes being closed, is not recognized, owing to inappreciation of the form and consistence of the object, and this even though the slightest tactile stimulus applied to the fingers or surface of the hand is felt and may be correctly localized. The sense of touch, pain, and temperature may be lowered, but usually not markedly unless the superior and inferior parietal lobules are involved in addition to the central gyri. Paræsthesias and vaso-motor disturbances are common accompaniments of paralyses of cortical origin.

(*b*) Irritative lesions cause localized spasms as described above. The most varied muscle groups corresponding to particular movement forms may be picked out. If the irritation be sudden and severe, typical attacks of Jacksonian epilepsy may occur. These convulsions are usually preceded and accompanied by subjective sensory impressions. Tingling or pain, or a sense of motion in the part, is often the *signal symptom* (Seguin), and is of great importance in determining the seat of the lesion. Here, too, the stereognostic sense is frequently involved.

Lesions are often both destructive and irritative, and we then have combinations of the symptoms produced by each. For instance, certain muscles may be paralyzed, and those represented near them in the cortex may be the seat of localized convulsions, or the paralyzed limb itself may be at times subject to convulsive spasms, or muscles which have been convulsed may become paralyzed. The close observation of the sequence of the symptoms in such cases often makes it possible to trace the progress of a lesion involving the motor cortex. In these cases the most frequent cause is a developing tumor, though sometimes local thickenings of the membranes of the brain, small abscesses, minute hæmorrhages, or fragments of a fractured skull must be held responsible.

In another section lesions involving the centres for the special senses are considered, and we shall simply refer to them here. The symptoms caused by lesions of the speech centres will be described under aphasia, and it is only necessary to note here the near situation of the motor speech area (Broca's centre) in the left inferior frontal convolution to the centres for the face and arm on that side, and to state that motor aphasia is often associated with monoplegia of the right side of the face and the right arm. Accompanying the paralysis, following a Jacksonian fit, of the right face or arm there is often a transient motor aphasia.

According to Flechsig, the sensori-motor centres are limited to tolerably circumscribed areas in the cortex, which differ from other portions in that they are provided with projection fibres which connect them with lower centres. The remaining areas of the cortex, amounting, he believes, to about two thirds of the whole, are devoid of projection fibres and are concerned entirely in associative activities. These latter areas, the "association centres" of Flechsig, are three in number: (1) The anterior association centre, including the whole of the frontal lobe in front of the somæsthetic area; (2) the middle association centre, corresponding to the cortex of the island of Reil; and (3) the large, posterior association centre, including the præcuneus, the superior and inferior parietal lobules, the supramarginal and angular gyri, and the whole of the temporal and occipital lobes except the auditory and visual sensory areas.

Flechsig attributes the higher psychic functions, especially those connected with the personality of the individual, to the anterior association centres, while the intellectual activities which have to do with knowledge of the external world he believes correspond to the functions of the large posterior association centre. Whether these views be true, and, if so, in how far they may be applied practically in the localization of diseases, especially of the mind, the future has to decide.

2. Centrum Semiovale.—Lesions in this part may involve either projection fibres (motor or sensory) or association fibres. If involvement of the motor path cause paralysis, this has the distribution of a cortical palsy when the lesion is near the cortex, and of a paralysis due to a lesion of the internal capsule when it is near that region. These lesions of the motor fibres may be associated with symptoms due to interruption in the other systems of fibres running in the centrum semiovale; there may be sensory disturbances—hemianæsthesia and hemianopia—and if the lesion is in the left hemisphere one of the different forms of aphasia may accompany the paralysis.

3. Corpus Callosum.—This may be congenitally absent without symptoms. An acute lesion involving a large portion of the corpus callosum may, however, yield symptoms suggestive of its localization in this region. In the case recorded by Reinhard, in which the situation of the lesion was suspected ante-mortem, there was disturbance of equilibration (without vertigo) and of the synergetic movements of both halves of the body. The autopsy revealed a gliosarcoma which had destroyed the posterior three fourths of the corpus callosum. In Bristowe's 4 cases there existed, as symptoms common to all, pain in the head and partial or complete hemiplegia, with gradual extension of the paralysis to the opposite side of the body. Toward the end of life there was disturbance of speech, difficulty in deglutition, incontinence of urine and fæces and dementia. Here the symptoms have in them nothing that can be looked upon as pathognomonic; indeed, many of the phenomena were doubtless dependent upon involvement of the projection and association fibres of the centrum semiovale.

In animals in which the corpus callosum has been cut experimentally progressive emaciation has been mentioned as a characteristic phenomenon.

4. **Internal Capsule** (Fig. 4).—Through this pass within a rather narrow area all, or nearly all, of the projection fibres (both motor and sensory) which are connected with the cerebral cortex. It is divided into an anterior limb, a knee, and a posterior limb, the latter consisting of a thalamo-lenticular portion (its anterior two thirds) and a retro-lenticular portion (its posterior third). In considering the effects of a given focal lesion involving the fibres of the internal capsule, it is not to be forgotten that the relations of the two limbs of the capsule to one another and to the knee vary considerably in different horizontal planes. Much of the confusion in the bibliography is dependent upon neglect to describe the horizontal level of the lesion, as well as its situation in an antero-posterior direction. The principal bundle passing through the anterior limb of the capsule is that which connects the frontal gyri and the medial bundle in the base of the peduncle (crus) with the nuclei of the pons. These fibres are centrifugal, and innervate chiefly the lower motor nuclei governing bilaterally innervated muscles, especially those of the eyes, head, neck, and probably those of the mouth, tongue, and larynx. In lower horizontal planes these fibres are situated near the knee of the capsule. It is the region of the knee of the capsule which transmits especially the fibres passing from the cerebral cortex to the nuclei of the facial, hypoglossal and third nerves. The path which supplies the nuclei governing the muscles used in speech passes through the knee.

The pyramidal tract goes through the thalamo-lenticular portion of the capsule. The motor fibres are arranged according to definite muscle groups, or rather movement forms, those for the movements of the arm being anterior to those for the leg. The number of fibres for a given muscle group corresponds rather to the degree of complexity of the movements than to the size of the muscles concerned. Thus the areas for the fingers and toes are relatively large.

The fibres to the somæsthetic area of the cortex—that is, those from the ventro-lateral group of nuclei of the thalamus and the tegmental radiations—carrying impulses concerned in general bodily sensation, pass upward through the posterior part of the thalamo-lenticular portion of the capsule. Some of these fibres pass through the anterior two thirds of the posterior limb alongside of the fibres of the pyramidal tract.

Through the retro-lenticular portion of the posterior limb, opposite the posterior third of the lateral surface of the thalamus, pass (1) the fibres carrying impulses concerned in the sensations of the opposite visual field (optic radiation from the lateral geniculate body to the visual sense area in the occipital cortex); (2) the fibres carrying impulses concerned in auditory sensations (radiation from the medial geniculate body to the auditory sense area in the cortex of the temporal lobe); (3) the fibres (probably centrifugal) connecting the cortex of the temporal lobe with the nuclei of the pons.

With this preliminary knowledge concerning the internal capsule, it is not difficult to understand the symptoms which result when it is diseased.

Since here all the fibres of the upper motor segment are gathered together in a compact bundle, a lesion in this region is apt to cause complete hemiplegia of the opposite side, followed later by contractures; and if the lesion involves the hinder portion of the posterior limb there is also hemianæsthesia, including even the special senses (Fig. 4). As a rule, however, lesions of the internal capsule do not involve the whole structure. The disease usually affects mainly either the anterior or posterior portions, and even in instances in which at first the symptoms point to total involvement, there is a disappearance often of a large part of the phenomena after a short time. Thus when the pyramidal tract is destroyed (lesion of the thalamo-lenticular portion of the capsule) the arm may be affected more than the leg, or *vice versa*. The facial paralysis is usually slight, though if the lesion be well forward in the capsule the paralysis of the face and tongue may be marked.

Hemianæsthesia alone without involvement of the motor fibres, due to disease of the capsule, is rare. There is usually also at least partial paralysis of the leg. When the retro-lenticular portion of the capsule is destroyed the hemianæsthesia is accompanied by hemianopsia, disturbance of hearing, and sometimes of smell and taste. The occurrence of hemichorea, marked tremor, or hemiathetosis after a capsular hemiplegia points to the involvement of the thalamus or of the hypothalamic region in the lesion.

Charcot and others have described cases in which as a result of disease of the internal capsule there has been paralysis of the face and leg without involvement of the arm. In such instances the lesion is linear, extending from the posterior part of the anterior limb of the internal capsule backward and lateralward to the leg region in the posterior limb of the capsule, the region for the arm escaping.

Capsular lesions when pure are not accompanied by aphasic symptoms, alexia, or agraphia. A "subcortical" motor aphasia may occur, if along with complete destruction of the anterior limb of the internal capsule on one side there be associated a lesion of the caudate nucleus on the opposite side large enough to interfere with the adjacent fibres going to the nuclei governing the muscles of speech.

5. **Crura (Cerebral Peduncles).**—From this level through the pons, medulla, and cord the upper and lower motor segments are represented, the first by the fibres of the pyramidal tracts and by the fibres which go from the cerebral cortex to the nuclei of the cerebral nerves, the latter by the motor nuclei and the nerve fibres arising from them. Lesions often affect

both motor segments, and produce paralyses having the characteristics of each. Thus a single lesion may involve the pyramidal tract and cause a spastic paralysis on the opposite side of the body, and also involve the nucleus or the fibres of one of the cerebral nerves, and so produce a lower segment paralysis on the same side as the lesion—crossed paralysis. In the crus the third and fourth cerebral nerves run near the pyramidal tract, and a lesion of this region is apt to involve them or their nuclei, causing partial paralysis of the muscles of the eye on the same side as the lesions, combined with a hemiplegia of the opposite side (Fig. 10, 3).

The optic tract also crosses the crus and may be involved, giving hemianopsia in the opposite halves of the visual fields.

If the tegmentum be the seat of a lesion which does not involve the base of the peduncle (or pes) there may be disturbances of cutaneous and muscular sensibility, ataxia, disturbances of hearing, or oculo-motor paralysis. An oculo-motor paralysis of one side, accompanied by a hemi-ataxia of the opposite side, appears to be especially characteristic of a tegmental lesion.

6. **Corpora Quadrigemina.**—Anatomical studies point to the view that the superior colliculus (anterior quadrigeminal body) represents the most important subcortical central organ for the control of the eye-muscle nuclei. This is supported to a certain extent by clinical evidence, though as yet but few cases have been carefully studied. Sight may be only slightly, if at all, disturbed when the superior colliculus is destroyed, and color vision may remain normal. The pupil is usually widened, and the pupillary reaction, both to light and on accommodation, interfered with. Apparently actual paralysis of the eye muscles does not occur unless the nucleus of the third nerve ventral to the aqueduct be also injured.

The inferior colliculus (posterior quadrigeminal body), on the other hand, has been shown by anatomical study to be an important way-station in the auditory conduction-path. A large part of the lateral lemniscus ends in its nucleus, and from it emerge medullated fibres which pass through the brachium quadrigeminum inferior to the medial geniculate body. Thence a large bundle runs through the retro-lenticular portion of the internal capsule to the auditory sense area in the cortex of the temporal lobe.

Weinland has collected 19 cases of tumors of the corpora quadrigemina from the bibliography; in 9 of these auditory disturbances were especially noted. Since the central auditory path of each side receives impulses from both ears, lesion of the colliculus on one side may dull the hearing on both sides, though the opposite ear is usually the more defective. Lesion of the inferior colliculus may be accompanied by disturbance of mastication, owing to paralysis of the descending (mesencephalic) root of the trigeminus. The fourth nerve may also be involved. The ataxia which sometimes accompanies lesions of the corpora quadrigemina is probably to be referred to disturbance in conduction in the medial lemniscus.

7. **Pons and Medulla Oblongata.**—Lesions involving the pyramidal tract, together with any one of the motor cerebral nerves of this region, cause crossed paralysis. A lesion in the lower part of the pons is apt to

cause a lower-segment paralysis of the face on the same side (destruction of the nucleus of the facial nerve or of its root fibres) and a spastic paralysis of the arm and leg on the opposite side (injury to pyramidal tract) (Fig. 10, 4). The abducens, the motor part of the trigeminus, and the hypoglossus nerves may also be paralyzed in the same manner. When the central fibres to the nucleus of the hypoglossus are involved a peculiar form of anarthria results. If the nucleus itself be diseased, swallowing is interfered with.

When the sensory fibres of the fifth nerve are interrupted, together with the sensory tract (the medial lemniscus or fillet) for the rest of the body, which has already crossed the middle line, there is a crossed sensory paralysis—i. e., disturbed sensation in the distribution of the fifth on the side of the lesion, and of all the rest of the body on the opposite side.

A paralysis of the external rectus muscle of one eye and of the internal rectus of the other eye (conjugate paralysis of the muscles which turn the eye to one side), in the absence of a "forced position" of the eyeballs, is highly characteristic of certain lesions of the pons. In such cases the internal rectus may still be capable of functioning on convergence, or when the eye to which it belongs is tested independently of that in which the external rectus is paralyzed. This form of paralysis is found, as a rule, only when the nodule lies just in front of the abducens or involves the nucleus itself, or includes, besides the root fibres of the abducens, that portion of the formatio reticularis that lies between them and the fasciculus longitudinalis medialis (von Monakow). The cases of conjugate paralysis just referred to may be complicated by other disturbances of the eye-muscle movements, in which case the interpretation of the symptoms may be rendered difficult. The facial nerve is often involved in these paralyses.

In lesions of the pons the patient often has a tendency to fall toward the side on which the lesion is, probably on account of implication of the middle peduncle of the cerebellum (brachium pontis). Still more frequent is the simple motor hemi-ataxia consequent upon lesion of the medial lemniscus, and perhaps of longitudinal bundles in the formatio reticularis. This is often accompanied by disturbance of muscular and cutaneous sensations. Only when the lesion is very extensive are there disturbances of hearing (involvement of the lateral lemniscus or corpus trapezoideum).

The symptoms produced by involvement of the different cerebral nerves will be considered in detail in another section.

8. **Cerebellum.**—The functions of this part of the brain are still under consideration. Luciani, whose monograph is exhaustive, regards it as " an end organ, directly or indirectly related to certain peripheral sensory organs and in direct efferent relationship with certain ganglia of the cerebro-spinal axis, and indirectly with the motor apparatus in general. It is functionally homogeneous, each part exercising the functions of the whole, but having special relations to the muscles of the corresponding side of the body " (Krauss).

Lesions of the lateral lobes affect the corresponding side of the body, while lesions of the middle lobe (vermis) affect both sides. Partial removal

62

is followed by transient muscular weakness; complete removal by extreme incoördination. Its one important function would appear to be the coördination of the muscular movements.

In monkeys the symptoms differ much at different periods after the operation. During the first five or six days irritation phenomena predominate. There is, according to Luciani, asthenia, atony, and astasia of the muscles on the side of the body operated upon. The animal cannot stand or walk. All these symptoms may gradually disappear in the course of a few months.

W. C. Krauss has analyzed the lesions and symptoms in 100 cases of disease of this part. The morbid conditions were as follows: Sarcoma in 22 cases; tubercle in 22; glioma in 18; abscess in 10; tumor of unspecified origin in 13; cyst in 7; and 1 case each of softening, endothelioma, cyst and sarcoma, cancer, gumma, fibroma, and hæmorrhage. The left lobe was affected 32 times, the right lobe 32 times, and the middle lobe 17 times. Thus tumor constituted by far the most important affection. There may be no symptoms whatever if it is in one hemisphere only and does not involve the middle lobe. There are not only instances of complete absence of one whole hemisphere, but also of extensive bilateral disease which throughout life have yielded no noticeable symptoms. Other portions of the brain appear to be able to take on the functions normally performed by the cerebellum.

The experiments of J. S. Risien Russell do not entirely confirm the observations of Luciani. In the first place, the occurrence of asthenia is not constant, and as to atony, while the patellar tendon reflexes are sometimes absent, they are as a rule intact in pure cerebellar lesions. There may be even muscular rigidity instead of atony. Russell's experiments make it seem likely that the cerebellar hemisphere of one side exercises constantly an inhibitory effect upon the activities of the cerebral hemisphere of the opposite side (probably by way of the brachium conjunctivum). Thus after removal of one cerebellar hemisphere he found that much milder faradic stimulation of the contra-lateral motor area would call forth movements of the arm and leg than that necessary to stimulate the homo-lateral motor area. The epileptic seizures following the administration of absinthe were far greater on the side of ablation. It is not impossible that the explanation of the epileptiform attacks by no means rare in cerebellar disease is here to be sought. The most common symptoms in tumor of the cerebellum are as follows:

Vertigo, which is more constant in this than in affections of any other region of the brain. Some believe this to be due to involvement of the nervus vestibularis or its nuclei of termination, by means of which the semicircular canals are connected with the cerebellum. The symptom was present in 48 of the cases of Krauss's collection, not reported in 43. The vertigo appears to be entirely independent of the ataxia. Though most frequently associated, either symptom may be present without the other. The vertigo of cerebellar disease is often associated with the feeling that objects are revolving about the body, or that the body itself is moving. *Headache* was present in 83 cases. *Vomiting* occurred in 69 cases, not reported in 23. *Optic neuritis* was found in 66 cases, not reported in 23. Very serious disturbances of vision may result from pressure on the aqueductus cerebri, leading to increased pressure in the third ventricle; this, through bulging of the floor, can directly injure the chiasm or optic nerve.

Of symptoms which are designated as more particularly cerebellar, *ataxia* is the most important. In cerebellar ataxia the gait is irregular and staggering, often zigzag, and in attempting to walk the patient sways to and fro like a drunken man (*démarche d'ivresse* of the French writers). As a rule, the patient walks and tends to fall toward the affected side, but the rule is not certain. The ataxia of cerebellar disease is to be sharply differentiated from the ataxia of tabes dorsalis, from cortical ataxia, and probably from the ataxia accompanying diseases of the tegmental portion of the pons and cerebral peduncle. Cerebellar ataxia is both static and dynamic. The opening or closing of the eyes is of less influence than in spinal ataxia. Very important for differential diagnosis is the fact that when the patient lies in bed movements tolerably well coördinated can be carried out. The coarse nature of the incoördination distinguishes cerebellar ataxia from that due to lesion of the cerebral cortex. In the latter the finer movements (buttoning, etc.) are especially apt to be involved, and there is usually hemi-paresis or mono-paresis, and often disturbance of muscular sense and of the stereognostic sense (von Monakow). Cerebellar ataxia may depend upon the withdrawal of the influence of the cerebellum upon the cerebrum.

Paresis of the trunk muscles, manifest in an inability to perform the movements of bending, erection, and lateral flexion of the trunk, may be present (Hughlings Jackson). Risien Russell holds that the paralysis is "probably directly due to the withdrawal of the cerebellar influence from the muscles."

Other less constant but suggestive symptoms are neuralgic pains in the region of the neck and occiput; blocking of the venæ Galeni and dilatation of the lateral ventricles, causing in children hydrocephalus; pressure on the mid-brain, pons, or medulla oblongata, producing paralysis of the cerebral nerves, rhythmical contractions of the head or extremities, nystagmus, tremor, anarthria, auditory or visual disturbances. There may be glycosuria and bilateral rigidity from pressure on the motor paths. Sudden death may occur. Forced movements, especially rotation of the trunk, forced positions (of the head or trunk), and a peculiar forced position of the eyes (one turned downward and to the side, the other upward and inward) are almost pathognomonic of disease of one brachium pontis (middle cerebellar peduncle).

The reflexes are very variable; they were absent in 12 cases. In pure cerebellar lesion they are probably intact or exaggerated, but when the cerebellar disease involves other structures, directly or indirectly, through action at a distance, or when there is associated disease of the spinal tracts, the reflexes may be abolished.

Symptoms of general mental disturbance may accompany cerebellar disease, but they are not characteristic. There is often irritability, enfeebled memory, and toward the end sopor and coma.

II. APHASIA.*

The speech mechanism consists of receptive, perceptive, and emissive centres in the cortex cerebri, disturbances of which cause *aphasia,* and centres in the medulla which preside over the muscles of articulation, disturbances of which produce *anarthria,* the condition of gradual loss of power of speech, such as occurs in bulbar paralysis. To the disturbances of speech resulting from lesion of the white fibres throwing the lower nuclei governing the speech muscles under the influence of the cortex, without primary injury to either the cortex of the nuclei in the medulla, the term *aphemia* has been applied (Bastian).

The studies of Dax, Broca, Bastian, Kussmaul, Wernicke, Lichtheim, and others have widened enormously our knowledge of speech disorders. Language is gradually acquired by imitation. During development in order that we may make ourselves understood (expressive components of speech), it is necessary that we learn to understand the expressions of others (perceptive speech components). Thus, in teaching a child to say *bell,* the sound of the uttered word enters the afferent path (auditory nerve) and reaches the auditory perceptive centre, from which an impulse is sent to the emissive or motor centre presiding over the nuclei in the medulla, through which the muscles of articulation are set in action. The arc in Lichtheim's schema (Fig. 9) is *a* A, M *m.* The child gradually acquires in this way *memories of the sounds of words,* which are stored at the centre A, and *motor memories*—the kinæsthetic memories of the coördinated muscular movements of the lips, tongue, and larynx necessary to utter words— which are stored at the centre M (glosso-kinæsthetic centre of Bastian). In a similar manner, when shown the bell, the child acquires *visual memories,* which are conveyed through the optic nerve to the visual perceptive centres, *o* O. So also with the memories of the sound of the bell when struck. The memory picture of the shape of the bell, the memory of the appearance of the word bell as written or printed, and the motor memories of the muscular movements required to write the word are distinct from each other; yet they are intimately connected, and form together what is termed the *word-image.* In addition to all this the child gradually acquires in his education ideas as to the use of the bell—intellectual conceptions—the centre for which is represented at I in the diagram. In volitional or intellectual speech, as in uttering the word *bell,* the path would be I, M *m,* and in writing the word, I, M, W, *h.* These various " memories " are as a rule stored or centred in the left hemisphere (see Fig. 3). When the word " bell " is heard, the mental state which results includes not only the activities of the auditory perception-centre, but also by association the activities

---

* A large number of valuable works on aphasia have appeared within the past few years, chief of which may be placed Bastian's recently issued monograph (1898). The works of Wyllie and Elder and the lectures of Bramwell (British Medical Journal, 1897– '98), the monograph of Collins, the text-book of C. K. Mills, and the various publications of Eskridge, von Monakow's volume in Nothnagel's Handbuch, and Miraillée's work are among the most important recent contributions.

of a whole series of cerebral centres, which in the manifold experiences of life have been occupied at one time or another in some way with some psychic attribute of the external object, or with combining and coördinating various impressions of it.

The relations of language (heard, read, spoken, and written) involves then (a) sensory perceptive centres (hearing and sight and, in the blind,

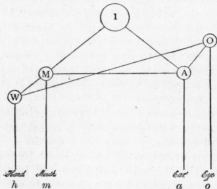

FIG. 9.—Lichtheim's schema. A, auditory area in cerebral cortex, in which are stored the memories of the sounds of words; a A, auditory conduction path from cochlea to temporal lobe; O, visual area in cerebral cortex, perception centre for written and printed words; o O, visual conduction path from retina to occipital lobe; M, speech centre in which are stored the memories of the muscular movements which produce spoken words (Bastian's glosso-kinæsthetic centre); M m, path along which impulses travel to innervate the lower nuclei which govern the muscles concerned in speech; W, area in cerebral cortex in which are stored the memories of the muscular movements concerned in writing (Bastian's cheiro-kinæsthetic centre); W h, path along which impulses travel to innervate the lower nuclei which govern the muscles used in writing; I, areas of association in cortex by means of which the activities of the various sensory perception centres may be united to higher units (conceptions, ideas, thoughts, etc.), and whence the centres M and W may be incited.

touch); (b) emissive or motor centres for speech and writing; and (c) higher psychical centres, through which we obtain an intellectual conception of what is said or written, and by which we express voluntarily our ideas in language.

Aphasic disturbances for convenience of description are arbitrarily divided into two chief forms—*sensory* and *motor*.

(1) **Sensory Aphasia; Apraxia; Word-blindness; Word-deafness.**—By apraxia is understood a condition in which there is loss or impairment of the power to recognize the nature and characteristics of objects. Persons so affected act "as if they no longer possessed such object memories, for they fail to recognize things formerly familiar. A fork, a cane, a pin, may be taken up and looked at by such a person, and yet held or used in a manner which clearly shows that it awakens no idea of its use. And this symptom, for which at first the term blindness of mind was used, is found to extend to other senses than that of sight. Thus the tick of a watch, the sound of a bell, a melody of music, may fail to arouse the idea which it

formerly awakened, and the patient has then deafness of mind; or an odor or taste no longer calls up the notion of the thing smelled or tasted; and thus it is found that each or all of the sensory organs, when called into play, may fail to arouse an intelligent perception of the object exciting them. For the general symptoms of inability to recognize the use or import of an object the term *apraxia* is now employed " (Starr).

Apraxia may occur alone, but more commonly is associated with varieties of sensory and motor aphasia. The patient may be able to read, but the words arouse no intelligent impression in his mind. While blind to memory-pictures aroused through sight, the perceptions may be stimulated by touch; thus there are instances on record of apraxic patients unable to read by sight, who could on tracing the letters by touch name them correctly. Of the forms of apraxia, mind-blindness and mind-deafness are the most important.

The cases of *mind-blindness* collected by Starr indicate that the lesion exists in the left hemisphere in right-handed persons, and in the right hemisphere in left-handed persons. The disease usually involves the angular and supramarginal gyri or the white matter beneath them. Blindness of the " mind's eye " may at times be functional and transitory, and is associated with many forms of mental disturbance. In a remarkable case reported by Macewen, the patient, after an injury to the head, had suffered with headache and melancholia, but there was no paralysis. He was psychically blind and though he could see everything perfectly well and could read letters, objects conveyed no intelligent impression. A man before his eyes was recognized as some object, but not as a man until the sounds of the voice led to the recognition through the auditory centres. The skull was trephined over the angular gyrus and the inner table was found to be depressed and a portion had been driven into the brain in this region. The patient recovered. Mind-blindness is the equivalent of visual amnesia. Other manifestations of mind-blindness are met with; thus a young man with secondary syphilis had several convulsive seizures, after one of which he remained unconscious for some time. On awakening, the memory-pictures of faces and places were a blank, and he neither knew his parents nor brothers, nor the streets of the town in which he lived; he had no aphasia proper, and no paralysis. Again, there may be complete tactile amnesia, as in the cases reported by C. W. Burr.

Word-blindness may occur alone or with motor aphasia. In uncomplicated cases the patient is no longer able to recall the appearances of words, and does not recognize them on a printed or written page. The patient may be able to pronounce the letters and can often write correctly, but he cannot read understandingly what he has written. It is rare, however, for the patient to be able to write with any degree of facility. There are instances in which the patient, unable to read, has yet been able to do mathematical problems and to recognize playing cards. The lesions in cases of word-blindness is, in a majority of cases, in the angular and supramarginal gyri on the left side. It is commonly associated with hemianopia, and not infrequently with mind-blindness (Fig. 3).

Mind-deafness is a condition in which sounds, though heard and perceived as such, awaken no intelligent perceptions. A person who knows nothing of French has mind-deafness so far as the French language is concerned, and though he recognizes the words as words when spoken, and can repeat them, they awaken no auditory memories. The musical faculties may be lost in aphasics, who may become note-deaf and unable to appreciate melodies or to read music (*amusia*). This may occur without the existence of motor aphasia, and, on the other hand, there are cases on record in which with motor aphasia for ordinary speech the patient could sing and follow tunes correctly. Mind-deafness is also known as auditory amnesia.

Word-deafness is a condition in which the patient no longer understands spoken language. The memory of the sound of the word is lost, and can neither be recalled nor recognized when heard. It is usually associated with other varieties of aphasia, though there are cases in which the patient has been able to read and write and speak. The lesion in word-deafness has been accurately defined in a number of cases to be in the posterior portion of the superior temporal convolution and the transverse temporal gyri on the left side (Fig. 3).

In *ordinary sensory aphasia* of Wernicke's type there is loss of power to understand spoken words and to repeat words pronounced before the patient. The patient, as a rule, cannot read (alexia), and is usually unable to express his thoughts in writing (agraphia). Spontaneous speech may be somewhat interfered with, and on account of the interference with speech control, resulting from the loss of memory of the sounds of words, there may be a little paraphasia.

In the so-called *pure word-deafness* (Wernicke's subcortical sensory aphasia) the symptoms differ from those of the most common form of sensory aphasia in that the power to read and to write are retained. Besides, there is but little if any paraphasia.

In the so-called *transcortical sensory aphasia* the patient has lost the power of understanding spoken words, although he is capable of spontaneous speech and also of repeating words pronounced before him. Spontaneous writing is impossible. He can read aloud from a manuscript or printed page, but does not understand what he reads. There is some paraphasia.

(2) **Ordinary motor or ataxic aphasia** is a condition in which the memory of the efforts necessary to pronounce words is lost, owing to disturbance in the emissive centres. This is the variety long ago recognized by Broca, the lesion of which was localized by him in the left inferior frontal convolution. The patient may not be able to utter a single word; more commonly he can say one or two words, such as "no," "yes," and he not infrequently is able to repeat words. When shown an object, though not able to name it, he may evidently recognize what it is. If told the name, he is, as a rule, unable to repeat it. A man knowing the French and German languages may lose the power of expressing his thoughts in them, while retaining his mother-tongue; or, if completely aphasic, may recover one before the other. As the third left frontal convolution is in close contact with the centres for the face and arm, these are not uncommonly involved, with the production of a partial or, in some instances, a complete right-

sided hemiplegia. *Alexia*, or inability to read, occurs with motor aphasia and also with word-blindness.

As a rule, in motor aphasia there is also inability to write—*agraphia*. When there is right brachial monoplegia it is difficult to test the capability, but there are instances of motor aphasia without paralysis, in which the power of voluntary writing is lost. The condition varies very much; thus a patient may not be able to write voluntarily or from dictation, and yet may copy perfectly. It is still a question whether there is a special writing centre. It has been placed by some writers at the base of the second frontal convolution, but it seems likely that it coincides with the motor area for the upper extremity. From the above type, which may be looked upon as the ordinary form of motor aphasia, two other varieties must be separated—viz., (1) pure word-dumbness and (2) the so-called transcortical motor aphasia.

Pure word-dumbness (subcortical motor aphasia of Lichtheim and Wernicke) is the term applied to that complex of symptoms occasionally met with, in which, though the power of spontaneous speech and of repeating words heard is lost, the individual can write, and can read to himself with understanding that which is written or printed. He is, of course, unable to read aloud.

Transcortical motor aphasia is the term applied by Wernicke to that form of motor aphasia studied first by Lichtheim in which the power to speak and write spontaneously is lost, though the patient can understand spoken and written words perfectly, can read aloud, can write to dictation, and can copy another individual's writing.

There is a form known as *mixed aphasia*, in which the patient understands what is said, and speaks even long sentences correctly, but he constantly tends to misplace words, and does not express his ideas in the proper words. It is precisely these cases which afford the most exquisite examples of paraphasia. All grades of this may be met with, from a state in which only a word or two is misplaced to an extreme condition in which the patient talks jargon. In these cases the association tract is interrupted between the auditory perceptive and the emissive centres, hence it is sometimes known as Wernicke's *aphasia of conduction*. The lesion is usually in the insula and in the convolutions which unite the frontal and temporal lobes. Lichtheim's schema, though out of accord with a number of facts, is extremely useful to the beginner, and will assist the student in obtaining a rational idea of the varieties of aphasia:

1. In the condition of apraxia or mind-blindness the ideation centres, I, are involved, often with the auditory and visual perceptive centres, A and O.

2. A lesion at A, the centre for the auditory memories of words (left superior temporal gyrus), is associated with word-deafness.

3. A lesion at O, the centre for visual memories (occipital cortex), causes word-blindness.

4. Interruption of the tracts uniting A M and O M causes the conduction aphasia of Wernicke—*paraphasia*.

5. Destruction of the centre M (Broca's convolution) causes ordinary motor aphasia, in which the patient cannot express thoughts in speech.

A lesion at M usually destroys also the power of writing. The centre for memories of the movements made in writing, W, is distinct from that of speech. It is called by Bastian the "cheiro-kinæsthetic" centre. A lesion at M, which would destroy the power of voluntary speech, might leave open the connections between O W and A W, by which the patient could copy or write from dictation. According to Wernicke's conception, pure word-deafness (subcortical sensory aphasia) would be due to a lesion in the path *a* A, transcortical sensory aphasia to a lesion in the path A I, pure word-dumbness (subcortical motor aphasia) to a lesion in the path M *m*, and transcortical motor aphasia to a lesion in the path I M. While undoubtedly there are groups of cases separable clinically corresponding to these various types, still pathological examinations have already shown that the nomenclature is faulty and will not stand, though the number of cases thus far thoroughly studied at autopsy does not suffice for the construction of a complete classification on a pathological basis.

The problems of aphasia are in reality excessively complicated, and the student must not for a moment suppose that cases are as simple as diagrams indicate. A majority of them are very complex, but with patience the diagnosis of the different varieties can often be worked out.

The following tests should be applied in each case of aphasia after having determined the presence or absence of paralyses, and whether the patient is right-handed or left-handed: (1) The power of recognizing the nature, uses, and relations of objects—i. e., whether apraxia is present or not; (2) the power to recall the name of familiar objects seen, smelled, or tasted, or of a sound when heard, or of an object touched; (3) the power to understand spoken words; (4) the capability of understanding printed or written language; (5) the power of appreciating and understanding musical tunes; (6) the power of voluntary speech—in this it is to be noted particularly whether he misplaces words or not; (7) the power of reading aloud and of understanding what he reads; (8) the power to write voluntarily and of reading what he has written; (9) the power to copy; (10) the power to write at dictation; and (11) the power of repeating words.

The *medico-legal aspects* of aphasia are of great importance. No general principle can be laid down, but each case must be considered on its merits. Langdon, in reviewing the whole question, concludes: "Sanity established, any legal document should be recognized when it can be proved that the person making it can understand fully its nature by any receptive channel (viz., hearing, vision, or muscular sense), and can, in addition, express assent or dissent with certainty to proper witnesses, whether this expression be by spoken speech, written speech, or pantomime."

Prognosis and Treatment.—In young persons the outlook is good, and the power of speech is gradually restored apparently by the education of the centres on the opposite side of the brain. In adults the condition is less hopeful, particularly in the cases of complete motor aphasia with right hemiplegia. The patient may remain speechless, though capable of understanding everything, and attempts at re-education may be futile. Partial recovery may occur, and the patient may be able to talk, but misplaces words. In sensory aphasia the condition may be only transient, and the different forms rarely persist alone without impairment of the powers of expression.

The education of an aphasic person requires the greatest care and patience, particularly if, as so often happens, he is emotional and irritable. It is best to begin by the use of detached letters, and advance, not too rapidly, to words of only one syllable. Children often make rapid progress, but in adults failure is only too frequent, even after the most painstaking efforts. In the cases of right hemiplegia with aphasia the patient may be taught to write with the left hand.

III. AFFECTIONS OF THE BLOOD-VESSELS.

1. Hyperæmia.

Congestion of the brain has in the past played an important part in cerebral pathology. Undoubtedly there are great variations in the amount of blood in the cerebral vessels; this is universally conceded, but how far these changes are associated with a definite group of symptoms is not quite so clear. The whole subject has recently been revised by R. Geigel, who rightly insists that the nutrition of the nerve-cells and the possibility of interchange of gases between the blood and the cerebral tissues is dependent not only upon the amount of blood in the cerebral vessels, but also upon its chemical constitution, and especially, it would appear, upon the velocity of the current in the cerebral capillaries. The speed of the blood flow in the cerebral capillaries depends, according to this writer, much more on the tension of the walls of the vessels than upon the height of the arterial pressure. In many of the conditions designated as " cerebral hyperæmia " there is really a condition of lowered pressure, for with flaccidity and widening of the cerebral arteries, due say to paralysis of the sympathetic, the arterial pressure remaining constant, there must follow as the result of the diminution of the tension of the vessel walls a decrease in the velocity of the blood-flow. On the other hand, spasm of the cerebral arteries, due say to irritation of the sympathetic, gives rise not to " anæmia " as generally is supposed, but through increase of vascular tension to a higher velocity of flow through the cerebral capillaries. It has been customary to describe cerebral hyperæmia as being either active or passive.

Thus *active hyperæmia* has been supposed to be associated with febrile conditions, with increased action of the heart, chilling of the surface, contraction of the superficial vessels, and with the suppression of certain customary discharges. Among other recognized causes are plethora, functional irritation, such as is associated with excessive brain work, and the action of certain substances, such as alcohol and nitrite of amyl.

Passive hyperæmia was said to result from obstruction in the cerebral sinuses and veins, engorgement in the lesser circulation, as in mitral stenosis, emphysema, from pressure on the superior cava by aneurisms and tumors, and in the venous engorgement which takes place in prolonged straining efforts. In its most intense form it is seen in the compression of the superior cava by tumors and in death from strangulation.

The anatomical changes in congestion of the brain are by no means striking. Such an active hyperæmia is never visible post mortem. The veins of the cortex are distended, the gray matter has a deeper color, and its vessels are full. The arteries at the base and in the Sylvian fissures contain blood. Nothing, however, can be more uncertain or indefinite than the post-mortem appearances of so-called hyperæmia of the brain. The most intense distention of the vessels is seen in early death during the specific fevers, or in the secondary passive congestion due to obstruction in the superior cava or in the lesser circulation. In a majority of these cases of so-called hyperæmia, while the total mass of blood in the brain may exceed the normal by a considerable amount, yet the velocity of the current is so much less than normal, that as a result the brain really has a smaller supply of blood than is normal—that is, the patient actually suffers from cerebral " anæmia " rather than from " hyperæmia."

Symptoms.—There are no characteristic or constant features of dilatation of the cerebral blood-vessels. It may exist in the most extreme grade without the slightest disturbance of the cerebral functions, as is witnessed frequently in the pressure by tumors on the superior vena cava. How far the headache and delirium of the early stage of the infectious fevers is to be assigned to dilatation of the blood-vessels of the brain it is not easy to determine. The headache, dizziness, and unpleasant sensations in aortic insufficiency and in some instances of hypertrophy of the heart have been attributed to the cerebral congestion.

As a separate clinical entity, congestion of the brain rarely comes under observation. I have no knowledge of instances associated with delirium, fever, insomnia, and convulsions, or of the so-called apoplectiform variety described by some writers. Very plethoric persons are subject to attacks of headache with flushing of the face and irritability of temper, attacks which may recur frequently and are sometimes relieved by bleeding at the nose. These have usually been attributed to congestion of the brain. When the so-called passive hyperæmia reaches a high grade, there may be torpor, dulness of the intellect, and ultimately deep coma.

Leube suggests that the symptoms usually referred to active hyperæmia in the acute infectious diseases, like diphtheria and erysipelas, or in the instances in which hypertrophy of the heart accompanies disease of the kidneys, may after all be toxic in origin, rather than due to alteration in the circulatory relations. At any rate, he believes that it is not possible to make a diagnosis of such a hyperæmia. Flushing of the face is by no means a safe guide. Possibly an examination of the eye-grounds may be helpful.

2. Anæmia.

This may be induced by loss of blood, either quickly, as in hæmorrhage, or gradually, as in the severe primary and secondary anæmias. The anæmia may be local and due to causes which interfere with the blood supply to the brain, as narrowing of the vessels by endarteritis, pressure, narrowing of the aortic orifice, or it may follow an unequal distribution of the blood in consequence of dilatation of certain vascular territories. Thus, rapid distention of the intestinal vessels, such as occurs after the removal of ascitic fluid, may cause sudden death from cerebral anæmia. The commonest illustration of this is the fainting fit from emotion, in which the blood supply to the brain is insufficient on account of the diminished arterial pressure. Anæmia of the cerebral vessels may be caused by pressure of fluid in the ventricles. The partial anæmia results from obliteration of branches of the circle of Willis by embolism or thrombosis. Ligature of one carotid sometimes causes a transient marked anæmia and disturbance of function on one side of the brain.

The anatomical condition of the brain in anæmia is very striking. The membranes are pale, only the large veins are full, the small vessels over the gyri are empty, and an unusual amount of cerebro-spinal fluid is present. On section both the gray and white matter look extremely pale and the cut surface is moist. Very few *puncta vasculosa* are seen.

Symptoms.—The effects of anæmia of the brain are well illustrated by a fainting fit in which loss of consciousness follows the heart weakness. When the result of hæmorrhage, there are drowsiness, giddiness, inability to stand, flashes of light, dark spots before the eyes, and noises in the ears; the respiration becomes hurried; the skin is cool and covered with sweat; the pupils are dilated, there may be vomiting, headache, or delirium, and gradually, if the bleeding continues, consciousness is lost and death may occur with convulsions. In ordinary syncope the loss of consciousness is usually transient and the recumbent posture alone may suffice to restore the patient to consciousness. In the more chronic forms of brain anæmia, such as result from the gradual impoverishment of the blood, as in protracted illness or in starvation, the condition known as irritable weakness results. Mental effort is difficult, the slightest irritation is followed by undue excitement, the patient complains of giddiness and noises in the ears, or there may be hallucinations or delirium. These symptoms are met with in an extreme grade as a result of prolonged starvation.

These symptoms are indistinguishable from those due to the so-called cerebral hyperæmia. The quality of the blood is deteriorated and the velocity of the blood-flow is diminished, so that the cerebral nutrition is interfered with. It is interesting to note that lack of suitable nutrition gives rise to phenomena of increased irritability in certain of the cerebral centres, at least for a time.

An interesting set of symptoms, to which the term *hydrencephaloid* was applied by Marshall Hall, occurs in the debility produced by prolonged diarrhœa in children. The child is in a semi-comatose condition with the eyes open, the pupils contracted, and the fontanelle depressed. In the earlier period there may be convulsions. The coma may gradually deepen, the pupils become dilated, and there may be strabismus and even retraction of the head, symptoms which closely simulate those of basilar meningitis.

3. Œdema of the Brain.

In the pathology of brain lesions œdema formerly played a *rôle* almost equal in importance to congestion. It occurs under the following conditions: In general atrophy of the convolutions, in which case the œdema is represented by an increase in the cerebro-spinal fluid and in that of the meshes of the pia. In extreme venous dilatation from obstruction, as in mitral stenosis or in tumors, there may be a condition of congestive œdema, in which, in addition to great filling of the blood-vessels, the substance of the brain itself is unusually moist. The most acute œdema is a local process found around tumors and abscesses. An intense infiltration, local or general, may occur in Bright's disease, and to it, as Traube suggested, certain of the uræmic symptoms may be due.

The *anatomical changes* are not unlike those of anæmia. When the œdema follows progressive atrophy, the fluid is chiefly within and beneath the membranes. The brain substance is anæmic and moist, and has a wet, glistening appearance, which is very characteristic. In some instances the œdema is more intense and local and the brain substance may look infiltrated with fluid. The amount of fluid in the ventricles is usually increased.

The *symptoms* are in great part those of lessened blood-flow, and are not well defined. As just stated, some of the cerebral features of uræmia may depend upon it. Of late years cases have been reported by Raymond, Tenneson, and Dercum, in which unilateral convulsions or paralysis have occurred in connection with chronic Bright's disease, and in which the condition appeared to be associated with œdema of the brain. The older writers laid great stress upon an apoplexia serosa, which may really have been a general œdema of the brain. Inasmuch as the instances in which œdema of the brain occurs are often those in which there is also intoxication, or anæmia, or both, it is probably impossible to say at the bedside definitely which of these possible factors is responsible for the symptoms in a given case.

4. Cerebral Hæmorrhage.

The bleeding may come from branches of either of the two great groups of cerebral vessels—the *basal,* comprising the circle of Willis and the central arteries passing from it and from the first portion of the cerebral arteries, or the *cortical group,* the anterior, middle, and the posterior cerebral vessels. In a majority of the cases the hæmorrhage is from the central branches, more particularly from those given off by the middle cerebral arteries in the anterior perforated spaces, and which supply the corpora striata and internal capsules. One of the largest of these branches which passes to the third division of the lenticular nucleus and to the anterior part of the internal capsule, the lenticulo-striate artery of Duret, is so frequently involved in hæmorrhage that it has been called by Charcot *the artery of cerebral hæmorrhage.* Hæmorrhages from this and from the lenticulo-thalamic artery include more than 60 per cent of all cerebral hæmorrhages. The bleeding may be into the substance of the brain, to which alone the term cerebral apoplexy is applied, or into the membranes, in which case it is termed meningeal hæmorrhage; both, however, are usually included under the terms intracranial or cerebral hæmorrhage.

Etiology.—The conditions which produce lesions of the blood-vessels play a very important part; thus the natural tendency to degeneration of the vessels in advanced life makes apoplexy much more common after the fiftieth year. It may, however, occur in children under ten. On account of the greater liability to arterial disease (associated probably with muscular exertion and the abuse of alcohol), men are more subject to cerebral hæmorrhage than women. Heredity was formerly thought to be an important factor in this affection, and the apoplectic *habitus* or build is still referred to. By this is meant a stout plethoric body of medium size, with a short neck. Heredity influences cerebral hæmorrhage entirely through the arteries, and there are families in which these degenerate early, usually in association with renal changes. The secondary hypertrophy of the heart brings with it serious dangers, which have already been discussed in the section upon arteries. The special factors in inducing arteriosclerosis—the abuse of alcohol, immoderate eating, syphilis, and prolonged muscular exertion—are found to be important antecedents in a large number of cases of cerebral hæmorrhage. Chronic lead poisoning and gout also may here be mentioned.

The endocarditis of rheumatism and other fevers may indirectly lead to apoplexy by causing embolism and aneurism of the vessels of the brain. Cerebral hæmorrhage occurs occasionally in the specific fevers and in profound alterations of the blood, as in leukæmia and pernicious anæmia. The actual exciting cause of the hæmorrhage is not evident in the majority of cases. The attack may be sudden and without any preliminary symptoms. In other instances violent exertion, particularly straining efforts, or the excited action of the heart in emotion may cause a rupture.

Morbid Anatomy.—The lesions causing apoplexy are almost invariably in the cerebral arteries, in which the following changes may lead directly to it:

(*a*) The production of miliary aneurisms, rupture of which is the most common cause of cerebral hæmorrhage. The origin of the miliary aneurisms is disputed. Charcot thought they resulted from changes in the *adventitia* (periarteritis). Others, with Eichler, Ziegler, and Birch-Hirschfeld, find the primary change in the *intima*. The weight of opinion at present, however, is on the side of the view that the *media* is first degenerated (Roth, Loewenthal). They occur most frequently on the central arteries, but also on the smaller branches of the cortical vessels. On section of the brain substance they may be seen as localized, small dark bodies, about the size of a pin's head. Sometimes they are seen in numbers upon the arteries when carefully withdrawn from the anterior perforated spaces. According to Charcot and Bouchard, who have described them, they are most frequent in the central ganglia. In apoplexy after the fortieth year if sought for they are rarely missed. The actual miliary aneurism, which by its rupture has occasioned the hæmorrhage, may be difficult to find, but if one pours water carefully on the area of hæmorrhage, or, better still, submerges the apoplectic mass for a time, it will usually be found possible to do so, and even to find the hole in its wall.

(*b*) Aneurism of the branches of the circle of Willis. These are by no means uncommon, and will be considered subsequently.

(*c*) Endarteritis and periarteritis in the cerebral vessels most commonly lead to apoplexy by the production of aneurisms, either miliary or coarse. There are instances in which the most careful search fails to reveal anything but diffuse degeneration of the cerebral vessels, particularly of the smaller branches; so that we must conclude that spontaneous rupture may occur without the previous formation of aneurism.

(*d*) Increased permeability of the walls of the vessels may account for hæmorrhages by *diapedesis* without actual rupture. Such hæmorrhages are not uncommon in cases of contracted kidney, grave anæmia, and various infections and intoxications.

The hæmorrhage may be meningeal, cerebral, or intraventricular.

Meningeal hæmorrhage may be outside the dura, between this membrane and the bone, or between the dura and arachnoid, or between the arachnoid and the pia mater. The following are the chief causes of this form of hæmorrhage: Fracture of the skull, in which case the blood usually comes from the lacerated meningeal vessels, sometimes from the torn sinuses. In these cases the blood is usually outside the dura or between it and the arachnoid. The next most frequent cause is rupture of aneurisms on the larger cerebral vessels. The blood is usually subarachnoid. An intracerebral hæmorrhage may burst into the meninges. A special form of meningeal hæmorrhage is found in the new-born, associated with injury during birth. And lastly, meningeal hæmorrhage may occur in the constitutional diseases and fevers. The blood may be in a large quantity at the base; in cases of ruptured aneurism, particularly, it may extend into the cord or upon the cortex. Owing to the greater frequency of the aneurisms in the middle cerebral vessels, the Sylvian fissures are often distended with blood.

Intracerebral hæmorrhage is most frequent in the neighborhood of the corpus striatum, particularly toward the outer section of the lenticular nucleus. The hæmorrhage may be small and limited to the lenticular body, the thalamus, and the internal capsule, or it may extend into the centrum semi-ovale, or burst into the lateral ventricle, or extend to the insula. Hæmorrhages confined to the white matter—the centrum semiovale—are rare. Localized bleeding may occur in the crura or in the pons. Hæmorrhage into the cerebellum is not uncommon, and usually comes from the superior cerebellar artery. The extravasation may be limited to the substance or rupture into the fourth ventricle. Twice I have known sudden death in girls under twenty-five to be due to cerebellar hæmorrhage.

Ventricular Hæmorrhage.—This occasionally but rarely is primary, coming from the vessels of the plexuses or of the walls. More often it is secondary, following hæmorrhage into the cerebral substance. It is not infrequent in early life and may occur during birth. Of 94 cases collected by Edward Sanders, 7 occurred during the first year, and 14 under the twentieth year. In the cases which I have seen in adults it has almost always been caused by rupture of a vessel in the neighborhood of the caudate nucleus. The blood may be found in one ventricle only, but more commonly it is in both lateral ventricles, and may pass into the third ventricle and through the aqueduct of Sylvius into the fourth ventricle, forming a complete mould in blood of the ventricular system. In these cases the clinical picture may be that of " *apoplexie foudroyante.*"

Subsequent Changes.—The blood gradually changes in color, and ultimately the hæmoglobin is converted into the reddish-brown hæmatoidin. Inflammation occurs about the apoplectic area, limiting and confining it, and ultimately a definite wall may be produced, inclosing a cyst with fluid contents. In other instances a cyst is not formed, but the connective tissue proliferates and leaves a pigmented scar. In meningeal hæmorrhage the effused blood may be gradually absorbed and leave only a staining of the membranes. In other cases, particularly in infants, when the effusion is cortical and abundant, there may be localized wasting of the convolutions and the production of a cyst in the meninges. Possibly certain of the cases of porencephaly are caused in this way.

Secondary degeneration follows, varying in character according to the location of the hæmorrhage and the actual damage done by it to nerve cells or their medullated axones. Thus, in persons dying some years after a cerebral apoplexy which has produced hemiplegia (lesion of the motor area in the cortex or of the pyramidal tract leading from it), the degeneration may be traced through the cerebral peduncle, the ventral part of the pons, the pyramids of the medulla, the fibres of the direct pyramidal tract of the cord of the same side, and the fibres of the crossed pyramidal tract on the opposite side. After hæmorrhages in the middle and inferior frontal gyri there follows degeneration of the frontal cerebro-cortico-pontal path, going through the anterior limb of the internal capsule and the medial portion of the basis pedunculi to the nuclei pontis; also degeneration of the fibres connecting the nucleus medialis thalami, and the anterior part of the nucleus lateralis thalami with the cortex (Flechsig, v. Monakow).

When the temporal gyri or their white matter are destroyed by a hæmorrhage the lateral segment of the basis pedunculi degenerates (Dejerine). Cerebellar hæmorrhage, especially if it injure the nucleus dentatus, may lead to degeneration of the brachium conjunctivum.

There may be slow degeneration in the lemniscus medialis, extending as far as the nuclei on the opposite side of the medulla oblongata, after hæmorrhages in the central gyri, hypothalamic region, or dorsal part of the pons. Hæmorrhages destroying the occipital cortex, or subcortical hæmorrhages injuring the optic radiations, occasion slow degeneration (cellulipetal) of the radiations from the lateral geniculate body, and after a time to marked atrophy or even disappearance of its ganglion cells.

Symptoms.—These may be divided into primary, or those connected with the onset, and secondary, or those which develop later after the early manifestations have passed away.

Primary Symptoms.—Premonitory indications are rare. As a rule, the patient is seized while in full health or about the performance of some every-day action, occasionally an action requiring strain or extra exertion.

Now and then instances are found in which there are sensations of numbness or tingling or pains in the limbs, or even choreiform movements in the muscles of the opposite side, the so-called prehemiplegic chorea. In other cases temporary disturbances of vision and of associated movements of the eye-muscles have been noted, but none of the prodromata of apoplexy (the so-called "warnings") is characteristic. The onset of the apoplexy, as cerebral hæmorrhage is usually called, varies greatly. There may be sudden loss of consciousness and complete relaxation of the extremities. In such instances the name *apoplectic stroke* is particularly appropriate. In other cases the onset is more gradual and the loss of consciousness may not occur for a few minutes after the patient has fallen, or after the paralysis of the limbs is manifest. In the typical apoplectic attack the condition is as follows: There is deep unconsciousness; the patient cannot be roused. The face is injected, sometimes cyanotic, or of an ashen-gray hue. The pupils vary; usually they are dilated, sometimes unequal, and always, in deep coma, inactive. If the hæmorrhage be so located that it can irritate the nucleus of the third nerve the pupils are contracted (hæmorrhages into the pons or ventricles). The respirations are slow, noisy, and accompanied with stertor. Sometimes the Cheyne-Stokes rhythm may be present. The chest movements on the paralyzed side may be restricted, in rare instances on the opposite side. The cheeks are often blown out during expiration, with spluttering of the lips. The pulse is usually full, slow, and of increased tension. The temperature may be normal, but is often found subnormal, and, as in a case reported by Bastian, may sink below 95°. In cases of basal hæmorrhage the temperature, on the other hand, may be high. The urine and fæces are usually passed involuntarily. Convulsions are not common. It may be difficult to decide whether the condition is apoplexy associated with hemiplegia or sudden coma from other causes. An indication of hemiplegia may be discovered in the difference in the tonus of the muscles on the two sides. If the arm or the leg is lifted, it drops "dead" on the affected side, while on the other it falls more slowly. Rigidity also may be present. In watching the movements of the facial muscles in the stertorous respiration it will be seen that on the paralyzed side the relaxation permits the cheek to be blown out in a more marked manner. The head and eyes may be turned strongly to one side—conjugate deviation. In such an event the turning is *toward* the side of the hæmorrhage.

In other cases, in which the onset is not so abrupt, the patient may not lose consciousness, but in the course of a few hours there is loss of power, unconsciousness gradually develops, and deepens into profound coma. This is sometimes termed ingravescent apoplexy. The attack may occur during sleep. The patient may be found unconscious, or wakes to find that the power is lost on one side. Small hæmorrhages in the territory of the central arteries may cause hemiplegia without loss of consciousness.

Usually within forty-eight hours after the onset of an attack, sometimes within from two to six hours, there is febrile reaction, and more or less constitutional disturbance associated with inflammatory changes about the hæmorrhage and absorption of the blood. The period of inflammatory reaction may continue for from one week to two months. The patient may die in this reaction, or, if consciousness has been regained, there may be delirium or recurrence of the coma. At this period the so-called early rigidity may develop in the paralyzed limbs. The so-called trophic changes may occur, such as sloughing or the formation of vesicles. The most serious of these is the sloughing eschar of the lower part of the back, or on the paralyzed side, which may appear within forty-eight hours of the onset and is usually of grave significance. The congestion at the bases of the lungs so common in apoplexy is regarded by some as a trophic change.

Conjugate Deviation.—In a right hemiplegia the eyes and head may be turned to the left side; that is to say, the eyes look toward the cerebral lesion. This is almost the rule in the conjugate deviation of the head and eyes which occurs early in hemiplegia. When, however, convulsions or spasm develop or the state of so-called early rigidity in hemiplegia, the conjugate deviation of the head and eyes may be in the opposite direction; that is to say, the eyes look away from the lesion and the head is rotated toward the convulsed side. This symptom may be associated with cortical lesions, particularly, according to some authors, when in the neighborhood of the supramarginal and angular gyri. It may also occur in a lesion of the internal capsule or in the pons, but in the latter situation the conjugate deviation is the reverse of that which occurs in other cases, as the patient looks away from the lesion, and in spasm or convulsion looks toward the lesion. In cases in which consciousness is restored and the patient improves, the unilateral paralysis which persists in cases in which the motor area, or the pyramidal tract in any part of its course, is involved is known as

Hemiplegia.—Hemiplegia is complete when it involves face, arm, and leg, or partial when it involves only one or other of these parts. This may be the result of a lesion (*a*) of the motor cortex; (*b*) of the pyramidal fibres in the corona radiata and in the internal capsule; (*c*) of a lesion in the cerebral peduncle; or (*d*) in the pons Varolii. The situation of the lesions and their effects are given in Fig. 10. Hæmorrhage is perhaps the most common cause, but tumors and spots of softening may also induce it. The special details of the hemiplegia may here be considered. The face (except in lesions in the lower part of the pons) is involved on the same side as the arm and leg. This results from the fact that the facial muscles stand in precisely the same relation to the cortical centres as those of the arm and leg, the fibres of the upper motor segment of the facial nerve from the cortex decussating just as do those of the nerves of the limbs. The facial paralysis is partial, involving only the lower portion of the nerve, so that the orbicularis oculi and the frontalis muscles are uninvolved. The signs of the facial paralysis are usually well marked. There may be a slight difficulty in elevating the eyebrows or in closing the eye on the paralyzed side, or in rare cases the facial paralysis is complete, but the movements may be present with emotion, as laughing or crying. The hypoglossal nerve also is involved. In consequence, the patient cannot put out the tongue straight, but it deviates toward the paralyzed side, inasmuch as the genio-hyo-glossus of the sound side is unopposed. With right hemiplegia there may be aphasia. Even without marked aphasia difficulty in speaking and slowness are common.

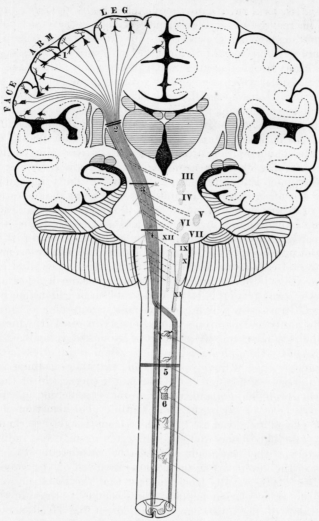

FIG. 10.—Diagram of motor path from right brain. The upper segment is black, the lower red. The nuclei of the motor cerebral nerves are shown on the left side; on the right side the cerebral nerves of that side are indicated. A lesion at 1 would cause upper segment paralysis in the arm of the opposite side—cerebral monoplegia; at 2, upper segment paralysis of the whole opposite side of the body—hemiplegia; at 3 (in the crus), upper segment paralysis of the opposite face, arm and leg, and lower segment paralysis of the eye muscles on the same side—crossed paralysis; at 4 (in the lower part of the pons), upper segment paralysis of the opposite arm and leg, and lower segment paralysis of the face and the external rectus on the same side—crossed paralysis; at 5, upper segment paralysis of all muscles represented below lesion, and lower segment paralysis of muscles represented at level of lesion—spinal paraplegia; at 6, lower segment paralysis of muscles localized at seat of lesion—anterior poliomyelitis. (Van Gehuchten, modified.)

The arm is, as a rule, more completely paralyzed than the leg. The loss of power may be absolute or partial. In severe cases it is at first complete. In others, when the paralysis in the face and arm is complete that of the leg is only partial. The face and arm may alone be paralyzed, while the leg escapes. Less commonly the leg is more affected than the arm, and the face may be only slightly involved.

Certain muscles escape in hemiplegia, particularly those associated in symmetrical movements, as those of the thorax and abdomen, a fact which Broadbent explains by supposing that as the spinal nuclei controlling these movements on both sides constantly act together, they may, by means of this intimate connection, be stimulated by impulses coming from only one side of the brain. The degree of permanent paralysis after a hemiplegic attack varies much in different cases. When the restitution is partial, it is always, as Wernicke has pointed out, certain groups of muscles which recover rather than others. Thus in the leg the residual paralysis concerns the flexors of the leg and the dorsal flexors of the foot—i. e., the muscles which, according to Ludwig Mann, are active in the second period of walking, shortening the leg, and bringing it forward while it swings. The muscles which lift the leg when it rests upon the ground, those used in the first period of walking, include the extensors of the leg and the plantar flexors of the foot. These "lengtheners" of the leg often recover almost completely in cases in which the paralysis is due to lesions of the pyramidal tract. In the arms the residual paralysis usually affects the muscle groups which oppose the thumb, those which rotate the arm outward, and the openers of the hand.

As a rule, there is at first no wasting of the paralyzed limbs.

Crossed Hemiplegia.—A paralysis in which there is loss of function in a cerebral nerve on one side with loss of power (or of sensation) on the opposite side of the body is called a crossed or alternate hemiplegia. It is met with in lesions, commonly hæmorrhage, in the crus, the pons, and the medulla (Fig, 10, 3 and 4).

(*a*) *Crus.*—The bleeding may extend from vessels supplying the corpus striatum, internal capsule, and optic thalamus, or the hæmorrhage may be primarily in the crus. In the classical case of Weber, on section of the lower part of the left crus an oblong clot 15 mm. in length lay just below the medial and inferior surface. The characteristic features of a lesion in this locality are paralysis of arm, face, and leg of the opposite side, and oculo-motor paralysis of the same side—the syndrome of Weber. Sensory changes have also been present. Hæmorrhage into the tegmentum is not necessarily associated with hemiplegia, but there may be incomplete paralysis of the oculo-motor nerve, with disturbance of sensation and ataxia on the opposite side of the body. The optic tract or the lateral geniculate body lying on the lateral side of the crus may be compressed, in which event there will be hemianopsia.

(*b*) *Pons and Medulla.*—Lesions may involve the pyramidal tract and one or more of the cerebral nerves. If at the lower aspect of the pons, the facial nerve may be involved, causing paralysis of the face on the same side and hemiplegia on the opposite side. The fifth nerve may be involved, with the fillet (the sensory tract), causing loss of sensation in the area of distribution of the fifth on the same side as the lesion and loss of sensation on the opposite side of the body.

Sensory Disturbances resulting from Cerebral Hæmorrhage.—These are variable. Hemianæsthesia may coexist with hemiplegia, but in many instances there is only slight numbing of sensation. When the hemianæsthesia is marked, it is usually the result of a lesion in the internal capsule involving the retrolenticular portion of the posterior limb. In C. L. Dana's study of sensory localization he found that anæsthesia of organic cortical origin was always limited or more pronounced in certain parts, as the face, arm, or leg, and was generally incomplete. Total anæsthesia was either of functional or subcortical origin. Marked anæsthesia was much more common in softening than in hæmorrhage. Complete hemianæsthesia is certainly rare in hæmorrhage. Disturbance of the special senses is not common. Hemianopia may exist on the same side as the lesion, and there may be diminution in the acuteness of the senses of hearing, taste, and smell. Gowers thinks that homonymous hemianopsia of the halves of the visual fields opposite to the lesion is very frequent, though often overlooked.

Psychic disturbances, variable in nature and degree, may result from cerebral hæmorrhage.

The Reflexes in Apoplectic Cases.—During the apoplectic coma all the reflexes are abolished, but immediately on recovery of consciousness they return, first on the non-hemiplegic side, later, sometimes only after weeks, on the paralyzed side. As to the time of return, especially of the patellar reflexes, marked differences are observable in individual cases. The deep reflexes later are increased on the paralyzed side, and ankle clonus may be present. The plantar and other superficial reflexes are usually diminished. The sphincters are not affected.

The *course* of the disease depends upon the situation and extent of the lesion. If slight, the hemiplegia may disappear completely within a few days or a few weeks. In severe cases the rule is that the leg gradually recovers before the arm, and the muscles of the shoulder girdle and upper arm before those of the forearm and hand. The face may recover quickly.

Except in the very slight lesions, in which the hemiplegia is transient, changes take place which may be grouped as

Secondary Symptoms.—These correspond to the chronic stage. In a case in which little or no improvement takes place within eight or ten weeks, it will be found that the paralyzed limbs undergo certain changes. The leg, as a rule, recovers enough power to enable the patient to get about, although the foot is dragged. Occasionally a recurrence of severe symptoms is seen, even without a new hæmorrhage having taken place. In both arm and leg the condition of *secondary contraction* or *late rigidity* comes on and is always most marked in the upper extremity. The arm becomes permanently flexed at the elbow and resists all attempts at extension. The wrist is flexed upon the forearm and the fingers upon the hand. The position of the arm and hand is very characteristic. There is frequently, as the contractures develop, a great deal of pain. In the leg the contracture is rarely so extreme. The loss of power is most marked in the muscles of the foot, and to prevent the toes from dragging, the knee in walking is much flexed, or more commonly the foot is swung round in a half-circle.

The reflexes are at this stage greatly increased. These contractures are permanent and incurable, and are associated with a secondary descending sclerosis of the motor path. There are instances, however, in which rigidity and contracture do not occur, but the arm remains flaccid, the leg having regained its power. This *hémiplégie flasque* of Bouchard is found most commonly in children. Among other secondary changes in late hemiplegia may be mentioned the following: Tremor of the affected limbs, post-paralytic chorea, the mobile spasm known as athetosis, arthropathies in the joints of the affected side, and muscular atrophy. Athetosis and post-hemiplegic chorea will be considered in the hemiplegia of children. The cool surface and thin glossy skin of a hemiplegic limb are familiar to all. A word may here be said upon the subject of muscular atrophy of cerebral origin.

As a rule, atrophy is not a marked feature in hemiplegia, but in some instances it does develop. It has been thought to be due in some cases to secondary alterations in the gray matter of the ventral horns, as in a case reported by Charcot. Recently, however, attention has been called by Senator, Quincke, and others to the fact that atrophy may follow as a direct result of the cerebral lesion, the ventral horns remaining intact. In Quincke's case, atrophy of the arm followed the development of a glioma in the anterior central convolution. The gray matter of the ventral horns was normal. These atrophies are most common in cortical lesions involving the domain of the third main branch of the Sylvian artery, and in central lesions involving the lenticulo-thalamic region. Their explanation is not clear. The wasting of cerebral origin, which occurs most frequently in children, and leads to hemiatrophy of the muscles along with stunted growth of the bones and joints, is to be sharply separated from the hemiatrophy of the muscles of the adult following within a relatively short time upon the hemiplegia.

Diagnosis.—There are three groups of cases which offer increasing difficulty in recognition.

(1) Cases in which the onset is gradual, a day or two elapsing before the paralysis is fully developed and consciousness completely lost, are readily recognized, though it may be difficult to determine whether the lesion is due to thrombosis or to hæmorrhage.

(2) In the sudden apoplectic stroke in which the patient rapidly loses consciousness, the difficulty in diagnosis may be still greater, particularly if the patient is in deep coma when first seen.

The first point to be decided is the existence of hemiplegia. This may be difficult, although, as a rule, even in deep coma the limbs on the paralyzed side are more flaccid and drop instantly when lifted; whereas, on the non-paralyzed side the muscles retain some degree of tonus. The reflexes may be increased on the affected side and there may be conjugate deviation of the head and eyes. Rigidity in the limbs of one side is in favor of a hemiplegic lesion. It is practically impossible in a majority of these cases to say whether the lesion is due to hæmorrhage, embolism, or thrombosis.

(3) Large hæmorrhage into the ventricles or into the pons may produce sudden loss of consciousness with complete relaxation, so that the condition may simulate coma from uræmia, diabetes, alcoholism, opium poisoning, or epilepsy.

The previous history and the mode of onset may give valuable information. In epilepsy, convulsions have preceded the coma; in alcoholism, there is a history of constant drinking, while in opium poisoning the coma develops more gradually; but in many instances the difficulty is practically very great, and on more than one occasion I have seen mortifying post-mortem disclosures under these circumstances. With diabetic coma the breath often smells of acetone. In ventricular hæmorrhage the coma is sudden and develops rapidly. The hemiplegic symptoms may be transient, quickly giving place to complete relaxation. Convulsions occur in many cases, and may be the very symptom to lead astray—as in a case of ventricular hæmorrhage which occurred in a puerperal patient, in whom, naturally enough, the condition was thought to be uræmic. Rigidity is often present. In hæmorrhage into the pons convulsions are frequent. The pupils may be strongly contracted, conjugate deviation may occur, and the temperature is apt to rise rapidly. The contraction of the pupils in pontine hæmorrhage naturally suggests opium poisoning. The difference in temperature in the two conditions is a valuable diagnostic point. The apoplectiform seizures of general paresis have usually been preceded by abnormal mental symptoms, and the associated hemiplegia is seldom permanent.

It may be impossible at first to give a definite diagnosis. In admissions to hospitals or in emergency cases the physician should be particularly careful about the following points: The examination of the head for injury or fracture; the urine should be tested for albumin, examined for sugar, and studied microscopically; a careful examination should be made of the limbs with reference to their degree of relaxation or the presence of rigidity, and the condition of the reflexes; the state of the pupils should be noted and the temperature taken. The odor of the breath (alcohol, acetone, chloroform, etc.) should be remarked. The most serious mistakes are made in the case of patients who are drunk at the time of the attack, a combination by no means uncommon in the class of patients admitted to hospital. Under these circumstances the case may erroneously be looked upon as one of alcoholic coma. It is best to regard each case as serious and to bear in mind that this is a condition in which, above all others, mistakes are common.

Prognosis.—From cortical hæmorrhage, unless very extensive, the recovery may be complete without a trace of contracture. This is more common when the hæmorrhage follows injury than when it results from disease of the arteries. Infantile meningeal hæmorrhage, on the other hand, is a condition which may produce idiocy or spastic diplegia.

Large hæmorrhages into the corona radiata, and especially those which rupture into the ventricles, rapidly prove fatal.

The hemiplegia which follows lesions of the internal capsule, the result of rupture of the lenticulo-striate artery, is usually persistent and followed by contracture. When the retro-lenticular fibres of the internal capsule are involved there may be hemianæsthesia, and later, especially if the thalamus be implicated, hemichorea or athetosis. In any case of cerebral apoplexy the following symptoms are of grave omen: persistence or deepening of the coma during the second and third day; rapid rise in temperature within the first forty-eight hours after the initial fall. In the reaction which takes place on the second or third day, the temperature usually rises, and its gradual fall on the third or fourth day with return of consciousness is a favorable indication. The rapid formation of bed-sores, particularly the malignant decubitus of Charcot, is a fatal indication. The occurrence of albumin and sugar, if abundant, in the urine is an unfavorable symptom.

When consciousness returns and the patient is improving, the question is anxiously asked as to the paralysis. The extent of this cannot be determined for some weeks. With slight lesions it may pass off entirely. If persistent at the end of a month some grade of permanent palsy is certain to remain, and gradually the late rigidity supervenes.

5. Embolism and Thrombosis (*Cerebral Softening*).

(*a*) **Embolism.**—The embolus usually enters the carotid, rarely the vertebral artery. In the great majority of cases it comes from the left heart and is either a vegetation of a fresh endocarditis or, more commonly, of a recurring endocarditis, or from the segments involved in an ulcerative process. Less often the embolus is a portion of a clot which has formed in the auricular appendix. Portions of clot from an aneurism, thrombi from atheroma of the aorta, or from the territory of the pulmonary veins, may also cause blocking of the branches of the circle of Willis. In the puerperal condition cerebral embolism is not infrequent. It may occur in women with heart-disease, but in other instances the heart is uninvolved, and the condition has been thought to be associated with the development of heart-clots, owing to increased coagulability of the blood. A majority of cases of embolism occur in heart-disease, 89 per cent (Saveliew). Cases are rare in the acute endocarditis of rheumatism, chorea, and febrile conditions. It is much more common in the secondary recurring endocarditis which attacks old sclerotic valves. The embolus most frequently passes to the left middle cerebral artery, as it enters the left carotid oftener than the right because of the more direct course of the blood in the former. The posterior cerebral and the vertebral are less often affected. A large plug may lodge at the bifurcation of the basilar. Embolism of the cerebral vessels is rare.

Embolism occurs more frequently in women, owing, no doubt, to the greater frequency of mitral stenosis. Contrary to this general statement, Newton Pitt's statistics of 79 cases at Guy's Hospital indicate, however, that males are more frequently affected; for in this series there were 44 males and 35 females. Saveliew gives 54 per cent in women.

(*b*) **Thrombosis.**—Clotting of blood in the cerebral vessels occurs (1) about an embolus, (2) as the result of a lesion of the arterial wall (either endarteritis with or without atheroma or, particularly, the syphilitic arteritis), (3) in aneurisms both coarse and miliary, and (4) very rarely as a direct result of abnormal conditions of the blood. Thrombosis occasionally follows ligation of the carotid artery. The thrombosis is most common in the middle cerebral and in the basilar arteries. According to Kolisko, softening of limited areas, sufficient to induce hemiplegia, may be caused by sudden collapse of certain cerebral arteries from cardiac weakness.

Anatomical Changes.—Degeneration and softening of the territory supplied by the vessels is the ultimate result in both embolism and thrombosis. Blocking in a terminal artery may be followed by infarction, in which the territory may either be deeply infiltrated with blood (hæmorrhagic infarction) or be simply pale, swollen, and necrotic (anæmic infarction). Gradually the process of softening proceeds, the tissue is infiltrated with serum and is moist, the nerve fibres degenerate and become fatty. The neuroglia is swollen and œdematous. The color of the softened area depends upon the amount of blood. The hæmoglobin undergoes gradual transformation, and the early red color may give place to yellow. Formerly much stress was laid upon the difference between *red*, *yellow*, and *white* softening. The red and yellow are seen chiefly on the cortex. Sometimes the red softening is particularly marked in cases of embolism and in the neighborhood of tumors. The gray matter shows many punctiform hæmorrhages—capillary apoplexy. There is a variety of yellow softening—the *plaques jaunes*—common in elderly persons, which occurs in the gray matter of the convolutions. The spots are from 1 to 2 cm. in diameter, sometimes are angular in shape, the edges cleanly cut, and the softened area is represented by either a turbid, yellow material, or in some instances there is a space crossed by fine trabeculæ, in the meshes of which there is fluid. White softening occurs most frequently in the white matter, and is seen best about tumors and abscesses. Inflammatory changes are common in and about the softened areas. When the embolus is derived from an infected focus, as in ulcerative endocarditis, suppuration may follow. The final changes vary very much. The degenerated and dead tissue elements are gradually but slowly removed, and if the region is small may be replaced by a growth of connective tissue and the formation of a scar. If large, the resorption results in the formation of a cyst. It is surprising for how long an area of softening may persist without much change.

The position and extent of the softening depend upon the obstructed artery. An embolus which blocks the middle cerebral at its origin involves not only the arteries to the anterior perforated space, but also the cortical branches, and in such a case there is softening in the neighborhood of the corpus striatum, as well as in part of the region supplied by the cortical vessels. The freedom of anastomosis between these branches varies a good deal. Thus, there are instances of embolism of the middle cerebral artery in which the softening has only involved the territory of the central branches, in which case blood has reached the cortex through the anterior and posterior cerebrals. When the middle cerebral is blocked (as is perhaps oftenest the case) beyond the point of origin of the central arteries, one or other of its branches is usually most involved. The embolus may lodge in the vessel passing to the third frontal convolution, or in the artery of the ascending frontal or ascending parietal; or it may lodge in the branch passing to the supramarginal and angular gyri, or it may enter the lowest branch which is distributed to the upper convolutions of the temporal lobe. These are practically terminal arteries, and instances frequently occur of softening limited to a part, at any rate, of the territory supplied by them. Some of the most accurate focalizing lesions are produced in this way.

Symptoms.—Extensive thrombotic softening may exist without any symptoms. It is not uncommon in the post-mortem examination of the bodies of elderly persons to find the *plaques jaunes* scattered over the convolutions. So, too, softening may take place in the "silent" regions, as they are termed, without exciting any symptoms. When the central or cortical branches of the middle cerebral arteries are involved the symptoms are similar to those of hæmorrhage from the same arteries. Permanent or transient hemiplegia results. When the central arteries are involved the softening in the internal capsule is commonly followed by permanent hemiplegia. There are certain peculiarities associated with embolism and with thrombosis respectively.

In *embolism* the patient is usually the subject of heart-trouble, or there exist some of the conditions already mentioned. The onset is sudden, without premonitory symptoms. When the embolism blocks the left middle cerebral artery the hemiplegia is usually associated with aphasia. In *thrombosis*, on the other hand, the onset is more gradual; the patient has previously complained of headache, vertigo, tingling in the fingers; the speech may have been embarrassed for some days; the patient has had loss of memory or is incoherent, or paralysis begins at one part, as the hand, and extends slowly, and the hemiplegia may be incomplete or variable. Abrupt loss of consciousness is much less common, and when the lesion is small consciousness is retained. Thus, in thrombosis due to syphilitic disease, the hemiplegia may come on gradually without the slightest disturbance of consciousness.

The hemiplegia following thrombosis or embolism has practically the characteristics, both primary and secondary, described under hæmorrhage.

The following may be the effects of blocking the different vessels: (*a*) *Vertebral.*—The left branch is more frequently plugged. The effects are involvement of the nuclei in the medulla and symptoms of acute bulbar paralysis. It rarely occurs alone; more commonly with

(*b*) Blocking of the *basilar artery*. When this is entirely occluded, there may be bilateral paralysis from involvement of both motor paths. Bulbar symptoms may be present; rigidity or spasm may occur. The temperature may rise rapidly. The symptoms, in fact, are those of apoplexy of the pons.

(*c*) The *posterior cerebral* supplies the occipital lobe on its medial surface and the greater part of the temporo-sphenoidal lobe. If the main stem be thrombosed there is hemianopia with sensory aphasia. Localized areas of softening may exist without symptoms. Blocking of the main occipital branch (arteria occipitalis of Duret), or of the arteria calcarina, passing to the cuneus may be followed by hemianopia. Hemianæsthesia may result from involvement of the posterior part of the internal capsule. Not infrequently symmetrical thrombosis of the occipital arteries of the two sides occurs, as in Förster's well-known case. Still more frequent is the occurrence of thrombosis of a branch of the posterior cerebral of one hemisphere and a branch of the middle cerebral of the other (von Monakow). It is in such cases that the most pronounced instances of apraxia are met with.

(d) *Internal Carotid.*—The symptoms are variable. As is well known, the vessel is in a majority of cases ligated without risk. In other instances transient hemiplegia follows; in others again the hemiplegia is permanent. These variations depend on the anastomoses in the circle of Willis. If these are large and free, no paralysis follows, but in cases in which the posterior communicating and the anterior communicating vessels are small or absent, the paralysis may persist. In No. 7 of my Elwyn series of cases of infantile hemiplegia, the woman, aged twenty-four, when six years old, had the right carotid ligated for abscess following scarlet fever, with the result of permanent hemiplegia. Blocking of the internal carotid within the skull by thrombosis or embolism is followed by hemiplegia, coma, and usually death. The clot is rarely confined to the carotid itself, but spreads into its branches and may involve the ophthalmic artery.

(e) *Middle Cerebral.*—This is the vessel most commonly involved, and, as already mentioned, if plugged before the central arteries are given off, permanent hemiplegia usually follows from softening of the internal capsule. Blocking of the branches beyond this point may be followed by hemiplegia, which is more likely to be transient, involves chiefly the arm and face, and if on the left side is associated with aphasia. The individual branches passing to the inferior frontal (producing typical motor aphasia if the disease be on the left side), anterior and posterior central gyri (usually causing total hemiplegia), to the supramarginal and angular gyri (giving rise, if the thrombosis be on the left side, probably without exception to the so-called pure (or subcortical) alexia, usually also to right-sided hemianopsia), or to the temporal gyri (in which event with left-sided thrombosis word-deafness results) may be plugged.

(f) *Anterior Cerebral.*—No symptoms may follow, and even when the branches which supply the paracental lobule and the top of the ascending convolutions are plugged the branches from the middle cerebral are usually able to effect a collateral circulation in these parts. Monoplegia of the leg may, however, result. Hebetude and dulness of intellect may occur with obstruction of the vessel.

There is unquestionably greater freedom of communication in the cortical branches of the different arteries than is usually admitted, although it is not possible, for example, to inject the posterior cerebral through the middle cerebral, or the middle cerebral from the anterior; but the absence of softening in some instances in which smaller branches are blocked shows how complete may be the compensation, probably by way of the capillaries. The dilatation of the collateral branches may take place very rapidly; thus a patient with chronic nephritis died about twenty-four hours after the hemiplegic attack. There were recent vegetations on the mitral valve and an embolus in the right middle cerebral artery just beyond the first two branches. The central portion of the hemisphere was swollen and œdematous. The right anterior cerebral was greatly dilated, and by measurement its diameter was found to be nearly three times that of the left.

Treatment of Cerebral Hæmorrhage and of Softening. —The patient should be placed on his back, with the head high, the neck free, kept absolutely quiet, and measures immediately taken to reduce the arterial pressure. Of these the most rapid and satisfactory is venesection, which should be practised whenever the arterial tension is much increased. With a small pulse of low tension and signs of cardiac weakness it is contra-indicated. The chief difficulty is in determining whether the apoplexy is really due to hæmorrhage, or to thrombosis or embolism, since in the latter group of cases bleeding probably does harm. As a rule, however, in middle-aged men with arterio-sclerosis, an accentuated aortic second sound, and hypertrophy of the left ventricle, bleeding is indicated. Horsley and Spencer have recently, on experimental grounds, recommended the practice, formerly employed empirically, of compression of the carotid, particularly in the ingravescent form; or even, in suitable cases, passing a ligature round the vessel. An ice-bag may be placed on the head and hot bottles to the feet. The bowels should be freely opened, either by calomel, or croton oil placed on the tongue. Counter-irritation to the neck or to the feet is not necessary. Catheterization of the bladder may be necessary, especially if the patient remain long unconscious. When dyspnœa, stertor, and signs of mechanical obstruction are present, the patient should be turned on the side, as recommended by Bowles. This procedure also lessens the liability to congestion of the lungs.

Special care should be taken to avoid bed-sores; and if bottles are used to the feet, they should not be too hot, since blisters may be readily caused by much lower temperature than in health. In the fever of reaction, aconite may be indicated, but should be cautiously used. Stimulants are not necessary, unless the pulse becomes feeble and signs of collapse supervene. No digitalis is to be given. During recovery the patient should be still kept entirely at rest, even in the mildest cases remaining in bed for at least fourteen days. The ice-bag should still be kept at the head. The diet should be light and no medicine other than some placebo should be administered, at least during the first month after the hæmorrhage. Attention should be paid to the position occupied by the paralyzed limb or limbs, which if swollen may be wrapped in cotton batting or flannel.

The treatment of *softening* from thrombosis or embolism is very unsatisfactory. Venesection is not indicated, as it lowers the tension and rather promotes clotting. If, as is often the case, the heart's action is feeble and irregular, stimulants and small doses of digitalis may be given with, if necessary, ether or ammonia. The bowels should be kept open, but it is not well to purge actively, as in hæmorrhage.

In the thrombosis which follows syphilitic disease of the arteries, and which is met with most frequently in men between twenty and forty (in whom the hemiplegia often sets in without loss of consciousness), the iodide of potassium should be freely used, giving from 20 to 30 grains three times a day, or, if necessary, larger doses. If the syphilis has been recent, mercurials by inunction are also indicated. Practically these are the only cases of hemiplegia in which we see satisfactory results from treatment.

Operative treatment has been suggested, and when the diagnosis of subdural hæmorrhage can be made it is justifiable. An attempt to reach a central hæmorrhage in the neighborhood of the internal capsule would only increase the damage to the brain substance. Very little can be done for the hemiplegia which remains. The damage is too often irreparable and permanent, and it is very improbable that iodide of potassium, or any other remedy, hastens in the slightest degree Nature's dealing with the blood-clot.

The paralyzed limbs may be gently rubbed once or twice a day, and this should be systematically carried out, in order to maintain the nutrition of the muscles and to prevent, if possible, contractures. The massage should not, however, be begun until at least ten days after the attack. The rubbing should be *toward* the body, and should not be continued for more than fifteen minutes at a time. After the lapse of a fortnight, or in severe cases a month, the muscles may be stimulated by the faradic current; faradic stimulation alternating with massage, especially if applied to the antagonists of the muscles which ordinarily undergo contracture, is of very great service, even in cases where there can be but little hope of any return of voluntary movement. When contractures develop, electricity properly applied at intervals may still be of some benefit along with the passive movements and frictions.

In a case of complete hemiplegia, the friends should at the outset be frankly told that the chances of full recovery are slight. Power is usually restored in the leg sufficient to enable the patient to get about, but in the majority of instances the finer movements of the hand are permanently lost. The general health should be looked after, the bowels regulated, and the secretions of the skin and kidneys kept active. In permanent hemiplegia in persons above the middle period of life, more or less mental weakness is apt to follow the attack, and the patient may become irritable and emotional.

And, lastly, when hemiplegia has persisted for more than three months and contractures have developed, it is the duty of the physician to explain to the patient, or to his friends, that the condition is past relief, that medicines and electricity will do no good, and that there is no possible hope of cure.

6. Aneurism of the Cerebral Arteries.

Miliary aneurisms are not included, but reference is made only to aneurism of the larger branches. The condition is not uncommon. There were 12 instances in my first 800 autopsies in Montreal.* This is a considerably larger proportion than in Newton Pitt's collection from Guy's Hospital, 19 times in 9,000 inspections.

Etiology.—Males are more frequently affected than females. Of my 12 cases 7 were males. The disease is most common at the middle period

---

* Canada Medical and Surgical Journal, vol. xiv.

of life. One of my cases was a lad of six. Pitt describes one at the same age. The chief causes are (a) endarteritis, either simple or syphilitic, which leads to weakness of the wall and dilatation; and (b) embolism. As pointed out by Church, these aneurisms are often found with endocarditis. Pitt, in his recent study of the subject, concludes that it is exceptional to find cerebral aneurism unassociated with fungating endocarditis. The embolus disappears, and dilatation follows the secondary inflammatory changes in the coats of the vessel.

Morbid Anatomy.—The middle cerebral branches are most frequently involved. In my 12 cases the distribution on the arteries was as follows: Internal carotid, 1; middle cerebral, 5; basilar, 3; anterior communicating, 3. Except in one case they were saccular and communicated with the lumen of the vessel by an orifice smaller than the circumference of the sac. In the 154 cases which make up the statistics of Lebert, Durand, and Bartholow the middle cerebral was involved in 44, the basilar in 41, internal carotid in 23, anterior cerebral in 14, posterior communicating in 8, anterior communicating in 8, vertebral in 7, posterior cerebral in 6, inferior cerebellar in 3 (Gowers). The size of the aneurism varies from that of a pea to that of a walnut. The hæmorrhage may be entirely meningeal with very slight laceration of the brain substance, but the bleeding may be, as Coats has shown, entirely within the substance.

Symptoms.—The aneurism may attain considerable size and cause no symptoms. In a majority of the cases the first intimation is the rupture and the fatal apoplexy. Distinct symptoms are most frequently caused by aneurism of the internal carotid, which may compress the optic nerve or the commissure, causing neuritis or paralysis of the third nerve. A murmur may be audible on auscultation of the skull. Aneurism in this situation may give rise to irritative and pressure symptoms at the base of the brain or to hemianopsia. In the remarkable case reported by Weir Mitchell and Dercum an aneurism compressed the chiasma and produced bilateral temporal hemianopsia.

Aneurism of the vertebral or of the basilar may involve the nerves from the fifth to the twelfth. A large sac at the termination of the basilar may compress the third nerves or the crura.

The diagnosis is, as a rule, impossible. The larger sacs produce the symptoms of tumor, and their rupture is usually fatal.

7. Endarteritis.

In no group of vessels do we more frequently see chronic degenerative changes than in those of the circle of Willis. The condition occurs as:

(a) *Arterio-sclerosis*, producing localized or diffused thickening of the intima with the formation of atheromatous patches or areas of calcification. In the later stages, as seen in elderly people, the arteries of the circle of Willis may be dilated, stiff, or almost universally calcified.

(b) *Syphilitic Endarteritis.*—As already mentioned under the section of syphilis, gummatous endarteritis is specially prone to attack the cerebral vessels. It has in itself no specific characters—that is to say, it is impossible in given sections to pick out an endarteritis syphilitica from an ordinary endarteritis obliterans. On the other hand, as already stated, the nodular periarteritis is never seen except in syphilis.

8. Thrombosis of the Cerebral Sinuses and Veins.

The condition may be primary or secondary. Lebert (1854) and Tonnele were among the first to recognize the condition clinically.

Primary thrombosis of the sinuses and veins is rare. It occurs (*a*) in children, particularly during the first six months of life, usually in connection with diarrhœa. It has, in my experience, been a rare condition. I have never seen an example of spontaneous thrombosis of the sinuses in a child, and only two instances, both in connection with meningitis, in which the cortical veins contained clots. Gowers believes that it is of frequent occurrence, and that thrombosis of the veins is not an uncommon cause of infantile hemiplegia.

(*b*) In connection with chlorosis and anæmia, the so-called *autochthonous sinus-thrombosis*. Brayton Ball has called attention to this interesting association, and has reported 1 case and collected 10 or 11 others from the literature. All were in girls with anæmia or chlorosis. The longitudinal sinus is most frequently involved. The thrombosis of the cerebral sinuses in such cases is usually associated with venous thromboses in other parts of the body, and the patients die, as a rule, in from one to three weeks.

(*c*) In the terminal stages of cancer, phthisis, and other chronic diseases thrombosis may gradually occur in the sinuses and cortical veins. To the coagulum developing in these conditions the term marantic thrombus is applied.

Secondary thrombosis is much more frequent and follows extension of inflammation from contiguous parts to the sinus wall. The common causes are disease of the internal ear, fracture, compression of the sinuses by tumor, or suppurative disease outside the skull, particularly erysipelas, carbuncle, and parotitis. In secondary cases the lateral sinus is most frequently involved. Of 57 fatal cases in which ear-disease caused death with cerebral lesions, there were 22 in which thrombosis existed in the lateral sinuses (Pitt). Tuberculous caries of the temporal bone is often directly responsible. The thrombus may be small, or may fill the entire sinus and extend into the internal jugular vein. In more than one half of these instances the thrombus was suppurating. The disease spreads directly from the necrosis on the posterior wall of the tympanum. According to Voltolini, the inflammation extends by way of the petroso-mastoid canal. It is not so common in disease of the mastoid cells.

Symptoms.—Primary thrombosis of the longitudinal sinus may occur without exciting symptoms and is found accidentally at the post mortem. There may be mental dulness with headache. Convulsions and vomiting may occur. In other instances there is nothing distinctive. In a patient who died under my care, at the Philadelphia Hospital, of phthisis, there was a gradual torpor, deepening to coma, without convulsions, localizing symptoms, or optic neuritis. The condition was thought to be due to a terminal meningitis. In the chlorosis cases the head symptoms have, as a rule, been marked. Ball's patient was dull and stupid, had vomiting, dilatation of the pupils, and double choked disks. Slight paresis of the left side occurred. An interesting feature in her case was the development of swelling of the left leg. In the cases reported by Andrews, Church, Tuckwell, Isambard Owen, and Wilks the patients had headache, vomiting, and delirium. Paralysis was not present. In Douglas Powell's case, with similar symptoms, there was loss of power on the left side. Bristowe reports a case of great interest in an anæmic girl of nineteen, who had convulsions, drowsiness, and vomiting. Tenderness and swelling developed in the position of the right internal jugular vein, and a few days later on the opposite side. The diagnosis was rendered definite by the occurrence of phlebitis in the veins of the right leg. The patient recovered.

The onset of such symptoms as have been mentioned in an anæmic or chlorotic girl should lead to the suspicion of cerebral thrombosis. In infants the diagnosis can rarely be made. Involvement of the cavernous sinus may cause œdema about the eyelids or prominence of the eyes.

In the *secondary thrombi* the symptoms are commonly those of septicæmia. For instance, in over 70 per cent of Pitt's cases the mode of death was by pulmonary pyæmia. This author draws the following important conclusions: (1) The disease spreads oftener from the posterior wall of the middle ear than from the mastoid cells. (2) The otorrhœa is generally of some standing, but not always. (3) The onset is sudden, the chief symptoms being pyrexia, rigors, pains in the occipital region and in the neck, associated with a septicæmic condition. (4) Well-marked optic neuritis may be present. (5) The appearance of acute local pulmonary mischief or of distant suppuration is almost conclusive of thrombosis. (6) The average duration is about three weeks, and death is generally from pulmonary pyæmia. The chief points in the diagnosis may be gathered from these statements.

Pitt records an interesting case of recovery in a boy of ten, who had otorrhœa for years and was admitted with fever, earache, tenderness, and œdema. A week later he had a rigor, and optic neuritis developed on the right side. The mastoid was explored unsuccessfully. The fever and chills persisting, two days later the lateral sinus was explored. A mass of foul clot was removed and the jugular vein was tied, after which the boy made a satisfactory recovery.

According to Griesinger there is often associated with thrombosis of the lateral sinus venous stasis and painful œdema behind the ear and in the neck. The external jugular vein on the diseased side may be less distended than on the opposite side, since owing to the thrombus in the lateral sinus the internal jugular vein is less full than on the normal side, and the blood from the external jugular can flow more easily into it (Gerhardt).

Treatment.—In marantic individuals roborants and stimulants are indicated. The position assumed in bed should favor both the arterial and venous circulation. The clothing should not restrict the neck, and care should be taken to avoid *bending* of the neck.

The internal administration of potassium iodide and calomel has been recommended in the autochthonous forms, but no treatment is likely to be of any avail.

The secondary forms, especially those following upon disease of the middle ear, are often amenable to operation, and, especially recently, many lives have been saved by surgical intervention after extensive sinus thrombosis. Macewen's work On Pyogenic Infective Diseases of the Brain and Spinal Cord contains the most exhaustive presentation of the subject of sinus thrombosis and its treatment.

9. HEMIPLEGIA IN CHILDREN.

Etiology.—Of 135 cases, 60 were in boys and 75 in girls. Right hemiplegia occurred in 79, left in 56. In 15 cases the condition was said to be congenital.

In a great majority the disease sets in during the first or second year; thus of the total number of cases, 95 were under two. Cases above the fifth year are rare, only 10 in my series. Neither alcoholism nor syphilis in the parents appears to play an important *rôle* in this affection. Difficult or abnormal labor is responsible for certain of the cases, particularly injury with the *forceps*. Trauma, such as falls or puncturing wounds, is more rare. The condition followed ligation of the common carotid in one case.

Infectious diseases. All the authors lay special stress upon this factor. In 19 cases in my series the disease came on during or just after one of the specific fevers. I saw one case in which during the height of vaccination convulsions developed, followed by hemiplegia. In a great majority of the cases the disease sets in with a convulsion, in which the child may remain for several hours or longer, and after recovery the paralysis is noticed.

Morbid Anatomy.—In an analysis which I have made of 90 autopsies reported in the literature, the lesions may be grouped under three headings:

(*a*) Embolism, thrombosis, and hæmorrhage, comprising 16 cases, in 7 of which there was blocking of a Sylvian artery, and in 9 hæmorrhage. A striking feature in this group is the advanced age of onset. Ten of the cases occurred in children over six years old.

(*b*) Atrophy and sclerosis, comprising 50 cases. The wasting is either of groups of convolutions, an entire lobe, or the whole hemisphere. The meninges are usually closely adherent over the affected region, though sometimes they look normal. The convolutions are atrophied, firm, and hard, contrasting strongly with the normal gyri. The sclerosis may be diffuse and widespread over a hemisphere, or there may be nodular projections—the hypertrophic sclerosis. Some of the cases show remarkable unilateral atrophy of the hemisphere. In one of my cases the atrophied hemisphere weighed 169 grammes and the normal one 653 grammes. The brain tissue may be a mere shell over a dilated ventricle.

(*c*) Porencephalus, which was present in 24 of the 90 autopsies. This term was applied by Heschel to a loss of substance in the form of cavities and cysts at the surface of the brain, either opening into and bounded by the arachnoid, and even passing deeply into the hemisphere, or reaching to the ventricle. In the study by Audrey of 103 cases of porencephalus, hemiplegia was mentioned in 68 cases.

Practically, then, in infantile hemiplegia cortical sclerosis and porencephalus are the important anatomical conditions. The primary change in the majority of these cases is still unknown. Porencephalia may result from a defect in development or from hæmorrhage at birth. The etiology is clear in the limited number of cases of hæmorrhage, embolism, and thrombosis, but there remains the large group in which the final change is sclerosis and atrophy. What is the primary lesion in these instances? The clinical history shows that in nearly all these cases the onset is sudden, with convulsions—often with slight fever. Strümpell believes that this condition is due to an inflammation of the gray matter—polio-encephalitis—a view which has not been very widely accepted, as the anatomical proofs are wanting. Gowers suggests that thrombosis may be present in some instances. This might probably account for the final condition of sclerosis, but clinically thrombosis of the veins rarely occurs in healthy children, which appear to be those most frequently attacked by infantile hemiplegia, and post-mortem proof is yet wanting of the association of thrombosis with the disease.

Symptoms.—(a) The onset. The disease may set in suddenly without spasms or loss of consciousness. In more than half the cases the child is attacked with partial or general convulsions and loss of consciousness, which may last from a few hours to many days. This is one of the most striking features in the disease. Fever is usually present. The hemiplegia, noticed as the child recovers consciousness, is generally complete. Sometimes the paralysis is not complete at first, but develops after subsequent convulsions. The right side is more frequently affected than the left. The face is commonly not involved.

(b) Residual symptoms. In some cases the paralysis gradually disappears and leaves scarcely a trace as the child grows up. The leg, as a rule, recovers more rapidly and more fully than the arm, and the paralysis may be scarcely noticeable. In a majority of cases, however, there is a characteristic hemiplegic gait. The paralysis is most marked in the arm, which is usually wasted; the forearm is flexed at right angles, the hand is flexed, and the fingers are contracted. Motion may be almost completely lost; in other instances the arm can be lifted above the head. Late rigidity, which almost always develops, is the symptom which suggested the name *hemiplegia spastica cerebralis* to Heine, the orthopædic surgeon who first accurately described these cases. It is, however, not constant. The limbs may be quite relaxed even years after the onset. The reflexes are usually increased. In several instances, however, I have known them to be absent. Sensation is, as a rule, not disturbed.

Aphasia is a not uncommon symptom, and occurred in 16 cases of my series—a smaller number than that given in the series of Wallenberg, Gaudard, and Sachs.

Mental Defects.—One of the most serious consequences of infantile hemiplegia is the failure of mental development. A considerable number of these cases drift into the institutions for feeble-minded children. Three grades may be distinguished—idiocy, which is most common when the hemiplegia has existed from birth; imbecility, which often increases with the development of epilepsy; and feeble-mindedness, a retarded rather than an arrested development.

Epilepsy.—Of the cases in my series, 41 were subjects of convulsive seizures, one of the most distressing sequels of the disease. The seizures may be either transient attacks of *petit mal,* true Jacksonian fits, beginning in and confined to the affected side, or general convulsions.

Post-hemiplegic Movements.—It was in cases of this sort that Weir Mitchell first described the post-hemiplegic movements. They are extremely common, and were present in 34 of my series. There may be either slight tremor in the affected muscles, or incoördinate choreiform movements—the so-called post-hemiplegic chorea—or, lastly,

Athetosis.—In this condition, described by Hammond, there are remarkable spasms of the paralyzed extremities, chiefly of the fingers and toes, and in rare instances of the muscles of the mouth. The movements are involuntary and somewhat rhythmical; in the hand, movements of adduction or abduction and of supination and pronation follow each other in orderly sequence. There may be hyperextension of the fingers, during which they are spread wide apart. This condition is much more frequent in children than in adults. In the latter it may be combined with hemianæsthesia, and the lesion is not cortical, but basic in the neighborhood of the thalamus. The movements are sometimes increased by emotion. They usually persist during sleep.

Treatment.—The possibility of injury to the brain in protracted labor and in forceps cases should be borne in mind by the practitioner. The former entails the greater risk. In infantile hemiplegia the physician at the outset sees a case of ordinary convulsions, perhaps more protracted and severe than usual. These should be checked as rapidly as possible by the use of the bromides, the application of cold or heat, and a brisk purge. During convulsions chloroform may be administered with safety even to the youngest children. When the paralysis is established not much can be hoped from medicines. In only rare instances does the paralysis entirely disappear. When the recovery is partial the "residual paralysis" is similar to that seen in other lesions of the upper motor segment. Thus in the lower extremity it is the flexors of the leg and the dorsal flexors of the foot which are most often permanently paralyzed (Wernicke). The indications are to favor the natural tendency to improve by maintaining the general nutrition of the child, to lessen the rigidity and contractures by massage and passive motion, and if necessary to correct deformities by mechanical or surgical measures. Much may be done by careful manipulation and rubbing and the application of a proper apparatus. In children the aphasia usually disappears. The epilepsy is a distressing and obstinate symptom, for which a cure can rarely be anticipated. Prolonged periods of quiescence are, however, not uncommon. In the Jacksonian fits the bromides rarely do good, unless there is much irritability and excitement.

Operative measures, which have been carried out in several cases, have not, as a rule, been successful. The liability to feeble-mindedness is the most serious outlook in the infantile cerebral palsies. In many cases the damage is irreparable, and idiocy and imbecility result. With patient training and with care many of the children reach a fair measure of intelligence and self-reliance.

IV. TUMORS, INFECTIOUS GRANULOMATA, AND CYSTS OF THE BRAIN.

The following are the most common varieties of new growths within the cranium:

(1) **Infectious Granulomata.**—(*a*) *Tubercle*, which may form large or small growths, usually multiple. Tuberculosis of the glands or bones may be coexistent, but the tuberculous disease of the brain may occur in the absence of other clinically recognizable tuberculous lesions. The disease is most frequent early in life. Three fourths of the cases occur under twenty, and one half of the patients are under ten years of age (Gowers). Of 299 cases of tumor in persons under nineteen collected from various sources by Starr, 152 were tubercle. The nodules are most numerous in the cerebellum and about the base.

(*b*) *Syphiloma* is most commonly found in the hemispheres or about the pons. The tumors are superficial, attached to the arteries or the meninges, and rarely grow to a large size. They may be multiple. The third nerve is particularly prone to syphilitic infiltration, and ptosis is common.

(2) **Tumors.**—(*c*) *Glioma and Neuroglioma.*—These vary greatly in appearance. They may be firm and hard, almost like an area of sclerosis, or soft and very vascular. They persist remarkably for many years. Klebs has called attention to the occurrence of elements in them not unlike ganglion-cells. Tumors of this character may contain the "Spinnen" or spider cells; enormous spindle-shaped cells with single large nuclei; cells like the ganglion-cells of nerve-centres with nuclei and one or more processes; and translucent, band-like fibres, tapering at each end, which result from a vitreous or hyaline transformation of the large spindle-cells. A separate type is also recognizable, in which the cells resemble the ependymal epithelium.

(*d*) *Sarcoma* occurs most commonly in the membranes of the brain and in the pons. It forms some of the largest and most diffusely infiltrating of intracranial growths. Like carcinoma, sarcoma of the brain is usually of very rapid growth.

(*e*) *Carcinoma* not infrequently is secondary to cancer in other parts. It is seldom primary. Occasionally cancerous tumors have been found in symmetrical parts of the brain.

(*f*) Other varieties occur, such as fibroid growths, which usually develop from the membranes; bony tumors, which grow sometimes from the falx, psammoma, and cholesteatoma. Fatty tumors are occasionally found on the corpus callosum.

(3) **Cysts.**—(*g*) These occur between the membranes and the brain, as a result of hæmorrhage or of softening. Porencephalus is a sequel of congenital atrophy or of hæmorrhage, or may be due to a developmental defect. Hydatid cysts have been referred to in the section on parasites. An interesting variety of cyst is that which follows severe injury to the skull in early life.

Symptoms.—(1) **General.**—The following are the most important: *Headache*, either dull, aching, and continuous, or sharp, stabbing, and paroxysmal. It may be diffused over the entire head; sometimes it is limited to the back or front. When in the back of the head it may extend down the neck (especially in tumors in the posterior fossa), and when in the front it may be accompanied with neuralgic pains in the face. Occasionally the pain may be very localized and associated with tenderness on pressure.

Optic neuritis occurs in four fifths of all the cases (Gowers). It is usually double, but occasionally is found in only one eye. A growth may develop slowly and attain considerable size without producing optic neuritis. On the other hand, it may occur with a very small tumor. J. A. Martin, from an extensive analysis of the literature with reference to the localizing value, concludes: When there is a difference in the amount of the neuritis in each eye it is more than twice as probable that the tumor is on the side of the most marked neuritis. It is constant in tumors of the corpora quadrigemina, present in 89 per cent of cerebellar tumors, and absent in nearly two thirds of the cases of tumor of the pons, medulla, and of the corpus callosum. It is least frequent in cases of tuberculous tumor; most common in cases of glioma and cystic tumors.

Vomiting is a common feature, and with headache and optic neuritis makes up the characteristic clinical picture of cerebral tumor. An important point is the absence of definite relation to the meals. A chemical examination shows that the vomiting is independent of digestive disturbances. It may be very obstinate, particularly in growths of the cerebellum and the pons.

Giddiness is often an early symptom. The patient complains of vertigo on rising suddenly or on turning quickly. *Mental Disturbance.*—The patient may act in an odd, unnatural manner, or there may be stupor and heaviness. The patient may become emotional or silly, or symptoms resembling hysteria may develop. *Convulsions*, either general and resembling true epilepsy or localized (Jacksonian) in character. There may be *slowing of the pulse*, as in all cases of increased intracranial pressure.

(2) **Localizing Symptoms.**—Focal symptoms often occur, but it must not be forgotten that these may be *indirectly* produced. The smaller the tumor and the less marked the general symptoms of cerebral compression, the more likely is it that any focal symptoms occurring are of *direct* origin.

(*a*) *Central Motor Area.*—The symptoms are either irritative or destructive in character. Irritation in the lower third may produce spasm in the muscles of the face, in the angle of the mouth, or in the tongue. The spasm with tingling may be strictly limited to one muscle group before extending to others, and this Seguin terms the *signal symptom*. The middle third of the motor area contains the centres controlling the arm, and here,

64

too, the spasm may begin in the fingers, in the thumb, in the muscles of the wrist, or in the shoulder. In the upper third of the motor areas the irritation may produce spasm beginning in the toes, in the ankles, or in the muscles of the leg. In many instances the patient can determine accurately the point of origin of the spasm, and there are important sensory disturbances, such as numbness and tingling, which may be felt first at the region affected.

In all cases it is important to determine, first, the point of origin, the *signal symptom;* second, the order or march of the spasm; and third, the subsequent condition of the parts first affected, whether it is a state of paresis or anæsthesia.

Destructive lesions in the motor zone cause paralysis, which is often preceded by local convulsive seizures; there may be a monoplegia, as of the leg, and convulsive seizures in the arm, often due to irritation in these centres. Tumors in the neighborhood of the motor area may cause localized spasms and subsequently, as the centres are invaded by the growth, paralysis occurs. On the left side, growths in the third frontal or Broca's convolution may cause motor aphasia.

(*b*) *Prefrontal Region.*—Neither motor nor sensory disturbance may be present. The general symptoms are often well marked. The most striking feature of growths in this region is mental torpor and gradual imbecility. In its extension downward the tumor may involve on the left side the lower frontal convolution and produce aphasia, or in its progress backward cause irritative or destructive lesions of the motor area. Exophthalmos on the side of the tumor may occur and be helpful in diagnosis, as in the case reported by Thomas and Keene.

(*c*) Tumors in the *parieto-occipital lobe* may grow to a large size without causing any symptoms. There may be word-blindness and mind-blindness when the angular gyrus and its underlying white matter is involved, and paraphasia.

(*d*) Tumors of the *occipital lobe* produce hemianopia, and a bilateral lesion may produce blindness. Tumors in this region on the left hemisphere may be associated with word-blindness and mind-blindness.

(*e*) Tumors in the *temporal lobe* may attain a large size without producing symptoms. In their growth they involve the lower motor centres. On the left side involvement of the first gyrus and the transverse temporal gyri (auditory sense area) may be associated with word-deafness.

(*f*) Tumors growing in the neighborhood of the *basal ganglia* produce hemiplegia from involvement of the internal capsule. Limited growths in either the nucleus caudatus or the nucleus lentiformis of the corpus striatum do not necessarily cause paralysis. Tumors in the thalamus opticus may also, when small, cause no symptoms, but increasing they may involve the fibres of the sensory portion of the internal capsule, producing hemianopia and sometimes hemianæsthesia. Growths in this situation are apt to cause early optic neuritis, and, growing into the third ventricle, may cause a distention of the lateral ventricles. In fact, pressure symptoms from this cause and paralysis due to involvement of the internal capsule are the chief symptoms of tumor in and about these ganglia. If the ventrolateral group of nuclei in the thalamus be involved there may be unilateral disturbances of cutaneous and muscular sense, hemichorea, or movement ataxia.

Growths in the *corpora quadrigemina* are rarely limited, but most commonly involve the crura cerebri as well. Ocular symptoms are marked. The pupil reflex is lost and there is nystagmus. In the gradual growth the third nerve is involved as it passes through the crus, in which case there will be oculo-motor paralysis on one side and hemiplegia on the other, a combination almost characteristic of unilateral disease of the crus.

(*g*) Tumors of the *pons* and *medulla*. The symptoms are chiefly those of pressure upon the nerves emerging in this region. In disease of the pons the nerves may be involved alone or with the pyramidal tract. Of 52 cases analyzed by Mary Putnam Jacobi, there were 13 in which the cerebral nerves were involved alone, 13 in which the limbs were affected, and 26 in which there was hemiplegia and involvement of the nerves. Twenty-two of the latter had what is known as alternate paralysis—i. e., involvement of the nerves on one side and of the limbs on the opposite side. In 4 cases there were no motor symptoms. In tuberculosis (or syphilis) a growth at the inferior and inner aspects of the crus may cause paralysis of the third nerve on one side, and of the face, tongue, and limbs on the opposite side (syndrome of Weber). A tumor growing in the lower part of the pons usually involves the sixth nerve, producing internal strabismus; the seventh nerve, producing facial paralysis; and the auditory nerve, causing deafness. Conjugate deviation of the eyes to the side opposite that on which there is facial paralysis also occurs. When the motor cerebral nerves are involved the paralyses are of the peripheral type (lower segment paralyses).

Tumors of the *medulla* may involve the cerebral nerves alone or cause in some instances a combination of hemiplegia with paralysis of the nerves. Paralyses of the nerves are helpful in topical diagnosis, but the fact must not be overlooked that one or more of the cerebral nerves may be paralyzed as a result of a much increased general intracranial pressure. Signs of irritation in the ninth, tenth, and eleventh nerves are usually present, and produce difficulty in swallowing, irregular action of the heart, irregular respiration, vomiting, and sometimes retraction of the head and neck. The hypoglossal nerve is least often affected. The gait may be unsteady or, if there is pressure on the cerebellum, ataxic. Occasionally there are sensory symptoms, numbness, and tingling. Toward the end convulsions may occur.

Diagnosis.—From the general symptoms alone the existence of tumor may be determined, for the combination of headache, optic neuritis, and vomiting is distinctive. A gradual increase in the intensity of the symptoms is usually seen. It must not be forgotten that severe headache and neuro-retinitis may be caused by Bright's disease. The localization must be gathered from the consideration of the symptoms above detailed and from the data given in the section on Topical Diagnosis of Diseases of the Brain. Mistakes are most likely to occur in connection with uræmia, hysteria, and general paralysis; but careful consideration of all the circumstances of the case usually enables the practitioner to avoid error. Auscultatory percussion is occasionally of service in localization.

Prognosis.—Syphilitic tumors alone are amenable to medical treatment. Tuberculous growths occasionally cease to grow and become calcified. The gliomata and fibromata, particularly when the latter grow from the membranes, may last for years. I have described a case of small, hard glioma, in which the Jacksonian epilepsy persisted for fourteen years. Hughlings Jackson has reported cases of glioma in which the symptoms lasted for over ten years. The more rapidly growing sarcomata usually prove fatal in from six to eighteen months. Death may be sudden, particularly in growths near the medulla; more commonly it is due to coma in consequence of gradual increase in the intracranial pressure.

Treatment.—(a) *Medical.*—If there is a suspicion of syphilis the iodide of potassium and mercury should be given. Nowhere do we see more brilliant therapeutical effects than in certain cases of cerebral gummata. The iodide should be given in increasing doses. In tuberculous tumors the outlook is less favorable, though instances of cure are reported, and there is post-mortem evidence to show that the solitary tuberculous tumors may undergo changes and become obsolete. A general tonic treatment is indicated in these cases. The headache usually demands prompt treatment. The iodide of potassium in full doses sometimes gives marked relief. An ice-cap for the head or, in the occipital headache, the application of the Paquelin cautery may be tried. The bromides are not of much use in the headache from this cause, and, as the last resort, morphia must be given. For the convulsions bromide of potassium is of little service.

(b) *Surgical.*—Tumors of the brain have been successfully removed by Macewen, Horsley, Keen, and others. The number of cases for operation, however, is small. Four fifths at least of all the cases are probably unsuitable, or of such a nature as to render an operation fatal. The most advantageous cases are the localized fibromata growing from the dura and only compressing the brain substance, as in Keen's remarkable case. The safety with which the exploratory operation can be made warrants it in all doubtful cases.

V. INFLAMMATION OF THE BRAIN.

1. ACUTE ENCEPHALITIS.

A focal or diffuse inflammation of the brain substance, usually of the gray matter (poliencephalitis), is met with (a) as a result of trauma; (b) in certain intoxications, alcohol, food poisoning, and gas poisoning; and (c) following the acute infections. The anatomical features are those of an acute hæmorrhagic poliencephalitis, corresponding in histological details with acute polio-myelitis. Focal forms are seen in ulcerative endocarditis, in which the gray matter may present deeply hæmorrhagic areas, firmer than the surrounding tissue. In the fevers there may be more extensive regions, involving two or three convolutions. This acute hæmorrhagic poliencephalitis superior is thought by Strümpell to be the essential lesion in infantile hemiplegia. Localizing symptoms are usually present, though they may be obscured in the severity of the general infection. The most typical encephalitis accompanies the meningitis in cerebro-spinal fever.

In acute mania, in delirium tremens, in chorea insaniens, in the maniacal form of exophthalmic goitre, and in the so-called cerebral forms of the malignant fevers the gray cortex is deeply congested, moist, and swollen, and with the recent finer methods of research will probably show changes which may be classed as encephalitis.

The *symptoms* are not very definite. In severe forms they are those of an acute infection; some cases have been mistaken for typhoid fever. The onset may be abrupt in an individual apparently healthy. Other cases have occurred in the convalescence from the fevers, particularly influenza. One of J. J. Putnam's cases followed mumps. The general symptoms are those which accompany all severe acute affections of the brain—headache, somnolence, coma, delirium, vomiting, etc. The local symptoms are very varied, depending on the extent of the lesions, and may be irritative or paralytic. Usually fatal within a few weeks, cases may drag on for weeks or months and recover.

2. ABSCESS OF THE BRAIN.

Etiology.—Suppuration of the brain substance is rarely if ever primary, but results, as a rule, from extension of inflammation from neighboring parts or infection from a distance through the blood. The question of idiopathic brain abscess need scarcely be considered, though occasionally instances occur in which it is extremely difficult to assign a cause. There are three important etiological factors:

(1) Trauma. Falls upon the head or blows, with or without abrasion of the skin. More commonly it follows fracture or punctured wounds. In this group meningitis is frequently associated with the abscess.

(2) By far the most important infective foci are those which arise in direct extension from disease of the middle ear or of the mastoid cells. From the roof of the mastoid antrum the infection readily passes to the sigmoid sinus and induces an infective thrombosis. In other instances the dura becomes involved, and a sub-dural abscess is formed, which may readily involve the arachnoid or the pia mater. In another group the inflammation extends along the lymph spaces, or the thrombosed veins, into the substance of the brain and causes suppuration. Macewen thinks that without local areas of meningitis the infective agents may be carried through the lymph and blood channels into the cerebral substance. Infection which extends from the roof of the mastoid process is most likely to be followed by abscess in the temporal lobe, while infection extending from the posterior wall causes most frequently sinus thrombosis and cerebellar abscess.

(3) In septic processes. Abscess of the brain is not often found in pyæmia. In ulcerative endocarditis multiple foci of suppuration are common. Localized bone-disease and suppuration in the liver are occasional causes. Certain inflammations in the lungs, particularly bronchiectasis, which was present in 17 of 38 cases of these so-called "pulmonal cerebral

abscesses" collected by R. T. Williamson, are liable to be followed by abscess. It is an occasional complication of empyema. Abscess of the brain may follow the specific fevers. Bristowe has called attention to its occurrence as a sequel of influenza. The largest number of cases occur between the twentieth and fortieth years, and the condition is more frequent in men than in women. Holt has collected 25 cases in children under five years of age, the chief causes of which were otitis media and trauma.

Morbid Anatomy.—The abscess may be solitary or multiple, diffuse or circumscribed. Practically any one of the different varieties of pyogenic bacteria may be concerned. The bacteriological examination often shows a mixture of different varieties. Occasionally cultures are sterile, owing to death of the bacteria. In the acute, rapidly fatal cases following injury the suppuration is not limited; but in long-standing cases the abscess is enclosed in a definite capsule, which may have a thickness of from 2 to 5 mm. The pus varies much in appearance, depending upon the age of the abscess. In early cases it may be mixed with reddish *débris* and softened brain matter, but in the solitary encapsulated abscess the pus is distinctive, having a greenish tint, an acid reaction, and a peculiar odor, sometimes like that of sulphuretted hydrogen. The brain substance surrounding the abscess is usually œdematous and infiltrated. The size varies from that of a walnut to that of a large orange. There are cases on record in which the cavity has occupied the greater portion of a hemisphere. Multiple abscesses are usually small. In four fifths of all cases the abscess is solitary. Suppuration occurs most frequently in the cerebrum, and the temporal lobe is more often involved than other parts. The cerebellum is the next most common seat, particularly in connection with ear-disease.

Symptoms.—Following injury or operation the disease may run an *acute* course, with fever, headache, delirium, vomiting, and rigors. The symptoms are those of an acute meningo-encephalitis, and it may be very difficult to determine, unless there are localizing symptoms, whether there is really suppuration in the brain substance. In the cases following ear disease the symptoms may at first be those of meningeal irritation. There may be irritability, restlessness, severe headache, and aggravated earache. Other striking symptoms, particularly in the more prolonged cases, are drowsiness, slow cerebration, vomiting, and optic neuritis. In the chronic form of brain abscess which may follow injury, otorrhœa, or local lung trouble, there may be a latent period ranging from one or two weeks to several months, or even a year or more. In the "silent" regions, when the abscess becomes encapsulated there may be no symptoms whatever during the latent period. During all this time the patient may be under careful observation and no suspicion be aroused of the existence of suppuration. Then severe headache, vomiting, fever, set in, perhaps with a chill. So, too, after a blow upon the head or a fracture the symptoms of the lesion may be transient, and months afterward cerebral symptoms of the most aggravated character may develop.

The localization of the lesion is often difficult. In or near the motor region there may be convulsions or paralysis, and it is to be remembered that an abscess in the temporal lobe may compress the lower motor centres and produce paralysis of the arm and face and on the left side cause aphasia. A large abscess may exist in the frontal lobe without causing paralysis, but in these cases there is almost always some mental dulness. In the temporal lobe, the common seat, there may be no focalizing symptoms. So also in the parieto-occipital region; though here early examination may lead to the detection of hemianopia. In abscess of the cerebellum vomiting is common. If the middle lobe is affected there may be staggering—cerebellar incoördination. Localizing symptoms in the pons and other parts are still more uncertain.

Diagnosis.—In the acute cases there is rarely any doubt. A consideration of possible etiological factors is of the highest importance. The history of injury followed by fever, marked cerebral symptoms, the development of rigors, delirium, and perhaps paralysis, make the diagnosis certain. In chronic ear-disease, such cerebral symptoms as drowsiness and torpor, with irregular fever, supervening upon the cessation of a discharge, should excite the suspicion of abscess. Cases in which suppurative processes exist in the orbit, nose, or naso-pharynx, or in which there has been subcutaneous phlegmon of the head or neck, a parotitis, a facial erysipelas, or tuberculous or syphilitic disease of the bones of the skull, should be carefully watched, and immediately investigated should cerebral symptoms appear. It is particularly in the chronic cases that difficulties arise. The symptoms resemble those of tumor of the brain; indeed, they are those of tumor plus fever. Choked disk, however, so commonly associated with tumor, is very frequently absent in abscess of the brain. In a patient with a history of trauma or with localized lung or pleural trouble, who for weeks or months has had slight headache or dizziness, the onset of a rapid fever, especially if it be intermittent and associated with rigors, intense headache, and vomiting, point strongly to abscess. The pulse-rate in cases of cerebral abscess is usually accelerated, but cases are not rare in which it is slowed. Macewen lays stress upon the value of percussion of the skull as an aid in diagnosis. The note, which is uniformly dull, becomes much more resonant when the lateral ventricles are distended in cerebellar abscess and in conditions in which the venæ Galeni are compressed.

It is not always easy to determine whether the meninges are involved with the abscess. Often in ear-disease the condition is that of meningo-encephalitis. Sometimes in association with acute ear-disease the symptoms may simulate closely cerebral meningitis or even abscess. Indeed, Gowers states that not only may these general symptoms be produced by ear-disease, but even distinct optic neuritis.

Treatment.—A remarkable advance has been made of late years in dealing with these cases, owing to the impunity with which the brain can be explored. In ear-disease free discharge of the inflammatory products should be promoted and careful disinfection practised. The treatment of injuries and fractures comes within the scope of the surgeon. The acute symptoms, such as fever, headache, and delirium, must be treated by rest, an ice-cap, and, if necessary, local depletion. In all cases, when a reasonable suspicion exists of the occurrence of abscess, the trephine should be used and the brain explored. The cases following ear-disease, in which the suppuration is in the temporal lobe or in the cerebellum, offer the most favorable chances of recovery. The localization can rarely be made accurately in these cases, and the operator must be guided more by general anatomical and pathological knowledge. In cases of injury the trephine should be applied over the seat of the blow or the fracture. In ear-disease the suppuration is most frequent in the temporal lobe or in the cerebellum, and the operation should be performed at the points most accessible to these regions. And, lastly, a most important, one might almost say essential, factor in the successful treatment of intracranial suppuration is an intelligent knowledge on the part of the surgeon of the work and works of William Macewen.

VI. HYDROCEPHALUS.

Definition.—A condition, congenital or acquired, in which there is a great accumulation of fluid within the ventricles of the brain.

The term hydrocephalus has also been applied to the collection of fluid between the cortex of the brain and the skull, known in this situation as *h. externus* or *h. ex vacuo*, a condition common in cases of atrophy of the brain substance, met with in old age, after hæmorrhages, softenings, or scleroses, in lingering and cachectic diseases, as cancer, chronic nephritis, chronic alcoholism, and sometimes in rickets. Occasionally the disease is caused by meningeal cysts. A true dropsy, however, of the arachnoid sac probably does not occur.

The cases may be divided into three groups—idiopathic internal hydrocephalus (serous meningitis), congenital or infantile, and secondary or acquired.

(1) **Serous Meningitis** (Quincke) (*Idiopathic Internal Hydrocephalus; Angio-neurotic Hydrocephalus*).—This remarkable form, described by Quincke, is very important, since a knowledge of the condition may explain very anomalous and puzzling cases. It is an ependymitis causing a serous effusion into the ventricles, with distention and pressure effects. It may be compared to the serous exudates in the pleura or in synovial membranes. It is not certain that the process is inflammatory, and Quincke likens it to the angio-neurotic œdema of the skin. In very acute cases the ependyma may be smooth and natural looking; in more chronic cases it may be thickened and sodden. The exudate does not differ from the normal, and if on lumbar puncture a fluid is removed of a specific gravity above 1.009, with albumin above two per one thousand, the condition is more likely to be hydrocephalus from stasis, secondary to tumor, etc.

Both children and adults are affected, the latter more frequently. In the acute form the condition is mistaken for tuberculous or purulent meningitis. There are headache, retraction of the neck, and signs of increased intracranial pressure, choked disks, slow pulse, etc. Fever is usually absent, but I have seen one case with recurring paroxysms of fever, and Morton Prince has described a similar one. In both the exudate was clear and the ependyma not acutely inflamed. Quincke has reported cases of recovery. In the chronic form the symptoms are those of tumor—general, such as headache, slight fever, somnolence, and delirium; and local, as exophthalmos, optic neuritis, spasms, and rigidity of muscles and paralysis of the cerebral nerves. Remarkable exacerbations occur, and the symptoms vary in intensity from day to day. Recovery may follow after an illness of many weeks, and some of the reported cases of disappearance of all symptoms of brain tumor belong in this category.

(2) **Congenital Hydrocephalus.**—The enlarged head may obstruct labor; more frequently the condition is noticed some time after birth. The cause is unknown. It has occurred in several members of the same family.

The anatomical condition in these cases offers no clew to the nature of the trouble. The lateral ventricles are enormously distended, but the ependyma is usually clear, sometimes a little thickened and granular, and the veins large. The choroid plexuses are vascular, sometimes sclerotic, but often natural looking. The third ventricle is enlarged, the aqueduct of Sylvius dilated, and the fourth ventricle may be distended. The quantity of fluid may reach several litres. It is limpid and contains a trace of albumin and salts. The changes in consequence of this enormous ventricular distention are remarkable. The cerebral cortex is greatly stretched, and over the middle region the thickness may amount to no more than a few millimetres without a trace of the sulci or convolutions. The basal ganglia are flattened. The skull enlarges, and the circumference of the head of a child of three or four years may reach 25 or even 30 inches. The sutures widen, Wormian bones develop in them, and the bones of the cranium become exceedingly thin. The veins are marked beneath the skin. A fluctuation wave may sometimes be obtained, and Fisher's brain murmur may be heard. The orbital plates of the frontal bone are depressed, causing exophthalmos, so that the eyeballs cannot be covered by the eyelids. The small size of the face, widening somewhat above, is striking in comparison with the enormously expanded skull.

Convulsions may occur. The reflexes are increased, the child learns to walk late, and ultimately in severe cases the legs become feeble and sometimes spastic. Sensation is much less affected than motility. Choked disk is not uncommon. The mental condition is variable; the child may be bright, but, as a rule, there is some grade of imbecility. The congenital cases usually die within the first four or five years. The process may be arrested and the patient may reach adult life. Cases of this sort are not very uncommon. Even when extreme, the mental faculties may be retained, as in Bright's celebrated patient, Cardinal, who lived to the age of twenty-nine, and whose head was translucent when the sun was shining behind him. Care must be taken not to mistake the rachitic head for hydrocephalus.

(3) **Acquired Chronic Hydrocephalus.**—This is stated to be occasionally primary (idiopathic)—that is to say, it comes on spontaneously in the adult without observable lesion. Dean Swift is said to have died of hydrocephalus, but this seems very unlikely. It is based upon the statement that "he (Mr. Whiteway) opened the skull and found much water in the brain," a condition no doubt of *h. ex vacuo*, due to the wasting associated with his prolonged illness and paralysis. In nearly all cases there is either

a tumor at the base of the brain or in the third ventricle, which compresses the venæ Galeni. The passage from the third to the fourth ventricle may be closed, either by a tumor or by parasites. More rarely the foramen of Magendie, through which the ventricles communicate with the cerebro-spinal meninges, becomes closed by meningitis. These conditions, occurring in adults, may produce the most extreme hydrocephalus without any enlargement of the head. Even when the tumor begins early in life there may be no expansion of the skull. In the case of a girl aged sixteen, blind from her third year, the head was not unusually large, the ventricles were enormously distended, and in the Rolandic region the brain substance was only 5 mm. in thickness. A tumor occupied the third ventricle. In a case of cholesteatoma of the floor of the third ventricle, in which the symptoms persisted at intervals for eight or nine years, the ventricles were enormously distended without enlargement of the skull. In other instances the sutures separate and the head gradually enlarges.

The symptoms of hydrocephalus in the adult are curiously variable. In the first case mentioned there were early headaches and gradual blindness; then a prolonged period in which she was able to attend to her studies. Headaches again supervened, the gait became irregular and somewhat ataxic. Death occurred suddenly. In the other case there were prolonged attacks of coma with a slow pulse, and on one occasion the patient remained unconscious for more than three months. Gradually progressing optic neuritis without focalizing symptoms, headache, and attacks of somnolence or coma are suggestive symptoms. These cases of acquired chronic hydrocephalus cannot be certainly diagnosed during life, though in certain instances the condition may be suspected.

Treatment.—Very little can be done to relieve hydrocephalus. Medicines are powerless to cause the absorption of the fluid. More rational is the system of gradual compression, with or without the withdrawal of small quantities of the fluid. The compression may be made by means of broad plasters, so applied as to cross each other on the vertex, and another may be placed round the circumference. In the meningitis serosa Quincke advises the use of mercury.

Of late years puncture of the ventricles, an operation which has been abandoned, has been revived; it has been resorted to in the meningitis serosa. When pressure symptoms are marked Quincke's procedure may be used. He recommends puncture of the subarachnoid sac between the third and the fourth lumbar vertebræ. At this point the spinal cord cannot be touched. The advantages are a slower removal of fluid and less danger of collapse.

VI. DISEASES OF THE PERIPHERAL NERVES.

I. NEURITIS (*Inflammation of the Bundles of Nerve Fibres*).

Neuritis may be *localized* in a single nerve, or *general,* involving a large number of nerves, in which case it is usually known as *multiple neuritis* or *polyneuritis.*

Etiology.—*Localized neuritis* arises from (*a*) cold, which is a very frequent cause, as, for example, in the facial nerve. This is sometimes known as rheumatic neuritis. (*b*) Traumatism—wounds, blows, direct pressure on the nerves, the tearing and stretching which follow a dislocation or a fracture, and the hypodermic injection of ether. Under this section come also the professional palsies, due to pressure in the exercise of certain occupations. (*c*) Extension of inflammation from neighboring parts, as in a neuritis of the facial nerve due to caries in the temporal bone, or in that met with in syphilitic disease of the bones, disease of the joints, and occasionally in tumors.

Multiple neuritis has a very complex etiology, the causes of which may be classified as follows: (*a*) The poisons of infectious diseases, as in leprosy, diphtheria, typhoid fever, small-pox, scarlet fever, and occasionally in other forms; (*b*) the organic poisons, comprising the diffusible stimulants, such as alcohol and ether, bisulphide of carbon and naphtha, and the metallic bodies, such as lead, arsenic, and mercury; (*c*) cachectic conditions, such as occur in anæmia, cancer, tuberculosis, or marasmus from any cause; (*d*) the endemic neuritis or beri-beri; and (*e*) lastly, there are cases in which none of these factors prevail, but the disease sets in suddenly after overexertion or exposure to cold.

Morbid Anatomy.—In neuritis due to the extension of inflammation the nerve is usually swollen, infiltrated, and red in color. The inflammation may be chiefly perineural or it may pass into the deeper portion—*interstitial* neuritis—in which form there is an accumulation of lymphoid elements between the nerve bundles. The nerve fibres themselves may not appear involved, but there is an increase in the nuclei of the sheath of Schwann. The myelin is fragmented, the nuclei of the internodal cells are swollen, and the axis cylinders present varicosities or undergo granular degeneration. Ultimately the nerve fibres may be completely destroyed and replaced by a fibrous connective tissue in which much fat is sometimes deposited—the *lipomatous neuritis* of Leyden.

In other instances the condition is termed *parenchymatous* neuritis, in which the changes are like those met with in the secondary or Wallerian degeneration, which follows when the nerve fibre is cut off from the cell body of the neurone to which it belongs. The medullary substance and the axis cylinders are chiefly involved, the interstitial tissue being but little altered or only affected secondarily. The myelin becomes segmented and divides into small globules and granules, and the axis cylinders become granular, broken, subdivided, and ultimately disappear. The nuclei of the sheath of Schwann proliferate and ultimately the fibres are reduced to a state of atrophic tubes without a trace of the normal structure. The muscles connected with the degenerated nerves usually show marked atrophic changes, and in some instances the change in the nerve sheath appears to extend directly to the interstitial tissue of the muscles—the *neuritis fascians* of Eichhorst.

Symptoms.—(*a*) **Localized Neuritis.**—As a rule the constitutional disturbances are slight. The most important symptom is pain of a boring or stabbing character, usually felt in the course of the nerve and in the parts to which it is distributed. The nerve itself is sensitive to pressure, probably, as Weir Mitchell suggests, owing to the irritation of its nervi nervorum. The skin may be slightly reddened or even œdematous over the seat of the inflammation. Mitchell has described increase in the temperature and sweating in the affected region, and such trophic disturbances as effusion into the joints and herpes. The function of the muscle to which the nerve fibres are distributed is impaired, motion is painful, and there may be twitchings or contractions. The tactile sensation of the part may be somewhat deadened, even when the pain is greatly increased. In the more chronic cases of local neuritis, such, for instance, as follow the dislocation of the humerus, the localized pain, which at first may be severe, gradually disappears, though some sensitiveness of the brachial plexus may persist for a long time, and the nerve cords may be felt to be swollen and firm. The pain is variable—sometimes intense and distressing; at others not causing much inconvenience. Numbness and formication may be present and the tactile sensation may be greatly impaired. The motor disturbances are marked. Ultimately there is extreme atrophy of the muscles. Contractures may occur in the fingers. The skin may be reddened or glossy, the subcutaneous tissue œdematous, and the nutrition of the nails may be defective. In the rheumatic neuritis subcutaneous fibroid nodules may develop.

A neuritis limited at first to a peripheral nerve may extend upward— the so-called ascending or migratory neuritis—and involve the larger nerve trunks, or even reach the spinal cord, causing subacute myelitis (Gowers). The condition is rarely seen in the neuritis from cold, or in that which follows fevers; but it occurs most frequently in traumatic neuritis. J. K. Mitchell, in his monograph On Injuries of Nerves (1895), concludes that the larger nerve trunks are most susceptible, and that the neuritis may spread either up or down, the former being the most common. The paralysis secondary to visceral disease, as of the bladder, may be due to an ascending neuritis. The inflammation may extend to the nerves of the other side, either through the spinal cord or its membranes, or without any involvement of the nerve centres, the so-called sympathetic neuritis. The electrical changes in localized neuritis vary a great deal, depending upon the extent to which the nerve is injured. The lesion may be so slight that the nerve and the muscles to which it is distributed may react normally to both currents; or it may be so severe that the typical reaction of degeneration develops within a few days—i. e., the nerve does not respond to stimulation by either current, while the muscle reacts only to the galvanic current and in a peculiar manner. The contraction caused is slow and lazy, instead of sharp and quick as in the normal muscle, and the AnC contraction is usually stronger than the CC contraction. Between these two extremes there are many different grades, and a careful electrical examination is most important as an aid to diagnosis and prognosis.*

The duration varies from a few days to weeks or months. A slight traumatic neuritis may pass off in a day or two, while the severer cases, such as follow unreduced dislocation of the humerus, may persist for months or never be completely relieved.

(*b*) **Multiple Neuritis.**—This presents a complex symptomatology. The following are the most important groups of cases:

(1) *Acute Febrile Polyneuritis.*—The attack follows exposure to cold or overexertion, or, in some instances, comes on spontaneously. The onset resembles that of an acute infectious disease. There may be a definite chill, pains in the back and limbs or joints, so that the case may be thought to be acute rheumatism. The temperature rises rapidly and may reach 103° or 104°. There are headache, loss of appetite, and the general symptoms of acute infection. The limbs and back ache. Intense pain in the nerves, however, is by no means constant. Tingling and formication are felt in the fingers and toes, and there is increased sensitiveness of the nerve trunks or of the entire limb. Loss of muscular power, first marked, perhaps, in the legs, gradually comes on and extends with the features of an ascending paralysis. In other cases the paralysis begins in the arms. The extensors of the wrists and the flexors of the ankles are early affected, so that there is foot and wrist drop. In severe cases there is general loss of muscular power, producing a flabby paralysis, which may extend to the muscles of the face and to the intercostals, and respiration may be carried on by the diaphragm alone. The muscles soften and waste rapidly. There may be only hyperæsthesia with soreness and stiffness of the limbs; in some cases, increased sensitiveness with anæsthesia; in other instances the sensory disturbances are slight. The clinical picture is not to be distinguished, in many cases, from Landry's paralysis; in others, from the subacute myelitis of Duchenne.

The course is variable. In the most intense forms the patient may die in a week or ten days, with involvement of the respiratory muscles or from paralysis of the heart. As a rule in cases of moderate severity, after persisting for five or six weeks, the condition remains stationary and then slow improvement begins. The paralysis in some muscles may persist for many months and contractures may occur from shortening of the muscles, but even when this occurs the outlook is, as a rule, good, although the paralysis may have lasted for a year or more.

(2) *Recurring Multiple Neuritis.*—Under the term *polyneuritis recurrens* Mary Sherwood has described from Eichhorst's clinic 2 cases in adults— in one case involving the nerves of the right arm, in the other both legs. In one patient there were three attacks, in the other two, the distribution in the various attacks being identical. The subject has recently been fully discussed by H. M. Thomas (Phila. Med. Jour., 1898, i).

---

* See under Facial Paralysis.

(3) *Alcoholic Neuritis.*—This, perhaps the most important form of multiple neuritis, was graphically described in 1822 by James Jackson, Sr., of Boston. Wilks recognized it as alcoholic paraplegia, but the starting-point of the recent researches on the disease dates from the observations of Dumenil, of Rouen. Of late years our knowledge of the disease has extended rapidly, owing to the researches of Huss, Leyden, James Ross, Buzzard, and Henry Hun. It occurs most frequently in women, particularly steady, quiet tipplers. Its appearance may be the first revelation to the physician or to the family of habits of secret drinking. The onset is usually gradual, and may be preceded for weeks or months by neuralgic pains and tingling in the feet and hands. Convulsions are not uncommon. Fever is rare. The paralysis gradually sets in, at first in the feet and legs, and then in the hands and forearms. The extensors are affected more than the flexors, so that there is wrist-drop and foot-drop. The paralysis may be thus limited and not extend higher in the limbs. In other instances there is paraplegia alone, while in the most extreme cases all the extremities are involved. In rare instances the facial muscles and the sphincters are also affected. The sensory symptoms are very variable. There are cases in which there are numbness and tingling only, without great pain. In other cases there are severe burning or boring pains, the nerve trunks are sensitive, and the muscles are sore when grasped. The hands and feet are frequently swollen and congested, particularly when held down for a few moments. The cutaneous reflexes as a rule are preserved. The deep reflexes are usually lost.

The course of these alcoholic cases is, as a rule, favorable, and after persisting for weeks or months improvement gradually begins, the muscles regain their power, and even in the most desperate cases recovery may follow. The extensors of the feet may remain paralyzed for some time, and give to the patient a distinctive walk, the so-called *steppage* gait, characteristic of peripheral neuritis. It is sometimes known as the pseudo-tabetic gait, although in reality it could not well be mistaken for the gait of ataxia. The foot is thrown forcibly forward, the toe lifted high in the air so as not to trip upon it. The heel is brought down first and then the entire foot. It is an awkward, clumsy gait, and gives the patient the appearance of constantly stepping over obstacles. Among the most striking features of alcoholic neuritis are the mental symptoms. Delirium is common, and there may be hallucinations with extravagant ideas, resembling somewhat those of general paralysis. In some cases the picture is that of ordinary delirium tremens, but the most peculiar and almost characteristic mental disorder is that so well described by Wilks, in which the patient loses all appreciation of time and place, and describes with circumstantial details long journeys which, he says, he has recently taken, or tells of persons whom he has just seen.

(4) *Multiple Neuritis in the Infectious Diseases.*—This has been already referred to, particularly in diphtheria, in which it is most common. The peripheral nature of the lesion in these instances has been shown by post-mortem examination. The outlook is usually favorable and, except in diphtheria, fatal cases are uncommon. Multiple neuritis in tuberculosis, dia-

betes, and syphilis is of the same nature, being probably due to toxic materials absorbed into the blood.

(5) *Arsenical and Saturnine Neuritis.*—The arsenical neuritis is not common; only a single instance of it has come under my observation. Only one case to my knowledge has followed the use of Fowler's solution in my ward or dispensary practice, although I am in the habit of giving in chorea and anæmia doses which might be regarded as excessive. The most common causes are accidental poisoning, as in the cases reported by Mills. In a case of E. G. Cutler the patient got the arsenic from green-paper tags, which he was in the habit of putting in his mouth. The general symptoms are not unlike those of alcoholic paralysis; the weakness of the extensors is marked and the *steppage* gait characteristic. The neuritis due to lead has been discussed in the consideration of lead poisoning. The special involvement of the motor nerves and the great frequency of the occurrence of wrist-drop are the peculiarities of this form. The changes in the cell bodies of the neurones in cases of poisoning with lead and arsenic have recently been studied by Lugaro by means of the method of Nissl.

A similar form of neuritis is caused by the bisulphide of carbon and by the protracted use of tea (M. A. Starr).

(6) *Endemic Neuritis, Beri-beri,* has been considered under the Infectious Diseases.

Anæsthesia Paralysis.—Here perhaps may most appropriately be considered the forms of paralysis following the use of anæsthetics. Much has been written in the past few years upon this subject, which has been very fully considered by Garrigues (American Journal of the Medical Sciences, 1897, i). There are two groups of cases:

1. Pressure paralysis, in which, owing to the position, the nerves have been compressed, either the humerus against the brachial plexus or the musculo-spiral against the table. The pressure most frequently occurs when the arm is elevated alongside the head, as in laparotomy done in the Trendelenberg position, or held out from the body, as in breast amputations. Instances of paralysis of the crural by Robb's leg-holder are also reported.

2. Paralysis from cerebral lesions during etherization. In one of Garrigues' cases paralysis followed the operation, and at the autopsy, seven weeks later, softening of the brain was found. Apoplexy or embolism may develop during the anæsthesia. In Montreal a cataract operation was performed on an old man. He did not recover from the anæsthetic; I found post mortem a cerebral hæmorrhage. A man was admitted to the Philadelphia Hospital on the 26th completely comatose; the day previously ether had been given for a minor operation. He never recovered consciousness, but remained deeply comatose, with great muscular relaxation, low temperature, 97.5°, and noisy respirations; he died on the 28th. There was, unfortunately, no autopsy. Epileptic convulsions may occur during the anæsthesia, and may even prove fatal. The possibility has to be considered of paralysis from loss of blood in prolonged operations, though I have no personal knowledge of any such cases.

And, lastly, a paralysis might result from the toxic affects of the ether in a very protracted administration.

Diagnosis.—The electrical condition in multiple neuritis is thus described by Allen Starr: "The excitability is very rapidly and markedly changed; but the conditions which have been observed are quite various. Sometimes there is a simple diminution of excitability, and then a very strong faradic or galvanic current is needed to produce contractions. Frequently all faradic excitability is lost and then the muscles contract to a galvanic current only. In this condition it may require a very strong galvanic current to produce contraction, and thus far it is quite pathognomonic of neuritis. For in anterior polio-myelitis, where the muscles respond to galvanism only, it does not require a strong current to cause a motion until some months after the invasion.

"The action of the different poles is not uniform. In many cases the contraction of the muscle when stimulated with the positive pole is greater than when stimulated with the negative pole, and the contractions may be sluggish. Then the reaction of degeneration is present. But in some cases the normal condition is found and the negative pole produces stronger contractions than the positive pole. A loss of faradic irritability and a marked decrease in the galvanic irritability of the muscle and nerve are therefore important symptoms of multiple neuritis."

There is rarely any difficulty in distinguishing the alcohol cases. The combination of wrist and foot drop with congestion of the hands and feet, and the peculiar delirium already referred to, is quite characteristic. The rapidly advancing cases with paralysis of all extremities, often reaching to the face and involving the sphincters, are more commonly regarded as of spinal origin, but the general opinion seems to point strongly to the fact that all such cases are peripheral. The less acute cases, in which the paralysis gradually involves the legs and arms with rapid wasting, simulate closely and are usually confounded with the subacute atrophic spinal paralysis of Duchenne. The diagnosis from locomotor ataxia is rarely difficult. The *steppage* gait is entirely different from that of tabes. There is rarely positive incoördination. The patient can usually stand well with the eyes closed. Foot-drop is not common in locomotor ataxia. The lightning pains are absent and there are no pupillary symptoms. The etiology, too, is of moment. The patient is recovering from a paralysis which has been more extensive, or from arsenical poisoning, or he has diabetes.

Treatment.—Rest in bed is essential. In the acute cases with fever, the salicylates and antipyrin are recommended. To allay the intense pain morphia or the hot applications of lead water and laudanum are often required. Great care must be exercised in treating the alcoholic form, and the physician must not allow himself to be deceived by the statements of the relatives. It is sometimes exceedingly difficult to get a history of spirit-drinking. In the alcoholic form it is well to reduce the stimulants gradually. If there is any tendency to bed-sores an air-bed should be used or the patient placed in a continuous bath. Gentle friction of the muscles may be applied from the outset, and in the later stages, when the atrophy is marked and the pains have lessened, massage is probably the most reliable means at our command. Contractures may be gradually overcome by passive movements and extension. Often, with the most extreme deformity from contracture, recovery is, in time, still possible. The interrupted current is useful when the acute stage is passed.

Of internal remedies, strychnia is of value and may be given in increasing doses. Arsenic also may be employed, and if there is a history of syphilis the iodide of potassium and mercury may be given.

II. NEUROMATA.

Tumors situated on nerve fibres may consist of nerve substance proper, the true neuromata, or of fibrous tissue, the false neuromata. The true neuroma usually contains nerve fibres only, or in rare instances ganglion cells. Cases of ganglionic or medullary neuroma are extremely rare; some of them, as Lancereaux suggests, are undoubtedly instances of malformation of the brain substance. In other instances, as in the case which I reported, the tumor is, in all probability, a glioma with cells closely resembling those of the central nervous system. The true fascicular neuroma occurs in the form of the small subcutaneous painful tumor—*tubercula dolorosa*—which is situated on the nerves of the skin about the joints, sometimes on the face or on the breast. It is not always made up of nerve fibres, but may be, as shown by Hoggan, an adenomatous growth of the sweat glands.

The true neuromata, as a rule, are not painful, and occasionally are found associated with the nerve fibres in various regions. Those which develop at the ends and along the course of the nerves of the stump after amputation consist of connective tissue and of medullated and non-medullated nerve fibres. The most remarkable form is the *plexiform neuroma*, in which the various nerve cords are occupied by many hundreds of tumors. The cases are usually congenital. The tumors occur in all the nerves of the body. One of the most remarkable is that described by Prudden, the specimens of which are in the medical museum of Columbia College, New York. There were over 1,182 distinct tumors distributed on the nerves of the body. R. W. Smith's splendid monograph on neuromata has been reprinted this year (1898) by the New Sydenham Society.

Neuromata rarely cause symptoms, except the subcutaneous painful tumor or those in the amputation stump. Here they may be very painful and cause great distress. Motor symptoms are sometimes present, particularly a constant twitching. Epilepsy has sometimes been associated, and relief has followed removal of the growths.

The only available treatment is excision. The subcutaneous painful tumor does not return, and excision completely relieves the symptoms. On the other hand, the amputation neuromata may recur.

III. DISEASES OF THE CEREBRAL NERVES.

OLFACTORY NERVES AND TRACTS.

The functions of these nerves may be disturbed at their origin, in the nasal mucous membrane, at the bulb, in the course of the tract, or at the centres in the brain. The disturbances may be manifested in subjective sensations of smell, complete loss of the sense, and occasionally in hyper-æsthesia.

(a) *Subjective Sensations; Parosmia.*—Hallucinations of this kind are found in the insane and in epilepsy. The aura may be represented by an unpleasant odor, described as resembling chloride of lime, burning rags, or feathers. In a few cases with these subjective sensations tumors have been found in the hippocampi. In rare instances, after injury of the head the sense is perverted—odors of the most different character may be alike, or the odor may be changed, as in a patient noted by Morell Mackenzie, who for some time could not touch cooked meat, as it smelt to her exactly like stinking fish.

(b) *Increased sensitiveness,* or *hyperosmia,* occurs chiefly in nervous, hysterical women, in whom it may sometimes be developed so greatly that, like a dog, they can recognize the difference between individuals by the odor alone.

(c) *Anosmia; Loss of the Sense of Smell.*—This may be produced by: (1) Affections of the origin of the nerves in the mucous membrane, which is perhaps the most frequent cause. It is by no means uncommon in association with chronic nasal catarrh and polypi. In paralysis of the fifth nerve, the sense of smell may be lost on the affected side, owing to interference with the secretion.

It is doubtful whether the cases of loss of smell following the inhalations of very foul or strong odors should come under this or under the central division.

(2) The lesions of the bulb or of the tracts. In falls or blows, in caries of the bones, and in meningitis or tumor, the bulbs or the olfactory tracts may be involved. After an injury to the head the loss of smell may be the only symptom. Mackenzie notes a case of a surgeon who was thrown from his gig and lighted on his head. The injury was slight, but the anosmia which followed was persistent. In locomotor ataxia the sense of smell may be lost, possibly owing to atrophy of the nerves.

(3) Lesions of the olfactory centres. There are congenital cases in which the structures have not been developed. Cases have been reported by Beevor, Hughlings Jackson, and others, in which anosmia has been associated with disease in the hemisphere. The centre for the sense of smell is placed by Ferrier in the uncinate gyrus. Flechsig describes (1) a frontal centre in the base of the frontal lobe and (2) a temporal centre in the uncus.

To test the sense of smell the pungent bodies, such as ammonia, which act upon the fifth nerve, should not be used, but such substances as cloves, peppermint, and musk. This sense is readily tested as a routine matter in brain cases by having two or three bottles containing the essential oils. In all instances a rhinoscopical examination should be made, as the condition may be due to local, not central causes. The *treatment* is unsatisfactory even in the cases due to local lesions in the nostrils.

OPTIC NERVE AND TRACT.

(1) *Lesions of the Retina.*

These are of importance to the physician, and information of the greatest value may be obtained by a systematic examination of the eye-grounds. Only a brief reference can here be made to the more important of the appearances.

(*a*) **Retinitis.**—This occurs in certain general affections, more particularly in Bright's disease, syphilis, leukæmia, and anæmia. The common feature in all these states is the occurrence of hæmorrhage and the development of opacities. There may also be a diffuse cloudiness due to effusion of serum. The hæmorrhages are in the layer of nerve fibres. They vary greatly in size and form, but often follow the course of vessels. When recent the color is bright red, but they gradually change and old hæmorrhages are almost black. The white spots are due either to fibrinous exudate or to fatty degeneration of the retinal elements, and occasionally to accumulation of leucocytes or to a localized sclerosis of the retinal elements. The more important of the forms of retinitis to be recognized are:

Albuminuric retinitis, which occurs in chronic nephritis, particularly in the interstitial or contracted form. The percentage of cases affected is from 15 to 25. There are instances in which these retinal changes are associated with the granular kidney at a stage when the amount of albumen may be slight or transient; but in all such instances it will be found that there is a marked arterio-sclerosis. Gowers recognizes a degenerative form (most common), in which, with the retinal changes, there may be scarcely any alteration in the disk; a hæmorrhagic form, with many hæmorrhages and but slight signs of inflammation; and an inflammatory form, in which there is much swelling of the retina and obscuration of the disk. It is noteworthy that in some instances the inflammation of the optic nerve predominates over the retinal changes, and one may be in doubt for a time whether the condition is really associated with the renal changes or dependent upon intracranial disease.

Syphilitic Retinitis.—In the acquired form this is less common than choroiditis. In inherited syphilis *retinitis pigmentosa* is sometimes met with.

Retinitis in Anæmia.—It has long been known that a patient may become blind after a large hæmorrhage, either suddenly or within two or three days, and in one or both eyes. Occasionally the loss may be permanent and complete. In some of these instances a neuro-retinitis has been found, probably sufficient to account for the symptoms. In the more chronic anæmias, particularly in the pernicious form, retinitis is common, as determined first by Quincke.

In *malaria* retinitis or neuro-retinitis may be present, as noted by

Stephen Mackenzie. It is seen only in the chronic cases with anæmia, and in my experience is not nearly so common proportionately as in pernicious anæmia.

Leukæmic Retinitis.—In this affection the retinal veins are large and distended; there is also a peculiar retinitis, as described by Liebreich. It is not very common. It existed in only 3 of 10 cases of which I have notes of examination of the retina. There are numerous hæmorrhages and white or yellow areas, which may be large and prominent. In one of my cases the retina post mortem was dotted with many small, opaque, white spots, looking like little tumors, the larger of which had a diameter of nearly 2 mm. In Case 13 of my series the leukæmia was diagnosed by Norris and De Schweinitz, at whose clinic the patient had applied on account of failing vision, from the condition of the eye-grounds alone.

Retinitis is also found occasionally in diabetes, in purpura, in chronic lead poisoning, and sometimes as an idiopathic affection.

(*b*) **Functional Disturbances of Vision.**—(1) *Toxic Amaurosis.*—This occurs in uræmia and may follow convulsions or come on independently. The condition, as a rule, persists only for a day or two. This form of amaurosis occurs in poisoning by lead, alcohol, and occasionally by quinine. It seems more probable that the poisons act on the centres and not on the retina.

(2) *Tobacco Amblyopia.*—The loss of sight is usually gradual, equal in both eyes, and affects particularly the centre of the field of vision. The eye-grounds may be normal, but occasionally there is congestion of the disks. On testing the color fields a central scotoma for red and green is found in all cases. Ultimately, if the use of tobacco is continued, organic changes may develop with atrophy of the disk.

(3) *Hysterical Amaurosis.*—More frequently this is loss of acuteness of vision—amblyopia—but the loss of sight in one or both eyes may apparently be complete. The condition will be mentioned subsequently under hysteria.

(4) *Night-blindness—nyctalopia*—the condition in which objects are clearly seen during the day or by strong artificial light, but become invisible in the shade or in twilight, and *hemeralopia*, in which objects cannot be clearly seen without distress in daylight or in a strong artificial light, but are readily seen in a deep shade or in twilight, are functional anomalies of vision which rarely come under the notice of the physician. It may occur in epidemic form.

(5) *Retinal hyperæsthesia* is sometimes seen in hysterical women, but is not found frequently in actual retinitis. I have seen it once, however, in albuminuric retinitis, and once, in a marked degree, in a patient with aortic insufficiency, in whose retinæ there were no signs other than the throbbing arteries.

(2) *Lesions of the Optic Nerve.*

(*a*) **Optic Neuritis** (*Papillitis; Choked Disk*).—In the first stage there is congestion of the disk and the edges are blurred and striated. In the second stage, the congestion is more marked, the swelling increases, the striation also is more visible. The physiological cupping disappears and hæmorrhages are not uncommon. The arteries present little change, the veins are dilated, and the disk may swell greatly. In slight grades of inflammation the swelling gradually subsides and occasionally the nerve recovers completely. In instances in which the swelling and exudate are very great, the subsidence is slow, and when it finally disappears there is complete atrophy of the nerve. The retina not infrequently participates in the inflammation, which is then a neuro-retinitis.

This condition is of the greatest importance in diagnosis. It may exist in its early stages without any disturbance of vision, and even with extensive papillitis the sight may for a time be good.

Optic neuritis is seen occasionally in anæmia and lead poisoning, more commonly in Bright's disease as neuro-retinitis. It occurs occasionally as a primary idiopathic affection. The frequent connection with intracranial disease, particularly tumor, makes its presence of great value to practitioners. The nature of the growth is without influence. In over 90 per cent of such instances the papillitis is bilateral. It is also found in meningitis, either the tuberculous or the simple form. In meningitis it is easy to see how the inflammation may extend down the nerve sheath. In the case of tumor it was thought at first that a choked disk resulted from increased pressure within the skull. It is now more commonly regarded, however, as a descending neuritis.

(*b*) **Optic Atrophy.**—This may be: (1) A primary affection. There is an hereditary form, in which the disease has developed in all the males of a family shortly after puberty. A large number of the cases of primary atrophy are associated with spinal disease, particularly locomotor ataxia. Other causes which have been assigned for the primary atrophy are cold, sexual excesses, diabetes, the specific fevers, alcohol, and lead.

(2) Secondary atrophy results from cerebral diseases, pressure on the chiasma or on the nerves, or, most commonly of all, as a sequence of papillitis.

The ophthalmoscopic appearances are different in the cases of primary and secondary atrophy. In the former, the disk has a gray tint, the edges are well defined, and the arteries look almost normal; whereas in the consecutive atrophy the disk has a staring opaque-white aspect, with irregular outlines, and the arteries are very small.

The symptom of optic atrophy is loss of sight, proportionate to the damage in the nerve. The change is in three directions: " (1) Diminished acuity of vision; (2) alteration in the field of vision; and (3) altered perception of color " (Gowers). The outlook in primary atrophy is bad.

(3) *Affections of the Chiasma and Tract.*

At the chiasma the optic nerves undergo partial decussation. Each optic tract, as it leaves the chiasma, contains nerve fibres which originate in the retinæ of both eyes. Thus, of the fibres of the right tract, part have come through the chiasma without decussating from the temporal half of the right retina, the other and larger portion of the fibres of the tract have decussated in the chiasma, coming as they do from the left optic nerve and the nasal half of the retina on the left side. The fibres which cross are in the middle portion of the chiasma, while the direct fibres are on each side. The following are the most important changes which ensue in lesions of the tract and of the chiasma:

(*a*) *Unilateral Affection of Tract.*—If on the right side, this produces loss of function in the temporal half of the retina on the right side, and on the nasal half of the retina on the left side, so that there is only half vision, and the patient is blind to objects on the left side. This is termed homonymous hemianopia or lateral hemianopia. The fibres passing to the right half of each retina being involved, necessarily the left half of each visual field is blind. The hemianopia may be partial and only a portion of the half field may be lost. The unaffected visual fields may have the normal extent, but in some instances there is considerable reduction. When the left half of one field and the right half of the other, or *vice versa*, are blind, the condition is known as heteronymous hemianopia.

(*b*) *Disease of the Chiasma.*—(1) A lesion involves, as a rule, chiefly the central portion, in which the decussating fibres pass which supply the inner or nasal halves of the retinæ, producing in consequence loss of vision in the outer half of each field, or what is known as temporal hemianopia.

(2) If the lesion is more extensive it may involve not only the central portion, but also the direct fibres on one side of the commissure, in which case there would be total blindness in one eye and temporal hemianopia in the other.

(3) Still more extensive disease is not infrequent from pressure of tumors in this region, the whole chiasma is involved, and total blindness results. The different stages in the process may often be traced in a single case from temporal hemianopia, then complete blindness in one eye with temporal hemianopia in the other, and finally complete blindness.

(4) A limited lesion of the outer part of the chiasma involves only the direct fibres passing to the temporal halves of the retinæ and inducing blindness in the nasal field, or, as it is called, nasal hemianopia. This, of course, is extremely rare. Double nasal hemianopia may occur as a manifestation of tabes and in tumors involving the outer fibres of each tract.

(4) *Affections of the Tract and Centres.*

The optic tract crosses the crus (cerebral peduncle) to the hinder part of the optic thalamus and divides into two portions, one of which (the lateral root) goes to the pulvinar of the thalamus, the lateral geniculate body, and to the anterior quadrigeminal body (superior colliculus). From these parts, in which the lateral root terminates, fibres pass into the posterior part of the internal capsule and enter the occipital lobe, forming the fibres of the optic radiation, which terminate in and about the cuneus, the region of the visual perceptive centre. The fibres of the medial division of the tract pass to the medial geniculate body and to the posterior quadrigeminal body. The medial root contains the fibres of the commissura inferior of v. Gudden, which are believed to have no connection with the

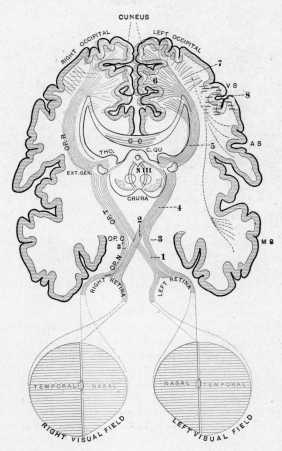

FIG. 11.—Diagram of visual paths. (From Vialet, modified.) OP. N., Optic nerve. OP. C., Optic chiasm. OP. T., Optic tract. OP. R., Optic radiations. GEN., Geniculate body. THO., Optic thalamus. C. QU., Corpora quadrigemina. C. C., Corpus callosum. V. S., Visual speech centre. A. S., Auditory speech centre. M. S., Motor speech centre. A lesion at 1 causes blindness of that eye; at 2, bi-temporal hemianopia; at 3, nasal hemianopia. Symmetrical lesions at 3 and 3′ would cause bi-nasal hemianopia; at 4, hemianopia of both eyes, with hemianopic pupillary inaction; at 5 and 6, hemianopia of both eyes, pupillary reflexes normal; at 7, amblyopia, especially of opposite eye; at 8, on left side, word-blindness.

retinæ. It is still held by some physiologists that the cortical visual centre is not confined to the occipital lobe alone, but embraces the occipito-angular region.

A lesion of the fibres of the optic path anywhere between the cortical centre and the chiasma will produce hemianopia. The lesion may be situated: (*a*) In the optic tract itself. (*b*) In the region of the thalamus, lateral geniculate body, and the corpora quadrigemina, into which the larger part of each tract enters. (*c*) A lesion of the fibres passing from the centres just mentioned to the occipital lobe. This may be either in the hinder part of the internal capsule or the white fibres of the optic radiation. (*d*) Lesion of the cuneus. Bilateral disease of the cuneus may result in total blindness. (*e*) There is clinical evidence to show that lesion of the angular gyrus may be associated with visual defect, not so often hemianopia as crossed amblyopia, dimness of vision in the opposite eye, and great contraction in the field of vision. Lesions in this region are associated with mind blindness, a condition in which there is failure to recognize the nature of objects.

The effects of lesions in the optic nerve in different situations from the retinal expansion to the brain cortex are as follows: (1) Of the optic nerve—total blindness of the corresponding eye; (2) of the optic chiasma, either temporal hemianopia, if the central part alone is involved, or nasal hemianopia, if the lateral region of each chiasma is involved; (3) lesion of the optic tract between the chiasma and the lateral geniculate body, produces lateral hemianopia; (4) lesion of the central fibres of the nerve between the geniculate bodies and the cerebral cortex produces lateral hemianopia; (5) lesion of the cuneus causes lateral hemianopia; and (6) lesion of the angular gyrus may be associated with hemianopia, sometimes crossed amblyopia, and the condition known as mind blindness. (See Fig. 11, with accompanying explanation.)

Diagnosis.—The student or practitioner must have a clear idea of the physiology of the nerve centres before he can appreciate the symptoms or undertake the diagnosis of lesions of the optic nerve. Having determined the presence of hemianopia, the question arises as to the situation of the lesion, whether in the tract between the chiasma and the geniculate bodies or in the central portion of the fibres between these bodies and the visual centres. This can be determined in some cases by the test known as Wernicke's *hemiopic pupillary inaction*. The pupil reflex depends on the integrity of the retina or receiving membrane, on the fibres of the optic nerve and tract which transmit the impulse, and the nerve centre at the termination of the optic tract which receives the impression and transmits it to the third nerve along which the motor impulses pass to the iris. If a bright light is thrown into the eye and the pupil reacts, the integrity of this reflex arc is demonstrated. It is possible in cases of lateral hemianopia so to throw the light into the eye that it falls upon the blind half of the retina. If when this is done the pupil contracts, the indication is that the reflex arc above referred to is perfect, by which we mean that the optic nerve fibres from the retinal expansion to the centre, the centre itself, and the third nerve are uninvolved. In such a case the conclusion would be justified that the cause of the hemianopia was central; that is, situated beyond the geniculate body, either in the fibres of the optic radiation or in the visual cortical centres. If, on the other hand, when the light is carefully thrown on the hemiopic half of the retina, the pupil remains inactive, the conclusion is justifiable that there is interruption in the path between the retina and the nucleus of the third nerve, and that the hemianopia is not central, but dependent upon a lesion situated in the optic tract. This test of Wernicke's is sometimes difficult to obtain. It is best performed as follows: " The patient being in a dark or nearly dark room with the lamp or gas-light behind his head in the usual position, I bid him look over to the other side of the room, so as to exclude accommodative iris movements (which are not necessarily associated with the reflex). Then I throw a faint light from a plane mirror or from a large concave mirror, held well out of focus, upon the eye and note the size of the pupil. With my other hand I now throw a beam of light, focussed from the lamp by an ophthalmoscopic mirror, directly into the optical centre of the eye; then laterally in various positions, and also from above and below the equator of the eye, noting the reaction at all angles of incidence of the ray of light." (Seguin.)

The significance of hemianopia varies. There is a functional hemianopia associated with migraine and hysteria. In a considerable proportion of all cases there are signs of organic brain-disease. In a certain number of instances of slight lesions of the occipital lobe hemiachromatopsia has been observed. The homonymous halves of the retina as far as the fixation point are dulled, or blind for colors. Hemiplegia is common, in which event the loss of power and blindness are on the same side. Thus, a lesion in the left hemisphere involving the motor tract produces right hemiplegia, and when the fibres of the optic radiation are involved in the internal capsule, there is also lateral hemianopia, so that objects in the field of vision to the right are not perceived. Hemianæsthesia is not uncommon in such cases, owing to the close association of the sensory and visual tracts at the posterior part of the internal capsule. Certain forms of aphasia also occur in many of the cases.

The optic aphasia of Freund may be mentioned here. The patient after an apoplectic attack, though able to recognize ordinary objects shown to him is unable to name them correctly. If he be permitted to touch the object he may be able to name it quickly and correctly. Freund's optic aphasia differs from mind-blindness, since in the latter affection the objects seen are not recognized. Optic aphasia, like word-blindness, never occurs alone, but is always associated with hemianopia, or mind-blindness, and often also with word-deafness. In the cases which have thus far come to autopsy there has always been a lesion in the white matter of the occipital lobe on the left side.

MOTOR NERVES OF THE EYEBALL.

Third Nerve (*Nervus oculomotorius*).—The nucleus of origin of this nerve is situated in the floor of the aqueduct of Sylvius; the nerve passes through the crus at the side of which it emerges. Passing along the wall of the cavernous sinus, it enters the orbit through the sphenoidal fissure and supplies, by its superior branch, the levator palpebræ superioris and the superior rectus, and by its inferior branch the internal and inferior recti muscles and the inferior oblique. Branches pass to the ciliary muscle and the constrictor of the iris. Lesions may affect the nucleus or the nerve in its course and cause either paralysis or spasm.

Paralysis.—A nuclear lesion is usually associated with the disease of the centres for the other eye muscles, producing a condition of general ophthalmoplegia. More commonly the nerve itself is involved in its course, either by meningitis, gummata, or aneurism, or is attacked by a neuritis, as in diphtheria and locomotor ataxia. Complete paralysis of the third nerve is accompanied by the following symptoms:

Paralysis of all the muscles, except the superior oblique and external rectus, by which the eye can be moved outward and a little downward and inward. There is divergent strabismus. There is ptosis or drooping of the upper eyelid, owing to paralysis of the levator palpebræ. The pupil is usually dilated. It does not contract to light, and the power of accommodation is lost. The most striking features of this paralysis are the external strabismus, with diplopia or double vision, and the ptosis. In very many cases the affection of the third nerve is partial. Thus the levator palpebræ and the superior rectus may be involved together, or the ciliary muscles and the iris may be affected and the external muscles may escape.

There is a remarkable form of recurring oculo-motor paralysis affecting chiefly women, and involving all the branches of the nerve. In some cases the attacks have come on at intervals of a month; in others a much longer period has elapsed. The attacks may persist throughout life. They are sometimes associated with pain in the head and sometimes with migraine. Mary Sherwood has collected from the literature 23 cases.

Ptosis is a common and important symptom in nervous affections. We may here briefly refer to the conditions under which it may occur: (*a*) A congenital, incurable form, which is frequently seen; (*b*) the form associated with definite lesion of the third nerve, either in its course or at its nucleus. This may come on with paralysis of the superior rectus alone or with paralysis of the internal and inferior recti as well. (*c*) There are instances of complete or partial ptosis associated with cerebral lesions without any other branch of the third nerve being paralyzed. The exact position of the cortical centre or centres is as yet unknown. (*d*) Hysterical ptosis, which is double and occurs with other hysterical symptoms. (*e*) Pseudo-ptosis, due to affection of the sympathetic nerve, is associated with symptoms of vaso-motor palsy, such as elevation of the temperature on the affected side with redness and œdema of the skin. Contraction of the pupil exists on the same side and the eyeball appears rather to have shrunk into the orbit. (*f*) In idiopathic muscular atrophy, when the face muscles are involved, there may be marked bilateral ptosis. And, lastly, in weak, delicate women there is often to be seen a transient ptosis, particularly in the morning.

Among the most important of the symptoms of the third-nerve paralysis are those which relate to the ciliary muscle and iris.

Cycloplegia, paralysis of the ciliary muscle, causes loss of the power of accommodation. Distant vision is clear, but near objects cannot be properly seen. In consequence the vision is indistinct, but can be restored by the use of convex glasses. This may occur in one or in both eyes; in the latter case it is usually associated with disease in the nuclei of the nerve. Cycloplegia is an early and frequent symptom in diphtheritic paralysis and occurs also in tabes.

Iridoplegia, or paralysis of the iris, occurs in three forms (Gowers).

(*a*) *Accommodative iridoplegia,* in which the pupil does not diminish in size during the act of accommodation. To test for this the patient should look first at a distant and then at a near object in the same line of vision.

(*b*) *Reflex Iridoplegia.*—The path for the iris reflex is along the optic nerve and tract to its termination, then to the nucleus of the third nerve, and along the trunk of this nerve to the ciliary ganglion, and so through the ciliary nerves to the eyes. Each eye should be tested separately, the other one being covered. The patient should look at a distant object in a dark part of the room; then a light is brought suddenly in front of the eye at a distance of three or four feet, so as to avoid the effect of accommodation. Loss of this iris reflex with retention of the accommodation contraction is known as the Argyll Robertson pupil.

(*c*) *Loss of the Skin Reflex.*—If the skin of the neck is pinched or pricked the pupil dilates reflexly, the afferent impulses being conveyed along the cervical sympathetic. Erb pointed out that this skin reflex is lost usually in association with the reflex contraction, but the two are not necessarily conjoined. In iridoplegia the pupils are often small, particularly in spinal disease, as in the characteristic small pupils of tabes—spinal myosis. Iridoplegia may coexist with a pupil of medium size.

Inequality of the pupils—aniscoria—is not infrequent in progressive paresis and in tabes. It may also occur in perfectly healthy individuals.

Spasm.—Occasionally in meningitis and in hysteria there is spasm of the muscles supplied by the third nerve, particularly the internal rectus and the levator palpebræ. The clonic rhythmical spasm of the eye muscles is known as *nystagmus,* in which there is usually a bilateral, rhythmical, involuntary movement of the eyeballs. The condition is met with in many congenital and acquired brain lesions, in albinism, and sometimes in coalminers.

Fourth Nerve (*Nervus trochlearis*).—This supplies the superior oblique muscle. In its course around the outer surface of the crus and in its passage into the orbit it is liable to be compressed by tumors, by aneurism, or in the exudation of basilar meningitis. Its nucleus in the upper part of the fourth ventricle may be involved by tumors or undergo degeneration with the other ocular nuclei. The superior oblique muscle acts in such a way as to direct the eyeball downward and rotates it slightly. The paralysis causes defective downward and inward movement, often too slight to be noticed. The head is inclined somewhat forward and toward the sound side, and there is double vision when the patient looks down.

Sixth Nerve (*Nervus abducens*).—This nerve emerges at the junction of the pons and medulla, then, passing forward, it enters the orbit and supplies the external rectus muscle. It is affected by meningitis at the base, by gummata or other tumors, and sometimes by cold. There is internal strabismus, and the eye cannot be turned outward. Diplopia occurs on looking toward the paralyzed side.

" When the nucleus is affected there is, in addition to paralysis of the external rectus, inability of the internal rectus of the opposite eye to turn that eye inward. As a consequence of this the axes of the eyes are kept parallel and both are conjugately deviated to the opposite side, away from the side of lesion. The reason of this is that the nucleus of the sixth nerve sends fibres up in the pons to that part of the nucleus of the opposite third nerve which supplies the internal rectus. We thus have paralysis of the internal rectus without the nucleus of the third nerve being involved, owing to its receiving its nervous impulses for parallel movement from the sixth nucleus of the opposite side. As the sixth nucleus is in such proximity to the facial nerve in the substance of the pons, it is frequently found that the whole of the face on the same side is paralyzed, and gives the electrical reaction of degeneration, so that with a lesion of the *left* sixth nucleus there is conjugate deviation of both eyes to the *right*—i. e., paralysis of the left external and the right internal rectus, and sometimes complete paralysis of the *left* side of the face " (Beevor).

General Features of Paralysis of the Motor Nerves of the Eye.—Gowers divides them into five groups:

(*a*) *Limitation of Movement.*—Thus, in paralysis of the external rectus, the eyeball cannot be moved outward. When the paralysis is incomplete the movement is deficient in proportion to the degree of the palsy.

(*b*) *Strabismus.*—The axes of the eyes do not correspond. Thus, paralysis of the internal rectus causes a divergent squint; of the external rectus, a convergent squint. At first this is only evident when the eyes are moved in the direction of the action of the weak muscle, but may become constant by the contraction of the opposing muscle. The deviation of the axis of the affected eye from parallelism with the other is called the primary deviation.

(*c*) *Secondary Deviation.*—If, while the patient is looking at an object, the sound eye is covered, so that he fixes the object looked at with the affected eye only, the sound eye is moved still further in the same direction—e. g., outward—with paralysis of the opposite internal rectus. This is known as secondary deviation. It depends upon the fact that, if two muscles are acting together, when one is weak and an effort is made to contract it, the increased effort—innervation—acts powerfully upon the other muscle, causing an increased contraction.

(*d*) *Erroneous Projection.*—" We judge of the relation of external objects to each other by the relation of their images on the retina; but we judge of their relation to our own body by the position of the eyeball as indicated to us by the innervation we give to the ocular muscles" (Gowers). With the eyes at rest in the mid-position, an object at which we are looking is directly opposite our face. Turning the eyes to one side, we recognize that object in the middle of the field or to the side of this former position. We estimate the degree by the amount of movement of the eyes, and when the object moves and we follow it we judge of its position by the amount of movement of the eyeballs. When one ocular muscle is weak, the increased innervation gives the impression of a greater movement of the eye than has really taken place. The mind, at the same time, receives the idea that the object is further on one side than it really is, and in an attempt to touch it the finger may go beyond it. As the equilibrium of the body is in a large part maintained by a knowledge of the relation of external objects to it obtained by the action of the eye muscles, this erroneous projection resulting from paralysis disturbs the harmony of these visual impressions and may lead to giddiness—ocular vertigo.

(e) *Double Vision.*—This is one of the most disturbing features of paralysis of the eye muscles. The visual axes do not correspond, so that there is a double image—diplopia. That seen by the sound eye is termed the true image; that by the paralyzed eye, the false. In simple or homonymous diplopia the false image is "on the same side of the other as the eye by which it is seen." In crossed diplopia it is on the other side. In convergent squint the diplopia is simple; in divergent it is crossed.

Ophthalmoplegia.—Under this term is described a chronic progressive paralysis of the ocular muscles. Two forms are recognized—ophthalmoplegia *externa* and ophthalmoplegia *interna*. The conditions may occur separately or together and are described by Gowers under nuclear ocular palsy.

Ophthalmoplegia externa.—The condition is one of more or less complete palsy of the external muscles of the eyeball, due usually to a slow degeneration in the nuclei of the nerves, but sometimes to pressure of tumors or to basilar meningitis. It is often, but not necessarily, associated with ophthalmoplegia interna. Siemerling, in a monograph on the subject, states that 62 cases are on record. In only 11 of these could syphilis be positively determined. The levator muscles of the eyelids and the superior recti are first involved, and gradually the other muscles, so that the eyeballs are fixed and the eyelids droop. There is sometimes slight protrusion of the eyeballs. The disease is essentially chronic and may last for many years. It is found particularly in association with general paralysis, locomotor ataxia, and in progressive muscular atrophy. Mental disorders were present in 11 of the 62 cases. With it may be associated atrophy of the optic nerve and affections of other cerebral nerves. Occasionally, as noted by Bristowe, it may be functional.

Ophthalmoplegia interna.—Jonathan Hutchinson applied this term to a progressive paralysis of the internal ocular muscles, causing loss of pupillary action and the power of accommodation. When the internal and external muscles are involved the affection is known as total ophthalmoplegia, and in a majority of the cases the two conditions are associated. In some instances the internal form may depend upon disease of the ciliary ganglion.

While, as a rule, ophthalmoplegia is a chronic process, there is an acute form associated with hæmorrhagic softening of the nuclei of the ocular muscles. There is usually marked cerebral disturbance. It was to this form that Wernicke gave the name polio-encephalitis superior.

Treatment of Ocular Palsies.—It is important to ascertain, if possible, the cause. The forms associated with locomotor ataxia are obstinate, and resist treatment. Occasionally, however, a palsy, complete or partial, may pass away spontaneously. The group of cases associated with chronic degenerative changes, as in progressive paresis and bulbar paralysis, is little affected by treatment. On the other hand, in syphilitic cases, mercury and iodide of potassium are indicated and are often beneficial. Arsenic and strychnia, the latter hypodermically, may be employed. In any case in which the onset is acute, with pain, hot fomentations and counter-irritation or leeches applied to the temple give relief. The direct treatment by electricity has been extensively employed, but probably without any special effect. The diplopia may be relieved by the use of prisms, or it may be necessary to cover the affected eye with an opaque glass.

FIFTH NERVE (*Nervus trigeminus*).

Paralysis may result from: (*a*) Disease of the pons, particularly hæmorrhage or patches of sclerosis. (*b*) Injury or disease at the base of the brain. Fracture rarely involves the nerve; on the other hand, meningitis, acute or chronic, and caries of the bone are not uncommon causes. (*c*) The branches may be affected as they pass out—the first division by tumors pressing on the cavernous sinus or by aneurism; the second and third divisions by growths which invade the spheno-maxillary fossa. (*d*) Primary neuritis, which is rare.

Symptoms.—(*a*) *Sensory Portion.*—Disease of the fifth nerve may cause loss of sensation in the parts supplied, including the half of the face, the corresponding side of the head, the conjunctiva, the mucosa of the lips, tongue, hard and soft palate, and of the nose of the same side. The anæsthesia may be preceded by tingling or pain. The muscles of the face are also insensible and the movements may be slower. The sense of smell is interfered with. There is disturbance of the sense of taste. There are, in addition, *trophic* changes; the salivary, lachrymal, and buccal secretions may be lessened, abrasions of the mucous membranes heal slowly, and the teeth may become loose. The eye inflames, the corneæ become cloudy and may ulcerate. It was formerly held that these symptoms only occurred when the Gasserian ganglion was affected, but of late years this has been completely removed for obstinate neuralgia without producing any trophic disturbance. This apparent contradiction is not yet explained. Herpes may develop in the region supplied by the nerve, usually the upper branch, and is associated with much pain, which may be peculiarly enduring, lasting for months or years (Gowers). In herpes zoster with the neuritis there may be slight enlargement of the cervical glands.

(*b*) *Motor Portion.*—The inability to use the muscles of mastication on the affected side is the distinguishing feature of paralysis of this portion of the nerve. It is recognized by placing the finger on the masseter and temporal muscles, and, when the patient closes the jaw, the feebleness of their contraction is noted. If paralyzed, the external pterygoid cannot move the jaw toward the unaffected side; and when depressed, the jaw deviates to the paralyzed side. The motor paralysis of the fifth nerve is almost invariably a result of involvement of the nerve after it has left the nucleus. Cases, however, have been associated with cortical lesions. Hirt concludes, from his case, that the cortical motor centre for the trigeminus is in the neighborhood of the lower third of the anterior central convolution.

Spasm of the Muscles of Mastication.—Trismus, the masticatory spasm of Romberg, may be tonic or clonic, and is either an associated phenomenon in general convulsions or, more rarely, an independent affection. In the tonic form the jaws are kept close together—lock-jaw—or can be separated only for a short space. The muscles of mastication can be seen in contraction and felt to be hard; the spasm is often painful. This tonic contraction is an early symptom in tetanus, and is sometimes seen in tetany. A form of this tonic spasm occurs in hysteria. Occasionally trismus follows exposure to cold, and is said to be due to reflex irritation from the teeth, the mouth, or caries of the jaw. It may also be a symptom of organic disease due to irritation near the motor nucleus of the fifth nerve.

Clonic spasm of the muscles supplied by the fifth occurs in the form of rapidly repeated contractions, as in " chattering teeth." This is rare apart from general conditions, though cases are on record, usually in women late in life, in whom this isolated clonic spasm of the muscles of the jaw has been found. In another form of clonic spasm sometimes seen in chorea, there are forcible single contractions. Gowers mentions an instance of its occurrence as an isolated affection.

(c) Gustatory.—Loss of the sense of taste in the anterior two thirds of the tongue, as a rule, follows paralysis of the fifth nerve. The gustatory fibres pass from the chorda tympani to the lingual branch of the fifth. Disease of the fifth nerve is, however, not always associated with loss of taste in the anterior part of the tongue, in which case either the taste fibres escape, or the disease is within the pons where these fibres are separate from those of sensation. It may be that the nervus intermedius of Wrisberg carries the taste fibres.

The *diagnosis* of disease of the trifacial nerve is rarely difficult. It must be remembered that the preliminary pain and hyperæsthesia are sometimes mistaken for ordinary neuralgia. The loss of sensation and the palsy of the muscles of mastication are readily determined.

Treatment.—When the pain is severe morphia may be required and local applications are useful. If there is a suspicion of syphilis, appropriate treatment should be given. Faradization is sometimes beneficial.

FACIAL NERVE.

Paralysis *(Bell's Palsy).*—The facial or seventh may be paralyzed by (1) lesions of the cortex—supranuclear palsy; (2) lesions of the nucleus itself; or (3) involvement of the nerve trunk in its tortuous course within the pons and through the wall of the skull.

1. *Supranuclear paralysis*, due to lesion of the cortex or of the facial fibres in the corona radiata or internal capsule, is, as a rule, associated with hemiplegia. It may be caused by tumors, abscess, chronic inflammation, or softening in the cortex or in the region of the internal capsule. It is distinguished from the peripheral form by well-marked characters—the persistence of the normal electrical excitability of both nerves and muscles and the absence of involvement of the upper branches of the nerve, so that the orbicularis palpebrarum and frontalis muscle are spared. In rare instances these muscles are paralyzed. A third difference is that in this form the voluntary movements are more impaired than the emotional. There are instances of cortical facial paralysis—monoplegia facialis—associated with lesions in the centre for the face muscles in the lower Rolandic region. Isolated paralysis, due to involvement of the nerve fibres in their path to the nucleus, is uncommon. In the great majority of cases supranuclear facial paralysis is part of a hemiplegia. Paralysis is on the same side as that of the arm and leg because the facial muscles bear precisely the same relation to the cortex as the spinal muscles. The nuclei of origin on either side of the middle line in the medulla are united by decussating fibres with the cortical centre on the opposite side (see Fig. 11). A few fibres reach the nucleus from the cerebral cortex of the same side (Mellus, Hoche).

2. The *nuclear paralysis* caused by lesions of the nerve centres in the medulla is not common alone; but is seen occasionally in tumors, chronic softening, and hæmorrhage. We have had one instance of its involvement in anterior polio-myelitis. In diphtheria this centre may also be involved. The symptoms are practically similar to those of an affection of the nerve fibre itself—infranuclear paralysis.

3. *Involvement of the Nerve Trunk.*—Paralysis may result from:

(*a*) Involvement of the nerve as it passes through the pons—that is, between its nucleus in the floor of the fourth ventricle and the point of emergence in the postero-lateral aspect of the pons. The specially interesting feature in connection with involvement of this part is the production of what is called alternating or *crossed paralysis*, the face being involved on the same side as the lesion, and the arm and leg on the opposite side, since the motor path is involved above the point of decussation in the medulla (Fig. 11). This occurs only when the lesion is in the lower section of the pons. A lesion in the upper half of the pons involves the fibres not of the outgoing nerve on the same side, but of the fibres from the hemispheres before they have crossed to the nucleus of the opposite side. In this case there would of course be, as in hemiplegia, paralysis of the face and limbs on the side opposite to the lesion. The palsy, too, would resemble the cerebral form, involving only the lower fibres of the facial nerve.

(*b*) The nerve may be involved at its point of emergence by tumors, gummata, meningitis, or occasionally may be injured in fracture of the base.

(*c*) In passing through the Fallopian canal the nerve may be involved in disease of the ear, particularly by caries of the bone in otitis media.

This is a common cause in children. I have seen two instances follow otitis in puerperal fever.

(*d*) As the nerve emerges from the styloid foramen it is exposed to injuries and blows which not infrequently cause paralysis. The fibres may be cut in the removal of tumors in this region, or the paralysis may be caused by pressure of the forceps in an instrumental delivery.

(*e*) Exposure to cold is the most common cause of facial paralysis, inducing a neuritis of the nerve within the Fallopian canal.

(*f*) Syphilis is not an infrequent cause, and the paralysis may develop early with the secondary symptoms.

(*g*) It may develop with herpes.

Facial diplegia is a rare condition occasionally found in affections at the base of the brain, lesions in the pons, simultaneous involvement of the nerves in ear disease, and in diphtheritic paralysis. Disease of the nuclei or symmetrical involvement of the cortex might also produce it. It may occur as a congenital affection. H. M. Thomas has described two cases in one family.

Symptoms.—In the peripheral facial paralysis all the branches of the nerve are involved. The face on the affected side is immobile and can neither be moved at will nor participate in any emotional movements. The skin is smooth and the wrinkles are effaced, a point particularly noticeable on the forehead of elderly persons. The eye cannot be closed, the lower lid droops, and the eye waters. On the affected side the angle of the mouth is lowered, and in drinking the lips are not kept in close apposition to the glass, so that the liquid is apt to run out. In smiling or laughing the contrast is most striking, as the affected side does not move, which gives a curious unequal appearance to the two sides of the face. The eye cannot be closed nor can the forehead be wrinkled. In long-standing cases, when the reaction of degeneration is present, if the patient tries to close the eyes while looking fixedly at an object the lids on the sound side close firmly, but on the paralyzed side there is only a narrowing of the palpebral orifice, and the eye is turned upward and outward by the inferior oblique. On asking the patient to show his upper teeth, the angle of the mouth is not raised. In all these movements the face is drawn to the sound side by the action of the muscles. Speaking may be slightly interfered with, owing to the imperfection in the formation of the labial sounds. Whistling cannot be performed. In chewing the food, owing to the paralysis of the buccinator, particles collect on the affected side. The paralysis of the nasal muscles is seen on asking the patient to sniff. Owing to the fact that the lips are drawn to the sound side, the tongue, when protruded, looks as if it were pushed to the paralyzed side; but on taking its position from the incisor teeth, it will be found to be in the middle line. The reflex movements are lost in this peripheral form. It is usually stated that the palate is paralyzed on the same side and that the uvula deviates. Both Gowers and Hughlings Jackson deny the existence of this involvement in the great majority of cases, and Horsley and Beevor have shown that these parts are innervated by the accessory nerve to the vagus.

When the nerve is involved within the canal between the genu and the origin of the chorda tympani, the sense of taste may be lost in the anterior part of the tongue on the affected side, owing probably to injury to the nervus intermedius of Wrisberg. When the nerve is damaged outside the skull the sense of taste is unaffected. Hearing is often impaired in facial paralysis, most commonly by preceding ear-disease. The paralysis of the stapedius muscle may lead to increased sensitiveness to musical notes. Herpes is sometimes associated with facial paralysis. Pain is not common, but there may be neuralgia about the ear. The face on the affected side may be swollen.

The *electrical reactions*, which are those of a peripheral palsy, have considerable importance from a prognostic standpoint. Erb's rules are as follows: If there is no change, either faradic or galvanic, the prognosis is good and recovery takes place in from fourteen to twenty days. If the faradic and galvanic excitability of the nerve is only lessened and that of the muscle increased to the galvanic current and the contraction formula altered (the contraction sluggish $AnC > CC$), the outlook is relatively good and recovery will probably take place in from four to six weeks; occasionally in from eight to ten. When the reaction of degeneration is present— that is, if the faradic and galvanic excitability of the nerves and the faradic excitability of the muscles are lost and the galvanic excitability of the muscle is quantitatively increased and qualitatively changed, and if the mechanical excitability is altered—the prognosis is relatively unfavorable and the recovery may not occur for two, six, eight, or even fifteen months.

The *course* of facial paralysis is usually favorable. The onset in the form following cold is very rapid, developing perhaps within twenty-four hours, but rarely is the paralysis permanent. Recurring attacks have been described; Sinkler mentions five. On the other hand, in the paralysis from injury, as by a blow on the mastoid process, the condition may remain. When permanent, the muscles are entirely toneless. In some instances contracture develops as the voluntary power returns, and the natural folds and the wrinkles on the affected side may be deepened, so that on looking at the face one at first may have the impression that the affected side is the sound one. This is corrected at once on asking the patient to smile, when it is seen which side of the face has the most active movement. Aretæus noted the difficulty sometimes experienced in determining which side was affected until the patient spoke or laughed.

The *diagnosis* of facial paralysis is usually easy. The distinction between the peripheral and central form is based on facts already mentioned.

Treatment.—In the cases which result from cold and are probably due to neuritis within the bony canal, hot applications first should be made; subsequently the thermo-cautery may be used lightly at intervals of a day or two over the mastoid process, or small blisters applied. If the ear is diseased, free discharge for the secretion should be obtained. The continuous current may be employed to keep up the nutrition of the muscles. The positive pole should be placed behind the ear, the negative one along the zygomatic and other muscles. The application can be made daily for a quarter of an hour and the patient can readily be taught to make it himself before the looking-glass. Massage of the muscles of the face is also useful. A course of iodide of potassium may be given even when there is no indication of syphilis.

In some of the traumatic cases the possibility of surgical interference may be considered. In a patient with chronic otitis media of twenty-three years' duration and secondary mastoid disease Bloodgood operated in May, 1896. Complete facial paralysis followed. Eight weeks later the facial nerve was exposed in its canal and found to be almost completely severed. The ends were brought together and the wound allowed to fill with blood-clot, which organized. Four months later the patient had improved, and one year and six months from the operation the power had returned to all the muscles except the occipito-frontalis and the depressor of the lower lip. The response to galvanic and faradic currents was normal.

Spasm.—The spasm may be limited to a few or involve all the muscles innervated by the facial nerve and may be unilateral or bilateral.

It is known also by the name of mimic spasm or of convulsive tic. Several different affections are usually considered under the name of facial or mimic spasm, but we shall here speak only of the simple spasm of the facial muscles, either primary or following paralysis, and shall not include the cases of habit spasm in children, or the *tic convulsif* of the French.

Gowers recognizes two classes—one in which there is an organic lesion, and an idiopathic form. It is thought to be due also to reflex causes, such as the irritation from carious teeth or the presence of intestinal worms. The disease usually occurs in adults, whereas the habit spasm and the *tic convulsif* of the French, often confounded with it, are most common in children. True mimic spasm occasionally comes on in childhood and persists. In the case of a school-mate, the affection was marked as early as the eleventh or twelfth year and still continues. When the result of organic disease, there has usually been a lesion of the centre in the cortex, as in the case reported by Berkeley, or pressure on the nerve at the base of the brain by aneurism or tumor.

Symptoms.—The spasm may involve only the muscles around the eye—blepharospasm—in which case there is constant, rapid, quick action of the orbicularis palpebrarum, which, in association with photophobia, may be tonic in character. More commonly the spasm affects the lateral facial muscles with those of the eye, and there is constant twitching of the side of the face with partial closure of the eye. The frontalis is rarely involved. In aggravated cases the depressors of the angle of the mouth, the levator menti, and the platysma myoides are affected. This spasm is confined to one side of the face in a majority of cases, though it may extend and become bilateral. It is increased by emotional causes and involuntary movements of the face. As a rule, it is painless, but there may be tender points over the course of the fifth nerve, particularly the supraorbital branch. Tonic spasm of the facial muscle may follow paralysis, and is said to result occasionally from cold.

The outlook in facial spasm is always dubious. A majority of the cases persist for years and are incurable.

Treatment.—Sources of irritation should be looked for and removed. When a painful spot is present over the fifth nerve, blistering or the application of the thermo-cautery may relieve it. Hypodermic injections of strychnia may be tried, but are of doubtful benefit. Weir Mitchell recommends the freezing of the cheek for a few minutes daily or every second day with the spray, and this, in some instances, is beneficial. Often the relief is transient; the cases return, and at every clinic may be seen half a dozen or more of such patients who have run the gamut of all measures without material improvement. Operative interference may be resorted to in severe cases, although not much can be expected of it.

AUDITORY NERVE.

The eighth, known also as *portio mollis* of the seventh pair, passes from the ear through the internal auditory meatus, and in reality consists of two separate nerves—the cochlear and vestibular roots. These two roots have entirely different functions, and may therefore be best considered separately. The cochlear nerve is the one connected with the organ of Corti, and is concerned in hearing. The vestibular nerve is connected with the vestibule and semicircular canals, and has to do with the maintenance of equilibrium.

The Cochlear Nerve.

The cortical centre for hearing is in the temporo-sphenoidal lobe. Primary disease of the auditory nerve in its centre or intracranial course is uncommon. More frequently the terminal branches are affected within the labyrinth.

(*a*) *Affection of the Cortical Centre.*—In the monkey, experiments indicate that the superior temporal gyrus represents the centre for hearing. In man the cases of disease indicate that it has the same situation, as destruction of this gyrus on the left side results in word-deafness, which may be defined as an inability to understand the meaning of words, though they may still be heard as sounds. The central auditory path extending to the cortical centre from the terminal nuclei of the cochlear nerve may be involved and produce deafness. This may result from involvement of the lateral lemniscus from the presence of a tumor in the corpora quadrigemina, especially if it involve the posterior quadrigeminal bodies from a lesion of the internal geniculate body, or it may be associated with a lesion of the internal capsule.

(*b*) *Lesions of the nerve at the base* of the brain may result from the pressure of tumors, meningitis (particularly the cerebro-spinal form), hæmorrhage, or traumatism. A primary degeneration of the nerve may occur in locomotor ataxia. Primary disease of the terminal nuclei of the cochlear nerve (nucleus nervi cochlearis dorsalis and nucleus nervi cochlearis ventralis) is rare. By far the most interesting form results from epidemic cerebro-spinal meningitis, in which the nerve is frequently involved, causing permanent deafness. In young children the condition results in deaf-mutism.

(*c*) In a majority of the cases associated with auditory-nerve symptoms the lesion is in the internal ear, either primary or the result of extension of disease of the middle ear. Two groups of symptoms may be produced—hyperæsthesia and irritation and diminished function or nervous deafness.

(1) *Hyperæsthesia and Irritation.*—This may be due to altered function of the centre as well as of the nerve ending. True hyperæsthesia—hyperacusis—is a condition in which sounds, sometimes even those inaudible to other persons, are heard with great intensity. It occurs in hysteria and occasionally in cerebral disease. As already mentioned, in paralysis of the stapedius low notes may be heard with intensity. In dysæsthesia, or dysacusis, ordinary sounds cause an unpleasant sensation, as commonly happens in connection with headache, when ordinary noises are badly borne.

Tinnitus aurium is a term employed to designate certain subjective sensations of ringing, roaring, ticking, and whirring noises in the ear. It is a very common and often a distressing symptom. It is associated with many forms of ear-disease and may result from pressure of wax on the drum. It is rare in organic disease of the central connections of the nerve. Sudden intense stimulation of the nerve may cause it. A form not uncommonly met with in medical practice is that in which the patient hears a continual *bruit* in the ear, and the noise has a systolic intensification, usually on one side. I have twice been consulted by physicians for this condition under the belief that they had an internal aneurism. A systolic murmur may be heard occasionally on auscultation. It occurs in conditions of anæmia and neurasthenia. Subjective noises in the ear may precede an epileptic seizure and are sometimes present in migraine. In whatever form tinnitus exists, though slight and often regarded as trivial, it occasions great annoyance and often mental distress, and has even driven patients to suicide.

The *diagnosis* is readily made; but it is often extremely difficult to determine upon what condition the tinnitus depends. The relief of constitutional states, such as anæmia, neurasthenia, or gout, may result in cure. A careful local examination of the ear should always be made. One of the most worrying forms is the constant clicking, sometimes audible many feet away from the patient, and due probably to clonic spasm of the muscles connected with the Eustachian tube or of the levator palati. The condition may persist for years unchanged, and then disappear suddenly. The pulsating forms of tinnitus, in which the sound is like that of a systolic *bruit*, are almost invariably subjective, and it is very rare to hear anything with the stethoscope. It is to be remembered that in children there is a systolic brain murmur, best heard over the ear, and in some instances appreciable in the adult.

(2) *Diminished Function or Nervous Deafness.*—In testing for nervous deafness, if the tuning-fork cannot be heard when placed near the meatus, but the vibrations are audible by placing the foot of the tuning-fork against the temporal bone, the conclusion may be drawn that the deafness is not due to involvement of the nerve. The vibrations are conveyed through the temporal bone to the cochlea and vestibule. The watch may be used for the same purpose, and if the meatus is closed and the watch is heard

66

better in contact with the mastoid process than when opposite the open meatus, the deafness is probably not nervous. Practically, disturbance of the function of the auditory nerve is not a very frequent symptom in brain-disease, but in all cases the function of the nerve should be carefully tested.

The Vestibular Nerve.

The most frequent symptoms met with in association with disease of the vestibular nerve and its central connections are vertigo, nystagmus, and loss of coördination of the muscles of the head, neck, and eyes.

Auditory Vertigo—Ménière's Disease.—In 1861 Ménière, a French physician, described an affection characterized by noises in the ear, vertigo (which might be associated with loss of consciousness), vomiting, and, in many cases, progressive loss of hearing. The term is now used to include all cases of sudden vertigo accompanied by noises in the ear and deafness. The frequency of vertigo with ear symptoms is striking. Thus, of 106 cases noted by Gowers, in which there was definite vertigo, in 94 ear symptoms were present, either tinnitus or deafness or both.

Symptoms.—The attack usually sets in suddenly with a buzzing noise in the ears and the patient feels as if he was reeling or staggering. He may feel himself to be reeling, or the objects about him may seem to be turning, or the phenomena may be combined. The attack is often so abrupt that the patient falls, though, as a rule, he has time to steady himself by grasping some neighboring object. There may be slight but transient loss of consciousness. In a few minutes, or even less, the vertigo passes off and the patient becomes pale and nauseated, a clammy sweat breaks out on the face, and vomiting may follow.

The deafness, which is always of a nervous character, may be in only one ear and is never complete. As a rule, the patients have no affection of the middle ear. The tinnitus is described as either a roaring or a throbbing sound. Ocular symptoms may be present; thus, jerking of the eyeballs or nystagmus may develop during the attack, or diplopia.

Labyrinthine vertigo is paroxysmal, coming on at irregular intervals. Sometimes weeks or months may elapse between the attacks; in other cases there may be several attacks in a day. The disease rarely occurs in young persons, is most frequent after the fortieth year, and is more common in men than in women.

The pathology of the disease has been much discussed, and there are many theories. It seems to be tolerably certain at present that the disturbances of equilibrium, including the vertigo, are dependent upon a disturbance of the functions of the vestibular nerve or of the organs with which this nerve is connected, either in its peripheral distribution or by means of its central connection. The auditory symptoms often accompanying it are doubtless always due to involvement of the cochlear nerve or its peripheral or central connections.

Diagnosis.—The combination of tinnitus with giddiness, with or without gastric disturbance, is sufficient to establish a diagnosis. There are other forms of vertigo from which it must be distinguished. The form known as gastric vertigo, which is associated with dyspepsia and occurs most commonly in persons of middle age, is, as a rule, readily distinguished by the absence of tinnitus or evidences of disturbance in the function of the auditory nerve. This variety of vertigo is much less common than Trousseau's description would lead us to believe. It is important to note the close connection of vertigo with ocular defects.

The cardio-vascular vertigo, one of the most common forms, occurs in cases of valvular disease, particularly aortic insufficiency, and as frequently in arterio-sclerosis.

Endemic Paralytic Vertigo.—In parts of Switzerland and France there is a remarkable form of vertigo described by Gerlier, which is characterized by attacks of paretic weakness of the extremities, falling of the eyelids, remarkable depression, but with retention of consciousness. It occurs also in northern Japan, where Miura says it develops paroxysmally among the farm laborers of both sexes and all ages. It is known there as *kubisagari*.

Aural vertigo must be carefully distinguished from attacks of *petit mal*, or, indeed, of definite epilepsy. It is rare in *petit mal* to have noises in the ear or actual giddiness, but in the aura preceding an epileptic attack the patient may feel giddy. Giddiness and transient loss of consciousness may be associated with organic disease of the brain, more particularly with tumor. Vomiting also may be present. A careful investigation of the symptoms will usually lead to a correct diagnosis.

The outlook in Ménière's disease is uncertain. While many cases recover completely, in others deafness results and the attacks recur at shorter intervals. In aggravated cases the patient constantly suffers from vertigo and may even be confined to his bed.

Treatment.—Bromide of potassium, in 20-grain doses three times a day, is sometimes beneficial. If there is a history of syphilis, the iodide should be administered. The salicylates are recommended, and Charcot advises quinine to cinchonism. In cases in which there is increase in the arterial tension, nitroglycerin may be given, at first in very small doses, but increasing gradually. It is not specially valuable in Ménière's disease, but in the cases of giddiness in middle-aged men and women associated with arterio-sclerosis it sometimes acts very satisfactorily. Correction of errors of refraction is sometimes followed by prompt relief of the vertigo.

GLOSSO-PHARYNGEAL NERVE (*Nervus glossopharyngeus*).

The ninth nerve contains both motor and sensory fibres and is also a nerve of the special sense of taste to the tongue. It supplies, by its motor branches, the stylo-pharyngeus and the middle constrictor of the pharynx. The sensory fibres are distributed to the upper part of the pharynx.

Symptoms.—Of nuclear disturbance we know very little. The pharyngeal symptoms of bulbar paralysis are probably associated with involvement of the nuclei of this nerve. Lesion of the nerve trunk itself is rare, but it may be compressed by tumors or involved in meningitis. Disturbance of the sense of taste may result from loss of function of this nerve, in which case it is chiefly in the posterior part of the tongue and soft palate. Gowers, however, states that there is no case on record in which loss of taste in these regions has been produced by disease of the roots of the glosso-pharyngeal; whereas, on the other hand, disease of the root of the fifth nerve may cause loss of taste on the back as well as the front of the tongue, as if the taste fibres of the glosso-pharyngeal came from the fifth.

The general disturbances of the sense of taste may here be briefly referred to. Loss of the sense of taste—*ageusia*—may be caused by disturbance of the peripheral end organs, as in affections of the mucosa of the tongue. This is very common in the dry tongue of fever or the furred tongue of dyspepsia, under which circumstances, as the saying is, everything tastes alike. Strong irritants too, such as pepper, tobacco, or vinegar, may dull or diminish the sense of taste. Complete loss may be due to involvement of the nerves either in their course or in the centres. Disturbance in the sense of taste is most commonly seen in involvement of the fifth nerve, and it may be that this nerve alone subserves the function. Perversion of the sense of taste—*parageusis*—is rarely found, except as an hysterical manifestation and in the insane. Increased sensitiveness is still more rare. There are occasional subjective sensations of taste, occurring as an aura in epilepsy or as part of the hallucinations in the insane.

To test the sense of taste the patient's eyes should be closed and small quantities of various substances applied. The sensation should be perceived before the tongue is withdrawn. The following are the most suitable tests: For bitter, quinine; for sweetness, a strong solution of sugar or saccharin; for acidity, vinegar; and for the saline test, common salt. One of the most important tests is the feeble galvanic current, which gives the well-known metallic taste.

Pneumogastric Nerve (*Nervus vagus*).

The tenth nerve has an important and extensive distribution, supplying the pharynx, larynx, lungs, heart, œsophagus, and stomach. The nerve may be involved at its nucleus along with the spinal accessory and the hypoglossal, forming what is known as bulbar paralysis. It may be compressed by tumors or aneurism, or in the exudation of meningitis, simple or syphilitic. In its course in the neck the trunk may be involved by tumors or in wounds. It has been tied in ligature of the carotid, and has been cut in the removal of deep-seated tumors. The trunk may be attacked by neuritis.

The affections of the vagus are best considered in connection with the distribution of the separate nerves.

(*a*) **Pharyngeal Branches.**—In combination with the glosso-pharyngeal the branches from the vagus form the pharyngeal plexus, from which the muscles and mucosa of the pharynx are supplied. In *paralysis* due to involvement of this either in the nuclei, as in bulbar paralysis, or in the course of the nerve, as in diphtheritic neuritis, there is difficulty in swallowing and the food is not passed on into the œsophagus. If the nerve on one side only is involved, the deglutition is not much impaired. In these cases the particles of food frequently pass into the larynx, and, when the soft palate is involved, into the posterior nares.

Spasm of the pharynx is always a functional disorder, usually occurring in hysterical and nervous people. Gowers mentions a case of a gentleman who could not eat unless alone, on account of the inability to swallow in the presence of others from spasm of the pharynx. This spasm is a well-marked feature in hydrophobia, and I have seen it in a case of pseudo-hydrophobia.

(*b*) **Laryngeal Branches.**—The superior laryngeal nerve supplies the mucous membrane of the larynx above the cords and the crico-thyroid muscle. The inferior or recurrent laryngeal curves around the arch of the aorta on the left side and the subclavian artery on the right, passes along the trachea and supplies the mucosa below the cords and all the muscles of the larynx except the crico-thyroid and the epiglottidean. Experiments have shown that these motor nerves of the pneumogastric are all derived from the spinal accessory. The remarkable course of the recurrent laryngeal nerves renders them liable to pressure by tumors within the thorax, particularly by aneurism. The following are the most important forms of paralysis:

(1) *Bilateral Paralysis of the Abductors.*—In this condition, the posterior crico-arytenoids are involved and the glottis is not opened during inspiration. The cords may be close together in the position of phonation, and during inspiration may be brought even nearer together by the pressure of air, so that there is only a narrow chink through which the air whistles with a noisy stridor. This dangerous form of laryngeal paralysis occurs occasionally as a result of cold, or may follow a laryngeal catarrh. The posterior muscles have been found degenerated when the others were healthy. The condition may be produced by pressure upon both vagi, or upon both recurrent nerves. As a central affection it occurs in tabes and bulbar paralysis, but may be seen also in hysteria. The characteristic symptoms are inspiratory stridor with unimpaired phonation. Possibly, as Gowers suggests, many cases of so-called hysterical spasm of the glottis are in reality abductor paralysis.

(2) *Unilateral Abductor Paralysis.*—This frequently results from the pressure of tumors or involvement of one recurrent nerve. Aneurism is by far the most common cause, though on the right side the nerve may be involved in thickening of the pleura. The symptoms are hoarseness or roughness of the voice, such as is so common in aneurism. Dyspnœa is not often present. The cord on the affected side does not move in inspiration. Subsequently the adductors may also become involved, in which case the phonation is still more impaired.

(3) *Adductor Paralysis.*—This results from involvement of the lateral crico-arytenoid and the arytenoid muscle itself. It is common in hysteria, particularly of women, and causes the hysterical aphonia, which may come on suddenly. It may result from catarrh of the larynx or from overuse of the voice. In laryngoscopic examination it is seen, on attempt at phonation, that there is no power to bring the cords together. In this connection the following table from Gowers' work will be found valuable to the student:

SYMPTOMS.	SIGNS.	LESION.
No voice; no cough; stridor only on deep inspiration.	Both cords moderately abducted and motionless.	Total bilateral palsy.
Voice low pitched and hoarse; no cough; stridor absent or slight on deep breathing.	One cord moderately abducted and motionless, the other moving freely, and even beyond the middle line in phonation.	Total unilateral palsy.
Voice little changed; cough normal; inspiration difficult and long, with loud stridor.	Both cords near together, and during inspiration not separated, but even drawn nearer together.	Total abductor palsy.
Symptoms inconclusive; little affection of voice or cough.	One cord near the middle line not moving during inspiration, the other normal.	Unilateral abductor palsy.
No voice; perfect cough; no stridor or dyspnœa.	Cords normal in position and moving normally in respiration, but not brought together on an attempt at phonation.	Adductor palsy.

Spasm of the Muscles of the Larynx.—In this the adductor muscles are involved. It is not an uncommon affection in children, and has already been referred to as laryngismus stridulus. Paroxysmal attacks of laryngeal spasm are rare in the adult, but cases are described in which the patient, usually a young girl, wakes at night in an attack of intense dyspnœa, which may persist long enough to produce cyanosis. Liveing states that they may replace attacks of migraine. They occur in a characteristic form in locomotor ataxia, forming the so-called laryngeal crises. There is a condition known as spastic aphonia, in which, when the patient attempts to speak, phonation is completely prevented by a spasm.

Disturbance of the sensory nerves of the larynx is rare.

Anœsthesia may occur in bulbar paralysis and in diphtheritic neuritis— a serious condition, as portions of food may enter the windpipe. It is usually associated with dysphagia and is sometimes present in hysteria. Hyperæsthesia of the larynx is rare.

(*c*) **Cardiac Branches.**—The cardiac plexus is formed by the union of branches of the vagi and of the sympathetic nerves. The vagus fibres subserve motor, sensory, and probably trophic functions.

(1) *Motor.*—The fibres which inhibit, control, and regulate the cardiac action pass in the vagi. Irritation may produce slowing of the action. Czermak could slow or even arrest the heart's action for a few beats by pressing a small tumor in his neck against one pneumogastric nerve, and it is said

that the same can be produced by forcible bilateral pressure on the carotid canal.   There are instances in which persons appear to have had voluntary control over the action of the heart.   Cheyne mentions the case of Colonel Townshend, "who could die or expire when he pleased, and yet by an effort or somehow come to life again, which it seems he had sometimes tried before he had sent for us."   Retardation of the heart's action has also followed accidental ligature of one vagus.   Irritation at the nuclei may also be accompanied with a neurosis of this nerve.   On the other hand, when there is complete paralysis of the vagi, the inhibitory action may be abolished and the acceleratory influences have full sway.   The heart's action is then greatly increased.   This is seen in some instances of diphtheritic neuritis and in involvement of the nerve by tumors, or its accidental removal or ligature.   Complete loss of function of one vagus may, however, not be followed by any symptoms.

(2) *Sensory* symptoms on the part of the cardiac branches are very varied.   Normally, the heart's action proceeds regularly without the participation of consciousness, but the unpleasant feelings and sensations of palpitation and pain are conveyed to the brain through this nerve.   How far the fibres of the pneumogastric are involved in angina it is impossible to say.   The various disturbances of sensation are described under the cardiac neuroses.

(*d*) **Pulmonary Branches.**—We know very little of the pulmonary branches of the vagi.   The motor fibres are stated to control the action of the bronchial muscles, and it has long been held that asthma may be a neurosis of these fibres.   The various alterations in the respiratory rhythm are probably due more to changes in the centre than in the nerves themselves.

(*e*) **Gastric and Œsophageal Branches.**—The muscular movements of these parts are presided over by the vagi and vomiting is induced through them, usually reflexly, but also by direct irritation, as in meningitis.   Spasm of the œsophagus generally occurs with other nervous phenomena.   Gastralgia may sometimes be due to cramp of the stomach, but is more commonly a sensory disturbance of this nerve, due to direct irritation of the peripheral ends, or is a neuralgia of the terminal fibres.   Hunger is said to be a sensation aroused by the pneumogastric, and some forms of nervous dyspepsia probably depend upon disturbed function of this nerve.   The severe gastric crises which occur in locomotor ataxia are due to central irritation of the nuclei.   Some describe exophthalmic goitre under lesions of the vagi.

SPINAL ACCESSORY NERVE (*Nervus accessorius*).

Paralysis.—The smaller or internal part of this nerve joins the vagus and is distributed through it to the laryngeal muscles.   The larger external part is distributed to the sterno-mastoid and trapezius muscles.

The nuclei of the nerve, particularly of the accessory part, may be involved in bulbar paralysis.   The nuclei of the external portion, situated as they are in the cervical cord, may be attacked in progressive degeneration of the motor nuclei of the cord.   The nerve may be involved in the exudation of meningitis, or be compressed by tumors, or in caries.   The *symptoms* of paralysis of the accessory portion which joins the vagus have already been given in the account of the palsy of the laryngeal branches of the pneumogastric. Disease or compression of the external portion is followed by paralysis of the sterno-mastoid and of the trapezius on the same side. In paralysis of one sterno-mastoid, the patient rotates the head with difficulty to the opposite side, but there is no torticollis, though in some cases the head is held obliquely. As the trapezius is supplied in part from the cervical nerves, it is not completely paralyzed, but the portion which passes from the occipital bone to the acromion is functionless. The paralysis of the muscle is well seen when the patient draws a deep breath or shrugs the shoulders. The middle portion of the trapezius is also weakened, the shoulder droops a little, and the angle of the scapula is rotated inward by the action of the rhomboids and the levator anguli scapulæ. Elevation of the arm is impaired, for the trapezius does not fix the scapula as a point from which the deltoid can work.

In progressive muscular atrophy we sometimes see bilateral paralysis of these muscles. Thus, if the sterno-mastoids are affected, the head tends to fall back; when the trapezii are involved, it falls forward, a characteristic attitude of the head in many cases of progressive muscular atrophy. Gowers suggests that lesions of the accessory in difficult labor may account for those cases in which during the first year of life the child has great difficulty in holding up the head. In children this drooping of the head is an important symptom in cervical meningitis, the result of caries.

The *treatment* of the condition depends much upon the cause. In the central nuclear atrophy but little can be done. In paralysis from pressure the symptoms may gradually be relieved. The paralyzed muscles should be stimulated by electricity and massage.

Accessory Spasm.—(*Torticollis; Wryneck.*)—The forms of spasm affecting the cervical muscles are best considered here, as the muscles supplied by the accessory are chiefly, though not solely, responsible for the condition. The following forms may be described in this section:

(*a*) *Congenital Torticollis.*—This condition, also known as fixed torticollis, depends upon the shortening and atrophy of the sterno-mastoid on one side. It occurs in children and may not be noticed for several years on account of the shortness of the neck, the parents often alleging that it has only recently come on. It affects the right side almost exclusively. A remarkable circumstance in connection with it is the existence of facial asymmetry noted by Wilks, which appears to be an essential part of this congenital form. It occurred in 6 cases reported by Golding-Bird. In congenital wryneck the sterno-mastoid is shortened, hard and firm, and in a condition of more or less advanced atrophy. This must be distinguished from the local thickening in the sterno-mastoid due to rupture, which may occur at the time of birth and produce an induration or muscle callus. Although the sterno-mastoid is almost always affected, there are rare cases in which the fibrous atrophy affects the trapezius. This form of wryneck in itself is unimportant, since it is readily relieved by tenotomy, but Golding-Bird states that the facial asymmetry persists, or indeed may, as shown by photographs in my case, become more evident. With reference to the pathology of the affection, Golding-Bird concludes that the facial asymmetry and the torticollis are integral parts of one affection which has a central origin and is the counterpart in the head and neck of infantile paralysis with talipes in the foot.

(b) *Spasmodic Wryneck.*—Two varieties of this spasm occur, the tonic and the clonic, which may alternate in the same case; or, as is most common, they are separate and remain so from the outset. The disease is most frequent in adults and, according to Gowers, more common in females. In this country it is certainly more frequent in males. Of the 8 or 10 cases which came under my observation in Montreal and Philadelphia, all were males. In females it may be an hysterical manifestation. There may be a marked neurotic family history, but it is usually impossible to fix upon any definite etiological factor. Some cases have followed cold; others a blow.

The *symptoms* are well defined. In the tonic form the contracted sterno-mastoid draws the occiput toward the shoulder of the affected side; the chin is raised, and the face rotated to the other shoulder. The sterno-mastoid may be affected alone or in association with the trapezius. When the latter is implicated the head is depressed still more toward the same side. In long-standing cases these muscles are prominent and very rigid. There may be some curvature of the spine, the convexity of which is toward the sound side. The cases in which the spasm is clonic are much more distressing and serious. The spasm is rarely limited to a single muscle. The sterno-mastoid is almost always involved and rotates the head so as to approximate the mastoid process to the inner end of the clavicle, turning the face to the opposite side and raising the chin. When with this the trapezius is affected, the depression of the head toward the same side is more marked. The head is drawn somewhat backward; the shoulder, too, is raised by its action. According to Gowers, the splenius is associated with the sterno-mastoid about half as frequently as the trapezius. Its action is to incline the head and rotate it slightly toward the same side. Other muscles may be involved, such as the scalenus and platysma myoides; and in rare cases the head may be rotated by the deep cervical muscles, the rectus and obliquus. There are cases in which the spasm is bilateral, causing a backward movement—the retro-collic spasm. This may be either tonic or clonic, and in extreme cases the face is horizontal and looks upward.

These clonic contractions may come on without warning, or be preceded for a time by irregular pains or stiffness of the neck. The jerking movements recur every few moments, and it is impossible to keep the head still for more than a minute or two. In time the muscles undergo hypertrophy and may be distinctly larger on one side than the other. In some cases the pain is considerable; in others there is simply a feeling of fatigue. The spasms cease during sleep. Emotion, excitement, and fatigue increase them. The spasm may extend from the muscles of the neck and involve those of the face or of the arms.

The disease varies much in its course. Cases occasionally get well, but the great majority of them persist, and, even if temporarily relieved, the disease frequently recurs. The affection is usually regarded as a functional neurosis, but it is possibly due to disturbance of the cortical centres presiding over the muscles.

Treatment.—Temporary relief is sometimes obtained; a permanent cure is exceptional. Various drugs have been used, but rarely with benefit. Occasionally, large doses of bromide will lessen the intensity of the spasm. Morphia, subcutaneously, has been successful in some reported cases, but there is the great danger of establishing the morphia habit. Galvanism may be tried. Counter-irritation is probably useless. Fixation of the head mechanically can rarely be borne by the patient. These obstinate cases fall ultimately into the hands of the surgeon, and the operations of stretching, division, and excision of the accessory nerve and division of the muscles have been tried. The last does not check the spasm, and may aggravate the symptoms. Temporary relief may follow, but, as a rule, the condition returns. Risien Russell thinks that resection of the posterior branches of the upper cervical nerves is most likely to give relief, and this has been done by Keen and others.

(*c*) The *nodding spasm* of children may here be mentioned as involving chiefly the muscles innervated by the accessory nerve. It may be a simple trick, a form of habit spasm, or a phenomenon of epilepsy (E. nutans), in which case it is associated with transient loss of consciousness. A similar nodding spasm may occur in older children. In women it sometimes occurs as an hysterical manifestation, commonly as part of the so-called salaam convulsion.

HYPOGLOSSAL NERVE.

This is the motor nerve of the tongue and for most of the muscles attached to the hyoid bone. Its cortical centre is probably the lower part of the anterior central gyrus.

Paralysis.—(1) *Cortical Lesion.*—The tongue is often involved in hemiplegia, and the paralysis may result from a lesion of the cortex itself, or of the fibres as they pass to the medulla. It does not occur alone and is considered with hemiplegia. There is this difference, however, between the cortical and other forms, that the muscles on both sides of the tongue may be more or less affected but do not waste, nor are their electrical reactions disturbed.

(2) *Nuclear* and *infra-nuclear* lesions of the hypoglossal result from slow progressive degeneration, as in bulbar paralysis or in locomotor ataxia; occasionally there is acute softening from obstruction of the vessels. The nuclei of both nerves are usually affected together, but may be attacked separately. Trauma and lead poisoning have also been assigned as causes. The fibres may be damaged by a tumor, and at the base by meningitis; or the nerve is sometimes involved in the condylar foramen by disease of the skull. It may be involved in its course in a scar, as in Birkett's case, or compressed by a tumor in the parotid region, as in a case at present under my care. As a result, there is loss of function in the nerve fibres and the tongue undergoes atrophy on the affected side. It is protruded toward the paralyzed side and may show fibrillary twitching.

The *symptoms* of involvement of one hypoglossal, either at its centre or in its course, are those of unilateral paralysis and atrophy of the tongue. When protruded, it is pushed toward the affected side, and there are fibrillary twitchings. The atrophy is usually marked and the mucous membrane on the affected side is thrown into folds. Articulation is not much impaired in the unilateral affection. There is a remarkable triad of symptoms, to which Hughlings Jackson first called attention—unilateral hemi-atrophy of the tongue, loss of power in the palate muscle, with paralysis of the larynx on the same side. When the disease is bilateral, the tongue lies almost motionless in the floor of the mouth; it is atrophied, and cannot be protruded. Speech and mastication are extremely difficult and deglutition may be impaired. If the seat of the disease is above the nuclei, there may be little or no wasting. The condition is seen in progressive bulbar paralysis and occasionally in progressive muscular atrophy.

The *diagnosis* is readily made and the situation of the lesion can usually be determined, since when supra-nuclear there is associated hemiplegia and no wasting of the muscles of the tongue. Nuclear disease is only occasionally unilateral; most commonly bilateral and part of a bulbar paralysis. It should be borne in mind that the fibres of the hypoglossal may be involved within the medulla after leaving their nuclei. In such a case there may be paralysis of the tongue on one side and paralysis of the limbs on the opposite side, and the tongue, when protruded, is pushed toward the sound side.

Spasm.—This rare affection may be unilateral or bilateral. It is most frequently a part of some other convulsive disorder, such as epilepsy, chorea, or spasm of the facial muscles. In some cases of stuttering, spasm of the tongue precedes the explosive utterance of the words. It may occur in hysteria, and is said to follow reflex irritation in the fifth nerve. The most remarkable cases are those of paroxysmal clonic spasm, in which the tongue is rapidly thrust in and out, as many as forty or fifty times a minute. In the case reported by Gowers the attacks occurred during sleep and continued for a year and a half. The spasm is usually bilateral. Wendt has reported a case in which it was unilateral. The prognosis is usually good.

IV. DISEASES OF THE SPINAL NERVES.

Cervical Plexus.

(1) **Occipito-cervical Neuralgia.**—This involves the nerve territory supplied by the second, the occipitalis major and minor, and the auricularis magnus nerves. The pains are chiefly in the back of the head and neck and in the ear. The condition may follow cold and is sometimes associated with stiffness of the neck or torticollis. Unless connected with it there exists disease of the bones or due to pressure of tumors, the outlook is usually good. There are tender points midway between the mastoid process and the spine and just above the parietal eminence, and between the sternomastoid and the trapezius. The affection may be due to direct pressure, in persons who carry very heavy loads on the neck.

(2) Affections of the Phrenic Nerve.—Paralysis may follow a lesion in the anterior horns at the level of the third and fourth cervical nerves, or may be due to compression of the nerve by tumors or aneurism. More rarely paralysis results from neuritis.

It may be part of a diphtheritic or lead palsy and is usually bilateral. When the diaphragm is paralyzed respiration is carried on by the intercostal and accessory muscles. When the patient is quiet and at rest little may be noticed, but the abdomen retracts in inspiration and is forced out in expiration. On exertion or even on attempting to move there may be dyspnœa. If the paralysis sets in suddenly there may be dyspnœa and lividity, which is usually temporary (W. Pasteur). Intercurrent attacks of bronchitis seriously aggravate the condition. Difficulty in coughing, owing to the impossibility of drawing a full breath, adds greatly to the danger of this complication, as the mucus accumulates in the tubes.

When the phrenic nerve is paralyzed on one side the paralysis may be scarcely noticeable, but careful inspection shows that the descent of the diaphragm is much less on the affected side.

The *diagnosis* of paralysis is not always easy, particularly in women, who habitually use this muscle less than men, and in whom the diaphragmatic breathing is less conspicuous. Immobility of the diaphragm is not uncommon, particularly in diaphragmatic pleurisy, in large effusions, and in extensive emphysema. The muscle itself may be degenerated and its power impaired.

Owing to the lessened action of the diaphragm, there is a tendency to accumulation of blood at the bases of the lungs, and there may be impaired resonance and signs of œdema. As a rule, however, the paralysis is not confined to this muscle, but is part of a general neuritis or an anterior polio-myelitis, and there are other symptoms of value in determining its presence. The outlook is usually serious. Pasteur states that of 15 cases following diphtheria, only 8 recovered. The treatment is that of the neuritis or polio-myelitis with which it is associated.

Hiccough.—Here may, perhaps, best be considered this remarkable symptom, caused by intermittent, sudden contraction of the diaphragm. The mechanism, however, is complex, and while the afferent impressions to the respiratory centre may be peripheral or central, the efferent are distributed through the phrenic nerve to the diaphragm, causing the intermittent spasm, and through the laryngeal branches of the vagus to the glottis, causing sudden closure as the air is rapidly inspired.

Obstinate hiccough is one of the most distressing of all symptoms, and may tax to the uttermost the resources of the physician. W. Langford Symes in a recent study groups the cases into:

(*a*) *Inflammatory*, seen particularly in affections of the abdominal viscera, gastritis, peritonitis, hernia, internal strangulation, appendicitis, suppurative pancreatitis, and in the severe forms of typhoid fever.

(*b*) *Irritative*, as in the direct stimulus of the diaphragm in the swallowing of very hot substances, local disease of the œsophagus near the diaphragm, and in many conditions of gastric and intestinal disorder, more particularly those associated with flatus.

(*c*) *Specific,* or, perhaps more properly, *idiopathic,* in which no evident causes are present. In these cases there is usually some constitutional taint, as gout, diabetes, or chronic Bright's disease. I have seen several instances of obstinate hiccough in the later stages of chronic interstitial nephritis.

(*d*) *Neurotic,* cases in which the primary cause is in the nervous system; hysteria, epilepsy, shock, or cerebral tumors. Of these cases the hysterical are, perhaps, the most obstinate.

The treatment is often very unsatisfactory. Sometimes in the milder forms a sudden reflex irritation will check it at once. Readers of Plato's Symposium will remember that the physician Eryximachus recommended to Aristophanes, who had hiccough from eating too much, either to hold his breath (which for trivial forms of hiccough is very satisfactory) or to gargle with a little water; but if it still continued, " tickle your nose with something and sneeze; and if you sneeze once or twice even the most violent hiccough is sure to go." The attack must have been of some severity, as it is stated subsequently that the hiccough did not disappear until Aristophanes had resorted to the sneezing.

Ice, a teaspoonful of salt and lemon-juice, or salt and vinegar, or a teaspoonful of raw spirits may be tried. When the hiccough is due to gastric irritation, lavage is sometimes promptly curative. I saw a case of a week's duration cured by a hypodermic injection of gr. $\frac{1}{8}$ of apomorphia. In obstinate cases the various antispasmodics have been used in succession. Pilocarpine has been recommended. One has sometimes to resort to hypodermics of morphia, or to inhalations of chloroform. The nitrite of amyl and nitroglycerin have been beneficial in some cases. Galvanism over the phrenic nerve, or pressure on the nerves, applied between the heads of the sterno-cleido-mastoid muscles may be used. Strong retraction of the tongue may give immediate relief.

BRACHIAL PLEXUS.

(1) **Combined Paralysis.**—The plexus may be involved in the supra-clavicular region by compression of the nerve trunks as they leave the spine, or by tumors and other morbid processes in the neck. Below the clavicle lesions are more common and result from injuries following dislocation or fracture, sometimes from neuritis. The most common cause of lesion of the brachial plexus is luxation of the humerus, particularly the subcoracoid form. If the dislocation is quickly reduced the symptoms are quite transient, and disappear in a few days. In severe cases all the branches of the plexus, or only one or two, may be involved. The most serious cases are those in which the dislocation is undetected or unreduced for some time, when the prolonged pressure on the nerves may cause complete and permanent paralysis of the arm. The muscles waste, the reaction of degeneration is present, and trophic changes in the skin are apt to occur. The medico-legal bearings of these cases are important, and may be thus briefly summarized: Direct injury, as by a fall or blow on the shoulder, resulting in great bruising of the nerves without dislocation, is occasionally followed by complete paralysis of the arm. A dislocation may be set immediately and

yet the lesion of the brachial plexus may be such as to cause permanent paralysis of the nerves. The dislocation may be reduced and the joint in subsequent movements slips out again. It has happened that by the time the surgeon sees the patient again, the damage has become irreparable.

Injuries and blows on the neck may cause partial paralysis of the arm, involving the deltoid, supraspinatus, infraspinatus, biceps, brachialis anticus, and the supinator. The injury may occur to the child during delivery.

A primary neuritis of the brachial plexus is rare. More commonly the process is an ascending neuritis from a lesion of a peripheral branch, involving first the radial or ulnar nerves, and spreading upward to the plexus, producing gradually complete loss of power in the arm.

(2) **Lesions of Individual Nerves of the Plexus.**—(*a*) *Long Thoracic Nerve* (*Serratus Palsy*).—This occurs chiefly in men. The nerve is injured in the posterior triangle of the neck, usually by direct pressure in the carrying of loads; cold may cause neuritis. It may be involved also in progressive muscular atrophy and in polio-myelitis anterior. When paralyzed the scapula on the affected side looks winged, which results from the projection of the angle and posterior border. This is particularly noticeable when the arm is moved forward, when the serratus no longer holds the scapula against the thorax. It is a well-defined and readily recognized form of paralysis. The onset is associated with, sometimes preceded by, neuralgic pains. The course is dubious, and many months may elapse before there is any improvement.

(*b*) *Circumflex Nerve.*—This supplies the deltoid and the teres minor. The nerve is apt to be involved in injuries, in dislocations, bruising by a crutch, or sometimes by extension of inflammation from the joint. Occasionally the paralysis arises from a pressure neuritis during an illness. As a consequence of loss of power in the deltoid, the arm cannot be raised. The wasting is usually marked and changes the shape of the shoulder. Sensation may also be impaired in the skin over the muscle. The joint may be relaxed and there may be a distinct space between the head of the humerus and the acromion. In other instances the ligaments are thickened, and a condition not unlike ankylosis may be produced, but which is readily distinguished on moving the arm.

(*c*) *Musculo-spiral Paralysis; Radial Paralysis.*—This is one of the most common of peripheral palsies, and results from the exposed position of the musculo-spiral nerve. It is often bruised in the use of the crutch, by injuries of the arm, blows, or fractures. It is frequently injured when a person falls asleep with the arm over the back of a chair, or by pressure of the body upon the arm when a person is sleeping on a bench or on the ground. It may be paralyzed by sudden violent contraction of the triceps. It is sometimes involved in a neuritis from cold, but this is uncommon in comparison with other causes. In the subcutaneous injection of ether the nerve may be accidentally struck and temporarily paralyzed. The paralysis of lead poisoning is the result of involvement of certain branches of this nerve.

A lesion when high up involves the triceps, the brachialis anticus, and the supinator longus, as well as the extensors of the wrist and fingers. Naturally, in lesions just above the elbow the arm muscles and the supinator longus are spared. The most characteristic feature of the paralysis is the wrist-drop and the inability to extend the first phalanges of the fingers and thumb. In the pressure palsies the supinators are usually involved and the movements of supination cannot be accomplished. The sensations may be impaired, or there may be marked tingling, but the loss of sensation is rarely so pronounced as that of motion.

The affection is readily recognized, but it is sometimes difficult to say upon what it depends. The sleep and pressure palsies are, as a rule, unilateral and involve the supinator longus. The paralysis from lead is bilateral and the supinators are unaffected. Bilateral wrist-drop is a very common symptom in many forms of multiple neuritis, particularly the alcoholic; but the mode of onset and the involvement of the legs and arms are features which make the diagnosis easy. The duration and course of the musculo-spiral paralyses are very variable. The pressure palsies may disappear in a few days. Recovery is the rule, even when the affection lasts for many weeks. The electrical examination is of importance in the prognosis, and the rules laid down under paralysis of the facial nerve hold good here.

The treatment is that of neuritis.

(d) *Ulnar Nerve*.—The motor branches supply the ulnar halves of the deep flexor of the fingers, the muscles of the little finger, the interossei, the adductor and the inner head of the short flexor of the thumb, and the ulnar flexor of the wrist. The sensory branches supply the ulnar side of the hand—two and a half fingers on the back, and one and a half fingers on the front. Paralysis may result from pressure, usually at the elbow-joint, although the nerve is here protected. Possibly the neuritis in the ulnar nerve in some cases of acute illness may be due to this cause. Gowers mentions the case of a lady who twice had ulnar neuritis after confinement. Owing to paralysis of the ulnar flexor of the wrist, the hand moves toward the radial side; adduction of the thumb is impossible; the first phalanges cannot be flexed, and the others cannot be extended. In long-standing cases the first phalanges are overextended and the others strongly flexed, producing the claw-hand; but this is not so marked as in the progressive muscular atrophy. The loss of sensation corresponds to the sensory distribution just mentioned.

(e) *Median Nerve*.—This supplies the flexors of the fingers except the ulnar half of the deep flexors, the abductor and the flexors of the thumb, the two radial lumbricales, the pronators, and the radial flexor of the wrist. The sensory fibres supply the radial side of the palm and the front of the thumb, the first two fingers and half the third finger, and the dorsal surfaces of the same three fingers.

This nerve is seldom involved alone. Paralysis results from injury and occasionally from neuritis. The signs are inability to pronate the forearm beyond the mid-position. The wrist can only be flexed toward the ulnar side; the thumb cannot be opposed to the tips of fingers. The second phalanges cannot be flexed on the first; the distal phalanges of the first and second fingers cannot be flexed; but in the third and fourth fingers this action can be performed by the ulnar half of the flexor profundus. The loss of sensation is in the region corresponding to the sensory distribution already mentioned. The wasting of the thumb muscles, which is usually marked in this paralysis, gives to it a characteristic appearance.

LUMBAR AND SACRAL PLEXUSES.

The *lumbar plexus* is sometimes involved in growths of the lymph-glands, in psoas abscess, and in disease of the bones of the vertebræ. Of its branches the *obturator nerve* is occasionally injured during parturition. When paralyzed the power is lost over the adductors of the thigh and one leg cannot be crossed over the other. Outward rotation is also disturbed. The *anterior crural nerve* is sometimes involved in wounds or in dislocation of the hip-joint, less commonly during parturition, and sometimes by disease of the bones and in psoas abscess. The special symptoms of affection of this nerve are paralysis of the extensors of the knee with wasting of the muscles, anæsthesia of the antero-lateral parts of the thigh and of the inner side of the leg to the big toe. This nerve is sometimes involved early in growths about the spine, and there may be pain in its area of distribution. Loss of the power of abducting the thigh results from paralysis of the *gluteal nerve*, which is distributed to the gluteus, medius, and minimus muscles.

The *sacral plexus* is frequently involved in tumors and inflammations within the pelvis and may be injured during parturition. Neuritis is common, usually an extension from the sciatic nerve.

Of the branches, the *sciatic nerve*, when injured at or near the notch, causes paralysis of the flexors of the legs and the muscles below the knee, but injury below the middle of the thigh involves only the latter muscles. There is also anæsthesia of the outer half of the leg, the sole, and the greater portion of the dorsum of the foot. Wasting of the muscles frequently follows, and there may be trophic disturbances. In paralysis of one sciatic the leg is fixed at the knee by the action of the quadriceps extensor and the patient is able to walk.

Paralysis of the *small sciatic nerve* is rarely seen. The gluteus maximus is involved and there may be difficulty in rising from a seat. There is a strip of anæsthesia along the back of the middle third of the thigh.

External Popliteal Nerve.—Paralysis involves the peronæi, the long extensor of the toes, tibialis anticus, and the extensor brevis digitorum. The ankle cannot be flexed, resulting in a condition known as foot-drop, and as the toes cannot be raised the whole leg must be lifted, producing the characteristic *steppage* gait seen in so many forms of peripheral neuritis. In long-standing cases the foot is permanently extended and there is wasting of the anterior tibial and peroneal muscles. The loss of sensation is in the outer half of the front of the leg and on the dorsum of the foot.

Internal Popliteal Nerve.—When paralyzed, plantar flexion of the foot and flexion of the toes are impossible. The foot cannot be adducted, nor can the patient rise on tiptoe. In long-standing cases talipes calcaneus follows and the toes assume a claw-like position from secondary contracture, due to overextension of the proximal and flexion of the second and third phalanges.

SCIATICA.

This is, as a rule, a neuritis either of the sciatic nerve or of its cords of origin. It may in some instances be a functional neurosis or neuralgia.

It occurs most commonly in adult males. A history of rheumatism or of gout is present in many cases. Exposure to cold, particularly after heavy muscular exertion, or a severe wetting are not uncommon causes. Within the pelvis the nerves may be compressed by large ovarian or uterine tumors, by lymphadenomata, by the fœtal head during labor; occasionally lesions of the hip-joint induce a secondary sciatica. The condition of the nerve has been examined in a few cases, and it has often been seen in the operation of stretching. It is, as a rule, swollen, reddened, and in a condition of interstitial neuritis. The affection may be most intense at the sciatic notch or in the nerve about the middle of the thigh.

Of the *symptoms*, pain is the most constant and troublesome. The onset may be severe, with slight pyrexia, but, as a rule, it is gradual, and for a time there is only slight pain in the back of the thigh, particularly in certain positions or after exertion. Soon the pain becomes more intense, and instead of being limited to the upper portion of the nerve, extends down the thigh, reaching the foot and radiating over the entire distribution of the nerve. The patient can often point out the most sensitive spots, usually at the notch or in the middle of the thigh; and on pressure these are exquisitely painful. The pain is described as gnawing or burning, and is usually constant, but in some instances is paroxysmal, and often worse at night. On walking it may be very great; the knee is bent and the patient treads on the toes, so as to relieve the tension on the nerve. In protracted cases there may be much wasting of the muscles, but the reaction of degeneration can seldom be obtained. In these chronic cases cramp may occur and fibrillar contractions. Herpes may develop, but this is unusual. In rare instances the neuritis ascends and involves the spinal cord.

The duration and course are extremely variable. As a rule it is an obstinate affection, lasting for months, or even, with slight remissions, for years. Relapses are not uncommon, and the disease may be relieved in one nerve only to appear in the other. In the severer forms the patient is bedridden, and such cases prove among the most distressing and trying which the physician is called upon to treat.

In the *diagnosis* it is important, in the first place, to determine whether the disease is primary, or secondary to some affection of the pelvis or of the spinal cord. A careful rectal examination should be made, and, in women, pelvic tumor should be excluded. Lumbago may be confounded with it. Affections of the hip-joint are easily distinguished by the absence of tenderness in the course of the nerve and the sense of pain on movement of the hip-joint or on pressure in the region of the trochanter. There are instances of sacro-iliac disease in which the patient complains of pain in the upper part of the thigh, which may sometimes radiate; but careful examination will readily distinguish between the affections. Pressure on the nerve trunks of the cauda equina, as a rule, causes bilateral pain and disturbances of sensation, and, as double sciatica is rare, these circumstances always suggest lesion of the nerve roots. Between the severe lightning pains of tabes and sciatica the differences are usually well defined.

Treatment.—The pelvic organs should be carefully and systematically examined. Constitutional conditions, such as rheumatism and gout, should receive appropriate treatment. In a few cases with pronounced rheumatic history, which come on acutely with fever, the salicylates seem to do good. In other instances they are quite useless. If there is a suspicion of syphilis, the iodide of potassium should be employed, and in gouty cases salines.

Rest in bed with fixation of the limb by means of a long splint is a most valuable method of treatment in many cases, one upon which Weir Mitchell has specially insisted. I have known it to relieve, and in some instances to cure, obstinate and protracted cases which had resisted all other treatment. Hydrotherapy is sometimes satisfactory, particularly the warm baths or the mud baths. Many cases are relieved by a prolonged residence at one of the thermal springs.

Antipyrin, antifebrin, and quinine, are of doubtful benefit.

Local applications are more beneficial. The hot iron or the thermocautery or blisters relieve the pain temporarily. Deep injections into the nerves give great relief and may be necessary for the pain. It is best to use cocaine at first, in doses of from an eighth to a quarter of a grain. If the pain is unbearable morphia may be used, but it is a dangerous remedy in sciatica and should be withheld as long as possible. The disease is so protracted, so liable to relapse, and the patient's *morale* so undermined by the constant worry and the sleepless nights, that the danger of contracting the morphia habit is very great. On no consideration should the patient be permitted to use the hypodermic needle himself. It is remarkable how promptly, in some cases, the injection of distilled water into the nerve will relieve the pain. Acupuncture may also be tried; the needles should be thrust deeply into the most painful spot for a distance of about 2 inches, and left for from fifteen to twenty minutes. The injection of chloroform into the nerve has also been recommended.

Electricity is an uncertain remedy. Sometimes it gives prompt relief; in other cases it may be used for weeks without the slightest benefit. It is most serviceable in the chronic cases in which there is wasting of the legs, and should be combined with massage. The galvanic current should be used; a flat electrode should be placed over the sciatic notch, and a smaller one used along the course of the nerve and its branches. In very obstinate cases nerve-stretching may be employed. It is sometimes successful; but in other instances the condition recurs and is as bad as ever.

VII. GENERAL AND FUNCTIONAL DISEASES.

I. ACUTE DELIRIUM (*Bell's Mania*).

Definition.—Acute delirium running a rapidly fatal course, with slight fever, and in which post mortem no lesions are found sufficient to account for the disease.

Cases are reported by many old writers under the term brain fever or phrenitis. Bell, at the time Superintendent of the McLean Asylum, described it * accurately under the designation, " a form of disease resembling some advanced stages of mania and fever."

The disease may set in abruptly or be preceded by a period of irritability, restlessness, and insomnia. The mental symptoms develop with rapidity and may quickly reach a grade of the most intense frenzy. There are the wildest hallucinations and outbreaks of great violence. The patient talks incessantly, but incoherently and unintelligibly. No sleep is obtained, and at last, worn out with the intensity of the muscular movements, the patient becomes utterly prostrated and assumes the sitting or recumbent posture. There may sometimes be definite salaam movements, and in a case which I saw at Westphal's clinic the patient incessantly made motions as if working a pump handle. After a period of intense bodily excitement, lasting for from twenty-four to thirty-six hours or longer, the patient can be examined, and presents the conditions which Bell described as typho-mania. The temperature ranges from 102° to 104°, or even higher. The tongue is dry, the pulse rapid and feeble; sometimes there are seen on the skin bullæ and pustules, and frequently sores from abrasion and self-inflicted injuries. Toward the close or, according to Spitzka, even during the development of the disease there may be lucid intervals. There may be petechiæ on the skin, and often there is marked congestion of the face and extremities. The duration of the disease is variable. Very acute cases may terminate within a week; others persist for two or even three weeks. The course of the disease is almost uniformly fatal. The anatomical condition is practically negative, or at any rate presents nothing distinctive. There is great venous engorgement of the vessels of the meninges and of the gray cortex. In two cases in which I made a careful microscopical examination of the gray matter there were perivascular exudation and leucocytes in the lymph sheaths and perigangliar spaces. In the inspection of fatal cases of acute delirium careful examination should be made of the lungs and ileum. It should be borne in mind that in a majority of the cases dying in this manner, there is engorgement of the bases of the lungs or even deglutition pneumonia.

The nature of the disease is quite unknown. Some of the cases suggest acute infection. Spitzka thinks that it is due to an autochthonous nerve poison.

---

* American Journal of Insanity, 1849.

Diagnosis.—There are several diseases which may present identical symptoms. As Bell remarks in his paper, the first glance in many cases suggests typhoid fever, particularly when the patient is seen after the violence of the mania has subsided. He gives two instances of this which were admitted from a general hospital. Enlargement of the spleen, the occurrence of spots, and the history give clews for the separation of the cases; but there are instances in which it is at first impossible to decide. Moreover, typhoid fever may set in with the most intense delirium. The existence of fever is the most deceptive symptom, and its combination with delirium and dry tongue so commonly means typhoid fever that it is very difficult to avoid error.

Acute pneumonia may come on with violent maniacal delirium and the pulmonary symptoms may be entirely masked.

Occasionally acute uræmia sets in suddenly with intense mania, and finally subsides into a fatal coma. The condition of the urine and the absence of fever would be important diagnostic features.

The character of the delirium is quite different from that of *mania a potu*. It may be extremely difficult to differentiate acute delirium from certain cases of cortical meningitis occurring in connection with pneumonia, ulcerative endocarditis or tuberculosis, or due to extension from disease of the ear. This sets in more frequently with a chill, and there may be convulsions.

Treatment.—Even though bodily prostration is apt to come on early and be profound, in the case of a robust man free venesection might be tried. I have been criticised for this advice, but repeat it. It is not at all improbable that some of the many cases of mania in which Benjamin Rush let blood with such benefit belonged to this class of affections. Considering its remarkable calming influence in febrile delirium, the cold bath or the cold pack should be employed. Morphia and chloroform may be administered and hyoscine and the bromides may be tried. Krafft-Ebing states that Solivetti has obtained good results by the use of ergotin. Unfortunately, as asylum reports show, the disease is almost uniformly fatal.

II. PARALYSIS AGITANS

(*Parkinson's Disease; Shaking Palsy*).

Definition.—A chronic affection of the nervous system, characterized by muscular weakness, tremors, and rigidity.

Etiology.—Men are more frequently affected than women. It rarely occurs under forty, but instances have been reported in which the disease began about the twentieth year. It is by no means an uncommon affection. Direct heredity is rare, but the patients often belong to families in which there are other nervous affections. Among exciting causes may be mentioned exposure to cold and wet, and business worries and anxieties. In some instances the disease has followed directly upon severe mental shock or trauma. Cases have been described after the specific fevers. Malaria is believed by some to be an important factor, but of this there is no satisfactory evidence.

Morbid Anatomy.—No constant lesions have been found. The similarity between certain of the features of Parkinson's disease and those of old age suggest that the affection may depend upon a premature senility of certain regions of the brain. Our organs do not age uniformly, but in some, owing to hereditary disposition, the process may be more rapid than in others. "Parkinson's disease has no characteristic lesions, but on the other hand it is not a neurosis. It has for an anatomical basis the lesions of cerebro-spinal senility, and which only differ from those of true senility in their early onset and greater intensity" (Dubief). The important changes are doubtless in the cerebral cortex.

Symptoms.—The disease begins gradually, usually in one or other hand, and the tremor may be either constant or intermittent. With this may be associated weakness or stiffness. At first these symptoms may be present only after exertion. Although the onset is slow and gradual in nearly all cases, there are instances in which it sets in abruptly after fright or trauma. When well established the disease is very characteristic, and the diagnosis can be made at a glance. The four prominent symptoms are tremor, weakness, rigidity, and the attitude.

Tremor.—This may be in the four extremities or confined to hands or feet; the head is not so commonly affected. The tremor is usually marked in the hands, and the thumb and forefinger display the motion made in the act of rolling a pill. At the wrist there are movements of pronation and supination, and, though less marked, of flexion and extension. The upper-arm muscles are rarely involved. In the legs the movement is most evident at the ankle-joint, and less in the toes than in the fingers. Shaking of the head is less frequent, but does occur, and is usually vertical, not rotatory. The rate of oscillation is about five per second. Any emotion exaggerates the movement. The attempt at a voluntary movement may check the tremor (the patient may be able to thread a needle), but it returns with increased intensity. The tremors cease, as a rule, during sleep, but persist when the muscles are at repose. The writing of the patient is tremulous and zigzag.

Weakness.—Loss of power is present in all cases, and may occur even before the tremor, but is not very striking, as tested by the dynamometer, until the late stages. The weakness is greatest where the tremor is most developed. The movements, too, are remarkably slow. There is rarely complete loss of power.

Rigidity may early be expressed in a slowness and stiffness in the voluntary movements, which are performed with some effort and difficulty, and all the actions of the patient are deliberate. This rigidity is in all the muscles, and leads ultimately to the characteristic

Attitude and Gait.—The head is bent forward, the back is bowed, and the arms are held away from the body and are somewhat flexed at the elbow-joints. The face is expressionless, and the movements of the lips are slow. The eyebrows are elevated, and the whole expression is immobile or mask-like, the so-called Parkinson's mask. The voice, as pointed out by Buzzard, is apt to be shrill and piping, and there is often a hesitancy in beginning a sentence; then the words are uttered with rapidity, as if the patient was in a hurry. This is sometimes in striking contrast to the scanning speech of insular sclerosis. The fingers are flexed and in the position assumed when the hand is at rest; in the late stages they cannot be extended. Occasionally there is overextension of the terminal phalanges. The hand is usually turned toward the ulnar side and the attitude somewhat resembles that of advanced cases of rheumatoid arthritis. In the late stages there are contractures at the elbows, knees, and ankles. The movements of the patient are characterized by great deliberation. He rises from the chair slowly in the stooping attitude, with the head projecting forward. In attempting to walk the steps are short and hurried, and, as Trousseau remarks, he appears to be running after his centre of gravity. This is termed festination or propulsion, in contradistinction to a peculiar gait observed when the patient is pulled backward, when he makes a number of steps and would fall over if not prevented—retropulsion.

The reflexes are normal in most cases, but in a few they are exaggerated.

Of sensory disturbances Charcot has noted abnormal alterations in the temperature sense. The patient may complain of subjective sensations of heat, either general or local—a phenomenon which may be present on one side only and associated with an actual increase of the surface temperature, as much as 6° F. (Gowers). In other instances, patients complain of cold. Localized sweating may be present. The mental condition rarely shows any change.

Variations in the Symptoms.—The tremor may be absent, but the rigidity, weakness, and attitude are sufficient to make the diagnosis. The disease may be hemiplegic in character, involving only one side or even one limb. Usually these are but stages of the disease.

Diagnosis.—In well-developed cases the disease is recognized at a glance. The attitude, gait, stiffness, and mask-like expression are points of as much importance as the oscillations, and usually serve to separate the cases from senile and other forms of tremor. Disseminated sclerosis develops earlier, and is characterized by the nystagmus, and the scanning speech, and does not present the *attitude* so constant in paralysis agitans. Yet Schultze and Sachs have reported cases in which the signs of multiple sclerosis have been associated with those of paralysis. The hemiplegic form might be confounded with post-hemiplegic tremor, but the history, the mode of onset, and the greatly increased reflexes would be sufficient to distinguish the two. The Parkinsonian face is of great importance in the diagnosis of the obscure and anomalous forms.

The disease is incurable. Periods of improvement may occur, but the tendency is for the affection to proceed progressively downward. It is a slow, degenerative process and the cases last for years.

Treatment.—There is no method which can be recommended as satisfactory in any respect. Arsenic, opium, and hyoscyamine may be tried, but the friends of the patient should be told frankly that the disease is incurable, and that nothing can be done except to attend to the physical comforts of the patient.

OTHER FORMS OF TREMOR.

(*a*) *Simple Tremor.*—This is occasionally found in persons in whom it is impossible to assign any cause. It may be transient or persist for an indefinite time. It is often extremely slight, and is aggravated by all causes which lower the vitality.

(*b*) *Hereditary Tremor.*—C. L. Dana has reported remarkable cases of hereditary tremor. It occurred in all the members of one family, and beginning in infancy continued without producing any serious changes.

(*c*) *Senile Tremor.*—With advancing age tremulousness during muscular movements is extremely common, but is rarely seen under seventy. It is always a fine tremor, which begins in the hands and often extends to the muscles of the neck, causing slight movement of the head.

(*d*) *Toxic tremor* is seen chiefly as an effect of tobacco, alcohol, lead, or mercury; more rarely in arsenical or opium poisoning. In elderly men who smoke much it may be entirely due to the tobacco. One of the commonest forms of this is the alcoholic tremor, which occurs only on movement and has considerable range. Lead tremor is considered under lead poisoning, of which it constitutes a very important symptom.

(*e*) *Hysterical tremor*, which usually occurs under circumstances which make the diagnosis easy, will be considered in the section on hysteria.

III. ACUTE CHOREA

(*Sydenham's Chorea ; St. Vitus's Dance*).

Definition.—A disease chiefly affecting children, characterized by irregular, involuntary contraction of the muscles, a variable amount of psychical disturbance, and a remarkable liability to acute endocarditis.

We shall speak here only of Sydenham's chorea. Senile chorea, chronic chorea, the prehemiplegic and post hemiplegic forms, and rhythmic chorea are totally different affections.

Etiology.—*Sex.*—Of 554 cases which I have analyzed from the Philadelphia Infirmary for Diseases of the Nervous System, 71 per cent were in females and 29 per cent in males. After puberty the percentage in females increases.

Age.—The disease is most common between the ages of five and fifteen. Of 522 cases, 380 occurred in this period. It is more common in the lower classes, and is rare among the negroes and native races of this continent. Morris J. Lewis has shown that the cases are most numerous when the mean relative humidity and barometric pressure are low.

Rheumatism.—A causal relationship between rheumatism and chorea has been claimed by many since the time of Bright. The English and French writers maintain the closeness of this connection; on the other hand, German authors, as a rule, regard the connection as by no means very close. Of 554 cases which I have analyzed, in 15.5 per cent there was a history of rheumatism in the family. In 88 cases, 15.8 per cent, there was a history of articular swelling, acute or subacute. In 33 cases there were pains, sometimes described as rheumatic, in various parts, but not associated with joint trouble. If we regard all such cases as rheumatic and add them to those with manifest articular trouble, the percentage is raised to nearly 21.

We find two groups of cases in which acute arthritis is present in chorea. In one, the arthritis antedates by some months or years the onset of the chorea, and does not recur before or during the attack. In the other group, the chorea sets in with or follows immediately upon the acute arthritis. In some instances it is impossible to decide whether the joint symptoms or the movements have appeared first. It is difficult to differentiate the cases of irregular pains without definite joint affection. It is probable that many of them are rheumatic, and yet I think it would be a mistake to regard as such all cases in children in which there are complaints of vague pains in the bones or muscles—so-called growing pains. It should never be forgotten, however, that a slight articular swelling may be the sole manifestation of rheumatism in a child—so slight, indeed, that the disease may be entirely overlooked.

Heart-disease.—Endocarditis is believed by some writers to be the cause of the disease. The particles of fibrin and vegetations from the valves pass as emboli to the cerebral vessels. On this view, which we shall discuss later, chorea is the result of an embolic process occurring in the course of a rheumatic endocarditis.

Infectious Diseases.—Scarlet fever with arthritic manifestations may be a direct antecedent. Sturges states that a history of previous whooping-cough occurs more frequently in choreic than in other children, but I find no evidence of this in the Infirmary records. With the exception of rheumatic fever, there is no intimate relationship between chorea and the acute diseases incident to childhood. It may be noted in contrast to this that the so-called canine chorea is a common sequel of distemper. Chorea has been known to develop in the course of an acute pyæmia, and to follow gonorrhœa and puerperal fever.

Anæmia is less often an antecedent than a sequence of chorea, and though cases develop in children who are anæmic and in poor health, this is by no means the rule. Chorea may develop in chlorotic girls at puberty.

Pregnancy.—A choreic patient may become pregnant; more frequently the disease occurs during pregnancy; sometimes it develops post partum. Buist, of Dundee (Trans. Edin. Obs. Soc., 1895), has tabulated carefully the recorded cases to that date. Of 226 cases, in 6 the chorea preceded the pregnancy; in 105 it occurred during the pregnancy; in 31 in recurrent pregnancies; 45 cases terminated fatally, and in 16 cases the chorea developed post partum. The alleged frequency in illegitimate primiparæ is not borne out by his figures. Beginning in the first three months were 108 cases, in the second three months 70 cases, in the last three months 25 cases. The disease is often severe, and maniacal symptoms may develop.

A tendency to the disease is found in certain families. In 80 cases there was a history of attacks of chorea in other members. In one instance both mother and grandmother had been affected. High-strung, excitable, nervous children are especially liable to the disease. *Fright* is considered a frequent cause, but in a large majority of the cases no close connection exists between the fright and the onset of the disease. Occasionally the attack sets in at once. Mental worry, trouble, a sudden grief, or a scolding may apparently be the exciting cause. The strain of *education*, particularly in girls during the third hemidecade, is a most important factor in the etiology of the disease. Bright, intelligent, active-minded girls from ten to fourteen, ambitious to do well at school, often stimulated in their efforts by teachers and parents, form a large contingent of the cases of chorea in hospital and private practice. Sturges has called special attention to this *school-made* chorea as one serious evil in our modern method of forced education. *Imitation*, which is mentioned as an exciting cause, is extremely rare, and does not appear to have influenced the onset in a single case in the Infirmary records.

The disease may rapidly follow an injury or a slight surgical operation. Reflex irritation was believed to play an important *rôle* in the disease, particularly the presence of worms or genital irritation; but I have met with no instance in which the disease could be attributed to either of these causes. Local spasm, particularly of the face—the habit chorea of Mitchell —may be associated with irritation in the nostrils and adenoid growths in the vault of the pharynx, as pointed out by Jacobi.

It has been claimed by Stevens that *ocular defects* lie at the basis of many cases of chorea, and that with the correction of these the irregular movements disappear. The investigations of De Schweinitz show that ocular defects do not occur in greater proportion in choreic than in other children. A majority of the cases in which operation has been followed by relief have been instances of *tic*, local or general.

Morbid Anatomy and Pathology.—No constant lesions have been found in the nervous system in acute chorea. Vascular changes, such as hyaline transformation, exudation of leucocytes, minute hæmorrhages, and thrombosis of the smaller arteries, have been described.

Embolism of the smaller cerebral vessels has been found, as might be expected in a disease with which endocarditis is so frequently associated; and, based upon this fact, Kirkes and others have supported what is known as the embolic theory of the disease. Endocarditis is by far the most frequent lesion in Sydenham's chorea. With no disease, not excepting rheumatism, is it so constantly associated. I have collected from the literature (to July, 1894) the records of 73 autopsies; there were 62 with endocarditis.* The endocarditis is usually of the simple variety, but the ulcerative form has occasionally been described.

We are still far from a solution of all the problems connected with chorea. Unfortunately, the word has been used to cover a series of totally diverse disorders of movement, so that there are still excellent observers who hold that chorea is only a symptom, and is not to be regarded as an etiological unit. The chorea of childhood, the disease which Sydenham described, presents, however, characteristics so unmistakable that it must

---

* Osler, Chorea and Choreiform Affections, 1894.

be regarded as a definite, substantive affection. We cannot discuss fully, but only indicate briefly, certain of the theories which have been advanced with regard to it. The most generally accepted view is that it is *a functional brain disorder* affecting the nerve-centres controlling the motor apparatus, an instability of the nerve-cells, brought about, one supposes by hyperæmia, another by anæmia, a third by psychical influences, a fourth by irritation, centric or peripheric. Of the actual nature of this derangement we know nothing, nor, indeed, whether the changes are primary and the result of a faulty action of the cortical cells or whether the impulses are secondarily disturbed in their course down the motor path. The predominance of the disease in females, and its onset at a time when the education of the brain is rapidly developing, are etiological facts which Sturges has urged in favor of the view that chorea is an expression of functional instability of the nerve-centres.

The *embolic theory* originally advanced by Kirkes has a solid basis of fact, but it is not comprehensive enough, as all of the cases cannot be brought within its limits. There are instances without endocarditis and without, so far as can be ascertained, plugging of cerebral vessels; and there are also cases with extensive endocarditis in which the histological examination of the brain, so far as embolism is concerned, was negative. In favor of the embolic view is the experimental production in animals of chorea by Rosenthal, and later by Money, by injecting fine particles into the carotids.

Lately, as indeed might be expected, chorea has been regarded as an *infectious disease*. Nothing definite has yet been determined. In favor of this view it has been urged, as it is impossible to refer the chorea to endocarditis or the endocarditis in all cases to rheumatism, that both have their origin in a common cause, some infectious agent, which is capable also, in persons predisposed, of exciting articular disease. Cases have been reported in scarlet fever with arthritic manifestations, in puerperal fever, and rheumatism, also after gonorrhœa, and such facts are suggestive at least of the association of the disease with infective processes. Possibly, as has been suggested by some writers, the paralytic conditions associated with chorea may be analogous to those which occur in typhoid and certain of the infectious diseases. On the other hand, there are conditions extremely difficult to harmonize with this view. The prominent psychical element is certainly one of the most serious objections, since there can be no doubt that ordinary chorea may rapidly follow a fright or a sudden emotion.

Symptoms.—Three groups of cases may be recognized—the mild, severe, and maniacal chorea.

Mild Chorea.—In this the affection of the muscles is slight, the speech is not seriously disturbed, and the general health not impaired. Premonitory symptoms are shown in restlessness and inability to sit still, a condition well characterized by the term " fidgets." There are emotional disturbances, such as crying spells, or sometimes night-terrors. There may be pains in the limbs and headache. Digestive disturbances and anæmia may be present. A change in the temperament is frequently noticed, and a docile, quiet child may become cross and irritable. After these symptoms have persisted for a week or more the characteristic involuntary movements begin, and are often first noticed at the table, when the child spills a tumbler of water or upsets a plate. There may be only awkwardness or slight incoördination of voluntary movements, or constant irregular clonic spasms. The jerky, irregular character of the movements differentiates them from almost every other disorder of motion. In the mild cases only one hand, or the hand and face, are affected, and it may not spread to the other side.

In the second grade, the *severe form*, the movements become general and the patient may be unable to get about or to feed or undress herself, owing to the constant, irregular, clonic contractions of the various muscle groups. The speech is also affected, and for days the child may not be able to talk. Often with the onset of the severer symptoms there is loss of power on one side or in the limb most affected.

The third and most extreme form, the so-called maniacal chorea, or *chorea insaniens*, is truly a terrible disease, and may develop out of the ordinary form. These cases are more common in adult women and may develop during pregnancy.

Chorea begins, as a rule, in the hands and arms, then involves the face, and subsequently the legs. The movements may be confined to one side —hemichorea. The attack begins oftenest on the right side, though occasionally it is general from the outset. One arm and the opposite leg may be involved. In nearly one fourth of the cases speech is affected; this may amount only to an embarrassment or hesitancy, but in other instances it becomes an incoherent jumble. In very severe cases the child will make no attempt to speak. The inability is in articulation rather than in phonation. Paroxysms of panting and of hard expiration may occur, or odd sounds may be produced. As a rule the movements cease during sleep.

A prominent symptom is muscular weakness, usually no more than a condition of paresis. The loss of power is slight, but the weakness may be shown by an enfeebled grip or by a dragging of the leg or limping. In his original account Sydenham refers to the " unsteady movements of one of the legs, which the patient drags." There may be extreme paresis with but few movements—the paralytic chorea of Todd. Occasionally a local paralysis or weakness remains after the attack.

It is doubtful whether choreic spasms extend to the muscles of organic life. The rapid action and disturbed rhythm of the heart present nothing peculiar to the disease, and there is no support for the view that irregular contractions occur in the papillary muscles.

Heart Symptoms.—*Neurotic.*—As so many of the subjects of chorea are nervous girls, it is not surprising that a common symptom is a rapidly acting heart. Irregularity, however, is not so special a feature in chorea as rapidity. The patients seldom complain of pain about the heart.

Hæmic Murmurs.—With anæmia and debility, not uncommon assocciates of chorea in the third or fourth week, we find a corresponding cardiac condition. The impulse is diffuse, perhaps wavy in thin children. The carotids throb visibly, and in the recumbent posture there may be pulsation in the cervical veins. On auscultation a systolic murmur is heard at the base, perhaps, too, at the apex, soft and blowing in quality.

Endocarditis.—As in rheumatism, so in chorea, acute valvulitis rarely gives evidence of its presence by symptoms. It must be sought, and clinical experience has shown that it is usually associated with murmurs at one or other of the cardiac orifices.

For the guidance of the practitioner the following statements may be made:

(1) In thin, nervous children a systolic murmur of soft quality is extremely common at the base, particularly at the second left costal cartilage, and is probably of no moment.

(2) A systolic murmur of maximum intensity at the apex, and heard also along the left sternal margin, is not uncommon in anæmic, enfeebled states, and does not necessarily indicate either endocarditis or insufficiency.

(3) A murmur of maximum intensity at apex, with rough quality, and transmitted to axilla or angle of scapula, indicates an organic lesion of the mitral valve, and is usually associated with signs of enlargement of the heart.

(4) When in doubt it is much safer to trust to the evidence of eye and hand than to that of the ear. If the apex beat is in the normal position, and the area of dulness not increased vertically or to the right of the sternum, there is probably no serious valvular disease.

(5) The endocarditis of chorea is almost invariably of the simple or warty form, and in itself is not dangerous; but it is apt to lead to those sclerotic changes in the valve which produce incompetency. Of 140 patients examined more than two years after the attack,* I found the heart normal in 51; in 17 there was functional disturbance, and 72 presented signs of organic heart-disease.

(6) Pericarditis is an occasional complication of chorea, usually in cases with well-marked rheumatism.

Sensory Disturbances.—Pain in the affected limbs is not common. Occasionally there is soreness on pressure. There are cases, usually of hemichorea, in which pain in the limbs is a marked symptom. Weir Mitchell has spoken of these as *painful choreas.* Tender points along the lines of emergence of the spinal nerves or along the course of the nerves of the limbs are rare.

Psychical disturbances are common, though in a majority of the cases slight in degree. Irritability of temper, marked wilfulness, and emotional outbreaks may indicate a complete change in the character of the child. There is deficiency in the powers of concentration, the memory is enfeebled, and the aptitude for study is lost. Rarely there is progressive impairment of the intellect with termination in actual dementia. Acute melancholia has been described (Edes). Hallucinations of sight and hearing may occur. Patients may behave in an odd and strange manner and do all sorts of meaningless acts. By far the most serious manifestation of

---

* Monograph on Chorea, 1894.

this character is the maniacal delirium, occasionally associated with the very severe cases—*chorea insaniens.* Usually the motor disturbance in these cases is aggravated, but it has been overlooked and patients have been sent to an asylum.

The psychical element in chorea is apt to be neglected by the practitioner. It is always a good plan to tell the parents that it is not the muscles alone of the child which are affected, but that the general irritability and change of disposition, so often found, really form part of the disease.

The condition of the *reflexes* in chorea is usually normal. Trophic lesions rarely occur in chorea unless, as some writers have done, we regard the joint troubles as arthropathies occurring in the course of a cerebrospinal disease.

Fever is not, as a rule, present in chorea unless complications exist. There may be the most intense and violent movements without any rise of temperature. I have seen instances, however, in which without apparently any visceral or articular disturbances there was slight daily fever. H. A. Hare states that in monochorea the temperature on the affected side may be elevated; but this is not an invariable rule. Fever is found with an acute arthritis, when there is marked endocarditis or pericarditis, though the former may certainly occur with little if any rise in temperature, and in the cases of maniacal chorea, in which the fever may range from 102° to 104°.

Cutaneous Affections.—The pigmentation, which is not uncommon, is due to the arsenic. Herpes zoster occasionally occurs. Certain skin eruptions, usually regarded as rheumatic in character, are not uncommon. Erythema nodosum has been described and I have seen several cases with a purpuric urticaria. There may, indeed, be the more aggravated condition of rheumatic purpura, known as Schönlein's *peliosis rheumatica.* Subcutaneous fibrous nodules, which have been noted by English observers in many cases of chorea, associated with rheumatism, are extremely rare in this country.

Duration and Termination.—From eight to ten weeks is the average duration of an attack of moderate severity. Chronic chorea rarely follows the minor disease which we have been considering. The cases described under this designation in children are usually instances of cerebral sclerosis or Friedreich's ataxia; but occasionally an attack which has come on in the ordinary way persists for months or years, and recovery ultimately takes place. A slight grade of chorea, particularly noticeable under excitement, may persist for months in nervous children.

The tendency of chorea to recur has been noticed by all writers since Sydenham first made the observation. Of 410 cases analyzed for this purpose, 240 had one attack, 110 had two attacks, 35 three attacks, 10 four attacks, 12 five attacks, and 3 six attacks. The recurrence is apt to be vernal.

Recovery is the rule in children. The statistics of out-patients' departments are not favorable for determining the mortality. A reliable estimate is that of the Collective Investigation Committee of the British Medical Association, in which 9 deaths were reported among 439 cases, about 2 per cent.

The paralysis rarely persists. Mental dulness may be present for a time, but usually passes away; permanent impairment of the mind is an exceptional sequence.

Diagnosis.—There are few diseases which present more characteristic features, and in a majority of instances the nature of the trouble is recognized at a glance; but there are several affections in children which may simulate and be mistaken for it.

(*a*) Multiple and diffuse cerebral sclerosis. The cases are often mistaken for ordinary chorea, and have been described in the literature as *chorea spastica*.

There are doubtless chronic changes in the cortex. As a rule, the movements are readily distinguishable from those of true chorea, but the simulation is sometimes very close; the onset in infancy, the impaired intelligence, increased reflexes and in some instances rigidity, and the chronic course of the disease, separate them sharply from true chorea.

(*b*) Friedreich's ataxia. Cases of this well-characterized disease were formerly classed as chorea. The slow, irregular, incoördinate movements, the scoliosis, the scanning speech, the early talipes, the nystagmus, and the family character of the disease are points which should render the diagnosis easy.

(*c*) In rare cases the paralytic form of chorea may be mistaken for polio-myelitis or, when both legs are affected, for paraplegia of spinal origin; but this can only be the case when the choreic movements are very slight.

(*d*) Hysteria may simulate chorea minor most closely, and unless there are other manifestations it may be impossible to make a diagnosis. Most commonly, however, the movements in the so-called hysterical chorea are rhythmic and differ entirely from those of ordinary chorea.

(*e*) As mentioned above, the mental symptoms in maniacal chorea may mask the true nature of the disease and patients have even been sent to the asylum.

Treatment.—Abnormally bright, active-minded children belonging to families with pronounced neurotic taint should be carefully watched from the ages of eight to fifteen and not allowed to overtax their mental powers. So frequently in children of this class does the attack of chorea date from the worry and stress incident to school examinations that the competition for prizes or places should be emphatically forbidden.

The treatment of the attack consists largely in attention to hygienic measures, with which alone, in time, a majority of the cases recover. Parents should be told to scan gently the faults and waywardness of choreic children. The psychical element, strongly developed in so many cases, is best treated by quiet and seclusion. The child should be confined to bed in the recumbent posture, and mental as well as bodily quiet enjoined. In private practice this is often impossible, but with well-to-do patients the disease is always serious enough to demand the assistance of a skilled nurse. Toys and dolls should not be allowed at first, for the child should be kept amused without excitement. The rest allays the hyper-excitability and reduces to a minimum the possibility of damage to the valve segments should endocarditis exist. Time and again have I seen very severe cases which had resisted treatment for weeks outside a hospital become quiet and the movements subside after two or three days of absolute rest in bed.

The child should be kept apart from other children and, if possible, from other members of the family, and should see only those persons directly concerned with the nursing of the case. Though irksome and troublesome to carry out, this is an important part of the treatment. In the latter period of the disease daily rubbings may be resorted to with great benefit.

The medical treatment of the disease is unsatisfactory; with the exception of arsenic, no remedy seems to have any influence in controlling the progress of the affection. Without any specific action, it certainly does good in many cases, probably by improving the general nutrition. It is conveniently given in the form of Fowler's solution, and the good effects are rarely seen until maximum doses are taken. It may be given as Martin originally advised (1813); he began "with five drops and increased one drop every day, until it might begin to disagree with the stomach or bowels." When the dose of 15 minims is reached, it may be continued for a week, and then again increased, if necessary, every day or two, until physiological effects are manifest. On the occurrence of these the drug should be stopped for three or four days. The practice of resuming the administration with smaller doses is rarely necessary, as tolerance is usually established and we can begin with the dose which the child was taking when the symptoms of saturation occurred. I have frequently given as much as 25 minims three times a day. Usually the signs of saturation are trivial but plain, and I have never seen any ill effects from the large doses, although I have heard recently of a case of arsenical neuritis due to the administration of Fowler's solution in chorea.

Of other medicines, strychnine, the zinc compounds, nitrate of silver, bromide of potassium, belladonna, chloral, and especially cimicifuga, have been recommended, and may be tried in obstinate cases.

For its tonic effect electricity is sometimes useful; but it is not necessary as a routine treatment. The question of gymnastics is an important one. Early in the disease, when the movements are active, they are not advisable; but during convalescence carefully graduated exercises are undoubtedly beneficial. It is not well, however, to send a choreic child to a school gymnasium, as the stimulus of the other children and the excitement of the romping, violent play is very prejudicial.

Other points in treatment may be mentioned. It is important to regulate the bowels and to attend carefully to the digestive functions. For the anæmia so often present preparations of iron are indicated.

In the severe cases with incessant movements, sleeplessness, dry tongue, and delirium, the important indication is to procure rest, for which purpose chloral may be freely given, and, if necessary, morphia. Chloroform inhalations may be necessary to control the intensity of the paroxysms, but the high rate of mortality in this class of cases illustrates how often our best endeavors are fruitless. The wet pack is sometimes very soothing and should be tried. As these patients are apt to sink rapidly into a low typhoid state with heart weakness, a supporting treatment is required from the outset.

Cases are found now and then which drag on from month to month without getting either better or worse and resist all modes of treatment. Change of air and scene is sometimes followed by rapid improvement, and in these cases the treatment by rest and seclusion should always be given a full trial.

In all cases care should be taken to examine the nostrils, and glaring ocular defects should be properly corrected either by glasses or, if necessary, by operation.

After the child has recovered from the attack, the parents should be warned that return of the disease is by no means infrequent, and is particularly liable to follow overwork at school or debilitating influences of any kind. These relapses are apt to occur in the spring. Sydenham advised purging in order to prevent the vernal recurrence of the disease.

IV. OTHER AFFECTIONS DESCRIBED AS CHOREA.

(*a*) **Chorea Major; Pandemic Chorea.**—The common name, St. Vitus's dance, applied to chorea has come to us from the middle ages, when under the influence of religious fervor there were epidemics characterized by great excitement, gesticulations, and dancing. For the relief of these symptoms, when excessive, pilgrimages were made, and in the Rhenish provinces, particularly to the Chapel of St. Vitus in Zebern. Epidemics of this sort have occurred also during this century, and descriptions of them among the early settlers in Kentucky have been given by Robertson and Yandell. It was unfortunate that Sydenham applied the term chorea to an affection in children totally distinct from this chorea major, which is in reality an hysterical manifestation under the influence of religious excitement.

(*b*) **Habit Spasm (Habit Chorea); Convulsive Tic** (of the French).

Two groups of cases may be recognized under the designation of habit spasm—one in which there are simply localized spasmodic movements, and the other in which, in addition to this, there are explosive utterances and psychical symptoms, a condition to which French writers have given the name *tic convulsif*.

(1) *Habit Spasm.*—This is found chiefly in childhood, most frequently in girls from seven to fourteen years of age (Mitchell). In its simplest form there is a sudden, quick contraction of certain of the facial muscles, such as rapid winking or drawing of the mouth to one side, or the neck muscles are involved and there are unilateral movements of the head. The head is given a sudden, quick shake, and at the same time the eyes wink. A not infrequent form is the shrugging of one shoulder. The grimace or movement is repeated at irregular intervals, and is much aggravated by emotion. A short inspiratory sniff is not an uncommon symp-

tom. The cases are found most frequently in children who are " out of sorts," or who have been growing rapidly, or who have inherited a tendency to neurotic disorders. Allied to or associated with this are some of the curious tricks of children. A boy at my clinic was in the habit every few moments of putting the middle finger into the mouth, biting it, and at the same time pressing his nose with the forefinger. Hartley Coleridge is said to have had a somewhat similar trick, only he bit his arm. In all these cases the habits of the child should be examined carefully, the nose and vault of the pharynx thoroughly inspected, and the eyes accurately tested. As a rule the condition is transient, and after persisting for a few months or longer gradually disappears. Occasionally a local spasm persists —twitching of the eyelids, or the facial grimace.

(2) *Tic Convulsif* (*Gilles de la Tourette's Disease*).—This remarkable affection, often mistaken for chorea, more frequently for habit spasm, is really a psychosis allied to hysteria, though in certain of its aspects it has the features of monomania. The disease begins, as a rule, in young children, occurring as early as the sixth year, though it may develop after puberty. There is usually a markedly neurotic family history. The special features of the complaint are:

(*a*) Involuntary muscular movements, usually affecting the facial or brachial muscles, but in aggravated cases all the muscles of the body may be involved and the movements may be extremely irregular and violent.

(*b*) Explosive utterances, which may resemble a bark or an inarticulate cry. A word heard may be mimicked at once and repeated over and over again, usually with the involuntary movements. To this the term *echolalia* has been applied. A much more distressing disturbance in these cases is *coprolalia*, or the use of bad language. A child of eight or ten may shock its mother and friends by constantly using the word *damn* when making the involuntary movements, or by uttering all sorts of obscene words. Occasionally actions are mimicked—*echokinesis*.

(*c*) Associated with some of these cases are curious mental disturbances; the patient becomes the subject of a form of obsession or a fixed idea. In other cases the fixed idea takes the form of the impulse to touch objects, or it is a fixed idea about words—onomatomania—or the patient may feel compelled to count a number of times before doing certain actions—arithmomania.

The disease is well marked and readily distinguished from ordinary chorea. The movements have a larger range and are explosive in character. Tourette regards the coprolalia as the most distinctive feature of the disease. The prognosis is doubtful. I have, however, known recovery to follow.

(*c*) **Saltatory Spasm** (*Latah; Myriachit; Jumpers*).—Bamberger has described a disease in which when the patient attempted to stand there were strong contractions in the leg muscles, which caused a jumping or springing motion. This occurs only when the patient attempts to stand. The affection has occurred in both men and women, more frequently in the former, and the subjects have usually shown marked neurotic tendencies. In many cases the condition has been transitory; in others it has persisted
68

for years. Remarkable affections similar to this in certain points occur as a sort of endemic neurosis. One of the most striking of these occurs among the " jumping Frenchmen " of Maine and Canada. As described by Beard and Thornton, the subjects are liable on any sudden emotion to jump violently and utter a loud cry or sound, and will obey any command or imitate any action without regard to its nature. The condition of echolalia is present in a marked degree. The " jumping " prevails in certain families.

A very similar disease prevails in parts of Russia and in Java, where it is known by the names of myriachit and latah, the chief feature of which is mimicry by the patient of everything he sees or hears.

(d) **Chronic Chorea** (*Huntington's Chorea*).—An affection characterized by irregular movements, disturbance of speech, and gradual dementia. It is frequently hereditary. The disease has no connection with Sydenham's chorea, and it is unfortunate that the term was applied to it. It was described by Huntington, of Pomeroy, Ohio, at the time a practitioner on Long Island, and he gave in three brief paragraphs the salient points in connection with the disease—namely, the hereditary nature, the association with psychical troubles, and the late onset—between the thirtieth and fortieth years. The disease seems common in this country, and many cases have been reported by Clarence King, Sinkler, and others. I have seen it in two Maryland families within the past few years. Under the term chronic chorea may be grouped the hereditary form and the cases which come on without family disposition, either at middle life or, more commonly, in the aged—senile chorea. It is doubtful whether the cases in children with chronic choreiform movements, often with mental weakness and spastic condition of the legs, should go into this category.

The hereditary character of the disease is very striking; it has been traced through four or five generations. Huntington's father and grandfather, also physicians, had treated the disease in the family which he described. Osborn, of East Hampton, L. I., writes (Jan. 28th, 1898) that the disease still continues to recur in certain families described by Huntington, as it has done, so it is said, for fully two centuries. An identical affection occurs without any hereditary disposition. The age of onset is late, rarely before the thirtieth or the thirty-fifth year.

The symptoms are very characteristic. The irregular movements are usually first seen in the hands, and the patient has slight difficulty in performing delicate manipulations or in writing. When well established the movements are disorderly, irregular, incoördinate rather than choreic, and have not the sharp, brusque motion of Sydenham's chorea. In the face there are slow, involuntary grimaces. In a well-developed case the gait is irregular, swaying, and somewhat like that of a drunken man. The speech is slow and difficult, the syllables are badly pronounced and indistinct, but not definitely staccato. The mental impairment leads finally to dementia.

Very few post mortems have been made. No characteristic lesions have been found. Atrophy of the convolutions, chronic meningo-encephalitis, and vascular changes have usually been present, the conditions which one would expect to find in chronic dementia. The recent study of two cases by Facklan (Arch. f. Psychiatrie, 30) confirms the view expressed in former editions that the disease is a chronic meningo-encephalitis with atrophy of the convolutions. The cord and peripheral nerves he found perfectly healthy. The affection is evidently a neuro-degenerative disorder, and has no connection with the simple chorea of childhood.

(*e*) **Rhythmic or Hysterical Chorea.**—This is readily recognized by the rhythmical character of the movements. It may affect the muscles of the abdomen, producing the salaam convulsion, or involve the sterno-mastoid, producing a rhythmical movement of the head, or the psoas, or any group of muscles. In its orderly rhythm it resembles the canine chorea.

V. INFANTILE CONVULSIONS (*Eclampsia*).

Convulsive seizures similar to those of epilepsy are not infrequent in children and in adults. The fit may indeed be identical with epilepsy, from which the condition differs in that when the cause is removed there is no tendency for the fits to recur. Occasionally, however, the convulsions in children continue and develop into true epilepsy.

Etiology.—A convulsion in a child may be due to many causes, all of which lead to an unstable condition of the nerve-centres, permitting of sudden, excessive, and temporary nervous discharges. The following are the most important of them:

(1) Debility, resulting usually from gastro-intestinal disturbance. Convulsions frequently supervene toward the close of an attack of entero-colitis and recur, sometimes proving fatal. Morris J. Lewis has shown that the death-rate in children from eclampsia rises steadily with that of gastro-intestinal disorders.

(2) Peripheral irritation. Dentition alone is rarely a cause of convulsions, but is often one of several factors in a feeble, unhealthy infant. The greatest mortality from convulsions is during the first six months, before the teeth have really cut through the gums. Other irritative causes are the overloading of the stomach with indigestible food. It has been suggested that some of these cases are toxic, owing to the absorption of poisonous ptomaines. Worms, to which convulsions are so frequently attributed, probably have little influence. Among other sources possible are phimosis and otitis.

(3) Rickets. The observation of Sir William Jenner upon the association of rickets and convulsions has been amply confirmed. The spasms may be laryngeal, the so-called child-crowing, which, though convulsive in nature, can scarcely be reckoned under eclampsia. The influence of this condition is more apparent in Europe than in this country, although rickets is a common disease, particularly among the colored people. Spasms, local or general, in rickets are probably associated with the condition of debility and malnutrition and with cranio-tabes.

(4) Fever. In young children the onset of the infectious diseases is frequently with convulsions, which often take the place of a chill in the adult.

It is not known upon what they depend. Scarlet fever, measles, and pneumonia are most often preceded by convulsions.

(5) Congestion of the brain. That extreme engorgement of the blood-vessels may produce convulsions is shown by their occasional occurrence in severe whooping-cough, but their rarity in this disease really indicates how small a part mechanical congestion plays in the production of fits.

(6) Severe convulsions usher in or accompany many of the serious diseases of the nervous system in children. In more than 50 per cent of the cases of infantile hemiplegia the affection follows severe convulsions. They less frequently precede a spinal paralysis. They occur with meningitis, tuberculous or simple, and with tumors and other lesions of the brain.

And, lastly, convulsions may occur immediately after birth and persist for weeks or months. In such instances there has probably been meningeal hæmorrhage or serious injury to the cortex.

The most important question is the relation of convulsions in children to true epilepsy. In Gowers' figures of 1,450 cases of epilepsy, the attacks began in 180 during the first three years of life. Of 460 cases of epilepsy in children which I have analyzed, in 187 the fits began within the first three years. Of the total list the greatest number, 74, was in the first year. In nearly all these instances there was no interruption in the convulsions. That convulsions in early infancy are necessarily followed by epilepsy in after life is certainly a mistake.

Symptoms.—The attack may come on suddenly without any warning; more commonly it is preceded by a stage of restlessness, accompanied by twitching and perhaps grinding of the teeth. It is rarely so complete in its stages as true epilepsy. The spasm begins usually in the hands, most commonly in the right hand. The eyes are fixed and staring or are rolled up. The body becomes stiff and breathing is suspended for a moment or two by tonic spasm of the respiratory muscles, in consequence of which the face becomes congested. Clonic convulsions follow, the eyes are rolled about, the hands and arms twitch, or are flexed and extended in rhythmical movements, the face is contorted, and the head is retracted. The attack gradually subsides and the child sleeps or passes into a state of stupor. Following indigestion the attack may be single, but in rickets and intestinal disorders it is apt to be repeated. Sometimes the attacks follow each other with great rapidity, so that the child never rouses but dies in a deep coma. If the convulsion has been limited chiefly to one side there may be slight paresis after recovery, or in instances in which the convulsions usher in infantile hemiplegia, when the child arouses, one side is completely paralyzed. During the fit the temperature is often raised. Death rarely occurs from the convulsion itself, except in debilitated children or when the attacks recur with great frequency. In the so-called hydrocephaloid state in connection with protracted diarrhœa convulsions may close the scene.

Diagnosis.—Coming on when the subject is in full health, the attack is probably due either to an overloaded stomach, to some peripheral irritation, or occasionally to trauma. Setting in with high fever and vomiting, it may indicate the onset of an exanthem, or occasionally be the primary symptom of encephalitis, or whatever the condition is which causes infantile hemiplegia. When the attack is associated with debility and with rickets the diagnosis is easily made. The carpopedal spasms and pseudo-paralytic rigidity which are often associated with rickets, laryngismus stridulus, and the hydrocephaloid state are usually confined to the hands and arms and are intermittent and usually tonic. The convulsions associated with tumor or which follow infantile hemiplegia are usually at first Jacksonian in character. After the second year convulsive seizures which come on irregularly without apparent cause and recur while the child is apparently in good health are likely to prove true epilepsy.

Prognosis.—Convulsions play an important part in infantile mortality. In Morris J. Lewis's table of deaths in children under ten, 8.5 per cent were ascribed to convulsions. West states that 22.35 per cent of deaths under one year are caused by convulsions, but this is too high an estimate for this country. In chronic diarrhœa convulsions are usually of ill omen. Those ushering in fevers are rarely serious, and the same may be said of the fits associated with indigestion and peripheral irritation.

Treatment.—Every source of irritation should be removed. If associated with indigestible food, a prompt emetic should be given, followed by an enema. The teeth should be examined, and if the gum is swollen, hot, and tense, it may be lanced; but never if it looks normal. When seen at first, if the paroxysm is severe, no time should be lost by giving a hot bath, but chloroform should be given at once, and repeated if necessary. A child is so readily put under chloroform and with such a small quantity that this precedure is quite harmless and saves much valuable time. The practice is almost universal of putting the child into a warm bath, and if there is fever the head may be douched with cold water. The temperature of the bath should not be above 95° or 96°. The very hot bath is not suitable, particularly if the fits are due to indigestion. After the attack an ice-cap may be placed upon the head. If there is much irritability, particularly in rickets and in severe diarrhœa, small doses of opium will be found efficacious. When the convulsions recur after the child comes from under the influence of chloroform it is best to place it rapidly under the influence of opium, which may be given as morphia hypodermically, in doses of from one twenty-fifth to one thirtieth of a grain for a child of one year. Other remedies recommended are chloral by enema, in 5-grain doses, and nitrite of amyl. After the attack has passed the bromides are useful, of which 5 to 8 grains may be given in a day to a child a year old. Recurring convulsions, particularly if they come on without special cause, should receive the most thorough and careful treatment with bromides. When associated with rickets the treatment should be directed to improving the general condition.

VI. EPILEPSY.

Definition.—An affection of the nervous system characterized by attacks of unconsciousness, with or without convulsions.

The transient loss of consciousness without convulsive seizures is known as *petit mal;* the loss of consciousness with general convulsive seizures is known as *grand mal.* Localized convulsions, occurring usually without loss of consciousness, are known as epileptiform, or more frequently as Jacksonian or cortical epilepsy.

Etiology.—*Age.*—In a large proportion of all cases the disease begins before puberty. Of the 1,450 cases observed by Gowers, in 422 the disease began before the tenth year, and three fourths of the cases began before the twentieth year. Of 460 cases of epilepsy in children which I have analyzed the age of onset in 427 was as follows: First year, 74; second year, 62; third year, 51; fourth year, 24; fifth year, 17; sixth year, 18; seventh year, 19; eighth year, 23; ninth year, 17; tenth year, 27; eleventh year, 17; twelfth year, 18; thirteenth year, 15; fourteenth year, 21; fifteenth year, 34. Arranged in hemidecades the figures are as follows: From the first to the fifth year, 229; from the fifth to the tenth year, 104; from the tenth to the fifteenth year, 95. These figures illustrate in a striking manner the early onset of the disease in a large proportion of the cases. It is well always to be suspicious of epilepsy developing in the adult, for in a majority of such cases the convulsions are due to a local lesion.

Sex.—No special influence appears to be discoverable in this relation, certainly not in children. Of 433 cases in my tables, 232 were males and 203 were females, showing a slight predominance of the male sex. After puberty unquestionably, if a large number of cases are taken, the males are in excess. The figures of Sieveking and Reynolds show that the disease is rather more prevalent in females than in males.

Heredity.—Much stress has been laid upon this by many authors as an important predisposing cause, and the statistics collected give from 9 to over 40 per cent. Gowers gives 35 per cent for his cases, which have special value apart from other statistics embracing large numbers of epileptics in that they were collected by him in his own practice. In our figures it appears to play a minor *rôle.* In the Infirmary list there were only 31 cases in which there was a history of marked neurotic taint, and only 3 in which the mother herself had been epileptic. In the Elwyn cases, as might be expected, the percentage is larger. Of the 126 there was in 32 a family history of nervous derangement of some sort, either paralysis, epilepsy, marked hysteria, or insanity. It is interesting to note that in this group, in which the question of heredity is carefully looked into, there were only two in which the mother had had epilepsy, and not one in which the father had been affected. Indeed, I was not a little surprised to find in the list of my cases that hereditary influences played so small a part. I have heard this opinion expressed by certain French physicians, notably Marie, who in writing also upon the question takes strong grounds against heredity as an important factor in epilepsy.

While, then, it may be said that direct inheritance is comparatively uncommon, yet the children of neurotic families in which neuralgia, insanity, and hysteria prevail are more liable to fall victims to the disease.

Chronic alcoholism in the parents is regarded by many as a potent predisposing factor in the production of epilepsy. Echeverria has analyzed 572 cases bearing upon this point and divided them into three classes, of which 257 cases could be traced directly to alcohol as a cause; 126 cases in which there were associated conditions, such as syphilis and traumatism; 189 cases in which the alcoholism was probably the result of the epilepsy. Figures equally strong are given by Martin, who found in 150 insane epileptics 83 with a marked history of parental intemperance. Of the 126 Elwyn cases, in which the family history on this point was carefully investigated, a definite statement was found in only 4 of the cases.

Syphilis.—This in the parents is probably less a predisposing than an actual cause of epilepsy, which is the direct outcome of local cerebral manifestations. There is no reason for recognizing a special form of syphilitic epilepsy. On the other hand, convulsive seizures due to acquired syphilitic disease of the brain are very common.

Alcohol.—Severe epileptic convulsions may occur in steady drinkers.

Of exciting causes fright is believed to be important, but is less so, I think, than is usually stated. Trauma is present in a certain number of instances. An important group depends upon a local disease of the brain existing from childhood, as seen in the post-hemiplegic epilepsy. Occasionally cases follow the infectious fevers. Masturbation has been stated to be a special cause, but its influence is probably overrated. A large group of convulsive seizures allied to epilepsy are due to some toxic agent, as in lead poisoning and in uræmia. Great stress was laid upon reflex causes, such as dentition and worms, the irritation of a cicatrix, some local affection, such as adherent prepuce, or a foreign body in the ear or the nose. In many of these cases the fits cease after the removal of the cause, so that there can be no question of the association between the two. In others the attacks persist. Genuine cases of reflex epilepsy are, I believe, rare. A remarkable instance of it occurred at the Philadelphia Infirmary for Diseases of the Nervous System in the case of a man with a testis in the inguinal canal, pressure upon which would cause a typical fit. Removal of the organ was followed by cure.

Epilepsy has been thought to be associated with disturbance of the heart's action, and some have spoken of a special cardiac epilepsy, particularly in cases in which there is palpitation or slowing of the action prior to the onset. Epileptic seizures may occur during the passage of a gallstone or occasionally during the removal of pleuritic fluid. Indigestion and gastric troubles are extremely common in epilepsy, and in many instances the eating of indigestible articles seems to precipitate an attack.

An attempt to associate genuine epilepsy with eye-strain has signally failed.

Symptoms.—(1) **Grand Mal.**—Preceding the fits there is usually a localized sensation, known as an *aura,* in some part of the body. This may be somatic, in which the feeling comes from some particular region in the periphery, as from the finger or hand, or is a sensation felt in the stomach or about the heart. The peripheral sensations preceding the fit are of great value, particularly those in which the aura always occurs in a definite region, as in one finger or toe. It is the equivalent of the signal symptom in a fit from a brain tumor. The varieties of these sensations are numerous. The epigastric sensations are most common. In these the patient complains of an uneasy sensation in the epigastrium or distress in the intestines, or the sensation may not be unlike that of heart-burn and may be associated with palpitation. These groups are sometimes known as pneumogastric auræ or warnings.

Of psychical auræ one of the most common, as described by Hughlings Jackson, is the vague, dreamy state, a sensation of strangeness or sometimes of terror. The auræ may be associated with special senses; of these the most common are the visual, consisting of flashes of light or sensations of color; less commonly, distinct objects are seen. The auditory auræ consist of noises in the ear, odd sounds, musical tones, or occasionally voices. Olfactory and gustatory auræ, unpleasant tastes and odors, are rare.

Occasionally the fit may be preceded not by an aura, but by certain movements; the patient may turn round rapidly or run with great speed for a few minutes, the so-called epilepsia procursiva. In one of the Elwyn cases the lad stood on his toes and twirled with extraordinary rapidity, so that his features were scarcely recognizable. At the onset of the attack the patient may give a loud scream or yell, the so-called epileptic cry. The patient drops as if shot, making no effort to guard the fall. In consequence of this epileptics frequently injure themselves, cutting the face or head or burning themselves. In the attack, as described by Hippocrates, "the patient loses his speech and chokes, and foam issues from the mouth, the teeth are fixed, the hands are contracted, the eyes distorted, he becomes insensible, and in some cases the bowels are affected. And these symptoms occur sometimes on the left side, sometimes on the right, and sometimes on both." The fit may be described in three stages:

(a) *Tonic Spasm.*—The head is drawn back or to the right, and the jaws are fixed. The hands are clinched and the legs extended. This tonic contraction affects the muscles of the chest, so that respiration is impeded and the initial pallor of the face changes to a dusky or livid hue. The muscles of the two sides are unequally affected, so that the head and neck are rotated or the spine is twisted. The arms are usually flexed at the elbows, the hand at the wrist, and the fingers are tightly clinched in the palm. This stage lasts only a few seconds, and then the

(b) *Clonic stage* begins. The muscular contractions become intermittent; at first tremulous or vibratory, they gradually become more rapid and the limbs are jerked and tossed about violently. The muscles of the face are in constant clonic spasm, the eyes roll, the eyelids are opened and closed convulsively. The movements of the muscles of the jaw are very forcible and strong, and it is at this time that the tongue is apt to be caught between the teeth and lacerated. The cyanosis, marked at the end of the tonic stage, gradually lessens. A frothy saliva, which may be blood-stained, escapes from the mouth. The fæces and urine may be discharged involuntarily. The duration of this stage is variable. It rarely lasts more than one or two minutes. The contractions become less violent and the patient gradually sinks into the condition of

(c) *Coma.* The breathing is noisy or even stertorous, the face congested, but no longer intensely cyanotic. The limbs are relaxed and the unconsciousness is profound. After a variable time the patient can be aroused, but if left alone he sleeps for some hours and then awakes, complaining only of slight headache or mental confusion.

In some cases one attack follows the other with great rapidity and consciousness is not regained. This is termed the *status epilepticus,* an exceptional condition, in which the patient may die of exhaustion, consequent upon the repeated attacks. In it the temperature is usually elevated.

After the attack the reflexes are sometimes absent; more frequently they are increased and the ankle clonus can usually be obtained. The state of the urine is variable, particularly as regards the solids. The quantity is usually increased after the attack, and albumin is not infrequently present.

Post-epileptic symptoms are of great importance. The patient may be in a trance-like condition, in which he performs actions of which subsequently he has no recollection. More serious are the attacks of mania, in which the patient is often dangerous and sometimes homicidal. It is held by good authorities that an outbreak of mania may be substituted for the fit. And, lastly, the mental condition of an epileptic patient is often seriously impaired, and profound defects are common.

Paralysis, which rarely follows the epileptic fit, is usually hemiplegic and transient.

Slight disturbances of speech also may occur; in some instances forms of sensory aphasia.

The attacks may occur at night, and a person may be epileptic for years without knowing it. As Trousseau truly remarks, when a person tells us that in the night he has incontinence of urine and awakes in the morning with headache and mental confusion, and complains of difficulty in speech owing to the fact that he has bitten his tongue; if, also, there are on the skin of the face and neck purpuric spots, the probability is very strong indeed that he is subject to nocturnal epilepsy.

(2) **Petit Mal.**—This is epilepsy without the convulsions. The attack consists of transient unconsciousness, which may come on at any time, accompanied or unaccompanied by a feeling of faintness and vertigo. Suddenly, for example, at the dinner table, the subject stops talking and eating, the eyes become fixed, and the face slightly pale. Anything which may have been in the hand is usually dropped. In a moment or two consciousness is regained and the patient resumes conversation as if nothing had happened. In other instances there is slight incoherency or the patient performs some almost automatic action. He may begin to undress himself and on returning to consciousness find that he has partially disrobed. He may rub his beard or face, or may spit about in a careless way. In other attacks the patient may fall without convulsive seizures. A definite aura is rare. Though transient, unconsciousness and giddiness are the most constant manifestations of *petit mal;* there are many other equivalent manifestations, such as sudden jerkings in the limbs, sudden tremor, or a sudden visual sensation. Gowers mentions no less than seventeen different manifestations of *petit mal.* Occasionally there are cases in which the patient

has a sensation of losing his breath and may even get red in the face. I have seen such attacks also in children.

After the attack the patient may be dazed for a few seconds and perform certain automatic actions, which may seem to be volitional. As mentioned, undressing is a common action, but all sorts of odd actions may be performed, some of which are awkward or even serious. One of my patients after an attack was in the habit of tearing anything he could lay hands on, particularly books. Violent actions have been committed and assaults made, frequently giving rise to questions which come before the courts. This condition has been termed masked epilepsy, or *epilepsia larvata*.

In a majority of the cases of *petit mal* convulsions finally occur, at first slight, but ultimately the *grand mal* becomes well developed, and the attacks may then alternate.

(3) **Jacksonian Epilepsy.**—This is also known as cortical, symptomatic, or partial epilepsy. It is distinguished from the ordinary epilepsy by the important fact that consciousness is retained or is lost late. The attacks are usually the result of irritative lesions in the motor zone, though there are probably also sensory equivalents of this motor form. In a typical attack the spasm begins in a limited muscle group of the face, arm, or leg. The zygomatic muscles, for instance, or the thumb may twitch, or the toes may first be moved. Prior to the twitching the patient may feel a sensation of numbness or tingling in the part affected. The spasm extends and may involve the muscles of one limb only or of the face. The patient is conscious throughout and watches, often with interest, the march of the spasm.

The onset may be slow, and there may be time, as in a case which I have reported, for the patient to place a pillow on the floor, so as to be as comfortable as possible during the attack. The spasms may be localized for years, but there is a great risk that the partial epilepsy may become general. The condition is due, as a rule, to an irritative lesion in the motor zone. Thus of 107 cases analyzed by Roland, there were 48 of tumor, 21 instances of inflammatory softening, 14 instances of acute and chronic meningitis, and 8 cases of trauma. The remaining instances were due to hæmorrhage or abscess, or were associated with sclerosis cerebri. Two other conditions may be mentioned, which may cause typical Jacksonian epilepsy—namely, uræmia and progressive paralysis of the insane. A considerable number of the cases of Jacksonian epilepsy are found in children following hemiplegia, the so-called post-hemiplegic epilepsy. The convulsions usually begin on the affected side, either in the arm or leg, and the fit may be unilateral and without loss of consciousness. Ultimately they become more severe and general.

Diagnosis.—In major epilepsy the suddenness of the attack, the abrupt loss of consciousness, the order of the tonic and clonic spasm, and the relaxation of the sphincters at the height of the attack are distinctive features. The convulsive seizures due to uræmia are epileptic in character and usually readily recognized by the existence of greatly increased tension and the condition of the urine. Practically in young adults hysteria causes the greatest difficulty, and may closely simulate true epilepsy. The following table from Gowers' work draws clearly the chief differences between them:

	EPILEPTIC.	HYSTEROID.
Apparent cause........	none.	emotion.
Warning	any, but especially unilateral or epigastric auræ.	palpitation, malaise, choking, bilateral foot aura.
Onset................	always sudden.	often gradual.
Scream..............	at onset.	during course.
Convulsion...........	rigidity followed by "jerking," rarely rigidity alone.	rigidity or "struggling," throwing about of limbs or head, arching of back.
Biting...............	tongue.	lips, hands, or other people and things.
Micturition...........	frequent.	never.
Defecation...........	occasional.	never.
Talking..............	never.	frequent.
Duration.............	a few minutes.	more than ten minutes, often much longer.
Restraint necessary...	to prevent accident.	to control violence.
Termination	spontaneous.	spontaneous or induced (water, etc.).

Recurring epileptic seizures in a person over thirty who has not had previous attacks is always suggestive of organic disease. According to H. C. Wood, whose opinion is supported by that of Fournier, in 9 cases out of 10 the condition is due to syphilis.

Petit mal must be distinguished from attacks of syncope, and the vertigo of Ménière's disease, of a cardiac lesion, and of indigestion. In these cases there is no actual loss of consciousness, which forms a characteristic though not an invariable feature of *petit mal*.

Jacksonian epilepsy has features so distinctive and peculiar that it is at once recognized. It is by no means easy, however, always to determine upon what the spasm depends. Irritation in the motor centres may be due to a great variety of causes, among which tumors and localized meningo-encephalitis are the most frequent; but it must not be forgotten that in uræmia localized epilepsy may occur. The most typical Jacksonian spasms also are not infrequent in general paresis of the insane.

Prognosis.—This may be given to-day in the words of Hippocrates: "The prognosis in epilepsy is unfavorable when the disease is congenital, and when it endures to manhood, and when it occurs in a grown person without any previous cause. . . . The cure may be attempted in young persons, but not in old."

Death during the fit rarely occurs, but it may happen if the patient falls into the water or if the fit comes on while he is eating. Occasionally the fits seem to stop spontaneously. This is particularly the case in the epilepsy in children which has followed the convulsions of teething or of the fevers. Frequency of the attacks and marked mental disturbance are unfavorable indications. Hereditary predisposition is apparently of no moment in the prognosis. The outlook is better in males than in females. The post-hemiplegic epilepsy is rarely arrested. Of the cases coming on in adults, those due to syphilis and to local affections of the brain allow a more favorable prognosis.

Treatment.—*General.*—In the case of children the parents should be made to understand from the outset that epilepsy in the great majority of cases is an incurable affection, so that the disease may interfere as little as possible with the education of the child. The subjects need firm but kind treatment. Indulgence and yielding to caprices and whims are followed by weakening of the moral control, which is so necessary in these cases. The disease does not incapacitate a person for all occupation. It is much better for epileptics to have some definite pursuit. There are many instances in which they have been persons of extraordinary mental and bodily vigor; as, for example, Julius Cæsar and Napoleon. One of the most distressing features in epilepsy is the gradual mental impairment which follows in a certain number of cases. If such patients become extremely irritable or show signs of violence they should be placed under supervision in an asylum. Marriage should be forbidden to epileptics. During the attack a cork or bit of rubber should be placed between the teeth and the clothes should be loosened. The patient should be in the recumbent posture. As the attack usually passes off with rapidity, no special treatment is necessary, but in cases in which the convulsion is prolonged a few whiffs of chloroform or nitrite of amyl or a hypodermic of a quarter of a grain of morphia may be given.

Dietetic.—The old authors laid great stress upon regimen in epilepsy. The important point is to give the patient a light diet at fixed hours, and on no account to permit overloading of the stomach. Meat should not be given more than once a day. There are cases in which animal food seems injurious. A strict vegetable diet has been warmly recommended. The patient should not go to sleep until the completion of gastric digestion.

Medicinal.—The bromides are the only remedies which have a special influence upon the disease. Either the sodium or potassium salt may be given. Sodium bromide is probably less irritating and is better borne for a long period. It may be given in milk, in which it is scarcely tasted. In all instances the dilution should be considerable. In adults it is well taken in soda water or in some mineral water. The dose for an adult should be from half a drachm to a drachm and a half daily. As Seguin recommends, it is often best to give but a single dose daily, about four to six hours before the attacks are most likely to occur. For instance, in the case of nocturnal epilepsy a drachm should be given an hour or two after the evening meal. If the attack occurs early in the morning, the patient should take a full dose when he awakes. When given three times a day it is best given after meals. Each case should be carefully studied to determine how much bromide should be used. The individual susceptibility varies and some patients require more than others. Fortunately, children take the drug well and stand proportionately larger doses than adults. Saturation is indicated by certain unpleasant effects, particularly drowsiness, mental torpor, and gastric and cardiac distress. Loss of palate reflex is one of the earliest indications that the system is under the influence of the bromides, and is a condition which should be attained. A very unpleasant feature is the development of acne, which, however, is no indication of bromism. Seguin states that the tendency to this is much diminished by giving the drug largely diluted in alkaline waters and administering from time to time full doses of arsenic. To be effectual the treatment should be continued for a prolonged period and the cases should be incessantly watched in order to prevent bromism. The medicine should be continued for at least two years after the cessation of the fits; indeed, Seguin recommends that the reduction of the bromides should not be begun until the patient has been three years without any manifestations. Written directions should be given to the mother or to the friends of the patient, and he should not himself be held responsible for the administration of the medicine. A book should be provided in which the daily number of attacks and the amount of medicine taken should be noted. The addition of belladonna to the bromide is warmly recommended by Black, of Glasgow. In very obstinate cases Flechsig uses opium, 5 or 6 grains, in three doses daily; then at the end of six weeks opium is stopped and the bromides in large amounts, 75 to 100 grains daily, are used for two months.

Among other remedies which have been recommended as controlling epilepsy are chloral, cannabis indica, zinc, nitroglycerin, and borax. Nitroglycerin is sometimes advantageous in *petit mal*, but is not of much service in the major form. To be beneficial it must be given in full doses, from 2 to 5 minims of the 1-per-cent solution, and increased until the physiological effects are produced. Counter-irritation is rarely advisable. When the aura is very definite and constant in its onset, as from the hand or from the toe, a blister about the part or a ligature tightly applied may stop the oncoming fit. In children, care should be taken that there is no source of peripheral irritation. In boys, adherent prepuce may occasionally be the cause. The irritation of teething, the presence of worms, and foreign bodies in the ears or nose have been associated with epileptic seizures.

The subjects of a chronic and, in most cases, a hopelessly incurable disease, epileptic patients form no small portion of the unfortunate victims of charlatans and quacks, who prescribe to-day, as in the time of the father of medicine, " purifications and spells and other illiberal practices of like kind."

Surgical.—In Jacksonian epilepsy the propriety of surgical interference is universally granted. It is questionable, however, whether in the epilepsy following hemiplegia, considering the anatomical condition, it is likely to be of any benefit. In idiopathic epilepsy, when the fit starts in a certain region—the thumb, for instance—and the signal symptom is invariable, the centre controlling this part may be removed. This procedure has been practised by Macewen, Horsley, Keen, and others, but time alone can determine its value. The traumatic epilepsy, in which the fit follows fracture, is much more hopeful.

The operation, *per se*, appears in some cases to have a curative effect. Thus of 50 cases of trephining for epilepsy in which nothing abnormal was found to account for the symptoms, 25 were reported as cured and 18 as improved. The operations have not been always on the skull, and White has collected an interesting series in which various surgical procedures have been resorted to, often with curative effect, such as ligation of the carotid artery, castration, tracheotomy, excision of the superior cervical ganglia, incision of the scalp, circumcision, etc.

VII. MIGRAINE (*Hemicrania; Sick Headache*).

Definition.—A paroxysmal affection characterized by severe headache, usually unilateral, and often associated with disorders of vision.

Etiology.—The disease is frequently hereditary and has occurred through several generations. Women and the members of neurotic families are most frequently attacked. It is an affection from which many distinguished men have suffered and have left on record an account of the disease, notably the astronomer Airy. Edward Liveing's work is the standard authority upon which most of the subsequent articles have been based. A gouty or rheumatic taint is present in many instances. Sinkler has called special attention to the frequency of reflex causes. Migraine has long been known to be associated with uterine and menstrual disorders. Nutritive disturbances are common, and attempts have been made by Haig and others to associate the attacks with disturbed uric-acid output. Certainly the amount of uric acid excreted just prior to and during an attack is reduced. Others regard the disease as a toxæmia from disordered intestinal digestion. Many of the headaches from eye-strain are of the hemicranial type. Brunton refers to caries of the teeth as a cause of these headaches, even when not associated with toothache. Cases have been described in connection with adenoid growths in the pharynx, and particularly with abnormal conditions of the nose. Many of the attacks of severe headaches in children are of this nature, and the eyes and nostrils should be examined with great care. Sinkler refers to a case in a child of two years, and Gowers states that a third of all the cases begin between the fifth and tenth years of age. The direct influences inducing the attack are very varied. Powerful emotions of all sorts are the most potent. Mental or bodily fatigue, digestive disturbances, or the eating of some particular article of food may be followed by the headache. The paroxysmal character is one of the most striking features, and the attacks may recur on the same day every week, every fortnight, or every month. Headaches of the migraine type may recur for years in connection with chronic Bright's disease.

Symptoms.—Premonitory signs are present in many cases, and the patient can tell when an attack is coming on. Remarkable prodromata have been described, particularly in connection with vision. Apparitions may appear—visions of animals, such as mice, dogs, etc. Transient hemianopia or scotoma may be present. In other instances there is spasmodic action of the pupil on the affected side, which dilates and contracts alternately, the condition known as *hippus*. Frequently the disturbance of vision is only a blurring, or there are balls of light, or zigzag lines, or the so-called fortification spectra (teichopsia), which may be illuminated with gorgeous colors. Disturbances of the other senses are rare. Numbness of the tongue and face and occasionally of the hand may occur with tingling.

More rarely there are cramps or spasms in the muscles of the affected side. Transient aphasia has also been noted. Some patients show marked psychical disturbance, either excitement or, more commonly, mental confusion or great depression. Dizziness occurs in some cases. The headache follows a short time after the prodromal symptoms have appeared. It is cumulative and expansile in character, beginning as a localized small spot, which is generally constant either on the temple or forehead or in the eyeball. It is usually described as of a penetrating, sharp, boring character. At first unilateral, it gradually spreads and involves the side of the head, sometimes the neck, and the pains may pass into the arm. In other cases both sides are affected. Nausea and vomiting are common symptoms. If the attack comes on when the stomach is full, vomiting usually gives relief. Vasomotor symptoms may be present. The face, for instance, may be pale, and there may be a marked difference between the two sides. Subsequently the face and ear on the affected side may become a burning red from the vaso-dilator influences. The pulse may be slow. The temporal artery on the affected side may be firm and hard, and in a condition of arterio-sclerosis— a fact which has been confirmed anatomically by Thoma. Few affections are more prostrating than migraine, and during the paroxysm the patient may scarcely be able to raise the head from the pillow. The slightest noise or light aggravates the condition.

The duration of the entire attack is variable. The severer forms usually incapacitate the person for at least three days. In other instances the entire attack is over in a day. The disease recurs for years, and in cases with a marked hereditary tendency may persist throughout life. In women the attacks often cease after the climateric, and in men after the age of fifty. Two of the greatest sufferers I have known, who had recurring attacks every few weeks from early boyhood, now have complete freedom.

The nature of the disease is unknown. Liveing's view, that it is a nerve storm or form of periodic discharge from certain sensory centres and is related to epilepsy, has found much favor. According to this view, it is the sensory equivalent of a true epileptic attack. Mollendorf, Latham, and others regard it as a vaso-motor neurosis, and hold that the early symptoms are due to vaso-constrictor and the later symptoms to vaso-dilator influences. The fact of the development of arterio-sclerosis in the arteries of the affected side is a point of interest bearing upon this view.

Treatment.—The patient is fully aware of the causes which precipitate an attack. Avoidance of excitement, regularity in the meals, and moderation in diet are important rules. I have known cases greatly benefitted by a strict vegetable diet. The treatment should be directed toward the removal of the conditions upon which the attacks depend. In children much may be done by watchfulness and care on the part of the mother in regulating the bowels and watching the diet of the child. Errors of refraction should be adjusted. On no account should such children be allowed to compete in school for prizes. A prolonged course of bromides sometimes proves successful. If anæmia is present, iron and arsenic should be given. When the arterial tension is increased a course of nitroglycerin may be tried. Not too much, however, should be expected of the preventive treatment of migraine. It must be confessed that in a very large proportion of the cases the headaches recur in spite of all we can do. Herter advises, so soon as the patient has any intimation of the attack, to wash out the stomach with water at 105°, and to give a brisk saline cathartic. During the paroxysm the patient should be kept in bed and absolutely quiet. If the patient feels faint and nauseated, a small cup of hot, strong coffee or 20 drops of chloroform give relief. Cannabis indica is probably the most satisfactory remedy. Seguin recommends a prolonged course of the drug. Antipyrin, antifebrin, and phenacetin have been much used of late. When given early, at the very outset of the paroxysm, they are sometimes effective. The doses which have been recommended of antifebrin and antipyrin are often dangerous, and I have seen in a case of migraine unpleasant collapse symptoms follow a 25-grain dose of antipyrin which the patient had taken on her own responsibility. Smaller, repeated doses are more satisfactory. Of other remedies, caffeine, in 5-grain doses of the citrate, nux vomica, and ergot have been recommended. Electricity does not appear to be of much service.

VIII. NEURALGIA.

Definition.—A painful affection of the nerves, due either to functional disturbance of their central or peripheral extremities or to neuritis in their course.

Etiology.—Members of neuropathic families are most subject to the disease. It affects women more than men. Children are rarely attacked. Of all causes, debility is the most frequent. It is often the first indication of an enfeebled nervous system. The various forms of anæmia are frequently associated with neuralgia. It may be a prominent feature at the onset of certain acute diseases, particularly typhoid fever. Malaria is believed to be a potent cause, but it has not been shown that neuralgia is more frequent in malarial districts, and the error has probably arisen from regarding periodicity as a special manifestation of paludism. It occasionally occurs in malarial cachexia. Exposure to cold is a cause in very susceptible persons. Reflex irritation, particularly from carious teeth, may induce neuralgia of the fifth nerve. The disease occurs sometimes in rheumatism, gout, lead poisoning, and diabetes. Persistent neuralgia may be a feature of latent Bright's disease.

Symptoms.—Before the onset of the pain there may be uneasy sensations, sometimes tingling in the part which will be affected. The pain is localized to a certain group or division of nerves, usually affecting one side. The pain is not constant, but paroxysmal, and is described as stabbing, burning, or darting in character. The skin may be exquisitely tender in the affected region, particularly over certain points along the course of the nerve, the so-called tender points. Movements, as a rule, are painful. Trophic and vaso-motor changes may accompany the paroxysm; the skin may be cool, and subsequently hot and burning; occasionally local œdema or erythema occurs. More remarkable still are the changes in the hair, which may become blanched (canities), or even fall out. Fortunately, such alterations are rare. Twitchings of the muscles, or even spasms, may be present during the paroxysm. After lasting a variable time—from a few minutes to many hours—the attack subsides. Recurrence may be at definite intervals—every day at the same hour, or at intervals of two, three, or even seven days. Occasionally the paroxysms develop only at the catamenia. This periodicity is quite as marked in non-malarial as in malarial regions.

Clinical Varieties, depending on the Nerve Groups affected.—(1) *Trifacial Neuralgia; Tic Douloureux; Prosopalgia.*—All the branches are rarely involved together. The ophthalmic is most often affected, but in severe attacks the pains, though more intense in one division, radiate over the other branches. At the outset there may be hyperæsthesia of the skin and sensitiveness of the mucous membrane. Pressure is painful at the points of emergence of the nerve trunk, and where the nerves enter the muscles. Sometimes in addition, as Trousseau pointed out, there are pains at the occipital protuberance and in the upper cervical spines. When the ophthalmic division is affected the eye may weep and the conjunctivæ are injected and painful. In the upper maxillary division there is a tender point where the nerve leaves the infraorbital canal, and the pain is specially marked along the upper teeth. In the lower branches, which are more frequently involved, there are painful points along the auriculo-temporal nerve and the pain radiates in the region of the ear along the lower jaw and teeth. The movements of mastication and speaking may be painful. Salivation is not uncommon. Herpes may occur about the eye or the lips. In protracted cases there may be atrophy or induration of the skin. Some of the forms of facial neuralgia are of frightful intensity and the recurring attacks render the patient's life almost insupportable.

(2) *Cervico-occipital neuralgia* involves the posterior branches of the first four cervical nerves, particularly the inferior occipital, at the emergence of which there is a painful point about half-way between the mastoid process and the first cervical vertebra. It may be caused by cold, and these nerves are often affected in cervical caries.

(3) *Cervico-brachial neuralgia* involves the sensory nerves of the brachial plexus, particularly in the cubital division. When the circumflex nerve is involved the pain is in the deltoid. The pain is most commonly about the shoulder and down the course of the ulnar nerve. There is usually a marked tender point upon this nerve at the elbow. This form rarely follows cold, but more frequently results from rheumatic affections of the joints, and trauma.

(4) *Neuralgia of the phrenic nerve* is rare. It is sometimes found in pleurisy and in pericarditis. The pain is chiefly at the lower part of the thorax on a line with the insertion of the diaphragm, and here may be painful points on deep pressure. Full inspiration is painful, and there is great sensitiveness on coughing or in the performance of any movement by which the diaphragm is suddenly depressed.

(5) *Intercostal Neuralgia.*—Next to the *tic douloureux* this is the most important form. It is most frequent in women and very common in hysteria and anæmia. The pain in caries and aneurism is felt in the intercostal

nerves. They are also the seat of the intense pain in inflammation of the pleura. The pain is often constant and exaggerated by movements. Pleurodynia is supposed by some to be local intercostal neuralgia, confined to one spot, usually along the course or at the exit of the nerves. Herpes zoster or zona occurs with the most aggravated form of intercostal neuralgia. The pain usually precedes the eruption, which consists of a series of pearly vesicles, which take two or three days to develop and gradually disappear. The eruption may occur without much pain. The most distressing feature in the complaint is the persistence in the pain after the eruption has subsided. The eruption and the neuralgia are in reality manifestations of neuritis. Changes have been found in the nerves and in the ganglia of the dorsal roots. The pain of zona may persist indefinitely, and it has been known to be so intractable that in despair the person has committed suicide.

(6) *Lumbar Neuralgia.*—The affected nerves are the posterior fibres of the lumbar plexus, particularly the ilio-scrotal branch. The pain is in the region of the iliac crest, along the inguinal canal, in the spermatic cord, and in the scrotum or labium majus. The affection known as irritable testis, probably a neuralgia of this nerve, may be very severe and accompanied by syncopal sensations.

(7) *Coccydynia.*—This is regarded as a neuralgia of the coccygeal plexus. It is most common in women, and is aggravated by the sitting posture. It is very intractable, and may necessitate the removal of the coccyx, an operation, however, which is not always successful. Neuralgias of the nerves of the leg have already been considered.

(8) *Neuralgias of the Nerves of the Feet.*

Painful Heel.—Both in women and men there may be about the heel severe pains which interfere seriously with walking—the pododynia of S. D. Gross. There may be little or no swelling, no discoloration, and no affection of the joints.

Plantar Neuralgia.—This is often associated with a definite neuritis, such as follows typhoid fever, and has been seen in an aggravated form in caisson disease (Hughes). The pain may be limited to the tips of the toes or to the ball of the great toe. Numbness, tingling, and hyperæsthesia or sweating may occur with it. Following the cold-bath treatment in typhoid fever it is not uncommon for patients to complain of great sensitiveness in the toes.

Metatarsalgia.—Morton's (Thomas G.) " painful affection of the fourth metatarso-phalangeal articulation " is a peculiar and very trying disorder, seen most frequently in women, and usually in one foot. Morton regards it as due to a pinching of the metatarsal nerve. The disease rarely gets well without operation. The red, painful neuralgia—erythromelalgia—is described under the vaso-motor and trophic disturbances.

(9) *Visceral Neuralgias.*—The more important of these have already been referred to in connection with the cardiac and the gastric neuroses. They are most frequent in women, and are constant accompaniments of neurasthenia and hysteria. The pains are most common in the pelvic region, particularly about the ovaries. Nephralgia is of great interest, for,

as has already been mentioned, the symptoms may closely simulate those of stone.

Treatment.—Causes of reflex irritation should be carefully removed. The neuralgia, as a rule, recurs unless the general health improves; so that tonic and hygienic measures of all sorts should be employed. Often a change of air or surroundings will relieve a severe neuralgia. I have known obstinate cases to be cured by a prolonged residence in the mountains, with an out-of-door life and plenty of exercise. A strict vegetable diet will sometimes relieve the neuralgia or headache of a gouty person. Of general remedies, iron is often a specific in the cases associated with chlorosis and anæmia. Arsenic, too, is very beneficial in these forms, and should be given in ascending doses. The value of quinine has been much overrated. It probably has no more influence than any other bitter tonic, except in the rare instances in which the neuralgia is definitely associated with malarial poisoning. Strychnine, cod-liver oil, and phosphorus are also advantageous. Of remedies for the pain, the new analgesics should first be tried—antipyrin, antifebrin, and phenacetin—for they are sometimes of service. Morphia should be given with great caution, and only after other remedies have been tried in vain. On no consideration should the patient be allowed to use the hypodermic syringe. Gelsemium is highly recommended. Of nervine stimulants, valerian and ether, which often act well together, may be given. Alcohol is a valuable though dangerous remedy, and should not be ordered for women. In the trifacial neuralgia nitroglycerin in large doses may be tried. Aconitia in doses of from one two-hundredth to one one-hundred-and-fiftieth of a grain may be tried. In gouty and rheumatic subjects cannabis indica and cimicifuga are recommended with the lithium salts.

Of local applications, the thermo-cautery is invaluable, particularly in zona and the more chronic forms of neuralgia. Acupuncture may be used, or aquapuncture, the injection of distilled water beneath the skin. Chloroform liniment, camphor and chloral, menthol, the oleates of morphia, atropia, and belladonna used with lanolin may be tried. Freezing over the tender point with ether spray is sometimes successful. The continuous current may be used. The sponges should be warm, and the positive pole should be placed near the seat of the pain. The strength of the current should be such as to cause a slight tingling or burning, but not pain.

The surgical treatment of intractable neuralgia embraces nerve stretching and excision. The latter is the more satisfactory, but too often the pain returns.

IX. PROFESSIONAL SPASMS; OCCUPATION NEUROSES.

The continuous and excessive use of the muscles in performing a certain movement may be followed by an irregular, involuntary spasm or cramp, which may completely check the performance of the action. The condition is found most frequently in writers, hence the term writer's cramp or scrivener's palsy; but it is also common in piano and violin players and in telegraph operators. The spasms occur in many other persons, such as milkmaids, weavers, and cigarette-rollers.

The most common form is writer's cramp, which is much more frequent in men than in women. Of 75 cases of impaired writing power reported by Poore, all of the instances of undoubted writer's cramp were in men. Morris J. Lewis states that in this country, in the telegrapher's cramp, women, who are employed a great deal in telegraphy, are much less frequently affected (only 4 out of 43 cases). Persons of a nervous temperament are more liable to the disease. Occasionally it follows slight injury.

Gowers states that in a majority of the cases a faulty method of writing has been employed, using either the little finger or the wrist as the fixed point. Persons who write from the middle of the forearm or from the elbow are rarely affected.

No anatomical changes have been found. The most reasonable explanation of the disease is that it results from a deranged action of the nerve centres presiding over the muscular movements involved in the act of writing, a condition which has been termed irritable weakness. " The education of centres which may be widely separated from each other for the performance of any delicate movement is mainly accomplished by lessening the lines of resistance between them, so that the movement, which was at first produced by a considerable mental effort, is at last executed almost unconsciously. If, therefore, through prolonged excitation, this lessened resistance be carried too far, there is an increase and irregular discharge of nerve energy, which gives rise to spasm and disordered movement. According to this view, the muscular weakness is explained by an impairment of nutrition accompanying that of function, and the diminished faradic excitability by the nutritional disturbance descending the motor nerves " (Gay).

Symptoms.—These may be described under five heads (Lewis).

(a) *Cramp* or *Spasm*.—This is often an early symptom and most commonly affects the forefinger and thumb; or there may be a combined movement of flexion and adduction of the thumb, so that the pen may be twisted from the grasp and thrown to some distance. Weir Mitchell has described a lock-spasm, in which the fingers become so firmly contracted upon the pen that it cannot be removed.

(b) *Paresis* and *Paralysis*.—This may occur with the spasm or alone. The patient feels a sense of weakness and debility in the muscles of the hand and arm and holds the pen feebly. Yet in these circumstances the grasp of the hand may be strong and there may be no paralysis for ordinary acts.

(c) *Tremor*.—This is most commonly seen in the forefinger and may be a premonitory symptom of atrophy. It is not an important symptom, and is rarely sufficient to produce disability.

(d) *Pain*.—Abnormal sensations, particularly a tired feeling in the muscles, are very constantly present. Actual pain is rare, but there may be irregular shooting pains in the arm. Numbness or soreness may exist. If, as sometimes happens, a subacute neuritis develops, there may be pain over the nerves and numbness or tingling in the fingers.

(*e*) *Vaso-motor Disturbances.*—These may occur in severe cases. There may be hyperæsthesia. Occasionally the skin becomes glossy, or there is a condition of local asphyxia resembling chilblains. In attempting to write, the hand and arm may become flushed and hot and the veins increased in size. Early in the disease the electrical reactions are normal, but in advanced cases there may be diminution of faradic and sometimes increase in the galvanic irritability.

Diagnosis.—A well-marked case of writer's cramp or palsy could scarcely be mistaken for any other affection. Care must be taken to exclude the existence of any cerebro-spinal disease, such as progressive muscular atrophy or hemiplegia. The physician is sometimes consulted by nervous persons who fancy they are becoming subject to the disease and complain of stiffness or weakness without displaying any characteristic features.

Prognosis.—The course of the disease is usually chronic. If taken in time and if the hand is allowed perfect rest, the condition may improve rapidly, but too often there is a strong tendency to recurrence. The patient may learn to write with the left hand, but this also may after a time be attacked.

Treatment.—Various prophylactic measures have been advised. As mentioned, it is important that a proper method of writing be adopted. Gowers suggests that if all persons wrote from the shoulder writer's cramp would practically not occur. Various devices have been invented for relieving the fatigue, but none of them are very satisfactory. The use of the type-writer has diminished very much the frequency of scrivener's palsy. Rest is essential. No measures are of value without this. Massage and manipulation, when combined with systematic gymnastics, give the best results. Poore recommends the galvanic current applied to the muscles, which are at the same time rhythmically exercised. In very obstinate cases the condition remains incurable. I saw a few years ago a distinguished gynæcologist who had had writer's cramp twenty years before, and who had all sorts of treatment, including the Wolff's method, without any avail. He still has it in aggravated form, but he can do all the finer manipulations of operative work without any difficulty.

The nutrition of the patients is apt to be much impaired, and cod-liver oil, strychnia, and other tonics will be found advantageous. Local applications are of little benefit. Tenotomy and nerve-stretching have been abandoned.

X. TETANY.

Definition.—An affection characterized by peculiar bilateral tonic spasms, either paroxysmal or continued, of the extremities.

Etiology.—The disease occurs under very different conditions, of which the following may be recognized:

(*a*) Epidemic tetany, also known as rheumatic tetany. In certain parts of the continent of Europe the disease has prevailed widely, particularly in the winter season. Von Jaksch, who has described an epidemic form occurring in young men of the working classes, sometimes with slight fever, regards the disease as infectious. This form is acute, lasting only two or three weeks and rarely proving fatal.

(b) A majority of the cases are found in association with debility following lactation and chronic diarrhœa, or in the malnutrition of rickets. From its occurrence in nursing women Trousseau called it nurse's contracture. It may also develop during pregnancy or recur in successive pregnancies. It has been found as a sequence of the acute fevers, and in some typhoid epidemics many cases have occurred.

(c) Tetany may follow removal of the thyroid gland. Thirteen cases, for example, followed 78 operations on enlarged thyroid in Billroth's clinic, and 6 of them proved fatal. James Stewart has reported an instance in which with the tetany there were symptoms of myxœdema, and no trace of the thyroid gland. Removal of the thyroid in dogs is followed by tetany.

(d) And, lastly, there is a form of tetany which is associated with dilatation of the stomach, particularly after the organ has been washed out.

On this continent true tetany is an extremely rare disease. Griffith has collected 72 cases, among which, however, cases of carpo-pedal spasm are included.

The nature of the disease is unknown; certain forms depend undoubtedly on loss of the function of the thyroid gland.

Symptoms.—In cases associated with general debility or in children with rickets the spasm is limited to the hands and feet. The fingers are bent at the metacarpo-phalangeal joint, extended at the terminal joints, pressed close together, and the thumb is contracted in the palm of the hand. The wrist is flexed, the elbows are bent, and the arms are folded over the chest. In the lower limbs the feet are extended and the toes adducted. The muscles of the face and neck are less commonly involved, but in severe cases there may be trismus, and the angles of the mouth are drawn out. The skin of the hands and feet is sometimes tense and œdematous. The spasms are usually paroxysmal and last for a variable time. In children the attack may pass off in a few hours. In some of the severer chronic cases in adults the stiffness and contracture may continue or even increase for many days, and the attack may last as long as two weeks. In the acute cases the temperature may be elevated and the pulse quickened. In the severe paroxysms there may be involvement of the muscles of the back and of the thorax, inducing dyspnœa and cyanosis. Certain additional features, valuable in diagnosis, are present.

Trousseau's symptom: "So long as the attack is not over, the paroxysms may be reproduced at will. This is effected by simply compressing the affected parts, either in the direction of their principal nerve trunks or over their blood-vessels, so as to impede the venous or arterial circulation."

Chvostek's symptom is shown in the remarkable increase in the mechanical excitability of the motor nerves. A slight tap, for example, in the course of the facial nerve will throw the muscles to which it is distributed into active contraction. Erb has shown that the electrical irritability of the nerves is also greatly increased, and Hofmann has demonstrated the heightened excitability of the sensory nerves, the slightest pressure on which may cause paræsthesia in the region of distribution.

Diagnosis.—The disease is readily recognized. It is a mistake to call instances of carpo-pedal spasm of children true tetany. It is common to find in rickety children or in cases of severe gastro-intestinal catarrh a transient spasm of the fingers or even of the arms. By many authors these are considered cases of mild tetany, and there are all grades in rickety children between the simple carpo-pedal spasm and the condition in which the four extremities are involved; but it is well, I think, to limit the term *tetany* to the severer affection.

With true tetanus the disease is scarcely ever confounded, as the commencement of the spasm in the extremities, the attitude of the hands, and the etiological factors are very different. Hysterical contractures are usually unilateral.

Treatment.—In the case of children the condition with which the tetany is associated should be treated. Baths and cold sponging are recommended and often relieve the spasm as promptly as in child-crowing. Bromide of potassium may be tried. In severe cases chloroform inhalations may be given. Massage, electricity, and the spinal ice-bag have also been used with success. Cases, however, may resist all treatment, and the spasms recur for many years. The thyroid extract should be tried. Gottstein reports relief in a case of long standing, and Bramwell reports one case of operative tetany and one of the idiopathic form successfully treated in this way.

XI. HYSTERIA.

Definition.—A state in which ideas control the body and produce morbid changes in its functions (Möbius).

Etiology.—The affection is most common in women, and usually appears first about the time of puberty, but the manifestations may continue until the menopause, or even until old age. Men, however, are by no means exempt, and of late years hysteria in the male has attracted much attention. It occurs in all races, but is much more prevalent, particularly in its severer forms, in members of the Latin race. In this country the milder grades are common, but the graver forms are rare in comparison with the frequency with which they are seen in France.

Children under twelve years of age are not very often affected, but the disease may be well marked as early as the fifth or sixth year. One of the saddest chapters in the history of human deception, that of the Salem witches, might be headed *hysteria in children*, since the tragedy resulted directly from the hysterical pranks of girls under twelve years of age.

Of predisposing causes, two are important—heredity and education. The former acts by endowing the child with a mobile, abnormally sensitive nervous organization. We see cases most frequently in families with marked neuropathic tendencies, the members of which have suffered from neuroses of various sorts. Education at home too often fails to inculcate habits of self-control. A child grows to girlhood with an entirely errone-ous idea of her relations to others, and accustomed to have every whim gratified and abundant sympathy lavished on every woe, however trifling, she reaches womanhood with a moral organization unfitted to withstand the cares and worries of every-day life. At school, between the ages of twelve and fifteen, the most important period in her life, when the vital energies are absorbed in the rapid development of the body, she is often cramming for examinations and cooped in close school-rooms for six or eight hours daily. The result too frequently is an active, bright mind in an enfeebled body, ill adapted to subserve the functions for which it was framed, easily disordered, and prone to react abnormally to the ordinary stimuli of life. Among the more direct influences are emotions of various kinds, fright occasionally, more frequently love affairs, grief, and domestic worries. Physical causes less often bring on hysterical outbreaks, but they may follow directly upon an injury or develop during the convalescence from an acute illness or be associated with disease of the generative organs. The name *hysteria* indicates how important was believed to be the part played by the uterus in the causation of the disease. Opinions differ a good deal on this question, but undoubtedly in many cases there are ova-rian and uterine disorders the rectification of which sometimes cures the disease. Sexual excess, particularly masturbation, is an important factor, both in girls and boys.

Symptoms.—A useful division is into the convulsive and non-convul-sive varieties.

Convulsive Hysteria.—(*a*) *Minor Forms.*—The attack most commonly follows emotional disturbance. It may set in suddenly or be preceded by symptoms, called by the laity "hysterical," such as laughing and crying alternately, or a sensation of constriction in the neck, or of a ball rising in the throat—the *globus hystericus.* Sometimes, preceding the convulsive movements, there may be painful sensations arising from the pelvic, ab-dominal, or thoracic regions. From the description these sensations re-semble auræ. They become more intense with the rising sensation of choking in the neck and difficulty in getting breath, and the patient falls into a more or less violent convulsion. It will be noticed that the fall is not sudden, as in epilepsy, but the subject goes down, as a rule, easily, often picking a soft spot, like a sofa or an easy-chair, and in the movements apparently exercises care to do herself no injury. Yet at the same time she appears to be quite unconscious. The movements are clonic and dis-orderly, consisting of to-and-fro motions of the trunk or pelvic muscles, while the head and arms are thrown about in an irregular manner. The paroxysm after a few minutes slowly subsides, then the patient becomes emotional, and gradually regains consciousness. When questioned the patient may confess to having some knowledge of the events which have taken place, but, as a rule, has no accurate recollection. During the at-tack the abdomen may be much distended with flatus, and subsequently a large amount of clear urine may be passed. These attacks vary greatly in character. There may be scarcely any movements of the limbs, but after a nerve storm the patient sinks into a torpid, semi-unconscious condition, from which she is roused with great difficulty. In some cases from this state the patient passes into a condition of catalepsy.

(*b*) *Major Forms; Hystero-epilepsy.*—This condition has been especially studied by Charcot and his pupils. Typical instances passing through the various phases are very rare in this country. The attack is initiated by certain prodromata, chiefly minor hysterical manifestations, either foolish or unseemly behavior, excitement, sometimes dyspeptic symptoms with tympanites, or frequent micturition. Areas of hyperæsthesia may at this time be marked, the so-called hysterogenic spots so elaborately described by Richet. These are usually symmetrical and situated over the upper dorsal vertebra, and in front in a series of symmetrically placed spots on the chest and abdomen, the most marked being those in the inguinal regions over the ovaries. Painful sensations or a feeling of oppression and a *globus* rising in the throat may be complained of prior to the onset of the convulsion, which, according to French writers, has four distinct stages: (1) Epileptoid condition, which closely simulates a true epileptic attack with tonic spasm (often leading to opisthotonos), grinding of the teeth, congestion of the face, followed by clonic convulsions, gradual relaxation, and coma. This attack lasts rather longer than a true epileptic attack. (2) Succeeding this is the period which Charcot has termed *clownism*, in which there is an emotional display and a remarkable series of contortions or of cataleptic poses. (3) Then in typical cases there is a stage in which the patient assumes certain attitudes expressive of the various passions—ecstasy, fear, beatitude, or erotism. (4) Finally consciousness returns and the patient enters upon a stage in which she may display very varied symptoms, chiefly manifestations of a delirium with the most extraordinary hallucinations. Visions are seen, voices heard, and conversations held with imaginary persons. In this stage patients will relate with the utmost solemnity imaginary events, and make extraordinary and serious charges against individuals. This sometimes gives a grave aspect to these seizures, for not only will the patient at this stage make and believe the statements, but when recovery is complete the hallucination sometimes persists. We seldom see in this country attacks having this orderly sequence. Much more commonly the convulsions succeed each other at intervals for several days in succession. Here is a striking difference between hystero-epilepsy and true epilepsy. In the latter the status epilepticus, if persistent, is always serious, associated with fever, and frequently fatal, while in hystero-epilepsy attacks may recur for days without special danger to life. After an attack of hystero-epilepsy the patient may sink into a state of trance or lethargy, in which she may remain for days.

Non-convulsive Forms.—So complex and varied is the clinical picture of hysteria that various manifestations are best considered according to the systems which are involved.

(1) **Disorders of Motion.**—(*a*) *Paralyses.*—These may be hemiplegic, paraplegic, or monoplegic. Hysterical diplegia is extremely rare. The paralysis either sets in abruptly or gradually, and may take weeks to attain its full development. *There is no type or form of organic paralysis which*

may not be simulated in hysteria. According to Weir Mitchell, the hemi-plegias are most frequent in the ratio of four on the left to one on the right side. The face is not affected; the neck may be involved, but the leg suffers most. Sensation is either lessened or lost on the affected side. The hysterical paraplegia is more common than hemiplegia. The loss of power is not absolute; the legs can usually be moved, but do not support the patient. The reflexes may be increased, though the knee-jerk is often normal. A spurious ankle clonus may sometimes be present. The feet are usually extended and turned inward in the equino-varus position. The muscles do not waste and the electrical reactions are normal. Other mani-festations, such as paralysis of the bladder or aphonia, are usually associ-ated with the hysterical paraplegia. Hysterical monoplegias may be facial, crural, or brachial. A condition of ataxia sometimes occurs with paresis. The incoördination may be a marked feature, and there are usually sensory manifestations.

(b) *Contractures and Spasms.*—An extraordinary variety of spasmodic affections occurs in hysteria, of which the most common are the follow-ing: The hysterical contractures may attack almost any group of volun-tary muscles and be of the hemiplegic, paraplegic, or monoplegic type. They may come on suddenly or slowly, persist for months or years, and disappear rapidly. The contracture is most commonly seen in the arm, which is flexed at the elbow and wrist, while the fingers tightly grasp the thumb in the palm of the hand; more rarely the terminal phalanges are hyperextended as in athetosis. It may occur in one or in both legs, more commonly the former. The ankle clonus is present; the foot is inverted and the toes are strongly flexed. These cases may be mistaken for lateral sclerosis and the difficulty in diagnosis may really be very great. The spastic gait is very typical, and with the exaggerated knee-jerk and ankle clonus the picture may be characteristic. In 1879 I frequently showed such a case at the Montreal General Hospital as a typical example of lat-eral sclerosis. The condition persisted for more than eighteen months and then disappeared completely. Other forms of contracture may be in the muscles of the hip, shoulder, or neck; more rarely in those of the jaws— hysterical trismus—or in the tongue. Remarkable indeed are the local con-tractures in the diaphragm and abdominal muscles, producing a phantom tumor, in which just below and in the neighborhood of the umbilicus is a firm, apparently solid growth. According to Gowers, this is produced by relaxation of the recti and a spasmodic contraction of the diaphragm, to-gether with inflation of the intestines with gas and an arching forward of the vertebral column. They are apt to occur in middle-aged women about the menopause, and are frequently associated with the symptoms of spu-rious pregnancy—*pseudo-cyesis.* The resemblance to a tumor may be strik-ing, and I have known skilful diagnosticians to be deceived. The only safeguard is to be found in complete anæsthesia, when the tumor entirely disappears. Some years ago I went by chance into the operating-room of a hospital and found a patient on the table under chloroform and the sur-geon prepared to perform ovariotomy. The tumor, however, had com-pletely disappeared with full anæsthesia. Mitchell has reported an instance of a phantom tumor in the left pectoral region just above the breast, which was tender, hard, and dense.

Clonic spasms are more common in hysteria in this country than contractures. The following are the important forms: *Rhythmic hysterical spasm.* This, unfortunately, is sometimes known as rhythmic chorea or hysterical chorea. The movements may be of the arm, either flexion and extension, or, more rarely, pronation and supination. Clonic contractions of the sterno-cleido-mastoid or of the muscles of the jaws or of the rotatory muscles of the head may produce rhythmic movements of these parts. The spasm may be in one or both psoas muscles, lifting the leg in a rhythmic manner eight or ten times in a minute. In other instances the muscles of the trunk are affected, and every few moments there is a bowing movement—salaam convulsions—or the muscles of the back may contract, causing strong arching of the vertebral column and retraction of the head. These movements may often alternate, as in a case in my wards, in which the patient on fine days had regular salaam convulsions, while on wet days the rhythmic spasm was in the muscles of the back and neck. Mitchell has described a rotatory spasm in which the patient rotated involuntarily, usually to the left. More unusual cases are those in which the contractions closely simulate paramyoclonus multiplex. Hysterical athetosis is a rare form of spasm. *Tremor* may be a purely hysterical manifestation, occurring either alone or with paralysis and contracture. It most commonly involves the hands and arms; more rarely the head and legs. The movements are small and quick. In the type *Rendu* the tremor may or may not persist during repose, but it is increased or provoked by volitional movements. Volitional or intentional tremor may exist, simulating closely the movements of insular sclerosis. Buzzard states that many instances of this disease in young girls are mistaken for hysteria.

(2) **Disorders of Sensation.**—*Anæsthesia* is most common, and usually confined to one half of the body. It may not be noticed by the patient. Usually it is accurately limited to the middle line and involves the mucous surfaces and deeper parts. The conjunctiva, however, is often spared. There may be hemianopia. This symptom may come on slowly or follow a convulsive attack. Sometimes the various sensations are dissociated and the anæsthesia may be only to pain and to touch. The skin of the affected side is usually pale and cool, and a pin-prick may not be followed by blood. With the loss of feeling there may be loss of muscular power. Curious trophic changes may be present, as in an interesting case of Weir Mitchell's, in which there was unilateral swelling of the hemiplegic side.

A phenomenon to which much attention has been paid is that of transference. By metallotherapy, the application of certain metals, the anæsthesia or analgesia can be transferred to the other side of the body. It has been shown, however, that this phenomenon may be caused by the electro-magnet and by wood and various other agents, and is probably entirely a mental effect. The subject has no practical importance, but it remains an interesting and instructive chapter in Gallic medical history.

Hyperæsthesia.—Increased sensitiveness and pains occur in various parts of the body. One of the most frequent complaints is of pain in the head, usually over the sagittal suture, less frequently in the occiput. This is described as agonizing, and is compared to the driving of a nail into the part; hence the name *clavus hystericus*. Neuralgias are common. Hyperæsthetic areas, the hysterogenic points, exist on the skin of the thorax and abdomen, pressure upon which may cause minor manifestations or even a convulsive attack. Increased sensitiveness exists in the ovarian region, but is not peculiar to hysteria. Pain in the back is an almost constant complaint of hysterical patients. The sensitiveness may be limited to certain spinous processes, or it may be diffuse. In hysterical women the pains in the abdomen may simulate those of gastralgia and of gastric ulcer, or the condition may be almost identical with that of peritonitis; more rarely the abdominal pains closely resemble those of appendix disease.

Special Senses.—Disturbances of taste and smell are not uncommon and may cause a good deal of distress. Of ocular symptoms, retinal hyperæsthesia is the most common, and the patients always prefer to be in a darkened room. Retraction of the field of vision is common and usually follows a convulsive seizure. It may persist for years. The color perception may be normal even with complete anæsthesia, and in this country the achromatopsia does not seem to be nearly so common an hysterical manifestation as in Europe. Hysterical deafness may be complete and may alternate or come on at the same time with hysterical blindness. Hysterical amaurosis may occur in children. One must carefully distinguish between functional loss of power and simulation.

(3) Visceral Manifestations.—*Respiratory Apparatus.*—Of disturbances in the respiratory rhythm, the most frequent, perhaps, is an exaggeration of the deeper breath, which is taken normally every fifth or sixth inspiration, or there may be a "catching" breathing, such as is seen when cold water is poured over a person. Hysterical dyspnœa is readily recognized, as there is no special distress and the pulse is usually normal. I have met with a remarkable case following trauma in which the respirations rose above 130 in the minute. Among laryngeal manifestations aphonia is the most frequent and may persist for months or even years without other special symptoms of the disease. Spasm of the muscles may occur with violent inspiratory efforts and great distress, and may even lead to cyanosis. Hiccough, or sounds resembling it, may be present for weeks or months at a time. Among the most remarkable of the respiratory manifestations are the hysterical cries. These may mimic the sounds produced by animals, such as barking, mewing, or grunting, and in France epidemics of them have been repeatedly observed. Extraordinary cries may be produced, either inspiratory or expiratory. I saw at Wagner's clinic at Leipsic a girl of thirteen or fourteen, who had for many weeks given utterance to a remarkable inspiratory cry somewhat like the whoop of whooping-cough, but so intense that it was heard at a long distance. It was incessant, and the girl was worn to a skeleton. Attacks of gaping, yawning, and sneezing may also occur.

The hysterical cough is a frequent symptom, particularly in young girls. It may occur in paroxysms, but is often a dry, persistent, croaking cough, extremely monotonous and unpleasant to hear. Sir Andrew Clark has called attention to a loud, barking cough (*cynobex hebetica*) occurring about the time of puberty, chiefly in boys belonging to neurotic families. The attacks, which last about a minute, recur frequently.

There is a peculiar form of hæmoptysis which may be very deceptive and lead to the diagnosis of pulmonary disorders. Wagner describes the sputum as a pale-red fluid—not so bright in color as in ordinary hæmoptysis; on settling it presents a reddish-brown sediment. It contains particles of food, pavement epithelium, red corpuscles, and micrococci, but no cylindrical or ciliated epithelium. It probably comes from the mouth or pharynx.

Digestive System.—Disturbed or depraved appetite, dyspepsia, and gastric pains are common in hysterical patients. The patient may have difficulty in swallowing the food, apparently from spasm of the gullet. There are instances in which the food seems to be expelled before it reaches the stomach. In other cases there is incessant gagging. In the hysterical vomiting the food is regurgitated without much effort and without nausea. This feature may persist for years without great disturbance of nutrition. The most striking and remarkable digestive disturbance in hysteria is the *anorexia nervosa* described by Sir William Gull. "To call it loss of appetite—anorexia—but feebly characterizes the symptom. It is rather an annihilation of appetite, so complete that it seems in some cases impossible ever to eat again. Out of it grows an antagonism to food which results at last and in its worst forms in spasm on the approach of food, and this in turn gives rise to some of those remarkable cases of survival for long periods without food" (Mitchell). As this goes on there may be an extreme degree of muscular restlessness, so that the patients wander about until exhausted. Nothing more pitiable is to be seen in practice than an advanced case of this sort. It is usually in a young girl, sometimes as early as the eleventh or twelfth, more commonly between the fifteenth and twentieth years. The emaciation is frightful, and scarcely exceeded by that of cancer of the œsophagus. The patient finally takes to bed, and in extreme cases lies upon one side with the thighs and legs flexed, and contractures may occur. Food is either not taken at all or only upon urgent compulsion. The skin becomes wasted, dry, and covered with bran-like scales. No food may be taken for several weeks at a time, and attempts to feed may be followed by severe spasms. Although the condition looks so alarming, these cases, when removed from their home surroundings and treated by Weir Mitchell's method, sometimes recover in a remarkable way. Death, however, may follow with extreme emaciation. In a fatal case under my care the girl weighed only 49 pounds. No lesions were found post mortem.

Among intestinal symptoms flatulency is one of the most distressing, and is usually associated with the condition of peristaltic unrest (Kussmaul). Frequent discharges of fæces may be due to disturbance in either the small or large bowel. An obstinate form of diarrhœa is found in some hysterical patients, which proves very intractable and is associated especially with the taking of food. It seems an aggravated form of the looseness of bowels to which so many nervous people are subject on emotion or the tendency which some have to diarrhœa immediately after eating.

An entirely different form is that produced by what Mitchell calls the irritable rectum, in which scybala are passed frequently during the day, sometimes with great violence. Constipation is more frequent, however, and may be due to a loss of power in the muscles of the bowel, or in the abdominal muscles. In extreme cases the bowels may not be moved for two or three weeks, leading to great accumulation of faeces. Other disturbances are ano-spasm or intense pain in the rectum apart from any fissure.

Cardio-vascular.—Rapid action of the heart on the slightest emotion, with or without the subjective sensation of palpitation, is often a source of great distress. A slow pulse is less frequent. Pains about the heart may simulate angina, the so-called hysterical or pseudo-angina, which has already been considered. Flushes in various parts are among the most common symptoms. Sweating occasionally occurs.

Among the more remarkable vaso-motor phenomena are the so-called stigmata or haemorrhages in the skin, such as were present in the celebrated case of Louise Lateau. In many cases these are undoubtedly fraudulent, but if, as appears credible, such bleeding may exist in the hypnotic trance, there seems no reason to doubt its occurrence in the trance of prolonged religious ecstasy.

Joint Affections.—To Sir Benjamin Brodie and Sir James Paget we owe the recognition of these extraordinary manifestations of hysteria. Perhaps no single affection has brought more discredit upon the profession, for the cases are very refractory, and finally fall into the hands of a charlatan or faith-healer, under whose touch the disease may disappear at once. Usually it affects the knee or the hip, and may follow a trifling injury. The joint is usually fixed, sensitive, and swollen. The surface may be cool, but sometimes the local temperature is increased. To the touch it is very sensitive and movement causes great pain. In protracted cases the muscles about the joint are somewhat wasted, and in consequence it looks larger. The pains are often nocturnal, at which time the local temperature may be much increased. While, as a rule, neuromimetic joints yield to proper management, there are interesting instances in the literature in which organic change has succeeded the functional disturbance. In the remarkable case reported in Weir Mitchell's lectures, the hysterical features were pronounced, and, on account of the chronicity, the disease of the knee-joint was considered organic by such an authority as Billroth. Sands found the joint surfaces normal, and the thickening to be due to inflammatory products outside the capsule.

Intermittent hydrarthrosis may be a manifestation of hysteria, occurring in the knee or other joints, sometimes with transient paresis.

Mental Symptoms.—The psychical condition of an hysterical patient is always abnormal, and the disease occupies the ill-defined territory between sanity and insanity. In a large number of cases the patients are really insane, particularly in the perversion witnessed in the moral sphere. Not the slightest dependence can be placed upon their statements, and they will for months or years deceive friends, relatives, and physician. This appears to result partly, but not wholly, from a morbid craving for sympathy. It is really due to an entire unhinging of the moral nature.

Hysterical patients may become insane and display persistent hallucinations and delirium, alternating perhaps with emotional outbursts of an aggravated character. For weeks or months they may be confined to bed, entirely oblivious to their surroundings, with a delirium which may simulate that of delirium tremens, particularly in being associated with loathsome and unpleasant animals. The nutrition may be maintained, but in these cases there is always a very heavy, foul breath. With seclusion and care recovery usually takes place within three or four months. At the onset of these attacks and during convalescence the patients must be incessantly watched, as a suicidal tendency is by no means uncommon. I have been accustomed to speak of this condition as the *status hystericus*.

Of hysterical manifestations in the higher centres that of trance is the most remarkable. This may develop spontaneously without any convulsive seizure, but more frequently, in this country at least, it follows hysteroid attacks. Catalepsy, a condition in which the limbs are plastic and remain in any position in which they are placed, may be present.

The Metabolism in Hysteria.—The studies of Gilles de la Tourette and Cathelineau, under Charcot's direction, have shown that in the ordinary forms of hysteria the urine does not show quantitative or qualitative changes, but in the severer types, characterized by convulsions, etc., there are important modifications: reduction in the urates and phosphates; the ratio of the earthy to the alkaline phosphates, normally 1 : 3, is 1 : 2, or even 1 : 1. The urine is also reduced in amount. They think that these changes might sometimes serve to differentiate convulsive hysteria from epilepsy, in which there is always an increase in the solid constituents after a seizure.

Hysterical Fever.—In hysteria the temperature, as a rule, is normal. The cases with fever may be grouped as follows: (*a*) Instances in which the fever is the sole manifestation. These are rare, but I have seen at least two cases in which the chronic course, the retention of the nutrition, and the entirely negative condition of the organs left no other diagnosis possible. In a case recently under observation the patient has had for four or five years an afternoon rise of temperature, reaching usually to 102° or 103°. She was well nourished and presented no pronounced hysterical symptoms, but there was a marked neurotic history on one side and a form of interrupted sighing respiration so often seen in hysteria.

(*b*) Cases of hysterical fever with spurious local manifestations. These are very troublesome and deceptive cases. The patient may be suddenly taken ill with pain in various regions and elevation of temperature. The case may simulate meningitis. There may be pain in the head, vomiting, contracted pupils, and retraction of the neck—symptoms which may persist for weeks—and some anomalous manifestation during convalescence may alone indicate to the physician that he has had to deal with a case of hysteria, and has not, as he perhaps flattered himself, cured a case of meningitis. Mary Putnam Jacobi, in a recent article on hysterical fever, mentions a case in the service of Cornil which was admitted with dyspnœa, slight cyanosis, and a temperature of 39° C. The condition proved to be hysterical. There is also an hysterical pseudo-phthisis with pain in the chest, slight fever, and the expectoration of a blood-stained mucus. The cases of hysterical peritonitis may also show fever.

(c) *Hysterical Hyperpyrexia.*—It is a suggestive fact that the cases of paradoxical temperatures reported of late years, in which the thermometer has registered 112° to 120° or more, have been in women. Fraud has been practised in some of these, but others have to be accepted, though their explanation is impossible under our known laws. Jacobi has reported a case in which the temperature rose to 148° F. (65.5° C.). The Omaha case, in which the temperature was recorded at 170° F., has, I am informed on good authority, proved a fraud.

Diagnosis.—Inquiry into the occurrence of previous manifestations and the mental conditions may give important information. These questions, as a rule, should not be asked the mother, who of all others is least likely to give satisfactory information about the patient's condition. The occurrence of the globus hystericus, of emotional attacks, of weeping and crying, are always suggestive. The points of difference between the convulsive attacks and true epilepsy were referred to in their description, and as a rule little difficulty is experienced in distinguishing between the two conditions. The hysterical paralyses are very variable and apt to be associated with anæsthesia. The contractures may at times be very deceptive, but the occurrence of areas of anæsthesia, of retraction of the visual field, and the development of minor hysterical manifestations, give valuable indications. The contractures disappear under full anæsthesia. Special care must be taken not to confound the spastic paraplegia of hysteria with lateral sclerosis.

The visceral manifestations are usually recognized without much difficulty. The practitioner has constantly to bear in mind the strong tendency in hysterical patients to practise deception.

Treatment.—The prophylaxis in hysteria may be gathered from the remarks on the relation of education to the disease. The successful treatment of hysteria demands qualities possessed by few physicians. The first element is a due appreciation of the nature of the disease on the part of the physician and friends. It is pitiable to think of the misery which has been inflicted on these unhappy victims by the harsh and unjust treatment which has resulted from false views of the nature of the trouble; on the other hand, worry and ill-health, often the wrecking of mind, body, and estate, are entailed upon the near relatives in the nursing of a protracted case of hysteria. The minor manifestations, attacks of the vapors, the crying and weeping spells, are not of much moment and rarely require treatment. The physical condition should be carefully looked into and the mode of life regulated so as to insure system and order in everything. A congenial occupation offers the best remedy for many of these manifestations. Any functional disturbance should be attended to and a course of tonics prescribed. Special attention should be paid to the action of the bowels.

Valerian and asafœtida are often of service. For the pains in various parts, particularly in the back, the thermo-cautery and static electricity will be found invaluable. Morphia should be withheld. In the convulsive seizures, particularly in the minor forms, it is often best, after settling the patient comfortably, to leave her. When she comes to, and finds herself alone and without sympathy, the attacks are less likely to be repeated. There is, as a rule, no cure for the hysterical manifestations of women, otherwise in good health, who are, as Mitchell says, "fat and ruddy, with sound organs and good appetites, but ever complain of pains and aches, and ever liable on the least emotional disturbance to exhibit a quaint variety of hysterical phenomena."

To treat hysteria as a physical disorder is, after all, radically wrong. It is essentially a mental and emotional anomaly, and the important element in the treatment is moral control. At home, surrounded by loving relatives who misinterpret entirely the symptoms and have no appreciation of the nature of the disease, the severer forms of hysteria can rarely be cured. The necessary control is impossible; hence the special value of the method introduced by Weir Mitchell, which is particularly applicable to the advanced cases which have become chronic and bedridden. The treatment consists in isolation, rest, diet, massage, and electricity. Separation from friends and sympathetic relatives must be absolute, and can rarely, if ever, be obtained in the individual's home. An essential element in the treatment is an intelligent nurse. No small share of the success which has attended the author of this plan has been due to the fact that he has persistently chosen as his allies bright, intelligent women. The details of the plan are as follows: The patient is confined to bed and not allowed to get up, nor, at first, in aggravated cases, to read, write, or even to feed herself. Massage is used daily, at first for twenty minutes or half an hour, subsequently for a longer period. It is essential as a substitute for exercise. The induction current is applied to the various muscles and to the spine. Its use, however, is not so essential as that of massage. The diet may at first be entirely of milk, 4 ounces every two hours. It is better to give skimmed milk, and it may be diluted with soda water or barley water and, if necessary, peptonized. After a week or ten days the diet may be increased, the amount of milk still being kept up. A chop may be given at midday, a cup of coffee or cocoa with toast or bread and butter or a biscuit with the milk. The patients usually fatten rapidly as the solid food is added, and with the gain there is, as a rule, a diminution or cessation of the nervous symptoms. The milk is the essential element in the diet, and is in itself amply sufficient.

The remarkable results obtained by this method are now universally recognized. The plan is more applicable to the lean than to fat, flabby hysterical patients. Not only is it suitable for the more obstinate varieties of hysteria with bodily manifestations, but in the cases with mental symptoms the seclusion and separation from relatives and friends are particularly advantageous. In the hysterical vomiting Debove's method of forced feeding may be used with benefit. For the innumerable minor manifestations of hysteria and for the simulations the indications for treatment are usually clear. Of late, hypnotism has been extensively used in the treatment of hysteria. Occasionally in cases of hysterical contractions or paralysis it is of benefit, but any one who has seen the development of this method

70

as practised at present in France must feel that it is a two-edged sword and that the constant repetition in the same patient is fraught with danger. In the cases in which we have tried it here the success has not been marked.

XII. NEURASTHENIA.

Definition.—A condition of weakness or exhaustion of the nervous system, giving rise to various forms of mental and bodily inefficiency.

The term, an old one, but first popularized by Beard, covers an ill-defined, motley group of symptoms, which may be either general and the expression of derangement of the entire system, or local, limited to certain organs; hence the terms cerebral, spinal, cardiac, and gastric neurasthenia.

Etiology.—The causes may be grouped as hereditary and acquired.

(a) *Hereditary.*—We do not all start in life with the same amount of nerve capital. Parents who have led irrational lives, indulging in excesses of various kinds, or who have been the subjects of nervous complaints or of mental trouble, may transmit to their children an organization which is defective in what, for want of a better term, we must call "nerve force." Such individuals start handicapped with a neuropathic predisposition, and furnish a considerable proportion of our neurasthenic patients. As van Gieson sonorously puts it, "the potential energies of the higher constellations of their association centres have been squandered by their ancestors."

Besides such forms of hereditary neuropathy, which we have to look upon as instances of injury to the germ-plasm derived from one or both of the parents, there have to be considered those cases in which during intra-uterine life there have been conditions which interfered with the proper development and nutrition of the embryo. So long as these individuals are content to transact a moderate business with their life capital, all may go well, but there is no reserve, and in the exigencies of modern life these small capitalists go under and come to us as bankrupts.

(b) *Acquired.*—The functions, though perverted most readily in persons who have inherited a feeble organization, may also be damaged in persons with no neuropathic predisposition by exercise which is excessive in proportion to the strength—i. e., by strain. The cares and anxieties attendant upon the gaining of a livelihood may be borne without distress, but in many persons the strain becomes excessive and is first manifested as *worry*. The individual loses the distinction between essentials and non-essentials, trifles cause annoyance, and the entire organism reacts with unnecessary readiness to slight stimuli, and is in a state which the older writers called irritable weakness. If such a condition be taken early and the patient given rest, the balance is quickly restored. In this group may be placed a large proportion of the neurasthenics which we see in this country, particularly among business men, teachers, and journalists. Neurasthenia may follow the infectious diseases, particularly influenza, typhoid fever, and syphilis. The abuse of certain drugs, alcohol, tobacco, morphine may lead to a high grade of neurasthenia, though the drug habit is more often a result rather than a cause of the neurasthenia. Other causes more subtle, yet potent, and less easily dealt with, are the worries attendant upon love affairs, religious doubts, and the sexual passion. Sexual excesses have undoubtedly been exaggerated as a cause of neurasthenia, but that they are responsible in a number of instances is certain.

The traumatic forms, especially those following upon railway accidents, will be separately considered.

Symptoms.—These are extremely varied, and may be general or localized; more often a combination of both. The appearance of the patient is suggestive, sometimes characteristic, but difficult to describe. Important information can be gained by the physician if he observe the patient closely as he enters the room—the way he is clothed, the manner in which he holds his body, his facial expression, and the humor which he is in. Loss of weight and slight anæmia may be present. The physical debility may reach a high grade and the patient may be confined to bed. Mentally the patients are usually low-spirited and despondent, in women frequently emotional.

The local symptoms may dominate the situation, and there have accordingly been described a whole series of types of the disease—cerebral, spinal, cardio-vascular, gastric, and sexual. In all forms there is a striking lack of accordance between the symptoms of which the patient complains and the objective changes discoverable by the physician. In nearly every clinical type of the disease the predominant symptoms are referable to pathological sensations and the psychic effects of these. Imperfect sleep is also complained of by a majority of patients, or, if not complained of, is found to exist on inquiry.

In the cerebral or psychic form the symptoms are chiefly connected with an inability to perform the ordinary mental work. Thus a row of figures cannot be correctly added, the dictation or the writing of a few letters is a source of the greatest worry, the transaction of petty details in business is a painful effort, and there is loss of power of fixed attention. With this condition there may be no headache, the appetite may be good, and the patient may sleep well. As a rule, however, there are sensations of fulness and weight or flushes, if not actual headache. Sleeplessness is a frequent concomitant of the cerebral form, and may be the first manifestation. Some of these patients are good-tempered and cheerful, but a majority are moody, irritable, and depressed.

Hyperæsthesia, especially to sensations of pain, is one of the main characteristics of almost all neurasthenic individuals. The sensations are nearly always referred to some special region of the body—the skin, eye muscles, the joints, the blood-vessels, or the viscera. It is frequently possible to localize a number of points painful to pressure (Valleix's points). In some patients there is marked vertigo, occasionally even resembling that of Ménière's disease.

If such pathological sensations continue for a long time the mood and character of the patient gradually alter. The so-called "irritable humor" develops. Many obnoxiously egoistic individuals met with in daily life are in reality examples of psychic neurasthenia. Everything is complained of. The individual demands the greatest consideration for his condition; feels that he has been deeply insulted if his desires are not always immediately granted. He may at the same time have but little consideration for others. Indeed, in the severer forms of the disease he may show a malicious pleasure in attempting to make people who seem happier than himself uncomfortable. Such patients complain frequently that they are "misunderstood" by their fellows.

In many cases the so-called "anxiety conditions" gradually develop; one scarcely ever sees a case of advanced neurasthenia without the existence of some form of "anxiety." In the simpler forms of anxiety (nosophobic) there may be only a fear of impending insanity or of approaching death or of apoplexy. More frequently the anxious feeling is localized somewhere in the body—in the præcordial region, in the head, in the abdomen, in the thorax, or more rarely in the extremities.

In some cases the anxiety becomes intense and the patients are restless, and declare that they do not know what to do with themselves. They may throw themselves upon a bed, crying and complaining, and making convulsive movements with the hands and feet. Suicidal tendencies are not uncommon in such cases, and patients may in desperation actually take their own lives.

Involuntary mental activity may be very troublesome; the patient complains that when he is overtired thoughts which he cannot stop or control run through his head with lightning-like rapidity. In other cases there is marked absence of mind, the individual's mind being so filled up owing to the overexcitability of latent memory pictures that he is unable to form the proper associations for ideas called up by external stimuli. Sometimes a patient complains that a definite word, a name, a number, a melody, or a song keeps running in his head in spite of all he can do to abolish it.

In the severer cases of psychic neurasthenia the so-called "phobias" are common. The most frequent form perhaps is *agoraphobia,* in which patients the moment they come into an open space are oppressed by an exaggerated feeling of anxiety. They seem "frightened to death," and commence to tremble all over; they complain of compression of the thorax and palpitation of the heart. They may break into profuse perspiration and assert that they feel as though chained to the ground or that they cannot move a step. It is remarkable that in some such cases the open space can be crossed if the individual be accompanied by some one, even by a child, or if he carry a stick or an umbrella! Other people are afraid to be left alone (monophobia), especially in a closed compartment (claustrophobia).

The fear of people and of society is known as anthropophobia. A whole series of other phobias have been described—batophobia, or the fear that high things will fall; pathophobia, or fear of disease; siderodromophobia, or fear of a railway journey; siderophobia or astrophobia, fear of thunder and lightning. Occasionally we meet with individuals who are afraid of everything and every one—victims of the so-called pantophobia.

The *special senses* may be disturbed, particularly vision. An aching or weariness of the eyeballs after reading a few minutes or flashes of light are common symptoms. The "irritable eye," the so-called nervous or neurasthenic asthenopia, is familiar to every family physician. According to

Binswanger, the essence of the asthenopic disturbance consists in pathological sensations of fatigue in the ciliary muscles or the medial recti.

There may be acoustic disturbances—hyperalgesia and even true hyperacusia.

One of the most common of all the symptoms of neurasthenia is the *pressure in the head* complained of by these patients. This symptom, variously described, may be diffuse, but is more frequently referred to some one region—frontal, temporal, parietal, or occipital.*

When the *spinal symptoms* predominate—spinal irritation or spinal neurasthenia—in addition to many of the features just mentioned, the patients complain of weariness on the least exertion, of weakness, pain in the back, intercostal neuralgiform pains, and of aching pains in the legs. There may be spots of local tenderness on the spine. The rachialgia may be spontaneous, or may be noticed only on pressure or movement. Occasionally there may be disturbances of sensation, particularly a feeling of numbness and tingling, and the reflexes may be increased. Visceral neuralgias, especially in connection with the genital organs, are frequently met with. The aching pain in the back or in the back of the neck is the most constant complaint in these cases. In women it is often impossible to say whether this condition is one of neurasthenia or hysteria. It is in these cases that the disturbances of muscular activity are most pronounced, and in the French writings *amyosthenia* particularly plays an important *rôle*. The symptoms may be irritative or paretic, or a combination of both. Disturbances of coördination are not uncommon in the severer forms. These are particularly prone to involve the associated movements of the eye muscles leading to asthenopic lack of accommodation. Drooping of one eyelid is very common, probably owing to insufficient innervation on the part of the sympathetic rather than to paresis of the nervus oculomotorius. Occasionally Romberg's symptom may be present, and the patient, or even his physician, may fear a beginning tabes. More rarely there is disturbance of such finely coördinated acts as writing and articulation, not unlike those seen at the onset of general paresis. Such symptoms are always alarming, and the greatest care must be taken in establishing a diagnosis. That they may be the symptoms of pure neurasthenia, however, can no longer be doubted.

The reflexes in neurasthenia are usually increased, the deep reflexes especially never being absent. The condition of the superficial reflexes is less constant, though these, too, are usually increased. The pupils are often dilated, and the reflexes are usually normal. There may be inequality of the pupils in neurasthenia, a point which Pelizaeus has especially emphasized.

In another type of cases the muscular weakness is extreme, and may go on even to complete motor helplessness. Very thorough examination is necessary before deciding as to the nature of the affection, since in some

---

* For an exhaustive consideration of the mental symptoms of neurasthenia, see the Shattuck Lecture, by Cowles (Boston Medical and Surgical Journal, 1891), as well as two German monographs, that of Binswanger (1896), and that of Löwenfeld. The French treatise of Bouveret (1891) is also valuable. F. C. Müller's Handbuch der Neurasthenie (Leipzig, 1893) contains an excellent bibliography of this subject.

instances serious mistakes have been made. Here belong the *atremia* of Neftel, the *akinesia algera* of Möbius, and the neurasthenic form of *astasia abasia* described by Binswanger.

In other cases the *cardio-vascular* symptoms are the most distressing, and may occur with only slight disturbance of the cerebro-spinal functions, though the conditions are nearly always combined. Palpitation of the heart, irregular and very rapid action (neurasthenic tachycardia), and pains and oppressive feelings in the cardiac region are the most common symptoms. The slightest excitement may be followed by increased action of the heart, sometimes associated with sensations of dizziness and anxiety, and the patients frequently have the idea that they suffer from serious disease of this organ. Attacks of pseudo-angina may occur.

Vaso-motor disturbances constitute a special feature of many cases. Flushes of heat, especially in the head, and transient hyperæmia of the skin may be very distressing symptoms. Profuse sweating may occur, either local or general, and sometimes nocturnal. The pulse may show interesting features, owing to the extreme relaxation of the peripheral arterioles. The arterial throbbing may be everywhere visible, almost as much as in aortic insufficiency. The pulse, too, may under these circumstances have a somewhat water-hammer quality. The capillary pulse may be seen in the nails, on the lips, or on the margins of a line drawn upon the forehead, and I have on several occasions seen pulsation in the veins of the back of the hand. A characteristic symptom in some cases is the *throbbing aorta*. This "preternatural pulsation in the epigastrium," as Allan Burns calls it, may be extremely forcible and suggest the existence of abdominal aneurism. The subjective sensations associated with it may be very unpleasant, particularly when the stomach is empty.

In women especially, and sometimes in men, the peripheral blood-vessels are contracted, the extremities are cold, the nose is red or blue, and the face has a pinched expression. These patients feel much more comfortable when the cutaneous vessels are distended, and resort to various means to favor this (wearing of heavy clothing, use of diffusible stimulants).

The general features of *gastro-intestinal neurasthenia* have been dealt with under the section of nervous dyspepsia. The connection of these cases with dilatation of the stomach, floating kidney, and the condition which Glénard calls *enteroptosis* has already been mentioned.

Sexual neurasthenia is a condition in which there is an irritable weakness of the sexual organs manifested by nocturnal emissions, unusual depression after intercourse, and often by a distressing dread of impotence. The mental condition of these patients is most pitiable, and they fall an easy prey to quacks and charlatans of all kinds.

Spermatorrhœa is the bugbear of the majority. They complain of continued losses, usually without accompanying pleasurable sensations. After defecation or micturition there may be seminal discharges. Microscopic examination sometimes reveals the presence of spermatozoa. Actual nervous impotence is not uncommon. The "painful testicle" is a well-known neurasthenic phenomenon.

In the severer cases, especially those bearing the stigmata of degeneration, there may be evidence of sexual perversion. The "damnable iteration" with which writers in our ranks "dish up" this unpleasant subject is proof positive that not all prophets speak to edification.

In females it is common to find a tender ovary, and painful or irregular menstruation.

In all forms of neurasthenia the condition of the urine is important. Many cases are complicated with the symptoms of the condition known as lithæmia, and so marked may this be that some have indeed made a special form of lithæmic neurasthenia. Polyuria may be present, but is more common in hysteria. With disturbed digestion the urates and oxalates may be in excess.

Diagnosis.—While in the majority of cases the diagnosis can readily be made, still there are instances in which it is very difficult. Neurasthenia overlaps hypochondria and hysteria on the one hand, and the psychoses and degenerative diseases of the nervous system on the other. The term has in the past been altogether too loosely used. Simple local disturbances and temporary general disturbances the result of sudden overexertion should scarcely be diagnosed as neurasthenia. Only when we have before us a clinical picture indicating general weakness of the nervous system in addition to the local disturbances, no matter how pronounced they are, is the diagnosis justifiable. Charcot has designated as neurasthenic stigmata certain fundamental and typical symptoms, such as the pain and pressure in the head, the disturbances of sleep, the rhachialgia and spinal hyperæsthesia, the muscular weakness, the nervous dyspepsia, the disturbances of the genital organs, and the typical mental phenomena (irritable humor, psychic depression, feelings of anxiety, intellectual fatigue, incapacity of decision, and the like). In addition to these cardinal symptoms of the disease, he described as secondary or accessory symptoms the feelings of dizziness and vertigo, the neurasthenic asthenopia, the circulatory, respiratory, secretory, and nutritive disturbances, disturbances of motility and sensation, the fever of neurasthenia, and neurasthenic idiosyncrasies. The anxiety conditions and various phobias, as well as the different varieties of tic and the occupation neuroses when they accompany neurasthenia, are regarded as complications dependent in the majority of instances upon faulty heredity. I must agree with Binswanger in emphasizing the importance for the diagnosis of the peculiar intellectual and emotional condition of the patient, as well as the disturbances of sleep.

Neurasthenia is a disease above all others which has to be diagnosed from the subjective statements of the patient, and from an observation of his general behavior rather than from the physical examination. The physical examination is of the highest importance in excluding other diseases likely to be confounded with it. That somatic changes occur and that physical signs are often to be made out is very true, and we owe to Löwenfeld especially a careful discussion of these points, but there is nothing typical or pathognomonic in these objective changes.

The hypochondriac differs from the neurasthenic in the excessive psychic distortion of the pathological sensations to which he is subject. He is the victim of actual delusions regarding his condition.

The confusion of neurasthenia with hysteria is still more frequent; in women especially a diagnosis of hysteria is often made when in reality the condition is one of neurasthenia. In the absence of hysterical paroxysms, of crises, and of those marked emotional and intellectual characteristics of the hysterical individual the diagnosis of hysteria should not be made. Of course, in many of the cases of hysteria definite hysterical stigmata (hysterical paralyses, convulsions, contractures, anæsthesias, alterations in the visual field, etc.) are present, and the diagnosis is not difficult.

Epilepsy is not likely to be confounded with neurasthenia if there be definite epileptic attacks, but the cases of *petit mal* may be puzzling.

The onset of exophthalmic goitre may be mistaken for neurasthenia, especially if there be no exophthalmos at the beginning. The emotional disturbances and the irritability of the heart may mislead the physician. In pronounced cases of nervous prostration the differential diagnosis from the various psychoses may be extremely difficult.

The two forms of organic disease of the nervous system with which neurasthenia is most likely to be confounded are tabes and general paresis. The symptoms of the spinal form of neurasthenia may resemble those of the former disease, while the symptoms of the psychic or cerebral form of neurasthenia may be very similar to those of general paresis. The diagnosis, as a rule, presents no difficulty if the physician be careful to make a thorough routine examination. It is only the superficial study of a case that is likely to lead one astray. In tabes especially a consideration of the sensory disturbances, of the deep reflexes, and of the pupillary findings will always establish the presence or absence of the disease. In general paresis there is sometimes more difficulty. The onset of general paresis is often characterized by the appearance of symptoms quite like those of ordinary neurasthenia, and the family physician may entirely overlook the grave nature of the malady. The mistake in the other direction is, however, perhaps just as common. A physician who once or twice has seen a case of general paresis develop out of what appeared to be one of pronounced neurasthenia is too prone afterward to suspect every neurasthenic to be developing the malign affection. The most marked symptoms, however, of psychic exhaustion do not justify a diagnosis of general paresis even when the history is suspicious, unless along with it definite paresis of the facial or muscles of articulation or of the pupils exist. A history of syphilis or of chronic alcoholism or morphinism associated with severe psychic exhaustion should, of course, put one always on his guard, and the physician should be sharply on the lookout for the appearance of intellectual defects, paraphasia, facial paresis, and sluggishness of the pupils.

Treatment.—*Prophylaxis.*—Many patients come under our care a generation too late for satisfactory treatment, and it may be impossible to restore the exhausted capital. The greatest care should be taken in the rearing of children of neuropathic predisposition. From a very early age they should be submitted to a process of " psychic hardening," every effort being made to strengthen the bodily and mental condition. Even in infancy the child should not be pampered. Later on the greatest care should be exercised with regard to food, sleep, and school work. Complaints of children should not be too seriously considered.

Much depends upon the example set by the parents. A restless, emotional, constantly complaining mother will rack the nervous system of a delicate child. In some instances, for the welfare of a developing boy or girl, the physician may find it necessary to advise its removal from home.

Neurotic children are especially liable during development to fits of temper and of emotional disturbance. These should not be too lightly considered. Above all, violent chastisement in such cases is to be avoided, and loss of temper on the part of the parent or teacher is particularly pernicious for the nervous system of the child. Where possible, in such instances, the best treatment is to put the obstreperous child immediately to bed, and if the excitement and temper continue a warm bath followed by a cool douch may be effective. If he be put to bed after the bath sleep soon follows.

Special attention is necessary at puberty in both boys and girls. If there be at this period any marked tendency to emotional disturbance or to intellectual weakness the child should be removed from school and every care taken to avoid unfavorable influences.

Personal Hygiene.—Throughout life individuals of neuropathic predisposition should obey scrupulously certain hygienic and prophylactic rules. Intellectual work especially should be judiciously limited and should alternate frequently with periods of repose. Excitement of all kinds should of course be avoided, and such individuals will do well to be abstemious in the use of tobacco, tea, coffee, and alcohol, if, indeed, they be permitted to use these substances at all. The habit, happily in this country becoming very common, of taking at least once a year a prolonged holiday away from the ordinary environment, in the woods, in the mountains, or at the seashore, should be urgently enjoined upon every neuropathic individual. In many instances it is found to be the greatest relief and rest if the patient can take his holiday away from his relatives.

During ordinary life nervous people should, during some portion of each day, pay rational attention to the body. Cold baths, swimming, exercises in the gymnasium, gardening, golf, lawn tennis, cricket, hunting, shooting, rowing, sailing, and bicycling are of value in maintaining the general nutrition. Such exercises are, of course, to be recommended only to individuals physically equal to them. If neurasthenia be once well developed the greatest care must be observed in the ordering of exercise. Many nervous girls have been completely broken down by following injudicious advice with regard to long walks.

Treatment of the Condition.—The treatment of neurasthenia when once established presents a varied problem to the thoughtful physician. Every case must be handled upon its own merits, no two, as a rule, requiring exactly the same methods. In general it will be the aim of the medical adviser to remove the patient as far as possible from the influences which have led to his downfall, and to restore to normal the nervous mechanisms which have been weakened by injurious influences. The general character of the individual, his physical and social status must of course be considered, and the therapeutic measures carefully adjusted to these.

Above all, the physician must first gain the confidence of his patient, and this he will not do if he be inattentive to the complaints of the individual, especially at first, or if he rudely tell the patient before he has carefully examined him and observed him for some time that his troubles are imaginary. As has been said, it is education more than medicine that these patients need, but the patients themselves do not wish to be educated; they come to the physician to be treated, and the educating process has to be disguised.

The diagnosis having been settled, the physician may assure the patient that with prolonged treatment, during which his coöperation with the physician is absolutely essential, he may expect to get well. He must be told that much depends upon himself and that he must make a vigorous effort to overcome certain of his tendencies, and that all his strength of will will be needed to further the progress of the cure. In the case of business or professional men, in whom the condition develops as a result of overwork or overstudy, it may be sufficient to enjoin absolute rest with change of scene and diet. A trip abroad, with a residence for a month or two in Switzerland, or, if there are symptoms of nervous dyspepsia, a residence at one of the Spas will usually prove sufficient. The excitement of the large cities abroad should be avoided. The longer the disease has lasted and the more intense the symptoms have been, the longer the time necessary for the restoration of health. In cases of any severity the patient must be told that at least six months' complete absence from business, under strict medical guidance, will be necessary. Shorter periods may of course be of benefit, which, however, as a rule, will be only temporary.

It will be wise in very many cases to treat the individual for a few weeks at least in a hospital or other institution before sending him away on a journey. In this preliminary treatment the greatest tact is required on the part of the medical attendant and nurse. The patient should not see the doctor too often after the first careful examination, although he should of course receive regular visits from him. The physician will make a mistake if he responds to frequent calls on the part of the patient between the periods of his regular visits. The choice of a nurse is by no means an easy matter. That she should be healthy, strong, and by no means nervous herself are among the first considerations. Sallow-faced, emotional, emaciated women can only do harm if detailed to the care of a nervous patient.

It will often be found advisable to make out a daily programme, which shall occupy almost the whole time of the patient. At first he need know nothing about this, the case being given over entirely to the nurse. As improvement advances, moderate physical and intellectual exercises, alternating frequently with rest and the administration of food, may be undertaken. Some one hour of the day may be left free for reading, correspondence, conversation, and games. In some instances the writing of letters is particularly harmful to the patient and must be prohibited or limited. Cultured individuals may find benefit from attention to drawing, painting, modelling, translating from a foreign language, the making of abstracts, etc., for short periods in the day.

In not a few cases, including a large proportion of neurasthenic women, a systematic Weir Mitchell treatment rigidly carried out should be tried (see Hysteria). For obstinate and protracted cases, particularly if combined with the chloral or morphia habit, no other plan is so satisfactory. The patient must be isolated from his friends, and any regulations undertaken must be strictly adhered to, the consent of the patient and his family having first been gained. If the case responds well to the treatment there should be a gain of from 2 to 4 pounds per week. The benefit is often extraordinary, individuals increasing in weight as much as from 50 to 80 pounds in the course of twelve weeks. The treatment of the gastric and intestinal symptoms so important in this condition has already been considered. For the irregular pains, particularly in the back and neck, the thermo-cautery is invaluable.

Hydrotherapy is indicated in nearly every case if it can be properly applied. Much can be done at home or in an ordinary hospital, but for systematic hydrotherapeutic treatment residence in a suitable sanitarium is necessary. I have found the wet pack of especial value. Particularly at night in cases of sleeplessness it is perhaps the best remedy against insomnia we have. Some patients gain rapidly in weight through the systematic use of the wet pack. Salt baths are more helpful to some patients. The various forms of douches, partial packs, foot baths, etc., may be valuable in individual cases. The Scotch douche is often invigorating in the milder cases.

Electrotherapy is of some value, though only in combination with psychic treatment and hydrotherapy. General and local faradization, galvanic electricity, and Franklinization may be used; in every case, however, with great caution and only by skilled operators.

Treatment by drugs should be avoided as much as possible. They are of benefit chiefly in the combating of single symptoms. A placebo is sometimes necessary for its psychic effect. Alcohol, morphia, chloral, or cocaine should never be given. The family physician is often responsible for the development of a drug habit. I have been repeatedly shocked by the loose, careless way in which physicians inject morphia for a simple headache or a mild neuralgia.

General tonics may be helpful, especially if the individual be anæmic. Arsenic and more often iron are then indicated. The value of phosphorus has been exaggerated. For the severer pains and nervous attacks some sedative may occasionally be necessary, especially at the beginning of the treatment. The bromides, especially a mixture of the salts of ammonium, potassium, and sodium may here be given with advantage. An occasional dose of phenacetin, antipyrin, or salipyrin may be required, but the less of these substances we can get along with the better. For the relief of sleeplessness all possible measures should be resorted to before the employment of drugs. The wet pack will usually suffice. If absolutely necessary to give a drug, sulphonal, trional, or amylene hydrate may be employed.

In cases in which the anxiety conditions are disturbing, the cautious use of opium in pill form may be necessary, since, as in the psychoses, opium here will sometimes yield permanent relief. A prolonged treatment with opium is, however, never necessary in neurasthenia.

XIII. THE TRAUMATIC NEUROSES

(Railway Brain and Railway Spine; Traumatic Hysteria).

Definition.—A morbid condition following shock which presents the symptoms of neurasthenia or hysteria or of both. The condition is known as "railway brain" and "railway spine."

Erichsen regarded the condition as the result of inflammation of the meninges and cord, and gave it the name railway spine. Walton and J. J. Putnam, of Boston, were the first to recognize the hysterical nature of many of the cases, and to Westphal's pupils we owe the name traumatic neurosis. For an excellent discussion of the whole question the reader is referred to Pearce Baily's recent work, On Accident and Injury; their Relation to Diseases of the Nervous System.

Etiology.—The condition follows an accident, often in a railway train, in which injury has been sustained, or succeeds a shock or concussion, from which the patient may apparently not have suffered in his body. A man may appear perfectly well for several days, or even a week or more, and then develop the symptoms of the neurosis. Bodily shock or concussion is not necessary. The affection may follow a profound mental impression; thus, an engine-driver ran over a child, and received thereby a very severe shock, subsequent to which the most pronounced symptoms of neurasthenia developed. Severe mental strain combined with bodily exposure may cause it, as in a case of a naval officer who was wrecked in a violent storm and exposed for more than a day in the rigging before he was rescued. A slight blow, a fall from a carriage or on the stairs may suffice.

Symptoms.—The cases may be divided into three groups: simple neurasthenia, cases with marked hysterical manifestations, and cases with severe symptoms indicating or simulating organic disease.

(a) *Simple Traumatic Neurasthenia.*—The first symptoms usually develop a few weeks after the accident, which may or may not have been associated with an actual trauma. The patient complains of headache and tired feelings. He is sleepless and finds himself unable to concentrate his attention properly upon his work. A condition of nervous irritability develops, which may have a host of trivial manifestations, and the entire mental attitude of the person may for a time be changed. He dwells constantly upon his condition, gets very despondent and low-spirited, and in extreme cases melancholia may develop. He may complain of numbness and tingling in the extremities, and in some cases of much pain in the back. The bodily functions may be well performed, though such patients usually have, for a time at least, disturbed digestion and loss in weight. The physical examination may be entirely negative. The reflexes are slightly increased, as in ordinary neurasthenia. The pupils may be unequal; the cardio-vascular changes already described in neurasthenia may be present in a marked degree. According as the symptoms are more spinal or more cerebral, the condition is known as railway brain or railway spine.

(2) *Cases with Marked Hysterical Features.*—Following an injury of any sort, neurasthenic symptoms, like those described above, may develop, and in addition symptoms regarded as characteristic of hysteria. The emotional element is prominent, and there is but slight control over the feelings. The patients have headache, backache, and vertigo. A violent tremor may be present, and indeed constitutes the most striking feature of the case. I have recently seen an engineer who developed subsequent to an accident a series of nervous phenomena, but the most marked feature was an excessive tremor of the entire body, which was specially manifest during emotional excitement. The most pronounced hysterical symptoms are the sensory disturbances. As first noted by Putnam and Walton, hemianæsthesia may occur as a sequence of traumatism. This is a common symptom in France, but rare in England and in this country. Achromatopsia may exist on the anæsthetic side. A second, more common, manifestation is limitation of the field of vision, similar to that which occurs in hysteria.

Remarkable disturbances may develop in some of these cases. A few months ago I saw a man who had been struck by an electric car, whose chief symptom was an extraordinary increase in the number of respirations. He was a stout, powerfully built man, and presented practically no other symptom than dyspnœa of the most extreme grade. At the time of observation his respirations were over 130 per minute, and he stated that they had been counted at over 150.

(3) *Cases in which the Symptoms suggest Organic Disease of the Brain and Cord.*—As a result of spinal concussion, without fracture or external injury, there may subsequently develop symptoms suggestive of organic disease, which may come on rapidly or at a late date. In a case reported by Leyden the symptoms following the concussion were at first slight and the patient was regarded as a simulator, but finally the condition became aggravated and death resulted. The post mortem showed a chronic pachymeningitis, which had doubtless resulted from the accident. The cases in this group about which there is so much discussion are those which display marked sensory and motor changes. Following an accident in which the patient has not received external injury a condition of excitement may develop within a week or ten days; he complains of headache and backache, and on examination sensory disturbances are found, either hemianæsthesia or areas on the skin in which the sensation is much benumbed; or painful and tactile impressions may be distinctly felt in certain regions, and the temperature sense is absent. The distribution may be bilateral and symmetrical in limited regions or hemiplegic in type. Limitation of the field of vision is usually marked in these cases, and there may be disturbance of the senses of taste and smell. The superficial reflexes may be diminished; usually the deep reflexes are exaggerated. The pupils may be unequal; the motor disturbances are variable. The French writers describe cases of

monoplegia with or without contracture, symptoms upon which Charcot lays great stress as a manifestation of profound hysteria. The combination of sensory disturbances—anæsthesia or hyperæsthesia—with paralysis, particularly if monoplegic, and the occurrence of contractures without atrophy and with normal electrical reactions, may be regarded as distinctive of hysteria.

In rare cases following trauma and succeeding to symptoms which may have been regarded as neurasthenic or hysterical, there are organic changes which may prove fatal. That this sequence occurs is demonstrated clearly by recent post-mortem examinations. The features upon which the greatest reliance can be placed as indicating organic change are optic atrophy, bladder symptoms, particularly in combination with tremor, paresis, and exaggerated reflexes.

The anatomical changes in this condition have not been very definite. When death follows spinal concussion within a few days there may be no apparent lesion, but in some instances the brain or cord has shown punctiform hæmorrhages. Edes has reported 4 cases in which a gradual degeneration in the pyramidal tracts followed concussion or injury of the spine; but in all these cases there was marked tremor and the spinal symptoms developed early or followed immediately upon the accident. Post mortems upon cases in which organic lesions have supervened upon a traumatic neurosis are extremely rare. Bernhardt reports an instance of a man, aged thirty-three, who in 1886 received a kick from a horse on the epigastrium and subsequently developed the symptom-complex of neurasthenia and hysteria with attacks of vertigo and great psychical depression. He afterward had more marked mental symptoms and attacks of unconsciousness. He committed suicide and the brain and cord showed a beginning multiple sclerosis in the white matter, which was possibly associated with an advanced grade of arterio-sclerosis. In a second case a man, aged forty-two, received a shock in a railway accident in July, 1884. He was rendered unconscious and had a slight injury in the buttock region. In a few weeks symptoms of traumatic neurosis developed, particularly great depression of spirits, with headache and sensory disturbances in the feet and hands. Tremor and great weakness were complained of when he attempted to work. There was no increase in the reflexes. The case was regarded as an instance of simulation and a defect in objective symptoms favored this view. Subsequently this judgment was reversed, but he did not improve. He died in January, 1889, with symptoms of cardiac dyspnœa. Macroscopically the brain and cord appeared normal. There was extreme arteriosclerosis, particularly of the vessels of the brain and cord. In the latter there were scattered areas of degeneration in the white substance, and degeneration in the sympathetic ganglia.

I have entered somewhat fully into this question because of its extreme importance and on account of the paucity of the observations upon cases which have subsequently developed symptoms of organic disease. Examples of it are extremely rare. So far as I know no case with autopsy has been reported in this country, nor have I seen an instance in which the clinical features pointed to an organic disease which had followed upon a traumatic neurosis.

Diagnosis.—A condition of fright and excitement following an accident may persist for days or even weeks, and then gradually pass away. The symptoms of neurasthenia or of hysteria which subsequently develop present nothing peculiar and are identical with those which occur under other circumstances. Care must be taken to recognize simulation, and, as in these cases the condition is largely subjective, this is sometimes extremely difficult. In a careful examination a simulator will often reveal himself by exaggeration of certain symptoms, particularly sensitiveness of the spine, and by increasing voluntarily the reflexes. Maunkopff suggests as a good test to take the pulse-rate before, during, and after pressure upon an area said to be painful. If the rate is quickened, it is held to be proof that the pain is real. This is not, however, always the case. It may require a careful study of the case to determine whether the individual is honestly suffering from the symptoms of which he complains. A still more important question in these cases is, Has the patient organic disease? The symptoms given under the first two groups of cases may exist in a marked degree and may persist for several years without the slightest evidence of organic change. Hemianæsthesia, limitation of the field of vision, monoplegia with contracture, may all be present as hysterical manifestations, from which recovery may be complete. In our present knowledge the diagnosis of an organic lesion should be limited to those cases in which optic atrophy, bladder troubles, and signs of sclerosis of the cord are well marked—indications either of degeneration of the lateral columns or of multiple sclerosis.

Prognosis.—A majority of patients with traumatic hysteria recover. In railway cases, so long as litigation is pending and the patient is in the hands of lawyers the symptoms usually persist. Settlement is often the starting-point of a speedy and perfect recovery. I have known return to health after the persistence of the most aggravated symptoms with complete disability of from three to five years' duration. On the other hand, there are a few cases in which the symptoms persist even after the litigation has been closed; the patient goes from bad to worse and psychoses develop, such as melancholia, dementia, or occasionally progressive paresis. And, lastly, in extremely rare cases, organic lesions may develop as a sequence of the traumatic neurosis.

The function of the physician acting as medical expert in these cases consists in determining (*a*) the existence of actual disease, and (*b*) its character, whether simple neurasthenia, severe hysteria, or an organic lesion. The outlook for ultimate recovery is good except in cases which present the more serious symptoms above mentioned. Nevertheless, it must be borne in mind that traumatic hysteria is one of the most intractable affections which we are called upon to treat. In the treatment of the traumatic neuroses the practitioner may be guided by the principles laid down in the preceding chapter, in which the treatment of neurasthenia in general has been described.

XIV. OTHER FORMS OF FUNCTIONAL PARALYSIS.

I. Periodical Paralysis.

I have already referred to the remarkable periodical paralysis of the ocular muscles, which may recur at intervals for many years. There is a form of periodical paralysis involving the general muscles, which may recur with great regularity, and which is also a "family" affection. Gold-flam has described a family in which twelve members were affected with this disease, the heredity being through the mother. In this country E. W. Taylor has described in one family 11 cases in five generations.

The clinical picture is very much alike in all the recorded cases. The paralysis involves, as a rule, the arms and legs. It comes on when the patients are in full health, and without any apparent cause, often during sleep. Sometimes it begins with weakness in the limbs, a sensation of weariness and sleepiness, not often with sensory symptoms. The paralysis is usually complete within the first twenty-four hours, beginning in the legs, to which in rare instances it is confined. The muscles of the neck are sometimes involved, and occasionally those of the tongue and pharynx. The cerebral nerves and the special senses are, as a rule, uninvolved. The attacks are afebrile, sometimes with low temperatures and slow pulse. The deep reflexes are reduced, sometimes abolished, and the skin reflexes may be feeble. One of the most remarkable features is the extraordinary reduction or complete abolition of the faradic excitability, both of muscles and of nerves.

Improvement begins sometimes in the course of a few hours or after a day or two, and the paralysis disappears completely, and the patient is perfectly well. As mentioned, the attacks may recur every few weeks, in some instances even daily; more commonly, an interval of one or two weeks elapses between the attacks. There may be signs of acute dilatation of the heart during the attack. After the fiftieth year the attacks usually cease.

II. Astasia; Abasia.

These terms, indicating respectively inability to stand and inability to walk, have been applied by Charcot and Blocq to diseased conditions characterized by loss of the power of standing or of walking, with retention of muscular power, coördination, and sensation. Blocq's definition is as follows: "A morbid state in which the impossibility of standing erect and walking normally is in contrast with the integrity of sensation, of muscular strength, and of the coördination of the other movements of the lower extremities." The condition forms a symptom group, not a morbid entity, and is probably a functional neurosis. Knapp in his monograph analyzes the 50 cases reported in the literature. Twenty-five of these were in men, 25 in women. In 21 cases hysteria was present; in 3, chorea; in 2, epilepsy; and in 4, intention psychoses. As a rule, the patients, though able to move the feet and legs perfectly when in bed, are either unable to walk properly or cannot stand at all. The disturbances have been very varied, and different forms have been recognized. The commonest, according to Knapp's analysis of the recorded cases, is the paralytic, in which the legs give out as the patient attempts to walk and "bend under him as if made of cotton." "There is no rigidity, no spasm, no incoördination. In bed, sitting, or even while suspended, the muscular strength is found to be good." Other cases are associated with spasm or ataxia; thus there may be movements which stiffen the legs and give to the gait a somewhat spastic character. In other instances there are sudden flexions of the legs, or even of the arms, or a saltatory, spring-like spasm. In a majority of the cases it is a manifestation of a neurosis allied to hysteria.

The cases, as a rule, recover, particularly in young persons. Relapses are not uncommon. The rest treatment and static electricity should be employed.

VIII. VASO–MOTOR AND TROPHIC DISORDERS.

I. RAYNAUD'S DISEASE.

Definition.—A vascular disorder, probably dependent upon vaso-motor influences, characterized by three grades of intensity: (*a*) Local syncope, (*b*) local asphyxia, and (*c*) local or symmetrical gangrene.

Local Syncope.—This condition is seen most frequently in the extremities, producing the condition known as dead fingers or dead toes. It is analogous to that produced by great cold. The entire hand may be affected with the fingers; more commonly only one or more of the fingers. This feature of the disease rarely occurs alone, but is generally associated with local asphyxia. The common sequence is as follows: On exposure to slight cold or in consequence of some emotional disturbance the fingers become white and cold, or both fingers and toes are affected. The pallor may continue for an indefinite time, though usually not more than an hour or so; then gradually a reaction follows and the fingers get burning hot and red. This does not necessarily occur in all the fingers together; one finger may be as white as marble, while the adjacent ones are of a deep red or plum color.

Local Asphyxia.—Chilblains form the mildest grade of this condition. It usually follows the local syncope, but it may come on independently. The fingers and toes are oftenest affected, next in order the ears; more rarely portions of the skin on the arms and legs. During an attack the fingers alone, sometimes the hands, also swell and become intensely congested. In the most extreme grade the fingers are perfectly livid, and the capillary circulation is almost stagnant. The swelling causes stiffness and usually pain, not acute, but due to the tension and distention of the skin. Sometimes there is marked anæsthesia. Pain of a most excruciating kind may be present. Attacks of this sort may recur for years, and be brought on by the slightest exposure to cold or in consequence of disturbances, either mental or, in some instances, gastric. Apart from this unpleasant symp-

71

tom the general health may be very good. The condition is always worse during the winter, and may be present only when the external temperature is low.

Local or Symmetrical Gangrene.—The mildest grade of this condition follows the local asphyxia, in the chronic cases of which small necrotic areas are sometimes seen at the tips of the fingers. Sometimes the pads of the fingers and of the toes are quite cicatricial from repeated slight losses of this kind. So also when the ears are affected there may be superficial loss of substance at the edge. The severer cases, which terminate in extensive gangrene, are fortunately rare.

In an attack the local asphyxia persists in the fingers. The terminal phalanges, or perhaps the end of only one finger, become black, cold, and insensible. The skin begins to necrose and superficial gangrenous blebs appear. Gradually a line of demarkation shows itself and a portion of one or more of the fingers sloughs away. The resulting loss of substance is much less than the appearance of the hand or foot would indicate, and a condition which looks as if the patient would lose all the fingers or half of a foot may result perhaps in only a slight superficial loss in the phalanges. In severer cases the greater portion of a finger or the tip of the nose may be lost. Occasionally the disease is not confined to the extremities, but affects symmetrical patches on the limbs or trunk, and may pass on to rapid gangrene. These severe types of cases occur particularly in young children, and death may result within three or four days. The attacks are usually very painful, and the motion of the part is much impaired. In some cases numbness and tingling persist for a long time.

The climax of this series of neuro-vascular changes is seen in the remarkable instances of extensive multiple gangrene. They are most common in children, and may progress with frightful rapidity. In the Medico-Chirurgical Society's Transactions, vol. xxii, there is an extraordinary case reported, in which the child, aged three, lost in this way both arms above the elbow, and the left leg below the knee. There also had been a spot of local gangrene on the nose. Spontaneous amputation occurred, and the child made a complete recovery. The cases are more frequent than has been supposed, and an illustration is given by Weeks, of Marion, Ohio, in which the boy had rheumatic pains in the legs, and purpuric blotches developed before the gangrene began (Medico-Surgical Bulletin, July 1, 1894).

There are remarkable concomitant symptoms in Raynaud's disease to which a good deal of attention has been paid of late years. Hæmoglobinuria may develop during an attack, or may take the place of an outbreak. In such instances the affection is usually brought on by cold weather. In a case reported by H. M. Thomas from my clinic, Raynaud's disease occurred for three successive winters and always in association with hæmoglobinuria. The attacks were sometimes preceded by a chill. Several cases of the kind are found in Barlow's appendix to his translation of Raynaud's paper for the New Sydenham Society. The onset with a chill, as in the case just mentioned, has doubtless given rise to the idea that the disease is in some way associated with ague. Cerebral symptoms, particularly mental torpor and transient loss of consciousness, have also been noticed in some cases. The case just mentioned with hæmoglobinuria had epilepsy with the attacks. Exposure on a cold day would bring on an epileptic seizure with the local asphyxia and bloody urine. Another patient, the subject for years of Raynaud's disease, has had many attacks of transient hemiplegia on one side or the other, when on the right side with aphasia. Since the second edition of this work was issued she died in an attack. Occasionally joint affections develop, particularly anchylosis and thickening of the phalangeal articulations. Southey has reported a case in which mania developed, and Barlow an instance in which the woman had delusions. Peripheral neuritis has been found in several cases.

The *pathology* of this remarkable disease is still obscure. Raynaud suggested that the local syncope was produced by contraction of the vessels, which seems likely. The asphyxia is dependent upon dilatation of the capillaries and small veins, probably with the persistence of some degree of spasm of the smaller arteries. There are two totally different forms of congestion, which may be shown in adjacent fingers; one may be swollen, of a vivid red color, extremely hot, the capillaries and all the vessels fully distended, and the anæmia produced by pressure may be instantaneously obliterated; the adjacent finger may be equally swollen, absolutely cyanotic, stone cold, and the anæmia produced by pressure takes a long time to disappear. In the latter case the arterioles are probably still in a condition of spasm.

Treatment.—In many cases the attacks recur for years uninfluenced by treatment. Mild attacks require no treatment. In the severer forms of local asphyxia, if in the feet, the patient should be kept in bed with the legs elevated. The toes should be wrapped in cotton-wool. The pain is often very intense and may require morphia. Carefully applied, systematic massage of the extremities is sometimes of benefit. Galvanism may be tried. Barlow advises immersing the affected limb in salt water and placing one electrode over the spine and the other in the water. Nitroglycerin has been warmly recommended by Cates.

II. ERYTHROMELALGIA (*Red Neuralgia*).

Definition.—" A chronic disease in which a part or parts—usually one or more extremities—suffer with pain, flushing, and local fever, made far worse if the parts hang down " (Weir Mitchell). The name signifies a painful, red extremity.

Symptoms.—In 1872 (Phila. Med. Times, November 23d), in a lecture on certain painful affections of the feet, Weir Mitchell described the case of a sailor, aged forty, who after an African fever began to have " dull, heavy pains, at first in the left and soon after in the right foot. There was no swelling at first. When at rest he was comfortable and the feet were not painful. After walking the feet were swollen. They scarcely pitted on pressure, but were purple with congestion; the veins were everywhere singularly enlarged, and the arteries were throbbing visibly. The whole foot was said to be aching and burning, but above the ankle there was neither swelling, pain, nor, flushing." As the weather grew cool he got relief. Nothing seemed to benefit him. This brief summary of Mitchell's first case gives an accurate clinical picture of the disease. His second communication, On a Rare Vaso-motor Neurosis of the Extremities, appeared in the Am. Jour. of the Medical Sciences for July, 1878, while in his Clinical Lessons on Nervous Diseases, 1897, will be found additional observations.

The disease is rare. Rost states that there are only about 40 instances in the literature. The feet are much more often affected than the hands. The pain may be of the most atrocious character. It is usually, but not always, relieved by cool weather; in one of my cases the winter aggravates the trouble. In a few cases (Elsner, Dehio, Rolleston) the affection has been complicated with Raynaud's disease.

Mitchell speaks of it as a ".painful nerve-end neuritis." Dehio suggests that there may be irritation in the cells of the ventral horns of the cord at certain levels. Excision of the nerves passing to the parts has been followed by relief. In one of Mitchell's cases gangrene of the foot followed excision of four inches of the musculo-cutaneous nerve and stretching of the posterior tibial. Sclerosis of the arteries was found.

III. ANGIO-NEUROTIC ŒDEMA.

Definition.—An affection characterized by the occurrence of local œdematous swellings, more or less limited in extent, and of transient duration. Severe colic is sometimes associated with the outbreak. There is a marked hereditary disposition in the disease.

Symptoms.—The œdema appears suddenly and is usually circumscribed. It may appear in the face; the eyelid is a common situation; or it may involve the lips or cheek. The backs of the hands, the legs, or the throat may be attacked. Usually the condition is transient, associated perhaps with slight gastro-intestinal distress, and the affection is of little moment. There may be a remarkable periodicity in the outbreak of the œdema. In Matas' case this periodicity was very striking; the attack came on every day at eleven or twelve o'clock. The disease may be hereditary through many generations. In the family whose history I reported, five generations had been affected, including twenty-two members. The swellings appear in various parts; only rarely are they constant in one locality. The hands, face, and genitalia are the parts most frequently affected. Itching, heat, redness, or in some instances, urticaria may precede the outbreak. Sudden œdema of the larynx may prove fatal. Two members of the family just referred to died of this complication. In one member of this family, whom I saw repeatedly in attacks, the swellings came on in different parts; for example, the under lip would be swollen to such a degree that the mouth could not be opened. The hands enlarge suddenly, so that the fingers cannot be bent. The attacks recur every three or four weeks. Accompanying them are usually gastro-intestinal attacks, severe colic, pain, nausea, and sometimes vomiting. It is quite possible that some of the cases of Leyden's intermittent vomiting may belong to this group. The colic is of great intensity and usually requires morphia. Arthritis apparently does not occur. Periodic attacks of cardialgia have also been met with during the outbreak of the œdema. Hæmoglobinuria has occurred in several cases.

The disease has affinities with urticaria, the giant form of which is probably the same disease. There is a form of severe purpura, often with urticarial manifestations, which is also associated with marked gastro-intestinal crises, and it is interesting to note that Schlesinger has reported a case in which a combination of erythromelalgia, Raynaud's disease, and acute œdema occurred. Quincke regards the condition as a vaso-motor neurosis, under the influence of which the permeability of the vessels is suddenly increased. Milroy, of Omaha, has described cases of hereditary œdema, twenty-two individuals in six generations, in which there existed from birth a solid œdema of one or of both legs, without any special inconvenience or any progressive increase of the disease.

Some years ago I described a remarkable vaso-motor neurosis characterized by *swelling and tumefaction of the whole arm on exertion.* My patient was a man, healthy in every other respect. Recently in Philadelphia a similar case has been observed. On the supposition that there might be pressure on the axillary vessels these were exposed, but nothing was found.

The *treatment* is very unsatisfactory. In the cases associated with anæmia and general nervousness, tonics, particularly large doses of strychnia, do good; but too often the disease resists all treatment. I have seen great improvement follow the prolonged use of nitroglycerin.

IV. FACIAL HEMIATROPHY.

An affection characterized by progressive wasting of the bones and soft tissues of one side of the face. The atrophy starts in childhood, but in a few cases has not come on until adult life. Perhaps after a trifling injury or disease the process begins, either diffusely or more commonly at one spot on the skin. It gradually spreads, involving the fat, then the bones, more particularly the upper jaw, and last and least the muscles. The wasting is sharply limited at the middle line, and the appearance of the patient is very remarkable, the face looking as if made up of two halves from different persons. There is usually change in the color of the skin and the hair falls. Owing to the wasting of the alveolar processes the teeth become loose and ultimately drop out. The eye on the affected side is sunken, owing to loss of orbital fat. There is usually hemiatrophy of the tongue on the same side. Disturbance of sensation and muscle twitching may precede or accompany the atrophy. In a majority of the cases the atrophy has been confined to one side of the face, but there are instances on record in which the disease was bilateral, and a few cases in which there were areas of atrophy on the back and on the arm of the same side. The disease is rare; only about 100 cases are in the literature (Möbius).

Of the autopsies, Mendel's alone is satisfactory. There was the terminal stage of an interstitial neuritis in all the branches of the trigeminus, from its origin to the periphery, most marked in the superior maxillary branch.

The disease is recognized at a glance. The facial asymmetry associated with congenital wryneck must not be confounded with progressive facial hemiatrophy. Other conditions to be distinguished are: Facial atrophy in anterior polio-myelitis, and more rarely in the hemiplegia of infants and adults; the atrophy following nuclear lesions and sympathetic nerve paralysis; acquired facial hemihypertrophy, such as in the case recorded by D. W. Montgomery, which may by contrast give to the other side an atrophic appearance; and, lastly, scleroderma (a closely related affection), if confined to one side of the face. The precise nature of the disease is still doubtful, but it is a suggestive fact that in many of the cases the atrophy has followed the acute infections. It is incurable.

V. ACROMEGALY.

Definition.—A dystrophy characterized by abnormal processes of growth, chiefly in the bones of the face and extremities.

The term was introduced by Marie, and signifies large extremities.

Etiology.—It occurs rather more frequently in women. The affection usually begins about the twenty-fifth year, though in some instances as late as the fortieth. Rheumatism, syphilis, and the specific fevers have preceded the development of the disease, but probably have no special connection with it. In this country many cases have now been reported.

Symptoms.—In a well-marked case the disease presents most characteristic features. The hands and feet are greatly enlarged, but are not deformed, and can be used freely. The hypertrophy is general, involving all the tissues, and gives a curious spade-like character to the hands. The lines on the palms are much deepened. The wrists may be enlarged, but the arms are rarely affected. The feet are involved like the hands and are uniformly enlarged. The big toe, however, may be much larger in proportion. The nails are usually broad and large, but there is no curving, and the terminal phalanges are not bulbous. The head increases in volume, but not as much in proportion as the face, which becomes much elongated and enlarged in consequence of the increase in the size of the superior and inferior maxillary bones. The latter in particular increases greatly in size, and often projects below the upper jaw. The alveolar processes are widened and the teeth separated. The soft parts also increase in size, and the nostrils are large and broad. The eyelids are sometimes greatly thickened, and the ears enormously hypertrophied. The tongue in some instances becomes greatly enlarged. Late in the disease the spine may be affected and the back bowed—kyphosis. The bones of the thorax may slowly and progressively enlarge. With this gradual increase in size the skin of the hands and face may appear normal. Sometimes it is slightly altered in color, coarse, or flabby, but it has not the dry, harsh appearance of the skin in myxœdema. The muscles are sometimes wasted. Changes in the thyroid have been found, but are not constant. The gland has been normal in some, atrophied in others, and in a third group of cases enlarged. Erb, who has made an elaborate study of the disease, has noticed an area of dulness over the manubrium sterni, which he thought possibly due to the persistence or enlargement of the thymus. Headache is not uncommon. Somnolence has been noted in many cases. Menstrual disturbance may occur early, and there may be suppression. *Ocular symptoms* are common. Hertel has analyzed 175 recorded cases, 92 of which presented eye complications. In three fourths of these the optic nerves were affected—usually atrophy, rarely neuritis. Bitemporal hemianopia is often an early sign. The disease may persist for fifteen, twenty, or more years.

Pathological Anatomy.—Furnival has recently analyzed the recorded autopsies, 34 in number. Changes in the pituitary gland were found in all, and in the majority there was hypertrophy or tumor. In 24 cases in which it was examined the thyroid was normal in 5, hypertrophied in one half; the thymus in 17 examined was absent in 7, hypertrophied in 3, and persistent in 7. In Osborne's case the heart was enormous, weighing 2 pounds 9 ounces.

Owing to the remarkable changes in the pituitary gland in acromegaly, it has been suggested that the disease is a nutritional disturbance analogous to myxœdema, and caused directly by disturbance in the function of this organ. The evidence from comparative anatomy and embryology shows that the pituitary body is a very " complex organ, consisting of an anterior secreting glandular organ; a water-vascular duct; a posterior, sensitive, nervous lobe, of which the last two—namely, the duct and the nervous lobe —were morphologically well developed and functioned in ancestral vertebrates, but have become obliterated and atrophied in structure and function forever above larval acraniates " (Andriezen, British Medical Journal, 1894, i). The pituitary body continues active, but the duct is obliterated " and the gland changed into a ductless gland; the secretion becomes an ' internal secretion,' " which is absorbed by the lymphatics. The extraordinary frequency with which the pituitary is involved in this disease lends weight to the view that it is, in the words of Woods Hutchinson, the growth centre, or at any rate the proportion regulator of the skeleton.

It has been suggested by Massalongo and others that gigantism and acromegaly are one and the same disease, both due to the superfunction of the pituitary gland. Certain persons exhibited as giants, or who have been " strong men " and wrestlers, have become acromegalic, and the skulls of some notable giants show enormous enlargement of the sella turcica.

There is a congenital progressive hypertrophy of one extremity or of a part of it or of one side of the body—the so-called *giant growth*, which does not appear to have any connection with acromegaly.

The treatment does not appear to have any influence upon the progress of the disease. The thyroid extract has been tried in many cases, without, so far as my personal experience goes, any benefit. Extract of the pituitary gland has also been used. The lung extract has been employed in some cases of pulmonary osteo-arthropathy. In a case of Caton's, of Liverpool, an unsuccessful attempt was made to extirpate the pituitary body.

OSTEITIS DEFORMANS (*Paget's Disease*).

In this remarkable affection the shafts of the long bones are chiefly involved, and in the head the bones of the cranium, but not those of the face. It is a rare disease. The bones enlarge and soften, and those bearing weight become unnaturally curved and misshapen. At its commencement, and sometimes through all its course, it is attended with pains in the affected bones.

The bone structure shows a mixture of rarefying osteitis, with the Haversian canals large and irregular, and of formative osteitis, with certain Haversian canals narrowed and lamellæ of recent formation.

There is an intimate relation between osteitis deformans and the formation of malignant tumors. Of 8 cases traced to the end, 5 died with cancer or sarcoma.

About 60 cases have now been recorded, most of them in England. Seven have been reported in America. The most typical case is one reported by Watson in the Johns Hopkins Hospital Bulletin for June, 1898. I saw the man first in July, 1897. At the age of forty-two he was strong and healthy, measuring 5 feet $11\frac{1}{4}$ inches in height. His tibiæ began to enlarge and bow forward and outward, the thoracic spine to curve, and the cranial bones to enlarge. This has steadily progressed. He is now sixty-two years of age. At present, owing to the bowing of the spine and lower extremities, his height is about 5 feet $2\frac{1}{2}$ inches, or $9\frac{1}{4}$ inches less than formerly. The circumference of his head has increased $3\frac{1}{16}$ inches. His thorax is almost perfectly quadrilateral. His intellect is unimpaired, and his general health is fairly good (Watson).

As Marie states, in Paget's disease the face is triangular with the base upward; in acromegaly it is ovoid or egg-shaped with the large end downward; while in myxœdema it is round and full-moon-shaped.

Concerning the etiology of the disease, absolutely nothing is known. No method of treatment has had the slightest influence upon its progress.

HYPERTROPHIC PULMONARY ARTHROPATHY.

Marie has given the name *hypertrophic pulmonary osteo-arthropathy* to a remarkable disorder, first recognized by Bamberger, characterized by enlargement of the hands and feet, and of the ends of the long bones, chiefly of the lower three fourths of the forearm and legs. Unlike acromegaly, the bones of the skull and of the face are not involved. The terminal phalanges are much spread with both transverse and longitudinal curves; the nails, too, are large and much curved over the ends of the phalanges. Scoliosis and kyphosis are rarely seen. The disease is very chronic, and in nearly all cases has been associated with some long-standing affection of the bronchi, lungs, or pleura (hence the name *pulmonary osteo-arthropathy*), of which sarcoma, chronic bronchitis, chronic tuberculosis, and empyema have been the most frequent. There are several instances in which the affection has developed in the subjects of syphilis. It occurs usually in adults and in the male sex. Thayer has reported 4 cases from my clinic and has collected 55 typical cases from the literature. Forty-three showed preceding pulmonary affection; of the remaining, 3 followed syphilis, 3 heart-disease, 2 chronic diarrhœa, 1 spinal caries, and 3 unknown causes.

The essential pathology of the disease is very obscure. Marie suggests that the toxines of the pulmonary disease are absorbed into the circulation and exercise an irritant action on the bony and articular structures, causing an ossifying periostitis. Thorburn thinks that it is a chronic tuberculous affection of a large number of bones and joints of a benign type.

Leontiasis Ossea.

Finally, in a remarkable condition known as *leontiasis ossea*, there is hyperostosis of the bones of the cranium, and sometimes those of the face. The description is largely based upon the skulls in museums, but Allen Starr has recently reported an instance in a woman, who presented a slowly progressing increase in the size of the head, face, and neck, the hard and soft tissues both being affected. He has applied to the condition the term *megalo-cephaly*. Putnam states that the disease begins in early life, often as a result of injury. There may be osteophytic growths from the outer or inner tables, which in the latter situation may give the symptoms of tumor.

Micromegaly.

A remarkable condition, the antithesis of acromegaly, has been described by Jonathan Hutchinson and Hastings Gilford (Lancet, 1896, ii, p. 1227) as " mixed premature and immature development." The name *micromegaly* is suggested by Gilford, who describes it as a disease of that part of the nervous system presiding over nutrition, which manifests itself in a smallness and immaturity of some parts or functions and a relative or actual largeness or prematurity of others.

VI. SCLERODERMA.

Definition.—A condition of localized or diffuse induration of the skin.

Lewin and Heller (Die Sclerodermie, Berlin, 1895) have recently collected from the literature 508 cases.

Two forms are recognized: the circumscribed, which corresponds to the keloid of Addison, and to morphœa; and the diffuse, in which large areas are involved.

The disease affects females more frequently than males. The cases occur most commonly at the middle period of life. The *sclerema neonatorum* is a different affection, not to be confounded with it. The disease is more common in this country than statistics indicate. I have reported 8 cases (Jour. of Genito-Urinary and Cutaneous Diseases, January, 1898), since which date I have seen 3 additional cases.

In the *circumscribed form* there are patches, ranging from a few centimetres in diameter to the size of the hand or larger, in which the skin has a waxy or dead-white appearance, and to the touch is brawny, hard, and inelastic. Sometimes there is a preliminary hyperæmia of the skin, and subsequently there are changes in color, either areas of pigmentation or of complete atrophy of the pigment—leucoderma. The sensory changes are rarely marked. The secretion of sweat is diminished or entirely abolished. The disease is more common in women than in men, and is situated most frequently about the breasts and neck, sometimes in the course of the nerves. The patches may develop with great rapidity, and may persist for months or years; sometimes they disappear in a few weeks.

The *diffuse form*, though less common, is more serious. It develops first in the extremities or in the face, and the patient notices that the skin is unusually hard and firm, or that there is a sense of stiffness or tension in making accustomed movements. Gradually a diffuse, brawny induration develops and the skin becomes firm and hard, and so united to the subcutaneous tissues that it cannot be picked up or pinched. The skin may look natural, but more commonly is glossy, drier than normal, and unusually smooth. With reference to the localization, in 66 observations the disease was universal; in 203, regions of the trunk were affected; in 193, parts of the head or face; in 287, portions of one or other of the upper extremities; and in 122, portions of the lower extremities. In 80 cases there were disturbances of sensation. The disease may gradually extend and involve the skin of an entire limb. When universal, the face is expressionless, the lips cannot be moved, mastication is hindered, and it may become extremely difficult to feed the patient. The hands become fixed and the fingers immobile, on account of the extreme induration of the skin over the joints. Remarkable vaso-motor disturbances are common, as extreme cyanosis of the hands and legs. In one of my cases tachycardia was present. The disease is chronic, lasting for months or years. There are instances on record of its persistence for more than twenty years. Recovery may occur, or the disease may be arrested. The patients are apt to succumb to pulmonary complaints or to nephritis. Rheumatic troubles have been noticed in some instances; in others, endocarditis. Raynaud's disease may be associated with it, as in 2 cases described by Stephen Mackenzie. I have seen an instance of the diffuse form in which the primary symptoms were those of local asphyxia of the fingers, and in which, with extensive scleroderma of the arms and hands and face, there were cyanosis and swelling of the skin of the feet without any brawny induration. The pigmentation of the skin may be as deep as in Addison's disease, for which cases have been mistaken; scleroderma may occur as a complication of exophthalmic goitre.

The remarkable dystrophy known as *sclerodactylie* belongs to this disorder. There are symmetrical involvements of the fingers, which become deformed, shortened, and atrophied; the skin becomes thickened, of a waxy color, and is sometimes pigmented. Bullæ and ulcerations have been met with in some instances, and a great deformity of the nails. The disease has usually followed exposure, and the patients are much worse during the winter, and are curiously sensitive to cold. There may be changes in the skin of the feet, but the deformity similar to that which occurs in the hand has not been noted. Some of the cases present in addition diffuse sclerodermatous changes of the skin of other parts. In Lewin and Heller's monograph there are 35 cases of isolated sclerodactylism, and 106 cases in which it was combined with scleroderma.

The pathology of the disease is unknown. It is usually regarded as a tropho-neurosis, probably dependent upon changes in the arteries of the skin leading to connective-tissue overgrowth. The thyroid has been found atrophied.

Treatment.—The patients require to be warmly clad and to be guarded against exposure, as they are particularly sensitive to changes in the weather. Warm baths followed by frictions with oil should be systematically used. I have tried the thyroid feeding thoroughly in the diffuse form without success. In a recent case of quite extensive localized scleroderma, after ten weeks' treatment, the patches are softer and the pigmentation much less intense. Salol in 15-grain doses three times a day is stated to have been successful in several cases.

AINHUM.

Here a brief reference may be made to the remarkable trophic lesion described by Da Silva Lima, which is met with in negroes in Brazil, Africa, India, and occasionally in the Southern States. It is confined to the toes, usually the little toe, and begins as a furrow on the line of the digito-plantar fold. This gradually deepens, the end of the toe enlarges, and, usually without inflammation or pain, the toe falls off. The process may last some years. Cases have been reported in this country by Hornaday, Pittman, F. J. Shepherd, and Morrison.

SECTION XI.

DISEASES OF THE MUSCLES.

I. MYOSITIS.

Definition.—Inflammation of the voluntary muscles.

A primary myositis occurs as an acute or subacute affection, and is probably dependent on some unknown infectious agent. Several characteristic cases have been described of late years. That of E. Wagner may be taken as a typical example. A tuberculous but well-built woman entered the hospital, complaining of stiffness in the shoulders and a slight œdema of the back of the hands and forearms. There was paræsthesia, the arms became swollen, the skin tense, and the muscles felt doughy. Gradually the thighs became affected. The disease lasted about three months. The post mortem showed slight pulmonary tuberculosis; all the muscles except the glutei, the calf, and abdominal muscles were stiff and firm, but fragile, and there were serous infiltration, great proliferation of the interstitial tissue, and fatty degeneration. Similar cases have been reported by Unverricht, Hepp, and Jacoby, of New York. In the case reported by Jacoby the muscles were firm, hard, and tender, and there was slight œdema of the skin. The duration of the cases is usually from one to three months, though there are instances in which it has been longer. The swelling and tenderness of the muscles, the œdema, and the pain naturally suggest trichinosis, and indeed Hepp speaks of it as a pseudo-trichinosis. The nature of the disease is unknown. Senator's case presented marked disorders of sensation, and there is a question whether the peripheral nerves are not involved with the muscles. Wagner suggests that some of these cases were examples of acute progressive muscular atrophy. The separation from trichinosis can be made only by removing a portion of the muscle. It has not yet been determined whether the eosinophilia described by Brown is peculiar to the trichinous myositis. There are septic cases in which a diffuse, purulent infiltration of the muscles of different regions occurs. Instances have been reported in which this has been described as the primary affection, the condition of the muscles even passing on to gangrene.

1148

Myositis Ossificans Progressiva.

Of this rare and remarkable affection 42 cases have been recorded (Matthes). The process begins within the neck or back, usually with swelling of the affected muscles, redness of the skin, and slight fever. After subsiding an induration remains, which becomes progressively harder as the transformation into bone takes place. The disease is very chronic, and ultimately may involve a majority of the skeletal muscles. Nothing is known of the etiology; the condition has often been associated with malformations.

II. MYOTONIA (*Thomsen's Disease*).

Definition.—An infection characterized by tonic cramp of the muscles on attempting voluntary movements. The disease received its name from the physician who first described it, in whose family it has existed for five generations.

While the disease is in a majority of cases hereditary, hence the name myotonia congenita, there are other forms of spasm very similar which may be acquired, and others still which are quite transitory.

Etiology.—All the typical cases have occurred in family groups; a few isolated instances have been described in which similar symptoms have been present. The disease is rare in this country and in England; it seems more common in Germany and in Scandinavia.

Symptoms.—The disease comes on in childhood. It is noticed that on account of the stiffness the children are not able to take part in ordinary games. The peculiarity is noticed only during voluntary movements. The contraction which the patient wills is slowly accomplished; the relaxation which the patient wills is also slow. The contraction often persists for a little time after he has dropped an object which he has picked up. In walking, the start is difficult; one leg is put forward slowly, it halts from stiffness for a second or two, and then after a few steps the legs become limber and he walks without any difficulty. The muscles of the arms and legs are those usually implicated; rarely the facial, ocular, or laryngeal muscles. Emotion and cold aggravate the condition. In some instances there is mental weakness. The sensation and the reflexes are normal. G. M. Hammond has reported three remarkable cases in one family, in which the disease began at the eighth year and was confined entirely to the arms. It was accompanied with some slight mental feebleness. The condition of the muscles is interesting. The patients appear and are muscular, and there is sometimes a definite hypertrophy of the muscles. The force is scarcely proportionate to the size. Erb has described a characteristic reaction of the nerve and muscle to the electrical currents—the so-called myotonic reaction, the chief feature of which is that normally the contractions caused by either current attain their maximum slowly and relax slowly, and vermicular, wave-like contractions pass from the cathode to the anode.

The disease is incurable, but it may be arrested temporarily. The nature of the affection is unknown. In the only autopsy made Dejerine and

Sottas have found hypertrophy of the primitive fibres with multiplication of the nuclei of all the muscles, including the diaphragm, but not the heart. The spinal cord and the nerves were intact. From Jacoby's recent studies it is doubtful whether these changes in the muscles are in any way characteristic or peculiar to the disease. No treatment for the condition is known.

III. PARAMYOCLONUS MULTIPLEX

(*Myoclonia*).

An affection, described by Friedreich, characterized by clonic contractions, chiefly of the muscles of the extremities, occurring either constantly or in paroxysms.

The cases have been chiefly in males, and the disease has followed emotional disturbance, fright, or straining. The contractions are usually bilateral and may vary from fifty to one hundred and fifty in the minute. Occasionally tonic spasms occur. They are not accompanied by any sensory disturbances. In the intervals between the attacks there may be tremors of the muscles. In the severe spasms the movements may be very violent; the body is tossed about, and it is sometimes difficult to keep the patient in bed. Gucci has described a family in which the affection has occurred in three generations.

Weiss has also noted heredity in four generations. According to this author the essential symptoms are continuous or paroxysmal muscular contractions, usually symmetrical and rhythmical, of muscles otherwise normal, which cease during sleep. There are neither psychical nor sensory disturbances. The condition is most common in young males, and is unaffected by treatment. Raymond groups this disease with fibrillary tremors, electric chorea (Henoch), tic non douloureux of the face, and the convulsive tic, under the name of *myoclonies*, believing that it is only one link in a chain of pathological manifestations in the degenerate.

INDEX.

1151

THE END.

REFERENCE-BOOK OF PRACTICAL THERAPEUTICS.

BY VARIOUS AUTHORS.

Edited by FRANK P. FOSTER, M. D.,

*Editor of " The New York Medical Journal " and of
Foster's " Encyclopædic Medical Dictionary."*

In two large 8vo volumes. Sold only by subscription.

THIS work is intended as a ready-reference book, in which the physician can find the most recent information concerning the uses and application of remedies ; their indications and counter-indications ; the various conditions in which they are indicated ; the forms in which drugs are best used, their doses, and the methods of administration.

" It is essentially a book for the practitioner, and is an up-to-date work of reference. Only so much of the physiological properties of drugs, their chemical, mineralogical, botanical, and zoölogical relations as are of direct bearing on their use in practice have been considered in the compilation of this work. . . . The ambitious physician will be pleased with this work."—*Canadian Medical Record.*

" With the second volume this excellent work is completed, and is rendered immediately available, by means of the general index and index of diseases and remedies, as a book of therapeutic reference. A supplement of nearly fifty pages bears witness to the rapid strides in medical science, since it is filled chiefly with matter relating to knowledge acquired since the appearance of the first volume. The work is well printed and well bound, and the brief articles on every subject relating to the treatment of disease are excellently written, and in the main satisfactory as to the information they impart."—*Medical Record.*

" A careful review of the second volume of this valuable work shows that there is nothing to criticise, and that the same care has been exercised by the various authors in their contributions that characterized those in the first volume. The editor has executed his difficult task well, and has added all the information that has been published in the journals on the different subjects since the original articles were written. So great has been the advance in therapeutics that it has been necessary to add an appendix, thus making the book thoroughly up to date in every particular."—*Medical Sentinel.*

D. APPLETON AND COMPANY, NEW YORK.

For Tonsalitis give

℞ Quinine Sulphate
Dovers Powders āā 24 gr
M et divid No 8
Sig one night and
morning use hot
foot Bath at night and
go to bed

For Tonsalitis give
Wood

℞ varatrum ʒ 3
morphine gr ½
water ʒ 2
Sig one teaspoonful
every 6 hours

Widals Reaction Lee-
Take a fresh culture and smear on
a slide look at it with the microscope
and you see the Bacilus moving
Then take a drop of a Typhoid fever
patient and put on it and it causes
the bacilus to clump and they stop
their motion

Jones

Fehlings solution
Copper sulphat   gr 90½
Neutral Tartrat of Potasin gr 3 c c H
Solution of costic soda fl oy H
distilted water to make   oy c c

Widal's Test for Typhoid fever

Page 38

Fever mixture composed of
Citrate of potash
Liquor ammonia acetate
Aromatic spirits of ammonia

a nervous inability to fix the mind
for any length of time

R̶ Carbonate of Soda ƷƷ } 1
    Tr opium ƷƷ   } 2
    Glycerine
    water   } ā

M Sig apply for Rheumatism